MATH TEACHING SERIES
STUDENTS • TEACHERS • PARENTS

A step-by-step
MATH TEACHING SERIES
for
Students, Teachers, **AND** Parents

GRADE LEVEL

8

ABOUT THE AUTHOR:

Nicholas Aggor is a parent and an ex-senior engineer with a master's degree in engineering, fully trained in the prestigious Six Sigma Blackbelt of Problem Solving, and a National Dean's List Scholar

www.MathTeachingSeries.com
Published by Nicholas Aggor Publisher, LLC.

Welcome to the Math Teaching Series

IF YOU ARE AN EDUCATOR…

This text and every text in the Math Teaching Series provide new "tools" designed to assist you in teaching mathematics. After listening and working with educators to assist all students, even those who struggle with math, we were able to build a step-by-step method to improve the delivery of effective instruction.

IF YOU ARE A PARENT…

We will guide your student to build skills and they will become competent. Study will progress with less stress and more peace as the student and you are able to work together toward success. Pride in accomplishment can come early and stay during the study effort with the system.

IF YOU ARE A STUDENT…

These texts were built to assist all students and allow them to earn respect for their efforts. Those who struggle can get the help they need in a process built to avoid becoming lost and stuck. You are guided and the course is designed to allow you to build competence in skills, which will allow you to feel confident!

Nicholas Aggor, an Author, an Engineer, a Parent

This series of texts is dedicated to making the playing field a more fair and equal process to all students with a well-constructed platform to deliver the lessons.

I believe there are always at least three parties to the success of education. With the student supported with a text built to this level of support, we are confident that the educators of the world will now receive "hands on" help as well for the student with parents, relatives, and others who are dedicated to the journey that can use this text.

I wish to thank all the teachers who help in the real life struggle to teach.

We have designed a new set of tools for students, teachers, and parents.

Nicholas Aggor

Texas Instruments images used with permission of the copyright owner.

Material extracted from TI-Nspire™ Math and Science Learning Technology and TI-Nspire™ Learning Handheld Quick Reference with permission of the publisher Copyright (2007), Texas Instruments Incorporated

ISBN: 978-0-9840609-3-1

School to Home Connection

You promise to work and I promise you will not get lost.

Math Teaching Series Lesson One

LEARN WHY TO WORK AND YOU WILL SUCCEED

- You are as rich and as intelligent as anyone while studying this book.
- Stay with me and work daily and you will see improved results.
- This is all about effort, so follow the pathways and you will improve.

LEARN HOW TO WORK AND YOU WILL SUCCEED

- Peace and quiet will allow focus. NO radio, television, games, and phones.
- Expect to win, to progress and keep score daily and results will improve.
- Your teachers are there to help and teach, so show them your work daily.

Daily Score Card

1. Students grade parents for providing scheduled studies time, homework time, bed time, quiet place to study, quiet place to do homework, and food.
2. Parents grade students for the effort the students make during the scheduled studies time, homework time, and bed time.
3. Teachers grade students during quizzes, homework, and tests.

Days	Studies Time	Quality Control at Home		Quality Control at School	Steps to Improve
		Students' Grading	Parents' Grading	Teachers' Grading	Improvement
Mon					
Tue					
Wed					
Thu					
Fri					
Sat					
Sun					

- Students earn good results with good work habits. Take pride in your efforts.
- Share your daily effort with your parents, guardians, your family, and friends.
- Seek advice and help from your math teachers on your journey to success.
- Parents should make copies of the score card for monitoring progress.

How to Use This Book Most Effectively

There is a consistent teaching method in the text to follow.

Your book contains Examples, with step-by-step demonstration of "how to" do the math problems. As you study, focus on learning the "how to" properly and the solutions offered throughout your text will teach you the methods to use.

Practice the Examples and come to know how to do the work. The Examples section will "teach you" the process in a step-by-step manner. This way, learning the correct methods will prevent you from getting lost or stuck. You will find each step to be connected and the pace will allow you to progress with confidence.

After following the Examples offered with understanding, work the chapter Exercise Problems. As you do the Exercise Problems, use the "hints" provided, as you need them, sending you back to the Examples. This will allow you to advance, and as you learn the steps properly, your confidence will strengthen.

Challenge questions are designed for you to excel in the area of study. Allow yourself time to work the Challenge Questions as they will strengthen your skills.

Word Problems provide Real World applications of the methods you are learning. You are provided with the "how to" method again, showing the step-by-step solutions to solve these questions properly. This will help to improve your math reasoning skills.

Learn to use the Table of Contents (front) and the Index of Terms (back) in this book. These are reference aids to quickly direct you to solutions.

TABLE OF CONTENTS - Grade 8

PATTERNS

Cumulative Review

1. Add or subtract.

    a. $4^2 - 2^2 =$ **b.** $3^2 + 2^2 =$ **c.** $5\dfrac{2}{3} - 2\dfrac{3}{4} =$ **d.** $1\dfrac{4}{5} + \dfrac{3}{4} =$

    Hint: Review the Math Teaching Series for grade 6 or 7.

2. Multiply or divide.

    a. $4^2 \times 2^2 =$ **b.** $4^2 \div 2^2 =$ **c.** $5\dfrac{1}{3} \times 2\dfrac{3}{4} =$ **d.** $3\dfrac{1}{2} \div \dfrac{3}{4} =$

    Hint: Review the chapter/section on Exponents and Fractions in the Math Teaching Series for grade 6 or 7.

3. Write each percent as a decimal.

    a. 20%   **b.** 5%   **c.** 10%   **d.** 0.5%

    Hint: Review the chapter on Percent in the Math Teaching Series for grade 7 or 8

4. Write each decimal as a percent.

    a. 0.2   **b.** 1.25   **c.** 0.75   **d.** 0.25

    Hint: Review the chapter on Decimal in the Math Teaching Series for grade 7 or 8.

5. Write each fraction as a percent.

    a. $\dfrac{1}{2}$ **b.** $\dfrac{2}{5}$ **c.** $\dfrac{3}{50}$ **d.** $\dfrac{6}{25}$

    Hint: Review the chapter on Percent in the Math Teaching Series for grade 7 or 8.

6. A farm is in the form of a square. A side of the farm is 2 miles long. Mary said that the perimeter of the farm is 8 miles, and the area of the farm is 8 square miles. Is her statement correct? Explain your answer.

    Hint: Review the Chapter/section in the Math Teaching Series for grade 6 or 7 on the Perimeter of a Square and the Area of a Square.

7. The product of two numbers is zero. John said that at least one of the numbers is zero. Is his statement correct? Explain your answer.

    Hint: Review the Chapter/section on Multiplication in the Math Teaching Series for grade 5 or 6.

8. Find the difference.

    a. $-4 - (-2) =$ **b.** $-6.3 - (-7.7) =$ **c.** $10.4 - (-6.6) =$ **d.** $7 - (-7) =$

    Hint: Review the chapter on Integers in the Math Teaching Series for grade 7 or 8.

9. Find the sum.

    a. $-8 + 12 =$ **b.** $-9 + (-9) =$ **c.** $12.8 + (-14.2) =$ **d.** $-11.6 + (-2.8) =$

    Hint: Review the chapter on Integers in the Math Teaching Series for grade 7 or 8.

10. Simplify the expression.

    a. $\dfrac{-12x}{-3}$ **b.** $(-5t)(4)$ **c.** $\dfrac{6a - 14a}{2}$ **d.** $3(5x - 8) - 4$

    Hint: Review the chapter on Order of Operations in the Math Teaching Series for grade 7 or 8.

11. Write 4% as a fraction. Hint: Review the chapter on Percent in the Math Teaching Series for grade 7 or 8.

12. What is 8% of 200? Hint: Review the chapter on Percent in the Math Teaching Series for grade 7 or 8.

13. Write 75% as a decimal. Hint: Review the chapter on Percent in the Math Teaching Series for grade 7 or 8.

14. Simplify:

    a. $r^2 \cdot r^3$ **b**. $t \cdot t^5$ **c**. $x^0 \cdot x^0$ **d**. $24 \cdot t^0$

    Hint: Review the chapter on Exponent in the Math Teaching Series for grade 7 or 8.

New Terms: **patterns**, **constant difference**, **terms**, **number sequence**, **two consecutive terms**

How to Identify Patterns

Generally, a **pattern** is a design used by dressmakers. Some of the earliest forms of patterns can be found in the adinkra cloth and the Ashanti kente cloth which are produced by the people of Ghana in West Africa. This is a sample of the Ashanti kente cloth pattern.

A sample of the Ashanti kente cloth.

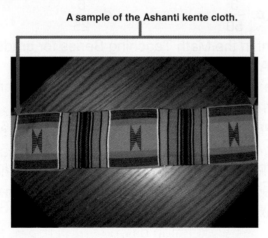

Each set of a **pattern** has a specific order of design, however, since some patterns are made by people, the order of a pattern can be changed. Similarly in mathematics, **a number sequence** is a group of numbers such that the numbers are called terms and the terms are in a certain order called **patterns**. For example, the pattern in a number sequence is always to add a certain number to the previous number to get the next number in the sequence or to subtract a certain number from the previous number to get the next number. In the sequence 1, 3, 5, 7, 9, ..., notice that 2 is added to the previous number to obtain the next number as follows:

$1 + 2 = 3$, $3 + 2 = 5$, $5 + 2 = 7$, $7 + 2 = 9$, and ... This information can be represented as shown:

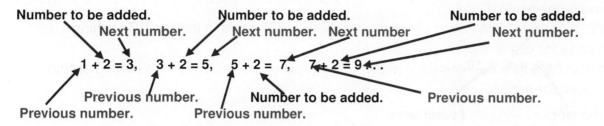

Number to be added.   Number to be added.   Next number   Number to be added.

Next number.   Next number.   Next number.

1 + 2 = 3,   3 + 2 = 5,   5 + 2 = 7,   7 + 2 = 9...

Previous number.   Number to be added.   Previous number.

Previous number.   Previous number.

Notice that the next number becomes the next previous number.

A **sequence** is formed by a list of numbers, called **terms** which are in a certain order. In a sequence, the first number is the first term, the second number is the second term, the third number is the third term, and so on as shown:

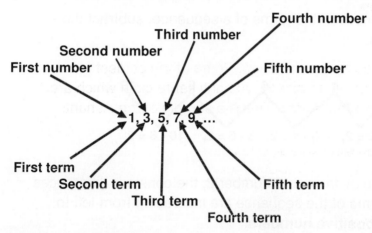

Fourth number

Third number

Second number

First number   Fifth number

1, 3, 5, 7, 9 ...

First term

Second term   Fifth term

Third term

Fourth term

If the difference between any two consecutive terms in a sequence is the same, then the difference is called a **constant difference or a common difference**, **see Example 2**. Two consecutive terms in a sequence means any two terms, such that the previous term is followed directly by the next term in order or according to the pattern of the sequence. The three dots, ..., after the last given number or term show that the sequence has more terms that are not listed.
A sequence that has constant differences or common differences is known as arithmetic or linear sequence.

Example 1
What are the first, third, and fourth terms of the sequence.
2, 4, 6, 8, 10, ...
Solution
The position of the terms in a sequence determine the name given to the term. For example, the term in the first position is the first term, the term in the second position is the second term, the term in the third position is the third term and so on. Therefore,

the solution is:

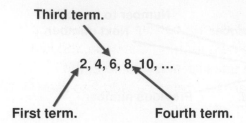

First term.   Third term.   Fourth term.

So, the first term is 2, the third term is 6, and the fourth term is 8.

Example 2

Find the constant differences of the terms of the sequence.

2, 4, 6, 8, 10, ...

Solution

Rule 1: To find the constant differences of the terms of a sequence, subtract the previous terms from the next terms.

Using rule 1, we can write:

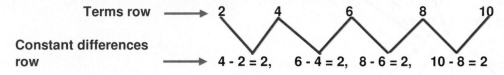

Terms row → 2   4   6   8   10

Constant differences row → 4 - 2 = 2,   6 - 4 = 2,   8 - 6 = 2,   10 - 8 = 2

Notice that since the terms increase by the same number 2, the constant differences are 2. Notice also that since the terms of the sequence are increasing from left to right, the constant differences are **positive numbers**.

Example 3

Find the constant differences of the terms of the sequence 15, 12, 9, 6, 3, ...

Solution

Rule 1: To find the constant differences of the terms of a sequence, subtract the previous terms from the next terms.

Using Rule 1, we can write:

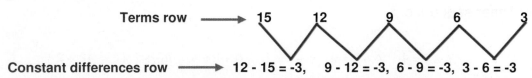

Terms row → 15   12   9   6   3

Constant differences row → 12 - 15 = -3,   9 - 12 = -3, 6 - 9 = -3, 3 - 6 = -3

Notice that since the terms decrease by the same number -3, the constant differences are -3. Notice also that since the terms of the sequence are decreasing from left to right, the constant differences are **negative numbers**.

Example 4

Find the next two terms of the sequence by using constant differences.
2, 4, 6, 8, 10, ...

Solution

To find the next two terms, we need to find the constant differences first, and then add the constant differences to the previous term to get the next term. In this case, the last term which is 10 becomes the previous term. From the solution of Example 2, the constant differences of the sequence 2, 4, 6, 8, 10, ... are 2. Therefore, add 2 to the last term given in the sequence to get the first next term as shown:

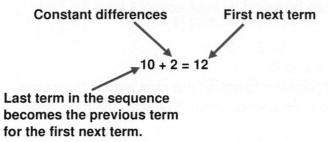

To find the second next term, the first next term becomes the previous term, and therefore, we should add 2 which is the constant differences to the first next term to get the second next term as shown:

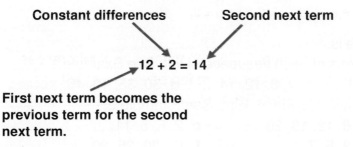

This is how the next two terms are obtained by adding the constant differences of 2 to the previous terms to get the next terms:

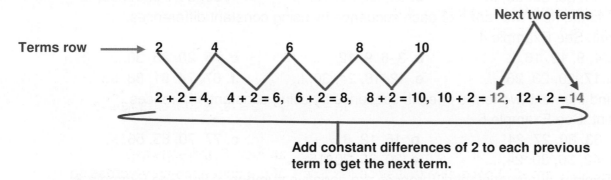

Example 5

Find the next two terms of the sequence 15, 12, 9, 6, 3, ... by using constant

5

differences.

Solution

From Example 3, the constant differences of the sequence 15, 12, 9, 6, 3, ..., are -3. Notice that each next term of the sequence 15, 12, 9, 6, 3, ..., is obtained by subtracting 3 from each previous terms. The last term of the sequence 15, 12, 9, 6, 3, ..., is 3. The first next term can be obtained by subtracting the constant difference from the last term of the sequence as shown:

$$3 - 3 = 0$$

The second next term of the sequence can be found by subtracting 3 from the first next term as shown:

$$0 - 3 = -3$$

The next two terms of the sequence are 0 and -3.

Notice that subtracting 3 from each previous term to obtain the next term is the same as adding the constant difference of -3 to each previous term to obtain the next term as shown:

$$3 + (-3) = 3 - 3 = 0 \qquad \text{Note:} + (- = -$$
$$0 + (-3) = 0 - 3 = -3 \qquad \text{Note:} + (- = -$$

Exercises

1. What is a number sequence?
2. Explain what a sequence is.
3. What are terms?
4. Explain what a constant difference is.
5. What are the first and the third terms of each sequence? Hint: See Example 1.
   a. 3, 6, 9, 12, 15, ...   **b**. 2, 5, 8, 11, ..   **c**. 4, 8, 12, 14, ..   **d**. 30, 35, 40, 45, ...
6. Find the constant differences of each sequence. Hint: See Example 2.
   a, 3, 6, 9, 12, 15, ...   **b**. 4, 8, 12, 16, 20, ...   **c**. 2, 5, 8, 11, ...
   d. 6, 8, 10, 12, 14, ...   **e**. 1, 3, 5, 7, ...   **f**. 15, 20, 25, 30, ...
7. Find the constant differences of each sequence. Hint: See Example 3.
   a. 10, 8, 6, 4, 2, ...   **b**. 73, 66, 59, 52, ...   **c**. 23, 20, 17, 14, ...
   d. 40, 36, 32, 28, ...   **e**. 30, 25, 20, 15, ...   **f**. 90, 80, 70, 60, 50, ...
8. Find the next two terms of each sequence by using constant differences.
   Hint: See Example 4.
   a. 4, 8, 12, 16, ...   **b**. 3, 6, 9, 12, ...   **c**. 15, 20, 25, 30, ...
   d. 17, 20, 23, 26, ...   **e**. 12, 18, 24, 30, ...   **f**. 67, 74, 81, 88, 95, ...
9. Find the next two terms of each sequence by using constant differences.
   Hint: See Example 5.
   a. 33, 30, 27, 24, ...   **b**. 16, 12, 8, ...   **c**. 77, 70, 63, 56, ...
   d. 42, 36, 30, 24, ...   **e**. 30, 25, 20, 15, ...   **f**. 19, 17,15, 13, ...
10. Explain when constant differences are negative numbers. Hint: See Example 3.
11. Explain when constant differences are positive numbers. Hint: See Example 2.

Challenge Questions

12. Find the constant differences of each sequence.

    a. 1, 6, 11, 16, 21, ...   **b.** 37, 34, 31, 28, 25, ...   **c.** 5, 10, 15, 20, 25, ...

    d. 65, 60, 55, 50, 45, ...   **e.** 10, 20, 30, 40, 50, ...   **f.** 11, 15, 19, 23, ...

13. Find the next two terms of each of the sequences in Exercise 12.

Answers to Selected Questions

5a. First term is 3 and third term is 9.

6a. 3   **7a.** -2   **8a** 20,24   **9a** -3

How to Solve Problems Using the Second Differences

Sometimes after finding the first difference of a sequence it can be observed that the first differences are not the same. Since the first differences are not constant, it will be impossible to find the next terms of the sequence. In this case, we should find the second differences by using the first differences as shown in Examples 1 and 2.

Example 1

Find the next four terms of the sequence 3, 13, 27, 45, 67, 93, ...

Solution

Step 1: Find the first differences.

Each next term minus the previous term gives the difference as shown:

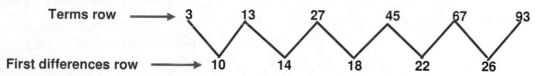

For example, 13 - 3 = 10 , 27 - 13 = 14, 45 - 27 = 18, 67 - 45 = 22, 93 - 67 = 26.

Step 2: Find the second differences.

Since the differences are not the same, find the second differences. Each second difference is found by subtracting the previous first difference from the next first difference as shown: 14 - 10 = 4, 18 - 14 = 4, 22 - 18 = 4, 26 - 22 = 4

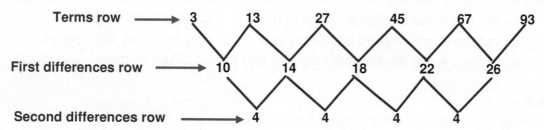

Step 3: Find the next four first differences (by working backward).

Since the numbers in the second differences row are all the same, that is 4, we can then add the second difference, which is 4, to the previous first differences to obtain the next four first differences as shown:

7

$26 + 4 = 30, 30 + 4 = 34, 34 + 4 = 38,$ and $38 + 4 = 42$

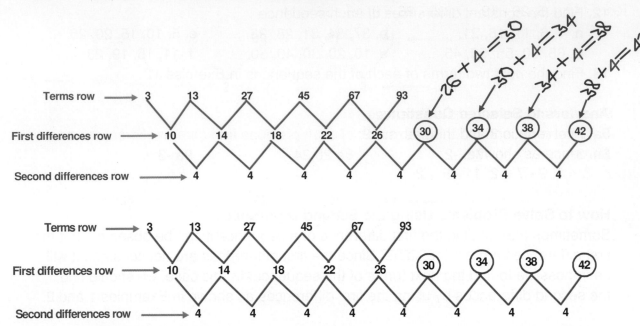

Step 4: Find the next four terms (by working backward).

Add the corresponding first differences found in Step 3 to the corresponding previous terms to obtain the next four terms of the sequence as shown:

$93 + 30 = 123, 123 + 34 = 157, 157 + 38 = 195, 195 + 42 = 237$

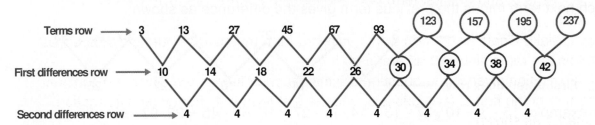

The next four terms of the sequence are 123, 157, 195, and 237.

Critical Thinking

Notice that: **a.** In Step 1, we worked forward to find the first differences.

b. In Step 2, we worked forward to find the second differences.

c. In Step 3, we worked backward to find the next four first differences.

d. In Step 4, we worked backward to find the next four terms.

Example 2

Find the first and the second differences of the sequence:

14, 19, 26, 35, 46, ...

Solution

Step 1: Find the first differences

To find the first differences, subtract each previous term from the next term to obtain

8

the first differences as shown:

19 - 14 = 5, 26 - 19 = 7, 35 - 26 = 9, 46 - 35 = 11

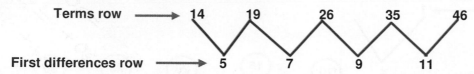

Step 2: Find the second differences.

To find the second differences, subtract each previous first difference from the next first difference as shown:

7 - 5 = 2, 9 - 7 = 2, 11 - 9 = 2

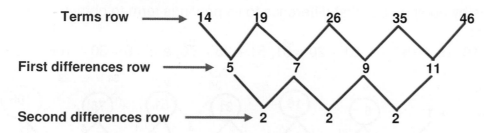

The first differences are 5, 7, 9, and 11. The second differences are 2.

Example 3

If the second differences of a sequence are a constant 5, the first of the first differences is 5, and the first term is 1, find the first 7 terms of the sequence.

Solution

Step 1: Make Chart 1 and then work backward from the constant second differences to obtain the remaining first differences.

The information given in the question are the second differences, which are constant 5, the first of the first differences is 5, and the first term is 1. Put all the information on Chart 1 as shown:

Chart 1

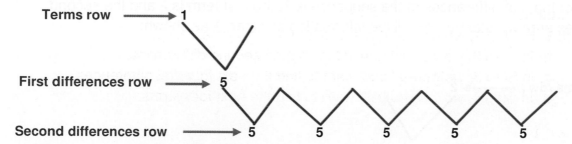

Using Chart 1, we have to work backward from the constant second differences of 5 to obtain the remaining first differences by adding the constant second differences of 5 to each previous first difference to obtain the next first difference as shown:

5 + 5 = 10, 10 + 5 = 15, 15 + 5 = 20, 20 + 5 = 25, and 25 + 5 = 30.

Chart 2

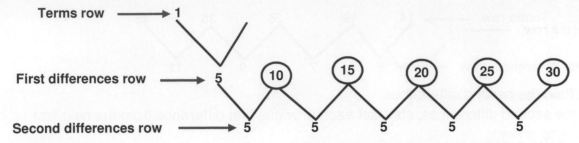

Step 2: Using Chart 2, we have to work backward from the first differences to obtain the remaining terms by adding each first difference to its previous term to obtain the next term as shown:

$1 + 5 = 6$, $6 + 10 = 16$, $16 + 15 = 31$, $31 + 20 = 51$, $51 + 25 = 76$, and $76 + 30 = 106$

Chart 3

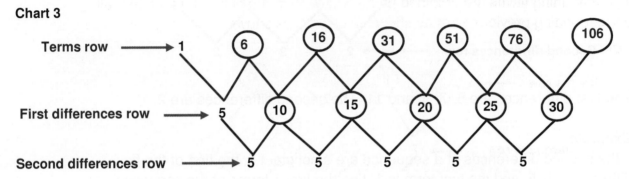

Therefore, the first seven terms of the series are: 1, 6, 16, 31, 51, 76, and 106.

Example 4

The first of the first differences of a sequence is 7. The first term is 2 and the second differences are a constant 3. Find the first 4 terms of the sequence.

Solution

The information given in the question are:
The first of the first differences of the sequence is 7, the first term is 2 and the second differences area constant 3. Put all the information on Chart 1 as shown:

Chart 1

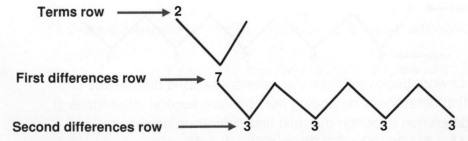

Use the constant second differences of 3 to find the next 3 first differences as shown in Chart 2 as shown:

Chart 2

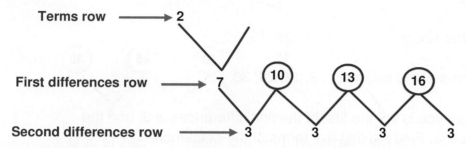

The remaining first differences are obtained by adding a constant 3 to the previous
first difference as shown:

7 + 3 = 10, 10 + 3 = 13, 13 + 3 = 16.

The remaining terms are obtained by adding each of the first difference to their
corresponding previous term as shown in Chart 3 as shown:

Chart 3

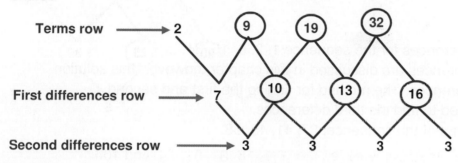

Therefore, the first four terms of the sequence are 2, 9, 19, and 52.

Exercises

1. Describe how you will find the next four terms of a sequence when you find out
   that the first differences of the sequence are not a constant or are not the same.
   Hint: See Example 1
2. Describe how you will find the remaining terms of a sequence when the first
   term, the first of the first difference and the constant second difference are
   given. Hint: See Example 4.
3. In solving sequence problems, when is it necessary to find the second differences?
   Hint; See Example 1.
4. Find the next three terms of each sequence. Hint: See Example 1.
   a. 9,16, 25, 36, 49, ...
   b. 1, 9, 24, 75, 111, ...
   c. 10, 30, 65, 115, 180, ...
   d. 61, 76, 92, 109, 127, ...

e. 3, 10, 21, 36, ...

5. Find the first and the second differences of the sequence:
   45, 67, 93, 123, 157, ...
   Hint: See Example 2.

6. Find the next term of the sequence 10, 13, 19, 28, 40, 55, ...
   Hint: See Example 4.

7. Find the next three terms of the sequence, 8, 16, 26, 38, ...
   Hint: See Example 1.

8. The first term of a sequence is 10, the first of the first differences is 3, and the constant differences are 3. Find the first five terms of the sequence.
   Hint: See Examples 3 and 4.

9. Find the next three terms of the sequence, 1, 5, 11, 19, 29, 41, ...
   Hint: See Example 4.

10. The first term of a sequence is 1, the first of the first differences is 4, and the constant differences are 2. Find the first five terms of the sequence.
    Hint: See Examples 3 and 4.

Challenge Questions

11. Find the constant differences for the sequence 1, 2, 6, 15, 31, ...
    Hint: The second differences are discussed in this chapter, however, this solution requires the third differences. The method for finding the first and second differences can be used to find the third differences.

12. Find the next two terms of the sequence, 37, 41, 48, 58, ...

Answers to Selected Questions

4a. 64, 81, 100   **4b**. 154, 204, 261   **12**. 71, 87

LINEAR PATTERNS

Example 1
A book club charges $10 membership fee and $15 per book purchased.

a. Show this information in a table by using constant differences. Show the total cost for purchasing 0 to 6 books.

b. Write an equation that represents the situation and then explain the equation.

c. Draw a graph of the equation in **b**.

d. From the graph, can you conclude that a data that has constant first differences is linear?

e. From the graph you have drawn, what is the name of the equation $c = 15n + 10$?

f. In the equation $c = 15n + 10$, what is the independent variable and what is the dependent variable?

g. How did you plot the graph with respect to the axis, dependent variables, and independent variables?

h. Describe how the first differences are used to write an equation for the total cost?

Solution

a. The information is represented in the table.

Number of books purchased (n)	0	1	2	3	4	5	6
Total cost ($)	10	25	40	55	70	85	100

Constant differences row ⟶ 15   15   15   15   15   15

Notice that when the number of books purchased is 0, the total cost is $10 due to the membership fee. Notice also that the total cost includes the cost of the number of books purchased and the membership fee. The constant difference can be obtained by subtracting the previous total cost from the next total cost.

b. Let the total cost of the books be **c**. Let **n** be the number of books purchased. We can then write an equation that represents the situation by observing the table in solution **a**, as:

Total cost = (Constant differences) × (Number of books) + (Membership fee)

$$c = 15 \times n + 10$$
$$c = 15n + 10$$

Notice that in the equation $c = 15n + 10$, 10 is the membership fee, and $15n$ is the cost of n books without the membership fee. Notice also that 15 is the first differences and it represents the price per book.

c. The graph of $c = 15n + 0$ is drawn by constructing a table first by choosing values for **n** and finding the corresponding values for **c** as shown:

n	c = 15n + 10	Points (n, c)
0	$c = 15 \times 0 + 10 = 0 + 10 = 10$	(0, 10)
1	$c = 15 \times 1 + 10 = 15 + 10 = 25$	(1, 25)
2	$c = 15 \times 2 + 10 = 30 + 10 = 40$	(2, 40)
3	$c = 15 \times 3 + 10 = 45 + 10 = 55$	(3, 55)

Plot the points (**n**, **c**) on a graph paper, and use a ruler and a pencil to connect the points as shown:

(The graph is on the next page.)

Books Purchased

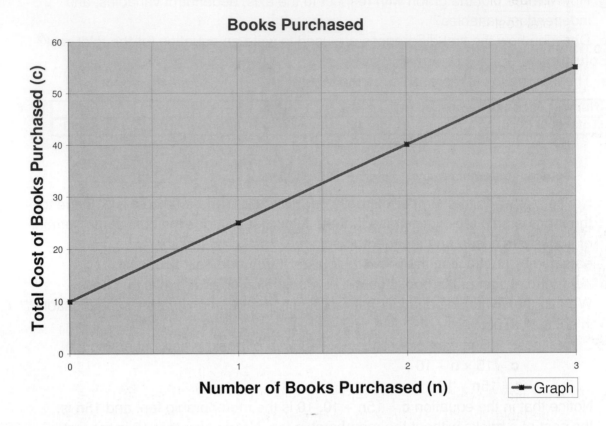

Number of Books Purchased (n)   ▪—Graph

d. Yes, since the graph or pattern is linear, I can conclude that if a data shows constant first differences, then the data is linear.

e. The graph of the equation **c** = 15**n** + 10 is a straight line, and therefore, the equation is a straight line or a linear equation.

f. In the graph of **c** = 15**n** + 10, **n** is the independent variable because **n** does not depend on **c** for the value of **n**. The value of **c** depends on the value chosen for **n**, and therefore, **c** is the dependent variable. Hint: Review the chapter on Graphs.

g. The graph is drawn such that the dependent variable is on the vertical axis and the independent variable is on the horizontal axis.

h. See the solutions to **a** and **b**.

Critical Point

Notice how several diverse questions can be asked about one equation as shown in Example 1. The solutions to Example 1 show many useful methods for answering mathematics questions involving an equation.

Example 2

The table shows the cost associated with being a member of a video club.

a. Find the first differences of the data

b. Write an equation to represent the data pattern.

c. Explain why the number of videos purchased is zero but the cost is $14.00

14

Number of videos purchased (n)	0	1	2	3	4
Total cost ($)		14	30	46	62	78

Solution

a. Find the first differences of the data by subtracting the previous terms from the next terms as shown:

30 - 14 = 16, 46 - 30 = 16, 62 - 46 = 16, 78 - 62 = 16

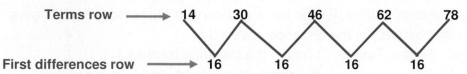

The first differences are 16.

b. The equation that represents the data pattern is:

total cost = (first differences) × (number of videos) + (membership fee)

$$c = 16 \times n + 14$$
$$c = 16n + 14$$

where c = total cost
16 = first difference
n = number of videos
14 = membership fees

c. Since the first differences are 16, the club, therefore, charges $16 per video. From the table, the cost for 0 videos is $14 because the membership fee of the club is $14.

Exercises

1. Explain how the first differences of a number sequence can be found.
2. Describe what a dependent variable is.
3. Describe what an independent variable is.
4. John said that, on a graph, the independent variable is on the horizontal axis and the dependent variable is on the vertical axis. Is his statement correct? Explain your answer.
5. A library club charges $8 membership fee and $3 per book borrowed.
   (Hint: See Examples 1 and 2.)
   a. Show this information in a table.
   b. Write an equation that represents the situation and then explain the equation.
   c. Draw a graph of the equation in **b**.
   d. From the graph can you conclude that a data that has constant first differences is linear?
   e. From the graph you have drawn, what is the name of the equation $c = 3n + 8$ where c is the total cost of the library books borrowed, and n is the number of books borrowed?

f. In the equation **c** = 3**n** + 8, what is the independent variable, and what is the dependent variable?

g. How did you plot the graph with respect to the axis, dependent variable, and the independent variable?

Challenge Questions

6. A car is traveling at 30 miles per hour. Write an equation to express the distance traveled in a given amount of time. Graph the equation with times from 0 to 4 hours. Hint: An equation that expresses the distance covered is:

$$\text{Distance} = \text{Rate} \times \text{Time} \quad \text{(This is the distance formula.)}$$

$$\mathbf{d} = 30\mathbf{t} \qquad \mathbf{d} = \text{distance covered, and } \mathbf{t} = \text{time taken}$$
to travel the distance in hours.

Complete the table and then draw the graph. Hint: See Example 1.

Time (hours), t	0	1	2	3	4
Distance (miles), d	0	30	60	?	?

7. John can walk 3 miles per hour. Write an equation to express the distance traveled in a given amount of time. Graph the equation for the times from 0 to 5 hours. Hint: See Challenge Question 6.

8. Mary said that a sequence that has first constant differences, has a linear graph. Is her statement true or false? Explain your answer.

CHAPTER 2

ORDER OF OPERATIONS

Quick Cumulative Review

1. Find each sum. Review Integers in the MathMasters Series for grade 7 or 8.
   a. -20 + (-21) =   **b.** -2.2 + (-3.8) =   **c.** -100 + 98 =   **d.** 3.9 + (-6.2)

2. Evaluate. Review the Order of Operations in the MathMasters Series for grade 7 or 8.
   a. 20 ÷ 4 · 5 + 4 =   **b.** 3 · 4 + 9 ÷ 2 =   **c.** 68 - 42 ÷ 6 =   **d.** 50 - 24 ÷ 3 - 7 =

3. Mary said that to divide by a fraction is the same as to multiply by the reciprocal of the fraction. Is her statement correct? Hint: Review the section on Dividing by a Fraction in the MathMasters Series for grade 6 or 7.

4. Explain what is meant by the reciprocal of a number. Hint: Review the section on the Reciprocal of Numbers in the MathMasters Series for grade 6.

5. John said that $\dfrac{3}{4} \div \dfrac{5}{12} = 8$. Is his statement correct? Give reasons for your answer.

6. Solve:

    a. $\dfrac{3}{7} \div \dfrac{3}{4} =$ **b.** $17 \div \dfrac{1}{5} =$ **c.** $\dfrac{6}{5} \times \dfrac{3}{15} =$ **d.** $\dfrac{3}{5} - \dfrac{2}{50} =$

    Hint: Review the sections on Fractions in the MathMasters Series for grade 6.

7. The measure of a side of a square is 10 ft.

    a. What is the perimeter of the square?

    b. What is the area of the square?

    Hint: Review the sections on Perimeter and Area in the MathMasters Series for grade 6.

8. $\sqrt{2} \times \sqrt{2} =$ 9. $\sqrt{4} \times \sqrt{4} =$ 10. $\sqrt{6 \times 6} =$ 11. $\sqrt{81} =$

New Terms
order of operations, **"PERMDAS"**, **exponents**, **square root**

Order of Operations
The order of operations is the sequence to follow in solving expressions involving parentheses, exponents, roots, multiplication, division, addition, and subtraction.

 **What have I learnt so far?**

Explaining the Order of Operations
Example 1
Explain the order of operations by:

a. Finding the total number of balls by addition only

b. Finding the total number of balls by using additions and multiplication. Show that the answer in **a** is the same as the answer in **b**.

c. Showing that if the addition operation is done before the multiplication operation in equation $[A]$ of solution **b**, a wrong answer is obtained.

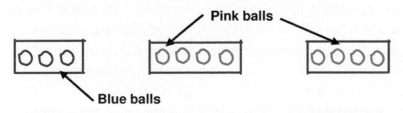

Pink balls

Blue balls

Solution
a The total number of balls by addition only = 3 blue balls + 4 pink balls + 4 pink balls.

                = 11 balls.

b. Alternate method:

Since there are 2 sets of 4 pink balls the total number of pink balls = 2 × 4 pink balls.
There are 3 blue balls also, therefore, the total number of balls

$$= 3 + 2 \times 4 \underline{\hspace{4cm}} [A]$$
$$= 3 + 8$$
$$= 11 \text{ balls.}$$

Therefore, the answer in the solution **a** is the same as the answer in solution **b**.

c. Note that in the solution **b**, the answer 11 is obtained because the multiplication operation was done before the addition operation in equation [A]. If the addition operation is done first before the multiplication operation in equation [A], a different and a wrong answer is obtained as shown:

3 + 2 x 4

5 x 4 = 20   **(This is a different and a wrong answer).**

Conclusion

We can conclude from Example 1 that the expression 3 + 2 × 4 could result in more than one value as the solution but only one value is the correct answer. Therefore, mathematicians have agreed on an order to follow when performing operations and this order is known as the **order of operations**.

The order of operations may be simplified as **PERMDAS** where:

Rule 1: **P** = Parentheses: Do the operations within the ( ) first if there are any.

Rule 2: **E** = Exponents: Do exponents second if there are any.

Rule 3: **R** = Roots: Do roots third if there are any. The roots refers to all types of roots.
(Examples of types of roots are: $\sqrt{}$, $\sqrt[3]{}$, $\sqrt[4]{}$, ...)

Rule 4: **M** = Multiplication and **D** = Divide from left to right: Do multiplication and division from left to right if there are any.

Rule 5: **A** = Add and **S** = Subtract from left to right: Do multiplication and division from left to right if there are any.

I can solve the problems too if only
I understand the concepts.

Addition and Subtraction
Example 2
Find the value of each expression.
a. 3 + 2 - 1   **b.** 22 - 2 + 4   **c.** 10 - 2 - 3
Solution
PERMDAS, specifically Rule 5 which states "**A** = Add and **S** = Subtraction from left to right" should be used to find the values of **a**, **b**, and **c**.
a. Using Rule 5 from left to right, we have to do the addition first before the

18

subtraction step-by-step as shown:
$$3 + 2 - 1 = 5 - 1 \qquad (3 + 2 = 5)$$
$$= 4$$

b. Using Rule 5 from left to right, we have to subtract first before the addition step-by-step as shown:
$$22 - 2 + 4 = 20 + 4 \qquad (22 - 2 = 20)$$
$$= 24 \qquad (20 + 4 = 24)$$

c. Using Rule 5 from left to right, we have to do the subtraction on the left first and then do the second subtraction step-by-step as shown:
$$10 - 2 - 3 = 8 - 3 \qquad (10 - 2 = 8)$$
$$= 5 \qquad (8 - 3 = 5)$$

Multiplication and Division
Example 3
Find the value of each expression

a. $9 \cdot 2 \div 3$ **b.** $24 \div 3 \cdot 2$ **c.** $60 \div 10 \div 2$

Solution

PERMDAS, specifically Rule 4, which states "**M** = Multiplication and **D** = Division from left to right" should be used to find the values of questions **a**, **b**, and **c**.

a. Using Rule 4 from left to right, we should do the multiplication before the division step-by-step as shown:
$$9 \cdot 2 \div 3 = 18 \div 3 \qquad (9 \cdot 2 - 18)$$
$$= 6 \qquad (18 \div 3 = 6)$$

b. Using Rule 4 from left to right, we should do the division before multiplication step-by-step as shown:
$$24 \div 3 \cdot 2 = 8 \cdot 2 \qquad (24 \div 3 = 8)$$
$$= 16 \qquad (8 \cdot 2 = 16)$$

c. Using Rule 4 from left to right, we should do the division at the left side first before doing the second division step-by-step as shown:
$$60 \div 10 \div 2 = 6 \div 2 \qquad (60 \div 10 = 6)$$
$$= 3 \qquad (6 \div 2 = 3$$

Addition, Subtraction, Multiplication, and Division
Example 4
Find the value of each expression.

a. $5 \cdot 3 - 4$ **b.** $24 - 4 \cdot 2$ **c.** $60 \div 10 + 5$

d. $7 - 60 \div 10$ **e.** $10 - 2 \cdot 3 + 4$ **f.** $10 + 2 \cdot 3 - 4$

g. $20 - 3 \cdot 4 + 6 \div 3$ **h.** $20 \div 5 \cdot 2 + 6 - 2$ **i.** $2 \cdot 8 \div 4$

j. $16 \div 4 \cdot 2$ **k.** $21 \div 3 + 3 \cdot 10$ **l.** $9 + 6 - 4 \cdot 2$ **m.** $2 + 4 \cdot 6$

Solution

PERMDAS, specifically Rule 4 which states, **M** = Multiplication and **D** = Division from left to right" and Rule 5 which states, "**A** = Add and **S** = Subtract from left to right" should be used to find the values of questions **a**, **b**, **c**, **d**, **e**, **f**, **g**, **h**, **i**, **j**, **k**, **l**, **and m** as shown:

a. Using **PERMDAS**, the multiplication should be done before subtraction step-by-step as shown:

$$5 \cdot 3 - 4 = 15 - 4 \qquad\qquad (5 \cdot 3 = 15)$$
$$= 11 \qquad\qquad (15 - 4 = 11)$$

b. Using **PERMDAS**, multiplication should be done before subtraction step-by-step as shown:

$$24 - 4 \cdot 2 = 24 - 8 \qquad\qquad (4 \cdot 2 = 8)$$
$$= 16 \qquad\qquad (24 - 8 = 16)$$

c. Using **PERMDAS**, division should be done before the addition step-by-step as shown:

$$60 \div 10 + 5 = 6 + 5 \qquad\qquad (60 \div 10 = 6)$$
$$= 11 \qquad\qquad (6 + 5 = 11)$$

d. Using **PERMDAS**, division should be done before subtraction step-by-step as shown:

$$7 - 60 \div 10 = 7 - 6 \qquad\qquad (60 \div 10 = 6)$$
$$= 1 \qquad\qquad (7 - 6 = 1)$$

e. Using **PERMDAS**, do multiplication, subtraction, and then addition step-by-step as shown:

$$10 - 2 \cdot 3 + 4 = 10 - 6 + 4 \qquad\qquad (2 \cdot 3 = 6)$$
$$= 4 + 4 \qquad\qquad (10 - 6 = 4)$$
$$= 8 \qquad\qquad (4 + 4 = 8)$$

f. Using **PERMDAS**, do multiplication, addition, and then subtraction step-by-step as shown:

$$10 + 2 \cdot 3 - 4 = 10 + 6 - 4 \qquad\qquad (2 \cdot 3 = 6)$$
$$= 16 - 4 \qquad\qquad (10 + 6 = 16)$$
$$= 12 \qquad\qquad (16 - 4 = 12)$$

g. Using **PERMDAS**, do the multiplication, division, subtraction, and then addition step-by-step as shown:

$$20 - 3 \cdot 4 + 6 \div 3 = 20 - 12 + 6 \div 3 \qquad\qquad (3 \cdot 4 = 12)$$
$$= 20 - 12 + 2 \qquad\qquad (6 \div 3 = 2)$$
$$= 8 + 2 \qquad\qquad (20 - 12 = 8)$$
$$= 10 \qquad\qquad (8 + 2 = 10)$$

h. Using **PERMDAS**, do the division, multiplication, addition, and then subtraction step-by-step as shown:

$$20 \div 5 \cdot 2 + 6 - 2 = 4 \cdot 2 + 6 - 2 \qquad\qquad (20 \div 5 = 4)$$
$$= 8 + 6 - 2 \qquad\qquad (4 \cdot 2 = 8)$$
$$= 14 - 2 \qquad\qquad (8 + 6 = 14)$$
$$= 12 \qquad\qquad (14 - 2 = 12)$$

i. Using **PERMDAS**, do the multiplication, and then the division step-by-step as shown:

$$2 \cdot 8 \div 4 = 16 \div 4 \qquad\qquad (2 \cdot 8 = 16)$$

$$= 4 \qquad\qquad (16 \div 4 = 4)$$

j. Using **PERMDAS**, do the division, and then the multiplication step-by-step as shown:

$$16 \div 4 \cdot 2 = 4 \cdot 2 \qquad\qquad (16 \div 4 = 4)$$
$$= 8 \qquad\qquad (4 \cdot 2 = 8)$$

k. Using **PERMDAS**, do the division, multiplication, and then the addition step-by-step as shown:

$$21 \div 3 + 3 \cdot 10 = 7 + 3 \cdot 10 \qquad\qquad (21 \div 3 = 7)$$
$$= 7 + 30 \qquad\qquad (3 \cdot 10 = 30)$$
$$= 37 \qquad\qquad (7 + 30 = 37)$$

l. Using **PERMDAS**, do multiplication, addition and then subtraction step-by-step as shown:

$$9 + 6 - 4 \cdot 2 = 9 + 6 - 8 \qquad\qquad (4 \cdot 2 = 8)$$
$$= 15 - 8 \qquad\qquad (9 + 6 = 15)$$
$$= 7 \qquad\qquad (15 - 8 = 7)$$

m. Using **PERMDAS**, do multiplication before addition step-by-step as shown:

$$2 + 4 \cdot 6 = 2 + 24 \qquad\qquad (4 \cdot 6 = 24)$$
$$= 26 \qquad\qquad (2 + 24 = 26)$$

It is not difficult, if I make the time to practise, I can become a "MathMaster".

Addition, Subtraction, Multiplication, Division, and Parentheses
Example 5
Find the value of each expression.

a. $2 \cdot (4 + 2)$ **b.** $(5 - 3) \cdot 3$ **c.** $24 \div (10 + 2)$ **d.** $(25 - 5) \div 4$

e. $(11 + 4) \cdot 2 + 3$ **f.** $6 + (10 - 3)$ **g.** $12 \div 3 \cdot (6 - 2)$ **h.** $3 \cdot (7 + 3) \div 5$

i. $6 \cdot 2 \div (8 - 6)$ **j.** $(16 + 4) \times (7 - 2)$ **k.** $13 + 8 \div (18 - 16)$ **l.** $(4 + 2 \cdot 5) \div 2$

m. $3 \cdot (11 - 2 \cdot 3 \div 6) \div (20 \div 4 - 3)$ **n.** $15 - (7 + 2)$ **o.** $(36 + 4) \times (5 - 2)$

p. $(19 - 9) - (7 - 5)$ **q.** $(23 - 19) + (7 + 3)$

Solution
PERMDAS is used to find the values of questions **a** to **q** as follows:

a. Do the addition inside of the parenthesis, and then multiply step-by-step as shown:

$$2 \cdot (4 + 2) = 2 \cdot 6 \qquad\qquad (4 + 2) = 6$$
$$= 12 \qquad\qquad (2 \cdot 6 = 12)$$

b. Do the subtraction inside of the **parenthesis**, and then multiply step-by-step as shown:

$$(5 - 3) \cdot 3 = 2 \cdot 3 \qquad\qquad (5 - 3) = 2$$
$$= 6 \qquad\qquad (2 \cdot 3 = 6)$$

c. Do the addition inside of the **parenthesis**, and then divide step-by-step as shown:

$$24 \div (10 + 2) = 24 \div 12 \qquad (10 + 2) = 12)$$
$$= 2 \qquad\qquad (24 \div 12 = 2)$$

d. Do the subtraction inside of the **parenthesis**, and then divide step-by-step as shown:

$$(25 - 5) \div 4 = 20 \div 4 \qquad (25 - 5) = 20$$
$$= 5 \qquad\qquad (20 \div 4 = 5)$$

e. Do the addition inside of the **parenthesis**, multiply, and then add step-by-step as shown:

$$(11 + 4) \cdot 2 + 3 = 15 \cdot 2 + 3 \qquad (11 + 4) = 15$$
$$= 30 + 3 \qquad\qquad (15 \cdot 2 = 30)$$
$$= 33 \qquad\qquad (30 + 3 = 33)$$

f. Do the subtraction inside of the **parenthesis**, and then add step-by-step as shown:

$$6 + (10 - 3) = 6 + 7 \qquad (10 - 3) = 7$$
$$= 13 \qquad\qquad (6 + 7 = 13)$$

g. Do the subtraction inside of the **parenthesis**, do the division, and then multiply step-by-step as shown:

$$12 \div 3 \cdot (6 - 2) = 12 \div 3 \cdot 4 \qquad (6 - 2 = 4)$$
$$= 4 \cdot 4 \qquad\qquad (12 \div 3 = 4)$$
$$= 16 \qquad\qquad (4 \cdot 4 = 16)$$

h. Do the addition inside of the **parenthesis**, do the multiplication, and then do the division step-by-step as shown:

$$3 \cdot (7 + 3) \div 5 = 3 \cdot 10 \div 5 \qquad (7 + 3) = 10$$
$$= 30 \div 5 \qquad\qquad (3 \cdot 10 = 30)$$
$$= 6 \qquad\qquad (30 \div 5 = 6)$$

i. Do the subtraction inside the **parenthesis**, do the multiplication, and then do the division step-by-step as shown:

$$6 \cdot 2 \div (8 - 6) = 6 \cdot 2 \div 2 \qquad (8 - 6) = 2$$
$$= 12 \div 2 \qquad\qquad (6 \cdot 2 = 12)$$
$$= 6 \qquad\qquad (12 \div 2 = 6)$$

j. Do the addition inside of the **parenthesis** on the left side, do the subtraction in the **parenthesis** on the right side, and then multiply step-by-step as shown:

$$(16 + 4) \times (7 - 2) = 20 \times (7 - 2) \qquad (16 + 4 = 20)$$
$$= 20 \times 5 \qquad\qquad (7 - 2 = 5)$$
$$= 100 \qquad\qquad (20 \times 5 = 100)$$

k. Do the subtraction inside of the **parenthesis**, do the division, and then do the addition step-by-step as shown:

$$13 + 8 \div (18 - 16) = 13 + 8 \div 2 \qquad (18 - 16) = 2$$
$$= 13 + 4 \qquad\qquad (8 \div 2 = 4)$$
$$= 17 \qquad\qquad (13 + 4 = 17)$$

l. Do the multiplication inside the **parenthesis**, do the addition inside of the **parentheses**, and then do the division step-by-step as shown:

$$(4 + 2 \cdot 5) \div 2 = (4 + 10) \div 2 \qquad (2 \cdot 5 = 10)$$
$$= 14 \div 2 \qquad\qquad (4 + 10 = 14)$$

$$= 7 \qquad\qquad (14 \div 2 = 7)$$

m. Do the operations inside of the **parenthesis** on the left side according to PERMDAS by multiplying, dividing, and then subtracting, then do the operations inside of the **parenthesis** on the right side according to PERMDAS by dividing, and then subtract. Finally, multiply and divide as shown step-by-step:

$$3 \cdot (11 - 2 \cdot 3 \div 6) \div (20 \div 4 - 3) =$$

$3 \cdot (11 - 2 \cdot 3 \div 6) \div (20 \div 4 - 3)$

$= 3 \cdot (11 - 6 \div 6) \div (20 \div 4 - 3)$ $\qquad\qquad$ $(2 \cdot 3 = 6)$

$= 3 \cdot (11 - 1) \div (20 \div 4 - 3)$ $\qquad\qquad$ $(6 \div 6 = 1)$

$= 3 \cdot 10 \div (20 \div 4 - 3)$ $\qquad\qquad$ $(11 - 1 = 10)$

$= 3 \cdot 10 \div (5 - 3)$ $\qquad\qquad$ $(20 \div 4 = 5)$

$= 3 \cdot 10 \div 2$ $\qquad\qquad$ $(5 - 3 = 2)$

$= 30 \div 2$ $\qquad\qquad$ $(3 \cdot 10 = 30)$

$= 15$ $\qquad\qquad$ $(30 \div 2 = 15)$

n. Do the addition inside of the **parenthesis**, and then do the subtraction step-by-step as shown:

$$15 - (7 + 2) = 15 - 9 \qquad\qquad (7 + 2 = 9)$$
$$= 6 \qquad\qquad (15 - 9 = 6)$$

o. Do the addition inside of the **parenthesis** at the left side, do the subtraction inside of the **parenthesis** at the right side, and then multiply step-by-step as shown:

$$(36 + 4) \times (5 - 2) = 40 \times (5 - 2) \qquad\qquad (36 + 4 = 40)$$
$$= 40 \times 3 \qquad\qquad (5 - 2 = 3)$$
$$= 120 \qquad\qquad (40 \times 3 = 120)$$

p. Do the subtraction inside of the **parenthesis** at the left side, do the subtraction inside of the **parenthesis** at the right side and then do the subtraction step-by-step as shown:

$$(19 - 9) - (7 - 5) = 10 - (7 - 5) \qquad\qquad (19 - 9 = 10)$$
$$= 10 - 2 \qquad\qquad (7 - 5 = 2)$$
$$= 8 \qquad\qquad (10 - 2 = 8)$$

q. Do the subtraction inside of the **parenthesis** at the left side, do the addition inside of the **parenthesis** at the right side, and then do the addition step-by-step as shown:

$$(23 - 19) + (7 + 3) = 4 + (7 + 3) \qquad\qquad (23 - 19 = 4)$$
$$= 4 + 10 \qquad\qquad (7 + 3 = 10)$$
$$= 14 \qquad\qquad (4 + 10 = 14)$$

Addition, Subtraction, Multiplication, Division, Parentheses, Exponents, and Roots

Quick Review

Exponents show repeated multiplication. Therefore, an exponent tells how many times a base is used as a factor as shown:

(a).

Exponent form.   Factor form.   Standard form.   Exponent

$$4^3 = 4 \cdot 4 \cdot 4 = 64 \qquad\qquad 4^3$$

Base   4 is used as a factor 3 times.

(b). $\quad 2^3 = 2 \cdot 2 \cdot 2 = 8$

In this section, "**Roots**" are actually referred to as **square roots**.

If $A = x^2$, then x is the square root of A. The square root of x^2 is written as $\sqrt{x^2} = x$ where $\sqrt{}$ is the symbol for square root. (**Note:** Finding the square root is similar to finding the length of a side of a square when the area of the square is known.) Review the section on the area of a square. Review the section on square root also.

For examples:

a. $\sqrt{4} = \sqrt{2^2} = 2$ **b.** $\sqrt{9} = \sqrt{3^3} = 3$ **c.** $\sqrt{16} = \sqrt{4^2} = 4$

d. $\sqrt{25} = \sqrt{5^2} = 5$ **e.** $\sqrt{36} = \sqrt{6^2} = 6$ **f.** $\sqrt{49} = \sqrt{7^2} = 7$

g. $\sqrt{64} = \sqrt{8^2} = 8$ **h.** $\sqrt{81} = \sqrt{9^2} = 9$ **i.** $\sqrt{100} = \sqrt{10^2} = 10$

Example 6

Find the value of each expression.

a. $(3^2 - \sqrt{9}) - \sqrt{16} + 2^2$ **b.** $2^2 \times \sqrt{25} + \sqrt{16}$ **c.** $\sqrt{36} + 4^2 - \sqrt{9}$

d. $(2^3 + \sqrt{25}) - (3^2 - \sqrt{36})^2$ **e.** $(\sqrt{81} - 2^2 + \sqrt{16}) \times (6^2 - 4^2 - 3^2) \div 2$

Solution

PERMDAS is used to find the values of questions **a** to **e** as shown:

a. Do the **exponent** and the **root** inside of the **parenthesis**, and then subtract inside of the **parentheses**, do the **exponent outside the parenthesis**, do the **root outside the parenthesis**, subtract, and then add step-by-step as shown:

$$(3^2 - \sqrt{9}) - \sqrt{16} + 2^2 = (9 - \sqrt{9}) - \sqrt{16} + 2^2 \qquad\qquad 3^2 = 9$$

$$= (9 - 3) - \sqrt{16} + 2^2 \qquad\qquad\qquad \sqrt{9} = 3$$

$$= 6 - \sqrt{16} + 2^2 \qquad\qquad\qquad\quad 9 - 6 = 3$$

$$= 6 - \sqrt{16} + 4 \qquad\qquad\qquad\quad 2^2 = 4$$

$$= 6 - 4 + 4 \qquad\qquad\qquad\qquad \sqrt{16} = 4$$

$$= 2 + 4 \qquad\qquad\qquad\qquad 6 - 4 = 2$$
$$= 6 \qquad\qquad\qquad\qquad\qquad 2 + 4 = 6$$

b. Do the **exponent**, do the **roots**, multiply, and then add step-by-step as shown:

$$2^2 \times \sqrt{25} + \sqrt{16} = 4 \times \sqrt{25} + \sqrt{16} \qquad\qquad 2^2 = 4$$
$$= 4 \times 5 + 4 \qquad\qquad \sqrt{25} = 5, \sqrt{16} = 4$$
$$= 20 + 4 \qquad\qquad 4 \times 5 = 20$$
$$= 24 \qquad\qquad 20 + 4 = 24$$

c. Do the **exponent**, do the **roots**, add, and then subtract step-by-step as shown:

$$\sqrt{36} + 4^2 - \sqrt{9} = \sqrt{36} + 16 - \sqrt{9} \qquad\qquad 4^2 = 16$$
$$= 6 + 16 - 3 \qquad\qquad \sqrt{36} = 6, \sqrt{9} = 3$$
$$= 22 - 3 \qquad\qquad 6 + 16 = 22$$
$$= 19 \qquad\qquad 22 - 3 = 19$$

d. Do the **exponent** and the **root** inside of the **parenthesis** on the left side, and then add, do the **exponent** and the **root** inside of the **parenthesis** on the right side, and then subtract, do the **exponent** inside of the **parentheses** on the right side, and finally subtract as shown step-by-step:

$$(2^3 + \sqrt{25}) - (3^2 - \sqrt{36})^2 = (8 + \sqrt{25}) - (3^2 - \sqrt{36})^2 \qquad\qquad 2^3 = 2 \cdot 2 \cdot 2 = 8$$
$$= (8 + 5) - (3^2 - \sqrt{36})^2 \qquad\qquad \sqrt{25} = 5$$
$$= 13 - (3^2 - \sqrt{36})^2 \qquad\qquad (8 + 9) = 13$$
$$= 13 - (9 - \sqrt{36})^2 \qquad\qquad 3^2 = 9$$
$$= 13 - (9 - 6)^2 \qquad\qquad \sqrt{36} = 6$$
$$= 13 - 3^2 \qquad\qquad (9 - 6)^2 = 3^2$$
$$= 13 - 9 \qquad\qquad 3^2 = 9$$
$$= 4 \qquad\qquad 13 - 9 = 4$$

e. Do the **operations** inside of the **parenthesis** at the left side according to **PERMDAS**, do the **operations** inside of the **parenthesis** at the right side according to **PERMDAS**, multiply the results, and then divide as shown step-by-step:

$$(\sqrt{81} - 2^2 + \sqrt{16}) \times (6^2 - 4^2 - 3^2) \div 2$$
$$= (\sqrt{81} - 4 + \sqrt{16}) \times (6^2 - 4^2 - 3^2) \div 2 \qquad\qquad 2^2 = 4$$
$$= (9 - 4 + 4) \times (6^2 - 4^2 - 3^2) \div 2 \qquad\qquad \sqrt{81} = 9, \sqrt{16} = 4$$
$$= (5 + 4) \times (6^2 - 4^2 - 3^2) \div 2 \qquad\qquad 9 - 4 = 5$$
$$= 9 \times (6^2 - 4^2 - 3^2) \div 2 \qquad\qquad 5 + 4 = 9$$
$$= 9 \times (36 - 16 - 9) \div 2 \qquad\qquad 6^2 = 36, 4^2 = 16, 3^2 = 9$$
$$= 9 \times (20 - 9) \div 2 \qquad\qquad 36 - 16 = 20$$
$$= 9 \times 11 \div 2 \qquad\qquad 20 - 9 = 11$$
$$= 99 \div 2 \qquad\qquad 9 \times 11 = 99$$

$$= 49\frac{1}{2}$$

$$99 \div 2 = 49\frac{1}{2}$$

━━━━━━━━━━━━━━━━━ **The notes and the generous worked examples have provided me with the conceptual understanding and the computational fluency to do my homework.**

Exercises

1. What is meant by the order of operations?

2. What does PERMDAS stands for?

3. Find the value of each expression. Hint: See Example 2.
Match similar exercises with similar examples.

   a. 8 + 4 - 3   **b**. 16 - 7 + 3   **c**. 16 - 5 - 8

   d. 32 - 10 + 5   **e**. 13 + 2 - 7   **f**. 24 - 6 - 10

4 Find the value of each expression. Hint: See Example 3.
Match similar exercises with similar examples.

   a. 10 · 2 ÷ 4   **b**. 15 ÷ 5 · 3   **c**. 36 ÷ 6 ÷ 6

   d. 28 ÷ 7 · 3   **e**. 24 ÷ 4 ÷ 3   **f**. 8 · 2 ÷ 4

5. Find the value of each expression. Hint: See Example 4.
Match similar exercises with similar examples.

   a. 6 · 4 - 3   **b**. 36 - 5 · 2   **c**. 30 ÷ 3 + 4

   d. 8 - 30 ÷ 5   **e**. 12 - 4 · 2 + 6   **f**. 5 + 3 · 4 - 2

   g. 16 - 2 · 5 + 4 ÷ 2   **h**. 14 ÷ 7 · 3 + 8 - 3   **i**. 4 · 6 ÷ 3

   j. 12 ÷ 3 · 4   **k**. 18 ÷ 6 + 2 · 6   **l**. 6 + 12 - 3 · 4   **m**. 7 + 2 · 4

6. Find the value of each expression. Hint: See Example 5.
Match similar exercises with similar examples.

   a. 4 · (7 + 3)   **b**. (7 - 5) · 2   **c**. 36 ÷ (4 + 2)

   d. (18 - 3) ÷ 5   **e**. (13 + 2) · 2   **f**. 8 + (24 - 9)

   g. 16 ÷ 4 · (8 - 6)   **h**. 2 · (5 + 4) ÷ 6   **i**. 8 · 3 ÷ (12 - 8)

   j. (12 + 6) × (9 - 7)   **k**. 11 + 3 ÷ (4 - 2)   **l**. (5 + 3 · 5) ÷ 2

   m. 4 · (12 - 3 · 4 ÷ 3)   **n**. 8 - (3 + 5)   **o**. (14 + 2) × (6 - 4)

   p. (9 - 3) - (13 - 7)   **q**. (15 - 8) + (4 + 8)

7. Find the value of each expression. Hint: See Example 6.
Match similar exercises with similar examples.

   a. $(2^2 - \sqrt{4}) - \sqrt{4} + 3^2$ **b**. $3^2 \times \sqrt{16} + \sqrt{9}$ **c**. $\sqrt{64} + 3^2 - \sqrt{9}$

   d. $(3^3 + \sqrt{9}) - (2^3 - \sqrt{25})^2$ **e**. $(\sqrt{100} - 3^2 + \sqrt{25}) \times (5^2 - 3^2 - 2^2)$

Challenge Questions

8 Find the value of each expression.

   a. 10 - 3 - 4   **b**. 17 - 8 + 2   **c**. 18 + 3 - 9   **d**. 36 ÷ 6 ÷ 3

e. $9 \cdot 2 \div 3$ **f.** $15 \div 3 \cdot 3$ **g.** $10 - 4 \div 2$ **h.** $8 - 2 \cdot 4 + 5$

i. $18 - 11 \cdot 2$ **j.** $12 \div 4 + 3$ **k.** $8 \cdot 4 - 5$ **l.** $5 \cdot 4 \div 2$

m. $12 - 3 \cdot 2 + 4 \div 2$ **n.** $24 \div 6 \cdot 2 + 9 - 7$ **o.** $16 \div 4 \cdot 3$

p. $24 \div 4 + 3 \cdot 4$ **q.** $8 + 3 \cdot 5$ **r.** $10 + 4 - 2 \cdot 4$ **s.** $3 \cdot 4 \div 2$

9. Find the value of each expression.

  a. $6 \cdot 3 \div (9 - 6)$ **b.** $(8 + 3) \cdot 4$ **c.** $24 \div (5 + 3)$ **d.** $3 \cdot (5 + 6)$

  e. $15 \div 3 \cdot (7 - 3)$ **f.** $3 \cdot (4 + 3) \div 3$ **g.** $(12 - 3) - (10 - 4)$

  h. $(10 - 4) \times (7 + 3)$ **i.** $(8 + 4 \div 2) \div 5$ **j.** $6 \cdot (14 - 3 \times 4 \div 3)$

  k. $(14 - 8) + (3 + 7)$ **l.** $3 \cdot (16 - 4 \cdot 2 \div 8)$ **m.** $(7 + 5 \cdot 5) \div 4$

10. Find the value of each expression.

  a. $\sqrt{81} - 2^3 + \sqrt{4}$ **b.** $3^2 \cdot \sqrt{4} - \sqrt{9}$ **c.** $4^2 - \sqrt{100} \div 2$

  d. $(4^2 + \sqrt{81}) - (2^3 - \sqrt{9})^2$ **e.** $(3^3 - \sqrt{16}) - \sqrt{16} + 3^2$

  f. $\sqrt{81} + 3^2 - \sqrt{16}$ **g.** $(4^2 - \sqrt{16}) - \sqrt{9} + 3^2$ **h.** $3^3 \cdot \sqrt{25} + \sqrt{36}$

Answers to Selected Questions

3a. 9   **4a.** 5   **5a.** 21   **6a.** 40   **7a.** 9

Extension of the Order of Operations Using PERMDAS
(A). Fraction Bar

The order of operations using PERMDAS can be **extended** to include **a fraction bar**. A fraction bar indicates that the operations in the numerator are done separately using PERMDAS, the operations in the denominator are also done separately using PERMDAS, and finally, the numerator is divided by the denominator.

Example 7

Find the value of each expression.

  a. $\dfrac{24 \div (7 - 3)}{9 - 3}$ **b.** $\dfrac{(16 - 4) - 2}{5 - 12 \div 4}$ **c.** $\dfrac{(15 - 7) \cdot 4}{16 - 4 \cdot 3}$ **d.** $\dfrac{3 \cdot 4 + 10}{12 \div 3 - 1}$

Solution

a. Considering the **numerator** and using PERMDAS, do the subtraction inside of the **parenthesis**, and then do the division. Considering the **denominator** and using PERMDAS, do the subtraction, and then divide the **numerator** by the **denominator** as shown step-by-step:

$$\frac{24 \div (7 - 3)}{9 - 3} = \frac{24 \div 4}{9 - 3} \qquad\qquad (7 - 3) = 4$$

$$= \frac{6}{9 - 3} \qquad\qquad 24 \div 4 = 6$$

$$= \frac{6}{6} \qquad\qquad 9 - 3 = 6$$

$$= 1 \qquad\qquad 6 \div 6 = 1$$

b. Considering the **numerator** and using PERMDAS, do the subtraction inside of the **parenthesis**, and then do the subtraction outside the parenthesis. Considering the **denominator** and using PERMDAS, do the division, and then the subtraction. Finally divide the **numerator** by the **denominator** as shown step-by-step:

$$\frac{(16 - 4) - 2}{5 - 12 \div 4} = \frac{12 - 2}{5 - 12 \div 4} \qquad\qquad (16 - 4) = 12$$

$$= \frac{10}{5 - 12 \div 4} \qquad\qquad 12 - 2 = 10$$

$$= \frac{10}{5 - 3} \qquad\qquad 12 \div 4 = 3$$

$$= \frac{10}{2} \qquad\qquad 5 - 3 = 2$$

$$= 5 \qquad\qquad 10 \div 2 = 5$$

c. Considering the **numerator** and using **PERMDAS**, do the subtraction inside the **parenthesis**, and then multiply. Considering the **denominator** and using PERMDAS, do the multiplication and subtraction, and finally, divide the **numerator** by the **denominator** step-by-step as shown:

$$\frac{(15 - 7) \cdot 4}{16 - 4 \cdot 3} = \frac{8 \cdot 4}{16 - 4 \cdot 3} \qquad\qquad (15 - 7) = 8$$

$$= \frac{32}{16 - 4 \cdot 3} \qquad\qquad 8 \cdot 4 = 32$$

$$= \frac{32}{16 - 12} \qquad\qquad 4 \cdot 3 = 12$$

$$= \frac{32}{4} \qquad\qquad 16 - 12 = 4$$

$$= 8 \qquad\qquad 32 \div 4 = 8$$

d. Considering the **numerator** and using PERMDAS, multiply, and then add. Considering the **denominator** and using PERMDAS, divide, and then subtract. Finally, divide the numerator by the denominator step-by-step as shown:

28

$$\frac{3 \cdot 4 + 10}{12 \div 3 - 1} = \frac{12 + 10}{12 \div 3 - 1} \qquad 3 \cdot 4 = 12$$

$$= \frac{22}{12 \div 3 - 1} \qquad 2 + 10 = 22$$

$$= \frac{22}{4 - 1} \qquad 12 \div 3 = 4$$

$$= \frac{22}{3} \qquad 4 - 1 = 3$$

$$= 7\frac{1}{3} \qquad 22 \div 3 = 7\frac{1}{3}$$

(B). Parentheses, Parenthesis, and Brackets

Parentheses is the plural form of parenthesis.

The symbol for a parenthesis is ( ) and the symbol for a bracket is [ ]. The brackets may be considered as another type of parentheses, and that the operations inside of the **parentheses** are done first according to PERMDAS **before** the operations inside of the **brackets** are done according to PERMDAS, and then we should do the remaining operations according to PERMDAS. The parentheses and brackets are used in expressions when further groupings of the numbers in the expression are necessary. Note that the operations should always be done within the **innermost grouping** symbols first.

Example 8

Find the value of each expression.

a. $[(9 - 5) + 3] \cdot 2$ **b.** $[(19 - 4) \div (12 - 9)] \cdot 3$

Solution

a. Do the subtraction inside of the **parentheses**, do the addition inside of the **bracket** next, and then multiply step-by-step as shown:

$$[(9 - 5) + 3] \cdot 2 = [4 + 3] \cdot 2 \qquad\qquad (9 - 5) = 4$$
$$= 7 \cdot 2 \qquad\qquad [4 + 3] = 7$$
$$= 14 \qquad\qquad 7 \cdot 2 = 14$$

b. Do the subtractions inside of **both parentheses**, do the division inside of the **bracket** next, and then multiply step-by-step as shown:

$$[(19 - 4) \div (12 - 9)] \cdot 3 = [15 \div 3] \cdot 3 \qquad (19 - 4) = 15, (12 - 9) = 3$$
$$= 5 \cdot 3 \qquad\qquad [15 \div 3] = 5$$
$$= 15 \qquad\qquad 5 \cdot 3 = 15$$

Example 9

Find the value of each expression.

a. $[(7 - 5)^2 + 3] \cdot 3$ **b.** $[(10 - 8)^3 \div (9 - 7)^2] \cdot 3$ **c.** $[(11 - 9)^2 \times (24 - 23)^2]^2 \cdot 2$

Solution

a. Do the operation inside of the **parenthesis**, do the operation in the **bracket**, and then multiply step-by-step as shown:

$$[(7 - 5)^2 + 3] \cdot 3 = [2^2 + 3] \cdot 3$$
$$= [4 + 3] \cdot 3$$
$$= 7 \cdot 3$$
$$= 21$$

$(7 - 5)^2 = 2^2$
$2^2 = 4$
$[4 + 3] = 7$
$7 \cdot 3 = 21$

b. Do the operations inside of both **parentheses**, do the operations in the **bracket**, and then multiply step-by-step as follows:

$$[(10 - 8)^3 \div (9 - 7)^2] \cdot 3 = [2^3 \div 2^2] \cdot 3$$
$$= [8 \div 4] \cdot 3$$
$$= 2 \cdot 3$$
$$= 6$$

$(10 - 8)^3 = 2^3, (9 - 7)^2 = 2^2$
$2^3 = 2 \cdot 2 \cdot 2 = 8, 2^2 = 2 \cdot 2 = 4$
$[8 \div 4] = 2$
$2 \cdot 3 = 6$

c. Do the operations inside of both **parentheses**, do the operations in the bracket, square the simplification inside the bracket, and then multiply step-by-step as shown:

$$[(11 - 9)^2 \times (24 - 23)^2]^2 \cdot 2 = [2^2 \times 1^2]^2 \cdot 2$$
$$= [4 \times 1]^2 \cdot 2$$
$$= 4^2 \cdot 2$$
$$= 16 \cdot 2$$
$$= 32$$

$(11 - 9)^2 = 2^2, (24 - 23)^2 = 1^2$
$2^2 = 4, 1^2 = 1$
$[4 \times 1]^2 = 4^2$
$4^2 = 4 \times 4 = 16$
$16 \cdot 2 = 32$

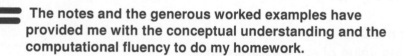 **The notes and the generous worked examples have provided me with the conceptual understanding and the computational fluency to do my homework.**

Exercises

1. Find the value of each expression. Hint: See Example 7. Match similar exercises with similar examples.

a. $\dfrac{18 \div (11 - 9)}{17 - 14}$ **b.** $\dfrac{(19 - 3) - 4}{6 - 9 \div 3}$ **c.** $\dfrac{(27 - 23) \cdot 4}{18 - 7 \cdot 2}$ **d.** $\dfrac{5 \cdot 3 + 5}{9 - 20 \div 5}$

2. Find the value of each expression. Hint: See Example 8. Match similar exercises with similar examples.

a. $[(12 - 7) + 4] \cdot 3$ **b.** $[(14 - 6) \div (16 - 12)] \cdot 2$

3. Find the value of each expression. Hint: See Example 9. Match similar exercises with similar examples.

a. $[(9 - 7)^2 + 6] \cdot 2$ **b.** $[(5 - 1)^2 \div (11 - 9)^2] \cdot 2$ **c.** $[(18 - 16)^2 \times (7 - 5)^2]^2 \cdot 2$

Challenge Questions

4. Find the value of each expression.

30

a. $\dfrac{4 \cdot 3 + 8}{11 - 36 \div 6}$ **b.** $\dfrac{(7 - 4) \cdot 5}{9 - 4}$ **c.** $[(7 - 3) + 2] \cdot 4$

d. $[(6 - 4)^3 \div (5 - 3)^2] \cdot 2$ **e.** $[(14 + 10) \div (8 - 2)] \cdot 2$ **f.** $[(3 + 1)^2 \times (13 - 11)^2] \cdot 2$

Answers to Selected Questions.
1a. 3   **2b.** 27   **3a.** 20

STEM-AND-LEAF PLOT

Cumulative Review

1. Mary said that to divide by a fraction is the same as multiplying by the reciprocal of the fraction. Is her statement correct? Hint: Review the section on the Division of Fractions in the MathTeaching Series for grade 6 or grade 7.
2. Divide, multiply, divide, subtract, or add. Hint: Review the section on the Division of Fractions in the MathTeaching Series for grade 6 or grade 7.

   a. $\dfrac{2}{5} \div \dfrac{4}{15} =$ **b.** $\dfrac{2}{5} \times \dfrac{4}{15} =$ **c.** $\dfrac{2}{5} + \dfrac{4}{15} =$ **d.** $\dfrac{2}{5} - \dfrac{4}{15} =$

3. Find the value of each expression. Hint: Review the chapter on the Order of Operations in the MathTeaching Series for grade 6 or grade 7.
   a. $12 + 3 \cdot 4 - 8$ **b.** $16 - 20 \div 4$ **c.** $7 \cdot 2 - 2$ **d.** $9 \div 3 \cdot 2$

New Terms
Stem-and-leaf plot, stem, leaf

A stem-and-leaf plot is a table that shows groups of data arranged by **place value**. (Review the section on **Place Value** in the MathTeaching Series for grade 5 if needed.) **A stem-and-leaf plot** is used to display and compare data.

How to Make a Stem-and-Leaf Plot
Example 1
Using the data values, (a) make a stem-and-leaf plot.
                        (b) explain how the stem-and-leaf plot is made.
    Ages of people in a club.
    Data values
    28   34   16   50   12   13
    34   14   7   16   25   19

31

16	9	28	50	55	19
74	36	8			

Solution

a). The tens digit of each number is its **stem**. The **stems** are listed from the least to the greatest. The **leaf** of each data value is written to the right of its stem, and they are written in order from the least to the greatest. The stem-and-leaf plot is shown below:

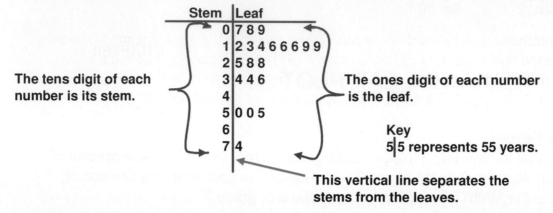

b). The stem-and-leaf plot is made from data values using the four items listed below:

1. Under the stems column, list the tens digit of every number in order from the least to the greatest and these tens digits becomes the stems. The data values contain one-digit numbers which are ones, so the stem column begins with zero because the ones has no place value for tens. The highest data is 74, and therefore, the tens digits under the stem column range from 0 to 7, and therefore, choose 0 to 7 as stems also.

2. Under the leaves column and beside each ten digit, write the ones digits of each number in order from least to greatest, and these ones digits become the leaves. For example, the data values for the stem-and-leaf plot:

2|5 8 8   are 25, 28, and 28.

tens   ones

3. The ones digits are written under the leaf column to the right of its stem, and they are written from the least to the greatest.

4. The "key" helps us to confirm the place values of the stem and leaf columns. For example, the key "5|5" means 55 years" and it confirms that the stem column is tens and the leaf column is ones.

Example 2

List the data values in the stem-and-leaf plot.

```
Stem │Leaf
     0│1 7 9
     1│4 4 8
     2│0 1 6
     3│0 0 9              Key
     4│4 5 6 8 9          1│4   means 14
     5│1 4
```

Solution

Using the information in Example 1, regarding the fact that the stem column is the tens column and the leaf column is the ones column and the key shows "1 | 4 means 14", which confirms that the stem column is tens and the leaf column is ones, the data values are: 1, 7, 9, 14, 14, 18, 20, 21, 26, 30, 30, 39, 44, 45, 46, 48, 49, 51, 54.

Example 3

a. Use the given data to make a stem-and-leaf plot.
b. How many teams have scores greater than 65?
c. How many leaves are in the stem-and-leaf plot?
d. Using the stem-and-leaf plot, what is the median?
e. Using the stem-and-leaf plot, what is the mode?
f. What is the range?

Teams	A	B	C	D	E	F	G	H	I	J	K	L	M	N
Scores per year	24	30	30	48	56	29	70	72	27	32	30	44	50	48

Solution

a The scores range from 24 to 72, so the stems are from 2 to 7, and the ones digits are written under the leaf column to the right of the stems, and they are written from the least to the greatest as shown:

```
Stem │Leaf
     2│4 7 9
     3│0 0 0 2
     4│4 8 8
     5│0 6
     6│                  key
     7│0 2               7│0   means 70.
```

b. There are two teams which have scores greater 65 and the scores are:

$$7│0\ 2\quad \text{which are 70 and 72.}$$

c. There are 14 leaves in the stem-and-leaf plot. The number of leaves is the same as the number of the scores.

d. The middle score is the median, however, since there are 14 scores, the middle score is the average of the 7th and the 8th scores.
The 7th leaf = 32 and the 8th leaf = 44.

33

Therefore, the average of the 7th and 8th scores

$$= \frac{\text{7th score} + \text{8th score}}{2}$$

$$= \frac{32 + 44}{2} = \frac{76}{2} = 38 \text{ scores.}$$

In order to find the median, the data needs to be arranged in order from the least to the greatest. **Note** that the stem-and-leaf plot already arranges the numbers in order from the least to the greatest.

e. The score that occurs the most is the mode. From the stem-and-leaf plot, the mode is:

3|0 0 0   which is 30, 30, and 30 because 30 occurs the most.

f. The **range is the largest score minus the smallest score** which is 72 - 24 = 48

Example 4

a. Use the data to make a stem-and-leaf plot. The weights are given to the nearest whole number.

b. Explain what

7|0 8   mean

c. What does

1 2|0 0   mean?

d. What is the mean?

People	A	B	C	D	E	F	G	H	I	J	K	L	M
Weight in lbs.	145	85	94	142	100	68	140	120	85	100	70	78	120

Solution

a. The numbers range from 68 to 145, and therefore, the stem should range from 6 to 14, and from the key the numbers under the leaf column are ones. The stem and leaf plot is shown as shown:

34

```
Stem Leaf
   6 8
   7 0 8
   8 5 5
   9 4
1 0 0 0
1 1
1 2 0 0                              key
1 3                                  14 0   means 140 lbs.
1 4 0 2 5
```

b.   7 0 8   means 70 lbs. and 78 lbs. (See similar explanation in Examples 1 and 2).
c.   1 2 0 0   means 120 lbs. and 120 lbs. (See similar explanation in Examples 1 and 2).

d. The mean is the same as the average.

$$\text{Mean} = \frac{\text{Sum of all the numbers}}{\text{Total number of the numbers}}$$

$$= \frac{68 + 70 + 78 + 85 + 85 + 94 + 100 + 100 + 120 + 120 + 140 + 142 + 145}{13}$$

$$= \frac{1347}{13}$$

= 103.6 lbs. You may use a calculator to obtain the answer.

Back-to-Back Stem-and-Leaf Plot
Example 5
a. What is a back-to-back stem-and-leaf plot?
b. What is the back-to-back stem-and-leaf plot used for?
Solution
a. A back-to-back stem-and-leaf plot is simply two stem-and-leaf plots joined together.
b. A back-to-back stem-and-leaf plot is used to compare two related sets of data.

How to Make a "Back-to-Back Stem-and-Leaf Plot"
Example 6
Describe how a back-to-back stem-and-leaf plot is made. Give an example.
A back-to-back stem-and-leaf plot is made as shown:
Record the stems in the center of the plot.
Record one set of the leaf at the left side of the stem and record the other set of the leaf at the right side of the stem as shown:

35

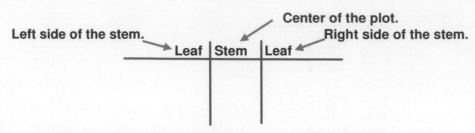

Center of the plot.

Left side of the stem.

Right side of the stem.

Leaf | Stem | Leaf

The key to the back-to-back stem-and-leaf plot can be written in two forms, (**a**) and (**b**).
Use back-to-back stem-and-leaf plot of the weights of boys and girls shown below
as an example.

Girls (weights in lbs.)	Stem	Boys (weights in lbs)
9 6 5	1	7 9
9 8 4	2	0 5
6 5 3 0	3	
8 7 2 1	4	3 6 8

The keys are:

(a) means 24 lbs. ⟵ 4 | 2 | 0 ⟶ means 20 lbs.
(Note that this key is
written in the reverse form).

(b)

| 4 | 3 means 43 lbs.
0 | 3 | means 30 lbs.
(Note that this key is written in the
reverse form).

Example 7

a. Use the given data to make a back-to-back stem-and-leaf plot.

Ages of males and females entering a certain library												
Females (years)	44	22	10	19	34	40	17	10	22	31	45	19	10
Males (years)	24	30	17	20	29	10	24	24	31	36	18	15	16

b. Find the median and the mode of the ages of the females.

c. What is the median and the mode of the ages of the males?

d. What is the range of the ages of the females?

e. What is the range of the ages of the males?

f. Comparing the ages of the females and the males, which range is smaller?

g. Which median is greater? Is this difference shown by the stem-and-leaf plot?
   How is this difference shown by the stem-and-leaf plot?

Solution

a. Using the information under "How to make a back-to-back stem-and-leaf plot" the
   back-to-back stem-and-leaf plot of the ages of the females and the males are
   drawn as follows:

Female	Stem	Males
9 9 7 0 0 0	1	0 5 6 7 8
2 2	2	0 4 4 4 9
4 1	3	0 1 6
5 4 0	4	

key:
Means 31 years ←——1│3│0 ——→ Means 30 years

b. The median is the middle leaf of the ages of the females, which is 22 years. (Count the ages under the leaf column to get to the middle age). The leaf that occurs the most is the mode. From the back-to-back stem-and-leaf plot, the age that occurs most is 10 years, and therefore, the mode is 10 years.

Note that   0 0 0 │1│   means 10, 10, and 10.

c. The median is the middle leaf of the ages of the males, which is 24 years. (Count the ages under the leaf column to get the middle age). The leaf that occurs the most is the mode. From the back-to-back stem-and-leaf plot, the age that occurs the most is 24 years, so the mode is 24 years.

Note that   │2│4 4 4 means 24, 24, and 24.

d. The range of the ages of the females is the greatest age minus the least age which is 45 - 10 = 35 years.

e. The range of the ages of the males is the greatest age minus the least age which is 36 - 10 = 26 years.

f. From the solution **d**, the range of the ages of the females is 35 years. From the solution **e**, the range of the males is 26 years. The range of the females' ages is greater than the range of the males' ages and this difference can be shown in the stem and leaf plot because the females' ages are spread more than the males' ages.

g. From solution **b**, the median age of the females is 22 years and from the solution **c**, the median age of the males is 24 years. Therefore, the median age of the males is greater than the median age of the females. The ages of the females are too close together to show any significant difference in the spread of the data (ages) on the stem-and-leaf plot.

Example 8
Use the back-to-back stem-and-leaf plot to answer the following questions.
   (a) Find the median for each set of data. Which median is greater? How is this difference shown by the stem-and-leaf plot?
   (b) Find the mode for each set of data.
   (c) Find the mean for each set of data.
   (d) What is the range for each set of data?
   (e) Which range is greater? How is this difference shown by the stem and leaf plot?

The time people use to find library books.
(Time to the nearest tenth of a minute).

Females	Stem	Males
9 8 7 5 1 0	7	2 4
6 5 3 1 1 0	8	5 7
7 5 4 3	9	2 3 5
8 6 4 3 3	10	2 3 4
2	11	0 2 5
	12	1
	13	3 7
	14	5 8
	15	
	16	3 8 9

key:
| 10 | 2   means 10.2 minutes
3 | 9 | means 9.3 minutes

Solution

Note that the key shows that the data under the leaf are not ones but rather tenths of a minute.

(**a**) The median age of the females' data is the middle leaf of the females' data. Since there are 22 data for the females, the middle terms are the 11th and the 12th terms of the data, which are 8.6 and 8.5 minutes. The average of the 11th and the 12th terms of the female data is the median of the females' data. So the

median of the females' data $= \dfrac{8.6 + 8.5}{2} = \dfrac{17.1}{2} = 8.55$ minutes.

(Hint: See the chapter/section on median.)
The median of the males' data is the middle leaf of the males' data.
Since there are 21 data for the males, the 11th data is the middle data which is 11.0 minutes. The median of the males' data is greater than the median of the females' data. The difference in the median between the females' and the males' data is shown by the stem-and-leaf plot because the females' data is clustered near the top.

(**b**) The leaf that occurs the most in each set of the data is the mode for the data. Considering the females' data, two numbers occur most which are 8.1 minutes and 10.3 minutes.

> **Note that 1 1 | 8 | means 8.1 and 8.1**
> **Note that 3 3 | 10 | means 10.3 and 10.3**

Considering the males' data, no data in the males' leaf occurs most, so the male data has no mode.

(**c**) Mean $= \dfrac{\text{Sum of all the data}}{\text{Total number of the data}}$

Considering the females' ages:
Mean $= (7.0 + 7.1 + 7.5 + 7.7 + 7.8 + 7.9 + 8.1 + 8.1 + 8.3 + 8.5 + 8.6 + 9.3 + 9.4$
$+ 9.5 + 9.7 + 10.3 + 10.3 + 10.4 + 10.6 + 10.8 + 11.2) \div 21$

$$= \frac{188.1}{21} = 8.96 = 9.0 \text{ minutes.}$$

Considering the males' ages:

$$\text{Mean} = \frac{\text{Sum of all the data}}{\text{Total number of the data}}$$

$$= 7.2 + 7.4 + 8.5 + 8.7 + 9.2 + +9.3 + 9.5 + 10.2 + 10.3 + 10.4 + 11.0 + 11.2$$
$$+ 11.5 + 12.1 + 13.3 + 13.7 + 14.5 + 14.8 + 16.3 + 16.8 + 16.9) \div 21$$

$$= \frac{242.8}{21} = 11.56 = 11.6 \text{ minutes} \qquad \text{(You may use a calculator.)}$$

(**d**) The range of each set of data is the largest time minus the smallest time. Considering the females, the largest time is 11.2 minutes and the smallest time is 7.0 minutes, and therefore, the range is:

$$11.2 - 7.0 = 4.2 \text{ minutes.}$$

Considering the males, the largest time is 16.9 minutes and the smallest time is 7.2 minutes, and therefore, the range = 16.9 - 7.2 = 9.7 minutes.

(**e**) From solution (**d**), the range of the females' data is 4.2 minutes and the range for the males' data is 9.7 minutes, and therefore, the males' range is greater than the females' range and this difference is shown by the stem-and-leaf plot because the females' data is clustered to the top while the males' data is spread.

Exercises

1. What is a stem-and-leaf plot?

2. What is a stem-and-leaf plot used for?

3. Use the data values to:

  (**a**) make a stem-and-leaf plot.

  (**b**) explain how the stem-and-leaf plot is made.

  Hint: See Example 1.

  Ages of people in a book club (ages in years).

15	17	34
22	38	34
34	45	62
40	60	28
15	65	29

4. Use the data values to make a stem-and-leaf plot.

  (**a**). Weight of people in lbs.   (**b**). Number of books per shelf

25	44	55	20
68	37	34	16
34	62	47	20

44	69	30
19	30	20
36	40	40

```
   16  20  59  37                          30  62  36
   77  32  25  32                          27  31  44
```
Hint: See Example 1.

5. List the data values in the following stem-and-leaf plots. Hint: See Example 2.

```
(a)  0│2 8 9          (b)  0│1 4 8 9        ©   0│0 3 5
     1│3                   1│7 8 9              1│0 0 4
     2│5 8 9               2│0 0 3 8            2│3
     3│0 0 0 5 8           3│4 9                3│4 8
     4│0 1 8 9             4│0 3 7 9            4│0 0 0 1
                           5│0 0 9              5│1 3 6 8
```

key: 4│0 means 40

key: 1│7 means 17   key: 3│4 means 34.

6a. Use the given data in tables 1 and 2 to make two separate stem-and-leaf plots.

Table 1

Teams	A	B	C	D	E	F	G	H	I	J
Scores per year	16	10	25	16	16	34	48	25	40	37

Table 2

Teams	A	B	C	D	E	F	G	H	I	J	K	L
Scores per year	9	27	17	35	27	17	30	34	27	35	42	30

6b. From each stem-and-leaf plot, how many teams have scored above 40 points per year?

6c. How many leaves are there in each stem-and-leaf plot?

6d. Find the median from each stem-and-leaf plot.

6e. Find the mode and the range of each stem-and-leaf plot.
Hint: See Example 3.

7a. Use the data to make a stem-and-leaf plot. The weights are given to the nearest whole number in lbs.

Animals	A	B	C	D	E	F	G	H	I	J	K	L
Weight in lbs.	77	30	29	37	30	48	44	56	70	54	61	48

7b. Explain the meaning of 3│007.

7c. Explain the meaning of 4│88.

7d. What is the mean of the data?
Hint: See Example 4.

8a. What is a back-to-back stem-and-leaf plot?

8b. What is a back-to-back stem-and-leaf plot used for?
Hint: See Example 5.

9. Describe how a back-to-back stem-and-leaf plot is made.
Hint: See Example 6.

10a. Use the given data to make a back-to-back stem-and-leaf plot.

Ages in years of people entering the library											
Females	29	20	50	42	20	32	19	21	50	32	20	20
Males	36	41	32	36	30	14	30	44	48	36	40	30

10b. Find the median and the mode of the ages of the females.

40

10c. Find the median and the mode of the ages of the males.

10d. What is the range of the ages of the males?

10e. What is the range of the ages of the females?

10f. Which range is smaller? How is the difference shown by the stem-and-leaf plot?
　　Hint: See Example 7.

11a. Use the given data to make a back-to-back stem-and-leaf plot.

Miles per gallon ratings of 4-cylinder and 6-cylinder cars.											
Model type	A	B	C	D	E	F	G	H	I	J	K
4-Cylinder	16	18	20	35	42	18	28	32	28	32	18
6-Cylinder	10	15	17	25	29	15	21	24	19	25	15

11b. Find the median and the mode of the 4-cylinder cars.

11c. Find the median and the mode of the 6-cylinder cars.

11d. What is the range of the 4-cylinder car data?

11e. What is the range of the 6-cylinder car data?
　　Hint: See Example 7.

12. Use the back-to-back stem-and-leaf plot to answer the questions:

　a. Find the median for each set of data. Which median is greater? How is this difference shown by the stem and leaf plot?

　b. Find the mode for each set of data.

　c. Find the mean for each set of data.

　d. What is the range for each set of data?

Ratings of miles per gallon for 4-cylinder and 6-cylinder cars.
Ratings to the nearest tenth of a mile per gallon.

```
        4-Cylinder   |   | 6-Cylinder
        ─────────────┼───┼────────────
                     | 14| 0 4
                     | 15| 3 5 7 9
                     | 16| 4 1
                     | 17|
                     | 18| 0 0 1
                     | 19| 5 8
                     | 20|
                     | 21|
           8 7 4 0 0 | 22|
               9 7 6 | 23|
             4 2 1 0 | 24|
```

key: | 15|3 means 15.3 mpg.
　　 6|23| means 23.6 mpg.
mpg means miles per gallon.

Hint: See Example 8

13. Create a stem-and-leaf plot of the data values.

　a. 54, 36, 48, 88, 93, 48, 50, 36, 50, 72, 61. Hint: See Example 3a

　b. 6.6, 9.4, 6.0, 7.4, 10.0, 8.7, 10.0, 6.0

　Hint: Although this problem is not a back-to-back stem-and-leaf plot, it is similar to Example 8 because the data values are in decimals (see the key of Example 8).

Challenge Questions

14. List the data values in the following stem-and-leaf plots.

(a)
```
0 | 2 3 4
1 | 0 0 1
2 | 8 9
3 |
4 | 4 8 9
5 | 0 0 0 2
```
key: 2 | 8 means 28.

(b)
```
1 | 0 0 0
2 | 4 8 9
3 | 2
4 | 7 8
5 | 0 5 8
6 | 1 1 14
```
key: 4 | 7 means 47.

©
```
1 | 7 9
2 | 0 0 4
3 | 4
4 |
5 | 1 3 8 9
6 | 4 7
```
key: 6 | 4 means 6.4

15. Use the data values to make stem-and-leaf plots.

a. Age of people in years.
```
17   25   23
25   17   23
18   19   18
20   23   17
24   24   19
38   39   42
```

b. Weight of people in lbs.
```
65   60   50
72   78   63
78   84   78
50   80   71
55   50   55
```

c. From the stem-and-leaf plot of **a** and **b**, find the median, mode, and range.

d. What does 1 | 99 mean?

e. What does 5 | 000 mean?

16a. Use the given data to make a back-to-back stem-and-leaf plot.

Ages of teachers in a certain school.						
Male (years)	24	36	55	47	50	36
Females (years)	23	41	28	32	30	23

16b. Find the mode, range, median, and mean of the ages of the male teachers.

16c. Find the mode, range, median, and mean of the ages of the female teachers.

17. Use the back-to-back stem-and-leaf plot to answer the following question.

What is the mode, range, median, and mean for the data set?

```
      8 6 | 10 | 0 1 4
          9 | 11 | 4
            | 12 | 5 6
      2 0 0 | 13 |
        4 2 | 14 | 3 1
```
key: 6 | 10 | means 10.6
      | 14 | 3 means 14.3

18. Find the mode, range, median, and mean of the following stem-and-leaf plot.

(a)
Stem	Leaf
2	0 0
3	1 2
4	2 3

key: 3 | 1 means 31.

(b)
Stem	Leaf
5	2 3
6	2 4
7	0 0 1

key: 7 | 0 means 7.0

©
Stem	Leaf
13	2 4
14	0 0 2

key: 13 | 2 means 132.

BOX-AND-WHISKER PLOTS

Now Terms
box-and-whiskers plot, quartile, interquartile range

A **box-and-whisker plot** shows sets of distribution of data into four groups, and each of the four groups contains about the same number of data. The **box-and-whisker plot is used to compare sets of data**. The **quartiles** separate or divide a data set into about four equal parts. The **interquartile range** is the upper quartile minus the lower quartile.

How to Make a Box-and-Whisker Plot

Example 1
Make a sketch of a box-and-whisker plot and show how the data is distributed at each section of the plot. Show the position of the first quartile, median, third quartile, and whiskers.

Solution
The box-and-whisker plot showing the first quartile, median, third quartile, and whiskers are shown as shown:

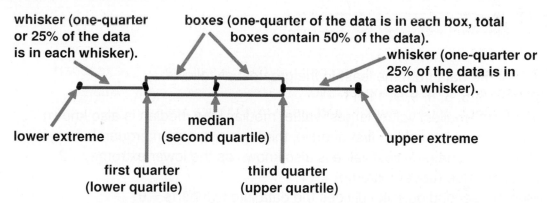

Critical Thinking - What Does the Length of the Box-and-Whisker Plot Tell You About the Data?
From the diagram in Example 1, there is one-quarter of the data in each whisker and in each box. So, a longer whisker or a longer box indicates that the data in that quartile or quartiles have a greater range. Similarly, a shorter whisker or box indicates that the data in that quartile or quartiles have a less range. A greater range indicates that the data in that quartile are more spread out. A less range indicates that the data in that quartile are less spread out.

The diagram below shows that the whisker at the left, which contains the data in the first quartile, is longer than any of the three other parts (second quartile, third quartile, and fourth quartile). So, the data in the first quartile is most spread out compared to the data in the other three quartiles.

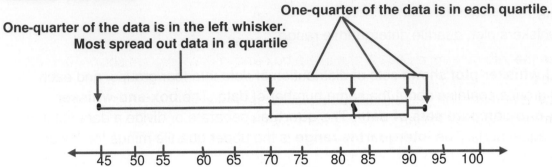

If the median line divides the box into two equal parts, then the data in the second, and the third quartiles are similarly spread out.

Example 2

a. Use the given data to find: smallest value, largest value, median (second quartile), lower quartile (first quartile), upper quartile (third quartile), and then make a box-and-whisker plot.

Data	11	5	2	6	11	9	5	3	8	9	4

b. Find the interquatile range.

c. Find the mode.

d. Find the mean.

Solution

a. Step 1: Order the data from the least to the greatest as follows:

2, 3, 4, 5, 5, 6, 8, 9, 9, 11, 11

Step 2: Find the smallest value, largest value, median (the median is also known as the second quartile), first quartile, third quartile, and interquartile range.

Smallest value (smallest value is also known as the lower extreme) = 2.

Largest value (upper extreme) = 11.

Median (second quartile) divides the data into two parts = 6.

First quartile (it is the median of the lower half of the data) = 4.

Third quartile (it is the median of the upper half of the data) = 9.

The information in Step 2 is illustrated in Figure 1.

(Figure 1 is shown on the next page.)

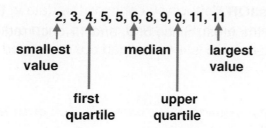

2, 3, 4, 5, 5, 6, 8, 9, 9, 11, 11

smallest value   median   largest value

first quartile   upper quartile

(Figure 1 is shown above.)

(Use the information in Step 2 to make a box-and-whisker plot as shown in Steps 3, 4, 5, and 6.)

Step 3: Draw a number line and plot the points smallest value, median, first quartile, third quartile, and the largest value from Step 2.

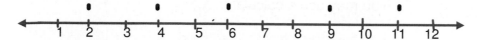

Step 4: Draw the vertical segments of the box with the three medians (or first quartile, second quartile, and the third quartile) identified.

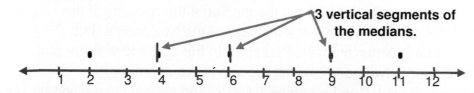

3 vertical segments of the medians.

Step 5: Draw **boxes** connecting the three vertical segments of the medians (or draw the **boxes** using the first, second, and third quartiles. The 3 vertical segments of the medians are the same as the 3 quartiles.)

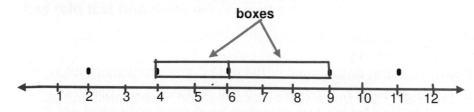

boxes

Step 6: Draw a **whisker** at each end of the box to the smallest and the largest numbers.

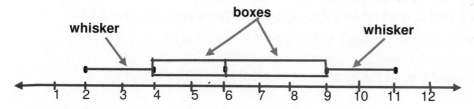

boxes

whisker   whisker

b. The interquartile range = Upper quartile - lower quartile

$\qquad\qquad$ = 9 - 4 $\quad$ From solution **a**, upper quartile = 9, and the lower quartile = 4.

$\qquad\qquad$ = 5

45

(The interquartile range is also known as **IQR**.)

c. The mode is the data value that occurs the most. Since 5, 9, and 11 occurred the most, the modes are 5, 9, and 11.

d. Mean $= \dfrac{\text{Sum of the numbers}}{\text{Number of the numbers.}}$

$$= \frac{2 + 3 + 4 + 5 + 5 + 6 + 8 + 9 + 9 + 11 + 11}{11}$$

$$= \frac{73}{11}$$

$= 6.6$ You may use a calculator.

Example 3

How is the median found in the stem-and-leaf plot and the box-and-whisker plot?

Solution

In the stem-and-leaf plot, the middle data item is the median if the quantity of the data item is an odd number or the median is the average of the two middle data items if the quantity of the data items is an even number. In the box-and-whisker plot, the median divides the data into two parts and the median is the segment that divides the box into two parts. Hint: See Examples 1 and 2, and review the section on stem-and-leaf plot.

Example 4

How are the smallest and the greatest data items found in the **stem-and-leaf plot** and the **box-and-whisker plot**?

Solution

In the **stem-and-leaf plot**, after the data values or the data items are written out in order, the first number is the smallest number and the last number is the greatest number. In the **box-and-whisker plot** the first data item on the left of the plot which is **the lower extreme is the least data item** and the last data item on the right of the plot which is the **upper extreme is the greatest data item**.

Hint: See Examples 1 and 2, and review the section on the stem-and-leaf plot.

Example 5

(**a**) Use the stem-and-leaf plot of the grades of students (in %) to make a box-and-whisker plot.

(**b**) Find the interquartile range of the data.

(**c**) Find the mean and the range.

(**d**) Find the mode.

46

Stem	Leaf
7	9
8	6 8 8 9
9	0 5

key: 9 | 0 means 90%

Solution

(**a**) The data items in the stem-and-leaf plot are already in numerical order from the smallest to the largest. The data values are 79 86, 88, 88, 89, 90, and 95. Use the description for lower extreme, first quartile, median, third quartile, and upper extreme in Example 2 to locate them as shown:

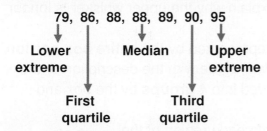

The **box-and-whisker plot** is shown below.

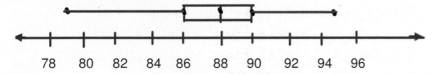

(**b**) Interquartile range = Third quartile - First quartile

$$= 90 - 86$$
$$= 4\%$$

(**c**) Mean = $\dfrac{\text{Sum of the data items}}{\text{Number of data items}}$

$$= \frac{79 + 86 + 88 + 88 + 89 + 90 + 95}{7}$$

$$= \frac{615}{7}$$

$= 87.857$ You may use a calculator to find $\dfrac{615}{7}$.

$= 88\%$ to the nearest whole number.

Range = Greatest data item - Least data item

$$= 95 - 79$$

$$= 16\%$$

The mode is the data item that occurs most.

$$= 88$$

Group Exercises

(a). Use the **stem-and-leaf plot** of the ages of students in a math club to draw a **box-and-whisker plot**.

```
0 | 2 2 3 4
1 | 0 0 1 1 2 3 9
```

(b) Find the median by using the **stem-and-leaf plot** and also by using a **box-and-whisker plot**.

(c) Considering the spread of the data items, explain why the upper whisker is longer than the upper portion of the box.

(d) Find the percent of the data items that are represented by the **entire box portion** of the box-and-whisker plot. Does your answer agree with the description of the box-and-whisker plot? Hint: The data is divided into **4 groups** by the box and whisker plot.

(e) Find the percent of the data items that fall into each region of the **box-and-whisker plot**? Does your answer agree with the description of the **box-and-whisker plot**. Hint: The data is divided into **4** groups by the box-and-whisker plot.

Example 6

Find the range, the first, and the third quartiles of the data set. Find the median of the data set.

93 84 78 88 91 88 89

Solution

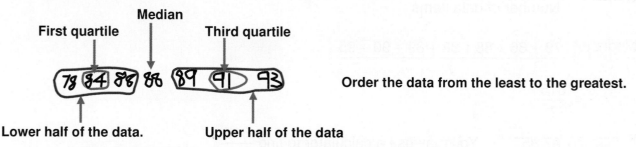

Order the data from the least to the greatest.

Range = Largest data item - Smallest data item.

= 93 - 78 (Largest data item = 93 and the smallest data item = 78.

= 15

First quartile = Median of the lower half of the data.

= 84

Third quartile = Median of the upper half of the data.

= 91

Median is the number that divides the data into two equal parts.

Median = 88.

Example 7

Find the range, median, the first, and third quartiles for the data set.

15 13 14 17 15 16 17 19 15 20 21 17

Solution

Order the data items from the smallest to the largest as follows:

13 14 15 15 15 16 17 17 17 19 20 21

Range = Largest value - Smallest value

$\quad$ = 21 - 13

$\quad$ = 8

We may group the data as follows to help us with the quartiles:

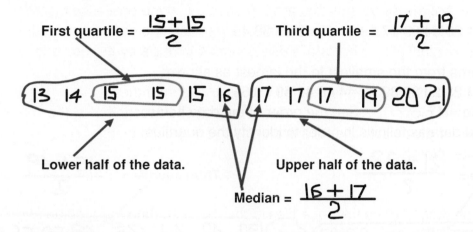

First quartile = $\dfrac{15+15}{2}$ $\quad$ Third quartile = $\dfrac{17+19}{2}$

13 14 15 15 15 16 17 17 17 19 20 21

Lower half of the data. $\quad$ Upper half of the data.

Median = $\dfrac{16+17}{2}$

The median is the average of the two middle numbers that divide the data into two equal parts when the total number of the data is an even number. (The data has a total of 12 numbers and 12 is an even number).

$$\text{Median} = \frac{16+17}{2}$$

$$= 16\frac{1}{2}$$

First quartile = Median of the lower half of the data.

$$= \frac{15+15}{2}$$

$$= \frac{30}{2}$$

$$= 15$$

Third quartile = Median of the upper half of the data.

$$= \frac{17 + 19}{2}$$

$$= \frac{36}{2}$$

$$= 18$$

Example 8

Find the smallest value, median, first quartile, third quartile, and the largest value for the data set.

50 22 17 23 56 21 23 64 23 17 19 44 42 49 39 36 45

Solution

Order the data items from the smallest to the largest as shown:

17 17 19 21 22 23 23 23 36 39 42 44 45 49 50 56 64

The smallest value = 17   See the order of the data items.

Group the ordered data as follows in order to identify the quartiles:

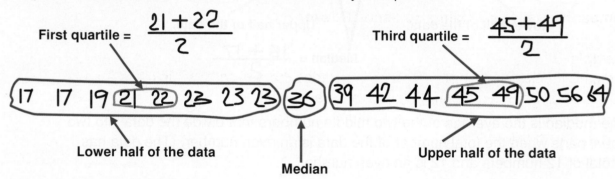

First quartile = $\dfrac{21 + 22}{2}$

Third quartile = $\dfrac{45 + 49}{2}$

Lower half of the data

Median

Upper half of the data

Median is the number that divides the data into two equal parts. So, the median is the number in the middle.

Median = 36

The first quartile is the median (middle number) of the lower half of the data.

First quartile = $\dfrac{21 + 22}{2}$ There is no middle number. Find the average of the two middle numbers.

$$= \frac{43}{2}$$

$$= 21.5$$

The third quartile is the median (middle number) of the upper half of the data.

Third quartile = $\dfrac{45 + 49}{2}$ There is no middle number. Find the average of the two middle numbers.

$$= \frac{94}{2} = 47$$

The largest value = 64.   See the order of the data items.

Example 9
(a) Select the values that can be found using a stem-and-leaf plot.
    1. upper quartile   **2.** median   **3.** range   **4.** mean
    5. mode   **6.** lower quartile   **7.** upper extreme   **8.** lower extreme
(b) Select the values that **cannot** be found using a box-and-whisker plot.
    1. upper quartile   **2.** interquartile range   **3.** range
    4. mean   **5.** mode   **6.** median
Solution
(a) All the values from 1 to 8 can be found using a stem and leaf plot.
(b) The mean and the mode cannot be found from the box-and-whisker plot.

Comparing Data Sets Using Box-and-Whisker Plot.

Example 10
Compare the box-and-whisker plots of the grades that the students in class A and class B obtained in geography. Which class has the higher
    (a) median   **(b)** range   **(c)** upper extreme
    (d) range of the middle half of the data
    (e) lower extreme

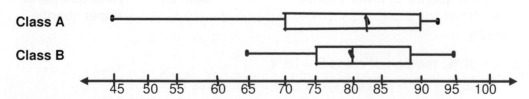

Solution
Use the scale in the diagram from 45 to 100 to compare the two box-and-whisker plots of the class A and the class B.
(a) Class A has the higher median.   See the diagram.
(b) Class A has the higher range because the distance between the upper extreme value and the lower extreme value is longer for class A.
   (We can subtract the lower extreme value from the upper extreme value of each set of the class (data) to find the class that has the higher range.)
(c) Class B has the higher upper extreme value because the extreme value of class B has bigger value than the extreme value of class A.

(**d**) The range of the middle half of the data is the length of the box which is greater for class A

(**e**) Class B has the higher "lower extreme" value.   See the diagram.

Example 11

For each box-and-whisker plot, find the values listed.

a. median   **b**. lower quartile   **c**. upper quartile
d. interquartile range   **e**. lower extreme   **f**. upper extreme   **g**. range

History test scores of students in class A and class B.

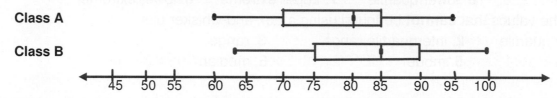

Solution

Redraw the box-and-whisker plots and link all the values to a position on the number line.

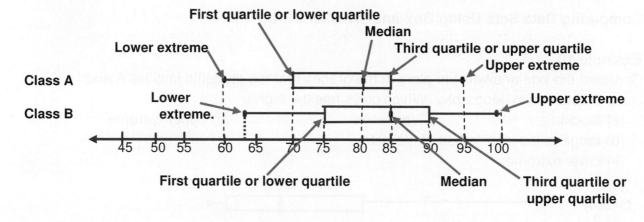

a. Median of class A = 80%, median of class B = 85%
b. Lower quartile of class A = 70% and the lower quartile of class B = 75%
c. Upper quartile of class A = 85% and the upper quartile of class B = 90%
d. Interquartile range of class A = Upper quartile - lower quartile
$$= 85\% - 70\% = 15\%$$
Interquartile range of class B = Upper quartile - lower quartile
$$= 90\% - 75\% = 15\%$$
e. Lower extreme of class A = 60% and lower extreme of class B = 63%
f. Upper extreme of class A = 95% and upper extreme of class B = 100%
g. Range of class A = Largest value - Smallest value = 95% - 60% = 35%
   Range of class B = Largest value - Smallest value = 100% - 63% = 37%

Exercises

1. Select the correct answer. The box-and-whisker plot shows the distribution of data into:
   a. two groups.   **b.** three groups.   **c.** four groups.   **d.** five groups.
   Hint: See Group Exercises, item (d), or see the preceding information.
2. Select the correct answer. Each group described in Exercise 1 contains about:
   a. twice the data.   **b.** three times the data.   **c.** the same number of data.
   Hint: See the preceding information.
3. The quartile separates or divides a data into about
   a. 5 equal parts.   **b.** 2 equal parts.   **c.** 3 equal parts.   **d.** 4 equal parts.
   e. 6 equal parts. Select the correct answer.
   Hint: See the preceding information.
4. **a.** What is the interquartile range (IQR)? Hint: See the preceding information.
   b. How are the data in the second and the third quartiles spread out when the median line divides the box into two equal parts?
   Hint: See the information/section under "Critical Thinking."
   c. Describe the range of a data that has a long whisker or box. Hint: See the information/section under "Critical Thinking."
   d. Complete the statement. A long whisker or box shows that the data in that quartile or quartiles have a _____ range. Hint: See the information/section under "Critical Thinking."
5. Describe how you would make a box-and-whisker plot and list all the data name that you would use in making the box-and-whisker plot.
   Hint: See Example 1.
6. Use the given data to make a box-and-whisker plot. Find the interquartile range, the mode, and the mean.
   a. 9, 6, 10, 11, 8, 7, 12, 9, 5, 8, 7
   b. 15, 14, 7, 10, 9, 6, 13, 8, 9, 7, 6
   c. 2, 7, 8, 3, 4, 5, 9, 3, 7, 8, 8
   Hint: See Example 2.
7. Describe in **your own words** how the median is found in the stem-and-leaf plot and the box-and-whisker plot. Hint: See Example 3.
8. Describe **in your own words** how the smallest and the largest data items are found in the stem-and-leaf plot and the box-and-whisker plot. Hint: See Example 4.
9 **a.** Use the stem-and-leaf plots A, B, and C of the grades of students in percent to make a box-and-whisker plot.
   b. Find the interquartile range of each set of data.
   c. Find the mean and the range of each set of data.
   d. Find the mode of each set of data.

A	
Stem	**Leaf**
7	5 8
8	0 0 3
9	1 8

Key: 7|5 means 75%.

B	
Stem	**Leaf**
6	8
7	8 9
8	0 1 3 7

Key: 6|8 means 68%

C	
Stem	**Leaf**
6	9
7	5 6
8	8 9
9	0 5

Key: 7|5 means 75%

Hint: See Example 5.

10. Find the range, the first, and the third quartiles of each set of data. Find the median of each set of data.

a. 65, 35, 72, 56, 60, 59, 45.

b. 98, 42, 38, 79, 82, 88, 56.

c. 77, 85, 23, 57, 48, 61, 68.

Hint: See Example 6.

11. Find the range, the median, the first, and the third quartiles for each data set.

a. 11, 14, 17, 10, 28, 18, 39, 44, 35, 12, 14, 15.

b. 19, 24, 3, 29, 13, 16, 9, 7, 13, 14, 7, 14.

c. 10, 8, 6, 4, 12, 8, 5, 6, 9, 12, 11, 7.

Hint: See Example 7.

12. Find the smallest value, median, first quartile, third quartile, and the largest value for each data set.

a. 7, 8, 9, 18, 9, 14, 17, 22, 27, 19, 11, 12, 10, 12, 13, 9, 26

b. 40, 32, 11, 16, 18, 21, 27, 12, 17, 13, 15, 14, 13, 9, 10, 16, 14

c. 13, 2, 7, 8, 2, 15, 11, 11, 12, 13, 14, 10, 8, 9

Hint: See Example 8.

13. The mean and mode cannot be found from the box-and-whisker plot. True or False? Hint: See Example 9.

14. Compare the box-and-whisker plots (A) and (B) for the grades in percent that students in class Y and class Z obtained in chemistry. Which class has the higher:

a. range.

b. range of the middle half of the data.

c. median.

d. lower quartile.

e. lower extreme.

f. upper quartile.

g. upper extreme.

(The box-and-whisker plots (A) and (B) are shown on the next page.)

Chemistry test scores in percent of students in classes Y and Z.

(B)

Chemistry test scores in percent of students in classes Y and Z.

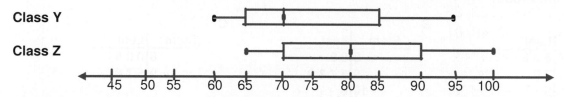

Hint: See Example 10 and notes.

15. For each set of the box-and-whisker plot X and Y, find the values listed.

    a. median.   **b**. range.   **c**. interquartile range.

    d. upper quartile.   **e**. lower quartile.   **f**. lower extreme.

    g. upper extreme.

Plot X

History test scores in percent of students in classes A and B.

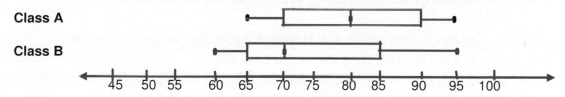

Plot Y

Science test scores in percent of students in classes A and class B.

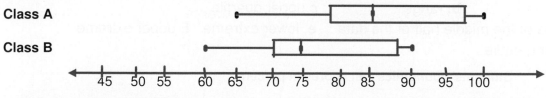

Hint: See Example 11

Challenge Questions

16. Use each given data to make a box-and-whisker plot. Find the interquartile range, range, mean, median, and mode.

    a. 10, 12, 7, 15, 11, 10, 13, 9, 12, 11, 14.

    b. 5, 8, 9, 12, 7, 13, 9, 7, 13, 10, 13.

17. Find the range, the first quartile, the third quartile, and the median of each of the data sets.

    a. 4, 10, 12, 14, 8, 11, 9

    b. 13, 19, 22, 14, 19, 10, 19

    c. 27, 21, 32, 18, 38, 18, 21

18. Use the stem-and-leaf plots A, B, and C of the grades of physics students in percent to:

    a. make a box-and-whisker plot.

    b. find the interquartile range.

    c. find the mean and the range.

    d. find the mode.

A

Stem	Leaf
6	0 8 8
7	7 9
8	5
9	8

Key: 7|7 means 77%.

B

Stem	Leaf
8	8 9
9	5 7 8 9
10	0

Key: 10|0 means 100%.

C

Stem	Leaf
8	0 0 6 8
9	5 7 8

Key: 8|0 means 80%.

19. Find the range, the median, the first, and the third quartiles of each data set.

    a. 5, 11, 17, 16, 9, 7, 18, 22, 28, 11, 15, 12

    b. 20, 28, 16, 35, 36, 18, 19, 22, 24, 12, 13, 10

    c. 10, 23, 9, 16, 28, 13, 15

    d. 11, 18, 28, 18, 15, 16, 11, 20, 22, 12, 11, 13, 17, 12, 14, 15, 10

    e. 19, 28, 14, 17, 15, 26, 38

20. Find the median, the range, the mode, the smallest value, the largest value, the first quartile, and the third quartile for each of the data set.

    a. 12, 13, 14, 28, 36, 18, 45,1 6, 19, 10, 13, 24, 26, 10, 15, 17, 16

    b. 11, 38, 24, 17, 19, 22, 22, 28, 10, 18, 14, 16, 27, 22, 15, 17, 17

21. Compare the box-and-whisker plots A and B of grades in percent obtained in economics class. Which class has the higher:

    a. median   **b.** range   **c.** upper quartile

    d. range of the middle half of the data   **e.** lower extreme **f.** upper extreme

    g. lower quartile

Students' economics test scores in percent

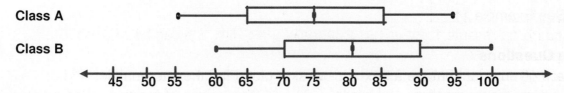

56

PERCENT

Percent Concept

The word **percent** means per one hundred. Percent may also be explained as a certain number out of 100. For example, 40 out of 100 students went to the zoo, means 40 percent went to the zoo and the 40 percent can be written as 40%. The 40% or 40 out of 100 can also be expressed as the fraction $\dfrac{40}{100}$.

The word percent is replaced by the symbol %. Note also that any common fraction that has a denominator of 100 can be expressed as a percent as shown:

(a) $\dfrac{12}{100} = 12\%$ **(b)** $\dfrac{8}{100} = 8\%$ **(c)** $\dfrac{99.9}{100} = 99.9\%$

(d) $\dfrac{300}{100} = 300\%$ **(e)** $\dfrac{100}{100} = 100\%$ **(f)** $\dfrac{2\frac{1}{2}}{100} = 2\frac{1}{2}\%$

(g) $\dfrac{\frac{1}{2}}{100} = \frac{1}{2}\%$ **(h)** $\dfrac{.8}{100} = .8\%$ **(i)** $\dfrac{1}{100} = 1\%$

Let us use the grid that has 100 squares to explain the concept of percent.

Λ									
A	B								
A						B			
A									
A									
A		B							
A									
A									
A			B						
A									

(a). Each square represents 1 out of 100 squares of the grid which can be expressed as one percent or 1%.

(b). There are 10 squares that contain the letter A, out of the 100 squares of the grid, and this can be expressed as 10 percent (10%) of the squares of the grid contain the letter A.

(c). There are 4 squares that contain the letter B, out of the 100 squares of the grid. This can be expressed as 4 percent (4%) of the squares of the grid contain the letter B.

Team Exercise

The class should be divided into four groups. Each group should use the grid to answer the following questions, and then report the answers to the class. The grid has a total of 100 squares.

What percent of the squares contain:

(**a**). Q   (**b**). P   (**c**). X   (**d**). M   (**e**). K

K		Q	X	K	P				P
	M							M	
P		Q						Q	
P				K					
					P				
	K		K						Q
P									
P			X		P		M		Q

Example 1

70 out of 100 is what percent?

Solution

Step 1: Express 70 out of 100 as a percent.

$$70 \text{ out of } 100 = \frac{70}{100} = 70\%$$

Therefore, 70 out of 100 is 70% .

Exercises

Express the following as a percent. Hint: See Example 1.

(**1**) 2 out of 100   (**2**) 28 out of 100   (**3**) 23 out of 100

(**4**) 100 out of 100   (**5**) $78\frac{1}{2}$ out of 100   (**9**) 48.5 out of 100

Answers to Selected Exercises

(**1**) 2%   (**2**) 28%

Express Percent as a Fraction

1. If we count 33 squares out of 100 squares of a grid, then we can represent the 33 squares out of the 100 squares as 33% or $\dfrac{33}{100}$.

2. **Team exercise**: Each team should sketch a grid that contains 100 squares. The grid should have a total of ten columns and ten rows. Each column and each row should contain ten squares. Each team should shade five columns which are joined together from one edge of the grid blue. Compare the five columns which are shaded blue, to the whole grid. Is the size of the five columns which are shaded blue about half the size of the whole grid? The five columns which are shaded blue contain 50 squares out of the 100 squares of the grid, and this can be expressed as $\dfrac{50}{100}$ or 50%, but the five columns which are shaded blue are half of the whole grid, so we can say:

$$\dfrac{50}{100} = 50\% = \dfrac{1}{2}$$

Rule: To express a percent as a fraction, put the percent number as a numerator over 100, and then reduce the fraction to the lowest term if possible.

Example 1
Change 37% to a fraction.
Solution
Using the rule to express a percent as a fraction, put the percent number as the numerator over 100, and then reduce the fraction to the lowest term if possible.

$$37\% = \dfrac{37}{100}$$

Example 2
Change 25% to a fraction.
Solution
Using the rule to express a percent as a fraction, put the percent number as the numerator over 100, and then reduce the fraction to the lowest term if possible.

$$25\% = \dfrac{25}{100} = \dfrac{\overset{1}{\underset{\underset{4}{20}}{\cancel{25}}}}{\underset{\underset{}{}}{\cancel{100}}} \qquad \text{Reduce to the lowest term by dividing by 5.}$$

$$= \dfrac{1}{4}$$

Example 3
Change 125% to a fraction.
Solution

Using the rule to express a percent as a fraction, put the percent number as the numerator over 100, and then reduce the fraction to the lowest term if possible.

$$125\% = \frac{125}{100}$$

$$= \frac{\overset{5}{\cancel{\underset{20}{\cancel{\underset{4}{125}}}}}}{\underset{20}{\cancel{100}}} \qquad \text{Reduce to the lowest term by dividing by 5.}$$

$$= \frac{5}{4}$$

Example 4

Express $22\frac{1}{2}$ % as a fraction.

Solution

Using the rule to express a percent as a fraction, put the percent number as the numerator over 100, and then reduce to the lowest term if possible.

$$22\frac{1}{2}\% = \frac{22\frac{1}{2}}{100}$$

$\dfrac{22\frac{1}{2}}{100}$ can be written as $22\frac{1}{2} \div 100$

$= \dfrac{45}{2} \div \dfrac{100}{1}$ (Note: $22\frac{1}{2} = \dfrac{45}{2}$ and $100 = \dfrac{100}{1}$. Refer to the chapter on fractions).

$= \dfrac{45}{2} \times \dfrac{1}{100}$ (Note: 100 is inverted which is the reciprocal of 100 and the division

symbol changes to a multiplication symbol because to divide by a fraction is the same as to multiply by the reciprocal of the fraction. Review the chapter on the division of fractions).

$= \dfrac{\overset{9}{\cancel{45}}}{2} \times \dfrac{1}{\underset{20}{\cancel{100}}}$ Reduce to the lowest term by dividing by 5.

$$= \frac{9}{2} \times \frac{1}{20} = \frac{9}{40}$$

Example 5

Change .4% to a fraction.

Solution

Using the rule to express a percent as a fraction, put the percent number as the numerator over 100, and then reduce the fraction to the lowest term if possible.

$$4\% = \frac{.4}{100}$$

$$= .4 \times \frac{1}{100} \qquad \text{Rearrange } \frac{.4}{100} \text{ as } .4 \times \frac{1}{100}.$$

$$= \frac{4}{10} \times \frac{1}{100} \qquad .4 = \frac{4}{10}, \text{ review the chapter on decimals.}$$

$$.4 \text{ is in a decimal form, and } \frac{4}{10} \text{ is in a fraction form.}$$

$$= \frac{\overset{1}{\cancel{4}}}{10} \times \frac{1}{\underset{25}{\cancel{100}}} \qquad \text{Divide by 4.}$$

$$= \frac{1}{10} \times \frac{1}{25}$$

$$= \frac{1}{250} \qquad 25 \times 10 = 250$$

The required fraction is $\frac{1}{250}$.

Example 6

Change .12% to a fraction.

Solution

Using the rule to express a percent as a fraction, put the percent number as the numerator over 100, and then reduce to the lowest term if possible.

$$.12\% = \frac{.12}{100}$$

$$= .12 \times \frac{1}{100} \qquad \text{Rearrange } \frac{.12}{100} \text{ as } .12 \times \frac{1}{100}.$$

$$= \frac{12}{100} \times \frac{1}{100}$$
$.12 = \frac{12}{100}$, review the chapter on decimals.

$.12$ is in a decimal form, and $\frac{12}{100}$ is in a fraction form.

$$= \frac{\overset{3}{\cancel{12}}}{\underset{25}{\cancel{100}}} \times \frac{1}{100}$$
Divide by 4.

$$= \frac{3}{25} \times \frac{1}{100}$$

$$= \frac{3}{2500}$$
$25 \times 100 = 2500$

The required fraction is $\frac{3}{2500}$.

Example 7
Change .124% to a fraction.
Solution
Using the rule to express a percent as a fraction, put the percent number as the numerator over 100, and then reduce to the lowest term if possible.

$$.124\% = \frac{.124}{100}$$

$$= .124 \times \frac{1}{100}$$
Rearrange $\frac{.124}{100}$ as $.128 \times \frac{1}{100}$.

$$= \frac{124}{1000} \times \frac{1}{100}$$
$.124 = \frac{124}{1000}$, review the chapter on decimals.

$.124$ is in a decimal form, and $\frac{124}{1000}$ is in a fraction form.

$$= \frac{\overset{31}{\cancel{124}}}{1000} \times \frac{1}{\underset{25}{\cancel{100}}}$$
Divide by 4.

$$= \frac{31}{1000} \times \frac{1}{25}$$

$$= \frac{31}{2500}$$
$25 \times 100 = 2500$

The required fraction is $\dfrac{31}{2500}$.

Exercises

1. Express the following percents as fractions and reduce the answers to the lowest terms if possible. Hint: See Examples 1, 2, and 3.
   - (a) 27%
   - (b) 20%
   - (c) 135%
   - (d) 90%
   - (e) 110%

2. Express the following percents as fractions and reduce the answers to the lowest terms if possible. Hint: See Example 4.
   - (a) $32\dfrac{1}{2}\%$
   - (b) $4\dfrac{2}{3}\%$
   - (c) $6\dfrac{3}{4}\%$
   - (d) $17\dfrac{1}{3}\%$
   - (e) $1\dfrac{1}{9}\%$

3. Express the following percents as fractions and reduce the answers to the lowest terms if possible. Hint: See Example 5.
   - (a) .2%
   - (b) .7%
   - (c) .5%
   - (d) .3%
   - (e) .8%

4. Express the following percents as fractions and reduce the answers to the lowest terms if possible. Hint: See Example 6.
   - (a) .14%
   - (b) .11%
   - (c) .15%
   - (d) .31%
   - (e) .70%

5. Express the following percents as fractions and reduce the answers to the lowest terms if possible. Hint: See Example 7.
   - (a) .114%
   - (b) .133%
   - (c) .115%
   - (d) .131%
   - (e) .105%

Challenge Exercises

6. Express the following percents as fractions and reduce the answers to the lowest terms if possible.
   - (a) .6%
   - (b) 75%
   - (c) $7\dfrac{3}{5}\%$
   - (d) .215%
   - (e) 135%

   - (f) 10%
   - (g) 6%
   - (h) .12%
   - (i) $6\dfrac{1}{2}\%$
   - (j) 110%

Answers to Selected Exercises

1(a) $\dfrac{27}{100}$ 1(b) $\dfrac{1}{5}$ 2(a) $\dfrac{13}{40}$ 2(b) $\dfrac{7}{150}$

3(a) $\dfrac{1}{50}$ 3(b) $\dfrac{7}{100}$ 4(a) $\dfrac{7}{5000}$ 4(b) $\dfrac{11}{10,000}$

5(a) $\dfrac{57}{50,000}$ 5(b) $\dfrac{133}{100,000,}$

REAL WORLD APPLICATIONS - WORD PROBLEMS
Express Percent as Fraction

Example 1
Yesterday, 2% of the students in a school were absent. What fraction of the students were absent?
Solution
Using the rule to express a percent as a fraction, write the percent number as the numerator over 100 and then reduce to the lowest term if possible.

$$2\% = \frac{2}{100}$$

$$= \frac{\overset{1}{\cancel{2}}}{\underset{50}{\cancel{100}}} \qquad \text{Reduce to the lowest term by dividing by 2.}$$

$$= \frac{1}{50}$$

The fraction of the students that were absent was $\frac{1}{50}$.

Example 2
A television set was reduced by 15%. What fraction of the price is the reduction?
Solution
Using the rule to express a percent as a fraction, write the percent number as the numerator over 100 and then reduce the fraction to the lowest term if possible.

$$15\% = \frac{15}{100}$$

$$= \frac{\overset{3}{\cancel{15}}}{\underset{20}{\cancel{100}}} \qquad \text{Reduce to the lowest term by dividing by 5.}$$

$$= \frac{3}{20}$$

The fraction of the price that was the reduction is $\frac{3}{20}$

Example 3
In a school, 65% of the students like soccer, what fraction of the students like soccer?
Solution

Using the rule to express a percent as a fraction, write the percent number as the numerator over 100, and then reduce the fraction to the lowest term if possible.

$$65\% = \frac{65}{100}$$

$$= \frac{\overset{13}{\cancel{65}}}{\underset{20}{\cancel{100}}} \qquad \text{Reduce to the lowest term by dividing by 5.}$$

$$= \frac{13}{20}$$

The fraction of the students that like soccer is $\frac{13}{20}$.

Example 4

A computer system was on sale at 10% off the regular price. What fraction of the regular price was the reduction?

Solution

Using the rule to express a percent as a fraction, write the percent number as the numerator over 100, and then reduce to the lowest term if possible.

$$10\% = \frac{10}{100} \qquad \text{The reduction was 10\%.}$$

$$= \frac{\overset{1}{\cancel{10}}}{\underset{10}{\cancel{100}}} \qquad \text{Reduce to the lowest term by dividing by 10.}$$

$$= \frac{1}{10}$$

The fraction of the regular price that was on sale is $\frac{1}{10}$.

Exercises

1. 25% of the students in a class went to the zoo. What fraction of the students went to the zoo? Hint: See Example 1.
2. A television set was reduced by 10%. What fraction of the price is the reduction? Hint: See Example 2.
3. 75% of the students in a class like science. What fraction of the students like science? Hint: See Example 3.
4. A car is on sale at 6% off the regular price. What fraction of the regular price is the

the reduction? Hint: See Example 4.

5. A house was sold at 8% off the original selling price. What is the fraction of the reduction of the price of the house? Hint: See Example 4.

6. 16% of the students in a class went to medical schools. What is the fraction of the students that went to medical schools? Hint: See Example 3.

Challenge Questions

7. 55% of the students at the Peki Secondary School are girls. What is the fraction of the girls in the school?

8. A printer was sold at 25% off the original price. What is the fraction of the reduction of the price of the computer?

Answers to Selected Exercises

1. $\dfrac{1}{5}$ 2. $\dfrac{1}{10}$ 3. $\dfrac{3}{4}$

Express Fractions as Percents

Recall that we already discussed the grid at the beginning of this chapter (Percent). One square out of the 100 squares in the grid can be written as 1% and this can be expressed as $\dfrac{1}{100}$. This means that if we have a fraction such as $\dfrac{1}{100}$ and we want to change the fraction which is $\dfrac{1}{100}$ to a percent, we have to multiply the fraction by 100, and then attach the % sign.

$$\frac{1}{100} \times 100$$

$$= \frac{1}{\cancel{100}} \times \overset{1}{\cancel{100}} \qquad \text{Do the division.}$$

$$= 1\%$$

Rule: To express a fraction as a percent multiply the fraction by 100, and then attach the % sign to the answer.

Example 1

Express $\dfrac{1}{10}$ as a percent.

Solution

Using the rule express the fraction as a percent by multiplying the fraction by 100, and then attach the % sign to the answer.

$$\frac{1}{10} \text{ as a percent} = \frac{1}{10} \times 100$$

$$= \frac{\overset{10}{\cancel{100}}}{\underset{1}{\cancel{10}}} \qquad \text{Reduce to the lowest term by dividing by 10.}$$

$$= 10\%$$

Example 2

Change $\dfrac{2}{15}$ to a percent.

Solution

Using the rule express the fraction as a percent by multiplying the fraction by 100, and then attach the % sign to the answer.

$$\frac{2}{15} \text{ as percent} = \frac{2}{15} \times 100$$

$$= \frac{2}{\underset{3}{\cancel{15}}} \times \overset{20}{\cancel{100}} \qquad \text{Reduce to the lowest term by dividing by 5.}$$

$$= \frac{40}{3} = 13\frac{1}{3}\% \qquad \text{Review the section on mixed numbers.}$$

Example 3

Change $\dfrac{3}{7}$ to a percent.

Solution

Using the rule express the fraction as a percent by multiplying the fraction by 100, and then attach the % sign to the answer.

$$\frac{3}{7} \text{ as a percent} = \frac{3}{7} \times 100$$

$$= \frac{300}{7}$$

$$= 42\frac{6}{7} \qquad \text{Review the section on mixed numbers.}$$

$\frac{3}{7}$ as a percent $= 42\frac{6}{7}$%.

Exercises

1. Express the following fractions as percents. Hint: See Example 1.

    a) $\frac{1}{2}$ **b)** $\frac{1}{4}$ **c)** $\frac{1}{5}$ **d)** $\frac{1}{15}$ **e)** $\frac{1}{25}$ **f)** $\frac{1}{50}$

2. Express the following fractions as percents. Hint: See Example 2.

    a) $\frac{2}{5}$ **b)** $\frac{3}{10}$ **c)** $\frac{4}{5}$ **d)** $\frac{4}{15}$ **e)** $\frac{1}{25}$ **f)** $\frac{7}{25}$

3. Change the following fractions to percents. Hint: See Example 3.

    a). $\frac{2}{3}$ **b).** $\frac{2}{7}$ **c).** $\frac{2}{9}$ **d).** $\frac{3}{8}$ **e).** $\frac{3}{11}$ **f).** $\frac{5}{12}$

Challenge Questions

4. Change the following fractions to percents.

    a) $\frac{4}{15}$ **b).** $\frac{1}{3}$ **c).** $\frac{1}{20}$ **d).** $\frac{7}{30}$ **e).** $\frac{7}{8}$ **f).** $\frac{4}{9}$

Answers to Selected Exercises

  1(a) 50%   **1(b)** 25%   **2(a)** 40%   **2(b)** 30%

  3(a) $66\frac{2}{3}$%   **3(b)** $28\frac{4}{7}$%

REAL WORLD APPLICATIONS – WORD PROBLEMS
Express Fractions as Percents

Example 1

Given that $\frac{4}{5}$ of the students in a high school like soccer. What percent of

the students like soccer?

Solution

Using the rule express the fraction as a percent by multiplying the fraction by 100,
and then attach the % sign to the answer.

Percent of the student population $= 100$%

Percent of $\frac{4}{5}$ of the students like soccer $= \frac{4}{5}$ of 100%

$$\downarrow \quad \downarrow \quad \downarrow$$

$$= \frac{4}{5} \times 100\%\text{"of" becomes a}$$

multiplication sign.

$$20\%$$

$$= \frac{4}{5} \times \overset{1}{\cancel{100\%}} \qquad \text{Divide by 5.}$$

$$= 4 \times 20\% = 80\%$$

Therefore, 80% of the students like soccer.

Example 2

A television set was reduced by $\frac{1}{5}$ off the regular price. What was the percent

of reduction in the price?

Solution

Using the rule express the fraction as a percent by multiplying the fraction by 100,
and then attach the % sign to the answer.

The percent of the original price of the television set = 100%

The percent of $\frac{1}{5}$ off the original price $= \frac{1}{5}$ of 100%

$$\downarrow \quad \downarrow \quad \downarrow$$

$$= \frac{1}{5} \times 100\% \qquad \text{"of" becomes a multiplication sign.}$$

$$= \frac{1}{\cancel{5}} \times \overset{20}{\cancel{100\%}} \qquad \text{Reduce to the lowest term by}$$

$$\qquad\qquad\qquad\qquad \text{dividing by 5.}$$

$$= 20\%$$

The percent of reduction in the price = 20%

Exercises

1. Given that $\frac{1}{25}$ of the workers in a plant are engineers, what percent of the workers
   are engineers? Hint: See Example 1.

2. A computer set was reduced by $\frac{1}{15}$ off the regular price. What was the
   percentage of reduction in price? Hint: See Example 2.

Challenge Questions

3. In 1990, the population of the Peki High School was 950 students. In 1991, the

students population increased by $\frac{1}{10}$.

a. What is the increase of the population of the students in 1991?

Hint: The increase of the population of the students $= \frac{1}{10} \times 950$

b. What is the percent increase of the population of the students?

c. What is the population of the students in 1991?

Hint: Population of the students in 1991

$\qquad$ = Population in 1990 + Increase in population.

4. A television set was increased by $\frac{3}{50}$ of the regular price. What was the percent increase in price?

Express Percent as a Decimal

Recall that we already discussed the grid at the beginning of this chapter (percent). One square out of the 100 squares in the grid can be written as 1% and this can be expressed as $\frac{1}{100}$. Recall from the chapter on decimal fractions that the fraction $\frac{1}{100}$ can be changed to a decimal by dividing 1 by 100 as shown:

$$100\overline{)1} = 100\overline{)100} \quad \begin{array}{r} .01 \\ \hline 100 \\ -100 \\ \hline 000 \end{array}$$

Therefore, $1\% = \frac{1}{100} = .01$. Note that 1% is changed to the decimal fraction .01 by dividing 1 by 100 or simply moving the decimal point in the percent number two places or two digits to the left.

Decimal point

Write 0 here to hold the place value.

$$1\% = .\,01 = .01$$

Move the imaginary decimal point behind 1 two places or two digits to the left.

Note: There is an imaginary decimal point behind the last digit of all whole numbers. (Review the chapter on decimal fractions).

Rule: To express a percent as a decimal fraction, move the decimal point in the percent number two places or two digits to the left of the decimal point, and ignore the percent sign.

Example 1

Express 25.5% as a decimal fraction.

Solution

Using the rule, to express a percent as a decimal fraction, move the decimal point in the percent number two places or two digits to the left of the decimal point, and ignore the percent sign as shown:

$$25.5\% = 25.5 = .255$$

Move the decimal point two places or two digits to the left.

Therefore, 25.5% = .255

Example 2

Express 25% as a decimal fraction.

Solution

Using the rule, to express a percent as a decimal fraction, move the decimal point in the percent number two places or two digits to the left of the decimal point, and ignore the percent sign as shown:

$$25\% = .25 = .25$$

Move the imaginary decimal point behind 25 two places or two digits to the left.

Therefore, 25% = .25

Note: There is an imaginary decimal point behind the last digit of every whole number.

Example 3

Express 2.55% as a decimal fraction.

Solution

Using the rule, to express a percent as a decimal fraction, move the decimal point in the percent number two places or two digits to the left of the decimal point, and ignore the percent sign.

Write a 0 here to hold the place value.

$$2.55\% = 2.55 = .0255$$

Move the decimal point two places or two digits to the left.

Therefore, 2.55% = .0255

Example 4
Express .255% as a decimal fraction.
Solution
Using the rule, to express a percent as a decimal fraction, move the decimal point in the percent number two places or two digits to the left of the decimal point, and ignore the percent sign.

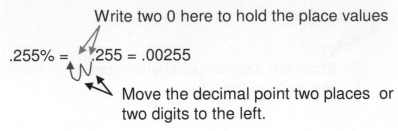

Write two 0 here to hold the place values

.255% = .255 = .00255

Move the decimal point two places or two digits to the left.

Therefore, .255% = .00255

Exercises

1. Express the following percents as decimals. Hint: See Example 1.
   (a) 28.1%   (b) 95.5%   (c) 64.9%   (d) 75.5%   (e) 95.3%
   (f) 12.4%   (g) 17.7%   (h) 55.6%   (i) 49.9%   (j) 99.9%
   (k) 39.8%   (l) 16.6%   (m) 11.1%   (n) 36.7%   (o) 57.8%

2. Express the following percents as decimals. Hint: See Example 2.
   (a) 26%   (b) 27%   (c) 99%   (d) 35%   (e) 64%
   (f) 75%   (g) 38%   (h) 45%   (i) 17%   (j) 19%
   (k) 11%   (l) 34%   (m) 17%   (n) 88%   (o) 96%

3. Express the following percents as decimals. Hint: See Example 3.
   (a) 3.22%   (b) 4.45%   (c) 7.1%   (d) 9.61   (e) 1.1%
   (f) 2.1%   (g) 9.9%   (h) 8.5%   (i) 6.25%   (j) 7.9%

4. Express the following percent as decimal. Hint: See Example 4.
   (a) .234%   (b) .641%   (c) .111%   (d) .2%   (e) .12%
   (f) .75%   (g) .35%   (h) .99%   (i) .1%   (j) .4%

Challenge Questions

5. Express the following percents as decimal fractions.
   (a) 72%   (b) 33.4%   (c) .01%   (d) 1.71%   (e) .09%
   (f) .3%   (g) 4.2%   (h) 13.1%   (i) 95%   (j) .88%

Answers to Selected Questions.
(1)(a) .281   2(a) .26   3(a) .0322   4(a) .00234

REAL WORLD APPLICATIONS – WORD PROBLEMS
Percent to Decimal Fractions

Example 1
Given that 12.32% of the items in a store are on sale, what decimal fraction of the items is on sale?
Solution
Using the rule to express a percent as a decimal fraction, move the decimal point in the percent number two places or two digits to the left of the decimal point, and ignore the percent sign.

$$12.32\% = 12.32 = .1232$$

Move the decimal point two places or two digits to the left.

The decimal fraction of the items on sale = .1232

Example 2
There are 7% of the boys at the Peki High School who work at the Peki Super Market. What is the decimal fraction of the boys that work at the Peki Super Market?
Solution
Using the rule to express a percent as a decimal fraction, move the decimal point in the percent number two places or two digits to the left of the decimal point, and ignore the percent sign.

Write a 0 here to hold the place value.

$$7\% = 7 = .07$$

Move the imaginary decimal point behind 7 to two places or two digits to the left.

Therefore, .07 is the decimal fraction of the boys.

Example 3
.64% of a certain concentration of orange drink is water. What is the decimal fraction of the concentration made of water?
Solution
Hint: Orange drink is made by mixing pure orange juice with water.
Using the rule to express a percent as a decimal fraction, move the decimal point in the percent number two places or two digits to the left of the decimal point, and ignore the percent sign.

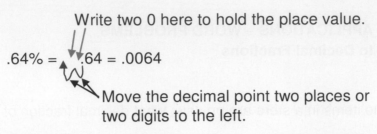

Write two 0 here to hold the place value.

.64% = .64 = .0064

Move the decimal point two places or
two digits to the left.

The decimal fraction of the concentration of the orange drink is .0064.

Exercises

1. Given that 17.2% of the computers in a certain store are on sale, what decimal fraction of the computers are on sale? Hint: See Example 1.
2. In a certain elementary school, 3% of the girls like soccer. What is the decimal fraction of the girls that like soccer? Hint: See Example 2.
3. The concentration of a certain orange drink is made up of .95% water. What is the decimal fraction of the concentration of water in the orange drink? Hint: See Example 3.

Challenge Questions

4. Given that the concentration of a certain drink is .5% water, what is the decimal fraction of the concentration of the water in the drink?
5. If 1% of the employees in a certain company prefer to take their vacation in the summer, what is the decimal fraction of the employees that prefer to take their vacation in the summer?
6. Mrs. Aggor went to the store to buy a shirt because 46.8% of the shirts were on sale. What is the decimal fraction of the shirts that are on sale?

Express Decimal Fractions as Percents

Note that expressing decimal fractions as percents is the opposite of expressing percents as decimal fractions, and therefore, the method of expressing decimal fractions as percents is the opposite of the method of expressing the percents as decimal fractions. Review the rule for expressing percents as decimal fractions in the preceding rule.

Rule: **To express decimal fractions as percent, move the decimal point two places or two digits to the right, and then attach the % sign.**

Example 1
Express .92 as a percent.
Solution
Using the rule to express decimal fractions as percents, move the decimal point two places or two digits to the right, and then attach the % sign.

Attach the % sign.

.92 = .92 = 92%

Move the decimal point two places or two digits to the right.

Therefore, .92 = 92%

Example 2

Change the following decimal fractions to percents:

(a) 1.87   (b) 1.8

Solution

(a). Using the rule to express decimal fractions as percents, move the decimal point two places or two digits to the right and then attach the % sign:

Attach the % sign.

1.87 = 1.87 = 187%

Move the decimal point two places or two digits to the right.

Therefore, 1.87 = 187%

(b). Using the rule to express decimal fractions as percents, move the decimal point two places or two digits to the right, and then attach the % sign.

Write a 0 here to hold the place value.

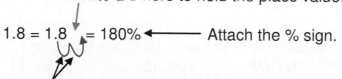

1.8 = 1.8 = 180% ◄────── Attach the % sign.

Move the decimal point two places or two digits to the right.

Example 3

Change the following decimal fractions to percents.

(a) .001   (b) .275   (c) 1.00

Solution

(a). Using the rule to express decimal fractions as percents, move the decimal point two places or two digits to the right, and then attach the % sign.

Attach the % sign.

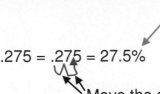

.001 = .001 = .1%

Move the decimal point two places or two digits to the right.

Therefore, .001 = .1%

(b). Using the rule to express decimal fractions as percents, move the decimal point two places or two digits to the right, and then attach the % sign.

Attach the % sign.

.275 = .275 = 27.5%

Move the decimal point two places or two digits to the right.

Therefore, .275 = 27.5%

(c). Using the rule to express decimal fractions as percents, move the decimal point two places or two digits to the right, and then attach the % sign.

Attach the % sign.

1.00 = 1.00 = 100%

Move the decimal point two places or two digits to the right.

Therefore, 1.00 = 100%

Exercises

1. Change the following decimal fractions to percents. Hint: See Example **1**.
   (**a**) .79   (**b**) .34   (**c**) .07   (**d**) .12   (**e**) .11
2. Change the following decimal fractions to percents. Hint: See Example **2(a)**.
   (**a**) 2.94   (**b**) 9.99   (**c**) 3.40   (**d**) 7.75   (**e**) 1.25
3. Change the following decimal fractions to percents. Hint: See Example **3(a)**.
   (**a**) 3.9   (**b**) 9.9   (**c**) 28.1   (**d**) 44.6   (**e**) 7.8
4. Change the following decimal fractions to percents. Hint : See Example **3(a)**.
   (**a**) .002   (**b**) .009   (**c**) .004   (**d**) 2.001   (**e**) 10.002
5. Change the following decimal fractions to percents. Hint: See Example **3(b)**.
   (**a**) .298   (**b**) .444   (**c**) .891   (**d**) .658   (**e**) .481
6. Change the following decimal fractions to percents. Hint: See Example 3(c).
   (**a**) 9.00   (**b**) 6.00   (**c**) 4.00   (**d**) 8.00   (**e**) 2.00

Challenge questions

7. Express the following decimal fractions as percents.

(a) .3   (b) 4.2   (c) 13.1   (d) 95   (e) .88

8. Express the following decimal fractions as percents.

(a) 1.1   (b) .001   (c) 1.78   (d) 7.0   (e) .09
(f) .90   (g) 3.0   (h) 1   (i) .21   (j) .01

Answers to Selected Exercises

1(a) 79%   2(a) 294%   3(a) 390%
4(a) 0.2%   5(a) 29.8%   6(a) 900%

REAL WORLD APPLICATIONS – WORD PROBLEMS
Express Decimal Fractions as Percents

Example 1
Given that .65 of the students in a certain school are girls, what percent of the students are girls?
Solution
Using the rule to express decimal fractions as percents, move the decimal point two places or two digits to the right, and then attach the % sign.

Attach the % sign.

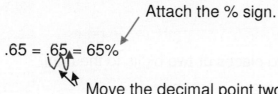

$$.65 = .65 = 65\%$$

Move the decimal point two places or two digits to the right.

The percent of the girls = 65%.

Example 2
John will make 1.9 profit in his investment.
Express his profit as a percent.
Solution
Using the rule to express decimal fractions as percents, move the decimal point two places or two digits to the right, and then attach the % sign.

Write a 0 here to hold the place value.

$$1.9 = 1.9 = 190\% \longleftarrow \text{Attach the \% sign.}$$

Move the decimal point two places or two digits to the right.

The percent profit = 190%.

Example 3

Given that .268 of the computers in a certain store were sold at a discount. What percent of the computers were sold at a discount ?

Solution

Using the rule to express decimal fractions as percents, move the decimal point two places or two digits to the right, and then attach the % sign:

Attach the % sign.

.268 = .268 = 26.8%

Move the decimal point two places or two digits to the right.

The percent of the computers sold at a discount was 26.8%

Example 4

Given that .022 of the students in a certain class study history, what is the percent of the students that study history?

Solution

Using the rule, to express decimal fractions as percents, move the decimal point two places or two digits to the right, and then attach the % sign.

Attach the % sign.

.022 = .022 = 2.2%

Move the decimal point two places or two digits to the right.

The percent of the students that study history is 2.2%

Exercises

1. Given that .75 of the students in a certain class are boys, what percent of the students are boys? Hint: See Example 1.
2. Eric made .078 profit on his investment. What is his percent profit? Hint: See Example 2 .
3. Given that .289 of the people who go to the zoo are children, what percent of the people who go to the zoo are children? Hint: See Example 3.
4. Given that .501 of the students in a certain class study chemistry, what percent of the students study chemistry? Hint: See Example 4.

Challenge Questions

5. Given that .018 of the animals in a certain zoo are lions, what percent of the animals are lions?
6. Given that .684 of the books in a certain library involve science, what is the percent of the books that involves science?

Key Facts - Summary

a. To change a percent to a common fraction, put the percent number over 100 as a denominator, and then reduce to the lowest terms if possible.

b. To change a common fraction to decimal fraction, move the decimal point in the numerator two places or two digits to the left if the denominator is 100, otherwise, just divide the numerator by the denominator.

c. To change a decimal fraction to a common fraction, count the number of the decimal places or the number of digits after the decimal point and this number of decimal places or the number of digits after the decimal point is equal to the number of zeros which form the denominator of the common fraction, and the actual number of the decimal fraction becomes the numerator as follows:

(1) .5 has one decimal place or one digit after the decimal point, so the denominator has one zero and the denominator is 10 and the numerator is 5 and the common fraction is $\dfrac{5}{10}$.

(2) .05 has two decimal places or two digits after the decimal point, so the denominator has two zeros and the denominator is 100 and the numerator is 5 and the common fraction is $\dfrac{5}{100}$.

(3) .005 has three decimal places or three digits after the decimal point, so the denominator has three zeros and the denominator is 1000, and the numerator is 5 and the common fraction is $\dfrac{5}{1000}$.

(4) .523 has three decimal places or three digits after the decimal point, therefore, the denominator has three zeros and the denominator is 1000 and the numerator is 523 and the common fraction is $\dfrac{523}{1000}$.

The table showing how to change decimal fractions to common fractions is on the next page.)

Decimal Fraction	No. of decimal places	No. of zeros in denominator	Common fraction
.5	1	1	$\dfrac{5}{10}$
.05	2	2	$\dfrac{5}{100}$
.005	3	3	$\dfrac{5}{1,000}$
.523	3	3	$\dfrac{523}{1,000}$
.0931	4	4	$\dfrac{931}{10,000}$
.74895	5	5	$\dfrac{74895}{100,000}$

(The table above summarizes how to change decimal fractions to common fractions.)

d. To change a common fraction to a percent, multiply the common fraction by 100, and then attach the % sign. For example,

$\dfrac{5}{100}$ is:

$$\dfrac{5}{100} \times 100$$

$$\dfrac{5}{\underset{1}{\cancel{100}}} \times \overset{1}{\cancel{100}} = 5\%$$

e. To change a percent to a decimal fraction, move the decimal point in the percent to two decimal places or two digits to the left, or just express the percent as a common fraction with 100 as the denominator and divide.

Exercises

1. Complete the table by filling in the columns for percents, fractions, and decimal fractions. Hint: See examples in the sections under percents, fractions, and decimals. See also the example in the second row of the table in this question.

Percents (%)	Fractions	Decimals or Decimal Fractions
5%	$\dfrac{5}{100}$	.05
65%		
16%		
	$\dfrac{17}{100}$	
	$\dfrac{73}{100}$	
		.008
		.08
		.8
2.1%		
.33%		

2. Complete the table by filling in the columns for decimal fractions, percents, and fractions. Hint: See examples under the sections in decimal fractions, percents, common fractions, and also see the two examples in the second and the third rows of the table in this question.

(The table is on the next page.)

Decimal fractions	Percent (%)	Common fractions
.8	$\dfrac{8}{10} \times 100 = 80\%$	$\dfrac{8}{10} = \dfrac{4}{5}$
.004	$\dfrac{4}{1000} \times 100 = .4\%$	$\dfrac{4}{1000} = \dfrac{1}{250}$
2.67		
85.8		
.561		
.018		
.o8		
.7		
9.49		
72.004		
.47		
.15		
$\dfrac{35}{100} = .35$	35%	$\dfrac{35}{100} = \dfrac{7}{20}$
	60%	
	160%	
	74.5%	
	9.8%	
	2%	
	13.11%	
12.5% = .125	$\dfrac{1}{8} \times 100 = 12.5\%$	$\dfrac{1}{8}$
		$\dfrac{272}{100}$
		$\dfrac{6}{12}$
		$\dfrac{9.7}{100}$
		$\dfrac{24\frac{1}{3}}{60}$
		$\dfrac{100}{100}$

3. Copy and complete the table by filling in the columns for common fractions,

82

decimal fractions and percents. Hint: See separate examples under the sections on decimal fractions, percents, and common fractions.

Common fraction	Decimal fraction	%
$\dfrac{57}{100}$		
$\dfrac{8}{24}$		
$\dfrac{7}{9}$		
$\dfrac{9.7}{100}$		
$\dfrac{5645}{100}$		
$\dfrac{18}{65}$		
	.358	
	.019	
	75.45	
	38.01	
	3.2	
	.6	
		2.5%
		275%
		1%
		60%
		4700.8%
		26.15%

Understanding 100%

(**1**) 100% means $\dfrac{100}{100} = \dfrac{1}{1} = 1$. 100% therefore means one whole of anything or the total of anything.

(**2**) If 100% of the employees at a certain company are women, it means that no men work at the company.

(**3**). If 100% of the students in grade 5B are boys, it means that all the students in grade 5B are boys.

(**4**) If 100% of the students visited the zoo yesterday, it means that all the students visited the zoo.

Understanding Percent

(**1**) If 70% of the students in a certain school are girls, it means that 100% − 70% = 30% are boys since the whole student population should be 100%.

(**2**) If 55% of the doctors in a certain hospital are women, then the percent of the male doctors is 100% − 55% = 45% since the whole doctor population in the hospital should be 100%.

(**3**) If 5% of a class is absent, it means that 100% − 5% = 95% of the students are present since the whole class should be 100%.

REAL WORLD APPLICATIONS – WORD PROBLEMS
Understanding Percent

Example 1

There are 48% of boys in a school. What is the percent of the girls?

Solution

The percent of the girls = 100% − 48% = 52%

Example 2

An advance school consists of students studying chemistry, physics, and biology. A student may study only one subject. Given that 25% of the students study chemistry and 30% of the students study biology, what is the percent of the students that study physics?

Solution

Total student population = 100%

Percent of students that study chemistry and biology = 25% + 30% = 55%.

Percent of students that study physics = 100% − 55% = 45%.

Example 3

A school has 800 students. If 55% of the student population are boys,

(**a**) what is the percent of girls in the school?

(**b**) how many girls are in the school?

Solution

(**a**) Total student population = 100%

    Percent of the boys = 55%

    Percent of the girls = 100% - 55% = 45%

(**b**) From solution (a), the percent of the girls = 45%

The number of the girls in the school = 45% of 800

$$= \frac{45}{100} \times 800 \qquad \text{Note: } 45\% = \frac{45}{100}, \text{ "of" is} \times.$$

$$= \frac{45}{\underset{1}{100}} \times \overset{8}{800} \qquad \text{Divide by 100.}$$

$$= 45 \times 8$$
$$= 360 \text{ girls}$$

Therefore, the number of the girls in the school is 360.

Example 4

A school has a population of 1,200 students. If 5 percent of the students are absent,
(a) what is the percent of the students present?
(b) what is the number of the students present?
(c) what is the number of the students absent?

Solution

(a) The percent of the whole student population = 100%
The percent of the students that are absent = 5%
The percent of the students that are present = 100% - 5% = 95%

(b) From the solution of (a), the percent of the students that are present = 95%
Student population of the school – 1,200
The number of the students present = 95% of the student population.

$$= 95\% \text{ of } 1,200$$

$$= \frac{95}{100} \times 1,200 \quad \text{Note: } 95\% = \frac{95}{100}, \text{ "of" is} \times.$$

$$= \frac{95}{\underset{1}{100}} \times \overset{12}{1,200} \quad \text{Divide by 100.}$$

$$= 95 \times 12$$
$$= 1140 \text{ students.}$$

Therefore, 1140 students were present.

(c) The number of students absent
$$= \text{Student population} - \text{Number of students present.}$$
$$= 1,200 - 1140$$

= 60 students.

Therefore, 60 students were absent.

Fractional Parts of Percents

The fractional part of a percent such as $\frac{1}{5}$% means $\frac{1}{5}$ out of 100. Recall that,

for example, 2% means 2 out of 100. Recall that 2% = $\frac{2}{100}$, and therefore,

$\frac{1}{5}$% = $\dfrac{\frac{1}{5}}{100}$.

Rule: **To express a fraction of a percent as a decimal fraction, write the fraction over 100, and then divide, ignoring the % sign.**

Example 1

Express $\frac{1}{5}$% as a decimal fraction

Solution

Using the rule to express a fraction of a percent as a decimal fraction, write the fraction over 100 and then divide, ignoring the % sign.

$$\frac{1}{5}\% = \dfrac{\frac{1}{5}}{100}$$

$$= \dfrac{\frac{1}{5}}{\frac{100}{1}} \quad \text{Change 100 to a fraction by writing 100 as } \frac{100}{1} = 100.$$

$$= \frac{1}{5} \times \frac{1}{100} \quad \text{Recall that to divide a fraction by another fraction, the}$$

top fraction ($\frac{1}{5}$) is multiplied by the inverted bottom

fraction ($\frac{1}{100}$). The inverted bottom fraction is called the

reciprocal.

$$= \frac{1 \times 1}{5 \times 100} = \frac{1}{500}$$

$$500\overline{)1} = 500\overline{)1.000} \\ \underset{0\,0\,0\,0}{\underline{-\ 1\,0\,0\,0}}$$

$$\overset{.002}{}$$

(Review the chapter on Dividing a Smaller Number by a Bigger Number.)

Therefore, $\dfrac{1}{5}\% = .002$

Example 2

Change $\dfrac{6}{8}\%$ to a decimal fraction.

Solution

Using the rule to express a fraction of a percent as a decimal fraction, write the fraction over 100, and then divide, ignoring the % sign.

$$\frac{6}{8}\% = \frac{\frac{6}{8}}{100}$$

$$= \frac{\frac{6}{8}}{\frac{100}{1}} \qquad \text{Change 100 to a fraction by writing 100 as } \frac{100}{1} = 100.$$

$$= \frac{6}{8} \times \frac{1}{100} \qquad \text{Recall that to divide a fraction by another fraction, the top}$$

fraction $(\dfrac{6}{8})$ is multiplied by the inverted bottom

fraction $(\dfrac{1}{100})$. The inverted bottom fraction is called the

reciprocal.

$$= \frac{\overset{3}{\cancel{6}}}{\underset{4}{\cancel{8}}} \times \frac{1}{100} \qquad \text{Divide the numerator and the denominator by 2.}$$

$$= \frac{3}{4} \times \frac{1}{100} = \frac{3 \times 1}{4 \times 100} = \frac{3}{400}$$

$$400\overline{)3} = 400\overline{)3.0000}^{\,.0075}$$

$$\begin{array}{r} -\underline{2800\downarrow} \\ 2000 \\ -\underline{2000} \\ 0000 \end{array}$$

(Review the chapter on Dividing a Smaller Number by a Bigger Number.)

Therefore, $\dfrac{6}{8}\% = .0075$

Example 3

Change $2\dfrac{1}{2}\%$ to decimal fraction.

Solution

Using the rule to express a fraction of a percent as a decimal fraction, write the fraction over 100, and then divide, ignoring the % sign.

$$2\frac{1}{2}\% = \frac{2\frac{1}{2}}{100}$$

$$= \frac{\frac{5}{2}}{100} \qquad \text{Change } 2\frac{1}{2} \text{ to an improper fraction of } \frac{5}{2}.$$

$$= \frac{\frac{5}{2}}{\frac{100}{1}} \qquad \text{Change 100 to a fraction by writing 100 as } \frac{100}{1} = 100.$$

$$= \frac{5}{2} \times \frac{1}{100} \qquad \text{Recall that to divide a fraction by another fraction,}$$
$$\text{the top fraction } (\frac{5}{2}) \text{ is multiplied by the inverted}$$
$$\text{bottom fraction } (\frac{1}{100}), \text{ which is the reciprocal.}$$

$$= \frac{\overset{1}{\cancel{5}}}{2} \times \frac{1}{\underset{20}{\cancel{100}}} \qquad \text{Divide numerator and denominator by 5.}$$

$$= \frac{1}{2} \times \frac{1}{20} = \frac{1 \times 1}{2 \times 20} = \frac{1}{40}$$

$$40\overline{)1} = 40\overline{\smash{)}1.000} \quad \begin{array}{r} .025 \\ \underline{-\ 80\downarrow} \\ 200 \\ \underline{-\ 200} \\ 000 \end{array}$$

(Review the chapter on Dividing a Smaller Number by a Bigger Number.)

Therefore, $2\frac{1}{2}\% = .025$

Exercises

1. Express the following fractions of percents as decimal. Round your answer to 3 decimal places. Hint: See Example 1.

(a) $\frac{1}{2}\%$ (b) $\frac{1}{4}\%$ (c) $\frac{1}{3}\%$ (d) $\frac{1}{10}\%$ (e) $\frac{1}{12}\%$

(f) $\frac{1}{7}\%$ (g) $\frac{1}{9}\%$ (h) $\frac{1}{15}\%$ (i) $\frac{1}{11}\%$ (j) $\frac{1}{20}\%$

2. Change the following fractions of percents to decimals. Round your answer to 3 decimal places. Hint: See Example 2.

(a) $\frac{2}{10}\%$ (b) $\frac{2}{5}\%$ (c) $\frac{3}{7}\%$ (d) $\frac{?}{7}\%$ (e) $\frac{3}{5}\%$

(f) $\frac{3}{5}\%$ (g) $\frac{3}{11}\%$ (h) $\frac{4}{15}\%$ (i) $\frac{5}{8}\%$ (j) $\frac{9}{10}\%$

3. Change the following mixed numbers of percents to decimals. Round your answer to 3 decimal places. Hint: See Example 3.

(a) $2\frac{1}{4}\%$ (b) $1\frac{1}{2}\%$ (c) $2\frac{2}{5}\%$ (d) $1\frac{3}{5}\%$ (e) $4\frac{3}{4}\%$

(f) $5\frac{2}{5}\%$ (g) $6\frac{5}{6}\%$ (h) $10\frac{2}{3}\%$ (i) $8\frac{2}{5}\%$ (j) $3\frac{3}{4}\%$

Challenge Questions

4. Change the following mixed numbers and fractions from percents to decimals.

(a) $2\frac{3}{4}\%$ (b) $\frac{1}{6}\%$ (c) $\frac{2}{9}\%$ (d) $2\frac{3}{5}\%$ (e) $\frac{1}{10}\%$

(f) $\dfrac{3}{8}$%   (g) $5\dfrac{5}{6}$%   (h) $\dfrac{1}{8}$%   (i) $7\dfrac{1}{7}$%   (j) $\dfrac{5}{7}$%

Answers to Selected Exercises
1(a) 0.005   **2(a)** 0.002   **3(a)** 0.023

REAL WORLD APPLICATIONS - WORD PROBLEMS
Express Fractions of Percents as Decimals

Example 1

Given that $\dfrac{3}{4}$% of the goods in a certain store are on sale, what is the decimal fraction

of the goods that are on sale?

Solution

Using the rule, to express a fraction of a percent as a decimal fraction, write the
fraction over 100, and then divide, ignoring the % sign.

$$\dfrac{3}{4}\% = \dfrac{\dfrac{3}{4}}{100}$$

$$= \dfrac{\dfrac{3}{4}}{\dfrac{100}{1}} \qquad \text{Change 100 to a fraction by writing 100 as } \dfrac{100}{1} = 100.$$

$$= \dfrac{3}{4} \times \dfrac{1}{100} \qquad \text{Recall that to divide a fraction by another fraction, the top}$$

fraction ($\dfrac{3}{4}$) is multiplied by the inverted bottom

fraction ($\dfrac{1}{100}$). The inverted bottom fraction is called the

reciprocal.

$$= \dfrac{3 \times 1}{4 \times 100} = \dfrac{3}{400}$$

$$400\overline{)3} = 400\overline{)3.0000} \atop {\begin{array}{r}.0075 \\ \underline{-2800\downarrow} \\ 2000 \\ \underline{-2000} \\ 0000\end{array}}$$

(Review the chapter on Dividing a Smaller Number by a Bigger Number.)

Therefore, $\dfrac{3}{4}\% = .0075$.

Example 2

The Agbeko Fish Pond has a lot of fish. Mr. Johnson owns $22\dfrac{1}{2}\%$ of the fish in the pond. What is the decimal fraction of the fish that is owned by Mr. Johnson?

Solution

Using the rule, to express a fraction of a percent as a decimal fraction, write the fraction over 100, and then divide, ignoring the % sign.

$$22\dfrac{1}{2}\% = \dfrac{22\dfrac{1}{2}}{100}$$

$$= \dfrac{\dfrac{45}{2}}{100} \qquad \text{Change } 22\dfrac{1}{2} \text{ to an improper fraction } (\dfrac{45}{2}).$$

$$= \dfrac{\dfrac{45}{2}}{\dfrac{100}{1}} \qquad \text{Change 100 to fraction by writing 100 as } \dfrac{100}{1} = 100.$$

$$= \dfrac{45}{2} \div \dfrac{100}{1} \qquad \text{Review division of fractions.}$$

$$= \dfrac{45}{2} \times \dfrac{1}{100} \qquad \text{Recall that to divide a fraction by another fraction,}$$

the top fraction is multiplied by the inverted bottom fraction ($\dfrac{1}{100}$). The inverted bottom fraction is called the reciprocal.

$$= \frac{\overset{9}{\cancel{45}}}{2} \times \frac{1}{\underset{20}{\cancel{100}}} \qquad \text{Divide the numerator and the denominator by 5.}$$

$$= \frac{9 \times 1}{2 \times 20} = \frac{9}{40}$$

$$40\overline{)9} \;=\; 40\overline{)9.000}$$

(handwritten long division showing:)
$$\begin{array}{r} .225 \\ 40\overline{)9.000} \\ -8\,0 \\ \hline 1\,00 \\ -\,80 \\ \hline 2\,00 \\ -\,200 \\ \hline 000 \end{array}$$

(Review the chapter on Dividing a Smaller Number by a Bigger Number.)

Therefore, $22\frac{1}{2}\% = .225$.

Exercises

1. A bank rate was increased by $\frac{3}{10}\%$, what is the decimal fraction of the increase? Hint: See Example 1.

2. The population of a certain country increased by $8\frac{1}{3}\%$ last year. What is the decimal fraction of the increase? Hint: See Example 2.

Challenge Questions.

3. Eric's academic performance has improved by $5\frac{1}{3}\%$. What is the decimal fraction of his improvement?

4. The number of books at the library has been reduced by $\frac{7}{10}\%$. What is the decimal fraction of the reduction of the books?

FRACTIONAL PARTS OF PERCENTS - Alternative Method

The preceding sections show how to change the fractional parts of percents to decimals. This section shows an alternative method of changing the fractional parts of percent to decimals.

Rule: To express a fraction of a percent as a decimal, change the common

fraction to a decimal fraction by dividing the numerator by the denominator, and then dividing the result by 100 by moving the decimal point two places or digits to the left, and then ignore the % sign.

Example 1

Express $\frac{2}{5}\%$ as a decimal.

Solution

Use the rule which states, to express a fraction of a percent as a decimal, change the common fraction to a decimal fraction by dividing the numerator by the denominator, and then divide the result by 100 by moving the decimal point two places or two digits to the left, and then ignore the % sign.

Step 1: Change the common fraction to a decimal fraction by dividing the numerator by the denominator.

$$\frac{2}{5} = 5\overline{)2.0} \quad \begin{array}{r} .4 \\ \underline{-20} \\ 00 \end{array}$$

$$\frac{2}{5}\% = .4\%$$

Step 2: Divide the result in Step 1 by 100 by moving the decimal point two places or two digits to the left.

Write two 0 here to hold the place value.

$$.4\% = \frac{.4}{100} = .4 = .004$$

Move the decimal point two places or two digits to the left.

Therefore, $\frac{2}{5}\% = .004$

Exercises

Use the preceding alternative method in Example 1 for "changing a fractional part of a percent to a decimal" to solve the exercises under the section, "Fractional Parts of Percent."

Find the Percent of a Number

Rule 1: To find the percent of a number, multiply the given percent by the given number.

Example 1

Find 5% of 80.

Solution

Using the rule to find the percent of a number, multiply the given percent by the given number.

$$5\% \text{ of } 80 = 5\% \times 80 \qquad \text{Note: "of" means to multiply.}$$

$$= \frac{5}{100} \times 80 \qquad \text{Note: } 5\% = \frac{5}{100}.$$

$$= \frac{\overset{1}{5}}{\underset{20}{\cancel{100}}} \times 80 \qquad \text{Divide by 5.}$$

$$= \frac{1}{\cancel{20}} \times \overset{4}{\cancel{80}} \qquad \text{Divide by 20.}$$

$$= \frac{4}{1} = 4$$

Therefore, 5% of 80 = 4

Rule 2: **To find the percent of a number, change the percent to a decimal fraction, and then multiply the decimal fraction equivalent of the percent by the number**.

Note: Rule 2 is an alternative method of finding the percent of a number.

Example 2

Find 5% of 80. Hint: Use Rule 2 in solving this problem. This problem is the same as Example 1.

Solution

Using Rule 2 to find the percent of a number, change the percent to a decimal fraction, and then multiply the decimal fraction equivalent of the percent by the number as shown:

Step 1: Change the percent to a decimal fraction.

Write a 0 here as a place holder.

$$5\% = \frac{5}{100} = 5 = .05$$

Move the imaginary decimal point behind
5 two places or two digits to the left.

Note: There is an imaginary decimal point behind the last digit of any whole number. (Review the chapter on Decimals.)

Step 2: Multiply the decimal fraction equivalent of the percent by the number as shown:

```
         80
     × .05      Review decimal multiplication.
        400
   +   000  ←  Write this 0 as a place holder.
       4.00
```

Therefore, 5% of 80 is 4.

Note that the methods used in Examples 1 and 2 give the same answer of 4.

Example 3

What is 1.7% of $50?

Solution

Using Rule 2 to find the percent of a number, change the percent to a decimal fraction, and then multiply the decimal fraction equivalent of the percent by the number as shown:

Step 1: Change the percent to a decimal fraction.

Write a 0 here as a place holder.

$$1.7\% = \frac{1.7}{100} = 1.7 = .017$$

Move the decimal point two places or .

Step 2: Multiply the decimal fraction equivalent of the percent by the number ($50) as shown:

```
          $50
      × .017
          350
          500  ←   Write a 0 here as a place holder.
   +    0000  ←   Write two 0s here as a place holder
       0.850
```

Move the decimal point three decimal places or 3 digits to

95

the left. Review decimal multiplication.

Therefore, 1.7% of $50 is $.85

Example 4

Find $6\frac{1}{4}$% of $28.14.

Solution

Using Rule 2 to find the percent of a number, change the percent to a decimal fraction, and then multiply the decimal fraction equivalent of the percent by the number as shown:

Step 1: Change the percent to a decimal fraction.

$$\frac{1}{4} = 4\overline{)1} = 4\overline{)1.00}$$

with long division showing .25 result:
.25
4)1.00
  8
  20
  20
  00

Write a 0 here as a place holder.
↓

$$6\frac{1}{4}\% = \frac{6\frac{1}{4}}{100} = \frac{6.25}{100} = .\;6.25 = .0625 \qquad \text{Note: } 6\frac{1}{4} = 6.25$$

↑
Move the decimal point two decimal places
or two digits to the left.

Step 2: Multiply the decimal fraction equivalent of the percent by the number ($28.14) as shown:

$$
\begin{array}{r}
\$28.14 \\
\times\ .0625 \\
\hline
14070 \\
56280 \quad \leftarrow \text{Write a 0 here as a place holder.} \\
+\ 1688400 \quad \leftarrow \text{Write two 0 here as a place holder.} \\
\hline
1.758750 \\
\end{array}
$$

↑
Move the decimal point 6 decimal places or 6 digits
to the left.

Therefore, $6\frac{1}{4}$ of $28.14 is $1.76 to the nearest hundredths or cent.

Exercises

1. Find 7% of the following numbers. Hint: See Example 1. Give your answer to three decimal places.

(a) 160   (b) 16.4   (c) 58.2   (d) 142.1

2. Find 15% of the following numbers. Hint: See Example 2. Give your answer to 3 decimal places.

(a) 35   (b) 46.2   (c) 10   (d) 242

3. Find 26% of the following numbers. Hint See Example 2. Give your answer to 3 decimal places.

(a) 24   (b) 78.51   (c) .01   (d) .8

4. Find 3.8% of the following amounts. Hint: See Example 3.

(a) $70   (b) $75   (c) $115   (d) $275

5. Find 35.8% of the following amounts. Hint: See Example 3.

(a) $48   (b) $12   (c) 28   (d) $36

6. Find $8\frac{1}{2}$% of the following amounts. Hint: See Example 4.

(a) $50.25   (b) $12.78   (c) $78.17   (d) 124.48

7. Find $16\frac{1}{4}$% of the following amounts. Hint: See Example 4.

(a) $24.25   (b) 47.34   (c) $66.48   (d) $164.28

8. Find $12\frac{1}{5}$% of the following numbers. Hint: See Example 4. Give your answer to 3 decimal places.

(a) 72   (b) 36.3   (c) 46.32   (d) 147.18

Challenge Questions

9. Find $\frac{1}{4}$% of 100. Hint : Review the section on "fractional parts of percent." Give your answer to 3 decimal places.

10. Find .8% of 64.12. Hint: Review the section on "Fractional parts of percent." Round your answer to 3 decimal places.

11. Find 7.8% of $36.87.

12. Find 8% of 1348. Round your answer to 3 decimal places.

13. Find $\frac{4}{5}$% of 125. Hint: Review the section on "Fractional parts of percent." Round your answer to 3 decimal places.

14. Find $24\frac{1}{4}$% of $78.36

Answers to Selected Questions

1(a) 11.200   4(a) $2.66   6(a) $4.27

REAL WORLD APPLICATIONS – WORD PROBLEMS
To Find the Percent of a Number.

Example 1

There are 20 students in a class. If 45% of the students are boys, how many boys are in the class?

Solution

Using Rule 2 to find the percent of a number, change the percent to a decimal fraction, and then multiply the decimal fraction equivalent of the percent by the number as shown:

Step 1: Change the percent to a decimal fraction

$$45\% = \frac{45}{100} = .45 = .45$$

$$\uparrow$$

Move the imaginary decimal point
2 decimal places to the left.

Step 2: Multiply the decimal fraction equivalent of the percent by the number (20) as shown:

$$
\begin{array}{r}
20 \\
\times\ .45 \\
\hline
100 \\
800 \quad \leftarrow \text{Write a 0 here as a place holder.} \\
\hline
9.00 \\
\end{array}
$$

$$\uparrow$$

Move the decimal point two decimal or
two digits to the left. Review the section on decimal multiplication.

The number of boys in the class is 9.

Example 2

An employee earns $9\frac{1}{2}$% commission. What is the commission earned on a sale of $3,580.28?

Solution

Using Rule 2 to find the percent of a number, change the percent to a decimal fraction, and then multiply the decimal fraction equivalent of the percent by the number as shown:

Step 1: Change the percent to a decimal fraction.

Need to fill this digit position with a zero as a place holder.
↓

$$9\frac{1}{2}\% \ = \ 9.5\% \ = \ \frac{9.5}{100} \ = \ 9.5 = .095$$

↑↑
Move the decimal point two decimal places or two digits to the left.

Step 2: Multiply the decimal fraction equivalent of the percent by the number (3,580.28) as shown:

```
        $3,580.28
    ×        .095
        1790140
       32222520    ←  Write a 0 here as a place holder.
    +  0000000     ←  Write two 0s here as place holders.
       $340.12660
```
↑
Move the decimal point 5 places to the left.
Review the section on decimal multiplication.

Therefore, $9\frac{1}{2}\%$ of $3,580.28 is $340.13 to the nearest cent.

Example 3
George's salary was $45,200. If his salary is increased by 12%,
(**a**) what is the increase in his salary?
(**b**) what is his new salary?
Solution
Using Rule 2 to find the percent of a number, change the percent to a decimal fraction, and then multiply the decimal fraction equivalent of the percent by the number as shown:
(**a**) **Step 1**: Change the percent to a decimal fraction.

$$12\% \ = \ \frac{12}{100} \ = \ .12 \ =$$

↑↑
Move the decimal point two decimal or two digits to the left.

Step 2: Multiply the decimal fraction equivalent of the percent by the number (45,200) as shown:

$$\begin{array}{r}
\$45,200 \\
\times \quad\quad .12 \\
\hline
90400 \\
+ \quad 452000 \\
\hline
\$5424.00
\end{array}$$

← Write a 0 here as a place holder.

⇈

Move the decimal point two
places or digits to the left.

Therefore, the increase in George's salary is $5424.00

(**b**) George's new salary = current salary + Increase in salary

$$= \$45,200.00 + \$5,424.00$$
$$= \$50,624.00$$

Example 4

Mr. Benson needs a 15% down payment on a new house. If the new house costs $200,000, how much of a down payment does Mr. Benson need?

Solution

Using Rule 2 to find the percent of a number, change the percent to a decimal fraction, and then multiply the decimal fraction equivalent of the percent by the number.

Step 1: Change the percent to a decimal fraction.

$$15\% = \frac{15}{100} = .15 = .15$$

⇈

Move the decimal point two decimal
places or two digits to the left.

Step 2: Multiply the decimal fraction equivalent of the percent by the
number (200,000).

$$\begin{array}{r}
\$200,000 \\
\times \quad\quad .15 \\
\hline
1000000 \\
+ \quad 2000000 \\
\hline
\$30,000.00
\end{array}$$

← Write a 0 here as a place holder.

⇈

Move two decimal places or
two digits to the left.

Therefore, the down payment is $30,000.00.

Exercises

1. In a school, 55% of the students are boys. If there are 500 students in the school,
   (a) how many boys are in the school?
   (b) how many girls are in the school? Hint: See Example 1.

2. An employee earns $13\frac{1}{4}$% commission. What is the commission earned on a sale of $6,258? Hint: See Example 2.

3. Ama's salary was $55,436.19. If her salary is increased by 5%,
   (a) what is the increase in her salary?
   (b) what is her new salary?
   Hint: See Example 3.

4. Seth bought a new house for $175,000. If he paid 8% down payment on the new house, how much did he pay for the new house? Hint: See Example 4.

Challenge Questions

1. Mr. Albert has to pay 14% down payment on a new house. If the new house cost $225,000, what is the down payment of Mr. Albert?

2. Elizabeth's current salary is increased by $12\frac{1}{2}$% . If her current salary is $55,200.78, what is the increment in her salary?

3. An employee earns $8\frac{1}{2}$% commission. What is the commission earned on a sale of $3,648.37?

4. The population of a school is 650 students. If 40% of the students are girls,
   (a) how many girls are in the school?
   (b) how many boys are in the school?

Percent of One Number Compared to Another Number

In mathematics, it is possible to find what percent a number is of another number, and this is really a ratio expressed in percent.

Rule: To find what percent a number is of another number, divide the first number by the second number, and then move the decimal point two places or two digits to the right in the quotient, and then attach the % sign.

Special note: Some students who may find it difficult in setting up the solution of the percent problems can use the "is of" ($\frac{is}{of}$) method. The facts in the rule can be stated as "a number is what percent of another number?", and this can be expressed generally as:

$$\frac{is}{of} = \frac{a\ number}{another\ number}$$

Example 1

Express 3 as a percent of 5.

Solution

The facts in the question can be stated as: "3 **is** what percent **of** 5?" and this can be expressed as:

$$\frac{\text{is}}{\text{of}} = \frac{3}{5}$$

Using the rule to find what percent of a number is of another number, divide 3 by 5 and then move the decimal point two places or two digits to the right in the quotient, and then attach the % sign.

Step 1: Divide the first number by the second number as shown:

$$\frac{3}{5} = 5\overline{)3} = 5\overline{)3.0}$$
$$\underline{-30}$$
$$00$$

quotient $.6$

Step 2: Change the .6 to a percent by moving the decimal point two places or two digits to the right, and then adding the percent sign, which is the same as multiplying .6 by 100.

Write a 0 here as a place holder.
↓
$.6 = .6 = 60\%$
↑↑
Move the decimal point two places or two digits to the right.

(Review the chapter on Decimal Fraction and Percent.)

Therefore, 3 is 60% of 5.

Example 2

Express the ratio 2 out of 10 as a percent to the nearest whole number.

Solution

The facts in the question can be stated as: "2 **is** what percent **of** 10?" and this can be expressed as:

$$\frac{\text{is}}{\text{of}} = \frac{2}{10}$$

Using the rule to find what percent a number is of another number, divide 2 by 10, and then move the decimal point two places or two digits to the right in the quotient, and then attach the % sign.

Step 1: "2 out of 10" is $\frac{2}{10}$ or simply divide 2 by 10.

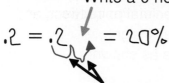

$$\frac{2}{10} = 10\overline{)2} = 10\overline{)2.0} \\ \underline{-2\,0} \\ 00$$

Step 2: Change .2 to a percent by moving the decimal point two places or two digits to the right, and then attach the percent sign.

Write a 0 here as a place holder.

.2 = .2 0 = 20%

Move the decimal point two places or two digits to the right.

Therefore, 2 is 20% of 10.

Exercises. Round all answers to the nearest whole number.
1. Express the following ratios as percents. Hint: See Example 2.
   (**a**) 1 out of 5   (**b**) 3 out of 10   (**c**) 3 out of 20
   (**d**) 4 out of 12   (**e**) 3 out of 9   (**f**) 2 out of 8
   (**g**) 2 out of 20   (**h**) 4 out of 100   (**i**) 20 out of 50
   (**j**) 12 out of 60   (**k**) 3 out of 15   (**l**) 8 out of 64
2. Express 2 as a percent of 8. Hint: See Example 1.
3. Express 10 as a percent of 100. Hint: See Example 1.
4. Express 5 as a percent of 25. Hint: See Example 1.
5. Express 6 as a percent of 24. Hint: See Example 1.
6. Express 40 as a percent of 90. Hint: See Example 1.
7. 15 is what percent of 125? Hint: See Example 1.

Challenge Questions
8. Express the following ratios as percents. Round your answers to the nearest whole number.
   (a) 25 out of 75   (b) 5 out of 65   (c) 6 out of 36
   (d) 35 out of 100   (e) 15 out of 100   (f) 50 out of 150
9. 25 is what percent of 125? Round your answer to the nearest whole number.
10. Express 4 as a percent of 48. Round your answer to the nearest whole number.

REAL WORLD APPLICATIONS – WORD PROBLEMS
Percent of One Number Compared to Another Number

Example 1
There are 8 girls and 12 boys in a class. What percent of the class is boys?

Solution

Total number of the students = 8 + 12 = 20 students.

The facts in the question can be stated as: "12 **is** what percent **of** 20?" and this can be expressed as:

$$\frac{is}{of} = \frac{12}{20}$$

Using the rule to find what percent a number is of another number, divide the number of boys by the total number of the students, and then move the decimal point two places or two digits to the right in the quotient, and then attach the % sign.

Step 1: Divide the number of boys by the total number of students as shown:

$$\frac{\text{Number of boys}}{\text{Total number of students}} = \frac{12}{20}$$

$$= \frac{\overset{3}{12}}{\underset{5}{20}} \qquad \text{Reduce to the lowest terms by dividing by 4.}$$

$$= \frac{3}{5}$$

$$\frac{3}{5} = 5\overline{)3} = 5\overline{)3.0} \quad \begin{array}{r} .6 \\ \hline -30 \\ \hline 0\ 0 \end{array}$$

Step 2: Change .6 to a percent by moving the decimal point 2 places to the right and then attach the percent sign which is the same as multiplying by 100.

Write a 0 here as a place holder.

.6 = .6 = 60%

Move the decimal point two places or two digits to the right.

Therefore, 60% of the class are boys.

Example 2

In a class of 24 students, 8 students like biology. What is the percent of the students that like biology?

Solution

The facts in the question can be stated as: "8 **is** what percent **of** 24?" and this can be expressed as:

$$\frac{\text{is}}{\text{of}} = \frac{8}{24}$$

Using the rule to find what percent a number is of another number, divide the number of students that like biology by the total number of the students, and then move the decimal point two places or two digits to the right in the quotient, and then attach the % sign.

Step1: Divide the number of students who like biology by the total number of students as shown:

$$\frac{\text{Number of students that like biology}}{\text{Total number of students}} = \frac{8}{24}$$

$$= \frac{\overset{1}{8}}{\underset{3}{24}} \qquad \text{Reduce to the lowest term by dividing by 8.}$$

$$= \frac{1}{3}$$

$$\frac{1}{3} = 3\overline{)1} = 3\overline{)1.000} \quad \begin{array}{r} .333 \\ \underline{-9} \\ 10 \\ \underline{-9} \\ 10 \\ \underline{-9} \\ 1 \end{array}$$

Step 2: Change .333 to a percent by moving the decimal point 2 places to the right, and then attach the percent sign as shown:

$$.333 = .333 = 33.3\%$$

Move the decimal point two places or two digits to the right.

Therefore, 33.3% of the students like biology.

Example 3

Judith earned $10.25 for baby-sitting. If she spent $2.50, what percent of the money did she spend?

Solution

The facts in the question can be stated as: "$2.50 **is** what percent **of** $10.25?" and this can be expressed as:

$$\frac{\text{is}}{\text{of}} = \frac{\$2.50}{\$10.25}$$

Using the rule to find what percent a number is of another number, divide the amount spent by the total amount earned, and then move the decimal point two places or two digits to the right in the quotient, and then attach the % sign.

Step 1: Divide the amount that she spent by the total amount that she earned.

$$\frac{\text{Amount spent}}{\text{Total amount earned}} = \frac{\$2.50}{\$10.25}$$

$$= .244 \quad \text{You may use a calculator to divide.}$$

Step 2: Change .244 to a percent by moving the decimal point two places to the right, and then adding the percent sign.

$$.244 = .244 = 24.4\%$$

Move the decimal point two places or two digits to the right.

Therefore, Judith spent 24.4% of her money.

Example 4

Helen earned $25,600 last year. If she saved $5,000, what percent of her income did she save?

Solution

The facts in the question can be stated as: "$5,000 **is** what percent **of** $25,600?" and this can be expressed as:

$$\frac{\text{is}}{\text{of}} = \frac{\$5,000}{\$25,600}$$

Using the rule to find what percent a number is of another number, divide the amount saved by the total amount earned, and then move the decimal point two places or two digits to the right in the quotient, and then attach the % sign.

Step 1: Divide the amount saved by the total amount earned.

$$\frac{\text{Amount saved}}{\text{Total Amount earned}} = \frac{\$5,000}{25,600}$$

$$= .195 \quad \text{You may use a calculator to divide.}$$

Step 2: Change .195 to a percent by moving the decimal point two places to the right, and then attach the % sign.

$$-195 = -195 = 19.5\%$$

Move the decimal point two places or two digits to the right.

Therefore, Helen saved 19.5% of what she earned last year.

Exercises

1. There are 10 boys and 15 girls in a certain class. What is the percent of the girls in the class? Hint: See Example 1.
2. In a class of 30 students, 5 of them like Chemistry. What is the percent of the students that like chemistry? Hint: See Example 2.
3. George earned $15 for baby-sitting. If he spent $5, what is the percent of the money that he spent? Hint: See Example 3.
4. If Hope made a down payment of $12 on a television set that cost $224, what is the percent of her down payment? Hint: See Example 4.

Challenge Questions

5. If Grace earned $8 for baby-sitting and she spent $2.50 of it, what is the percent of the money that she spent?
6. Robert made a down payment of $20 on a computer that cost $350. What is the percent of his down payment?
7. There are 26 students in a class. If 10 of the students like history, what is the percent of the students that like history?
8. A certain class consists of 6 girls and 14 boys. What percent of the class is boys?

Explanation of Percent Rate, Base, and Percentage

A percent statement can be 10% of 50 is 5. In this statement, 10 is the **percent rate**, 50 is known as the **base**, and 5 is the **percentage**. If two of the parts in a percent problem are known, the third part can be found by the **equation method** or the **proportion method**.

Finding a Number When a Percent of it is Known.

The two methods by which we can find a number when a percent of it is known are:
   (**1**). by the use of an equation.
   (**2**). by the use of a proportion.

Equation Method

Let us solve the question, 50% of what number is 2?
Let the number be *n*.

We can then set up an equation as follows:

$$50\% \text{ of } n = 2$$

$$50\% \times n = 2 \qquad \text{Note that "of" is the same as multiplication}$$

$$50\% \times n = 2 \text{ \rule{4cm}{0.4pt}}[A]$$

To find the value of n, divide each side of equation $[A]$ by 50% as follows:

$$\frac{50\% \times n}{50\%} = \frac{2}{50\%}$$

$$\frac{\overset{1}{\cancel{50\%}} \times n}{\underset{1}{\cancel{50\%}}} = \frac{2}{50\%}$$

$$n = \frac{2}{50\%} \text{ \rule{5cm}{0.4pt}}[B]$$

$$n = \frac{2}{\dfrac{50}{100}} \qquad \text{Note } 50\% = \frac{50}{100}$$

$$n = 2 \div \frac{50}{100}$$

$$n = 2 \times \frac{100}{50} \qquad \text{Review division by fractions.}$$

To divide by a fraction, is the same as to multiply by the reciprocal of the fraction.

$$n = 2 \times \frac{\overset{2}{\cancel{100}}}{\underset{1}{\cancel{50}}}$$

$$n = 2 \times 2$$

$$n = 4$$

Therefore, 50% of 4 is 2.

Note: We can also write equation $[A]$ which is $50\% \times n = 2$, in the decimal form as:

$$.5 \times n = 2 \qquad\qquad 50\% = \frac{50}{100} = \frac{1}{2} = .5$$

Divide both sides of the equation $.5 \times n = 2$ by $.5$ to obtain the value of n.

$$\frac{.5 \times n}{.5} = \frac{2}{.5}$$

$$\frac{\overset{1}{\cancel{.5}} \times n}{\underset{1}{\cancel{.5}}} = \frac{2}{.5}$$

Do the division.

$$n = \frac{2}{.5}$$

$$n = \frac{2}{\frac{1}{2}} \qquad\qquad .5 = \frac{1}{2}$$

$$n = 2 \times \frac{2}{1}$$

To divide by a fraction is the same as to multiply by the reciprocal of the fraction.

$$n = 4$$

Rule: Using equation $[\text{B}]$, we can state a rule as shown: **To find a number when the percent of the number is known and the number that the percent represents is also known, divide the number by the percent.**

Proportion Method

Hint: Review the chapter on Proportion.

Let us now use proportion to solve the same question, 50% of what number is 2?

Let the number be n.

Write a proportion as shown:

Part   Part

$$\frac{50}{100} = \frac{2}{n}$$

Whole   Whole

Note that $\frac{50}{100} = 50\%$

$$\frac{50}{100} \underset{\nwarrow\nearrow}{\searrow\swarrow} \frac{2}{n}$$

Cross products of equivalent ratios are equal.
Cross products of the ratios in a proportion are equal.

$$50n = 100 \times 2 \text{\textemdash}\!\text{\textemdash}\![\text{C}]$$

Divide both sides of equation $[\text{C}]$ by 50 in order to obtain the value of n as shown:

$$\frac{50n}{50} = \frac{100 \times 2}{50}$$

$$\frac{50n}{50} = \frac{100 \times 2}{50}$$

$$\frac{n}{1} \quad \frac{2}{1}$$

$$n = 2 \times 2 = 4$$

Therefore, 50% of 4 is 2.

Note that both the "Equation Method" and the "Proportion Method" give the same answer of 4, and so **the student may use the method that he/she is more comfortable with**.

Example 1

If a 10% reduction in price of an item is equal to $20.00, find the original price by
a. using the rule or the equation method.
b. using the proportion method.

Solution

a. Using the rule or the equation method

Using the rule divide the $20.00 by 10% to obtain the original price of the items as shown:

$$\frac{\$20}{10\%} = \frac{\$20}{\frac{10}{100}} \qquad\qquad 10\% = \frac{10}{100}$$

$$= \$20 \div \frac{10}{100}$$

$$= \$20 \times \frac{100}{10} \qquad\qquad \text{Review division by fractions.}$$

$$= \$20 \times \frac{\overset{10}{\cancel{100}}}{\underset{1}{\cancel{10}}}$$

$$= \$20 \times 10 = \$200$$

Therefore, the original price is $200.

b. Using the Proportion Method

Hint: Review the chapter on Proportion.
Let us now use proportion to solve Example 1.
Let the original price be x.

Write a proportion as shown:

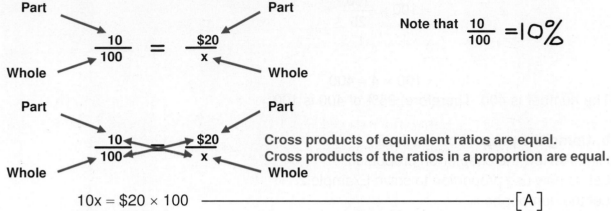

Note that $\dfrac{10}{100} = 10\%$

Cross products of equivalent ratios are equal.
Cross products of the ratios in a proportion are equal.

$$10x = \$20 \times 100 \quad\text{———————————————[A]}$$

Divide both sides of equation [A] by 10 in order to obtain the value of x as follows:

$$\dfrac{10x}{10} = \dfrac{\$20 \times 100}{10}$$

$$\dfrac{\overset{x}{\cancel{10}x}}{\underset{1}{\cancel{10}}} = \dfrac{\$20 \times \overset{10}{\cancel{100}}}{\underset{1}{\cancel{10}}} \qquad \text{Do the division.}$$

$$x = \$20 \times 10 = \$200$$

Therefore, the original price is $200.

Example 2

25% of what number is 100?

a. Find the number by using the rule or the equation method.
b. Find the number by using the proportion method.

Solution

a. Using the rule or the equation method

Using the rule, divide 100 by 25% as shown:

$$\dfrac{100}{25\%} = \dfrac{\dfrac{100}{25}}{100} \qquad \textbf{Note:}\ 25\% = \dfrac{25}{100}$$

$$\dfrac{\dfrac{100}{25}}{100} = 100 \div \dfrac{25}{100}$$

$$= 100 \times \dfrac{100}{25} \qquad \text{Review division by fractions.}$$

$$= 100 \times \frac{\overset{4}{\cancel{100}}}{\underset{1}{\cancel{25}}}$$

$$= 100 \times 4 = 400$$

The number is 400. Therefore, 25% of 400 is 100.

b. Using the proportion method

Hint: Review the chapter on proportion.

Let us now use proportion to solve Example 2.

Let the number be x.

Write a proportion as shown:

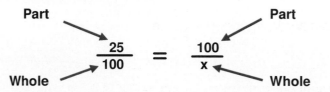

Note that $\frac{25}{100} = 25\%$

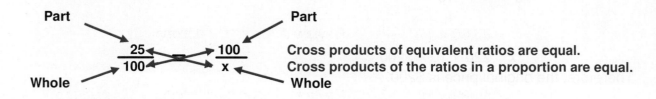

Cross products of equivalent ratios are equal.
Cross products of the ratios in a proportion are equal.

$$25x = 100 \times 100 \quad\text{————————[A]}$$

Divide both sides of equation [A] by 25 in order to obtain the value of x as shown:

$$\frac{25x}{25} = \frac{100 \times 100}{25}$$

$$\frac{\overset{x}{\cancel{25x}}}{\underset{1}{\cancel{25}}} = \frac{\overset{4}{\cancel{100}} \times 100}{\underset{1}{\cancel{25}}}$$ Do the division.

$$x = 4 \times 100 - 400$$

The number is 400. Therefore, 25% of 400 is 100.

Example 3

$5.80 is $\frac{1}{2}$% of what amount?

112

a. Find the amount by using the rule or the equation method.

b. Find the amount by using the proportion method.

Solution

a. Using the rule or the equation method

Using the rule, divide the $5.80 by $\frac{1}{2}$% as shown:

$$\frac{\$5.80}{\frac{1}{2}\%} = \frac{\$5.80}{\frac{\frac{1}{2}}{100}} \qquad \text{Note that } \frac{1}{2}\% = \frac{\frac{1}{2}}{100}$$

$$= \$5.80 \div \frac{\frac{1}{2}}{100} \qquad \text{Review division by fractions.}$$

$$= \$5.80 \times \frac{100}{\frac{1}{2}} \qquad \text{Review division by fractions, } \frac{\frac{1}{2}}{100} \text{ is inverted.}$$

$$= \$5.80 \times 100 \div \frac{1}{2} \qquad \text{Review division by fractions.}$$

$$= \$5.80 \times 100 \times \frac{2}{1} \qquad \text{Review division by fractions, } \frac{1}{?} \text{ is inverted.}$$

$$= \$5.80 \times 100 \times 2$$

$$= \$11.60 \times 100 \qquad\qquad \$5.80 \times 2 = \$11.60$$

$$= \$1160$$

The amount is $1160. Therefore, $5.80 is $\frac{1}{2}$% of $1160.

b. Using the proportion method

Hint: Review the chapter on proportion.

Let us now use proportion to solve Example 3.

Let the amount be x.

Write a proportion as shown:

Part

$$\frac{\$5.80}{x} = \frac{\frac{1}{2}}{100} \qquad \text{Note that } \frac{\frac{1}{2}}{100} = \frac{1}{2}\%$$

Whole

Part

Whole

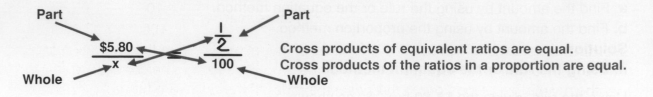

$$\frac{1}{2}x = \$5.80 \times 100 \hspace{4cm} \text{[A]}$$

Multiply both sides of equation [A] by 2 in order to obtain the value of x as follows:

$$\frac{1}{2}x \cdot 2 = \$5.80 \times 100 \cdot 2$$

$$\frac{1}{\overset{1}{\cancel{2}}}x \cdot \overset{}{\cancel{2}} = \$5.80 \times 100 \cdot 2 \hspace{2cm} \text{Do the division.}$$

$$x = \$5.80 \times 100 \cdot 2$$
$$x = \$1160$$

The amount is \$1160. Therefore, \$5.80 is $\frac{1}{2}$% of \$1160.

Summary of the Equation Method

1. Write an equation in a decimal form to solve the percent statement: 15% of x is 65.
The required equation is:

$$0.15 \cdot x = 65 \hspace{3cm} \text{[A]}$$

Hint: x can be found if both sides of the equation [A] are divided by 0.15.

2. Write an equation in a decimal form to solve the percent statement: 25% of 90 is n.
The required equation is:

$$0.25 \cdot 90 = n$$

Hint: n can be found if 0.25 is multiplied by 90.

3. Write an equation for x of 36 is 24 in a form so that you can solve for x.
The required equation is:

$$x \cdot 36 = 24 \hspace{3cm} \text{[A]}$$

Hint: x can be found if both sides of the equation [A] are divided by 36.
The value of x can be expressed in decimal or in percent by multiplying by 100.

Summary of the Proportion Method

1. Write a proportion to solve the equation: 10% of 64 is x.
The required proportion is:

$$\frac{10}{100} = \frac{x}{64}$$ Notice that $10\% = \frac{10}{100}$.

Hint: When writing a proportion, the order of the ratios that form the proportion are very important, otherwise the solution of the proportion will not be correct. Review the chapter on proportion. In this case, the order of the ratios are formed by using "part divided by whole" as shown:

Part → Part →

$$\frac{10}{100} = \frac{x}{64}$$

Whole → Whole →

Hint: x can be found by cross multiplying the ratios of the proportion and then dividing both sides of the equation formed by 100.

2. Write a proportion to solve the equation: 28% of x is 49.
   The required proportion is:

$$\frac{28}{100} = \frac{49}{x}$$ Notice that $28\% = \frac{28}{100}$.

Hint: When writing a proportion, the order of the ratios that form the proportion are very important, otherwise the solution of the proportion will not be correct. Review the chapter on proportion. In this case, the order of the ratios are formed by using "part divided by whole." as shown:

Part → Part →

$$\frac{28}{100} = \frac{49}{x}$$

Whole → Whole →

Hint: x can be found by cross multiplying the ratios of the proportion and then dividing both sides of the equation formed by 28.

3. Write a proportion to solve the equation: x% of 85 is 25.
   The required proportion is:

$$\frac{x}{100} = \frac{25}{85}$$ Notice that $x\% = \frac{x}{100}$.

Hint: When writing a proportion, the order of the ratios that form the proportion are very important, otherwise the solution of the proportion will not be correct. Review the chapter on proportion. In this case, the order of the ratios are formed by using "part divided by whole," as shown:

Part → Part →

$$\frac{x}{100} = \frac{25}{85}$$

Whole → Whole →

Hint: x can be found by cross multiplying the ratios of the proportion, and then

115

dividing both sides of the equation formed by 85.

Exercises

You may setup similar equations as shown under the "Summary of the Equation Method" and the "Summary of the Proportion Method" in solving Exercises 1 to 12 as needed.

1. If a 15% reduction in the price of an item is equal to $45.00, find the original price. Hint: See Example 1.

2. 22% of what number is 48? Round your answer to the nearest whole number. Hint: See Example 2.

3. $4.50 is $\frac{1}{5}$% of what amount? Hint: See Example 3.

4. $\frac{1}{4}$% of what number is 28? Hint: See Example 3.

5. $7.75 is 5% of what amount? Hint: See Example 2.

6. $28.45 is 45% of what amount? Hint: See Example 2.

7. 65% of what number is 160? Hint: See Example 2.

8. Write a proportion to solve each of the following equations:

    a. 30% of x is 40.   **b.** 54% of n is 72.   **c.** 15% of x is 65.

    d. 2% of k is 64.   **e.** 5% of x is 60.   **f.** 70% of p is 35.

    Hint: See the "Summary of the Proportion Method," item 2.

9. Solve each proportion in exercise 8.

    Hint: See the "Summary of the Proportion Method," item 2.

Challenge Questions

10. 30% of what number is 90?

11. 15% of what number is 125?

12. $10.25 is $\frac{1}{4}$% of what amount?

13. If a 6% reduction in the price of an item is $16.25, what is the cost of the item?

14. $6.75 is 5% of what amount?

15. 34% of what number is 24?

16. Write a proportion to solve each of the following equations:

    a. 60% of p is 9.   **b.** 20% of n is 80.   **c.** 4% of x is 36.

Answers to Selected Exercises

1. $300   **2.** 218.18   **8a.** $\dfrac{30}{100} = \dfrac{4}{x}$ **8d.** $\dfrac{2}{100} = \dfrac{64}{k}$

REAL WORLD APPLICATIONS - WORD PROBLEMS
Finding a Number When a Percent of it is Known
Example 1
A shirt was sold on a sale at 20% reduction. If the amount of the reduction was $10, what was the original price of the shirt?
Solution
Using the rule, the original price of the shirt can be found by dividing the reduction amount by the percent of the reduction, as shown:

$$\frac{\$10}{20\%} = \frac{\$10}{\frac{20}{100}} \qquad \text{Note that } 20\% = \frac{20}{100}$$

$$= \$10 \div \frac{20}{100} \qquad \text{Review division by fractions.}$$

$$= \$10 \times \frac{100}{20} \qquad \text{Review division by fractions, } \frac{20}{100} \text{ is inverted.}$$

To divide by a fraction is the same as multiplying by the reciprocal of the fraction.

$$= \$10 \times \frac{\overset{5}{\cancel{100}}}{\underset{1}{\cancel{20}}} \qquad \text{Divide by 20.}$$

$$= \$10 \times 5 = \$50$$

Therefore, the original price of the shirt is $50.

Example 2
Mr. Apreaku earns a commission of 10.2% of sales. If he earns $98.65 in commission, find the amount of his sales.
Solution
Using the rule, the amount of the sale can be found by dividing the commission earned by the percent of the commission, as shown:

$$\frac{\$98.65}{10.2\%} = \frac{\$98.65}{\frac{10.2}{100}} \qquad \text{Note that } 10.2\% = \frac{10.2}{100}$$

$$= \$98.65 \div \frac{10.2}{100} \qquad \text{Review division by fractions.}$$

$$= \$98.65 \times \frac{100}{10.2} \qquad \text{Review division by fractions, } \frac{10.2}{100} \text{ is inverted.}$$

$= \$967.156$ Once you setup the solution, you may use a calculator to calculate the final answer.

Therefore, the amount of his sale was $967.16 to the nearest cent.

Example 3

If 45% of the students in a school are girls, and there are 490 girls, find the total number of students.

Solution

Using the rule, divide the number of girls by the percent of the girls to obtain the total number of students.

$$\frac{490}{45\%} = \frac{490}{\dfrac{45}{100}} \qquad \text{Note that } 45\% = \frac{45}{100}$$

$$= 490 \div \frac{45}{100}$$

$$= 490 \times \frac{100}{45} \qquad \text{Review division by fractions, } \frac{45}{100} \text{ is inverted.}$$

To divide by a fraction is the same as to multiply by the reciprocal of the fraction.

$$= 490 \times \frac{\overset{20}{\cancel{100}}}{\underset{9}{\cancel{45}}}$$

$$= \frac{490 \times 20}{9} = 1088.8 \qquad \text{(You may use a calculator)}$$

The total number of students is 1089 to the nearest whole number

Exercise

1. A computer part was on sale at a 15% reduction. If the amount of the reduction was $30.00, what was the original price of the computer part? Hint: See Example 1.
2. Mr. Wilson earns a commission of 8.5% of sales. If he earns $425.00 in commission, find the amount of his sales. Hint: See Example 2.
3. If 60% of the students in a school are girls and there are 300 girls in the school, what is the total number of students in the school? Round your answer to the nearest whole number. Hint: See Example 3.

Challenge Questions

4. If 35% of the students in a school study geography, and there are 275 students

who study geography, how many students are in the school? Round your answer to the nearest whole number.

5. Mrs. Collins earns a commission of 12.5% of sales. If she earns $65.75 in commission, find the amount of her sales.

6. An advanced calculator was on sale at a 5% reduction. If the amount of the reduction was $15.25, what was the original price of the calculator?

REAL WORLD APPLICATIONS - WORD PROBLEMS
Percent of Increase or Decrease

The percent of increase or decrease is the increase or decrease expressed as a percent.

Percent of Increase
Example 1
Mary was making $5.00 per hour for baby–sitting and her earnings has been increased to $6.0 per hour. What is the percent of the increase?
Solution
Step 1: Her increase per hour can be calculated by subtracting her original earning per hour from her new earning per hour as follows:

$$\textbf{Increase per hour} = \textbf{New earnings per hour} - \textbf{original earning per hour}$$
$$= \$6.00 - \$5.00$$
$$= \$1.00$$

Step 2: Fraction of the increase per hour is calculated by dividing the increase per hour by the original earning per hour as follows:

$$\textbf{Fraction of increase per hour} = \frac{\textbf{Increase per hour}}{\textbf{Original earning per hour}}$$

$$= \frac{\$1.00}{\$5.00} = \frac{1}{5}$$

$$\frac{1}{5} = 5\overline{)1} = 5\overline{)\begin{array}{r}.2\\1.0\\-1\,0\\\hline 00\end{array}}$$

Therefore, the decimal fraction of increase = .2

Step 3: Change the fraction of increase to percent by moving the decimal point of the decimal fraction of the increase 2 places or two digits to the right which is the same as multiplying the decimal fraction of the increase by 100.

Percent increase = decimal fraction of increase × 100

119

$$= .2 \times 100$$

Write a 0 here as a place holder.

Attach the % sign.

$$= .2 \times 100 = .2 = 20\%$$

Move the decimal point two places or two digits to the right.

Therefore, the percent increase = 20%

Rule 1: To find the percent of increase, divide the increase by the original number, and then move the decimal point 2 places to the right or multiply the quotient by 100, and attach the % sign.

Example 2

What are the 3 major steps in finding the percent of increase?

Solution

The 3 major steps in finding percent of increase are:

Step 1: Find the increase by subtracting the original number from the new number.

Step 2: Find the fraction of the increase by dividing the increase by the original number.

Step 3: Change the fraction of the increase to percent by moving the decimal point 2 places or two digits to the right or by multiplying the quotient by 100.

Example 3

The weekly allowance of George was increased from $10 to $12. What is the percent of increase?

Solution

Step 1: Find the increase in his allowance by subtracting the original allowance from the new allowance.

Increase = New allowance – Original allowance
$$= \$12 - \$10$$
$$= \$2$$

Step 2: Find the fraction of the increase by dividing the increase by the original allowance as shown:

$$\textbf{Fraction of the increase} = \frac{\textbf{Increase}}{\textbf{Original allowance}}$$

$$= \frac{\$2}{\$10} = \frac{2}{10}$$

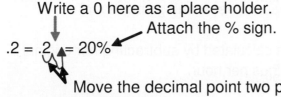

$$\frac{2}{10} = 10\overline{)2.0}$$

= .2 This is the decimal fraction of the increase.

Step 3: Change the decimal fraction of the increase to a percent by moving the decimal point of the decimal fraction of the increase two places or two digits to the right, and then attach the % sign, which is the same as multiplying the decimal fraction of the increase by 100.

Write a 0 here as a place holder.

Attach the % sign.

.2 = .2 = 20%

Move the decimal point two places or two digits to the right.

The percent of increase = 20 %.

Alternative method: Shortcut method for percent of increase.
When the students understand the steps for finding the percent of increase, the students may use shortcut in solving the problems. The formula is:

$$\textbf{Percent of increase} = \frac{\textbf{Increase}}{\textbf{Original number}} \times \textbf{100}$$

Let us solve Example 3 using the shortcut method.

$$\textbf{Percent of increase} = \frac{\textbf{Increase}}{\textbf{Original number}} \times \textbf{100}$$

$$= \frac{2}{10} \times 100$$

$$= \frac{2}{10} \times \overset{10}{100} \qquad \text{Divide by 10.}$$

$$= 2 \times 10 = 20\%$$

Therefore, the percent of increase = 20%.

Note that the shortcut method is useful when the numerators can be divided by the denominators evenly so that there will be no decimal fractions involved.

Group Exercise

The class should be divided into four groups and each group should solve Example 1 using the shortcut method, and then report their solution to the whole class.

Rule 2: The formula for finding the percent of increase is:

$$\text{Percent of increase} = \frac{\text{Increase}}{\text{Original number}} \times 100$$

Percent of Decrease

Example 4

Joyce was making $5.00 per hour for baby-sitting. Her earnings were decreased to $3.00 per hour. What is the percent of decrease in her earnings per hour?

Solution

Step 1: The decrease in her payment can be calculated by subtracting her original earnings per hour from her new earnings per hour.

$$\textbf{Decrease} = \textbf{New payment per hour} - \textbf{Original payment per hour}$$
$$= \$5.00 - \$3.00 = \$2.00$$

Step 2: The fraction of the decrease is calculated by dividing the decreased amount per hour by the original earnings per hour.

$$\textbf{Fraction of the decrease} = \frac{\textbf{Decrease amount per hour}}{\textbf{Original payment per hour}}$$

$$= \frac{\$2.00}{\$5.00} = \frac{2}{5}$$

$$\frac{2}{5} = 5\overline{)2.0} \quad \begin{array}{r} .4 \\ \hline 2.0 \\ -20 \\ \hline 00 \end{array}$$

Fraction of the decrease = .4   Note that .4 is the decimal fraction of the decrease.

Step 3: Change the decimal fraction of the decrease to a percent by moving the decimal point of the decimal fraction two places or two digits to the right, and then attach the % sign, which is the same as multiplying the decimal fraction of the decrease by 100.

Write a 0 here as a place holder.

Attach the % sign.

$$.4 = .40 = 40\%$$

Move the decimal point two places or two digits to the right.

122

Therefore, the percent of decrease in her earnings per hour is 40%.

Rule 3: To find the percent of decrease, divide the decrease by the original number, and move the decimal point two places or two digits to the right, and then attach the % sign, which is the same as multiplying the quotient by 100.

Example 5
What are the 3 major steps in finding the percent of a decrease?
Solution
The 3 major steps for finding the percent of the decrease are:

Step 1: Find the decrease by subtracting the original number from the new number.

Step 2: Find the fraction of the decrease by dividing the decreased amount by the original number.

Step 3: Change the decimal fraction of the decrease to a percent by moving the decimal point two places or two digits to the right, which is the same as multiplying the decimal fraction of the decrease by 100.

Shortcut method for percent decrease - Group exercise
When the students understand the steps for finding the percent of decrease, the student may use the shortcut in solving the problems. The formula is:

$$\textbf{Percent of decrease} = \frac{\textbf{Decrease}}{\textbf{Original number}} \times \textbf{100}$$

Rule 4: The formula for finding the percent of decrease is:

$$\textbf{Percent of decrease} = \frac{\textbf{Decrease}}{\textbf{Original number}} \times \textbf{100}$$

Divide the class into four groups and each group should solve Example 4 using the shortcut method and then report their solution to the class.

Example 6
The weekly allowance of Grace was reduced from $15.00 to $12.00. What is the percent of reduction in her weekly allowance?
Solution

Step 1: Find the reduction in her allowance by subtracting the new allowance from the original allowance.

$$\textbf{Reduction in allowance} = \textbf{Original allowance} - \textbf{New allowance}$$
$$= \$15.00 - \$12.00$$
$$= \$3.00$$

Step 2: Find the fraction of the reduction by dividing the reduction in allowance by the original allowance.

$$\text{Fraction of the reduction} = \frac{\text{Reduction}}{\text{Original allowance}}$$

$$= \frac{\$3.00}{\$15.00} = \frac{3}{15}$$

$$\frac{3}{15} = 15\overline{)3.0} \\ \begin{array}{r} .2 \\ \hline -30 \\ \hline 00 \end{array}$$

The fraction of the reduction = .2. **Note** that .2 is the decimal fraction of the reduction.

Step 3: Change the decimal fraction of the reduction to a percent by moving the decimal point of the decimal fraction of the reduction two places or two digits to the right, and then attach the % sign, which is the same as multiplying the decimal fraction of the reduction by 100.

Write a 0 here as a place holder

Attach the % sign.

.2 = .2 = 20%

Move the decimal point two places or two digits to the right.

The percent of reduction is 20%

Alternative Method - Shortcut Method.

Let us solve Example 6 using the shortcut method.

$$\text{Percent of reduction} = \frac{\text{Reduction}}{\text{Original number}} \times 100$$

$$= \frac{\$3.00}{\$15.00} \times 100$$

$$= \frac{\overset{1}{\cancel{\$3.00}}}{\underset{5}{\underset{1}{\cancel{\$15.00}}}} \times \overset{20}{\cancel{100}} \qquad \text{Divide by 3 and then by 5.}$$

$$= 20\%$$

Therefore, the percent of reduction = 20%.

Note that the shortcut method is useful when the numerator can be divided by the denominator evenly so that the quotient will not be a decimal fraction.

Group Project

The class should be divided into four groups. Each group should cut four sale coupons from the newspaper and bring them to school. Each group should use the sale coupons to make the table below. Each group should calculate the percent of decrease in price.

Items	Original price	Amount saved by coupon	Percent of decrease
Bread			
Cereal			
Medicine			
Kool–Aid			

Which group found the highest percent of reduction? Compare the group exercise to Examples 1 to 6. Each group should list the similarities and differences between the group exercise and the Examples 1 to 6.

Exercises

1. $20 is increased to $24, what is the percent of increase? Hint: See Examples 1, 2, and 3.

2. $45 is increased to $54, what is the percent of increase? Hint: See Examples 1, 2, and 3.

3. Two weeks ago, John was given 6 oranges. Last week, he was given 8 oranges. What is the percent of increase of the oranges? Hint: See Examples 1, 2, and 3.

4. Two months ago, Mr. Johnson was paid $230 and last month, he was paid $245. What is the percent of increase in his payment? Hint: See Examples 1, 2, and 3.

5. Maggie earned $16,500 last year, and this year she will earn $17,000. What is the percent of increase? Hint: See Examples 1, 2, and 3.

6. The population of a school last year was 535 students. This year, the enrollment is 643 students. What is the percent of increase? Hint: See Examples 1, 2, and 3.

7. Mrs. Jackson bought a car for $10,000 and she sold it for $12,000. What was the percent of profit? Hint: Percent profit is the same as percent of increase. See Examples 1, 2, and 3.

8. Rebecca's rent was increased from $595 to $610. What was the percent of increase? Hint: See Examples 1, 2, and 3.

9. What is the percent of decrease if:
   (a) $12 is decreased to $7? Hint: See Examples 4 and 5.
   (b) $15 is decreased to $9? Hint: See Examples 4 and 5.
   (c) $150 is decreased to $140? Hint: See Examples 4 and 5.
   (d) $348 is decreased to $292? Hint: See Examples 4 and 5.

10. Last year, Samuel was paid $6 per hour for baby-sitting. This year, he is being paid $4 per hour for baby-sitting. What is the percent of decrease? Hint: See Examples 4 and 5.

11. Mr. Collins weighed 190 pounds and after dieting for nine months, his weight was 175 pounds. What percent of his weight did he lose? Hint: See Examples 4 and 5.

12. A computer part selling for $120.00 was reduced to $100.00. What was the percent of decrease? Hint: See Examples 4, 5, and 6.

Challenge Questions

13. The enrollment of the students in a school decreased from 455 students to 395 students. What is the percent of decrease?

14. Mr. Watson bought a car for $15,440 and sold it for $16,000. What is the percent of increase?

15. Nick's rent was $725 last year. This year, his rent is $750. What is the percent of increase in his rent?

16. A furniture set, which was selling for $1,250, was reduced to $1,200. What is the percent of the reduction?

17. Two years ago, Amanda saved $400, and last year she saved $425. What is the percent of increase?

Answers to Selected Exercises

1. 20%   5. 3.03%   9(a) 41.67%   11. 7.89%

Cumulative Review

1. Find: (Round your answer to 2 decimal places.)
   (a) 2 out of 125   (b) 5% of 100   (c) 15% of 52.50

2. Change each percent to a decimal. Round the answer to 2 decimal places.

   (a) 1%   (b) $8\frac{1}{2}$%   (c) 120%

   (d) 15%   (e) 12%   (f) 45%

3. Write the following ratios as percents. Round your answer to 2 decimal places.
   (a) 2 out of 5   (b) 9 out of 10   (c) 8 out of 20
   (d) 7 out of 49   (e) 15 out of 125   (f) 3 out of 12

4. Change each decimal to a percent. Round your answer to 2 decimal places.
   (a) .5   (b) .48   (c) .34
   (d) 4.98   (e) .08   (f) .002
   (g) .7   (h) 1.25   (i) .041

5. Round the following answers to 2 decimal places.
   (a) 25 is what percent of 125?
   (b) Find what percent 15 is of 100?
   (c) 12% of what amount is $150?
   (d) If 45% of a number is 200, find the number.

(e) $\dfrac{2}{5}$% of what number is 75?

6. Find the percent of increase or decrease. Round off to 1 decimal place.
   (a) A school's enrollment of 425 students increased to 475 students.
   (b) John's expenses increased from $225 per week to $310 per week .
   (c) Gertrude's weight decreased from 170 pounds to 140 pounds.

More Cumulative Review

1. Change the following to decimal fractions. Round off each answer to the nearest hundredth.

   (a) $\dfrac{1}{5}$ (b) $\dfrac{9}{10}$ (c) $\dfrac{4}{7}$ (d) $\dfrac{3}{8}$ (e) $\dfrac{5}{12}$

   (f) $\dfrac{4}{9}$ (g) $\dfrac{5}{14}$ (h) $\dfrac{5}{9}$ (i) $\dfrac{2}{7}$ (j) $\dfrac{13}{15}$

2. $120 \div .24 =$ 3. $5.04 \times .09 =$ 4. $.91 + 784.1 =$

5. $91 - 7.989 =$ 6. $45.381 - 2.492 =$ 7. $.41 \times .98 =$

8. $\dfrac{1}{2} \div \dfrac{1}{2} =$ 9. $\dfrac{3}{4} \div \dfrac{3}{8} =$ 10. $\dfrac{5}{7} \times \dfrac{14}{2} =$

11. $.4 \div 10 =$ 12. $18.7 \times 100 =$ 13. $78 \times 10 =$

14. $\$24.64 \times .23 =$ 15. $36.93 \div 3 =$ 16. $56 \div 1{,}000 =$

17. $2\dfrac{1}{2} \div 3\dfrac{1}{3} =$ 18. $3\dfrac{2}{4} \div 4\dfrac{2}{3} =$ 19. $4\dfrac{3}{4} \times 2\dfrac{1}{2} =$

20. Change each percent to a decimal.

    (a) 12%   (b) 15.5%   (c) $4\dfrac{1}{2}$%   (d) 9%

21. Change each decimal to a percent.
    (a) .002   (b) .7   (c) .95   (d) 4.12
22. Write each decimal as a word phrase:
    (a) 4.44   (b) 5.09   (c) .038   (d) 2.009
23. Write each word phrase as a decimal:
    (a) Nine tenths.   (b) Fourteen thousandths.
    (c) Eight and three hundred fifteen ten–thousandths.
    (d) Twelve thousandths.

127

24. (a) $8 \div \dfrac{1}{4} =$ (b) $\dfrac{3}{4} \div 12 =$ (c) $\dfrac{7}{8} \div \dfrac{21}{24} =$

POWER OF NUMBERS

In the grid diagram, there are 5 rows and 5 columns of blocks. The total number of blocks in the grid can be written as 5 • 5 where the dot (•) means multiplication.

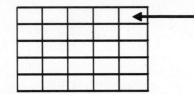 — **One block**

Total number of blocks = 5 x 5 = 25

The total number of the blocks is 5×5 which may be written as 5 • 5 which may further be written as 5^2 where the 5 is the base and 2 is the exponent as shown below:

$$5 \cdot 5 = 5^{\overset{\text{exponent}}{2}}$$

base

The **exponent** 2 shows how many times the base 5 is used as a factor
5^2 is known as "5 squared" or 5 to the second power. Similarly, instead of writing the same factor several times, the factor can be written once and the exponent can be used as shown:

$$5 \cdot 5 \cdot 5 = 5^3 \qquad \text{which is 5 to the third power.}$$
$$5 \cdot 5 \cdot 5 \cdot 5 = 5^4 \qquad \text{which is 5 to the fourth power.}$$
$$5 \cdot 5 \cdot 5 \cdot 5 \cdot 5 = 5^5 \qquad \text{which is 5 to the fifth power.}$$

In general, $n \cdot n \cdot n \cdot n \cdot n \cdot n \cdot \ldots = n^x$ which is n to the xth power.

Rule 1: The value of any number or any representation of a number such as a, b, n, x, or y to the power 0 is 1. For example, $1^0 = 1$, $2^0 = 1$, $100^0 = 1$, $n^0 = 1$, $x^0 = 1$, and $y^0 = 1$.

Example 1
How do you read 10^4 ?
Solution
10^4 is read as "10 to the power 4."

Example 2
(a) Write 8 in the exponential form.

(b) Write 24 in the exponential form.
(c) Write 60 in the exponential form.

Solution

(a) Use the prime factorization method under the section of prime factorization to find the prime factors of 8 as shown:

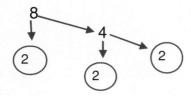

The prime factorization of 8 is 2 · 2 · 2.

Factor form

$$8 = 2 \cdot 2 \cdot 2 = 2^3$$

Therefore,

Standard form.   Exponential form

(b) From the chapter on prime factorization Example 1, the prime factors of 24 are:

$$2 \cdot 2 \cdot 2 \cdot 3$$

Therefore, the exponential form of 24 is:

$$24 = 2 \cdot 2 \cdot 2 \cdot 3 = 2^3 \cdot 3$$

Standard form   Exponential form

(c) From the chapter on prime factorization, Example 2, the prime factors of 60 are:

$$2 \cdot 2 \cdot 3 \cdot 5.$$

Therefore, the exponential form of 60 is:

$$60 = 2 \cdot 2 \cdot 3 \cdot 5 = 2^2 \cdot 3 \cdot 5$$

Standard form.   Exponential form

Example 3

(a) Find the value of 4^3
(b) Find the value of 3^4
(c) Find the value of $2 \cdot 3^2$
(d) $2 \cdot 3^2 \cdot 4^2 =$
(e) Find the value of $2^2 \cdot 3 \cdot 5^2$

Solution

(a) $4^3 = 4 \times 4 \times 4 = 64$
(b) $3^4 = 3 \times 3 \times 3 \times 3 = 81$
(c) $2 \cdot 3^2 = 2 \times 3 \times 3 = 18$

(d) $2 \cdot 3^2 \cdot 4^2 = 2 \times 3 \times 3 \times 4 \times 4 = 288$

(e) $2^2 \cdot 3 \cdot 5^2 = 2 \times 2 \times 3 \times 5 \times 5 = 300$

Example 4

(a) Find the value of 6^1

(b) Find the value of 4^0

(c) Find the value of $6^1 \cdot 4^0 \cdot 2^2$

(e) Find the value of $3^0 \cdot 20^0 \cdot x^0$

Solution

(a) $6^1 = 6$

(b) $4^0 = 1$ **Notice that any number to the power of 0 is equal to 1, therefore, $4^0 = 1$.**

(c) $6^1 \cdot 4^0 \cdot 2^2 = 6 \times 1 \times 2 \times 2 = 24$ Note $4^0 = 1$

(d) $2^0 \cdot 5^1 \cdot 6^2 = 1 \times 5 \times 6 \times 6 = 180$ Note $2^0 = 1$

(e) $3^0 \cdot 20^0 \cdot x^0 = 1 \times 1 \times 1 = 1$ Note $3^0 = 1, 20^0 = 1, x^0 = 1$

Example 5

Complete each equation:

(a) $a \cdot a \cdot b \cdot b \cdot b = a^2$?   (b) $2 \cdot 2 \cdot 3 \cdot 5 \cdot 5 = 2^2 \cdot 3$?

(c) $2 \cdot x \cdot 4 \cdot y \cdot x = 8x^2$?   (d) $3 \cdot x \cdot y \cdot 2 \cdot y = ?x$?

(e) $a^0 \cdot 4 = ? \cdot 4$ (f) $a^0 \cdot b^0 \cdot 3 \cdot 3 \cdot 4 = ? ? 3^2 \cdot 4$

Solution

(a) $a \cdot a \cdot b \cdot b \cdot b = a^2b^3$ (b^3 because there are 3 bases of b).

                                   (a^2 because there are 2 bases of a).

(b) $2 \cdot 2 \cdot 3 \cdot 5 \cdot 5 = 2^2 \cdot 3 \cdot 5^2$ (5^2 because there are 2 bases of 5).

                                   (2^2 because there are 2 bases of 2).

                                   (3 because there is 1 base of 3).

(c) $2 \cdot x \cdot 4 \cdot y \cdot x = 8x^2y$ (y because there is 1 base of y).

                                   (x^2 because there are 2 bases of x).

                                   (8 because $2 \cdot 4 = 8$).

(d) $3 \cdot x \cdot y \cdot 2 \cdot y = 6xy^2$ (6 and y^2 because $3 \times 2 = 6$ and there are 2 bases of y).

                                   (x because there is 1 base of x).

(e) $a^0 \cdot 4 = 1 \cdot 4$ (Note: $a^0 = 1$)

(f) $a^0 \cdot b^0 \cdot 3 \cdot 3 \cdot 4 = 1 \cdot 1 \cdot 3^2 \cdot 4$ (Note: $a^0 = 1$, and $b^0 = 1$)

                                   (3^2 because there are 2 bases of 3).

Exercises

1. Explain what is meant by the base and the exponent of a number in the exponential form.

2. How do you read the following: Hint: See Example 1.

(a) 2^5 (b) 3^4 (c) 10^3 (d) 100^2

(e) 9^1 (f) 12^3 (g) 5^3 (h) 2^6

3. Write the following in the exponential form. Hint: See Example 2.

(a) 9 (b) 12 (c) 16 (d) 18 (e) 20
(f) 32 (g) 45 (h) 25 (i) 36 (j) 27
(k) 21 (l) 27 (m) 35 (n) 99 (o) 64

4. Find the following values. Hint: See Example 3.

(a) 2^4 (b) 8^2 (c) $2^3 \cdot 3^2$ (d) $3^2 \cdot 4^2$

(e) $2 \cdot 3^2 \cdot 5^2$ (f) $2^2 \cdot 4 \cdot 5^2$ (g) $2 \cdot 3^2 \cdot 4$ (h) $2^3 \cdot 3 \cdot 4^2$

(i) $3 \cdot 4 \cdot 5^2$ (j) $2 \cdot 3^2 \cdot 6$ (k) $2 \cdot 2 \cdot 4^2$ (l) $2^2 \cdot 3^2 \cdot 4$

(m) 10^2 (n) 9^2 (o) $2 \cdot 10^3$ (p) $3^2 \cdot 8^2$

5. Find the following values. See Example 4.

(a) 100^0 (b) 9^1 (c) $2^0 \cdot 3^2$ (d) $2^2 \cdot 4^0 \cdot 5^1$

(e) $2^2 \cdot 3 \cdot 4^2$ (f) $2^3 \cdot 3^0 \cdot 4^2$ (g) $3^2 \cdot 5^0 \cdot 6^2$ (h) $4^0 \cdot 2^2 \cdot 3^2$

(i) $2^0 \cdot 3^1 \cdot 5^0$ (j) $6^0 \cdot 10^0 \cdot 15^0$ (k) $2^0 \cdot 3^0 \cdot 5^0$ (l) $2^2 \cdot 6^2 \cdot 9^0$

(m) $3^2 \cdot 5^0 \cdot 8^0$ (n) $2^3 \cdot 3^2 \cdot 4^0$ (o) $100^0 \cdot 200^0 \cdot 300^0$ (p) $10^2 \cdot 4^2$

6. Complete each equation. See Example 5.

(a) $a \cdot a \cdot b \cdot b = a^2 \,?$ (b) $2 \cdot 3 \cdot 3 \cdot 5 = 2 \cdot \,? \cdot 5$ (c) $2 \cdot 2 \cdot 2 \cdot x \cdot x = \,? \, x^2$
(d) $3 \cdot x \cdot 2 \cdot y \cdot x = \,? \cdot x^2 \cdot y$ (e) $2 \cdot a \cdot b \cdot 3 \cdot a \cdot = 6 \,? \, b$ (f) $4 \cdot x \cdot y \cdot 2 \cdot y = 8 \, x \,?$
(g) $a \cdot a \cdot a \cdot b = \,? \, b$ (h) $3 \cdot a \cdot x \cdot 4 \cdot a \cdot x = \,? \, a^2 \,?$ (i) $a^0 \cdot b^0 \cdot 2 \cdot 2 = 1 \,? \, 2^2$
(j) $2 \cdot 2 \cdot 4^0 \cdot a^0 = 2^2 \cdot \,? \cdot 1$ (k) $x^0 \cdot y^0 \cdot z^0 = \,? \,? \,?$ (l) $4 \cdot y \cdot x \cdot b \cdot 2 \cdot y \cdot b = \,? \,? \, x \, y^2$

Challenge Questions

7. Find the value.

(a) $7^2 \cdot 9^0 =$ (b) 150^0 (c) $2^0 \cdot 5^2 \cdot 7^0 =$ (d) $5^2 \cdot a^0 \cdot b^2$

8. Complete the equation.

(a) $3 \cdot a \cdot b \cdot a \cdot b = 3a^2 \,?$ (b) $4 \cdot a \cdot b \cdot 3 \cdot a \cdot b = \,? \, a^2 b^2$

Answers to Selected Questions.

3(a). 3^2 4(a). 16 5(a). 1

EXPONENTS

An exponent shows how many times a base is used as a factor. For example,

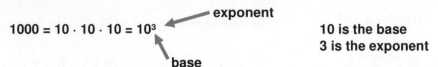

$$1000 = 10 \cdot 10 \cdot 10 = 10^3$$

exponent

base

10 is the base
3 is the exponent

The exponent of 3 shows that the base which is 10 is used as a factor of 1000 three times. "10^3" is read as "10 to the third power or "10 cubed."

Multiplying Powers With the Same Base.
The factors of any power such as 5^4 may be grouped in different ways as shown:
$5 \cdot 5 \cdot 5 \cdot 5 = 5^4$ ————————————————[A]
$(5 \cdot 5 \cdot 5) \cdot 5 = 5^3 \cdot 5^1 = 5^4$ ————————————[B]
$(5 \cdot 5) \cdot (5 \cdot 5) = 5^2 \cdot 5^2 = 5^4$ ————————————[C]
$5 \cdot (5 \cdot 5 \cdot 5) = 5^1 \cdot 5^3 = 5^4$ ————————————[D]
By observing equation [A], we can write:
$5 \cdot 5 \cdot 5 \cdot 5 = 5^1 \cdot 5^1 \cdot 5^1 \cdot 5^1 = 5^{1+1+1+1} = 5^4$
By observing equation [B], we can write:
$(5 \cdot 5 \cdot 5) \cdot 5 = 5^3 \cdot 5^1 = 5^{3+1} = 5^4$
By observing equation [C], we can write:
$(5 \cdot 5) \cdot (5 \cdot 5) = 5^2 \cdot 5^2 = 5^{2+2} = 5^4$
By observing equation [D], we can write:
$5 \cdot (5 \cdot 5 \cdot 5) = 5^1 \cdot 5^3 = 5^{1+3} = 5^4$
Therefore, observing equations [A], [B], [C], and [D], to multiply powers with the same base, use the same base, and then add the exponents such that in general,
$\mathbf{b^m \cdot b^n = b^{m+n}}$

Example 1
Multiply and write each product as one power.
a. $6^2 \cdot 6^7$ **b.** $7^3 \cdot 3^2$ **c.** $8^3 \cdot 8$ **d.** $4^2 \cdot a^2 \cdot 4^3 \cdot a^5$ **e.** $7^2 \cdot 7^6 \cdot 7^4$
Solution
a. $6^2 \cdot 6^7 = 6^{2+7}$ Add the exponents since the bases 6 and 6 are the same.
                        Generally, $\mathbf{b^m \cdot b^n = b^{m+n}}$
        $= 6^9$ $2 + 7 = 9$

132

b. $7^3 \cdot 3^2 = 7^3 \cdot 3^2$ The bases 7 and 3 are not the same so their exponents cannot be combined.

c. $8^3 \cdot 8 = 8^3 \cdot 8^1$ 8 is the same as 8^1

$\quad = 8^{3+1}$ Add the exponents since the bases 8 and 8 are the same. Generally, $\mathbf{b}^m \cdot \mathbf{b}^n = \mathbf{b}^{m+n}$

$\quad = 8^4$ $3 + 1 = 4$

d. $4^2 \cdot a^2 \cdot 4^3 \cdot a^5 = (4^2 \cdot 4^3) \cdot (a^2 \cdot a^5)$ Grouping the like bases together.

$\quad = 4^{2+3} \cdot a^{2+5}$ Add the exponents of the like bases.

$\quad = 4^5 \cdot a^7$ $2 + 3 = 5$ and $2 + 5 = 7$. The bases **4** and **a** are not the same so we cannot combine them.

e. $7^2 \cdot 7^6 \cdot 7^4 = 7^{2+6+4}$ Add the exponents because the bases 7, 7, and 7 are the same.

$\quad = 7^{12}$ $2 + 6 + 4 = 12$.

Example 2

Multiply using exponents.

a. $9^3 \cdot x^4 \cdot 2^4 \cdot 9 \cdot x^3 \cdot 2^n$

b. $n^2 \cdot k^3 \cdot n^4 \cdot k^2 \cdot n$

Solution

a. $9^3 \cdot x^4 \cdot 2^4 \cdot 9 \cdot x^3 \cdot 2^n = (9^3 \cdot 9) \cdot (x^4 \cdot x^3) \cdot (2^4 \cdot 2^n)$ Grouping the like bases.

$\quad = (9^3 \cdot 9^1) \cdot (x^4 \cdot x^3) \cdot (2^4 \cdot 2^n)$ **Note**: 9 is the same as 9^1.

$\quad = 9^{3+1} \cdot x^{4+3} \cdot 2^{4+n}$ Add the exponents of the like bases.

$\quad = 9^4 \cdot x^7 \cdot 2^{4+n}$ We can no longer combine the exponents because the bases 9, x, and 2 are not the same.

b. $n^2 \cdot k^3 \cdot n^4 \cdot k^2 \cdot n = (n^2 \cdot n^4 \cdot n) \cdot (k^3 \cdot k^2)$ Grouping the like bases of n and k.

$\quad = (n^2 \cdot n^4 \cdot n^1) \cdot (k^3 \cdot k^2)$ **Note**: n is the same as n^1.

$\quad = n^{2+4+1} \cdot k^{3+2}$ Add the exponents of the like bases.

$\quad = n^7 \cdot k^5$ We can no longer combine the exponents because the bases n and k are not the same.

Dividing Powers With the Same Base

Let us observe what happens when we divide powers with the same base as shown:

$$\frac{4^6}{4^4} = \frac{4 \cdot 4 \cdot 4 \cdot 4 \cdot 4 \cdot 4}{4 \cdot 4 \cdot 4 \cdot 4} = \frac{4 \cdot 4 \cdot 4 \cdot 4 \cdot 4 \cdot 4}{4 \cdot 4 \cdot 4 \cdot 4} = 4 \cdot 4 = 4^2 \quad \text{_____[A]}$$

It should then be observed from equation $[A]$ that $\dfrac{4^6}{4^4} = 4^{6-4} = 4^2$

Therefore, to divide powers with the same base, use the same base, and then subtract the exponents, such that in general $\dfrac{b^m}{b^n} = b^{m-n}$, and $b \neq 0$. The symbol $\neq$ means "is

not equal to." Note that $b \neq 0$ because if $b = 0$, then $\dfrac{b^m}{b^n} = \dfrac{0^m}{0^n}$, but it is impossible to

divide by 0.

Example 3
Divide and write each quotient as one power.

a. $\dfrac{6^5}{6^3}$ **b.** $\dfrac{n^5}{n^2}$ **c.** $\dfrac{m^6}{n^4}$

Solution

a. $\dfrac{6^5}{6^3} = 6^{5-3} = 6^2$ Subtract the exponents since the bases 6 and 6 are

the same. Generally, $\dfrac{b^m}{b^n} = b^{m-n}$, $b \neq 0$.

b. $\dfrac{n^5}{n^2} = n^{5-2} = n^3$ Subtract the exponents since the bases n and n

are the same. Generally, $\dfrac{b^m}{b^n} = b^{m-n}$, $b \neq 0$.

c. $\dfrac{m^6}{n^4}$ Cannot combine the exponents because the bases

m and n are not the same.

Example 4
Simplify each expression. Your answer should be in exponents.

a. $\dfrac{3^4 \cdot n^6}{n^2 \cdot 3^2}$ **b.** $\dfrac{x^7 \cdot y^8 \cdot 2^8}{y^6 \cdot 2^5 \cdot x^3}$ **c.** $\dfrac{12^7 \cdot n^6 \cdot y^5 \cdot x^4}{12^4 \cdot y^2 \cdot x \cdot k^2}$

Solution

a. $\dfrac{3^4 \cdot n^6}{n^2 \cdot 3^2} = 3^{4-2} \cdot n^{6-2}$ Subtract the exponents of the like bases.

$\dfrac{3^4}{3^2} = 3^{4-2}$, $\dfrac{n^6}{n^2} = n^{6-2}$. Generally, $\dfrac{b^m}{b^n} = b^{m-n}$, $b \neq 0$.

$= 3^2 \cdot n^4$ $4 - 2 = 2$ and $6 - 2 = 4$.

b. $\dfrac{x^7 \cdot y^8 \cdot 2^8}{y^6 \cdot 2^5 \cdot x^3} = x^{7-3} \cdot y^{8-6} \cdot 2^{8-5}$ Subtract the exponents of the like bases.

$$\frac{x^7}{x^3} = x^{7-3}, \quad \frac{y^8}{y^6} = y^{8-6}, \quad \frac{2^8}{2^5} = 2^{8-5}$$

$$= x^4 \cdot y^2 \cdot 2^3 \qquad\qquad 7 - 3 = 4, \ 8 - 6 = 2 \text{ and } 8 - 5 = 3.$$

c. $\dfrac{12^7 \cdot n^6 \cdot y^5 \cdot x^4}{12^4 \cdot y^2 \cdot x \cdot k^2} = \dfrac{12^{7-4} \cdot n^6 \cdot y^{5-2} \cdot x^{4-1}}{k^2}$ Subtract the exponents of

the like bases.

$$= \frac{12^3 \cdot n^6 \cdot y^3 \cdot x^3}{k^2}$$ For example: $\dfrac{12^7}{12^4} = 12^{7-4} = 12^3$

$$\frac{y^5}{y^2} = y^{5-2} = y^3$$

$$\frac{x^4}{x} = \frac{x^4}{x^1} = x^{4-1} = x^3$$

Note that $x = x^1$.

Zero Power

It can be shown that 1 can be expressed as a fraction with the numerator and the denominator of the fraction having the same base and the same exponents and subtracting the exponents will result in a zero exponent as follows:

$$1 = \frac{3^2}{3^2} = 3^{2-2} = 3^0$$

Therefore, $1 = 3^0$

Therefore, the zero power of any number except 0 equals 1 such that in general

$b^0 = 1$ **and** $b \neq 0$.

Example 5

Evaluate

a. 7^0 **b.** $5^6 \ 5^{-6}$ **c.** $\dfrac{10^4}{10^4}$ **d.** $\dfrac{n^5}{n^5}$

e. $\dfrac{12^7 \cdot y^5 \cdot 4^3}{12^7 \cdot y^5 \cdot 4^2}$ **f.** $\dfrac{4^5 \cdot 3^4 \cdot n^9 \cdot 3^{-4}}{4^5 \cdot n^9}$

Solution

a. $7^0 = 1$ The zero power of any number except 0 equals 1.

b. $5^6 \cdot 5^{-6} = 5^{6 + (-6)}$ To multiply powers with the same base, use the same base, and then add the exponents such that in general,

135

$$5^6 \cdot 5^{-6} = 5^{6-6}$$
$$= 5^0$$
$$= 1$$

$b^m \cdot b^n = b^{m+n}$.

Note: $+ (- = -$, therefore, $6 + (-6) = 6 - 6$.

$6 - 6 = 0$.

The zero power of any number except 0 is 1.

c. $\dfrac{10^4}{10^4} = 10^{4-4}$

To divide powers with the same base, use the same base

and then subtract the exponents such that in general

$\dfrac{b^m}{b^n} = b^{m-n}$ and $b \neq 0$.

$= 10^0$

$4 - 4 = 0$

$= 1$

The zero power of any number except 0 is 1

d. $\dfrac{n^5}{n^5} = n^{5-5}$

To divide powers with the same base, use the same base,

and then subtract the exponents such that in general

$\dfrac{b^m}{b^n} = b^{m-n}$, and $b \neq 0$.

$= n^0$

$5 - 5 = 0$.

$= 1$

The zero power of any number except 0 is 1.

e. $\dfrac{12^7 \cdot y^5 \cdot 4^3}{12^7 \cdot y^5 \cdot 4^2} = 12^{7-7} \cdot y^{5-5} \cdot 4^{3-2}$

To divide powers with the same base, use

the same base, and then subtract the exponents such that in general

$\dfrac{b^m}{b^n} = b^{m-n}$ and $x \neq 0$.

$= 12^0 \cdot y^0 \cdot 4^1$

$= 1 \cdot 1 \cdot 4$

$= 4$

$7 - 7 = 0,\ 5 - 5 = 0$ and $3 - 2 = 1$.

$12^0 = 1,\ y^0 = 1,$ and $4 = 4$.

f. $\dfrac{4^5 \cdot 3^4 n^9 \cdot 3^{-4}}{4^5 \cdot n^9} = 4^{5-5} \cdot 3^{4+(-4)} \cdot n^{9-9}$

To divide powers with the same base, use

the same base, and then subtract the exponents such that in general $\dfrac{b^m}{b^n} = \mathbf{b}^{m-n}$

and $b \neq 0$. For examples: $\dfrac{4^5}{4^5} = 4^{5-5}$

136

$$\frac{n^9}{n^9} = n^{9-9}$$

To multiply powers with the same base, use the same base, and then add the exponents such that in general $b^m \cdot b^n = b^{m+n}$.

For example: $3^4 \cdot 3^{-4} = 3^{4+(-4)}$.

$$= 4^0 \cdot 3^{4-4} \cdot n^0$$
$$= 4^0 \cdot 3^0 \cdot n^0$$
$$= 1 \cdot 1 \cdot 1$$
$$= 1$$

Note: $+ (- = -$, for an example, $3^{4+(-4)} = 3^{4-4}$.
$5 - 5 = 0$, $4 - 4 = 0$ and $9 - 9 = 0$.

The zero power of any number except 0 is 1.

Negative Exponents and Dividing With Exponent.

We can show that $10^{-1} = \dfrac{1}{10}$ as follows:

$$\frac{10^2}{10^3} = \frac{10 \cdot 10}{10 \cdot 10 \cdot 10}$$

$$\frac{10^2}{10^3} = \frac{\cancel{10} \cdot \cancel{10}}{\cancel{10} \cdot \cancel{10} \cdot 10}$$

Divide by 10

$$\frac{10^2}{10^3} = \frac{1}{10} \rule{6cm}{0.4pt} [A]$$

But $\dfrac{10^2}{10^3} = 10^{2-3}$

To divide powers with the same base, use the same base, and then subtract the exponents such that in general $\dfrac{b^m}{b^n} = b^{m-n}$ and $b \neq 0$. For an example,

$$\frac{10^2}{10^3} = 10^{2-3}.$$

$$\frac{10^2}{10^3} = 10^{-1} \rule{6cm}{0.4pt} [B]$$

Note: $2 - 3 = -1$.

Comparing equation [A] and equation [B], it can be written that:

137

$$10^{-1} = \frac{1}{10^1} = \frac{1}{10}$$
Note that equation [A] is the same as equation [B].

Therefore, in general, $b^{-n} = \frac{1}{b^n}$ for all real numbers and $b \neq 0$. It can therefore, be stated in general that: **A base with a negative exponent is equal to I divided by that base with a positive exponent**.

Example 6
Evaluate.

a. 4^{-3} **b.** $(-4)^{-3}$ **c.** $\dfrac{(-4)^2}{(-4)^3}$ **d.** $\dfrac{(6-4)^3}{(9-7)^6}$ **e.** $(4 \cdot 3)^4 \cdot (2 \cdot 6)^{-6}$ **f.** $2^3 \cdot 2^{-2} \cdot 2^{-3}$

Solution

a. $4^{-3} = \dfrac{1}{4^3}$ In general, $b^{-n} = \dfrac{1}{b^n}$, $b \neq 0$.

$\quad = \dfrac{1}{4 \cdot 4 \cdot 4}$ $4^3 = 4 \cdot 4 \cdot 4$

$\quad = \dfrac{1}{64}$ $4 \cdot 4 \cdot 4 = 64$

b. $(-4)^{-3} = \dfrac{1}{(-4)^3}$ In general, $b^{-n} = \dfrac{1}{b^n}$, and $b \neq 0$.

$\quad = \dfrac{1}{(-4) \cdot (-4) \cdot (-4)}$ $(-4)^3 = (-4) \cdot (-4) \cdot (-4)$

$\quad = \dfrac{1}{-64} = -\dfrac{1}{64}$ Note: $(-4) \cdot (-4) = +16 = 16$, but $(-4) \cdot (-4) \cdot (-4) = -64$ because the product of odd number negative signs is negative. Therefore, $(-) \cdot (-) \cdot (-) = -$. Hint: Review multiplication involving negative numbers.

c. $\dfrac{(-4)^2}{(-4)^3} = (-4)^{2-3}$ To divide powers with the same base, use the same base and then subtract the exponents, such that in general $\dfrac{b^m}{b^n} = b^{m-n}$ and $b \neq 0$.

$\dfrac{(-4)^2}{(-4)^3} = (-4)^{-1}$ Note: $2 - 3 = -1$

$= \dfrac{1}{(-4)^1}$ In general, $b^{-n} = \dfrac{1}{b^n}$, and $b \neq 0$.

$= \dfrac{1}{-4}$ Note: $\dfrac{1}{(-4)^1} = \dfrac{1}{(-4)} = \dfrac{1}{-4}$.   Any number with exponent 1 is

the same number.

d. $\dfrac{(6-4)^3}{(9-7)^6} = \dfrac{2^3}{2^6}$ Do the operations inside the parentheses first.

Hint: See the section on the order of operations.
6 - 4 = 2 and 9 - 7 = 2.

$= 2^{3-6}$ To divide powers with the same base, use the same
base, and then subtract the exponents, such that in general

$\dfrac{b^m}{b^n} = b^{m-n}$, and $b \neq 0$.

$= 2^{-3}$ 3 - 6 = -3

$= \dfrac{1}{2^3}$ In general, $b^{-n} = \dfrac{1}{b^n}$, $b \neq 0$

$= \dfrac{1}{2 \cdot 2 \cdot 2}$ $2^3 = 2 \cdot 2 \cdot 2$

$= \dfrac{1}{8}$ $2 \cdot 2 \cdot 2 = 8$.

e. $(4 \cdot 3)^4 \cdot (2 \cdot 6)^{-6}$ $= 12^4 \cdot 12^{-6}$ Do the operations inside the parentheses first.
Hint: See the section on order of operations.

$= 12^{4 + (-6)}$ To multiply powers with the same base, use
the same base, and then add the exponents,
such that in general, $b^m \cdot b^n = b^{m+n}$

$= 12^{4-6}$ Note: + (- = -, for example, $12^{4 + (-6)} = 12^{4-6}$.

$= 12^{-2}$ 4 - 6 = -2

$= \dfrac{1}{12^2}$ In general, $b^{-n} = \dfrac{1}{b^n}$, and $b \neq 0$.

$= \dfrac{1}{12 \cdot 12}$ $12^2 = 12 \cdot 12 = 144$.

$= \dfrac{1}{144}$

f. $2^3 \cdot 2^{-2} \cdot 2^{-3} = 2^{3 + (-2) + (-3)}$

To multiply powers with the same base, use the same base, and then add the exponents, such that in general, $b^m \cdot b^n = b^{m+n}$.

$= 2^{3-2-3}$

Note: $+(- = -$, such that $+ (-2) = -2$ and $+ (-3) = -3$.

$= 2^{3-5}$

$-2 - 3 = -5$.

$= 2^{-2}$

$3 - 5 = -2$.

$= \dfrac{1}{2^2}$

In general, $b^{-n} = \dfrac{1}{b^n}$, and $b \neq 0$.

$= \dfrac{1}{2 \cdot 2}$

$2^2 = 2 \cdot 2$

$= \dfrac{1}{4}$

$2 \cdot 2 = 4$

Example 7
Simplify

$$\dfrac{5}{3^{-2}}$$

Solution

$$\dfrac{5}{3^{-2}} = \dfrac{5}{\dfrac{1}{3^2}}$$

In general, $b^{-n} = \dfrac{1}{b^n}$, and $b \neq 0$. Therefore, $3^{-2} = \dfrac{1}{3^2}$.

$$= 5 \div \dfrac{1}{3^2}$$

$$= 5 \times \dfrac{3^2}{1}$$

To divide by a fraction, multiply by the reciprocal of the fraction. Hint: Review Division by Fractions.

$$= 5 \times 3 \times 3$$

$3^2 = 3 \times 3$

$$= 45$$

Example 8

Simplify. $\dfrac{15x^5y^3}{5x^2y}$

Solution

$$\dfrac{15x^5y^3}{5x^2y} = \dfrac{\overset{3}{\cancel{15}}x^5y^3}{\underset{1}{\cancel{5}}x^2y} = \dfrac{3x^5y^3}{x^2y}$$

Divide the numerical coefficients by 5.

140

$$= \frac{3x^5y^3}{x^2y} = 3x^{5-2}y^{3-1}$$

Subtract the exponents of the powers of the denominator from the exponents of the powers with the same base in the numerator. Note that $y = y^1$.

$$= 3x^3y^2$$

Example 9

Simplify. **a.** $\dfrac{-36a^5bc^4}{6a^2bc^3}$ **b.** $\dfrac{18p^5k^9}{-6p^2k^6}$

Solution

a. $\dfrac{-36a^5bc^4}{6a^2bc^3} = \dfrac{\overset{-6}{\cancel{-36}}a^5bc^4}{\underset{1}{\cancel{6}}a^2bc^3} = \dfrac{-6a^5bc^4}{a^2bc^3}$

Divide the numerical coefficients by 6.

$$= \frac{-6a^5bc^4}{a^2bc^3} = -6a^{5-2}b^{1-1}c^{4-3}$$

Subtract the exponents of the powers of the denominator from the exponents of the powers with the same base in the numerator. Note that $b = b^1$.

$$= -6a^3b^0c^1$$
$$= -6a^3 \cdot 1 \cdot c^1 \qquad\qquad b^0 = 1.$$
$$= -6a^3c \qquad\qquad c^1 = c.$$

b. $\dfrac{18p^5k^9}{-6p^2k^6} = \dfrac{\overset{3}{\cancel{18}}p^5k^9}{\underset{-1}{\cancel{-6}}p^2k^6} = \dfrac{3p^5k^9}{-p^2k^6}$

Divide the numerical coefficients by 6.

$$= -3p^{5-2}k^{9-6}$$

Subtract the exponents of the powers of the denominator from the exponents of the powers with the same base in the numerator. Note that in general, $\dfrac{a}{-b} = $ a certain negative number and $b \neq 0$.

$$= -3p^3k^3$$

Example 10

141

Simplify $\quad \dfrac{-24p^7k^5}{-8p^3k^2}$

Solution

$$\dfrac{-24p^7k^5}{-8p^3k^2} = \dfrac{\overset{3}{\cancel{-24}}p^7k^5}{\underset{1}{\cancel{-8}}p^3k^2} = \dfrac{3p^7k^5}{p^3k^2}$$

Divide the numerical coefficients by -8.

$$= \dfrac{3p^7k^5}{p^3k^2} = 3p^{7-3}k^{5-2}$$

Subtract the exponents of the powers of the denominator from the exponents of the powers with the same base in the numerator.
Note $-8 \div (-8) = 1$, $-24 \div (-8) = 3$.

$$= 3p^4k^3 \qquad\qquad 7 - 3 = 4 \text{ and } 5 - 2 = 3.$$

Exercises

1. What is an exponent?
2. What is a base?
3. Multiply and write each product as one power. Hint: See Examples 1a, 1c, and 1e.
   - **a.** $3^4 \cdot 3^7$
   - **b.** $9^5 \cdot 9$
   - **c.** $5^4 \cdot 5^6 \cdot 5^3$
   - **d.** $4^4 \cdot 4^2$
   - **e.** $5^4 \cdot 5^6 \cdot 5^3$
   - **f.** $6^2 \cdot 6 \cdot 6^4$
4. Multiply and write each product as one power. Hint: See Example 1b and 1d.
   - **a.** $3^4 \cdot n^5$
   - **b.** $5^3 \cdot 4^6$
   - **c.** $a^4 \cdot b^3$
5. Multiply using exponents. Hint: See Example 2a.
   - **a.** $4^3 \cdot n^5 \cdot 3^4 \cdot n^2 \cdot 4^2$
   - **b.** $k^4 \cdot 7^2 \cdot k^3 \cdot 7^4 \cdot k^5$
6. Multiply using exponents. Hint: See Example 2a.
   - **a.** $b^4 \cdot w^4 \cdot n \cdot b^2 \cdot n^3 \cdot w^2$
   - **b.** $x^4 \cdot v \cdot k^2 \cdot v^2 \cdot x^2$
   - **c.** $p^4 \cdot n^7 \cdot d^2 \cdot p^2 \cdot n^2$
   - **d.** $a^2 b^4 \cdot c^3 \cdot a^3 \cdot c^2$
7. Divide and write each quotient as one power. Hint: See Example 3a.
   - **a.** $\dfrac{4^7}{4^2}$
   - **b.** $\dfrac{9^{14}}{9^6}$
   - **c.** $\dfrac{7^4}{7^3}$
   - **d.** $\dfrac{6^6}{6^4}$
8. Divide and write each quotient as one power. Hint: See Example 3b.
   - **a.** $\dfrac{n^9}{n^4}$
   - **b.** $\dfrac{w^5}{w^2}$
   - **c.** $\dfrac{k^8}{k^5}$
   - **d.** $\dfrac{b^5}{b^3}$
9. Divide and write each quotient as one power. Hint: See Example 3c.
   - **a.** $\dfrac{k^4}{m^3}$
   - **b.** $\dfrac{12^5}{11^4}$
   - **c.** $\dfrac{x^7}{b^5}$
   - **d.** $\dfrac{7^5}{6^4}$

10. Simplify each expression. Hint: See Example 4a and 4b.

a. $\dfrac{5^8 \cdot k^5}{k^3 \cdot 5^4}$

b. $\dfrac{4^4 \cdot x^5 \cdot y^6}{y^2 \cdot x^3 \cdot 4^2}$

c. $\dfrac{w^7 \cdot u^5 \cdot x^4 \cdot 3^3}{x^2 \cdot u^3 \cdot 3^2 \cdot w^7}$

11. Simplify each expression. Hint: See Example 4c.

a. $\dfrac{11^6 \cdot w^9 \cdot y^5 \cdot 6^5}{y^3 \cdot w^6 \cdot 11^4 \cdot 6^3 \cdot v^2}$

b. $\dfrac{k^6 \cdot 2^2 \cdot 10^3}{10^9 \cdot 2^4 \cdot k^3 \cdot x}$

12. Evaluate. Hint: See Example 5a.

a. 10^0 **b.** 1^0 **c.** 29^0 **d.** 100^0

13. Evaluate. Hint: See Example 5b.

a. $2^7 \cdot 2^{-7}$ **b.** $6^{10} \cdot 6^{-10}$ **c.** $8^5 \cdot 8^{-5}$ **d.** $9^8 \cdot 9^{-8}$

14. Evaluate. Hint: See Example 5c.

a. $\dfrac{3^4}{34}$ **b.** $\dfrac{8^7}{8^7}$ **c.** $\dfrac{5^9}{5^9}$ **d.** $\dfrac{2^{10}}{2^{10}}$

15. Evaluate. Hint: See Example 5d.

a. $\dfrac{k^8}{k^8}$ **b.** $\dfrac{n^{10}}{n^{10}}$ **c.** $\dfrac{p^5}{p^5}$ **d.** $\dfrac{j^8}{j^8}$

16. Evaluate. Hint: See Example 6a.

a. 5^{-2} **b.** 4^{-2} **c.** 6^{-3} **d.** 3^{-3}

17. Evaluate. Hint: See Example 6b.

a. $(-3)^{-2}$ **b.** $(-2)^{-3}$ **c.** $(-5)^{-3}$ **d.** $(-4)^{-4}$

18. Evaluate. Hint: See Example 6c.

a. $\dfrac{(-3)^2}{(-3)^3}$ **b.** $\dfrac{(-3)^2}{(-3)^4}$ **c.** $\dfrac{(-5)^2}{(-5)^4}$ **d.** $\dfrac{(-4)^2}{(-4)^4}$

19. Evaluate. Hint: See Example 6d.

a. $\dfrac{(5-3)^2}{(6-4)^3}$ **b.** $\dfrac{(7-5)^3}{(8-6)^5}$ **c.** $\dfrac{(9-6)^2}{(7-4)^4}$ **d.** $\dfrac{(5-1)^2}{(9-5)^4}$

20. Evaluate. Hint: See Example 6e.

a. $(3 \cdot 2)^3 \cdot (6 \cdot 1)^{-5}$ **b.** $(4 \cdot 4)^4 \cdot (8 \cdot 2)^{-6}$

c. $(2 \cdot 2)^4 \cdot (4 \cdot 1)^{-6}$ **d.** $(2 \cdot 6)^{-6} \cdot (4 \cdot 3)^4$

21. Evaluate. Hint: See Example 6f.

a. $2^4 \cdot 2^{-6} \cdot 2^{-2}$ **b.** $3^{-2} \cdot 3^4 \cdot 3^{-3}$ **c.** $4^2 \cdot 4^{-3} \cdot 4^2 \cdot 4^{-2}$

22. Simplify. Hint: See Example 7.

a. $\dfrac{4}{3^{-2}}$ **b.** $\dfrac{3}{2^{-4}}$ **c.** $\dfrac{12}{3^{-3}}$ **d.** $\dfrac{5}{4^{-2}}$

23. Simplify. Hint: See example 8

a $\dfrac{16x^4y^5}{4x^2y}$ **b** $\dfrac{25x^6y^3}{5x^2y^2}$ **c** $\dfrac{9p^7k^3}{3p^2k}$ **d** $\dfrac{12x^{15}y^3}{4x^{12}y}$

24. Simplify. Hint: See Example 9

a. $\dfrac{-12a^9bc^{14}}{6a^3bc^6}$ **b.** $\dfrac{30w^{15}x^{11}}{-10w^2x^6}$ **c.** $\dfrac{-18a^5b^3c^{10}}{2a^2bc^6}$ **d.** $\dfrac{36wp^{12}x^{13}}{-9wp^2x^6}$

25. Simplify. Hint: See Example 10

a. $\dfrac{-24p^7k^5}{-8p^3k^2}$ **b.** $\dfrac{-21x^9k^7}{-7x^5k^2}$ **c.** $\dfrac{-36s^{17}k^8}{-9s^3k^2}$ **d.** $\dfrac{-22x^7k^5}{-11x^3k^5}$

Challenge Questions

26. Multiply using exponents.

  a. $n^4 \cdot 3^3 \cdot 4^2 \cdot 3^2 \cdot 4^2$ **b.** $x^6 \cdot y^4 \cdot x^2 \cdot y$

27. Evaluate

  a. 17^0 **b.** 10^{-2} **c.** $11^{-12} \cdot 11^{-12}$ **d.** $\dfrac{2}{3^{-2}}$

  e. $\dfrac{4}{3^{-2}}$ **f.** $k^4 \cdot k^{-4}$ **g.** $\dfrac{(-2)^2}{(-2)^4}$ **h.** $(4 \cdot 3)^2 \cdot (2 \cdot 6)^{-4}$

  i. $2^{-3} \cdot 2^{-2} \cdot 2^3$ **j.** $3^{-3} \cdot 3^2 \cdot 3^{-3}$ **k.** $4^4 \cdot 4^{-6}$ **l.** $(3 \cdot 2)^2 \cdot (2 \cdot 3)^{-4}$

  m. $\dfrac{v^5}{v^2}$ **n.** $\dfrac{9^7}{9^5}$ **o.** $(-3)^{-3}$ **p.** 3^{-3}

  q. $\dfrac{2^3}{2^3}$ **r.** $\dfrac{2}{4^{-2}}$ **s.** $\dfrac{m^n}{m^x}$ **t.** $\dfrac{9^0 \cdot n^{-7} \cdot w^5 \cdot k^{-4}}{n^{-2} \cdot w^{-2} \cdot k^2 \cdot 7^0}$

28. Simplify

  a. $4^6 \cdot y^4 \cdot x^5$ **b.** $\dfrac{(7-6)^3}{(8-6)^2}$ **c.** $\dfrac{(9-7)^2}{(7-5)^4}$ **d.** $\dfrac{(5-2)^2}{(9-6)^3}$

  e. $\dfrac{5^0 \cdot n^3 \cdot p^5}{n^{-4} \cdot w^2}$ **f.** $\dfrac{t^{-3}}{t^3}$ **g.** $\dfrac{t^3}{t^{-3}}$ **h.** $(2 \cdot 6)^{-6} \cdot (4 \cdot 3)^6$

  i. $x^3 \cdot x^5 \cdot x^0 \cdot x$ **j.** $x^4 \cdot c^9 \cdot y^3 \cdot c^9 \cdot y^0$ **k.** $y \cdot y^0$

29. Simplify.

  a $\dfrac{24x^8y^9}{4x^3y}$ **b.** $\dfrac{42w^{12}x^7}{-6w^5x^3}$ **c.** $\dfrac{18x^{10}y^4}{3x^4y^2}$ **d.** $\dfrac{-28x^7k^9}{-7x^4k^2}$

  e. $\dfrac{-15x^5k^8}{-3x^5k^2}$ **f.** $\dfrac{-18a^6b^7c^{10}}{3a^2bc^8}$ **g.** $\dfrac{-32s^{11}k^7}{-8s^3k^5}$ **h.** $\dfrac{28x^{18}y^9}{4x^{10}y^6}$

Answers to Selected Questions.

3a. 3^{11} **4a.** Cannot combine as one power because the bases are different.

6a. $b^6 \cdot w^6 \cdot n^4$

9a. Quotient cannot be written as one power because the bases are different.

13a. 1   **18a.** $-\dfrac{1}{3}$ **22a.** 36

SCIENTIFIC NOTATION

Scientific notation can be used to write large numbers in the standard form **more easily**. A large number written in scientific notation is a mathematical statement expressed as **a product of two factors** as follows:

   The first factor is a number that is at least 1 but less than 10 and the second factor is a power of 10.

So, to change the standard form of a number to scientific notation, multiply the first factor (that is at least 1 but less than 10) by the second factor (that is a power of 10) as shown:

   Standard form = Scientific notation

               = **(first factor that is at least 1 but less than 10)** × **(second factor that is a power of 10.)**

Example 1

Write 640,000,000 in scientific notation.

Solution

Step 1: Find the first factor of 640,000,000 by counting the number of places the decimal point in the standard form must be moved to the left to form a number that is at least 1 but less than 10 as shown:

First factor

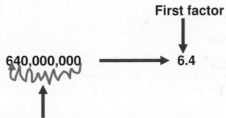

640,000,000 ⟶ 6.4

Move the decimal point 8 places to the left.

Note that there is an imaginary decimal point after every whole number,

145

review the chapter on decimals.

Step 2: Find the second factor of 640,000,000 by using the fact that since the decimal point in step 1 is moved 8 places to the left, the exponent of 10 is 8. The exponent of 10 is 8 can be written as shown:

Second factor

↓

Exponent of 10 is 8 = 10^8

Step 3: Write the number (640,000,000) in the scientific notation as the product of the two factors of 6.4 and 10^8 as shown:

$$640,000,000 = 6.4 \times 10^8$$

Example 2

Write 72,000,000,000 in the scientific notation.

Solution

Step 1: Find the first factor of 72,000,000,000 by counting the number of places the decimal point in the standard form must be moved to the left to form a number that is at least 1 but less than 10 as shown:

First factor

↓

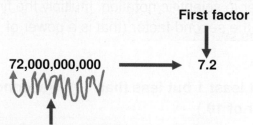

72,000,000,000 ⟶ 7.2

Move the decimal point 10 places to the left.

Note that there is an imaginary decimal point after every whole number, review the chapter on Decimals.

Step 2: Find the second factor of 72,000,000,000 by using the fact that since the decimal point in Step 1 is moved 10 places to the left, the exponent of 10 is 10. The exponent of 10 is 10 can be written as shown:

Second factor

↓

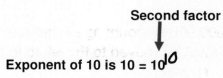

Exponent of 10 is 10 = 10^{10}

Step 3: Write the number (72,000,000,000) in the scientific notation as the product of the two factors of 7.2 and 10^{10} as shown:

$$72{,}000{,}000{,}000 = 7.2 \times 10^{10}$$

Example 3
Write 3,960,000 in the scientific notation.

Solution

Step 1: Find the first factor of 3,960,000 by counting the number of places the decimal point in the standard form must be moved to the left to form a number that is at least 1 but less than 10 as shown:

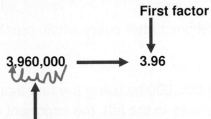

First factor

3,960,000 ⟶ 3.96

Move the decimal point 6 places to the left.

Note that there is an imaginary decimal point after every whole number, review the chapter on decimals.

Step 2: Find the second factor of 3,960,000 by using the fact that since the decimal point in step 1 is moved 6 places to the left, the exponent of 10 is 6. The exponent of 10 is 6 can be written as shown:

Second factor

Exponent of 10 is 6 = 10^6

Step 3: Write the number (3,960,000) in the scientific notation as the product of the two factors of 3.96 and 10^6 as shown:

$$3{,}960{,}000 = 3.96 \times 10^6$$

Example 4
Write 59,738,100,000,000 in the scientific notation.

Solution

Step 1: Find the first factor of 59,738,100,000,000 by counting the number of places the decimal point in the standard form must be moved to the left to form a number that is at least 1 but less than 10 as shown:

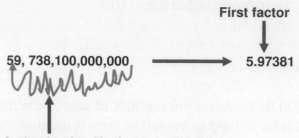

First factor

$59,738,100,000,000 \longrightarrow 5.97381$

Move the decimal point 13 places to the left.

Note that there is an imaginary decimal point after every whole number, review the chapter on decimals.

Step 2: Find the second factor of 59,738,100,000,000 by using the fact that since the decimal point in step 1 is moved 13 places to the left, the exponent of 10 is 13. The exponent of 10 is 13 can be written as shown:

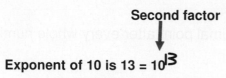

Second factor

Exponent of 10 is $13 = 10^{13}$

Step 3: Write the number 59,738,100,000,000 in the scientific notation as the product of the two factors of 5.97381 and 10^{13} as shown:

$$59,738,100,000,000 = 5.97381 \times 10^{13}$$

Example 5

Explain why each of the numbers is not written in the scientific notation.

a. $7.5 + 10^6$ **b.** 15×10^7 **c.** 6.2×8^5 **d.** 0.876×10^9

Solution

a. The scientific notation is written as the product of two factors but $7.5 + 10^6$ is not a product, but rather an addition.

b. The scientific notation is written as the product of two factors such that the first factor must be at least 1 but less than 10, but in 15×10^7, the first factor which is 15 is rather more than 10.

c. The scientific notation is written as the product of two factors such that the second factor is an exponent or power of 10, but in 6.2×8^5, the second factor is 8^5 but 8^5 is not an exponent or power of 10.

d. The scientific notation is written as the product of two factors such that the first factor must be at least 1 but less than 10, but in 0.876×10^9, the first factor which is 0.876 is less than 1.

How to Write Scientific Notations of Numbers Less Than 1.
In order to write the scientific notation of numbers that are less than 1, the decimal point in the number **must be moved to the right and must be placed behind the first non-zero digit so as to obtain a number that is at least 1**.
Since the decimal point is moved to the right, **the exponent must be negative**. Recall that a scientific notation is still a mathematical statement expressed as the product of two factors such that the first factor is at least 1 but less than 10 and the second factor is a power of 10.

Example 6
Write 0.0000004 in the scientific notation.
Solution
Step 1: Find the first factor of 0.0000004 by counting the number of places the decimal point in the decimal notation **must be moved to the right** to form a number that is at least 1 but less than 10 as shown:

First factor

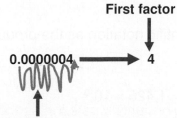

0.0000004 $\longrightarrow$ 4

Move the decimal point 7 places to the right.

Step 2: Find the second factor of 0.0000004 by using the fact that since the decimal point in Step 1 is moved 7 places to the **right**, the exponent of 10 is **-7**. The exponent of 10 is -7 can be written as shown:

Second factor

Exponent of 10 is -7 = 10^{-7}

Step 3: Write the number 0.0000004 in the scientific notation as the product of the two factors 4 and 10^{-7} as shown:

$$0.0000004 = 4 \times 10^{-7}$$

Example 7
Write 0.000001426 in the scientific notation.
Solution
Step 1: Find the first factor of 0.000001426 by counting the number of places the decimal point must be **moved to the right** to form a number that is at least 1 but less than 10 as shown:

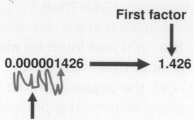

First factor

0.000001426 ———→ 1.426

Move the decimal point 6 places to the right.

Step 2: Find the second factor of 0.000001426 by using the fact that since the decimal point in step 1 is moved 6 places to the right, the exponent or the power of 10 is -6. The exponent of 10 is -6 can be written as shown:

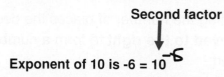

Second factor

Exponent of 10 is -6 = 10^{-6}

Step 3: Write the number 0.000001426 in the scientific notation as the product of the two factors 1.426 and 10^{-6} as shown:

$$0.000001426 = 1.426 \times 10^{-6}$$

How to Write Scientific Notation in the Standard Notation

In order to write the scientific notation as the standard notation, two rules should be followed:

Rule 1: If the exponent of the base of the scientific notation is positive, it means that the decimal point in the scientific notation should be moved to the **right** according to the magnitude of the exponent. Hint: See Example 8a.

Example of the scientific notation with positive exponent is:

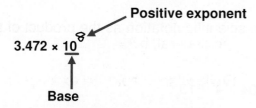

Positive exponent

3.472×10^{8}

Base

Rule 2: If the exponent of the base of the scientific notation is negative, it means that the decimal point in the scientific notation should be moved to the **left** according to the magnitude of the exponents. Hint: See Example 8b.

Example of the scientific notation with negative exponent is:

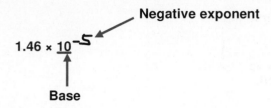
Negative exponent

1.46 × 10⁻⁵

Base

Example 8
Write each scientific notation in the standard notation.

a. 3.472×10^8 **b.** 1.46×10^{-5} **c.** -6.3×10^6

Solution

a. $3.472 \times 10^8 = 3.472 \times 100,000,000$ $10^8 = 100,000,000$

= 3.472

Move the decimal point 8 places to the right.
See rule 1.

Write the zeros here as place holders.
 Review the chapter on decimals.

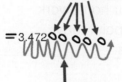
= 3.472 0 0 0 0 0

Move the decimal point 8 places to the right.
See rule 1.

347,200,000

Note that a detailed explanation is provided for the understanding of the concept, however, the detailed explanation may not be necessary in solving your homework exercises. The student should understand and apply how the decimal point may be moved to the right or left as needed in order to solve their exercises.

b. $1.46 \times 10^{-5} = 1.46 \times \dfrac{1}{10^5}$ In general, $b^{-n} = \dfrac{1}{b^n}$ and $b \neq 0$.

Review the chapter on exponents.

$= 1.46 \times \dfrac{1}{100,000}$

$= \dfrac{1.46}{100,000}$

151

= 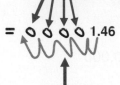 1.46

Move the decimal point 5 places to the left.
See rule 2.

Write the zeros here as place holders.
           Review the chapter on decimals.

= 0 0 0 0 1.46

Move the decimal point 5 places to the left.
See rule 2.

$$= 0.0000146$$

Note that the detailed explanation is provided for the understanding of the concept, however, the detailed explanation may not be necessary in solving your homework exercises. The student should understand and apply how the decimal point may be moved to the right or left as needed in order to solve their exercises.

c. $-6.3 \times 10^6 = -6.3 \times 1{,}000{,}000$ $10^6 = 1{,}000{,}000$

= -6.3

Move the decimal point 6 places to the right.
See rule 1.

Write zeros here as place holders.
           Review the chapter on decimals.

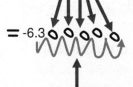
= -6.3 0 0 0 0 0

Move the decimal point 6 places to the right.
See rule 1.

$$= -6300000$$

Note that the detailed explanation is provided for the understanding of the concept, however, the detailed explanation may not be necessary in solving your homework exercises. The student should understand and apply how the decimal point may be moved to the right or left as needed in order to solve their exercises.

Exercises

1. Describe how you would write 4.8969×10^7 in the standard notation. Hint: See the preceding notes.
2. Describe how you would write 0.00038 in the scientific notation. Hint: See Example 6.
3. The scientific notation can be used to write large numbers in standard form more easily. True or False? Hint: See the preceding notes.
4. The scientific notation is made up of two factors. True or False? Hint: See the preceding notes.
5. Write the following numbers in the scientific notation. Hint: See Example 1.
   a. 530,000,000
   b. 720,00
   c. 480,000,000
   d. 940,000,000,000
   e. 670,00
   f. 110,000,000
6. Write the following numbers in the scientific notation. Hint: See Example 2.
   a. 64,000,000
   b. 55,000,000
   c. 78,000
   d. 12,000,000
   e. 99,000
   f. 84,000,000,000
7. Write the following numbers in the scientific notation. Hint: See Example 3.
   a. 5,870,000
   b. 7,250,000
   c. 6,740,000
   d. 2,940,000,000
   e. 4,390,000,000
   f. 8,390,000
8. Write the following numbers in the scientific notation. Hint: See Example 4.
   a. 47,891,200,000
   b. 98,147,300,000
   c. 57,284,000
   d. 64,734,300,000,000
   e. 38,234,400,000
   f. 49,195,000
9. Explain why each number is not written in the scientific notation. Hint: See Example 5.
   a. $2.9 + 10^7$
   b. 12×10^4
   c. 4.5×9^{10}
   d. 0.491×10^8
   e. $5.7 + 10^8$
   f. 0.34×10^7
10. Write the following numbers in the scientific notation. Hint: See Example 6.
   a. 0.000006
   b. 0.00009
   c. 0.000002
   d. 0.0008
   e. 0.0003
   f. 0.0000007
11. Write the following numbers in the scientific notation. Hint: See Example 7.
   a. 0.00004135
   b. 0.000741
   c. 0.000000148
   d. 0.00000278
   e. 0.00389
   f. 0.0091
12. Write each scientific notation in the standard form. Hint: See Example 8.
   a. 4.731×10^5
   b. 1.246×10^{-7}
   c. -5.71×10^4
   d. 9.81×10^7
   e. 3.46×10^{-5}
   f. 8.1×10^8
   g. 1.2×10^{-6}
   h. -5.7×10^4
   i. 3.481×10^9
   j. 4.793×10^6
   k. -7.4×10^7
   l. 7.34×10^{-4}
   m. -9.31×10^7
   n. 5.712×10^5
   o. 6.341×10^{-7}

Answers to Selected Questions

5a. 5.3×10^8 **6a.** 6.4×10^7 **7a.** 5.87×10^6 **8a.** 4.78912×10^{10}
10a. 6×10^{-6} **11a.** 4.135×10^{-5} **12a.** 473100

Challenge Questions

13. Write each number in the scientific notation.

    a. 72,000,000   **b.** 0.000002   **c.** 0.0000192

    d. 94,000,000   **e.** 1,000,000,000   **f.** 4000,000,000

    g. 77,000,000   **h.** 142,000,000   **i.** 298,000

    j. 8,000,000,000   **k.** 272,000   **l.** 0.00078

    m. 0.00000418   **n.** 0.0009   **o.** 22,000,000,000

14. Explain why each of the following is not in scientific notation.

    a. 0.491×10^4 **b.** $3.7 + 10^{16}$ **c.** 38×10^4

    d. 4.81×6^5 **e.** 4.9×7^8 **f.** 50×10^6

15. Write each number in the standard notation.

    a. 3.12×10^6 **b.** 1.7×10^9 **c.** 1.48×10^{-4}

    d. -2.4×10^5 **e.** 3.6×10^4 **f.** -4.8×10^4

    g. 7.1×10^{-5} **h.** 4.2×10^{-4} **i.** -2.2×10^6

CHAPTER 8

AVERAGE, MEAN, RANGE, MODE, AND MEDIAN

Average

Explanation 1

In its simplest form, an average is to share or divide anything equally. For example, how can we share or divide 6 oranges equally between 2 girls? We can share the 6 oranges equally such that each girl will receive 3 oranges as shown:

Six oranges to be shared equally.

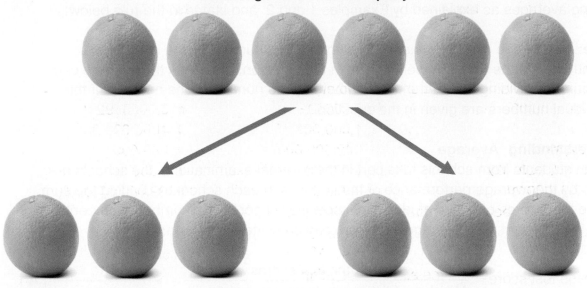

Equal share of 3 oranges   **Equal share of 3 oranges**

From the above picture, we are able to divide 6 oranges equally between 2 girls by dividing the total number of the oranges by the number of people who are to receive the share. Similarly, **an average is the total number divided by the number of the numbers**, and in this case the number of the numbers involves 2 girls which can be written as shown:

$$\text{Average} = \frac{\text{Total number of oranges}}{\text{Number of people}} = \frac{6}{2} = 3 \text{ oranges}$$

Explanation 2

Assume that a girl has 2 oranges and another girl has 4 oranges and they are requested to share the oranges equally, then they have to add the oranges together, and then divide the total number of the oranges or the sum of the oranges by 2 or the number of the girls. Similarly, sharing the oranges equally is the same as finding the average which can be stated as follows: **an average is the sum of numbers divided by the number of the numbers**. This average can be written as shown:

$$\text{Average} = \frac{\text{Sum of oranges}}{\text{Number of people}} = \frac{2+4}{2} = \frac{6}{2} = 3$$

Conclusion from Explanations 1 and 2.

In Explanation 1, we find the average by dividing "Total number of oranges" by "Number of people," but in Explanation 2, the average is found by dividing the "Sum of oranges" by "Number of people." We can then combine Explanations 1 and 2 together to write that **an average is the total or the sum of the numbers**

155

divided by the number of the numbers. Therefore, there are two methods of finding averages as explained by Examples 1 and 2, and stated in the rule below:

Rule: An average can be found by dividing the total number by the number of the numbers if the total number is given in the question, otherwise the average can be found by dividing the sum of the numbers by the number of the numbers if the individual numbers are given in the question.

Understanding Average

When students from schools take part in the external examinations, the schools are rated by the average performance of the students in each school by dividing the sum of the test scores of all the students in a specific school by the number of students who took the test. The average test score can be written as shown:

$$\text{Average test score} = \frac{\text{Sum of the test scores}}{\text{Number of the students who took the test}} \quad\quad\quad [A]$$

Group Exercise

The class should be divided into four groups and without using any students' names, each group should be given the test scores of the last weekly test. Each group should find the average test score of the last weekly test by completing the tables as shown and using the average equation, which is equation $[A]$.

Test scores :

Student #	1	2	3	4	5	6	7	8	. . .	N
Test score	?	?	?	?	?	?	?	?	. . .	?

Each group should report out the average test score to the whole class.
Each group should discuss the following 4 questions and to list and report out their answer with reasons to the whole class.
1. Are the average test score from the 4 groups the same?
2. How could the average test score be improved? When each student's test score is increased by 2, what happens to the average test score? Is the average test score higher when the individual test score is increased by 2?
3. Could you name some external tests that your school participates in?
4. What factors will lower the average test score? When the individual test score is lowered by 2, does the average test score becomes lower?

Example 1

(**a**). The test scores of five students out of a maximum score of 10 are 8, 7, 9, 10, and 6. Find the average test score of the students.
(**b**). The total age of 5 boys is 20 years. What is their average age?

Solution

(**a**). Using the formula, the average test score is:

$$\text{Average test score} = \frac{\text{Sum of the test scores}}{\text{Number of the students that took the test}} \quad\text{————————— [A]}$$

Sum of the test scores $= 8 + 7 + 9 + 10 + 6 = 40$
Number of the students that took the test $= 5$

$$\text{Average test score} = \frac{40}{5} \qquad \text{See equation } [A]$$

$$= \frac{\overset{8}{\cancel{40}}}{\underset{1}{\cancel{5}}} \qquad \text{Divide by 5.}$$

Therefore, the average test score is 8.

(**b**). The total age of the 5 boys $= 20$ years
The number of the boys $= 5$
Using the formula:

$$\text{Average} = \frac{\text{Total number (ages)}}{\text{Number of people}} = \frac{20}{5}$$

$$= \frac{\overset{4}{\cancel{20}}}{\underset{1}{\cancel{5}}} \qquad \text{(Divide by 5).}$$

Therefore, the average age of the 5 boys is 4 years.

Example 2

Find the average of the following numbers:

$$1\frac{1}{2}, \ 2\frac{3}{4}, \ 3\frac{2}{3}, \ 2\frac{1}{2}$$

Solution

Using the formula, the average of the numbers is:

$$\text{Average number} = \frac{\text{Sum of the numbers}}{\text{Number of the numbers}} \quad\text{————————— [A]}$$

Sum of the numbers $= 1\dfrac{1}{2} + 2\dfrac{3}{4} + 3\dfrac{2}{3} + 2\dfrac{1}{2}$

Number of the numbers $= 4$ (There are 4 numbers involved.)

Add the numbers as follow: (Review the Addition of Mixed Numbers).

$$1\dfrac{1}{2} = 1\dfrac{1}{2} \times \dfrac{6}{6} = 1\dfrac{6}{12}$$

$$2\dfrac{3}{4} = 2\dfrac{3}{4} \times \dfrac{3}{3} = 2\dfrac{9}{12}$$

$$3\dfrac{2}{3} = 3\dfrac{2}{3} \times \dfrac{4}{4} = 3\dfrac{8}{12}$$

$$2\dfrac{1}{2} = 2\dfrac{1}{2} \times \dfrac{6}{6} = 2\dfrac{6}{12}$$

$$8\dfrac{29}{12} = 8 + 2\dfrac{5}{12} = 10\dfrac{5}{12} \quad \text{(Review Division of Fractions)}$$

Sum of the numbers $= 10\dfrac{5}{12}$

Using equation [A]:

$$\text{Average number} = \dfrac{10\dfrac{5}{12}}{4} \quad \text{(There are 4 numbers.)}$$

$$= 10\dfrac{5}{12} \div 4$$

$$= 10\dfrac{5}{12} \times \dfrac{1}{4} \quad \text{(Review the Division of Fractions - multiply by reciprocal of 4.)}$$

Note: The reciprocal of any number $= 1 \div$ the number

$$= \dfrac{125}{12} \times \dfrac{1}{4} \quad \text{(Review the Multiplication of Mixed Fractions.)}$$

$$= \dfrac{125}{48} = 2\dfrac{29}{48}$$

Therefore, the average number is $2\dfrac{29}{48}$

Example 3

The average age of 8 children is 9 years. If the ages of seven of the children are 6,

$8\frac{1}{2}$, 4, 10, 11, 12, and 9, how old is the 8th child?

Solution

Sum of the ages of the 7 children $= 6 + 8\frac{1}{2} + 4 + 10 + 11 + 12 + 9 = 60\frac{1}{2}$ years.

Total ages of the 8 children $= 8 \times$ average age of the 8 children.
$$= 8 \times 9 \text{ years}$$
$$= 72 \text{ years.}$$

Age of 8th child = Total age of the 8 children − Sum of the ages of the 7 children
$$= 72 \text{ years} - 60\frac{1}{2} \text{ years}$$
$$= 11\frac{1}{2} \text{ years.}$$

Therefore, the age of the 8th child is $11\frac{1}{2}$ years.

Mean, Range, Mode, and Median.
The **mean** is the same as the average.
The **range** is the difference between the biggest number and the smallest number in a data.

Example 4
The table shows the ages of 9 students.

Students #	1	2	3	4	5	6	7	8	9
Ages	16	14	13	14	17	15	14	12	11

a. Find the range of the ages of the students.
b. Find the mean age of the students.
c. By conducting a group exercise, find the range of the data by using a line plot.
d. Find the mode of the data.
e. By using the line plot in Example 4c, how would you find the mode of the data?
f. Find the median age of the students.
g. By using the line plot of Example 4c, how would you find the median age of the students?

Solution

a. From the table, the student # 5 has the highest age of 17 years and the student #9 has the lowest age of 11 years.
Therefore, the range = Highest age - Lowest age
$$= 17 \text{ years} - 11 \text{ years} = 6 \text{ years.}$$

b. Let us find the mean age of the students as follows:

Sum of the ages of the students $= 16 + 14 + 13 + 14 + 17 + 15 + 14 + 12 + 11$

$= 126$ years

The number of students $= 9$ From the table, 9 students are listed.

The mean of the ages of the students $= \dfrac{\text{Sum of the ages of the students}}{\text{Number of the students}}$

$= \dfrac{126 \text{ years}}{9}$

$= 14$ years   Review the division of integers.

Therefore, the mean age of the students is 14 years.

c. Group Exercise

The class should be divided into four groups. Each group should complete the line plot of the ages of all the 9 students, using x for each mark as started below.

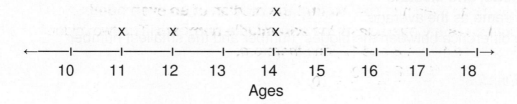

How could the range be determined from the line plot?

Answer: The x at the extreme left side of the line plot indicates the lowest age and the x at the extreme right side of the line plot indicates the highest age.

Subtract the lowest age from the highest age to obtain the range.

d. The **mode** is the number that occurs most often. From the table, the age 14 years occurs 3 times which is the age that occurs most often, and therefore, 14 is the mode.

e. Group Exercise

From the completed line plot, how could you find the mode?

Answer: **The age column which has the most "x" indicates the mode**. Which age column has the most "x"? What is then the mode from the line plot? The mode is the data that appears most.

f. The **median** is the middle number when data is listed in numerical order. Numerical order means to list the data from the least number to the greatest number, in order without omission. We can write the ages of the 9 students in numerical order as shown:

$$11, 12, 13, 14, 14, 14, 15, 16, 17$$
$$\uparrow$$

This 14 is the middle number when the data is listed in numerical order, and therefore, this 14 is the median.

g. Group Exercise

From the completed line plot, how could you find the median?
Answer: The x's on the line plot are already in numerical order, and therefore, by counting the x from left to right on the line plot, **we should be able to locate the x which is at the middle of the data and this middle x is the median**. What is the median from the line plot?

Special Method for Finding Median

The median is the middle number when data is listed in numerical order. However, if the data is an even number of numbers, there will be no middle number as the median as shown:

$$6, 8, 12, 14$$

The numbers 6, 8, 12, and 14 have no middle number because the number of the numbers is 4 which is an even number. **To find the median of an even number of numbers, the median is the average of the two middle numbers**. The two middle numbers of 6, 8, 12, and 14 are 8 and 12, and therefore,

the average of 8 and 12 $= \dfrac{8 + 12}{2} = \dfrac{20}{2} = 10.$

Therefore, the median of 6, 8, 12, and 14 is 10.

How to Solve Multi-Step Problems Involving Mean.

Example 5

The mean of the ages of 3 boys is 5 years. How old should the fourth boy be such that the mean of the 4 boys will be 8 years?
Solution
The method of solving this problem involves finding the total ages of the 3 boys and then let x represents the age of the fourth boy. We can then find the sum of the ages of all the 4 boys, we can also find the mean of the ages of all the four boys. Finally, we can equate the mean of the ages of the 4 boys to 8 years, and then solve for x which is the age of the fourth boy as shown:

Total ages of the 3 boys = 3 × Mean age of the 3 boys.
$\qquad\qquad\qquad$ = 3 × 5 years $\qquad$ Mean age of the 3 boys = 5 years.
$\qquad\qquad\qquad$ = 15 years
Let the age of the fourth boy = x years
Total age of all the 4 boys = 15 years + x years

$$\text{Mean of the ages of the 4 boys} = \frac{\text{Sum of the ages of the 4 boys}}{\text{Total number of boys}}$$

$$= \frac{15 + x}{4}$$

Since the question gives us the mean of the 4 boys is 8 years, we can equate $\frac{15 + x}{4}$ to 8, and then solve for x which is the age of the fourth boy as shown:

$$\frac{15 + x}{4} = 8$$

$$\frac{15 + x}{4} = \frac{8}{1} \qquad \text{8 is the same as } \frac{8}{1}.$$

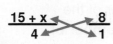

Cross products of a proprotion are equal. A proportion is a statement that two ratios are equal. Review the chapter on proportion.

$(15 + x) \times 1 = 4 \times 8$	Review the chapter on Proportion.
$15 \times 1 + x \times 1 = 4 \times 8$	Multiply to eliminate the bracket.
$15 + x = 32$	$4 \times 8 = 32.$
$15 - 15 + x = 32 - 15$	Subtract 15 from both sides of the equation $15 + x = 32$ in order to obtain x.
$0 + x = 17$	$15 - 15 = 0$ and $32 - 15 = 17.$
$x = 17$	

Therefore, the fourth boy should be 17 years.

The notes and the generous worked examples have provided me with conceptual understanding and computational fluency to do my homework.

Exercises

1. **(a)** Explain what is meant by average, mean, range, mode, and median.
   (b) Six boys are given $24. What is the average amount each boy will receive?
   Hint: See Example **1(a)**.
   (c). If 8 students are to share 16 apples, what is the average number of the apples will each student receive? Hint: See Example **1(b)**.
2. What is the average of 4, 5, 2, and 1? Hint: See Example **1(a)**.
3. Find the average of the following numbers: Hint: See Examples **1(a)** and 2.

(a) 2.1, 6.4, 2.8, 1.2, 2.5

(b) $1\frac{1}{2}$, $6\frac{2}{3}$, $1\frac{5}{6}$

(c) 22, 5, 14, 6, 8

(d) 4, 7, 8, 11, 2, 6, 3, 9, 13

(e) 14, 16, 8, 10, 7, 5

(f) 77, 43

(g) $2\frac{2}{3}$, $1\frac{3}{4}$, $3\frac{1}{4}$, $\frac{1}{3}$

(h) 1, 3, 9, 11, 4, 3, 12

(i) 14, 24, 31, 16

(j) 5, 10, 12, 14, 6

(k) 8, 5, 2   (l) 10, 6, 8, 4   (m) 2, 7, 5, 1, 10

4. From the given data, find the range. Hint: See the section under Range.
   See Example **4a**.

(a) 3, 4, 7, 28

(b) 101, 7, 2, 94

(c) 38, 49, 86, 99, 31, 2

(d) 2, 8, 4, 35, 44

(e) 39, 98, 401, 30, 11

(f) 15, 25, 7, 5

5. Find the median. Hint: See the section on Median. See Example **4f**.

(a) 4, 8, 1, 6, 4   (b) 9, 5, 8   (f) 7, 12, 3

(g) 4.2, 3.1, 6.4, 1.8, 6.2   (h) $7\frac{1}{2}$, $6\frac{1}{3}$, $8\frac{3}{4}$, $6\frac{2}{3}$, $7\frac{1}{4}$ (i) 6.3, 4.7, 8.4

6. Find the median. Hint: See the section on the Special Method of Finding the
   Median.

(a) 2, 8, 5, 3   (b) 3, 7, 8, 1   (c) 12, 2, 4, 6, 1, 3

(d) 12, 4   (e) 4, 6   (f) 3, 4, 8, 2, 7, 9

(g) 110, 112, 100, 98   (h) 2.4, 2.8, 4.2, 6.4   (i) $7\frac{1}{2}$, $6\frac{2}{3}$, $2\frac{2}{3}$, $1\frac{3}{4}$

7. Find the mode. Hint: See the section on Mode. See Example 4d.

(a) 2, 3, 7, 8, 2, 9, 3, 2   (b) 4, 1, 6, 9, 4, 2, 4, 1

(c) 9, 11, 6, 7, 9, 4, 9   (d) 1, 4, 6, 1, 7, 1, 2, 6, 4

(e) 4, 1, 5, 1, 6, 5, 8, 5   (f) 2, 6, 9, 4, 6, 2, 6

8. Find the mode and the range. Hint: See the section on Mode and Range.
   See Examples **4a** and **4d**.

(a) 12, 14, 4, 12, 3, 1, 12, 14   (b) 19, 24, 6, 19, 4, 2

(c) 3, 6, 9, 10, 6, 24, 4   (d) 1, 4, 5, 6, 5, 13, 5

(e) 2.5, 6.8, 4.1, 3, 6.8, 7.2   (f) $4\frac{1}{2}$, $1\frac{7}{8}$, $6\frac{4}{5}$, $1\frac{7}{8}$, 2

(g) $2\frac{3}{4}$, $1\frac{1}{2}$, $8\frac{3}{7}$, $2\frac{3}{4}$, 6, $2\frac{3}{4}$ (h) 1.5, 7.5, 2.5, 2.5, 1.5, 2.5, 1.5

9. The mean of 3 numbers is 2. What is the fourth number such that the mean of
   all the four numbers should be 5. Hint: See Example **5**.

10. The mean age of 2 girls is 4 years. What should be the age of the third girl
    such that the mean of all three girls should be 6 years? Hint: See Example **5**.

11. The mean of 5 numbers is 7, what should be the sixth number for the mean
    of all the 6 numbers to be 4? Hint: See Example **5**.

12. The mean of the ages of 3 girls is 14 years, what should be the age of the fourth

girl such that the mean age of all the 4 girls should be 12 years old? Hint: See Example **5**.

Challenge Questions
13. Find the average. Round off your answer to the nearest whole number.

(**a**) 2, 6, 14   (**b**) 14, 28, 31, 43   (**c**) 2.4, 6.9, 1.3

(**d**) 1.6, 10.4   (**e**) 36, 54, 104, 64   (**f**) 3, 7, 8, 4, 9

(**g**) $2\frac{3}{4}$, 3, $4\frac{1}{2}$, $2\frac{1}{4}$ (**h**) $10\frac{3}{4}$, $11\frac{1}{4}$ (**i**) 4.4, 6.9, 3.3

14. Find the range and the mode.

(**a**) 1, 7, 6, 1, 4, 1, 9   (**b**) 14, 2, 8, 1.4   (**c**) 2.2, 4.8, 2.2, 4

(**d**) 8, 10, 17, 10, 34, 10   (**e**) 2, 2, 4, 8, 4, 9, 4   (**f**) 6, 7, 11, 14, 7

15. Find the mean.

(**a**) 2, 3, 4   (**b**) 10, 22   (**c**) 1.2, 4.3, 3.5

(**d**) $14\frac{2}{6}$, $82\frac{2}{3}$, 2   (**e**). 31, 3   (**f**). 12, 6, 12

16. Find the mean.

(**a**) 2, 9, 7, 1, 4   (**b**) 1, 6, 8, 2, 10, 3   (**c**) 2, 4, 1, 8

(**d**) 2.2, 4.2, 6.8, 1.8   (**e**) $1\frac{1}{4}$, $6\frac{1}{2}$, $2\frac{1}{4}$ (**f**) 7, 9

17. The mean of 3 numbers is 6. What should be the fourth number such that the mean of all the four numbers should be 10?

Answers to Selected Questions
1(**b**) $4.00   **3**(**a**) 3   **4**(**a**) 25   **9**. 14

REAL WORLD APPLICATIONS - WORD PROBLEMS

1. The average test score of 5 students is 12. If the test score of 4 students are 10, 13, 10, and 14, what is the test score of the 5th student? Hint: See Example **3** under the chapter Average.

2. The ages of three students are 9, 10, and 11 years. Find their average age. Hint: See Example **1** under chapter Average.

Challenge Questions.
3. The average age of 6 employees is 25 years. If the ages of 4 of the employees

are 20, 21, 30, and 23 years, what is the total ages of the 2 remaining employees?

4. The weekly test scores of 6 students are 90%, 78%, 89%, 98%, 86%, and 65%. What is the average test score of the students?

5. Make a line plot of the following data and using the line plot explain how you would obtain the mode, range, mean, and the median. Hint: Number the number line from 0 to 30.

8, 12, 16, 28, 2, 18, 12, 4, 8, 12, 10, 12, 2, 2, 28.

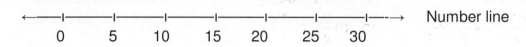

Number line

0   5   10   15   20   25   30

ALGEBRAIC EXPRESSIONS

An algebraic expression is formed by numbers, variables and the operations of addition, subtraction, division, multiplication, powers, and roots as shown in Table 1:

Table 1

Word Phrases	Operations needed	Examples of expressions
1. A number **plus** 2. 2. A number **increased** by 2. 3. 2 **more** than a number. 4. **Add** 2 to a number.	+	Let x be the number, and therefore, the expression is **x + 2.**
1. **Subtract** 3 from a number. 2. A number **decreased** by 3. 3. 3 **less** than a number. 4. A number **minus** 3. 5. **Difference** of a number and 3.	—	Let n be the number, and therefore, the expression is **n - 3.**
1. 4 **divided** into a number. 2. A number **divided** by 4. 3. **Quotient** of a number and 4.	÷	Let k be the number, and therefore, the expression is **k ÷ 4.**
1. **Product** of 5 and a number. 2. 5 **multiplied** by a number. 3. 5 **times** a number.	×	Let y be the number, and therefore, the expression is **5 × y = 5y.**
1. A number to the **power** a.	Power	Let 2 be the number, and therefore, the expression is 2^a.
1. **Root** of a number x.	√	Let x represent the number, and therefore, the expression is $\sqrt{x}$.

Key point: Understand and know the relationship between the words in **bold** under the "word phrase" column and the corresponding "operations needed" column in Table 1. For example, **more** means addition and **less** means subtraction.

Exercises or Group Exercises.

1. Write an algebraic expression for each word phrase. Hint: See examples of the expressions in table 1.

a. 10 more than k.	**b**. 8 less than x.	**c**. P minus 6.
d. w decreased by 15.	**e**. the quotient of 6 and p.	**f**. Product of 2 and k.
g. 7 multiplied by v.	**h**. Difference of 9 and b.	**i**. Subtract 1 from n.
j. 5 times k.	**k**. Add 11 to y.	**l**. Increase 12 by x.
m. z to the power 6.	**n**. Root of k.	**o**. 8 to the power w.

Complex Word Phrases

It is possible to combine some of the word phrases in Table 1 to form complex word phrases as shown in Table 2:

(Table 2 is shown on the next page.)

Table 2

Key Words	Word Phrases	Examples of expressions
more, products	2 **more** than the **product** of 4 and k.	4k is the **product** of 4 and k, and therefore, the expression is 4k + 2.
less, product	4 **less** than the **product** of 6 and k.	6k is the **product** of 6 and k, and therefore, the expression is 6k - 4.
less, divide	10 **less** than m **divided** by 7.	m **divided** by 7 is m ÷ 7, and therefore, the expression is m ÷ 7 - 10.
more, divide	10 **more** than m **divided** by 7.	m **divided** by 7 is m ÷ 7, and therefore, the expression is m ÷ 7 + 10.
times, sum	3 **times** the **sum** of n and 5.	The **sum** of n and 5 is n + 5, and therefore, the expression is 3(n + 5).
times, difference	8 **times** the **difference** of x and 6.	The **difference** of x and 6 is x - 6, and therefore, the expression is 8(x - 6).
times, product	2 **times** the **product** of k and 5.	The **product** of k and 5 is 5k, and therefore, the expression is 2 × 5k = 10k.
times, quotient	**Twice** the **quotient** of p and 58.	The **quotient** of p and 58 is p ÷ 58, and therefore, the expression is 2(p ÷ 58).
plus, product	2 **plus** the **product** of 3 and y.	The **product** of 3 and y is 3y, and therefore, the expression is 3y + 2.
minus, product	2 **minus** the **product** of 3 and y.	The **product** of 3 and y is 3y, and therefore, the expression is 2 - 3y.
fraction, sum	**Five-sixth** the **sum** of k and 3.	The **sum** of k and 5 is k + 5, and therefore, the expression is $\frac{5}{6}$(k + 3).

Key Points: 1. Understand and know the relationship among the "key words" column the "word phrase column," and the "examples of expressions column."

2. **Note** that each complex word phrase has at least two operations and it is important that the student should know which operation should be done first. In Table 2, the operations to be done first are in bold under the column "examples of expressions."

Exercises

1. Write an algebraic expression for each word phrase. Hint: See the examples in

Table 2 and also watch for the key words in Table 2.

   a. 10 more than the product of 7 and w.   **b**. 1 less than the product of 8 and k.

   c. 3 less than k divided by 6.   **d**. 6 times the sum of w and 10.

   e. 4 times the difference of y and 2.   **f**. 7 plus the product of 6 and k.

   g. 20 minus the product of 5 and w.   **h**. 2 more than k divided by 6.

   i. 8 times the product of m and 10.   **j**. Twice the quotient of 60 and w.

   k. Four times the quotient of 100 and p.   **l**. One-third the sum of w and 12.

   m. One-third the difference between 32 and p.

Challenge Questions

2. Write the expression for the following word phrases.

   a. w more than 5 times k.   **b**. 11 more than p times n.

   c. n less than 4 times b.   **d**. 100 decreased by 3 times w.

   e. w less than twice n.   **f**. Half the quotient of w and k.

   g. 6 times the product of p and k.   **h**. Half the difference between k and 3.

(Once you understand how to write expressions, you can then write and solve equations in the chapter on equations using an "equal to" symbol to show that two expressions are equal.)

Evaluation of Expressions
Example 1

Evaluate each expression for a = 2, b = 3, c = 2.1, and d = 4.

   a. $a + d$ **b**. $\dfrac{b}{a}$ **c**. $(ac) + 10$ **d**. $\dfrac{14}{a} - 3$

   e. $\dfrac{d}{a} + c$ **f**. $3bc$ **g**. $(d - c) - a$ **h**. $b + \dfrac{d}{a}$

Solution

a. Substitute 2 for a and 4 for d into the expression a + d as shown:

$$a + d = 2 + 4$$
$$= 6$$

b. Substitute 3 for b and 2 for a into the expression $\dfrac{b}{a}$ as shown:

$$\frac{b}{a} = \frac{3}{2}$$
$$= 1\frac{1}{2}$$

c. Substitute 2 for a and 2 .1 for c into the expression (ac) + 10 as shown:

$$(ac) + 10 = (2 \times 2.1) + 10$$
$$= 4.2 + 10$$
$$= 14 \cdot 2$$

d. Substitute 2 for a into the expression $\frac{14}{a}$ - 3 as shown:

$$\frac{14}{a} - 3 = \frac{14}{2} - 3$$
$$= 7 - 3 \qquad\qquad 14 \div 2 = 7$$
$$= 4$$

e. Substitute 4 for d, 2 for a, and 2.1 for c into the expression $\frac{d}{a}$ + c as shown:

$$\frac{d}{a} + c = \frac{4}{2} + 2.1$$
$$= 2 + 2.1$$
$$= 4.1$$

f. Substitute 3 for b and 2.1 for c into the expression 3bc as shown:
$$3bc = 3 \times 3 \times 2.1$$
$$= 9 \times 2.1 \qquad\qquad 3 \times 3 = 9$$
$$= 18.9$$

g. Substitute 4 for d, 2.1 for c and 2 for a into the expression (d - c) - a as shown:
$$(d - c) - a = (4 - 2.1) - 2$$
$$= 1.9 - 2 \qquad\qquad 4 - 2.1 = 1.9$$
$$= -.1 \qquad\qquad 1.9 - 2 = -.1$$

h. Substitute 3 for b, 4 for d, and 2 for a into the expression b $+\frac{d}{a}$ as shown:

$$b + \frac{d}{a} = 3 + \frac{4}{2}$$
$$= 3 + 2 \qquad\qquad 4 \div 2 = 2$$
$$= 5$$

Exercises

1. Evaluate each expression for a = 8, b = 2, c = 1, and d = 4. Hint: Match similar exercises with the similar examples in Example 1.

a. db

b. $\frac{a}{d}$ + b

c. d + c

d. (ab) + 4

e. $\frac{12}{b}$ + 4

f. $\frac{d}{c}$ + b

g. (a - d) - b

h. c + $\frac{d}{b}$

Challenge Questions

2. Evaluate each expression for m = 9, n = 2, w = 3, and p = 4.

a. mn

b. $\frac{18}{w}$ - p

c. (m - p) - w

d. n + $\frac{m}{w}$

e. $\frac{p}{n}$ + m

f. $\frac{24}{p}$ + m

g. p + nw

h. mp + n

EQUATIONS

New words: **equations**, **variable**, **solution and solve**.

An **equation** uses an "equal to" symbol to show that two expressions are equal.
The examples of equations are:

$2x + 1 = 4 - x$, $w + 4 = 10$, $5n = 15$, and $\dfrac{25}{5} = 5$.

An equation is therefore, similar to a seesaw such that the weight of the people on one side of the seesaw **is equal to** the weight of the people at the other side of the seesaw when the beam of the seesaw is horizontal or balanced.

Beam of the seesaw

Group Exercise

The class may be divided into four groups and under the supervision of the teacher, and other adults, the students should balance the beam of a seesaw to demonstrate that an equation is similar to a balanced beam of a seesaw.

The **variable** in an equation is the unknown value in an equation. For example, x is the variable in the equation $2x + 1 = 4 - x$.

The **solution** to an equation is the value of the variable in the equation. To **solve** an equation means that we should **find the value of the variable**.

Solving Equations Using Addition

We can simply state the "**addition property of equality**" as shown:

When the same number is added to both sides of an equation, the resulting equation still has equal values at both sides of the equation.

Addition Property of Equality

Adding the same number to both sides of an equation.	Algebra
Add 4 to both sides of the equation $3 + 6 = 9$ as shown: $3 + 6 = 9$ $\underline{+4 \quad +4}$ $3 + 10 = 13$ Note that the resulting value of both sides of the equation after adding 4 to both sides of the equation is the same, which is 13	$x = w$ $x + z = w + z$

Example 1

Solve for n in the equation $n - 6 = 12$. Check your answers.

Solution

The basic method of solving for n is to isolate the variable n.

$n - 6 = 12$

$n - 6 + 6 = 12 + 6$ Add 6 to both sides of the equation in order to isolate the variable n.

         $n = 18$ $-6 + 6 = 0$

Check Your Answer

$n - 6 = 12$

$18 - 6 = 12$ Substitute 18 for n in the original equation.

     $12 = 12$ Since the right side of the equation is equal to the left side, the answer is correct.

Example 2

Solve for t in the equation $8 = t - 4$. Check your answer.

Solution

The basic method for solving for t is to isolate t.

$8 = t - 4$

$8 + 4 = t - 4 + 4$ Add 4 to both sides of the equation in order to isolate t.

$12 = t + 0$ $8 + 4 = 12$ and $-4 + 4 = 0$

$12 = t$

Check Your Answer

8 = t - 4

8 = 12 - 4   Substitute 12 for t in the original equation.

8 = 8   Since the left side of the equation is equal to the right
                   side of the equation, the answer is correct.

Example 3

Solve for w in the equation 10 = -2 - w. Check your answer.

Solution

The basic method for solving for w is to isolate w.

10 = -2 - w

10 + 2 = -2 + 2 - w   Add 2 to both sides of the equation in order to isolate w.

12 = 0 - w   -2 + 2 = 0

12 = -w

12(-1) = -w(-1)   Multiply both sides of the equation by -1 in order to
                          change -w to w because we are asked to solve for w but
                          not -w.

-12 = w   **Note**: 12(-1) = -12 and -w(-1) = +w = w.

Check Your Answer

10 = -2 - w

10 = -2 - (-12)   Substitute w = -12, into the original equation.

10 = -2 + 12   -(-12) = +12

10 = 10   -2 + 12 = 10

                         Since the left side of the equation is equal to the right side
                         of the equation, the answer is correct.

Solving Equations Using Subtraction

We can simply state the "**subtraction property of equality**" as follows:

When the same number is subtracted from both sides of an equation, the resulting
equation still has equal values at both sides of the equation.

Subtract the same number from both sides of an equation.	Algebra
Subtracting 4 from both sides of the equation $10 + 8 = 18$ as shown: $10 + 8 = 18$ $\quad - 4 \quad - 4$ $10 + 4 = 14$ Note that the resulting value of both sides of the equation after subtracting 4 from both sides of the equation is the same which is 14.	$x = w$ $x - z = w - z$

Example 4

Solve for x in the equation $x + 3 = 16$. Check your answer.

Solution

The basic method for solving for x is to isolate x.

$x + 3 = 16$

$x + 3 - 3 = 16 - 3$ Add 3 to both sides of the equation in order to isolate x.

$\quad x + 0 = 13$ $+3 - 3 = 0$

$\quad\quad x = 13$

Check Your Answer

$x + 3 = 16$

$13 + 3 - 16$ Substitute $x - 13$ into the original equation.

$\quad 16 = 16$ Since the left side of the equation is equal to the right side of the equation, the answer is correct.

Example 5

Solve for y in the equation $12 = 3 + y$. Check your answer.

Solution

The basic method for solving for y is to isolate y.

$12 = 3 + y$

$12 - 3 = 3 - 3 + y$ Subtract 3 from both sides of the equation in order to isolate y.

$\quad 9 = 0 + y$ $12 - 3 = 9$ and $3 - 3 = 0$.

$\quad 9 = y$

Check Your Answer

$12 = 3 + y$

$12 = 3 + 9$ Substitute $y = 9$ into the original equation.

$12 = 12$ Since the left side of the equation is equal to the right side of the equation, the answer is correct.

Applications

Example 6
The sum of two numbers is 19. One of the numbers is 11. What is the other number?
Solution
Let the other number be n.
The sum of the two numbers is 19, therefore:

n + 11 = 19

n + 11 - 11 = 19 - 11   Subtract 11 from both sides of the equation in order to
                          isolate n.

   n + 0 = 8   +11 - 11 = 0 and 19 -11 = 8.

      n = 8

Example 7
When 2 is subtracted from a number the difference is 13. What is the number?
Solution
Let the number be n.
When 2 is subtracted from the number the difference is 13, therefore:

n - 2 = 13

n - 2 + 2 = 13 + 2   Add 2 to both sides of the equation to isolate n.

  n + 0 = 15   - 2 + 2 = 0 and 13 + 2 = 15.

     n = 15

Exercises
1. What is a variable in an equation?
2. What is meant by the solution of an equation?
3. Solve for the variable in each equation. Check your answer.
   Hint: See Example 1 and Example 2.
   a. x - 4 = 10   **b.** w - 3 = 11   **c.** 15 = y - 5
   d. p - 7 = -3   **e.** 8 = 6 + y   **f.** w - 6 = 14
4. Solve for the variable in each equation. Check your answer.
   Hint: See Example 3.
   a. 14 = 2 - k   **b.** 8 = 6 - w   **c.** 4 - w = 12
   d. 3 - p = 9   **e.** 12 = w + 4   **f.** 7 + w = 14
5. Solve for the variable in each equation. Check your answer.
   Hint: See Example 4 and Example 5.
   a. x + 2 = 6   **b.** x + 14 = 14   **c.** 11 = p + 10
   d. 13 = 14 + t   **e.** 12 = w + 4   **f.** 7 + w = 14
6. The sum of two numbers is 25. One of the numbers is 15. What is the other
   number? Hint: See Example 6.

7. When 4 is subtracted from a number, the difference is 29. What is the number?
Hint: See Example 7

Challenge Questions

8. Solve for the variable in each equation.

a. $n + 14 = 16$ **b.** $12 - p = 14$ **c.** $x - 5 = 9$ **d.** $12 - t = 4$
e. $2 - e = 7$ **f.** $w + 2 = 6$ **g.** $6 + w = 10$ **h.** $9 + t = 11$

9. When 13 is subtracted from a number, the difference is 24. What is the number?

10. The sum of two numbers is 55. One of the numbers is 27. What is the other number?

11. Mary's age in years minus 8 is 29. How old is Mary. Hint: Let x = Mary's age in years.

Answers to Selected Questions

   3a. 14   **4a.** -12

Solving Equations by Dividing

To solve for the variable in an equation where the variable forms a multiplication equation, use the "**division property of equality**" to obtain the solution.

We can simply state **the division property of equality** as:

When the same non-zero number is used to divide both sides of an equation, the resulting equation still has equal values on both sides of the equation.

Division Property of Equality

Divide both sides of the equation by the same non-zero number.	Algebra
Dividing both sides of the equation $5 \times 4 = 20$ by the same non-zero number of 2 as shown: $$\frac{5 \times 4}{2} = \frac{20}{2}$$ $$10 = 10$$ Note that the resulting value of both sides of the equation after dividing both sides of the equation by 2 is the same which is 10	$w = p$ $$\frac{w}{x} = \frac{p}{x}$$ x is a non-zero number.

Example 8
Solve and check your answer.
a. 5n = 25 **b**. 21 = 3x
Solution
a. The basic method to solve for n is to isolate n.
  5n = 25

$$\frac{5n}{5} = \frac{25}{5}$$ Divide both sides of the equation by 5 in order to isolate n.

$$\frac{\overset{n}{\cancel{5}n}}{\underset{1}{\cancel{5}}} = \frac{\overset{5}{\cancel{25}}}{\underset{1}{\cancel{5}}}$$

  n = 5.

Check Your Answer
5n = 25
5 · 5 = 25   Substitute 5 for n in the original equation.
  25 = 25   Since the left side of the equation is equal to the right side
          of the equation, the answer is correct

b. The basic method to solve for x is to isolate x.
  21 = 3x

$$\frac{21}{3} = \frac{3x}{3}$$ Divide both sides of the equation by 3 in order to isolate x.

$$\frac{\overset{7}{\cancel{21}}}{\underset{1}{\cancel{3}}} = \frac{\overset{x}{\cancel{3x}}}{\underset{1}{\cancel{3}}}$$

  7 = x

Check Your Answer
21 = 3x
21 = 3 · 7   Substitute 7 for x in the original equation.
21 = 21   Since the left side of the equation is equal to the right side
          of the equation, the answer is correct.

176

Solving Equations by Multiplication

To solve for the variable in an equation where the variable forms a division equation, use the "**multiplication property of equation**," to obtain the solution.

We can simply state the **multiplication property of equality** as:

when the same number is used to multiply both sides of an equation, the resulting equation still has equal values on both sides of the equation.

Multiplication Property of Equality

Multiplying both sides of the equation by the same number.	Algebra
Multipying both sides of the equation $4 \times 3 = 12$ by the same number 2 as shown: $4 \times 3 = 12$ $4 \times 3 \times 2 = 12 \times 2$ $12 \times 2 = 12 \times 2$ $24 = 24$ Note that the resulting value of both sides of the equation after multiplying both sides of the equation by 2 is the same, which is 24	$w = p$ $wx = px$

Example 9

Solve for x and check your answer.

a. $\dfrac{x}{4} = 7$ **b.** $\dfrac{5}{x} = \dfrac{1}{2}$

Solution

a. The basic method for solving for x is to isolate x.

$$\frac{x}{4} = 7$$

$$\frac{x}{4} \times 4 = 7 \times 4 \qquad \text{Multiply both sides of the equation by 4 in order to isolate x.}$$

The 4 on the left side cancels out as shown below.

$$\frac{x}{\underset{1}{\cancel{4}}} \times \overset{1}{\cancel{4}} = 28$$

$$x = 28$$

177

Check Your Answer

$$\frac{x}{4} = 7$$

$$\frac{28}{4} = 7 \qquad \text{Substitute 28 for x in the original equation}$$

$$\frac{\overset{7}{\cancel{28}}}{\underset{1}{4}} = 7 \qquad \text{Divide by 4.}$$

$$7 = 7 \qquad \text{Since the left side of the equation is equal to the right side of the equation, the answer is correct.}$$

b. The basic method for solving for x is to isolate the x.

$$\frac{5}{x} = \frac{1}{2}$$

$$\frac{5}{x} \cdot x = \frac{1}{2} \cdot x \qquad \text{Multiply both sides of the equation by x in order to eliminate the x on the left side of the equation as a denominator when the x cancels out on the left side of the equation as shown:}$$

$$\frac{5}{\underset{1}{\cancel{x}}} \cdot \cancel{x} = \frac{1}{2} \cdot x$$

$$5 = \frac{x}{2}$$

$$5 \cdot 2 = \frac{x}{2} \cdot 2 \qquad \text{Multiply both sides of the equation by 2 in order to isolate x when the 2 cancels out on the right side of the equation as shown:}$$

$$5 \cdot 2 = \frac{x}{\underset{1}{\cancel{2}}} \cdot \overset{1}{\cancel{2}}$$

$$10 = x$$

Check Your Answer

$$\frac{5}{x} = \frac{1}{2}$$

$$\frac{5}{10} = \frac{1}{2}$$ Substitute 10 for x in the original equation.

$$\frac{\overset{1}{\cancel{5}}}{\underset{2}{\cancel{10}}} = \frac{1}{2}$$

$$\frac{1}{2} = \frac{1}{2}$$ Since the left side of the equation is equal to the right side of the equation, the answer is correct.

Applications
Hint: Review the chapter on "Algebraic Expressions."

Example 10
A number divided by 4 equals 8. What is the number? Hint: See Example **9a**.
Solution

Let the number be x. The number divided by 4 equals 8, therefore, $\frac{x}{4} = 8$.

The basic method for obtaining x **is to isolate the x**.

$$\frac{x}{4} \cdot 4 = 8 \cdot 4$$ Multiply both sides of the equation by 4 in order to isolate the x when the 4 cancels out on the left side of the equation as shown:

$$\frac{x}{\underset{1}{\cancel{4}}} \cdot \overset{1}{\cancel{4}} = 8 \cdot 4$$

$$x = 32$$

Example 11
a. John scored 3 times as many points as Nick. If John scored 24 points, how many points did Nick score? Hint: See Example 8.
b. A CD cost 3 times as much as an LP. If the CD cost $18.00, how much did the LP cost? Hint: See Example 8.
Solution
a. **Step 1**: Set up the equation.

Let the number of the points scored by Nick = x.
John scored 3 times as many points as Nick and John scored 24 points.
Therefore:

$$3x = 24$$

Step 2: Solve the equation. The basic method for solving for x is to isolate the x.

$$\frac{3x}{3} = \frac{24}{3}$$ Divide both sides of the equation by 3 in order to isolate the x.

$$\frac{\overset{x}{\cancel{3x}}}{\underset{1}{\cancel{3}}} = \frac{\overset{8}{\cancel{24}}}{\underset{1}{\cancel{3}}}$$

$$x = 8 \text{ points.}$$

b. Step 1: Set up the equation. Hint: Review the chapter on the "Algebraic Expressions."
Let the cost of the LP = x.
A CD cost 3 times as much as an LP and the CD cost $18.00, therefore:
$$18 = 3x$$

Step 2: Solve the equation.
The basic method for solving for x is to isolate the x by dividing both sides of the equation by 3 as shown:
$$18 = 3x$$

$$\frac{18}{3} = \frac{3x}{3}$$ Divide both sides of the equation by 3 in order to isolate the x.

$$\frac{\overset{6}{\cancel{18}}}{\underset{1}{\cancel{3}}} = \frac{\overset{x}{\cancel{3x}}}{\underset{1}{\cancel{3}}}$$

$$6 = x$$
$$x = \$6.00$$

Exercises

1. Solve and check your answer. Hint : See Example 8.

   a. $3x = 15$ **b.** $12 = 4x$ **c.** $36 = 9y$
   d. $4p = 28$ **e.** $3y = 27$ **f.** $5w = 45$

2. Solve and check your answer. Hint : See Example 9.

a. $\dfrac{x}{3} = 10$ **b.** $\dfrac{y}{5} = 2$ **c.** $\dfrac{p}{4} = 3$ **d.** $\dfrac{w}{5} = 6$

e. $\dfrac{3}{x} = \dfrac{1}{3}$ **f.** $\dfrac{2}{y} = \dfrac{1}{5}$ **g.** $\dfrac{1}{4} = \dfrac{3}{w}$ **h.** $\dfrac{p}{3} = 6$

3. A number divided by 3 equals 21.
   What is the number? Hint: See Example 10.
4. Elizabeth has 3 times as many CD's as Nancy.
   If Elizabeth has 9 CD's how many CD's does Nancy have? Hint: See Example 11.
5. A number divided by 5 equals 9. What is the number? Hint: See Example 10.

Challenge Questions
6. Solve for the variable and check your answer.

   a. $6x = 42$ **b.** $\dfrac{p}{5} = 3$ **c.** $64 = 4x$ **d.** $\dfrac{4}{p} = \dfrac{1}{3}$

7. A number divided by 4 equals 6. What is the number?
8. Samuel made 4 times as much money this week for baby-sitting as George.
   If Samuel made $36.00, how much did George make?

Solving Two Step Equations
Example 12
Solve $2x + 1 = 9$.
Solution
Step 1: Isolate 2x by subtracting 1 from both sides of the equation.

   $2x + 1 = 9$.

   $2x + 1 - 1 = 9 - 1$ Subtract 1 from both sides of the equation in order to isolate the term with x in it which is 2x.

   $2x = 8$

Step 2: Isolate x by dividing both sides of the equation by 2.

   $\dfrac{2x}{2} = \dfrac{8}{2}$ Divide both sides of the equation by 2 in order to isolate the x.

   $\dfrac{\overset{x}{\cancel{2x}}}{\underset{1}{\cancel{2}}} = \dfrac{\overset{4}{\cancel{8}}}{\underset{1}{\cancel{2}}}$

   $x = 4$

Example 13

Solve: **a.** $3y - 5 = -20$ **b.** $\dfrac{w}{8} + 6 = 2$ **c.** $12 = \dfrac{n}{3} - 4 \cdot 2$ **d.** $28 = 10n - 12$

181

Solution

a. $3y - 5 = -20$

Step 1: Isolate $3y$.

$3y - 5 + 5 = -20 + 5$ Add 5 to both sides of the equation in order to isolate the term with y which is $3y$.

$3y + 0 = -15$ $-5 + 5 = 0$ and $-20 + 5 = -15$.

$= -15$

Step 2: Isolate y

$3y = -15$

$$\frac{3y}{3} = -\frac{15}{3}$$ Divide both sides of the equation by 3 in order to isolate the y.

$$\frac{\overset{y}{\cancel{3y}}}{\cancel{3}_1} = -\frac{\overset{5}{\cancel{15}}}{\cancel{3}_1}$$

$y = -5$

b. $\frac{w}{8} + 6 = 2$

Step 1: Isolate $\frac{w}{8}$.

$\frac{w}{8} + 6 - 6 = 2 - 6$ Subtract 6 from both sides of the equation in order to isolate the term with w which is $\frac{w}{8}$.

$6 - 6 = 0$ and $2 - 6 = -4$

$\frac{w}{8} + 0 = -4$

$\frac{w}{8} = -4$

Step 2: Isolate w.

$\frac{w}{8} \times 8 = -4 \times 8$ Multiply both sides of the equation by 8 in order to eliminate the 8 as a denominator, and then isolate w.

$\frac{w}{\cancel{8}} \times \overset{1}{\cancel{8}} = -4 \times 8$ Divide by 8.

$$w = -32$$

c. $12 = \dfrac{n}{3} - 4 \cdot 2$

Step 1: Isolate $\dfrac{n}{3}$.

$$12 + 4 \cdot 2 = \dfrac{n}{3} - 4 \cdot 2 + 4 \cdot 2$$
Add $4 \cdot 2$ to both sides of the equation in order to isolate the term with n which is $\dfrac{n}{3}$. $4 \cdot 2 = 8$ and $-4 \cdot 2 + 4 \cdot 2 = 0$ or $-8 + 8 = 0$.

$$12 + 8 = \dfrac{n}{3} + 0$$

$$20 = \dfrac{n}{3}$$

Step 2: Isolate n.

$$20 \times 3 = \dfrac{n}{3} \times 3$$
Multiply both sides of the equation by 3 in order to eliminate the 3 as a denominator, and then isolate n.

$$20 \times 3 = \dfrac{n}{\overset{1}{\cancel{3}}} \times \overset{1}{\cancel{3}}$$

$$60 = n$$

d. $28 = 10n - 12$

Step 1: Isolate 10n.

$$28 + 12 = 10n - 12 + 12$$
Add 12 to both sides of the equation in order to isolate the term with n which is 10n. $28 + 12 = 40$ and $-12 + 12 = 0$.

$$40 = 10n$$

Step 2: Isolate n.

$$\dfrac{40}{10} = \dfrac{10n}{10}$$
Divide both sides of the equation by 10 in order to isolate n.

$$\dfrac{\overset{4}{\cancel{40}}}{\underset{1}{\cancel{10}}} = \dfrac{\overset{n}{\cancel{10n}}}{\underset{1}{\cancel{10}}}$$

$$4 = n$$

REAL WORLD APPLICATIONS - WORD PROBLEMS
Applications and Solving Two-Step Equations

Hint: Review the chapter on "Algebraic Expression."

Example 14

Gertrude wants to buy a DVD for $45.00. She already has $5.00. If she earns $4.00 an hour for baby-sitting, how many hours must she work to earn the money she needs?

Solution

Step 1: Let n be the number of hours that Gertrude must work.

Step 2: Write an equation based on the information.

She earns $4.00 an hour for baby-sitting and from Step 1, she must work for n hours, and therefore, the total money that she makes baby-sitting is:

4n dollars.

But she already has $5.00, therefore, the total money that she needs is 4n + 5 dollars. The total money that she needs which is 4n + 5 dollars must be equal to the cost of the DVD which is $45.00. Therefore:

$$4n + 5 = 45$$

Step 3: Solve the equation by isolating the n.

(Note that once the equation is set up, we can then use the two-step equation solving method such as in Example 12 and Example 13 to find n.)

$$4n + 5 = 45$$

$4n + 5 - 5 = 45 - 5$ Subtract 5 from both sides of the equation in order to isolate the term with n, which is 4n.

$4n = 40$ +5 - 5 = 0 and 45 - 5 = 40.

$$\frac{4n}{4} = \frac{40}{4}$$ Divide both sides of the equation by 4 in order to isolate n.

$$\frac{\overset{1}{\cancel{4}}n}{\underset{1}{\cancel{4}}} = \frac{\overset{10}{\cancel{40}}}{\underset{1}{\cancel{4}}}$$

$$n = 10 \text{ hours.}$$

Example 15

If a number is divided by 5 and then 3 is subtracted, the result is 2. What is the number?

Solution

Step 1: Let x be the number

Step 2: Write an equation based on the information in the question.

The number is divided by 5 and from step 1, the number is x, and therefore,

the number divided by $5 = \dfrac{x}{5}$.

If 3 is subtracted from the number divided by 5, the result is 2, and therefore,

$\dfrac{x}{5} - 3 = 2$

Step 3: Solve the equation by isolating the x.

(**Note** that once the equation is set up, we can then use the two-step equation solving method such as in Example 12 and Example 13 to find x.)

$$\dfrac{x}{5} - 3 = 2$$

$$\dfrac{x}{5} - 3 + 3 = 2 + 3 \qquad \text{Add 3 to both sides of the equation in order to isolate}$$

$$\text{the term in x which is } \dfrac{x}{5}.$$

$$\dfrac{x}{5} = 5 \qquad \text{-3 + 3 = 0 and 2 + 3 = 5.}$$

$$\dfrac{x}{5} \times 5 = 5 \times 5 \qquad \text{Multiply both sides of the equation by 5 in order to}$$

$$\text{isolate x.}$$

$$x = 25$$

Example 16

If you divide a number by 4 and 5 is added to the result, you get 11. What is the number?

Solution

Step 1: Let p be the number.

Step 2: Write an equation based on the information in the question. The number is divided by 4 and from Step 1, the number is p, and therefore, the number

divided by $4 = \dfrac{p}{4}$.

If 5 is added to the number divided by 4, the result is 11, and therefore,

$\dfrac{p}{4} + 5 = 11$

Step 3: Solve the equation by isolating the p.

(**Note** that once the equation is set up, we can then use the two-step equation solving method such as in Example 12 and Example 13 to find p.)

$$\frac{p}{4} + 5 = 11$$

$$\frac{p}{4} + 5 - 5 = 11 - 5$$ Subtract 5 from both sides of the equation in

order to isolate the term in p which is $\frac{p}{4}$.

$$\frac{p}{4} = 6$$ +5 - 5 = 0 and 11 - 5 = 6.

$$\frac{p}{4} \times 4 = 6 \times 4$$ Multiply both sides of the equation by 4 in order to

isolate p.

$$\frac{p}{\overset{\displaystyle 4}{\underset{\displaystyle 1}{4}}} \times \overset{1}{4} = 6 \times 4$$

$$p = 24$$

Example 17
Four more than the product of 8 and a number is 36. What is the number?

Solution

Step 1: Let the number be m.

Step 2: Write an equation based on the information in the question.

The product of 8 and the number is 8m because, from Step 1, the number is m. Therefore, 4 more than the product of 8 and the number is 8m + 4. Then if 4 more than the product of 8 and the number is 36, this statement can be written as:

8m + 4 = 36

Step 3: Solve the equation by isolating the m.

(**Note** that once the equation is set up, we can then use the two-step equation solving method such as in Example 12 and Example 13 to find m.)

8m + 4 = 36

8m + 4 - 4 = 36 - 4   Subtract 4 from both sides of the equation in
order to isolate the term with m, which is 8m.

8m = 32   +4 - 4 = 0 and 36 - 4 = 32

$$\frac{8m}{8} = \frac{32}{8}$$ Divide both sides of the equation by 8 in order to

isolate m.

$$\frac{8m}{8} = \frac{32}{8}$$

$$\frac{m}{1} \quad \frac{4}{1}$$

$$m = 4$$

Example 18

Five less than the product of 6 and a number is 31. What is the number?

Solution

Step 1: Let the number be x.

Step 2: Write an equation based on the information in the question.

The product of 6 and the number will be 6 · x or 6x because, from Step 1, the number is x. Therefore, 5 less than the product of 6 and the number will be 6x - 5. Then, if five less than the product of 6 and the number is 31, the statement will be:

$$6x - 5 = 31$$

Step 3: Solve the equation by isolating the x.

(**Note** that once the equation is set up, we can then use the two-step equation solving method such as in Example 12 and Example 13 to find x.)

$$6x - 5 = 31$$

$$6x - 5 + 5 = 31 + 5 \qquad \text{Add 5 to both sides of the equation in order to isolate the term in x which is 6x.}$$

$$6x = 36 \qquad -5 + 5 = 0 \text{ and } 31 + 5 = 36$$

$$\frac{6x}{6} = \frac{36}{6} \qquad \text{Divide both sides of the equation by 6 in order to isolate x.}$$

$$\frac{x}{1} \quad \frac{6}{1}$$
$$\frac{6x}{6} = \frac{36}{6}$$
$$\frac{}{1} \quad \frac{}{1}$$

$$x = 6$$

Example 19

John earned $30.00 washing cars. He earned $6.00 less than 3 times what Mary earned. How much did Mary earn?

Solution

Step 1: Let k be the money that Mary earned.

Step 2: Write an equation based on the information in the question.

3 times what Mary earned = 3k because from Step 1, k is the money that Mary earned. The expression $6.00 less than 3 times what Mary earned can be stated as: 3k - 6.

$30.00 is $4.00 less than 3 times what Mary earned and this statement can be written as: 3k - 6 = 30

Step 3: Solve the equation by isolating the k.

$$3k - 6 = 30$$

$$3k - 6 + 6 = 30 + 6 \qquad \text{Add 6 to both sides of the equation in order to isolate the term in k which is 3k.}$$

$$3k = 36 \qquad -6 + 6 = 0 \text{ and } 30 + 6 = 36.$$

$$\frac{3k}{3} = \frac{36}{3} \qquad \text{Divide both sides of the equation by 3 in order to isolate the k.}$$

$$\frac{\overset{1}{\cancel{3}}k}{\underset{1}{\cancel{3}}} = \frac{\overset{12}{\cancel{36}}}{\underset{1}{\cancel{3}}}$$

$$k = \$12$$

Exercises

1. Solve for x, y, w, or p in each equation.
   Hint: See Example 12.

   a. $4x + 3 = 15$ **b.** $2y + 4 = 12$ **c.** $5 + 3p = 20$
   d. $2p + 6 = 18$ **e.** $4w + 4 = 24$ **f.** $5w + 6 = 26$

2. Solve for x, y, w, or p in each equation.
   Hint: See Examples **13a** and **13d**.

   a. $4x - 3 = 9$ **b.** $3p - 6 = 24$ **c.** $5y - 3 = 12$
   d. $6p - 5 = 19$ **e.** $4w - 4 = 16$ **f.** $-4 + 3y = 11$
   g. $-3 + 3w = 12$ **h.** $-5 + 4x = 15$ **j.** $3p - 3 = 18$

3. Solve for x or w. Hint: See Examples **13b** and **13c**.

   a. $24 = \frac{x}{3} + 4.1$ **b.** $\frac{w}{5} - 2 = 7$ **c.** $13 = \frac{w}{2} - 7$ **d.** $8 = \frac{x}{3} + 6.3$

4. Solve for w or p. Hint: See Example **13d**.

   a. $12 = 3w - 3$ **b.** $9 = 4p - 1$ **c.** $7 = 5p - 8$ **d.** $6 = 3w - 3$

5. Mary wants to buy a camera for $64. She already has $14. If she earns $5 an hour for baby-sitting, how many hours must she work to earn the money she needs?
   Hint: See Example 14.

6. If a number is divided by 4 and then 5 is subtracted the result is 4. What is the

number? Hint: See Example 15.

7. If you divide a number by 3 and add 6 to the result, you get 16. What is the number? Hint: See Example 16.

8. Seven more than the product of 6 and a number is 31. What is the number? Hint: See Example 17.

9. Three less than the product of 5 and a number is 22. What is the number? Hint: See Example 18

10. Judith earned $24 baby-sitting. She earned $4 less than twice what Mary earned. How much did Mary earned? Hint: See Example 19.

Challenge Questions

11. Solve for x, y, w, or p in each equation.

   a. $3w - 7 = 23$

   b. $4x + 5 = 41$

   c. $6x - 2 = 22$

   d. $-4 + 4p = 28$

   e. $6 + 7p = 27$

   f. $4y + 3 = 27$

   g. $9 = \dfrac{w}{4} + 8$

   h. $\dfrac{y}{4} - 2.4 = 3$

   j. $8 = 4p - 8$

12. Five less than the product of 8 and a number is 27. What is the number?

13. Nine more than the product of 4 and a number is 19. What is the number?

14. If you divide a number by 4 and add 11 to the result, you get 15. What is the number?

15. Nick earned $36 baby-sitting. He earned $18 less than three times what John earned. How much did John earned?

16. George wants to buy a copy of the "Mathmasters series" book for $37. He already has $17. If he earns $6 an hour baby-sitting, how many hours does he have to work to earn the money he needs?

Answers to Selected Questions

2f. $-4 + 3y = 11$

$-4 + 4 + 3y = 11 + 4$ Add 4 to both sides of the equation to isolate 3y.

$3y = 15$

$\dfrac{3y}{3} = \dfrac{15}{3}$ Divide both sides of the equation by 3 in order to isolate y.

$y = 5$

MULTI-STEP EQUATION SOLVING

Equations With Like Terms or Variables.

Equations with like terms are equations with the same types of variables. For example, in the equation $6x + 2x = 24$, the terms $6x$ and $2x$ have the same type of variable in x, and therefore, we say that the equation $6x + 2x = 24$ has like terms in x. The general method for solving equations with like terms is to isolate all the like terms to one side of the equation add or subtract the like terms, then divide to isolate the variable.

Example 1

Solve for x, k, or w.

a. $6x + 2x = 24$ **b.** $5k - 2k = 9$ c. $3w + 12 = 5w$

Solution

a. $6x + 2x = 24$

Step 1: Add the like terms.

$$8x = 24 \qquad\qquad 6x + 2x = 8x$$

Step 2: Divide both sides of the equation by 8 to isolate x.

$$\frac{8x}{8} = \frac{24}{8}$$

$$\frac{\overset{x}{\cancel{8x}}}{\underset{1}{\cancel{8}}} = \frac{\overset{3}{\cancel{24}}}{\underset{1}{\cancel{8}}}$$

$$x = 3$$

b. $5k - 2k = 9$

Step 1: Subtract the like terms.

$$3k = 9 \qquad\qquad 5k - 2k = 3k.$$

Step 2: Divide both sides of the equation by 3 to isolate k.

$$\frac{3k}{3} = \frac{9}{3}$$

$$\frac{\overset{k}{\cancel{3k}}}{\underset{1}{\cancel{3}}} = \frac{\overset{3}{\cancel{9}}}{\underset{1}{\cancel{3}}}$$

$$k = 3$$

c. $3w + 12 = 5w$

Step 1: Isolate all the like terms to one side by subtracting 3w from both sides of the equation.

$$3w - 3w + 12 = 5w - 3w$$
$$12 = 2w \qquad\qquad 3w - 3w = 0 \text{ and } 5w - 3w = 2w.$$

Step 2: Divide both sides of the equation by 2 in order to isolate w.

$$\frac{12}{2} = \frac{2w}{2}$$

$$\frac{\overset{6}{\cancel{12}}}{\underset{1}{\cancel{2}}} = \frac{\overset{w}{\cancel{2w}}}{\underset{1}{\cancel{2}}}$$

$$6 = w$$

Example 2

Solve for x, k, or w.

a. $8x - 1 - 3x = 24$ **b**. $9w + 3 = 6w + 15$ **c**. $-8k - 5 = 4k - 29$

Solution

a. $8x - 1 - 3x = 24$

Step 1: Isolate the like terms to one side of the equation by adding 1 to both sides of the equation.

$$8x - 1 + 1 - 3x = 24 + 1$$
$$8x - 3x = 25 \qquad\qquad -1 + 1 = 0$$

Step 2: Combine the like terms by subtracting 3x from 8x.

$$5x = 25 \qquad\qquad 8x - 3x = 5x$$

Step 3: Isolate x by dividing both sides of the equation by 5.

$$\frac{5x}{5} = \frac{25}{5}$$

$$\frac{\overset{x}{\cancel{5x}}}{\underset{1}{\cancel{5}}} = \frac{\overset{5}{\cancel{25}}}{\underset{1}{\cancel{5}}}$$

$$x = 5$$

b. $9w + 3 = 6w + 15$

Step 1: Isolate the like terms to one side of the equation by subtracting 6w from both sides of the equation and also subtracting 3 from both sides of the equation.

$$9w + 3 - 3 - 6w = 6w - 6w + 15 - 3$$
$$9w - 6w = 12 \qquad\qquad 3 - 3 = 0, 6w - 6w = 0 \text{, and } 15 - 3 = 12.$$

Step 2: Combine the like terms by subtracting 6w from 9w.

$$3w = 12 \qquad\qquad 9w - 6w = 3w$$

Step 3: Isolate w by dividing both sides of the equation by 3.

$$\frac{3w}{3} = \frac{12}{3}$$

$$\frac{\overset{w}{\cancel{3w}}}{\underset{1}{\cancel{3}}} = \frac{\overset{4}{\cancel{12}}}{\underset{1}{\cancel{3}}}$$

$$w = 4$$

c. -8k - 5 = 4k - 29

Step 1: Isolate the like terms to one side of the equation by adding 8k to both sides of the equation and also by adding 29 to both sides of the equation.

$$-8k + 8k -5 + 29 = 4k + 8k -29 + 29$$

$$24 = 4k + 8k \qquad\qquad -8k + 8k = 0, -5 + 29 = 24$$
$$\text{and } -29 + 29 = 0.$$

Step 2: Combine the like terms by adding 4k to 8k.

$$24 = 12k$$

Step 3: Isolate k by dividing both sides of the equation by 12.

$$\frac{24}{12} = \frac{12k}{12}$$

$$\frac{\overset{2}{\cancel{24}}}{\underset{1}{\cancel{12}}} = \frac{\overset{k}{\cancel{12}}}{\underset{1}{\cancel{12}}}$$

$$2 = k \text{ or } k = 2$$

Example 3

Solve for x, y, or w.

a. $\dfrac{4}{5} = x + \dfrac{3}{4}$ **b.** $y - 1\dfrac{1}{2} = 2\dfrac{1}{3}$ **c.** $\dfrac{6}{7} = w - \dfrac{2}{3}$

Solution

a. $\dfrac{4}{5} = x + \dfrac{3}{4}$ **Type of equation: Addition type**

Step 1: Isolate x by subtracting $\dfrac{3}{4}$ from both sides of the equation.

$$\frac{4}{5} - \frac{3}{4} = x + \frac{3}{4} - \frac{3}{4}$$

$$\frac{4}{5} - \frac{3}{4} = x \qquad\qquad\qquad \frac{3}{4} - \frac{3}{4} = 0$$

Step 2: Subtract $\frac{3}{4}$ from $\frac{4}{5}$ to obtain the value of x.

$$\frac{4}{5} - \frac{3}{4} = x$$

$$\frac{16 - 15}{20} = x \qquad\qquad\qquad \text{LCD (least common denominator)} = 20.$$

$$\frac{1}{20} = x \qquad\qquad\qquad 16 - 15 = 1$$

b. $y - 1\frac{1}{2} = 2\frac{1}{3}$ **Type of equation: Subtraction type**

Step 1: Isolate y to one side of the equation by adding $1\frac{1}{2}$ to both sides of the equation.

$$y - 1\frac{1}{2} + 1\frac{1}{2} = 2\frac{1}{3} + 1\frac{1}{2}$$

$$y = 2\frac{1}{3} + 1\frac{1}{2} \qquad\qquad -1\frac{1}{2} + 1\frac{1}{2} = 0$$

Step 2: Add $2\frac{1}{3}$ to $1\frac{1}{2}$ to obtain the value of y.

$$y = 2\frac{1}{3} + 1\frac{1}{2}$$

$$2\frac{1}{3} \cdot \frac{2}{2} = \frac{2}{6} \; \checkmark \text{LCD} \qquad\qquad \text{Review Addition of Fractions.}$$

$$\underline{+ \; 1\frac{1}{2} \cdot \frac{3}{3} = \frac{3}{6} \; \checkmark \text{LCD}} \qquad\qquad \text{Review Addition of Fractions.}$$

$$3\frac{5}{6} \qquad\qquad\qquad 2 + 1 = 3 \text{ and } \frac{2}{6} + \frac{3}{6} = \frac{5}{6}$$

$$y = 3\frac{5}{6}$$

c. $\frac{6}{7} = w - \frac{2}{3}$ **Type of equation: Subtraction type**

Step 1: Isolate w to one side of the equation by adding $\frac{2}{3}$ to both sides of the equation.

$$\frac{6}{7} + \frac{2}{3} = w - \frac{2}{3} + \frac{2}{3}$$

$$\frac{6}{7} + \frac{2}{3} = w \qquad\qquad -\frac{2}{3} + \frac{2}{3} = 0$$

Step 2: Add $\frac{6}{7}$ to $\frac{2}{3}$ in order to obtain the value of w.

$$\frac{6}{7} + \frac{2}{3} = w$$

$$\frac{18 + 14}{21} = w \qquad\qquad\qquad LCD = 21$$

$$\frac{32}{21} = w \qquad\qquad\qquad \text{Review Addition of Fractions.}$$

$$1\frac{11}{21} = w$$

Example 4

Solve for m and w.

a. $2.4 = m - 0.17$ **b.** $w + 1.5 = 3.16$

Solution

a. $2.4 = m - 0.17$ **Type of equation: Subtraction type**

Step 1: Isolate m to one side of the equation by adding 0.17 to both sides of the equation.

$$2.4 + 0.17 = m - 0.17 + 0.17$$
$$2.4 + 0.17 = m \qquad\qquad\qquad -0.17 + 0.17 = 0$$

Step 2: Add 2.4 to + 0.17 in order to obtain the value of m.

$$\begin{array}{r} 2.4 \\ + \underline{0.17} \\ 2.57 \end{array}$$

Therefore, 2.57 = m or m = 2.57

b. $w + 1.5 = 3.16$ **Type of equation: Addition type**

Step 1: Isolate w to one side of the equation by subtracting 1.5 from both sides of the equation.

$$w + 1.5 - 1.5 = 3.16 - 1.5$$
$$w = 3.16 - 1.5 \qquad\qquad 1.5 - 1.5 = 0$$

Step 2: Subtracting 1.5 from 3.16 to obtain the value of w.

$$\begin{array}{r} 3.16 \\ - 1.5 \\ \hline 1.66 \end{array}$$

$$w = 1.66$$

Exercises

1. What is meant by like terms?

2. Solve for x, y, or k in each equation. Hint: See Example 1.

   a. $4x + 3x = 21$ **b.** $7y - 2y = 25$ **c.** $2k + 18 = 5k$

   d. $3y + 27 = 12y$ **e.** $6k + 2k = 32$ **f.** $5x - 2x = 30$

3. Solve for x, k, or w. Hint: See Example 2.

   a. $7x - 2 - 4x = 31$ **b.** $4w + 4 = 2w$ **c.** $-5k - 3 = 3k - 27$

   d. $6w + 12 = 3w$ **e.** $-6k - 4 = 2k - 20$ **f.** $3w + 4 - 2x = 23$

4. Solve for w, x, or y. Hint: See Example 3.

   a. $\dfrac{4}{5} = x + \dfrac{1}{2}$ **b.** $y - 1\dfrac{1}{3} = 2\dfrac{1}{4}$ **c.** $\dfrac{4}{5} - w \quad \dfrac{1}{2}$

   d. $w - 1\dfrac{1}{4} = 3\dfrac{1}{2}$ **e.** $\dfrac{3}{4} = y + \dfrac{1}{3}$ **f.** $\dfrac{2}{3} = x - \dfrac{2}{3}$

5. Solve for m or w. Hint: See Example 4.

   a. $3.8 = m - 0.24$ **b.** $w + 1.7 = 4.19$ **c.** $w + 1.5 = 3.21$

   d. $4.2 = w - 0.33$ **e.** $m + 2.8 = 3.18$ **f.** $5.3 = w - 0.12$

Challenge Questions

6. Solve for x, y, or w in each equation.

   a. $5y - 7 - 3y = 10$ **b.** $6.7 = x - 2.4$ **c.** $4w - 2w = 6$

   d. $-4y - 2 = 3y - 16$ **e.** $8.4 = x - 2.33$ **f.** $\dfrac{3}{4} = w + \dfrac{1}{2}$

   g. $x - 2\dfrac{1}{2} = 1\dfrac{3}{4}$ **h.** $3y + 16 = 7y$ **i.** $\dfrac{4}{5} = w - \dfrac{1}{3}$

Distributive Property with Equations.

The distributive property states that for any number a, b, and c:

a(b + c) = ab + ac

a(b - c) = ab - ac.

This distributive property is used in simplifying expressions.

Distributive Law with a Positive on the Outside

Example 1

Simplify each expression.

a. $2(x + 4)$ **b.** $2(x - 4)$ **c.** $3(2n + 6)$ **d.** $6(4 - 2g)$

Solution

a. $2(x + 4)$

     $2(x + 4) = 2 \cdot x + 2 \cdot 4$ Distributive property; **a(b + c) = ab + ac**.

           $= 2x + 8$

b. $2(x - 4)$

     $2(x - 4) = 2 \cdot x - 2 \cdot 4$ Distributive property; **a(b - c) = ab - ac**.

           $= 2x - 8$

c. $3(2n + 6)$

     $3(2n + 6) = 3 \cdot 2n + 3 \cdot 6$ Distributive property; **a(b + c) = ab + ac**

           $= 6n + 18$

d. $6(4 - 2g)$

     $6(4 - 2g) = 6 \cdot 4 - 6 \cdot 2g$ Distributive property; **a(b - c) = ab - ac**.

           $= 24 - 12g$.

Exercises

Simplify each expression. Hint: See Example 1.

1. $4(a + 2)$ **2.** $3(2x - 6)$ **3.** $6(y + 2)$ **4.** $8(2w - 5)$

5. $4(10 - 3a)$ **6.** $3(w - 1)$ **7.** $5(3g - 4)$ **8.** $3(a + 5)$

9. $7(2x + 4)$ **10.** $4(3y - 5)$ **11.** $6(2 - 46)$ **12.** $4(3 + 2x)$

13. $5(2a + 1)$ **14.** $6(a + b)$ **15.** $2(3c - 2)$ **16.** $3(2y - 8)$

Distributive Law with a Negative on the Outside

During multiplication or division (see Example 2):

         1. If all the symbols are positive the answer is positive.

         2. If the number of negative symbols is an even number, then the
            answer is positive.

3. If the number of negative symbols is an odd number, then the answer is negative.

Example 2
Simplify each expression.

   a. -2(3 + 4x)   **b.** -3(-4 + 2a)   **c.** -4(-2x - 6)

   d. -(-2a - 4)   **e.** -(2a + 6)   **f.** -(-3x + 5)

Solution

a. -2(3 + 4x)

$$-2(3 + 4x) = -2 \cdot 3 + (-2)(4x)$$
$$= -6 - 8x$$

Distribution property; -**a**(**b** + **c**) = -**ab** + (-**a**)**c**.
Note, odd number of negative symbols = -
(-)(+) = -, therefore, -2 · 3 = -6

↓ ↓
(-)(+) = -

Note, odd number of negative symbols = -
+(-)(+) = -, therefore, + (-2)(4x) = -8x

↓ ↓ ↓
+ (-)(+) = -

b. -3(-4 + 2a)

$$-3(-4 + 2a) = (-3)(-4) + (-3)(2a)$$
$$= 12 - 6a$$

Distributive property; -**a**(-**b** + **c**) = (-**a**)(-**b**) + (-**a**)(**c**).
Note, even number of negative symbols = +
(-)(-) = +, therefore, (-3)(-4) = +12 = 12.
Note, odd number of negative symbols = -
+(-)(+) = -, therefore, + (-3)(2a) = -6a.

↓ ↓ ↓
+ (-) (+) = -

c. -4(-2x - 6)

$$-4(-2x - 6) = (-4)(-2x) - (-4)(6)$$
$$= 8x + 24$$

Distributive property; -**a**(-**b** - **c**) = (-**a**)(-**b**) - (-**a**)(**c**).
Note, even number of negative symbols = +
(-)(-) = +, therefore, (-4)(-2x) = +8x = 8x.

↓ ↓
(-) (-) = +

Note, even number of negative symbols = +
(-)(-)(+) = +, therefore, -(-4)(6) = +24 = 24

↓ ↓ ↓
- (-) (+) = +

d. -(-2a - 4)

$$-(-2a - 4) = -2(-a) - (-4)$$
$$= 2a + 4$$

Distributive property; -(-**b** - **c**) = -(-**b**) - (-**c**)
Note, even number of negative symbols = +
(-)(-) = +, therefore, -2 (-a) = +2a = 2a.

↓ ↓
(-) (-) = +

Note, even number of negative symbols = +

$$(-)(-) = +, \text{ therefore, } - (-4) = +4 = 4.$$
$$\downarrow \downarrow$$
$$(-)(-) = +$$

e. -(2a + 6)

   -(2a + 6) = -(2a) + (-)(6)   Distributive property; -(**b** + **c**) = -**b** + (-)(**c**).

          = -2a - 6   Note, odd number of negative symbols = -

                                    Hint: See Example 2a.

f. -(-3x + 5)

   -(-3x + 5) = -(-3x) + (-)(5)   Distributive property

          = 3x - 5   See the preceding examples.

Exercises

1. Simply each expression. Hint: See Example **2a**.

   a. -2(4 + 5a)   **b**. -4(3 + 4x)   **c**. -3(4x + 2)

   d. -5(3y + 6)   **e**. -6(2 + 3w)   **f**. -3(2w + 4)

2. Simplify each expression. Hint: See Example **2b**.

   a. -2(-2 + 2w)   **b**. -3(-4 + 6a)   **c**. -4(-5 + 3w)

   d -5(-6 + 3a)   **e** -2(-3 + 2x)   **f**. -3(-3 + 4a)

3. Simplify each expression. Hint: See Example **2c**.

   a. -3(-3x - 2)   **b**. -2(-6x - 4)   **c**. -5(-7a - 6)

   d. -4(-4y - 3)   **e**. -6(-2w - 5)   **f**. -3(-5w - 5)

4. Simplify each expression. Hint: See Example **2d**.

   a. -3(3a - 3)   **b**. -(-4w - 5)   **c**. -(-6y - 7)

   d. -(-5x - 4)   **e**. -(-7a - 6)   **f**. -(4x - 5)

5. Simplify each expression. Hint: See Example **2e**.

   a. -(3x + 4)   **b**. -4(w + 7)   **c**. -(3a + 6)

   d -(-4y + 5)   **e**. -4(a + 6)   **f**. -(5w + 3)

6. Simplify each expression. Hint: See Example **2f**.

   a. -(-4a + 2)   **b**. -(-3y + 4)   **c**. -(-5w + 3)

   d. -(-3x + 4)   **e**. -(-6y + 2)   **f**. -(-2x + 8)

Challenge Questions

7. Simplify each expression.

   a. -(-3a - 4)   **b**. -2(-4 - 3y)   **c**. -4(6 + 7w)

   d. -(-3w + 6)   **e**. -3(-2w - 3)   **f**. -2(-5 + 3a)

Answers to Selected Questions

1a. -8 - 10a   **2a**. 4 - 4w   **3a**. 9x + 6

4a. -9 + 9a   **5a**. -3x - 4   **6a**. 4a - 2.

Distributive Law with Equations.

Example 1

Solve for y. $2(4 + y) = 12$

Solution

$2(4 + y) = 12$

Step 1: Simplify the equation.

$2 \cdot 4 + 2 \cdot y = 12$ Distributive property

$8 + 2y = 12$ $2 \cdot 4 = 8$

Step 2: Isolate 2y by subtracting 8 from both sides of the equation.

$8 - 8 + 2y = 12 - 8$

$2y = 4$ $8 - 8 = 0$ and $12 - 8 = 4$.

Step 3: Isolate y by dividing both sides of the equation by 2.

$$\frac{2y}{2} = \frac{4}{2}$$

$$\frac{\overset{y}{\cancel{2y}}}{\underset{1}{\cancel{2}}} = \frac{\overset{2}{\cancel{4}}}{\underset{1}{\cancel{2}}}$$

$$y = 2$$

Rules

Two rules are needed when dividing as shown:

Rule 1: If the symbols (+, -) of the numerator and the denominator are the same, the symbol of the answer is **positive**.

For example, $\frac{-a}{-a} = +1 = 1$ and $\frac{+a}{+a} = \frac{a}{a} = 1$.

Rule 2: If the symbols (+, -) of the numerator and the denominator are different, the symbol of the answer is **negative**.

For example, $\frac{-a}{a} = -1$ and $\frac{a}{-a} = -1$

Example 2

Solve for x. $-3(2x + 3) = -15$

Solution

$-3(2x + 3) = -15$

Step 1: Simplify the equation.

$-3 \cdot (2x) -3 \cdot (+3) = -15$ Distributive property.

$-6x - 9 = -15$ Note, odd number of negative symbols = -

Step 2: Isolate -6x to one side of the equation by adding 9 to both sides of the equation.

$$-6x - 9 + 9 = -15 + 9$$
$$-6x = -6 \qquad\qquad -9 + 9 = 0 \text{ and } -15 + 9 = -6.$$

Step 3: Isolate x to one side of the equation by dividing both sides of the equation by -6.

$$\frac{-6x}{-6} = \frac{-6}{-6}$$

$$\frac{\overset{x}{\cancel{-6x}}}{\cancel{-6}} = \frac{\overset{1}{\cancel{-6}}}{\cancel{-6}} \qquad\qquad \text{Hint: Rule 1 is used here.}$$
$$\quad 1 \qquad\quad 1$$

$$x = 1$$

Example 3

Solve for w. $\qquad -2(2w - 3) = 12$

Solution

$-2(2w - 3) = 12$

Step 1: Simplify the equation.

$\qquad -2 \cdot 2w - 2 \cdot (-3) = 12 \qquad$ Distributive property.

$\qquad -4w + 6 = 12 \qquad\qquad$ Note, odd number of negatives = -

$\qquad\qquad\qquad\qquad\qquad\qquad$ -(+) = -, therefore, $-2 \cdot (2w) = -4w$.

$\qquad\qquad\qquad\qquad\qquad\qquad\qquad \downarrow \qquad \downarrow$

$\qquad\qquad\qquad\qquad\qquad\qquad\qquad\quad - \quad (+) = -$

$\qquad\qquad\qquad\qquad\qquad\qquad$ Note, even number of negatives = +.

$\qquad\qquad\qquad\qquad\qquad\qquad$ -(-) = +, therefore, $-2 \cdot (-3) = +6 = 6$.

$\qquad\qquad\qquad\qquad\qquad\qquad\qquad\quad \downarrow \qquad \downarrow$

$\qquad\qquad\qquad\qquad\qquad\qquad\qquad\quad - \quad (-) = +.$

Step 2: Isolate -4w to one side of the equation by subtracting 6 from both sides of the equation.

$\qquad -4w + 6 - 6 = 12 - 6$

$\qquad\qquad -4w = 6 \qquad\qquad +6 - 6 = 0 \text{ and } 12 - 6 = 6.$

Step 3: Isolate w to one side of the equation by dividing both sides by -4.

$$\frac{-4w}{-4} = \frac{6}{-4}$$

$$\frac{\overset{w}{\cancel{-4w}}}{\cancel{-4}} = \frac{\overset{3}{\cancel{6}}}{\cancel{-4}} \qquad\qquad \text{Hint: Rule 1 is used for } \frac{-4w}{-4} \text{ and Rule 2 is}$$
$$\quad 1 \qquad -2 \qquad\qquad\qquad \text{used for } \frac{6}{-4}.$$

$$w = \frac{3}{-2}$$

$$w = -1\frac{1}{2}$$

Example 4

Solve for w.   -(2w - 4) = -14

Solution

-(2w - 4) = -14

Step 1: Simplify the equation.

-(2w - 4) = -14

(-)2w - (-)4 = -14   Distributive property.

-2w + 4 = -14   Note, odd number of negative numbers = -.

-(+) = -, therefore, -(2w) = -2w.

↓↓

-(+) = -

Note, even number of negatives = +

-(-) = +, therefore, -(-4) = +4 = 4

↓↓

-(-) = +

Step 2: Isolate -2w to one side of the equation by subtracting 4 from both sides of the equation.

-2w + 4 - 4 = -14 - 4

-2w – -18   +4 - 4 = 0 and -14 - 4 = -18.

Step 3: Isolate w to one side of the equation by dividing both sides of the equation by -2.

$$\frac{-2w}{-2} = \frac{18}{-2}$$

$$\frac{\overset{w}{-2w}}{-2} = \frac{\overset{-9}{18}}{-2}$$ Hint: Rule 1 is used for $\frac{-2w}{-2}$ to obtain +w = w and

$$\overset{1}{} \quad \overset{1}{}$$ Rule 2 is used for $\frac{18}{-2}$ to obtain -9.

w = -9

Example 5

Solve for b.   2b + 3(b - 4) = 4

201

Solution

$2b + 3(b - 4) = 4$

Step 1: Simplify the equation.

$2b + 3 \cdot 2b - 3 \cdot 4 = 4$ Distributive property

$2b + 6b - 12 = 4$

Step 2: Combine the like terms.

$8b - 12 = 4$ $2b + 6b = 8b$.

Step 3: Isolate 8b to one side of the equation by adding 12 to both sides of the equation.

$8b - 12 + 12 = 4 + 12$

$8b = 16$ $-12 + 12 = 0$ and $4 + 12 = 16$

Step 4: Isolate b to one side of the equation by dividing both sides of the equation by 8.

$$\frac{8b}{8} = \frac{16}{8}$$

$$\frac{\overset{1}{\cancel{8}}b}{\cancel{8}} = \frac{\overset{2}{\cancel{16}}}{\cancel{8}}$$

$$b = 2$$

Example 6

Solve for x. $9x + 5 - 2(3x + 6) = 14$

Solution

$9x + 5 - 2(3x + 6) = 14$

Step 1: Simplify the equation.

$9x + 5 - 2(3x) + (-2)(6) = 14$ Distributive property

$9x + 5 - 6x - 12 = 14$

Step 2: Combine the like terms.

$3x - 7 = 14$ $9x - 6x = 3x$ and $5 - 12 = -7$

Step 3: Isolate 3x to one side of the equation by adding 7 to both sides of the equation.

$3x - 7 + 7 = 14 + 7$

$3x = 21$ $-7 + 7 = 0$ and $14 + 7 = 21$

Step 4: Isolate x by dividing both sides of the equation by 3.

$$\frac{3x}{3} = \frac{21}{3}$$

$$\frac{x}{3x} \stackrel{7}{=} \frac{21}{3}$$
$$\frac{}{1} \quad \frac{}{1}$$

$$x = 7$$

Example 7
Solve for n. $2(3 - n) = 16 - 2(3 + 2n)$
Solution
$2(3 - n) = 16 - 2(3 + 2n)$
Step 1: Simplify the equation.
$2 \cdot 3 - 2 \cdot n = 16 - 2 \cdot 3 + (-2)(2n)$ Distributive property.
$6 - 2n = 16 - 6 - 4n$ $+ (-2)(2n) = -2(2n) = -2 \cdot 2n = -4n$
Step 2: Isolate the like terms to the left side of the equation by adding 4n to both
         sides of the equation and also subtracting 6 from both sides of the equation.
         $6 - 6 - 2n + 4n = 16 - 6 - 6 - 4n + 4n$
            $-2n + 4n = 4$ $6 - 6 = 0$, $16 - 6 - 6 = 4$, and $-4n + 4n = 0$
              $2n = 4$
Step 3: Isolate n to one side of the equation by dividing both sides of the equation
         by 2.
$$\frac{2n}{2} = \frac{4}{2}$$

$$\frac{\overset{n}{2n}}{\underset{n}{2}} = \frac{\overset{2}{4}}{\underset{1}{2}}$$

$$n = 2$$

Example 8
Solve for n. $8n - 3(4 - 2n) = 6(n + 1)$
Solution
$8n - 3(4 - 2n) = 6(n + 1)$
Step 1: Simplify the equation.
         $8n - 3 \cdot 4 - (-3)(2n) = 6 \cdot n + 6 \cdot 1$ Distributive property.
            $8n - 12 + 6n = 6n + 6$ Hint: See previous examples.
Step 2: Isolate the like terms to the left side of the equation by subtraction 6n
         from both sides of the equation and also by adding 12 to both sides of
         the equation.

$$8n - 12 + 12 + 6n - 6n = 6n - 6n + 6 + 12$$
$$8n = 6 + 12 \qquad -12 + 12 = 0 \text{ and } 6n - 6n = 0.$$
$$8n = 18$$

Step 3: Isolate n by dividing both sides of the equation by 8.

$$\frac{8n}{8} = \frac{18}{8}$$

$$\frac{\overset{n}{\cancel{8n}}}{\underset{1}{\cancel{8}}} = \frac{18}{8}$$

$$n = 2\frac{2}{8} = 2\frac{1}{4} \qquad \text{Review the reduction of fractions to the}$$

lowest terms.

Group Exercises

1. Using Rule 1, give the correct answer.

   a. $\dfrac{-6}{-2} =$ **b.** $\dfrac{-10}{-5} =$ **c.** $\dfrac{8}{4} =$ **d.** $\dfrac{-64}{-8} =$

2. Using Rule 2, give the correct answer:

   a. $\dfrac{-8}{-2} =$ **b.** $\dfrac{10}{-5} =$ **c.** $\dfrac{-8}{4} =$ **d.** $\dfrac{64}{-8}$

Exercises

1. Solve for x, y, or w. Hint: See Example 1.
   a. $3(2 + x) = 12$ **b.** $4(5 + w) = 28$ **c.** $2(3 + y) = 15$

2. Solve for x, y, or w. Hint: See Example 2.
   a. $-2(3x + 3) = -12$ **b.** $-4(3y + 2) = -32$ **c.** $-5(2w + 1) = -15$

3. Solve for x, y, or w. Hint: See Example 3.
   a. $-3(2w - 4) = 24$ **b.** $-4(3y - 2) = 32$ **c.** $-5(2x - 2) = 30$

4. Solve for x, y, or w. Hint: See Example 4.
   a. $-(3w - 3) = -15$ **b.** $-(4y - 5) = -29$ **c.** $-(5x - 6) = -31$

5. Solve for y. Hint: See Example 5.
   a. $3y + 3(3y - 4) = 12$ **b.** $2y + 4(2y - 5) = 10$ **c.** $5y + 3(4y - 2) = 11$

6. Solve for w, x, or y. Hint: See Example 6.
   a. $10w + 7 - 3(2w + 3) = 14$ **b.** $14x + 10 - 4(3x + 2) = 6$ **c.** $15y - 3(4y + 4) + 8 = 8$

7. Solve for w, x, or y. Hint: See Example 7.
   a. $3(4 - w) = 30 - 4(2 + w)$ **b.** $2(5 - 3x) = 28 - 3(3 + 3x)$ **c.** $4(2 - 2y) = -2(4 + 5y) + 28$

8. Solve for w, x, or y. Hint: See Example 8.
   a. $5w - 2(3 - 2w) = 4(w + 1)$ **b.** $2y - 2(8 - 3y) = 3(4 - 2y)$ **c.** $4x - 3(4 - 2x) = 2(2x + 2)$

Challenge Questions

9. Solve for w, x, or y.

a. $-(3x + 16) = 1$ b. $-2(2w - 3) = -10$ c. $6y + 2(2y - 3) = 14$

d. $2(3 - 2w) = 20 - 3(2 + 4w)$ e. $6w - 3(1 - w) = 3(w + 3)$

Answers to Selected Questions

1a. 2   **2a.** 1   **3a.** -2

REAL WORLD APPLICATIONS - WORD PROBLEMS

Multi-Step Equation Solving

Review the section on "**Algebraic Expressions**" first so that you may be able to write the equations correctly.

Group Review

Write the following phrases in mathematical terms.

1. 8 less than three times **a** is: $3a - 8$

2. x decreased by 4 times a number is: $x - 4n$ where n is the number.

3. y more than 3 times k is: $3k + y$

4. 4 less than 10 times a number is: $10n - 4$ where n is the number.

Example 1

If 4 is increased by twice a number, the result is 20.

What is the number?

Solution

Setup: Let the number be x, and therefore, twice the number = 2x. We can write 4 increased by 2x as $4 + 2x$.

The result of 4 increased by 2x is 20, therefore,

$$4 + 2x = 20$$

Step 1: Isolate 2x to one side of the equation by subtracting 4 from both sides of the equation.

$$4 - 4 + 2x = 20 - 4 \qquad\qquad 4 - 4 = 0 \text{ and } 20 - 4 = 16.$$
$$2x = 16$$

Step 2: Isolate x to one side of the equation by dividing both sides of the equation by 2.

$$\frac{2x}{2} = \frac{16}{2}$$

$$\frac{\overset{x}{\cancel{2x}}}{\underset{1}{\cancel{2}}} = \frac{\overset{8}{\cancel{16}}}{\underset{1}{\cancel{2}}}$$

$$x = 8$$

Example 2

3 times a number is subtracted from 8 more than 5 times the number the result is 48.

a. What is the number?

b. Check your answer.

Solution

a. Setup: Let the number be n. Therefore, 3 times the number is 3n. We can write 8 more than 5 times the number as $5n + 8$. We can write 3n subtracted from $5n + 8$ as $5n + 8 - 3n$, and therefore, we can write that the result of $5n + 8 - 3$ is 48 as:

$$5n + 8 - 3n = 48$$

Step 1: Isolate the like terms to one side of the equation by subtracting 8 from both sides of the equation.

$$5n + 8 - 8 - 3n = 48 - 8$$
$$5n - 3n = 40$$

Step 2: Combine like terms by subtracting 3n from 5n.

$$2n = 40$$

Step 3: Isolate n to one side of the equation by dividing both sides of the equation by 2.

$$\frac{2n}{2} = \frac{40}{2}$$

$$\frac{\overset{n}{\cancel{2n}}}{\underset{1}{\cancel{2}}} = \frac{\overset{20}{\cancel{40}}}{\underset{1}{\cancel{2}}}$$

$$n = 20$$

b. To check the answer $n = 20$, substitute 20 for n in the original equation $5n + 8 - 3n = 48$ to see if the result will be 48 or not. If the result is 48, then the answer $n = 20$ is correct, but if the result is not 48, then the answer $n = 20$ is not correct.

$5n + 8 - 3n = 48$ then becomes $5 \times 20 + 8 - 3 \times 20 = 48$

$$100 + 8 - 60 = 48$$

$$108 - 60 = 48 \quad \text{Review order of operations.}$$
$$48 = 48$$

The answer n = 20 is correct.

Example 3

If 4 times Mary's age is increased by 10 more than 3 times her age the result is 59.

a. How old is Mary?

b. Check your answer.

Solution

a. **Setup**: Let Mary's age be x, and therefore, 4 times Mary's age = 4x. We can write 10 more than 3 times her age as 3x + 10. The result of 4x increased by 3x + 10 is 59 can be written as:

$$4x + 3x + 10 = 59$$

Step 1: Isolate the like terms to one side of the equation by subtracting 10 from both sides of the equation.

$$4x + 3x + 10 - 10 = 59 - 10$$
$$4x + 3x = 49 \qquad 10 - 10 = 0 \text{ and } 59 - 10 = 49.$$

Step 2: Combine the like terms by adding 4x and 3x together.

$$7x = 49$$

Step 3: Isolate x to one side of the equation by dividing both sides of the equation by 70.

$$\frac{7x}{7} = \frac{49}{7}$$

$$\frac{\overset{x}{\cancel{7x}}}{\underset{1}{\cancel{7}}} = \frac{\overset{7}{\cancel{49}}}{\underset{1}{\cancel{7}}}$$

$$x = 7 \text{ years.}$$

b. To check the answer x = 7 years, substitute 7 for x in the original equation 4x + 3x + 10 = 59 to see if the result will be 59 or not. If the result is 59 then the answer x = 7 years is correct, but if the result is not 59, then the answer x = 7 years is not correct.

$$4x + 3x + 10 = 59 \text{ then becomes } 4 \times 7 + 3 \times 7 + 10 = 59$$
$$28 + 21 + 10 = 59$$
$$59 = 59$$

The answer x = 7 years is correct.

Exercises

1. If 6 is increased by twice a number, the result is 40. Find the number.
   Hint: See Example 1.

2. If 8 is increased by 4 times a number, the result is 24. Find the number.

Hint: See Example 1.

3. If 4 times a number is subtracted from 12 more than 6 times the number, the result is 36.

    a. Find the number.   **b**. Check your answer.

Hint: See Example 2.

4. If 3 times John's age is increased by 10 more than 5 times his age, the result is 74.

    a. How old is John?   **b**. Check your answer.

Hint: See Example 3.

Challenge Questions

5. If 2 is increased by twice a number, the result is 20. Find the number.

6. If 4 times Chase's age is increased by 8 more than twice his age, the result is 44.

a. How old is Chase?   **b**. Check your answer.

7. If twice Samuel's age is increased by 4 more than 4 times his age, the result is 48.

    a. How old is Samuel?   **b**. Check your answer.

CHAPTER 11

FACTORING OF QUADRATIC FUNCTIONS/EXPRESSIONS/EQUATIONS

How to Factor Quadratic Functions

Since $2 \times 3 = 6$, 2 and 3 are said to be the factors of 6. Similarly since $(x + 2)(x - 6) = x^2 - 4x - 12$, $(x + 2)$ and $(x - 6)$ are said to be the factors of $x^2 - 4x - 12$. It can be shown that $(x + 2)(x - 6) = x^2 - 4x - 12$ by multiplying each term in the first parenthesis by each term in the second parenthesis as shown:

$(x + 2)(x - 6) = x^2 + (x)(-6) + 2x + (2)(-6)$

$\qquad\qquad\qquad = x^2 - 6x + 2x - 12 \qquad\qquad (x)(-6) = -6x$ and $(2)(-6) = -12$

$\qquad\qquad\qquad = x^2 - 4x - 12 \qquad\qquad\qquad -6x + 2x = -4x$

An algebraic expression such as $x^2 - 4x - 12$ does not necessarily have factors just as in arithmetic a number such as 7 is said to be a prime number because it has factors of only one and itself (the factors of 7 are 1 and 7).

Example 1

Factor the expression $x^2 + 7x + 10$.

Solution

The goal of factoring is to fill in the parenthesis in the statement as shown:

208

$x^2 + 7x + 10 = (\quad)(\quad)$

The first term in the given expression $x^2 + 7x + 10$ is x^2 and this can be obtained only by putting x first in each parentheses as shown:

$x^2 + 7x + 10 = (x\quad)(x\quad)$

The next term to consider is the last term in the given expression which is 10. This number (10) is the product of the last terms in the two parentheses and the choices are 10 and 1, -10 and -1, 5 and 2 or -5 and -2. Therefore, the possibilities to be considered are:

    a. $(x + 10)(x + 1) = x^2 + 11x + 10$

    b. $(x - 10)(x - 1) = x^2 - 11x + 10$

    c. $(x + 5)(x + 2) = x^2 + 7x + 10$ (This gives the given expression).

    d. $(x - 5)(x - 2) = x^2 - 7x + 10$

Notice that in the equations a, b, c, and d, the coefficients of x on the right side of the equations is the sum of the last numbers in the two parentheses, for example, considering equation a:

$$11 = 10 + 1,$$

considering equation b:

$$-11 = -10 + (-1),$$

considering equation c:

$$7 = 5 + 2,$$

considering equation d:

$$-7 = -5 + (-2).$$

The combination that satisfies the given expression of $x^2 + 7x + 10$ is the equation **c**. Therefore, the factors of $x^2 + 7x + 10$ are $(x + 5)$ and $(x + 2)$ or we can state that $x^2 + 7x + 10 = (x + 5)(x + 2)$.

(Note that it does not matter which parentheses comes first because $(x + 2)(x + 5)$ is the same as $(x + 5)(x + 2)$.

Representation of the Factors of $x^2 + 7x + 10$ in a Diagram form.

The factors of the function $x^2 + 7x + 10$ is shown in a diagram form in Example 1 under the topic "How to Use Zeros to Find the Vertex of a Parabola" which is under the applications of the "Quadratic Functions" and it is summarized as shown:

The **three necessary conditions** for the factors of the function $x^2 + 7x + 10$ to be $(x + 5)$ and $(x + 2)$ are shown below with diagrams as shown:

    1. **The product of the first terms in each parenthesis, for example, x · x must be equal to the first term of the function which is x^2.**

    2. **The product of the last terms of each parenthesis which is 5 · 2 must be equal to the last term of the function which is 10.**

    3. **The product of the outside terms which is x · 2 added to the product of the inside terms which is 5 · x must be equal to the middle term of the function which is 7x.**

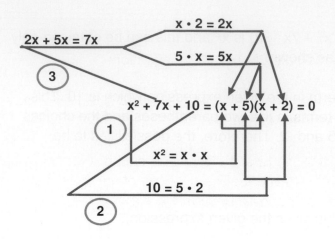

① gives the first term.

② gives the last term.

③ gives the middle term.

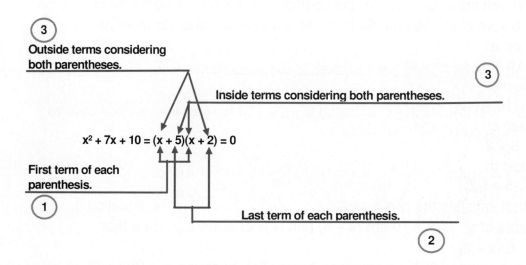

Example 2

Factor the expression $x^2 - 9x + 8$

Solution

The goal of factoring is to fill in the parentheses in the equation:

$x^2 - 9x + 8 = ($ $)($ $)$

As in Example 1, the first term in the expression $x^2 - 9x + 8$ is x^2 which can be obtained by putting x first in each parenthesis as shown:

$x^2 - 9x + 8 = (x$ $)(x$ $)$.

The last term is +8 which is the product of +4 and +2, -4 and -2, +8 and +1 or -8 and -1. Out of all of these pairs of numbers only -8 and -1 add up to -9 which is the coefficient for the middle term. Therefore, the factors of $x^2 - 9x + 8$ are (x - 8) and (x - 1) or we can state that:

$x^2 - 9x + 8 = (x - 8)(x - 1)$

Example 3

Factor the expression $x^2 - 4x - 12$
Solution
The goal of the factorization is to fill in the parentheses in the equation:
$x^2 - 4x - 12 = ($ $)($ $)$.
As in Example 1, the first term in the expression $x^2 - 4x - 12$ is x^2 and it can be obtained by putting x first in each of the parenthesis as shown:
$x^2 - 4x - 12 = (x$ $)(x$ $)$.
The last term in the expression $x^2 - 4x - 12$ is -12 and -12 is a product of -12 and +1, +12 and -1. -6 and +2, +6 and -2, -4 and +3 or +4 and -3. The only pair of numbers that give -4 as the coefficient for the middle term is -6 and +2 because -6 + 2 = -4.
Therefore, $x^2 - 4x - 12 = (x - 6)(x + 2)$

Example 4
Factor the expression $x^2 + 2x - 15$.
Solution
The goal of factoring is to fill in each parentheses in the statement:
$x^2 + 2x - 15 = ($ $)($ $)$.
As in Example 1, the first term in the expression $x^2 + 2x - 15$ is x^2 which can be obtained by putting x first in each parenthesis as follows:
$x^2 + 2x - 15 = (x$ $)(x$ $)$.
The last term in the expression $x^2 + 2x - 15$ is -15, and -15 is the product of -15 and +1, +15 and -1, -5 and +3 or +5 and -3. The only pair of numbers that give +2 as the coefficient for the middle term of the expression $x^2 + 2x - 15$ is +5 and -3 because +5 - 3 = + 2. Therefore, $x^2 + 2x - 15 = (x + 5)(x - 3)$.

Exercises
1. Factor each expression. Hint: See Example 1. Show your method.
   a. $x^2 + 4x + 3$ **b.** $a^2 + 13a + 36$ **c.** $m^2 + 5m + 6$ **d.** $x^2 + 7x + 10$
   e. $x^2 + 6x + 9$ **f.** $x^2 + 3x + 2$ **g.** $n^2 + 7n + 12$ **h.** $x^2 + 13x + 12$
2. Factor each expression. Hint: See Example 2. Show your method.
   a. $x^2 - 8x + 12$ **b.** $n^2 - 7n + 12$ **c.** $x^2 - 3x + 2$ **d.** $a^2 - 8a + 7$
   e. $n^2 - 8n + 15$ **f.** $x^2 - 6x + 5$ **g.** $x^2 - 14x + 49$ **h.** $a^2 - 10a + 21$
   i. $x^2 - 9x + 20$ **j.** $x^2 - 8x + 16$
3. Factor each expression. Hint: See Example 3. Show your method.
   a. $x^2 - 7x - 18$ **b.** $n^2 - 5n - 6$ **c.** $x^2 - 2x - 3$ **d.** $a^2 - 4a - 12$
   e. $n^2 - 5n - 14$ **f.** $x^2 - 3x - 10$
4. Factor each expression. Hint: See Example 4. Show your method.
   a. $m^2 + 3m - 18$ **b.** $x^2 + 8x - 20$ **c.** $x^2 + 5x - 6$ **d.** $x^2 + 11x - 12$
   e. $x^2 + 5x - 14$ **f.** $n^2 + 5n - 6$ **g.** $x^2 + 3x - 10$ **h.** $x^2 + 6x - 16$
   i. $x^2 + 8x - 48$

Challenge Questions.

5. Show why each expression does not have factors. Hint: Use the methods for finding the factors of an expression and if you cannot find the factors, it means that the expression does not have factors.

   a. $x^2 - 7x - 7$ **b.** $x^2 + x + 1$ **c.** $n^2 + n + 14$ **d.** $x^2 + 6x - 16$

   e. $x^2 + 8x + 9$ **f.** $x^2 + 3x - 2$

6. Find the factors of each expression.

   a. $x^2 - 2x - 8$ **b.** $n^2 + 6n + 8$ **c.** $k^2 - 6k + 8$ **d.** $x^2 + 2x - 8$

Applications of Factoring of Equations/Functions/Expressions

The application of factoring of function/expressions can be found under "Applications of Quadratic Functions" and "How to Use Zeros to Find the Vertex of a Parabola."

Answers to Selected Questions

1a. $(x + 1)(x + 3)$ **2a.** $(x - 2)(x - 6)$ **2b.** $(a + 4)(a + 9)$ **3a.** $(x + 2)(x - 9)$

3b. $(n + 1)(n - 6)$ **4a.** $(m - 3)(m + 6)$ **4b.** $(x - 2)(x + 10)$ **4f.** $(n - 1)(n + 6)$

More Trinomials

We have already discussed the simple factors of the quadratic expressions of the type $x^2 - 2x - 15 = (x - 5)(x + 3)$. There are more types of this expression where the coefficient of x^2 is not one. The following examples illustrate some of these types of the quadratic expressions. The factors of these types of quadratic expressions should always be found by inspection, and then the results should be checked by multiplication.

Example 1

Factor the expression $2x^2 + 7x - 15$.

Solution

The first term in the quadratic expression $2x^2 + 7x - 15$ is $2x^2$, which is the product of $2x$, and x. Therefore, we can write the quadratic expression $2x^2 + 7x - 15$ as shown:

   $2x^2 + 7x - 15 = (2x \,...)(x \,...)$

The last term of the quadratic expression $2x^2 + 7x - 15$ is -15, which is the product of -15 and 1, 15 and -1, -1 and 15, 1 and -15, -5 and 3, 5 and -3, -3 and 5 or 3 and -5. Therefore, the possible factors of the quadratic expression $2x^2 + 7x - 15$ are:

$(2x - 15)(x + 1)$	$(2x - 5)(x + 3)$
$(2x + 15)(x - 1)$	$(2x + 5)(x - 3)$
$(2x - 1)(x + 15)$	$(2x - 3)(x + 5)$
$(2x + 1)(x - 15)$	$(2x + 3)(x - 5)$

All the possible factors give $2x^2$ as the first term of the quadratic expression

$2x^2 + 7x - 15$ when the first number in the first parenthesis is multiplied by the first number in the second parenthesis. Also, all the possible factors give -15 as the last term when the last number in each first parenthesis is multiplied by the last number in each second parenthesis.

The only factor that gives +7x as the middle term when the product of the first number in the first parenthesis and the last number in the second parenthesis is added to the product of the last number in the first parenthesis and the first number in the second parenthesis is as shown:

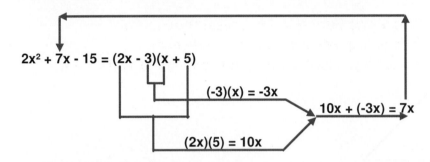

$$2x^2 + 7x - 15 = (2x - 3)(x + 5)$$

$$(-3)(x) = -3x$$

$$(2x)(5) = 10x$$

$$10x + (-3x) = 7x$$

Therefore, $2x^2 + 7x - 15 = (2x - 3)(x + 5)$.

With practice, it will be found unnecessary to write down all the possibilities of the factors before selecting the correct one.

Example 2

Factor the expression $2x^2 - 5x + 3$

Solution

The first term of the quadratic expression $2x^2 - 5x + 3$ is $2x^2$ which is the product of $2x$ and x. Therefore, we can write the quadratic expression as:

$$2x^2 - 5x + 3 = (2x \ldots)(x \ldots)$$

The last term of the quadratic expression $2x^2 - 5x + 3$ is +3 which is the product of 1 and 3, 3 and 1, -1 and -3, or -3 and -1.

Therefore, all the possible factors of the quadratic expression $2x^2 - 5x + 3$ are:

$(2x + 1)(x + 3)$ $(2x - 1)(x - 3)$

$(2x + 3)(x + 1)$ $(2x - 3)(x - 1)$

Two of the factors $(2x + 1)(x + 3)$ and $(2x + 3)(x + 1)$ need not to be written down and may be discarded at once, because they could not possibly produce a minus sign for the middle term of the given quadratic expression. Therefore, we will select the correct quadratic factor of $2x^2 - 5x + 3$ from the factors $(2x - 1)(x - 3)$ and $(2x - 3)(x - 1)$.

Both factors of $(2x - 1)(x - 3)$ and $(2x - 3)(x - 1)$ give $2x^2$ as the first term of the quadratic expression of $2x^2 - 5x + 3$ when the first number in the first parenthesis is multiplied by the first number in the second parenthesis and also both factors give + 3 as the last term when the last number in each first parenthesis is multiplied by the last number in each last parenthesis.

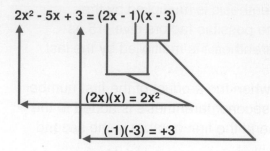

$2x^2 - 5x + 3 = (2x - 1)(x - 3)$

$(2x)(x) = 2x^2$

$(-1)(-3) = +3$

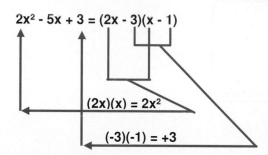

$2x^2 - 5x + 3 = (2x - 3)(x - 1)$

$(2x)(x) = 2x^2$

$(-3)(-1) = +3$

The only product of $(2x - 3)(x - 1)$ which are the factors $(2x - 3)$ and $(x - 1)$, gives $-5x$ as the middle term when the product of the first number in the first parenthesis and the last number in the second parenthesis is added to the product of the last number in the first parenthesis and the first number in the second parenthesis as follows:

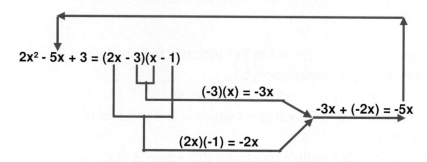

$2x^2 - 5x + 3 = (2x - 3)(x - 1)$

$(-3)(x) = -3x$

$-3x + (-2x) = -5x$

$(2x)(-1) = -2x$

Therefore, the factors of $2x^2 - 5x + 3 = (2x - 3)(x - 1)$.

Example 3
Factor the expression $6n^2 - 7n - 3$.
Solution
The first term of the quadratic expression is $6n^2$ which is the product of $6n$ and n, or $3n$ and $2n$. Therefore, we can write the quadratic expression as:

$$6n^2 - 7n - 3 = (6n...)(n...) \text{ or } (3n...)(2n...).$$

The last term of the quadratic expression $6n^2 - 7n - 3$ is -3 which is the product of -1 and 3, 1 and -3, -3 and 1, or 3 and -1.
Therefore, all the possible factors of the quadratic expression $6n^2 - 7n - 3$ are:

$$(6n - 1)(n + 3) \qquad (3n - 1)(2n + 3)$$

$$(6n + 1)(n - 3) \qquad\qquad (3n + 1)(2n - 3)$$
$$(6n - 3)(n + 1) \qquad\qquad (3n - 3)(2n + 1)$$
$$(6n + 3)(n - 1) \qquad\qquad (3n + 3)(2n - 1)$$

All the factors give $6n^2$ as the first term of the quadratic expression $6n^2 - 7n - 3$ when the first number of each parenthesis is multiplied by the first number in the second parenthesis. All the factors also give -3 as the last term of the quadratic expression $6n^2 - 7n - 3$ when the last number in the first parenthesis is multiplied by the last number of the second parenthesis. The only product, $(3n + 1)(2n - 3)$, which has factors $(3n + 1)$ and $(2n - 3)$, gives $-7n$ as the middle term when the product of the first number in the first parenthesis and the last number in the second parenthesis are added to the product of the last number in the first parenthesis and the first number in the second parenthesis as shown:

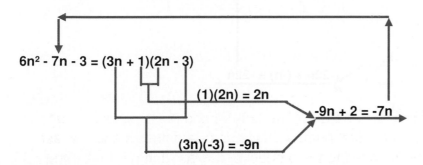

Therefore, the factors of $6n^2 - 7n - 3 = (3n + 1)(2n - 3)$.

Example 4

Factor the expression $7 - 22n + 3n^2$

Solution

The first term of the expression $7 - 22n + 3n^2$ is 7, which is the product of 7 and 1.
Therefore, we can write the expression $7 - 22n + 3n^2$ as:
$$7 - 22n + 3n^2 = (7...)(1...)$$
The last term of the expression $7 - 22n + 3n^2$ is $3n^2$ which is the product of $3n$ and n, with like signs as shown:
$$3n \text{ and } n, \ n \text{ and } 3n, \ -3n \text{ and } -n, \ \text{and } -n \text{ and } -3n.$$
Therefore, all the possible factors of the expression $7 - 22n + 3n^2$ are:
$$(7 + 3n)(1 + n) \qquad\qquad (7 - 3n)(1 - n)$$
$$(7 + n)(1 + 3n) \qquad\qquad (7 - n)(1 - 3n)$$
The factors $(7 + 3n)(1 + n)$ and $(7 + n)(1 + 3n)$ should be discarded as they could not possibly produce a minus sign for the middle term of the given expression.
Considering the remaining two factors which are $(7 - 3n)(1 - n)$ and $(7 - n)(1 - 3n)$ we can write:
$$(7 - 3n)(1 - n) = (7)(1) - (7)(n) - (3n)(1) - (3n)(-n)$$
$$= 7 - 7n - 3n + 3n^2$$
$$= 7 - 10n + 3n^2 \qquad\qquad\qquad -(3n)(-n) = +3n^2$$

215

and $(7 - n)(1 - 3n) = (7)(1) - (7)(3n) - (n)(1) - (n)(-3n)$ $(-n)(-3n) = -(n)(-3n)$
$(7 - n)(1 - 3n) = 7 - 21n - n + 3n^2$ $- (n)(-3n) = + 3n^2$
$= 7 - 22n + 3n^2$ $- 21n - n = -22$

Since the product of the factors $(7 - n)(1 - 3n)$ equal $7 - 22n + 3n^2$ which is the expression in the question, the required factors of $7 - 22n + 3n^2$ are $(7 - n)(1 - 3n)$. Or, we can state that $(7 - n)(1 - 3n)$ are the required factors of the expression $7 - 22n + 3n^2$ because the product of the first number in the first parenthesis and the last number in the second parenthesis added to the product of the last number in the first parenthesis and the first number in the second parenthesis equal $-22n$ which is the middle term of the expression $7 - 22n + 3n^2$ as shown:

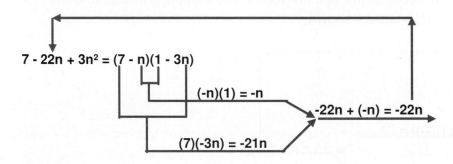

Example 5

Factor the expression $2x^2 + 23x + 45$

Solution

The first term of the quadratic expression $2x^2 + 23x + 45$ is $2x^2$ which is the product of $2x$ and x. Therefore, we can write the quadratic expression as:

$2x^2 + 23x + 45 = (2x...)(x...)$.

The last term of the quadratic expression $2x^2 + 23x + 45$ is $+45$ which is the product of:

1 and 45, -1 and -45, 45 and 1, -45 and -1,
9 and 5, -9 and -5, 5 and 9, -5 and -9,
3 and 15, -3 and -15, 15 and 3, or -15 and -3.

Therefore, all the possible factors of the quadratic expression $2x^2 + 23x + 45$ are:

$(2x + 1)(x + 45)$	$(2x + 9)(x + 5)$	$(2x + 3)(x + 15)$
$(2x - 1)(x - 45)$	$(2x - 9)(x - 5)$	$(2x - 3)(x - 15)$
$(2x + 45)(x + 1)$	$(2x + 5)(x + 9)$	$(2x + 15)(x + 3)$
$(2x - 45)(x - 1)$	$(2x - 5)(x - 9)$	$(2x - 15)(x - 3)$

Similar to Example 4, all the factors involving minus signs should be discarded at once because they could not possibly produce a positive sign for the middle term of the given expression, for example:

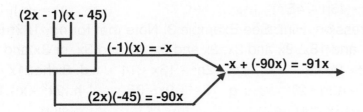

But -91x is not the same as the middle term of the expression which is +23x and more importantly, the middle term does not have a minus sign. Therefore, we have to discard $(2x-1)(x-45)$ as the required factor of the expression $2x^2 + 23x + 45$. Similarly, we have to discard all the possible factors of $2x^2 + 23x + 45$ which contain minus signs.

So, we can now consider factors with positive signs only as the possible factors of $2x^2 + 23x + 45$ which are:

$(2x + 1)(x + 45)$ $(2x + 9)(x + 5)$ $(2x + 3)(x + 15)$
$(2x + 45)(x + 1)$ $(2x + 5)(x + 9)$ $(2x + 15)(x + 3)$

Of all the factors with positive signs, only $(2x + 5)(x + 9)$ produce the middle term of $+23x$ of the expression $2x^2 + 23x + 45$ when the product of the first number in the first parenthesis and the last number in the second parenthesis is added to the product of the last number in the first parenthesis and the first number in the second parenthesis as shown:

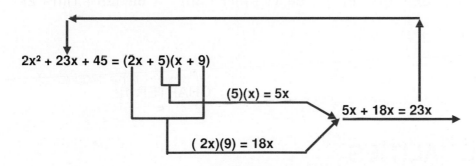

Therefore, $(2x + 5)(x + 9)$ is the correct factors of $2x^2 + 23x + 45$.

Exercises

1. Describe how you can find the middle term of a quadratic expression when you are given the factors of a quadratic expression. Hint: See the preceding explanation.
2. Factor each quadratic expression. Hint: See Example 1. Note that for **2f**, $15y^2$ is the product of 15y and y, y and 15y, 3y and 5y, or 5y and 3y.
   a. $3x^2 + x - 2$ **b.** $2n^2 + 5n - 3$ **c.** $3x^2 + 2x - 1$ **d.** $3n^2 + 7n - 6$
   e. $3n^2 + 8n - 35$ **f.** $15y^2 + 17y - 18$ **g.** $4x^2 + 12x - 7$ **h.** $3n^2 + 3n - 18$
3. Factor each quadratic expression. Hint: See Example 2. Note that for **3d**, $12x^2$ is the product of 12x and x, x and 12x, 6x and 2x, 2x and 6x, 3x and 4x, or 4x and 3x.
   a. $2x^2 - 5x + 2$ **b.** $2n^2 - 3n + 1$ **c.** $3y^2 - 11y + 6$ **d.** $12x^2 - 11x + 2$
   e. $8n^2 - 17n + 9$ **f.** $2p^2 - 15p + 27$ **g.** $4x^2 - 12y + 5$ **h.** $2y^2 - 10y + 12$

i. $4y^2 - 20y + 25$ **j.** $8n^2 - 46n + 45$

4. Factor each quadratic expression. Hint: See Example 3. Note that for **4g**, $18x^2$ is the product of 18x and x, x and 18x, 9x and 2x, 2x and 9x, 6x and 3x, or 3x and 6x.

    a. $2x^2 - 5x - 3$ **b.** $5y^2 - 9y - 2$ **c.** $12n^2 - 13x - 14$ **d.** $8x^2 - 21x - 9$

    e. $3x^2 - 14x - 24$ **f.** $5n^2 - 42n - 27$ **g.** $18x^2 - 9x - 35$ **h.** $2x^2 - x - 1$

    i. $3x^2 - 5x - 8$ **j.** $3x^2 - 13x - 30$

5. Factor each expression. Hint: See Example 4.

    a. $1 + 4n + 3n^2$ **b.** $35 + 30x - 5x^2$ **c.** $7 - 20y - 3y^2$ **d.** $5 - 8n - 4n^2$

6. Factor each expression. Hint: See Example 5.

    a. $2n^2 + 5n + 2$ **b.** $7x^2 + 22x + 3$ **c.** $2n^2 + 5n + 3$

Challenge Questions

7. Factor the expressions.

    a. $7n^2 + 10n + 3$ **b.** $3n^2 - 4n + 1$ **c.** $2y^2 - 5y + 3$ **d.** $1 + 3m + 2m^2$

    e. $2n^2 - 15n - 27$ **f.** $5 - 7x - 6x^2$ **g.** $10x^2 - 41x - 45$ **h.** $2y^2 - 7y + 5$

    i. $2x^2 - 15x + 25$ **j.** $8n^2 - 10n + 3$

Answers to Selected Questions.

2a. $(3x - 2)(x + 1)$ **2e.** $(3n - 7)(n + 5)$ **3a.** $(x - 2)(2x - 1)$ **3i.** $(2x - 5)(2x - 5)$

4a. $(x - 3)(2x + 1)$ **4e.** $(3x + 4)(x - 6)$ **5a.** $(1 + n)(1 + 3n)$ **6a.** $(2n + 1)(n + 2)$

CHAPTER 12

INEQUALITIES

The statement that uses > and < to show that two quantities are not equal is an **inequality**. The symbols for inequalities, their meanings, examples, and their solutions are shown in the table below:

Table 1

Symbols	Meaning	Examples	Solutions
<	is less than.	x < 10 means x is less than 10.	Every number less than 10 is a solution.
>	is greater than	x > -3 means x is greater than -3.	Every number greater than -3 is a solution.
≤	is less than or equal to.	x ≤ 6 means x is less than or equal to 6.	Every number less than 6 or equal to 6 is a solution.
≥	is greater than or equal to.	y ≥ -2 means y is greater or equal to -2.	Every number greater than -2 or equal to -2 is a solution.

218

Conclusions From Table 1

1. Notice that the information under the column "Solutions" shows that:
   a. An inequality may have **more than one solution**.
   b. Values that make **the inequality true** are solutions of the inequality.
2. Notice that the information under the column "Examples" shows that:
   a. An inequality may contain a variable, as in the inequality $x < 10$. In this inequality, x is the variable.
   b. An inequality may not contain a variable, as in the inequality $3 > -3$.

Example 1

a. Is the number 2 one of the solutions of $x < 8$?

b. Are -9, 0, and $9\frac{1}{2}$ also solutions of $x < 10$?

Solution

a. Yes, the number 2 is one of the solutions of $x < 8$, because $2 < 8$ is true. Hint: The meaning of the symbol < in Table 1 is used in deciding the solution.

b. Yes, -9, 0, and $9\frac{1}{2}$ are also solutions of $x < 10$ because -9, 0, and $9\frac{1}{2}$ are less than 10. Hint: The meaning of the symbol < in Table 1 is used in deciding the solution.

Example 2

Are $-2\frac{1}{2}$, 0, and 100 also solutions of $x > -3$?

Solution

Yes, $-2\frac{1}{2}$, 0, and 100 are also solutions of $x > -3$ because $-2\frac{1}{2}$, 0, and 100 are greater than -3. Hint: The meaning of the symbol > in Table 1 is used in deciding the solution.

Example 3

Are -99, 0, and $\frac{1}{4}$ also solutions of $x \leq \frac{1}{3}$?

Solution

Yes, -99, 0, and $\frac{1}{4}$ are also solutions of $x \leq \frac{1}{3}$ because -99, 0, and $\frac{1}{4}$ are less than $\frac{1}{3}$. Hint: The meaning of the symbol $\leq$ in Table 1 is used in deciding the solution.

Example 4

a. Are $\frac{1}{8}$, 0, and 50 also solutions of $y \geq -\frac{1}{4}$?

b. Are -10, −1, and $-\frac{3}{4}$ also solutions of $y \geq -\frac{1}{4}$?

Solutions

a. Yes, $\frac{1}{8}$, 0, and 50 are also solutions of $y \geq -\frac{1}{4}$ because $\frac{1}{8}$, 0, and 50 are greater

than $-\frac{1}{4}$. Hint: The meaning of the symbol $\geq$ in Table 1 is used in deciding the solution.

b. No, -10, −1, and $-\frac{3}{4}$ are not also solutions of $y \geq -\frac{1}{4}$ because -10, −1, and $-\frac{3}{4}$ are

less than $-\frac{1}{4}$. Hint: The meaning of the symbol $\geq$ in Table 1 is used in deciding

the solution, additionally, the graphical solution of inequalities on a number line (which is the next section) may help more in the understanding of the solution of Example 4b.

How to Graph the Solutions of Inequalities on the Number Line

There are three main steps in graphing all the solutions of inequalities as shown:

Step 1: Draw a number line as shown:

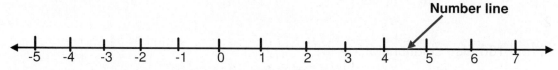

Number line

Step 2: Find the solutions of the inequality and use:

    a. a hollow dot to show that a specific number is not a solution as shown:

The hollow dot shows that 4 is not a solution.

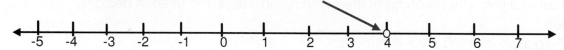

    b. a solid dot to show that a specific number is also a solution as shown:

The solid dot shows that 4 is a solution.

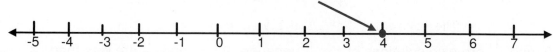

Step 3: Start at the:

    a. hollow dot and color over the solutions you have found as shown:

The hollow dot shows that 4 is not a solution.

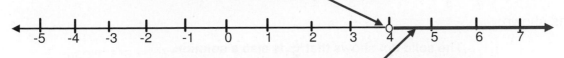

Color over the solutions that you have found.
For example, the red color is the solution for x > 4.

b. solid dot and color over the solutions you have found as shown:

The solid dot shows that 4 is also a solution.

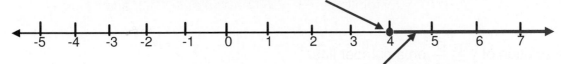

Color over the solutions that you have found.
For example, the red color is the solution for x ≥ 4.

Note: **1.** You may combine Step 1, Step 2, and Step 3 in solving problems.
2. The red color arrow on the number line shows that the solutions go on forever.

Example 5
Graph the solution of $x < 6$ on a number line.
Solution
Every number less than 6 is a solution of $x < 6$. Let us graph the solution as shown:

The hollow dot shows that 6 is not a solution

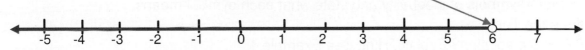

Example 6
Graph the solution of $x > 3$ on a number line.
Solution
Every number greater than 3 is a solution to $x > 3$. Let us graph the solution as shown:

The hollow dot shows that 3 is not a solution

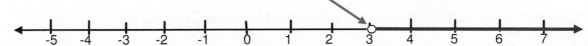

Example 7
Graph the solution of $x \leq \dfrac{1}{3}$ on a number line.

Solution

Every number less than $\frac{1}{3}$ or equal to $\frac{1}{3}$ is a solution to $x \leq \frac{1}{3}$. Let us graph the solution as shown:

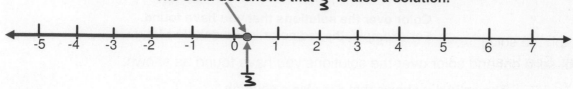

The solid dot shows that $\frac{1}{3}$ is also a solution.

Example 8

Graph the solution of $y \geq -\frac{1}{4}$ on a number line.

Solution

Every number that is greater than or equal to $-\frac{1}{4}$ are solutions to $y \geq -\frac{1}{4}$. Let us graph the solution as shown:

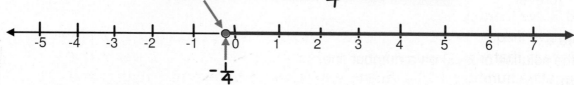

The solid dot shows that $-\frac{1}{4}$ is also a solution.

Exercises or Group Exercises

1. List the four symbols of inequality and state what each symbol means.
   Hint: See the Table 1.

2. If $x < 6$, is 5 a solution? Explain. Hint: See Example 1.

3. If $x < 3$, are -11 and 0 also solutions? Hint: See Example 1.

4. If $x < 8$, is 10 a solution? Explain. Hint: See Example 1.

5. If $x > 2$, is 10 a solution? Explain. Hint: See Example 2.

6. If $x > 2$, is 0 a solution? Explain. Hint: See Example 2.

7. If $y > 14$, is 13 a solution? Explain. Hint: See Example 4b.

8. Are -50, 0, and $\frac{1}{4}$ also solutions to $x \leq \frac{1}{2}$? Explain. Hint: See Example 3.

9. Are -1, 0, and $\frac{1}{8}$ also solutions to $x \leq \frac{2}{3}$? Explain. Hint: See Example 3.

10. Are 0, 1, and 20 also solutions to $y \geq -1$? Explain. Hint: See Example 4a.

11. Are -2, 0, 1, and 100 also solutions to $y \geq -3$? Explain. Hint: See Example 4a.

12. Graph the solutions of the following inequalities on a number line.
   Hint: See Example 5.
   a. $x < 4$ **b.** $x < 7$ **c.** $y < 2$ **d.** $x < -3$

13. Graph the solutions of the following inequalities on a number line.

Hint: See Example 6.

a. x > 2   **b.** x > 5   **c.** x > -2   **d.** y > 0

14. Graph the solutions of the following inequalities on a number line.
    Hint: See Example 7.

a. $x \leq \frac{1}{2}$ **b.** $x \leq 4$ **c.** $y \leq -2$ **d.** $x \leq 5$

15. Graph the solutions of the following inequalities on a number line.
    Hint: See Example 8.

a. $y \geq -\frac{1}{2}$ **b.** $y \geq 3$ **c.** $x \geq -2$ **d.** $y \geq 1$

Challenge Questions

16. Graph the solutions of the following inequalities on a number line.

a. $x \geq 0$ **b.** $x \leq 0$ **c.** $x \geq -1$ **d.** $x < -2$

e. $y \leq -5$ **f.** $y < -6$ **g.** $y > 6$ **h.** $x > -4$

17. Explain why -2 is one of the solutions of $x \geq -3$

18. Explain why -4 is not a solution of $x \geq -3$

How to Solve Inequalities

How to solve inequalities is much the same as how to solve equations, but the **only difference is that when both sides of an inequality are multiplied or divided by a negative number, the inequality symbol must be reversed. Regard this as Rule 1.**

Example 1

Solve for x.

$x + 7 \leq 3$

Solution

$x + 7 \leq 3$

$x + 7 - 7 \leq 3 - 7$ Subtract 7 from both sides of the equation in order to eliminate the 7 at the left side of the equation so that x alone will remain at the left side of the equation. $7 - 7 = 0$ and $3 - 7 = -4$.

$x + 0 \leq -4$

$x \leq -4$

Example 2

Solve for x.

$x - 5 \leq -6$

Solution

$x - 5 \leq -6$

$x - 5 + 5 \leq -6 + 5$ Add 5 to both sides of the equation in order to eliminate the -5 from the left side of the equation so

x + 0 ≤ -1   that only x remains at the left side of the equation.
x ≤ -1   -5 + 5 = 0 and -6 + 5 = -1.

Example 3
Solve for n

n + 6 ≥ -4

Solution

n + 6 ≥ -4

n + 6 - 6 ≥ -4 -6   Subtract 6 from both sides of the inequality so that
                             only n remains at the left side of the inequality.

n + 0 ≥ -10   6 - 6 = 0 and -4 - 6 = -10

n   ≥ -10

Example 4
Solve for t.

$\dfrac{t}{4} \geq -8$

Solution

$\dfrac{t}{4} \geq -8$

$\dfrac{t}{4} \times 4 \geq -8 \times 4$ Multiply both sides of the inequality by 4 in order
                             to eliminate the denominator of 4 from the left side
                             of the inequality so that only t should remain at the
                             left side of the inequality.

$\dfrac{t}{\underset{1}{\overset{1}{4}}} \times 4 \geq -32$ Divide by 4 and also -8 × 4 = -32

t ≥ -32

Example 5
Solve for y. -2y ≤ - 5

Solution

-2y ≤ -5

$\dfrac{-2y}{-2} \geq \dfrac{-5}{-2}$ Divide both sides of the inequality by -2 and **reverse** the
                             inequality symbol so that only y should remain at the left
        ↑   side of the equation. **See Rule 1.**
(Reverse the symbol).

$$\frac{\cancel{-2}y}{\cancel{-2}} \geq \frac{\cancel{-5}}{\cancel{-2}}$$

$$\quad 1$$

Note: The negative symbols attached to the numerators and the denominators cancel out each other.

$$y \geq \frac{5}{2}$$

$$\geq 2\frac{1}{2}$$

Example 6
Solve for k.

$$\frac{k}{-3} > 6$$

Solution

$$\frac{k}{-3} > 6$$

$$\frac{k}{-3} \times (-3) < 6 \times (-3)$$

$\uparrow$
(Reverse the symbol).

Multiply both sides of the inequality by -3 in order to eliminate the denominator on the left side of the inequality so that only k remains at the left side of the inequality. **See Rule 1**.

$$\frac{k}{\cancel{-3}} \times (\cancel{-3}) < -18$$

$$\quad 1$$

Note: The negative symbols at the left side of the inequality cancel out and also $6 \times (-3) = -18$.

$$k < -18$$

Example 7
Solve for p.

$$-4p \geq 12$$

Solution

$$-4p \geq 12$$

$$\frac{-4p}{-4} \leq \frac{12}{-4}$$

$\uparrow$
(Reverse the symbol).

Divide both sides of the inequality by -4 in order to eliminate the -4 from the left side of the inequality so that only p should remain at the left side of the inequality, and then **reverse** the inequality symbol. **See Rule 1**.

$$\frac{\cancel{-}4p}{\cancel{-}4} \leq -3$$

$$\frac{1}{}$$

Note: The negative symbols that are attached to the inequality cancel out to give positive p which is simply written as p, also $4p \div 4 = p$ and $12 \div (-4) = -3$.

$p \leq -3$

Exercises

1. Judith said that when both sides of an inequality are multiplied or divided by a negative number, the symbol of the inequality is reversed.
Is her statement true or false?

2. Solve for x, n, and k. Hint: See Example 1, 2, and 3.

    a. $x + 10 \leq 12$ **b.** $n + 2 \geq 3$ **c.** $k - 4 \leq -3$

    d. $n + 11 \geq -3$ **e.** $x - 3 \leq 4$ **f.** $k + 3 < -5$

3. Solve for x, n, and k. Hint: See Example 4.

    a. $\dfrac{k}{6} \geq -2$ **b.** $\dfrac{n}{4} \leq 3$ **c.** $\dfrac{x}{2} > 4$

    d. $\dfrac{n}{3} < -6$ **e.** $\dfrac{k}{3} > -4$ **f.** $\dfrac{x}{5} \leq 4$

4. Solve for x, n, and k. Hint: See Examples 5 and 7.

    a. $-2y < -8$ **b.** $-3n < 12$ **c.** $-4k \geq 16$

    d. $-3x \geq -2$ **e.** $-5y > 25$ **f.** $-6k \leq 36$

    g. $-4k \geq 8$ **h.** $-2n \leq -24$ **i.** $-7x > -21$

5. Solve for x, n, and k. Hint: See Example 6.

    a. $\dfrac{k}{-4} < 2$ **b.** $\dfrac{n}{-3} \geq 3$ **c.** $\dfrac{n}{-5} \leq -2$

    d. $\dfrac{n}{-5} > -3$ **e.** $\dfrac{x}{-4} < -12$ **f.** $\dfrac{n}{-2} > 0$

Challenge Questions

6. Solve for x, n, and k.

    a. $\dfrac{x}{3} > 5$ **b.** $\dfrac{k}{-2} \leq -1$ **c.** $\dfrac{n}{-5} \geq -2$

    d. $k + 4 \geq -7$ **e.** $n - 6 < 3$ **f.** $x - 8 \leq -4$

Answers to Selected Questions

2a. $x \leq 2$ **3a.** $k \geq -12$ **4a.** $y > 4$ **5a.** $k > -8$

Cumulative Review

1. Solve for w in each equation.

a. $2w = 12$ **b.** $\dfrac{w}{5} = 4$ **c.** $\dfrac{2}{3} \times w = 6$

2. The average age of two boys is 8 years. What is their total ages? Hint: You may use the formula for finding averages.

3. $25 \times 5 =$ **4.** $2.5 \times 5 =$ **5.** $2.5 \times .5 =$

4. Find the measure of the angles for b and x in each parallelogram.

a.

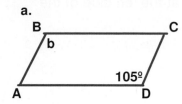

b.

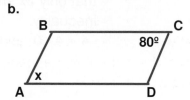

c.

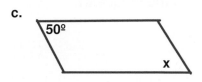

d.

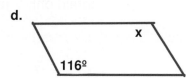

5. By considering each right angle, find the measure of x.

a..

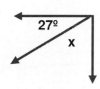

b.

c.

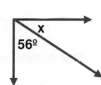

d.

e.

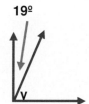

f.

SOLVING MULTI-STEP INEQUALITY

Solving Two-step Inequalities

Solving two-step inequalities is much like solving two-step equations, but the symbol of the inequality is reversed when both sides of the inequality are multiplied or divided by a negative number. Regard this statement again as **Rule 1**.

Example 1
Solve and graph 2x - 4 > 2.
Solution
2x - 4 > 2

2x - 4 + 4 > 2 + 4   Add 4 to both sides of the inequality in order to eliminate -4 from the left side of the inequality so that only 2x should remain at the left side of the inequality.

2x + 0 > 6   -4 + 4 = 0, and 2 + 4 = 6

2x > 6

$$\frac{2x}{2} > \frac{6}{2}$$ Divide both sides of the inequality by 2 in order to obtain only x at the left side of the inequality.

$$\frac{\overset{x}{\cancel{2x}}}{\underset{1}{2}} > \frac{\overset{3}{\cancel{6}}}{\underset{1}{2}}$$

x > 3
This is the graph of x > 3.

The hollow dot shows that 3 is not a solution

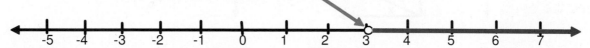

Example 2
Solve and graph -8 < 4x + 4
Solution
-8 < 4x + 4

-8 - 4 < 4x + 4 - 4   Subtract 4 from both sides of the inequality in order to eliminate the 4 at the right side of the inequality so that only 4x should remain at the right side of the inequality.

-12 < 4x + 0   -8 - 4 = -12, and 4 - 4 = 0

$$\frac{-12}{4} < \frac{4x}{4}$$ Divide both sides of the inequality by 4 so that only x remains at the right side of the inequality.

$$\frac{\overset{-3}{\cancel{-12}}}{\underset{1}{4}} < \frac{\overset{x}{\cancel{4x}}}{\underset{1}{4}}$$ **Note** that the inequality symbol is not reversed

because the inequality is not divided by a negative number.

-3 < x

The graph of x > -3 is shown below.

The hollow dot shows that -3 is not a solution

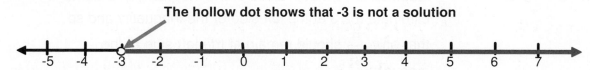

Example 3
Solve and graph -3x + 7 ≤ 4
Solution

-3x + 7 ≤ 4

-3x + 7 - 7 ≤ 4 - 7   Subtract 7 from both sides of the inequality in order to eliminate the 7 on the left side of the inequality so that only -3x should remain at the left side of the inequality.

-3x + 0 ≤ -3   7 - 7 = 0, 4 - 7 = -3.

-3x ≤ -3

$$\frac{-3x}{-3} \geq \frac{-3}{-3}$$

   ↑

(Reverse the symbol).

Divide both sides of the inequality by -3 so that only x should remain at the left side of the inequality, and then **reverse** the inequality symbol. Hint: **See Rule 1.**

$$\frac{\cancel{-3}x}{\cancel{-3}} \geq \frac{\cancel{-3}}{\cancel{-3}}$$

  x   1

  1   1

Note: The negative symbols cancel out so that the answer becomes positive.

x ≥ 1

The graph of x ≥ 1 is shown below.

The solid dot shows that 1 is also a solution.

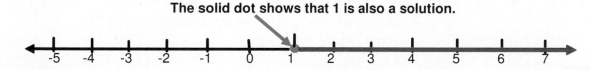

Example 4

Solve and graph $\dfrac{n}{-4} + 3 > -6$

Solution

229

$$\frac{n}{-4} + 3 > -6$$

$$\frac{n}{-4} + 3 - 3 > -6 -3$$

Subtract 3 from both sides of the inequality in order to eliminate the 3 at the left side of the inequality and so that only $\frac{n}{-4}$ should remain at the left side of the inequality.

$$\frac{n}{-4} + 0 > -9$$

$3 - 3 = 0$, and $-6 - 3 = -9$

$$\frac{n}{-4} > -9$$

$$\frac{n}{-4} \times (-4) < -9 \times (-4)$$

↑
(Reverse the symbol).

Multiply both sides of the inequality by -4 so that the denominator -4 is eliminated so that only n should remain at the left side of the inequality, and then **reverse** the inequality symbol. Hint: **See Rule 1.**

$$\frac{n}{\cancel{4}} \times (\cancel{4}) < -9 \times (-4)$$

Divide the left side of the inequality by 4.

$$n < 36$$

$-4 \div (-4) = 1$, and $-9 \times (-4) = 36$
Note: The negative symbols on the left side of the inequality cancel out to become positive and the negative symbols at the right side of the inequality are multiplied with each other to become positive.

The graph of $n < 36$ is shown below.

The hollow dot shows that 36 is not a solution.

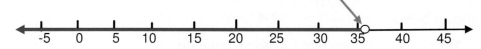

Exercises

1. The symbol of a two-step inequality is reversed whenever the inequality is multiplied or divided by a negative number. Is this statement true or false?

2. Solve and graph each inequality. Hint: See Examples 1 and 2.

a. $3x - 5 > 7$ b. $-5 < 2x - 9$ c. $4n + 2 < 6$

d. $5y + 1 \leq 11$ e. $2n - 3 \geq 7$ f. $3x + 6 \geq 12$

g. $6n - 4 > 8$ h. $3n + 16 < 12$ i. $-6 \geq 3n + 3$

3. Solve and graph each inequality. Hint: See Example 3.

    a. $-2x + 5 \le 9$ **b.** $8 + 3x < 14$ **c.** $3x - 4 > 8$

    d. $-4x - 6 \ge 10$ **e.** $-6 - 2x \le -2$ **f.** $5n + 3 < 13$

    g. $4n + 6 > -6$ **h.** $5 - 3x > 8$ **i.** $-7n - 20 \le -27$

4. Solve and graph each inequality. Hint: See Example 4.

    a. $\dfrac{x}{-2} + 4 > -1$ **b.** $\dfrac{n}{-3} - 2 \le 3$ **c.** $\dfrac{k}{-4} - 5 < -4$

    d. $-2 + \dfrac{k}{-3} > -4$ **e.** $6 + \dfrac{n}{-4} \le 7$ **f.** $\dfrac{x}{-6} + 7 > 9$

Challenge Questions

5. Solve and graph each inequality.

    a. $-3n + 2 > -4$ **b.** $\dfrac{n}{-3} - 2 \le 4$ **c.** $7x - 4 > 3$

    d. $4x + 3 \le 11$ **e.** $4 + \dfrac{k}{-2} \ge 6$ **f.** $\dfrac{n}{3} - 4 \le -2$

Answers to Selected Questions

2a.   **X > 4**

The hollow dot shows that 4 is not a solution.

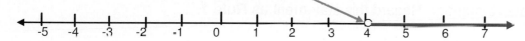

3a.   **-3 < x**

The hollow dot shows that -3 is not a solution.

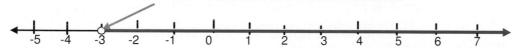

4a.   **X < 10**

The hollow dot shows that 10 is not a solution.

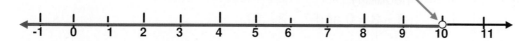

2a. X > 4

The hollow dot shows that 4 is not a solution.

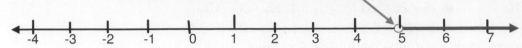

3a. x $\geq$ -2

The solid dot shows that -2 is also a solution.

4a. x < 10

The hollow dot shows that 10 is not a solution.

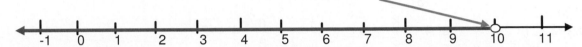

How to Solve Multi-step Inequalities

Solving multi-step inequalities is much like solving an equation but the symbols of the inequalities must be reversed whenever both sides of the inequalities are multiplied or divided by a negative number. Regard this statement as **Rule 1**.

Example 1

Solve and graph 4n - 3 - 2n > 7

Solution

4n - 3 - 2n > 7

2n - 3 > 7   Combine like terms. 4n - 2n = 2n

2n - 3 + 3 > 7 + 3   Add 3 to both sides of the inequality in order to eliminate the -3 at the left side of the inequality so that only 2n should be left at the left side of the inequality.

2n > 10   -3 + 3 = 0 and 7 + 3 =10.

$\dfrac{2n}{2} > \dfrac{10}{2}$ Divide both sides of the inequality by 2 in order to obtain only n at the left side of the inequality.

$\dfrac{\overset{1}{\cancel{2}}n}{\underset{1}{\cancel{2}}} > \dfrac{\overset{5}{\cancel{10}}}{\underset{1}{\cancel{2}}}$

n > 5

The graph of n > 5 is shown below.

The hollow dot shows that 5 is not a solution.

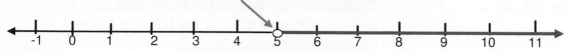

Example 2

Solve and graph the inequality $3x + 2 \leq 6x - 7$

Solution

$3x + 2 \leq 6x - 7$

$3x - 3x + 2 \leq 6x - 3x - 7$ Subtract 3x from both sides of the inequality in order to eliminate the 3x at the left side of the inequality.

$0 + 2 \leq 3x - 7$ $3x - 3x = 0$ and $6x - 3x = 3x$.

$\quad 2 \leq 3x - 7$

$2 + 7 \leq 3x - 7 + 7$ Add 7 to both sides of the inequality in order to eliminate the -7 at the right side of the inequality so that only 3x should remain at the right side of the inequality.

$\quad 9 \leq 3x$ $2 + 7 = 9$ and $-7 + 7 = 0$.

$\dfrac{9}{3} \leq \dfrac{3x}{3}$ Divide each side of the inequality by 3 in order to obtain only x at the right side of the inequality.

$\dfrac{\overset{3}{\cancel{9}}}{\underset{1}{\cancel{3}}} \leq \dfrac{\overset{x}{\cancel{3x}}}{\underset{1}{\cancel{3}}}$

$3 \leq x$

The graph of $3 \leq x$ is shown below.

The solid dot shows that 3 is also a solution.

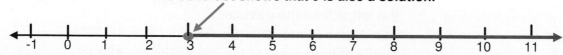

Example 3

Solve and graph the inequality $4 - 6x \geq 8 - 4x$

Solution

$\quad\quad 4 - 6x \geq 8 - 4x$

$4 - 6x + 4x \geq 8 - 4x + 4x$ Combine like terms by adding 4x to both sides

$4 - 2x \geq 8$

$4 - 4 - 2x \geq 8 - 4$

of the inequality in order to eliminate -4x at the right side of the inequality.

$-4x + 4x = 0$ and $-6x + 4x = -2x$.

Subtract 4 from both sides of the inequality in order to eliminate the 4 at the left side of the inequality and so that only -2x should remain at the left side of the inequality.

$-2x \geq 4$

$4 - 4 = 0$ and $8 - 4 = 0$.

$$\frac{-2x}{-2} \leq \frac{4}{-2}$$

↑

(Reverse the symbol).

Divide both sides of the inequality by -2 in order to obtain only x at the left side of the inequality and then **reverse** the inequality symbol.

Hint: See Rule 1.

$$\begin{array}{cc} x & -2 \\ \dfrac{\cancel{2}x}{\cancel{2}} \leq & \dfrac{4}{-2} \\ 1 & 1 \end{array}$$

Note: The negative symbols on the left side of the inequality cancel out and also $4 \div (-2) = -2$.

$x \leq -2$

The graph of $x \leq -2$ is as shown:

The solid dot shows that -2 is also a solution.

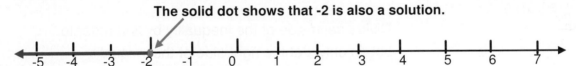

Example 4

Solve and graph the inequality $-2n + 3 < -7 - 4n$

Solution

$-2n + 3 < -7 - 4n$

$-2n + 2n + 3 < -7 - 4n + 2n$

Move or combine all the "ns" to the right side of the inequality by adding 2n to both sides of the inequality in order to eliminate the -2n at the left side of the inequality so that only 3 remains at the left side of the inequality.

$-2n + 2n = 0$ and $-4n + 2n = -2n$

$3 < -7 - 2n$

$3 + 7 < -7 + 7 - 2n$

Add 7 to both sides of the inequality in order to eliminate the -7 at the right side of the inequality so that only -2n should remain at the right side of the inequality.

$10 < -2n$

$3 + 7 = 10$ and $-7 + 7 = 0$.

$$\frac{10}{-2} > \frac{-2n}{-2}$$

$\uparrow$
(Reverse the symbol).

Divide both sides of the inequality by -2 in order to obtain only n at the right side of the inequality and **reverse** the inequality symbol. **Hint: See Rule 1.**

$$\frac{\overset{-5}{\cancel{10}}}{-2} > \frac{\overset{n}{\cancel{-2n}}}{\cancel{-2}}$$
$$\quad 1 \qquad 1$$

Note: The negative symbols at the right side of the inequality cancel out and also $10 \div (-2) = -5$.

$-5 > n$
The graph of $-5 > n$ is as shown:

The hollow dot shows that -5 is not a solution.

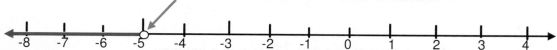

Example 5

Solve and the graph the inequality $\frac{1}{3} \geq \frac{n}{2} - \frac{5}{6}$.

Note how the LCD (least common denominator) is used to solve this problem. Review the LCD.

Solution

$$\frac{1}{3} \geq \frac{n}{2} - \frac{5}{6}$$

$$\frac{1}{3} \times 6 \geq (\frac{n}{2} - \frac{5}{6})6$$

Multiply both sides of the inequality by the LCD of the fractions $\frac{1}{3}$, $\frac{n}{2}$, and $\frac{5}{6}$ which is 6 in order to change the fractions to whole numbers.

$$\frac{6}{3} \geq (\frac{n}{2})6 - (\frac{5}{6})6$$

Distributive property, for an example,
$a(b - c) = ab - ac$.

$$\frac{\overset{2}{\cancel{6}}}{\cancel{3}} \geq (\frac{n}{\cancel{2}})\overset{3}{\cancel{6}} - (\frac{5}{\cancel{6}})\overset{1}{\cancel{6}}$$
$$\quad 1 \qquad 1 \qquad 1$$

$\frac{6}{3} = 2$, $(\frac{n}{2})6 = 3n$, and $(\frac{5}{6})6 = 5$

$2 \geq 3n - 5$

$2 + 5 \geq 3n - 5 + 5$

Add 5 to both sides of the inequality in order to eliminate the -5 at the right side of the inequality and also to obtain only 3n at the right side of the

235

$7 \geq 3n$

inequality.

$2 + 5 = 7$ and $-5 + 5 = 0$.

$\dfrac{7}{3} \geq \dfrac{3n}{3}$

Divide both sides of the inequality by 3 in order to obtain only n at the right side of the inequality.

$2\dfrac{1}{3} \geq \dfrac{\overset{1}{\cancel{3n}}}{\cancel{3}}$

$2\dfrac{1}{3} \geq n$

The graph of $2\dfrac{1}{3} \geq n$ is as shown:

The solid dot shows that $2\frac{1}{3}$ is also a solution.

Example 6

Solve and graph the inequality $-\dfrac{3x}{4} + \dfrac{2}{3} > -\dfrac{x}{2} + \dfrac{7}{8}$

Note how the LCD (least common denominator) is used to solve the problem.

Solution

$-\dfrac{3x}{4} + \dfrac{2}{3} > -\dfrac{x}{2} + \dfrac{7}{8}$

$(-\dfrac{3x}{4} + \dfrac{2}{3})24 > (-\dfrac{x}{2} + \dfrac{7}{8})24$

Multiply both sides of the inequality by the LCD of the fraction $\dfrac{3x}{4}, \dfrac{2}{3}, \dfrac{x}{2}$, and $\dfrac{7}{8}$ which is 24 in order to change the fractions into whole numbers.

$(-\dfrac{3x}{4})24 + (\dfrac{2}{3})24 > (-\dfrac{x}{2})24 + (\dfrac{7}{8})24$

Distributive property, for example, $a(b + c) = ab + ac$.

$(-\dfrac{3x}{\underset{1}{\cancel{4}}})\overset{6}{\cancel{24}} + (\dfrac{2}{\underset{1}{\cancel{3}}})\overset{8}{\cancel{24}} > (-\dfrac{x}{\underset{1}{\cancel{2}}})\overset{12}{\cancel{24}} + (\dfrac{7}{\underset{1}{\cancel{8}}})\overset{3}{\cancel{24}}$

Divide separately as shown.

236

$(-3x)6 + (2)8 > (-x)12 + (7)3$

$-18x + 16 > -12x + 21$

$-18x + 12x + 16 > -12x + 12x + 21$
    Combine like terms of x by adding 12x to both sides of the inequality in order to eliminate the -12x at the right side of the inequality.

$-6x + 16 > 0 + 21$
    $-18x + 12x = -6x$, and $-12x + 12x = 0$.

$-6x + 16 > 21$

$-6x + 16 - 16 > 21 - 16$
    Subtract 16 from both sides of the inequality in order to eliminate the 16 at the left side of the inequality so that only -6x should remain on the left side of the inequality.

$-6x + 0 > 5$
    $16 - 16 = 0$, and $21 - 16 = 5$.

    $-6x > 5$

$\dfrac{-6x}{-6} < \dfrac{5}{-6}$
    Divide both sides of the inequality by -6 so that only x remains at the right side of the inequality and then **reverse** the inequality symbol because you are dividing by a negative number.

↑

(Reverse the symbol).
    Hint: See Rule 1

$\dfrac{\cancel{-6}x}{\cancel{-6}} < \dfrac{5}{-6}$
    Note: The negative symbols at the left side of the inequality cancel out.

1

$x < -\dfrac{5}{6}$

The graph of $x < -\dfrac{5}{6}$ is as follows:

The hollow dot shows that $-\dfrac{5}{6}$ is not a solution.

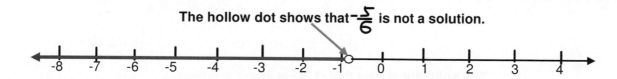

Exercises

1. Whenever both sides of an equality are multiplied or divided by a negative number, the inequality symbol must be_____.

2. Solve and graph the following inequalities. Hint: See Examples 1 and 2.

    a. $4x - 2 - 2x > 6$ **b.** $4x - 2 - 3x < 5$ **c.** $2x + 2 \leq 5x - 7$

d. $3 + 6n \geq 3n - 15$ **e.** $4n + n - 3 > 12$ **f.** $4 - 2n < 3n - 6$

3. Solve and graph the following inequalities. Hint: See Example 4.

    a. $-2x + 8 > -5x - 1$ **b.** $-6n + 5 \geq -2n + 21$

    c. $3k - 5k + 7 \leq -1$ **d.** $-1 - 3n < 15 - 7n$

4. Solve and graph the following inequalities. Hint: See Examples 5 and 6.

    a. $\dfrac{1}{4} \leq \dfrac{n}{-3} - \dfrac{1}{6}$ **b.** $\dfrac{n}{4} - \dfrac{3}{8} > \dfrac{1}{2}$ **c.** $\dfrac{1}{2} + \dfrac{2n}{3} > \dfrac{5}{6}$

    d. $\dfrac{-3n}{4} + \dfrac{1}{2} \geq \dfrac{n}{2} - \dfrac{3}{4}$ **e.** $\dfrac{2}{3} - \dfrac{5n}{9} \leq -\dfrac{n}{3} + \dfrac{4}{9}$ **f.** $-\dfrac{n}{6} - \dfrac{2}{3} < \dfrac{2}{3} - \dfrac{5n}{6}$

Challenge Questions

5. Solve and graph the following inequalities.

    a. $5x + 2 < 2x + 8$ **b.** $6 - 2n > 5n - 8$ **c.** $\dfrac{3x}{4} - \dfrac{3}{8} \geq \dfrac{1}{4} + \dfrac{x}{8}$

    d. $5k + 5 < 13 + k$ **e.** $\dfrac{4}{5} - \dfrac{3x}{5} \leq -\dfrac{4}{5} - \dfrac{x}{10}$ **f.** $9 - 6n - 1 > -2n$

Answers to Selected Questions

    2a.   **X > 4**

The hollow dot shows that 4 is not a solution.

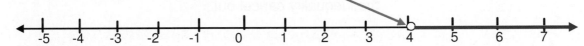

    3a.   **-3 < x**

The hollow dot shows that -3 is not a solution.

    4a. $-1\frac{1}{4} \geq n$

The solid dot shows that $-1\frac{1}{4}$ is also a solution.

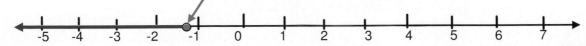

INEQUALITIES IN TWO VARIABLES

The graph of a line or a linear equation divides the coordinate plane into three sets of points as shown:

1. Points that are on the line which is called the **boundary line**.

2. Points that are above the boundary line.

3. Points that are below the boundary line.

Let us graph the line of the equation $y = x - 2$ as shown:

when $x = 0$, $y = x - 2$ becomes $y = 0 - 2$ Substitute $x = 0$ into $y = x - 2$.

$$y = -2$$

when $y = 0$, $y = x - 2$ becomes $0 = x - 2$ Substitute $y = 0$ into $y = x - 2$.

$$0 + 2 = x - 2 + 2$$ Add 2 to both sides of the equation

$0 = x - 2$ in order to obtain the value of x.

$$2 = x$$ $-2 + 2 = 0$

Therefore, when $x = 0$, $y = -2$ which is the point $(0, -2)$ and when $y = 0$, $x = 2$ which is the point $(2, 0)$. We can locate these points, $(0, -2)$ and $(2, 0)$ on the graph paper and then connect the two points with a pencil and a ruler.

The equation of the graph of the line is $y = x - 2$. The line divides the coordinate plane into three sets of points as shown:

the set of points that are on the line,

the set of points at the shaded region or above the boundary line,

the set of points at the region not shaded or below the boundary line.

Therefore, the sets of points in the coordinate plane are divided by using these three statements as shown:

Equality: $y = x - 2$ (Set of points on the line or on the boundary line).

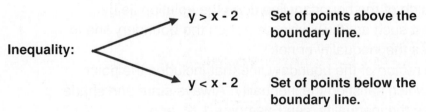

Inequality:

$y > x - 2$ **Set of points above the boundary line.**

$y < x - 2$ **Set of points below the boundary line.**

The graph of the line $y = x - 2$ with the three sets of points is as shown on the next page:

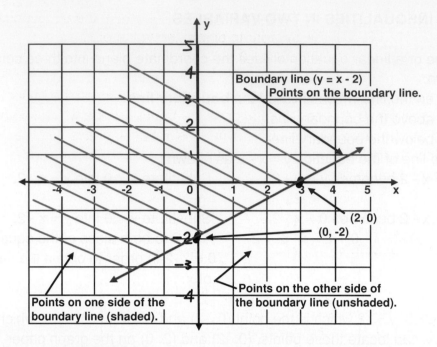

Boundary line (y = x - 2)
Points on the boundary line.

(2, 0)
(0, -2)

Points on the other side of the boundary line (unshaded).

Points on one side of the boundary line (shaded).

How to Graph Inequalities

There are three main steps in graphing inequalities as shown:

Step 1: Draw the boundary line of the inequality by initially using the equality sign such that:

    a. If the inequality symbol is $\leq$ or $\geq$, then the line is included in the solution, and therefore, draw a continuous line as the boundary line as ——————.

    b. If the inequality symbol is $<$ or $>$, then the line is not a solution to the inequality because no points can be on the boundary line as a solution of the inequality, and therefore, draw a dotted line for the boundary line such as - - - - .

Step 2: Determine on which side of the boundary line does the solution lie by choosing a simple point such as (0, 0) which is not on the boundary line to test if the point satisfies the inequality or not.

Step 3: Shade the part of the region of the boundary line that includes the point selected in Step 2 or which satisfied the inequality. Always state and shade the region that satisfies the inequality, see Examples 1, 2, and 3.

Example 1

Graph the inequality $y > x + 2$.

Solution

Step 1: Draw the boundary line of the inequality.

    Draw the boundary line with the equation $y = x + 2$ by using any two points as shown:

    When $x = 0$, $y = x + 2$ becomes $y = 0 + 2 = 2$.   Substitute $x = 0$.

    Therefore, the point $(x, y) = (0, 2)$ is on the boundary line.

    When $y = 0$, $y = x + 2$ becomes $0 = x + 2$.

        $0 = x + 2$ _____[A]

240

$0 - 2 = x + 2 - 2$ Subtract 2 from both sides of the equation [A] in order to obtain the value of x.

$-2 = x$ $2 - 2 = 0$.

$x = -2$

Therefore, when $y = 0$, $x = -2$, the point $(x, y) = (-2, 0)$ is also on the boundary line. Use the points $(0, 2)$ and $(-2, 0)$ to draw the boundary line which should be a dotted line because the inequality symbol is $>$ which means that the solution set of the points are not on the boundary line (See Step 1b under "How to Graph Inequalities.")

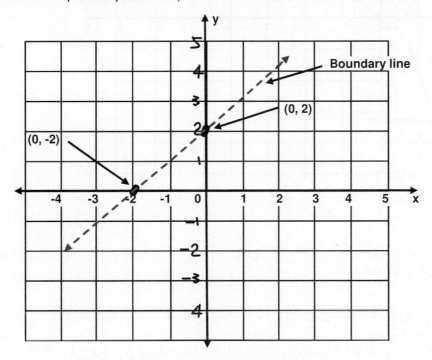

Step 2: Determine on which side of the boundary line does the solution lie. Take any simple point such as $(0, 0)$ which is not on the boundary line to test if the point satisfies the inequality or not as shown:

Substitute the point $(0, 0)$ into the original inequality to test if the point $(0, 0)$ satisfies the inequality or not as shown:

$y > x + 2$ Original inequality.

$0 > 0 + 2$ Substitute $x = 0$ and $y = 0$ into the original inequality.

$0 > 2$ This is not true, therefore, we should shade the side of the boundary line that does not contain the point $(0, 0)$.

Step 3: Shade the part of the boundary line that satisfies the solution of the inequality. Since $0 > 2$ is not true, $(0, 0)$ is not a solution of $y > x + 2$, and therefore, shade the side of the boundary line that does not include $(0, 0)$ as the solution to the inequality $y > x + 2$ as shown:

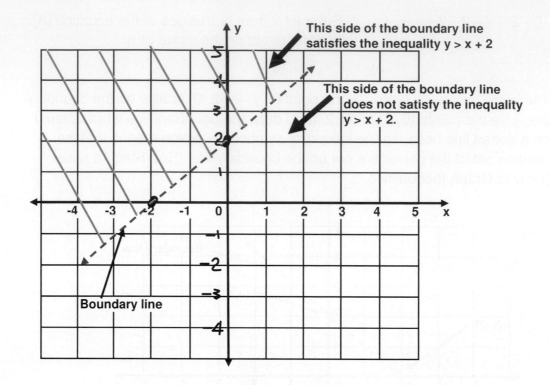

This side of the boundary line satisfies the inequality y > x + 2

This side of the boundary line does not satisfy the inequality y > x + 2.

Boundary line

Example 2
Solve the inequality x + 2y - 4 < 0

Solution

First write the inequality in the slope-intercept form of y = mx + b as shown:

x + 2y - 4 < 0	
x + 2y - 4 + 4 < 4	Add 4 to both sides of the equation x + 2y - 4 < 0 to eliminate the 4 at the left side of the equation.
x + 2y < 4	- 4 + 4 = 0
x - x + 2y < 4 - x	Subtract x from both sides of the equation x + 2y < 4 in order to eliminate the x at the left side of the equation.
2y < 4 - x _____ [A]	
	x - x = 0

$$\frac{2y}{2} < \frac{4 - x}{2}$$

Divide both sides of equation [A] by 2 in order to obtain the value of y and also to obtain the slope-intercept form of y = mx + b.

$$\frac{2y}{2} < \frac{4}{2} - \frac{x}{2}$$

Separate the right side of the equation $\frac{2y}{2} < \frac{4 - x}{2}$ in order to obtain the slope intercept form of y = mx + b.

242

$$\frac{\overset{1}{\cancel{2}}y}{\cancel{2}} < \frac{\overset{2}{\cancel{4}}}{\cancel{2}} - \frac{x}{2}$$

Divide by 2 as shown.

$$y < 2 - \frac{x}{2}$$

$$y < -\frac{x}{2} + 2$$

Rearrange the terms in the slope intercept form of $y = mx + b$.

Now let us graph $y < -\frac{x}{2} + 2$.

Step 1: Draw the boundary line of the inequality.

Draw the boundary line with the equation $y = -\frac{x}{2} + 2$ by using any two points

as shown:

When $x = 0$, $y = -\frac{x}{2} + 2$ becomes $y = -\frac{0}{2} + 2 = 2$.   Substitute $0 = x$.

Therefore, the point $(x, y) = (0, 2)$ is on the boundary line.

When $y = 0$, $y = -\frac{x}{2} + 2$ becomes $0 = -\frac{x}{2} + 2$.   Substitute $0 = y$.

$$0 = -\frac{x}{2} + 2 \underline{\hspace{3cm}}[B]$$

$$0 - 2 = -\frac{x}{2} + 2 - 2$$

Subtract 2 from both sides of the equation [B] in order to eliminate the 2 at the right side of the equation and also to isolate the term in x.

$$-2 = -\frac{x}{2}$$ $2 - 2 = 0$

$$-2(-2) = -\frac{x}{2}(-2)$$

Multiply both sides of the equation by -2 in order to obtain the value of x.

$$-2(-2) = -\frac{x}{\overset{1}{\cancel{2}}}(\overset{-1}{\cancel{-2}})$$ Dividing.

$$4 = x$$ $-2(-2) = 4$ and $-x(-1) = x$.

$$x = 4$$

Therefore, when $y = 0$, $x = 4$, the point $(x, y) = (4, 0)$ is also on the boundary line.
Use the points $(0, 2)$ and $(4, 0)$ to draw the boundary line which should be a
dotted line because the inequality symbol is < which means that the solution

points are not on the boundary line.

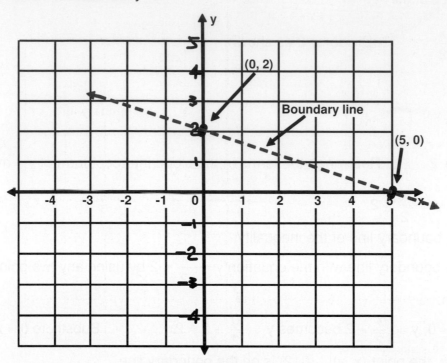

Step 2: Determine on which side of the boundary line does the solution lie. Take any simple point such as (0, 0) which is not on the boundary line to test if the point satisfies the inequality or not as shown:

Substitute the point (0, 0) into the original inequality to test if the point (0, 0) satisfies the inequality or not as shown:

$x + 2y - 4 < 0$ Original inequality.

$0 + 2(0) - 4 < 0$ Substitute $x = 0$ and $y = 0$ into the original inequality.

$0 + 0 - 4 < 0$

$-4 < 0$

Since $-4 < 0$ is true, (0, 0) is a solution of $x + 2y - 4 < 0$, and therefore, shade the side of the boundary line that includes the point (0, 0) as the solution to the inequality as shown:

(The shaded region is shown on the graph on the next page.)

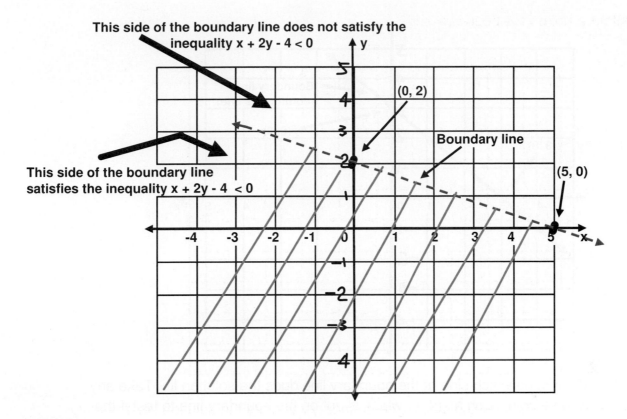

This side of the boundary line does not satisfy the inequality x + 2y - 4 < 0

(0, 2)

Boundary line

(5, 0)

This side of the boundary line satisfies the inequality x + 2y - 4 < 0

Example 3

Graph the inequality y ≤ x + 3

Solution

Step 1: Draw the boundary line of the inequality. Draw the boundary line with the equation y = x + 3 by using any two points as shown:

When x = 0, y = x + 3 becomes y = 0 + 3 = 3.   Substitute x = 0.

Therefore, the point (x, y) = (0, 3) is on the boundary line.

When y = 0, y = x + 3 becomes 0 = x + 3.   Substitute y = 0.

  0 = x + 3 _____[A]

  0 - 3 = x + 3 - 3   Subtract 3 from both sides of equation [A] in order to isolate the term in x or to obtain the value of x.

     -3 = x   0 - 3 = -3 and 3 - 3 = 0.

Therefore, when y = 0, x = -3, and therefore, the point (x, y) = (-3, 0) is also on the boundary line. Use the two points (0, 3) and (-3, 0) to draw the boundary line which should be a continuous line because the inequality symbol is ≤ which means that the solution points are on the boundary line.

245

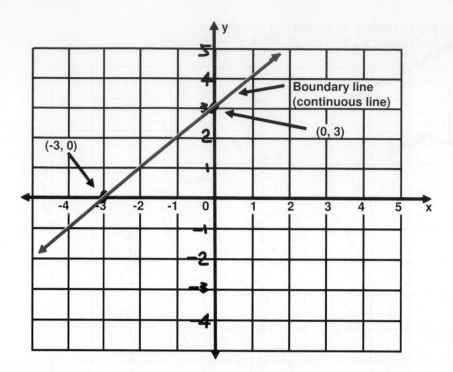

Step 2: Determine which side of the boundary line does the solution lie. Take any simple point such as (0, 0) which is not on the boundary line to test if the point satisfies the inequality or not as shown:

Substitute the point (0, 0) into the original inequality to test if the point (0, 0) satisfies the inequality or not as shown:

$y \leq x + 3$ Original inequality.

$0 \leq 0 + 3$ Substitute $x = 0$ and $y = 0$ into the original equation.

$0 \leq 3$

Since $0 \leq 3$ is true, (0, 0) is a solution of $y \leq x + 3$, and therefore, shade the side of the boundary line that includes the point (0, 0) as the solution to the inequality as shown:

(The shaded region is shown on the graph on the next page.)

This side of the boundary line does not satisfy the inequality y ≤ x + 3.

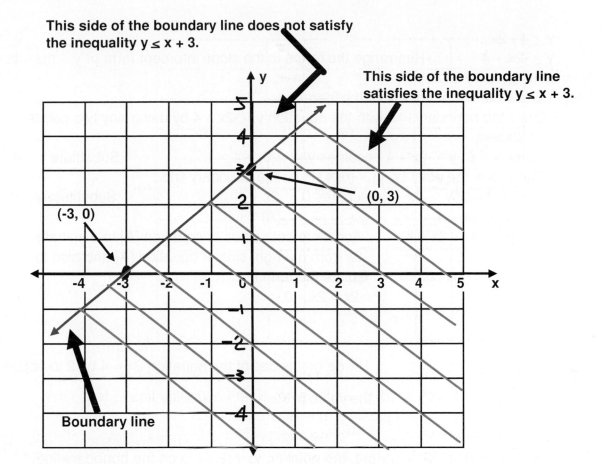

This side of the boundary line satisfies the inequality y ≤ x + 3.

(0, 3)

(-3, 0)

Boundary line

Example 4

Graph $2y + 4x \geq 8$

Solution

First write the inequality $2y + 4x \geq 8$ in the slope-intercept form of $y = mx + b$ as shown:

$2y + 4x \geq 8$

$2y + 4x - 4x \geq 8 - 4$ Subtract 4x from both sides of the equation to obtain 2y.

$2y \geq 8 - 4x$ $4x - 4x = 0$.

$\dfrac{2y}{2} \geq \dfrac{8 - 4x}{2}$ Divide both sides of the equation $2y \geq 8 - 4x$ by 2 to obtain

the value of y.

$\dfrac{2y}{2} \geq \dfrac{8}{2} - \dfrac{4x}{2}$ Separate the right side of the equation $\dfrac{2y}{2} \geq \dfrac{8 - 4x}{2}$ to

obtain the slope-intercept form of $y = mx + b$.

$\begin{matrix} & y & & 4 & & 2x \\ \dfrac{2y}{2} & \geq & \dfrac{8}{2} & - & \dfrac{4x}{2} \\ & 1 & & 1 & & 1 \end{matrix}$ Dividing by 2.

$y \geq 4 - 2x$

$y \geq -2x + 4$ Rearrange the terms in the slope intercept form of $y = mx + b$.

Now let us graph $y \geq -2x + 4$.

Step 1: Draw the boundary line of the inequality.

Draw the boundary line with the equation $y = -2x + 4$ by using any two points as shown:

When $x = 0$, $y = -2x + 4$ becomes $y = -2(0) + 4 = 4$.   Substitute $x = 0$.

Therefore, the point $(x, y) = (0, 4)$ is on the boundary line.

When $y = 0$, $y = -2x + 4$ becomes $0 = -2x + 4$.   Substitute $y = 0$.

$0 = -2x + 4$ _____[A]

$0 + 2x = -2x + 2x + 4$ Add $2x$ to both sides of equation [A] to eliminate $-2x$ from the right side of equation [A] and also to isolate the term in x.

$2x = 4$ $-2x + 2x = 0$.

$$\frac{\overset{1}{\cancel{2}}x}{\underset{1}{\cancel{2}}} = \frac{\overset{2}{\cancel{4}}}{\underset{1}{\cancel{2}}}$$ Divide both sides of the equation $2x = 4$ by 2 to obtain the value of x.

$x = 2$

When $y = 0$, $x = 2$, therefore, the point $(x, y) = (2, 0)$ is on the boundary line. Use the two points $(0, -4)$ and $(2, 0)$ which are on the boundary line to draw the boundary line which should be a continuous line because the inequality symbol is $\geq$ which means that the solution points are on the boundary line.

(The graph showing the boundary line is shown on the next page.)

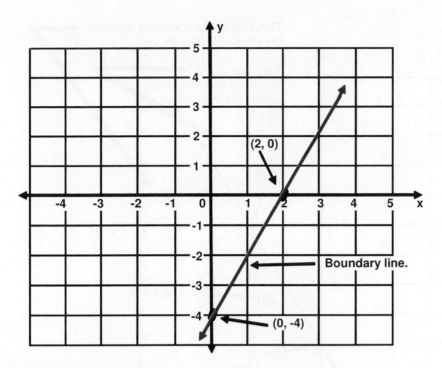

Step 2: Determine which side of the boundary line does the solution lie. Take any simple point such as (0, 0) which is not on the boundary line to test if the point satisfies the inequality or not as shown:

Substitute the point (0, 0) into the original inequality to test if the point (0, 0) satisfies the inequality or not as shown:

$2y + 4x \geq 8$ Original inequality.

$2(0) + 4(0) \geq 8$ Substitute $x = 0$ and $y = 0$ into the original equation.

$0 + 0 \geq 8$

$0 \geq 8$

Since $0 \geq 8$ is not true, (0, 0) is not a solution of $2y + 4x \geq 8$, and therefore, shade the side of the boundary line that does not include (0, 0) as the solution to the inequality as shown:

(The shaded area of the graph is shown on the next page.)

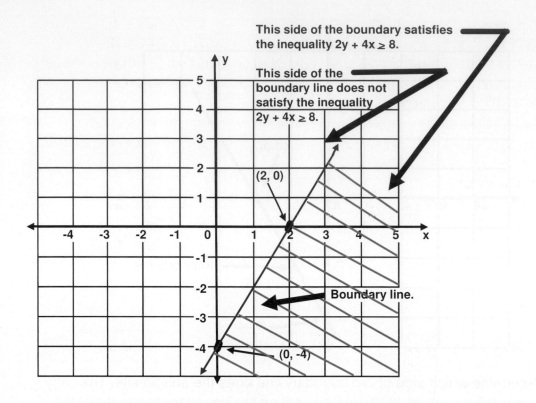

This side of the boundary satisfies the inequality $2y + 4x \geq 8$.

This side of the boundary line does not satisfy the inequality $2y + 4x \geq 8$.

(2, 0)

Boundary line.

(0, -4)

Exercises

1. Name the three sets of points that a linear equation divides the coordinate plane into. Hint: See the instructions in your book.

2. The dotted line in the graph of an inequality shows that the solution set of the inequality is not on the line. (True or False?).

3. When a graph of an inequality is a continuous or a solid line, it means that the solution set of points are not on the boundary line. (True or False?).
   Hint: See your textbook.

4. What are the three main steps that you would follow in graphing an inequality? Hint: See your textbook.

5. Graph each of the following inequalities. Hint: See Example 1.

    a. $y > x + 4$ **b.** $y > x + 1$ **c.** $y > x - 1$

    d. $-y > 2x - 1$ **e.** $y > -2x + 2$ **f.** $y > 3x + 2$

    g. $y > 3x - 2$ **h.** $y > 2x - 2$ **i.** $y > 3x - 1$

6. Solve each of the following inequalities. Hint: See Example 2.

    a. $x + 2y + 1 < 0$ **b.** $x + 2y - 1 < 0$ **c.** $2y + 2x < 1$

    d. $2x + 3y < 2$ **e.** $y < 2x - 1$ **f.** $2y < x + 2$

7. Graph each inequality. Hint: See Example 3.

    a. $y \leq x + 1$ **b.** $y \leq x + 2$ **c.** $y \leq x - 1$

    d. $y \leq 2x + 2$ **e.** $y \leq 2x - 1$ **f.** $y \leq 3x + 2$

8. Graph each inequality. Hint: See Example 4.

a. $2y + 3x \geq 2$ **b.** $2y \geq 2x + 4$ **c.** $2x + 2y \geq 4$

d. $x + 2y \geq 3$ **e.** $-2x + 2y \geq 3$ **f.** $3y + 4x \leq 12$

9. Tell whether each ordered pair is a solution of each inequality. Hint: Use the similar idea in Examples 1, 2, 3, and 4 where (0, 0) is substituted in the original inequality to test if (0, 0) is a solution set or not.

a. $y > 3x + 1$,   (0, 2)   **b.** $y < 2x - 3$,   (0, 0)   **c.** $y \geq x - 4$,   (2, 4)

d. $y \leq 4x - 2$,   (1, 4)   **e.** $y < -2x + 1$,   (3, 2)   **f.** $y \leq -3x + 4$,   (0, 0)

Challenge Questions

10. Graph each inequality.

   a. $4x + y \leq 2$ **b.** $y > x - 5$ **c.** $x - 2y \geq 1$

   d. $3x - 3y > 3$ **e.** $y \leq 6x - 4$ **f.** $3x + 2y - 4 > 0$

SIMULTANEOUS LINEAR INEQUALITIES IN TWO VARIABLES

What is meant by the solution set of a system of inequalities in x and y? The solution set of a system of inequalities in x and y is the **region of the intersection of the solution of all the individual inequalities represented on the same graph paper**. Every point in the intersecting region satisfies the system of the inequalities. A system of linear inequalities is a collection of linear inequalities.

How to Find the Solution Set of Simultaneous Linear Inequalities in Two Variables.

There are four main steps in finding the solution set of simultaneous linear inequalities in two variables as shown:

Step 1: Graph each inequality or the boundary line on the same coordinate plane by initially changing the inequality symbol to an equality symbol and then assign x = 0 and find y, also assign y = 0 and find x, and:

   (a). if the inequality symbol is $\leq$ or $\geq$, then the boundary line is included in the solution, and therefore, draw a continuous or solid line as the boundary line as _____.

   (b). if the inequality symbol is < or >, then the boundary line is not included in the solution, and therefore, draw a dotted line as the boundary line as _ _ _.

Step 2: Pick a point that is not on the boundary line and test the point to determine if the point is a solution to each inequality or not by substituting the point into each original inequality and then shade each solution set of each inequality.

Step 3: The intersection of the solution sets of the shaded region of the individual inequalities is the solution of the inequalities.

Step 4: Test a point from the intersection of the shaded region to determine if the point satisfies both inequalities or not.

Example 1

Solve the two inequalities by graphing.

$y \leq 2x - 1$

$y > -x + 2$

Solution

Step 1: Graph each inequality on the same coordinate plane.

To graph each inequality, initially change all the inequality symbols to equality symbols, find the value of y when $x = 0$, and then find the value of x when $y = 0$.

Considering $y \leq 2x - 1$ which initially becomes $y = 2x - 1$.

When $x = 0$, $y = 2x - 1$ becomes $y = 2(0) - 1 = -1$.   Substitute $x = 0$.

Therefore the point $(x, y) = (0, -1)$ is on $y = 2x - 1$.

When $y = 0$, $y = 2x - 1$ becomes $0 = 2x - 1$ Substitute $y = 0$.

$0 = 2x - 1$_____[A]

Subtract 2x from both sides of the equation [A] in order to isolate the 2x at the right side of the equation [A] as shown:

$0 - 2x = 2x - 2x - 1$

$-2x = -1$ $2x - 2x = 0$

Divide both sides of the equation $-2x = -1$ by -2 in order to obtain the value of x as shown:

$$\frac{-2x}{-2} = \frac{-1}{-2}$$

$$\frac{\overset{x}{\cancel{-2x}}}{-2} = \frac{-1}{-2}$$ A negative number divided by another negative number

1 results in a positive number.

$$x = \frac{1}{2}$$ A negative number divided by another negative number

results in a positive number.

Therefore, the point $(x, y) = (\frac{1}{2}, 0)$ is on $y \leq 2x - 1$.

Considering $y \geq -x + 2$ which initially becomes $y = -x + 2$.

When $x = 0$, $y = -x + 2$ becomes $y = -(0) + 2 = 2$.   Substitute $x = 0$.

Therefore, the point $(x, y) = (0, 2)$ is on $y = -x + 2$.

When $y = 0$, $y = -x + 2$ becomes $0 = -x + 2$.   Substitute $y = 0$.

$0 = -x + 2$_____[C]

Add x to both sides of equation [C] in order to eliminate -x from the right side of the equation $[C]$ as shown:

$0 + x = -x + x + 2$

$x = 2$ $-x + x = 0$

Therefore, the point $(x, y) = (2, 0)$ is on $y < -x + 2$.

Graph the two points $(0, -1)$ and $(\frac{1}{2}, 0)$ for the equation $y = 2x - 1$, and also graph

the points $(0, 2)$ and $(2, 0)$ for the equation $y = -x + 2$ as shown:

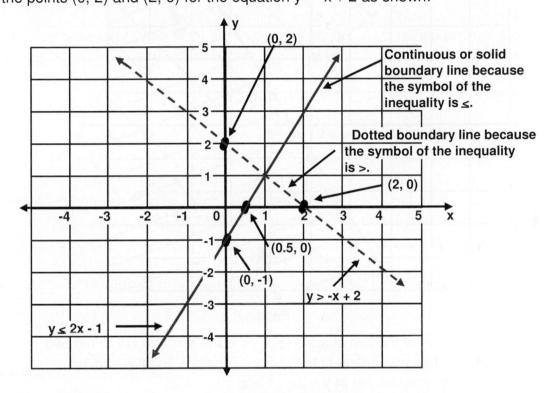

Step 2: Pick a point that is not on the boundary line and test the point to determine if the point is a solution to each inequality or not by substituting the point into each inequality and then shade each solution set of each inequality as shown:

Considering the inequality $y \leq 2x - 1$ and pick a point $(0, 0)$ to test for the solution set.

$y \leq 2x - 1$

$0 \leq 2(0) - 1$ Substitute $x = 0$ and $y = 0$.

$0 \leq -1$ This is not true.

Since $0 \leq -1$ is not true, shade the region that does not contain the point $(0, 0)$ and this region is labelled P.

Considering the inequality $y > -x + 2$ and again pick a point $(0, 0)$ to test for the solution set.

$y > -x + 2$

$0 > -0 + 2$ Substitute $x = 0$ and $y = 0$.

$0 > 2$

Since 0 > 2 is not true, shade the region that does not contain the point (0, 0) and this region is labelled K.

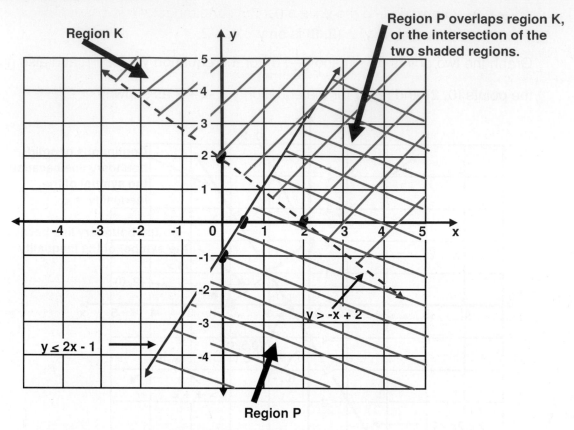

Region K

Region P overlaps region K, or the intersection of the two shaded regions.

$y \leq 2x - 1$

$y > -x + 2$

Region P

Step 3: The intersection of the two shaded regions is the solution set of the two inequalities. The intersection of the shaded region P and the shaded region K is the solution set of $y \leq 2x - 1$ and $y > -x + 2$.

Step 4: Check the solution by testing a point inside the intersecting region. The point (3, 0) is in the intersecting region, and therefore, substitute the point (3, 0) into the inequalities $y \leq 2x - 1$ and $y > -x + 2$ to check the solution set as shown:

Considering $y \leq 2x - 1$

$0 \leq 2(3) - 1$ Substitute x = 3 and y = 0.

$0 \leq 6 - 1$

$0 \leq 5$ which is true.

Considering $y > -x + 2$

$0 > -3 + 2$ Substitute x = 3 and y = 0.

$0 > -1$ This is true.

Therefore, the intersection of the two shaded regions is the solution set of the two inequalities.

Exercises

1. Describe how you would find the solution set of simultaneous linear inequalities in two variables. Hint: See your textbook.
2. Solve each pair of the inequalities by graphing. Hint: See Example 1.

    a. $y \leq -x + 9$ **b.** $y \leq -2x - 1$ **c.** $y \leq 3x - 4$
        $y < -2x + 12$ $y > x + 3$ $y < -2x + 6$

    d. $y > -2x - 6$ **e.** $2y + x \geq 8$ **f.** $x + y \geq 5$
        $y \leq -4x + 7$ $2x + y \leq 4$ $x - 2y < 8$

REAL WORLD APPLICATIONS OF INEQUALITIES IN TWO VARIABLES

How to Solve Real World Problems Involving Simultaneous Linear Inequalities.

The steps for solving word problems involving simultaneous linear inequalities are:

1. Write down the inequalities from the given question.
2. Graph each inequality and shade each solution set of each inequality.
3. Determine the region of intersection of all the shaded solution set regions.

Example 1

A machine produces x boxes of blue pencils and y boxes of red pencils each hour. The maximum minutes required to make a blue pencil is 3 minutes and the maximum minutes required to make a red pencil is 6 minutes.

a. Write the three inequalities that represent the information given.
b. Shade the region of the graph that is the solution set of each inequality.
c. What are the coordinates of each vertex that forms the region of the solution
    set of the inequalities?

Solution

a. If x represents the boxes of blue pencils and y represents the boxes of red pencils
    made in 1 hour, then we can write the following inequalities:

      $3x + 6y \leq 60$ 1 hour = 60 minutes
          $x \geq 0$ We cannot have negative boxes of blue pencils.
          $y \geq 0$ We cannot have negative boxes of red pencils.

b. To find the solution set of all the inequalities, graph each inequality in the solution
    of Example 1**a**, and then determine each solution set by shading the region which
    satisfies each solution set as shown:

    To graph $3x + 6y \leq 60$, $3x + 6y \leq 60$ becomes $3x + 6y = 60$, assign a value to x,
    and then find the corresponding value of y as shown:

    When x = 0, $3x + 6y = 60$ becomes $3(0) + 6y = 60$ Substitute x = 0

$$0 + 6y = 60$$
$$6y = 60$$

$$\frac{6y}{6} = \frac{60}{6}$$ Divide both sides of the equation by 6 in order to

obtain the value of y.

$$\frac{\overset{y}{\cancel{6}y}}{\underset{1}{\cancel{6}}} = \frac{\overset{10}{\cancel{60}}}{\underset{1}{\cancel{6}}}$$ Dividing by 6.

$$y = 10$$

When x = 0, y = 10, and therefore, the point (0, 10) is on the line
3x + 6y = 60. Now assign a value to y and then find the corresponding value
of x as shown:

When y = 0, 3x + 6y = 60 becomes 3x + 6(0) = 60   Substitute y = 0.
$$3x + 0 = 60$$
$$3x = 60$$

$$\frac{3x}{3} = \frac{60}{3}$$ Divide both sides of the equation 3x = 60 by 3

in order to obtain the value of x.

$$\frac{\overset{x}{\cancel{3}x}}{\underset{1}{\cancel{3}}} = \frac{\overset{20}{\cancel{60}}}{\underset{1}{\cancel{3}}}$$ Divide

When y = 0, x = 20, and therefore, the point (20, 0) is on the line 3x + 6y = 60.
Let us graph the equation 3x + 6y = 60 with the two points (0, 10)
and (20, 0), and also to determine the region of the solution set as shown:
Figure 1.

(Figure 1 is on the next page.)

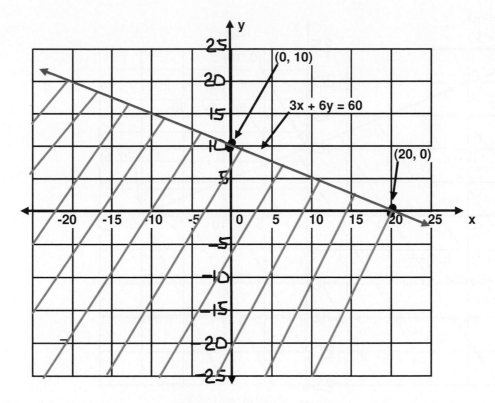

(Figure 1 is shown above.)

Substitute the point (0, 0) into the inequality $3x + 6y \leq 60$ in order to determine the region of the solution set as shown:

$3(0) + 6(0) \leq 60$ Substitute x = 0 and y = 0.

    $0 + 0 \leq 60$

      $0 \leq 60$ This is true.

Since $0 \leq 60$ is true, the region that includes the point (0, 0) is shaded, see the shaded region in Figure 1. Therefore, the shaded region in Figure 1 is the solution set of $3x + 6y \leq 60$.

Let us graph the inequality $x \geq 0$ by changing $x \geq 0$ to $x = 0$ and then determine which region of x = 0 is the solution set for $x \geq 0$ as shown:

x = 0 is the y-axis, and therefore, the graph of x = 0 is the y-axis. Let us pick a point (1, 1) to determine if (1, 1) is in the region of the solution set of $x \geq 0$ as shown:

      $x \geq 0$

      $1 \geq 0$ Substitute x = 1 into $x \geq 0$.

Since $1 \geq 0$ is true, the region that includes the point (1,1) is shaded, see Figure 2.

(Figure 2 is on the next page.)

257

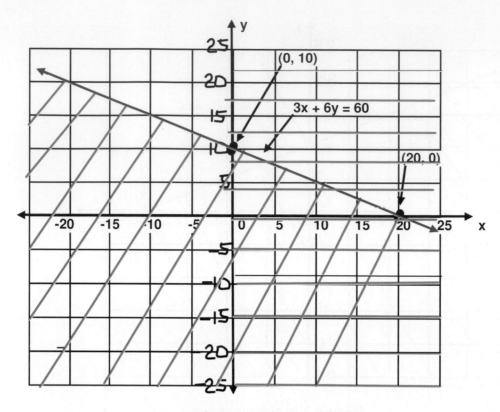

(Figure 2 is shown above.)

Let us graph the inequality $y \geq 0$ by changing $y \geq 0$ to $y = 0$ and then determine which region of $y = 0$ is the solution set of $y \geq o$ as shown:

$y = 0$ is the x-axis, and therefore, the graph of $y = 0$ is the x-axis.

Let us pick a point (1, -1) to determine if (1, -1) is in the region of the solution set of $y \geq 0$ as shown:

$$y \geq 0$$
$$-1 \geq 0 \qquad \text{Substitute } y = -1 \text{ into } y \geq 0.$$
$$-1 \geq 0 \qquad \text{This is not true.}$$

Since $-1 \geq 0$ is not true, we pick a point at the other region of the line $y = 0$. We can pick the point (1, 1) such that:

$$y \geq 0$$
$$1 \geq 0 \qquad \text{Substitute } y = 1 \text{ into } y \geq 0.$$
$$1 \geq 0 \qquad \text{This is true.}$$

Since $1 \geq 0$ is true, the point (1, 1) is in the region of the solution set of $y \geq 0$. Therefore, the region of the solution set of $y \geq 0$ is shaded. Note that $y = 0$ is the same as the x-axis, see Figure 3.

(Figure 3 is on the next page.)

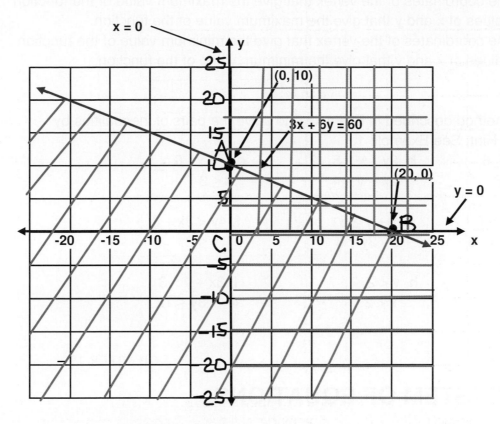

(Figure 3 is shown above.)

Therefore, the region of the solution set of $3x + 6y \leq 60$, $x \geq 0$ and $y \geq 0$ is the region where all the shaded parts intersect. This is the region enclosed by the triangle ABC in the Figure 3.

c. The coordinates of the vertices of the solution set of the inequalities $3x + 6y \leq 60$, $x \geq 0$, and $y \geq 0$ are the coordinates of the triangle ABC in Figure 3 as shown:

A(0,10), B(20,0), and C(0, 0).

How to Find the Maximum or the Minimum Value of a Function

The following steps can be followed in order to find the maximum or the minimum value of a function using the knowledge of inequalities in two variables:

1. Write down the function, for example, write down the function in x and y.
2. Substitute each coordinate of the vertices of the polygon that form the solution set of all the inequalities into the function (for example profit function) in order to determine the values of the function at the coordinates of each vertex.
3. Select the value of the function which is the largest as the maximum value of the function.
4. Select the value of the function which is the smallest as the minimum value of the function.

5. Select the coordinates of the vertex that give the maximum value of the function as the values of x and y that give the maximum value of the function.

6. Select the coordinates of the vertex that give the minimum value of the function as the values of x and y that give the minimum value of the function.

Exercises

1. Use the method described in Example 1 to solve the pairs of inequalities by graphing. Hint: See Example 1.

a. $x + 2y \leq 6$
   $x - y \leq 6$

b. $2y + x \geq 8$
   $2x + y \leq 4$

c. $y < x - 6$
   $y \leq 3$

d. $3x - 2y > 0$
   $2x + 3y < -3$

e. $x + y \geq 5$
   $x - 2y < 8$

f. $4y < 3x + 8$
   $y \leq 2$

g. $x \geq 5$
   $0 < y$

h. $y < 2$
   $x < 2$

i. $3x + y > 3$
   $4x + 3y \leq 12$

CHAPTER 13

SYSTEM OF EQUATIONS

Cumulative Review

1. Find each sum.
   a. $-21 + (-21) =$ **b.** $-2.1 + (-3.9) =$ **c.** $-100 + 95 =$ **d.** $3.7 + (-6.3)$
   Review the chapter on the Order of Operations if you cannot solve any of the questions.

2. Evaluate.
   a. $20 \div 4 \cdot 5 + 2 =$ **b.** $3 \cdot 3 + 9 \div 2 =$ **c.** $61 - 42 \div 6 =$ **d.** $50 - 24 \div 3 - 3 =$
   Review the chapter on the Order of Operations if you cannot solve any of the questions.

3. Mary said that to divide by a fraction is the same as to multiply by the reciprocal of the fraction. Is her statement correct? Hint: Review the section on Dividing by a Fraction in the MathMasters Series for grade 6.

4. Explain what is meant by the reciprocal of a number. Hint: Review the section on the Reciprocal of Numbers in the MathMasters Series for grade 6.

5. John said that $\dfrac{3}{4} \div \dfrac{5}{12} = 8$. Is his statement correct? Give reasons for your answer.

6. Solve:

   a. $\dfrac{3}{7} \div \dfrac{12}{4} =$ **b.** $17 \div \dfrac{17}{5} =$ **c.** $\dfrac{6}{5} \times \dfrac{3}{15} =$ **d.** $\dfrac{3}{5} - \dfrac{3}{50} =$

   Hint: Review the chapter on Fractions in the MathMasters Series for grade 6.

260

7. The measure of a side of a square is 8 ft.

    a. What is the perimeter of the square?

    b. What is the area of the square?

        Hint: Review the chapter on Perimeter and Area in the MathMasters Series for grade 6.

8. Describe how you will find the median, mean, and the mode of a data. Hint: Review the chapter of the MathMasters Series on Median, Mean, and Mode for grade 7.

Systems of Equations

Simultaneous equations are equations that have a common point (x, y) that satisfies both equations simultaneously or at the same time, and the point (x, y) is said to be the solution of the simultaneous equations. Simultaneous equations are usually called **systems of equations**. The three methods for solving simultaneous equations are **graphical**, **elimination by addition or subtraction**, and **substitution**.

Graphical Method

The graphical method for solving equations simultaneously is to draw the graph of each equation on the same coordinate plane and the point of the intersection of the lines of each equation is the solution of the equations.

Example 1

Solve the pair of the equations graphically.

$$y = x + 1$$
$$y = 3x - 2$$

Solution

Step 1: Create a table for $y = x + 1$ and $y = 3x - 2$ by assigning a value to x and then finding the corresponding value for y as shown:

Table for $y = x + 1$

x	y = f(x) = x + 1	y	(x, y)
-1	y = f(-1) = -1 + 1 = 0	0	(-1, 0)
0	y = f(0) = 0 + 1 = 1	1	(0, 1)
1	y = f(1) = 1 + 1 = 2	2	(1, 2)

Table for $y = 3x - 2$

x	y = f(x) = 3x - 2	y	(x, y)
-1	y = f(-1) = 3(-1) - 2 = -3 - 2 = -5	-5	(-1, -5)
0	y = f(0) = 3(0) - 2 = 0 - 2 = -2	-2	(0, -2)
1	y = f(1) = 3(1) - 2 = 3 - 2 = 1	1	(1, 1)

Note: When drawing a graph of a linear equation, it is not necessary to plot more than three points for each equation.

Step 2: Plot the graph of each equation using the (x, y) points in the tables for each equation. Use a ruler to draw a line through the points of each equation as shown:

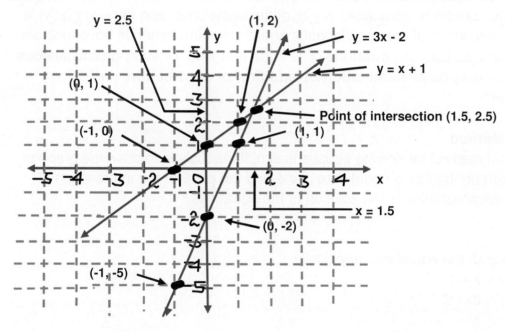

Step 3: Graphical analysis

From the graph, since the lines intersect or cross each other at the point $(1\frac{1}{2}, 2\frac{1}{2})$, then $(1\frac{1}{2}, 2\frac{1}{2})$ or $x = 1\frac{1}{2}$ and $y = 2\frac{1}{2}$ are the solutions of

the pair of the equations. Note that $(1\frac{1}{2}, 2\frac{1}{2})$ is the same as (1.5, 2.5).

Step 4: Check your answer.

You can check your answer by substituting the values of the solutions into the original equations as shown:

The original equations are:

$$y = x + 1$$
$$y = 3x - 2$$

From Step 3, the solution is $(1\frac{1}{2}, 2\frac{1}{2})$ or $x = 1\frac{1}{2}$ and $y = 2\frac{1}{2}$.

Substitute $(1\frac{1}{2}, 2\frac{1}{2})$, or $x = 1\frac{1}{2}$ and $y = 2\frac{1}{2}$ into the equation $y = x + 1$ as shown:

$$y = x + 1$$

$$2\frac{1}{2} = 1\frac{1}{2} + 1 \qquad\qquad\qquad\qquad x = 1\frac{1}{2}$$

$$2\frac{1}{2} = 2\frac{1}{2} \qquad\qquad\qquad\qquad 1\frac{1}{2} + 1 = 2\frac{1}{2}$$

Since the left side of the equation equals the right side of the equation, $x = 1\frac{1}{2}$ and $y = 2\frac{1}{2}$ are the correct solutions of $y = x + 1$.

Substitute $(1\frac{1}{2}, 2\frac{1}{2})$ or $x = 1\frac{1}{2}$ and $y = 2\frac{1}{2}$ into the equation $y = 3x - 2$ as shown:

$$y = 3x - 2$$

$$2\frac{1}{2} = 3(1\frac{1}{2}) - 2 \qquad\qquad\qquad x = 1\frac{1}{2} \text{ and } y = 2\frac{1}{2}$$

$$2\frac{1}{2} = 3(\frac{3}{2}) - 2 \qquad\qquad\qquad\qquad 1\frac{1}{2} = \frac{3}{2}$$

$$2\frac{1}{2} = \frac{9}{2} - 2 \qquad\qquad\qquad 3(\frac{3}{2}) = 3 \times \frac{3}{2} = \frac{9}{2}$$

$$2\frac{1}{2} = 4\frac{1}{2} - 2 \qquad\qquad\qquad\qquad \frac{9}{2} = 4\frac{1}{2}$$

$$2\frac{1}{2} = 2\frac{1}{2} \qquad\qquad\qquad\qquad 4\frac{1}{2} - 2 = 2\frac{1}{2}$$

Since the left side of the equation equals the right side of the equation, $x = 1\frac{1}{2}$ and $y = 2\frac{1}{2}$ are the correct solutions to $y = x + 1$ and $y = 3x - 2$.

Example 2
Solve graphically the pair of equations.

$$x - 2y = 1$$
$$2x + y = 2$$

Solution

Step 1: Rearrange each equation so that y is isolated and this will help in creating a table for the equation as shown:

$$x - 2y = 1$$

$$x - x - 2y = 1 - x$$ Subtract x from both sides of the equation to isolate -2y.

$$-2y = 1 - x \underline{\hspace{4cm}}[A]$$

$$x - x = 0$$

Divide both sides of the equation [A] by -2 to obtain the value of y as shown:

$$\frac{-2y}{-2} = \frac{1 - x}{-2}$$

$$\frac{-2\overset{y}{\cancel{y}}}{\underset{1}{\cancel{-2}}} = \frac{1 - x}{-2} \qquad \text{Divide}$$

$$y = \frac{1 - x}{-2} \underline{\hspace{5cm}}[B]$$

The second equation is $2x + y = 2$ $\underline{\hspace{3cm}}$[C]

Again, rearrange each equation so that y is isolated and this will help in creating a table for the equation as shown:

Subtract 2x from both sides of equation [C] in order to isolate y as shown:

$$2x - 2x + y = 2 - 2x$$

$$0 + y = 2 - 2x \qquad\qquad 2x - 2x = 0$$

$$y = -2x + 2 \underline{\hspace{3cm}}[D]$$

Rearranging the terms.

Step 2: Create a table for equations [B] and [D] by assigning a value to x and then finding the corresponding value for y as shown:

Table for Equation $y = \dfrac{1 - x}{-2}$

x	$y = f(x) = \dfrac{1 - x}{-2}$	y	(x, y)
-1	$y = f(-1) = \dfrac{1 - (-1)}{-2} = \dfrac{1 + 1}{-2} = \dfrac{2}{-2} = -1$	-1	(-1, -1)
0	$y = f(0) = \dfrac{1 - 0}{-2} = \dfrac{1}{-2} = \dfrac{1}{-2}$	$-\dfrac{1}{2}$	$(0, -\dfrac{1}{2})$
1	$y = f(1) = \dfrac{1 - 1}{-2} = \dfrac{0}{-2} = 0$	0	(1, 0)

Table for Equation y = -2x + 2

x	y = f(x) = -2x + 2	y	(x , y)
-1	y = f(-1) = -2(-1) + 2 = 2 + 2 = 4	4	(-1, 4)
0	y = f(0) = -2(0) + 2 = 0 + 2 = 2	2	(0, 2)
1	y = f(1) = -2(1) + 2 = -2 + 2 = 0	0	(1, 0)

Note: When drawing a graph of a linear equation using a chart, it is not necessary to plot more than three points for each equation.

Step 3: Plot the graph of each equation using the points (x, y) in the table for each equation. Use a ruler or a straight edge to draw a line through the points plotted for each equation as shown:

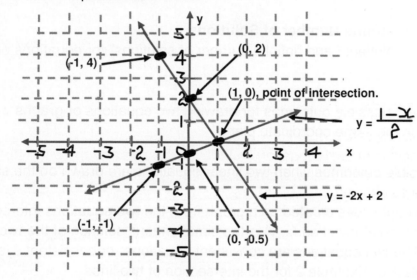

Note on the graph that the point (0, -0.5) is the same as $(0, -\frac{1}{2})$.

Step 4: Graph analysis:

From the graph, we can see that the lines intersect or cross each other at point (1,0). The point (1, 0) or x = 1 and y = 0 is the solution of the pair of the equations.

Step 5: Check your answer:

You can check your answer by substituting the values of the solution into the original equation as shown:

The original equations are:

$$x - 2y = 1$$
$$2x + y = 2$$

From Step 4, the solution is (1, 0).

Substitute (1, 0) or x = 1 and y = 0 into the equation x - 2y = 1 as shown:

$$x - 2y = 1$$

265

$$1 - 2(0) = 1$$
$$1 - 0 = 1$$
$$1 = 1$$

$x = 1$ and $y = 0$.

Since the left side of the equation equals the right side of the equation, $x = 1$ and $y = 0$ is the correct solution of $x - 2y = 1$.

Substitute $(1, 0)$ or $x = 1$ and $y = 0$ into the original equation $2x + y = 2$ as shown:

$$2x + y = 2$$
$$2(1) + 0 = 2$$
$$2 + 0 = 2$$
$$2 = 2$$

$x = 1$ and $y = 0$.

Since the left side of the equation equals the right side of the equation, $x = 1$ and $y = 0$ is the correct solution of $2x + y = 2$. Therefore, $(1, 0)$ or $x = 1$ and $y = 0$ is the correct solution to both $x - 2y = 1$ and $2x + y = 2$.

No Solutions and Infinite Number of Solutions
(How to solve "no solutions" and "infinite number of solutions" for equations or graphs.)

Example 3
Describe fully the 3 possible outcomes for drawing two equations or graphs simultaneously on the same coordinate plane.

Solution

There are 3 possible outcomes when two linear equations are drawn on the same coordinate plane as shown:

1. If the two straight lines created on a graph from the two equations intersect, then the point of intersection (x, y) is the simultaneous solution of the two equations. The two equations are consistent equations, or consistent systems. See Example 1 or Example 2 for the intersection of two lines.

2. If the two straight lines created on the graph from the two equations are parallel, (that is, there is no intersection), then the two equations have no simultaneous solution, and the two equations are called inconsistent equations or inconsistent systems. An example of inconsistent equations with graphs are as shown:

Let us consider equations **$x + y = 2$** and **$2x + 2y = 8$**.

$x + y = 2$ becomes $y = -x + 2$ when x is subtracted from both sides of the equation.

$$x + y - x = 2 - x$$
$$y = 2 - x$$
$$y = -x + 2$$

$2x + 2y = 8$ becomes $y = \dfrac{-2x + 8}{2}$ when $2x$ is subtracted from both sides of the equation and the result is divided by 2.

$$2x - 2x + 2y = 8 - 2x$$
$$2y = 8 - 2x$$

$$\frac{2y}{2} = \frac{8 - 2x}{2}$$

$$y = \frac{8 - 2x}{2}$$

The numerator of $y = \frac{8 - 2x}{2}$ can be switched to obtain $y = \frac{-2x + 8}{2}$.

Now we can create a table for $y = -x + 2$ and $y = \frac{-2x + 8}{2}$.

Table of y = -x + 2

x	y = f(x) = -x + 2	y	(x, y)
-1	y = f(-1) = -(-1) + 2 = 1 + 2 = 3	3	(-1, 3)
0	y = f(0) = 0 + 2 = 2	2	(0, 2)
1	y = f(1) = -1 + 2 = 1	1	(1, 1)

Table of $y = \frac{-2x + 8}{2}$

x	$y = f(x) = \frac{-2x + 8}{2}$	y	(x, y)
-1	$y = f(-1) = \frac{-2(-1) + 8}{2} = \frac{2 + 8}{2} = \frac{10}{2} = 5$	5	(-1, 5)
0	$y = f(0) \frac{-2(0) + 8}{2} = \frac{8}{2} = 4$	4	(0, 4)
1	$y = f(1) = \frac{-2(1) + 8}{2} = \frac{-2 + 8}{2} = \frac{6}{2} = 3$	3	(1, 3)

Plot the graph of each equation using the points (x, y) in the table for each equation. Use a ruler or a straight edge to draw a line through the points plotted of each equation as shown:

(The graph is shown on the next page.)

267

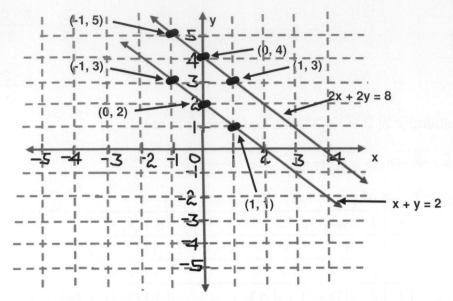

3. If the same straight line is created twice on the same coordinate plane, by two equations, then the equations are dependent and every point on the line represents a solution to the two equations. Since there are an infinite number of points on a line, there are an infinite number of simultaneous solutions to the two equations.

These types of equations with simultaneous solutions are also referred to as consistent equations or consistent system. An example of consistent equations or consistent system by graph is as shown:

$$x + y = 1 \underline{\hspace{5cm}} [A]$$
$$2x + 2y = 2 \underline{\hspace{5cm}} [B]$$

Notice that when equation $[A]$ is multiplied by 2 it will give equation $[B]$. Therefore, the graph of equation $[A]$ is the same as the graph of equation $[B]$. Subtract x from both sides of equation $[A]$ to obtain the value of y and create a table for x and y as shown:

$$x + y = 1$$
$$x - x + y = 1 - x \qquad\qquad \text{Subtract x from both sides of the equation } [A].$$
$$y = 1 - x$$

Now we can make a table of $y = 1 - x$ as shown:

x	y = f(x) = 1 - x	y	(x, y)
-1	y = f(-1) = 1 - (-1) = 1 + 1 = 2	2	(-1, 2)
0	y = f(0) = 1 - 0 = 1	1	(0, 1)
1	y = f(1) = 1 - 1 = 0	0	(1, 0)

Plot the graph of each equation using the points (x, y) in the table for each equation. Use a ruler or a straight edge to draw a line through the points plotted for each equation as shown:

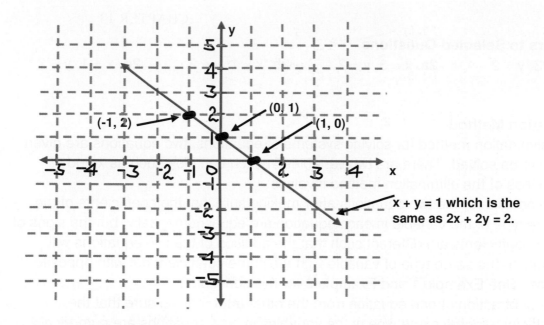

(-1, 2)   (0, 1)   (1, 0)

x + y = 1 which is the
same as 2x + 2y = 2.

Exercises

1. Solve the following pairs of equations graphically. Check your answers.
   Hint: See Example 1.

   a. y = x + 2
   y = 2x - 3

   b. y = 2x + 1
   y = 3x - 3

   c. y = x - 1
   y = -x + 5

2. Solve the following pairs of equations graphically. Check your answers.
   Hint: See Example 2. Hint: Review how to solve for y in each equation
   before making the tables.

   a. x - y = 1
   x + 2y = 7

   b. x + y = 3
   3x - y = 1

   c. y = 2x + 2
   3x + 2y = 4

   d. x + 3y = 0
   x - 3y = 6

   e. 3y = 2x + 8
   x + y = 1

   f. x - y = 0
   3x - y + 2 = 0

   g. y = x + 1
   x + y = 3

   h. 2x + y = 0
   x + 2y = 3

   i. 3x + y = 11
   y = 2x - 4

3. Explain what is meant by "there are an infinite number of simultaneous solutions to
   two equations." Hint: See Example 3.

4. Explain in one sentence how two lines on a graph can have no solutions.
   Hint: See Example 3.

5. Explain by graphing and algebraically how each pair of equations may have one
   solution, no solution, or infinitely many solutions. Hint: See Example 3.

   a. x + y = 1
   3x + 3y = 3

   b. x + y = 2
   2x + 2y = 8

   c. 2x - y = 1
   x + 2y = 3

6. Using the solutions from Exercise 5, determine which sets of equations form
   consistent or inconsistent equations or systems. Hint: See Example 3.

Answers to Selected Questions

1c. $x = 3$, $y = 2$ **2a.** $x = 3$, $y = 2$ **2b.** $x = 1$, $y = 2$ **2g.** $x = 1$, $y = 2$

Elimination Method

In the elimination method for solving systems of equations, two equations are given that are to be solved. There are two variables in each equation such as x and y. The process of the elimination method involves:

1. The addition of the two equations after making sure that the coefficients of the same type of the variable in each equation are equal numerically, but the signs of their coefficients are different such that the addition of the two equations will eliminate the same type of variable with the same coefficient but with opposite signs. See Example 1 and Example 2 for this concept.

2. The subtraction of one equation from the other after making sure that the coefficients of the same type of the variables in both equations are numerically equal, and with the same signs such that the subtraction of one equation from the other will eliminate the same variable type with equal numerical coefficient and with the same sign. See Examples 3 and 4 for this concept.

Example1

Solve the equations by using the elimination method.

$$x + y = 4$$
$$2x - y = 5$$

Solution

Step 1: Add both of the equations to eliminate y.

The coefficient of y in the equation $x + y = 4$ is 1 and the sign of the coefficient is positive. The coefficient of y in the equation $2x - y = 5$ is -1, so the sign of the coefficient of y is negative. This means that the coefficients of y in both equations are the same, but their signs are opposite so we can add the two equations together in order to eliminate y as follows:

Add.

$$
\begin{array}{r}
x + y = 4 \\
2x - y = 5 \\
\hline
3x \quad = 9
\end{array}
$$ [A]

Note: $+y - y = 0$

Divide both sides of equation [A] by 3 in order to obtain the value of x as shown:

$$\frac{3x}{3} = \frac{9}{3}$$

$$\frac{\overset{1}{\cancel{3}}x}{\underset{1}{\cancel{3}}} = \frac{\overset{3}{\cancel{9}}}{\underset{3}{\cancel{3}}}$$

$$x = 3$$

Step 2: Substitute x = 3 into either of the original equations to obtain the value of y.

Now substitute x = 3 into either of the original equations, such as x + y = 4 in order to find the value of y as shown:

x + y = 4	
3 + y = 4	Substitute x = 3.
3 - 3 + y = 4 - 3	Subtract 3 from both sides of the equation to obtain the value of y.
y = 1	3 - 3 = 0 and 4 - 3 = 1.

The solution of the systems of equations is x = 3 and y = 1 or the point (3, 1).

Example 2

Find the values of x and y if x + y = 2 and 3x - 2y = 1. Use the elimination method.

Solution

The equations are:

$$x + y = 2 \underline{\hspace{4cm}}[A]$$
$$3x - 2y = 1 \underline{\hspace{4cm}}[B]$$

Step 1: Eliminate the variable y by the addition of the two equations.

Let us eliminate the variable y by the addition of equation [A] and [B]. However, the coefficient of y in equation [A] is 1, but the coefficient of y in equation [B] is 2. Although their signs are opposite, we cannot eliminate y by adding equations [A] and [B]. We should first make the coefficients of y in equations [A] and [B] the same as shown:

Multiply both sides of equation [A] by 2 so that the coefficient of y in equation [A] will become the same as the coefficient of y in equation [B] as shown:

2(x + y) = 2 · 2	Multiply both sides of the equation by 2.
2x + 2y = 4 \underline{\hspace{2cm}}[C}	

Equation [A] now becomes equation [C]. Now let us add equation [C] and equation [B] together as shown:

Add

$$\begin{array}{r} 2x + 2y = 4 \\ 3x - 2y = 1 \\ \hline 5x \quad\quad = 5 \underline{\hspace{3cm}}[D] \\ +2y - 2y = 0 \end{array}$$

Divide both sides of equation [D] by 5 in order to obtain the value of x as shown:

$$\frac{5x}{5} = \frac{5}{5}$$

271

$$\frac{\overset{1}{\cancel{5}}x}{\underset{1}{\cancel{5}}} = \frac{\overset{1}{\cancel{5}}}{\underset{1}{\cancel{5}}}$$

$$x = 1$$

Step 2: Substitute $x = 1$ into the original equation to obtain the value of y.
Now substitute $x = 1$ into either of the original equations such as
$x + y = 2$ in order to find the value of y as shown:

$x + y = 2$	
$1 + y = 2$	Substitute $x = 1$.
$1 - 1 + y = 2 - 1$	Subtract 1 from both sides of the equation in order to obtain the value of y.
$y = 1$	$1 - 1 = 0$ and $2 - 1 = 1$

Therefore, the values of x and y are $x = 1$ and $y = 1$ or the solution is the point (1, 1).

Example 3
Solve the system of equations. Use the elimination method.

$$x - y = 1$$
$$x + 2y = 7$$

Solution
The equations are:

$x - y = 1$ _____[A]
$x + 2y = 7$ _____[B]

Step 1: Eliminate the variable x by subtracting equation [B] from equation [A].
It will be easier to eliminate x because the coefficients of x in both equation [A] and equation [B] are 1 and both of the coefficients have positive signs.
Therefore, we can subtract equation [B] from equation [A] in order to eliminate the variable x as shown:
Subtract.

$$x - y = 1$$
$$\underline{x + 2y = 7}$$
$$x - x - y - (+2y) = 1 - 7$$
$$0 - y - 2y = -6 \qquad\qquad x - x = 0, -(+ = -, -(+2y = -2y$$
$$-3y = -6 \text{ _____[C]}$$
$$\qquad\qquad\qquad\qquad -y - 2y = -3y$$

Divide both sides of equation [C] by -3 in order to obtain the value of y as shown:

$$\frac{-3y}{-3} = \frac{-6}{-3}$$

$$\frac{-3y}{-3} = \frac{-6}{-3}$$

$$y = 2$$

Step 2: Substitute y = 2 into either of the original equations to obtain the value of x.

Now substitute x = 2 into either of the original equations such as x - y = 1 in order to find the value of x as shown:

$$x - y = 1$$
$$x - 2 = 1 \qquad \text{Substitute } y = 2.$$
$$x - 2 + 2 = 1 + 2 \qquad \text{Add 2 to both sides of the equation in order to obtain the value of x.}$$
$$x = 3 \qquad\qquad -2 + 2 = 0$$

The solution to the system of equation is x = 3 and y = 2 or the point (3, 2).

Example 4

Use the method of elimination to solve for x and y if x + 2y = 5 and 2x + y = 4.

Solution

The equations are:

$$x + 2y = 5 \qquad\qquad\qquad\qquad \text{[A]}$$
$$2x + y = 4 \qquad\qquad\qquad\qquad \text{[B]}$$

Step 1: Eliminate the variable x by subtracting equation [B] from equation [A].

Let us eliminate the variable x by subtracting equation [B] from equation [A]. The coefficient of x in equation [A] is 1 but the coefficient of x in equation [B] is 2, and therefore, we cannot eliminate x by subtracting equation [B] from equation [A]. In order to eliminate x by subtraction, we have to make the coefficients of x in the equation [A] be the same as the coefficient of the x in equation [B] by multiplying both sides of equation [A] by 2 as shown:

$$2(x + 2y) = 5 \cdot 2 \qquad \text{Multiply both sides of equation [A] by 2.}$$
$$2x + 2 \cdot 2y = 10$$
$$2x + 4y = 10 \qquad\qquad\qquad \text{[C]}.$$

Equation [A] then becomes equation [C].

Now let us subtract equation [B] from equation [C] as shown:

Subtract.

$$2x + 4y = 10$$
$$2x + y = 4$$
$$\overline{2x - 2x + 4y - y = 10 - 4}$$
$$3y = 6 \qquad\qquad\qquad \text{[D]}$$

$$2x - 2x = 0, \; 4y - y = 3y, \; \text{and } 10 - 4 = 6$$

Divide both sides of equation [D] by 3 in order to obtain the value of y as shown:

$$\frac{3y}{3} = \frac{6}{3}$$

$$\frac{\overset{y}{\cancel{3y}}}{\underset{1}{\cancel{3}}} = \frac{\overset{2}{\cancel{6}}}{\underset{1}{\cancel{3}}}$$

$$y = 2$$

Step 2: Substitute y = 2 into either of the original equations to obtain the value of x. Now substitute y = 2 into any of the original equations such as x + 2y = 5 in order to find the value of x as shown:

x + 2y = 5	
x + 2 • 2 = 5	Substitute y = 2.
x + 4 = 5	
x + 4 - 4 = 5 - 4	Subtract 4 from both sides of the equation in order to obtain the value of x.
x = 1	4 - 4 = 0 and 5 - 4 = 1

Therefore, the solutions of the system of equations is x = 1 and y = 2 or the point (1, 2).

How to Solve System of Equations or Functions by Modifying Both Equations Given Before Eliminating One Variable.

At times the coefficients in the system of equations are such that even modifying just one of the two equations will not create the same type of variable with the same coefficient as the second equation so that one type of the variables can be eliminated by subtraction (see Example 4, Step 1). In this situation, both the two equations or functions given should be modified first in order to create equal coefficients for the same type of variable such as x or y in both equations. So that the variable with the same type of coefficients can be eliminated by either the addition (see Example 5, Method A) or the subtraction (see Example 5, Method B) method.

Example 5

Solve the system of equations.

$$3x + 2y = 12$$
$$5x - 3y = 1$$

Solution

Method A

a. The given equations are:

$$3x + 2y = 12 \underline{\hspace{4cm}}[A]$$
$$5x - 3y = 1 \underline{\hspace{4cm}}[B]$$

Step 1: To eliminate the variable y.

Notice from the two given equations that we cannot just modify the coefficients of either of the variables of equation [A] to be equal to the coefficients of the variables x or y of equation [B]. Therefore, we have to modify both equations [A] and [B] first in order to create equal coefficients for the same type of variable such as x or y in both equation [A] and [B] so that when equation [A] is **added** to equation [B], one type of the variable (y) will be eliminated as shown:

Add

$$9x + 6y = 36 \underline{\qquad} C]$$ Multiply equation [A] by 3 such that $3(3x + 2y) = 12 \cdot 3$

$$\underline{10x - 6y = 2 \underline{\qquad} [D]}$$ Multiply equation [B] by 2 such that $2(5x - 3y) = 1 \cdot 2$.

$$19x \qquad = 38$$ Add equations [C] and [D] to eliminate y.

$$+6y - 6y = 0$$

Divide both sides of the equation $19x = 38$ by 19 in order to obtain the value of x as shown:

$$\frac{19x}{19} = \frac{38}{19}$$ Divide both sides of the equation by 19.

$$\frac{\overset{x}{\cancel{19x}}}{\underset{1}{\cancel{19}}} = \frac{\overset{2}{\cancel{38}}}{\underset{1}{\cancel{19}}}$$

$$x = 2$$

Step 2: Substitute $x = 2$ into either of the original equations [A] or [B] in order to obtain the value of y. Now substitute $x = 2$ into either of the original equations such as $3x + 2y = 12$ or $5x - 3 = 1$ in order to find the value of y as shown:

$$3x + 2y = 12$$

$$3 \cdot 2 + 2y = 12 \qquad \text{Substitute } x = 2.$$

$$6 + 2y = 12 \underline{\qquad} [E]$$

$$6 - 6 + 2y = 12 - 6 \qquad \text{Subtract 6 from both sides of the equation [E]}$$
in order to isolate 2y.

$$2y = 6 \qquad 6 - 6 = 0 \text{ and } 12 - 6 = 6$$

Divide both sides of the equation $2y = 6$ by 2 in order to obtain the value of y as shown:

$$\frac{2y}{2} = \frac{6}{2}$$ Divide both sides of the equation by 2.

$$\frac{\overset{y}{\cancel{2y}}}{\underset{1}{\cancel{2}}} = \frac{\overset{3}{\cancel{6}}}{\underset{1}{\cancel{2}}}$$

$$y = 3$$

275

The solution of the system of equations is $x = 2$ and $y = 3$ or in other words, the lines intersect at the point $(2, 3)$.

Method B

Step 1: Let us rather eliminate x first so that we can find the value of y first.

The original given equations are:

$3x + 2y = 12$ _____[F]	
$5x - 3y = 1$ _____[G]	
$15x + 10y = 60$ _____[H]	Multiply equation [F] by 5.
$15x - 9y = 3$ _____[I]	Multiply equation [G] by 3.
$15x - 15x + 10y - (-9y) = 60 - 3$	Subtract equation [I] from equation [H] to eliminate x.
$10y + 9y = 57$	$15x - 15x = 0, - (-9y) = + 9y.$
$19y = 57$	$10y + 9y = 19y, 60 - 3 = 57.$

Divide both sides of the equation $19y = 57$ by 19 in order to obtain the value of y as shown:

$$\frac{19y}{19} = \frac{57}{19} \qquad \text{Divide both sides of the equation by 19.}$$

$$\frac{\overset{y}{\cancel{19y}}}{\underset{1}{\cancel{19}}} = \frac{\overset{3}{\cancel{57}}}{\underset{1}{\cancel{19}}}$$

$$y = 3$$

Step 2: Substitute $y = 3$ into either of the original equations, which are equation [F] or equation [G] in order to obtain the value of x.

Now substitute $y = 3$ into either of the original equations such as $3x + 2y = 12$ or $5x - 3y = 1$ in order to find the value of x as shown:

$3x + 2y = 12$	
$3x + 2 \cdot 3 = 12$	Substitute $y = 3$.
$3x + 6 = 12$	$2 \cdot 3 = 6.$
$3x + 6 - 6 = 12 - 6$	Subtract 6 from both sides of the equation in order to isolate 3x.
$3x = 6$	$6 - 6 = 0, 12 - 6 = 6.$

Divide both sides of the equation $3x = 6$ by 3 in order to obtain the value of x as shown:

$$\frac{3x}{3} = \frac{6}{3} \qquad \text{Divide both sides of the equation by 3.}$$

$$\frac{\overset{1}{\cancel{3}x}}{\underset{1}{\cancel{3}}} = \frac{\overset{2}{\cancel{6}}}{\underset{1}{\cancel{3}}}$$

$$x \quad 2$$

$$y = 2$$

The solutions of the system of equations is $x = 2$ and $y = 3$ or in other words, the lines intersect at the point (2, 3).

Note that both Method A and Method B give the same solution of $x = 2$ and $y = 3$.

Substitution Method

The substitution method involves finding the value of either x or y in one of the two given equations and then substituting the value of the variable found into the second equation in order to find the value of the second variable. The substitution method is most appropriate when the coefficient of either x or y, or both x and y are 1 in order to avoid complicated fractional computations as in Example 3.

Example 1

Solve the system of equations using the substitution method.

$$2x + y = 7$$
$$3x - 2y = 7$$

Solution

The original equations are:

$$2x + y = 7 \underline{\hspace{4cm}} [A]$$
$$3x - 2y = 7 \underline{\hspace{4cm}} [B]$$

Step 1: Find the value of y in the first equation and then substitute it in the second equation to obtain the value of x.

Since the coefficient of y in the first equation is 1, it is easier to find the value of y in the first equation, and then substitute it into the second equation to obtain the value of x as shown:

$$2x + y = 7 \underline{\hspace{4cm}} [A]$$

$$2x - 2x + y = 7 - 2x \qquad \text{Subtract } 2x \text{ from both sides of equation } [A]$$
in order to obtain the value of x.

$$0 + y = 7 - 2x \qquad 2x - 2x = 0$$

$$y = 7 - 2x$$

Now substitute $y = 7 - 2x$ into the equation [B] and then solve for x as shown:

$$3x - 2y = 7 \underline{\hspace{4cm}} [B]$$

$$3x - 2(7 - 2x) = 7 \qquad \text{Substitute } y = 7 - 2x.$$

$$3x - 2 \cdot 7 - 2(-2x) = 7$$

$3x - 14 + 4x = 7$ $-2(-2) = +4$ and $-2(-2x) = +4x$

$7x - 14 = 7$ $3x + 4x = 7x$

$7x - 14 + 14 = 7 + 14$ Add 14 to both sides of the equation in order to isolate $7x$.

$7x - 0 = 21$ $-14 + 14 = 0$

$7x = 21$

Divide both sides of the equation $7x = 21$ by 7 in order to obtain the value of x.

$$\frac{7x}{7} = \frac{21}{7}$$ Divide both sides of the equation by 7.

$$\frac{\overset{x}{\cancel{7x}}}{\underset{1}{\cancel{7}}} = \frac{\overset{1}{\cancel{21}}}{\underset{1}{\cancel{7}}}$$

$$x = 3$$

Step 2: Substitute $x = 3$ into either of the original equations, to obtain the value of y.

Now substitute $x = 3$ into $2x + y = 7$ as shown:

$2x + y = 7$

$2 \cdot 3 + y = 7$ Substitute $x = 3$

$6 + y = 7$ $2 \cdot 3 = 6$

$6 - 6 + y = 7 - 6$ Subtract 6 from both sides of the equation in order to obtain the value of y.

$0 + y = 1$ $6 - 6 = 0$ and $7 - 6 = 1$.

$y = 1$

The solution of the system of equations is $x = 3$ and $y = 1$ or in other words, the lines intersect at point (3, 1).

Exercises

1. Solve the system of equations by using the elimination method.
Hint: See Example 1.

a. $x + 2y = 7$ **b.** $4x + 2y = -8$ **c.** $x + 3y = 0$ **d.** $2x - 2y = 2$

     $3x - 2y = -3$ $6x - 2y = -27$ $x - 3y = 6$ $x + 2y = 7$

e. $3x + 2y = 10$ **f.** $10x + 2y = 0$

     $8x - 2y = 12$ $3x - 2y = 13$

2. Solve the system of equations by using the elimination method.
Hint: See Example 2.

a. $3x + 2y = 10$ **b.** $5x + y = 0$ **c.** $x - 2y = 1$ **d.** $2x + y = 7$

     $4x - y = 6$ $3x - 2y = 13$ $2x - y = 2$ $3x - 2y = 7$

e. $5x + y = 0$ **f.** $x + y = 29$
     $3x - 2y = 13$ $2x - 2y = 6$

3. Solve the system of equations by using the elimination method.
   Hint: See Example 3.

   a. $x - y = 1$ **b.** $5x + 3y = 1$ **c.** $x - y = 0$ **d.** $2x - 4y = 2$
       $x + y = 5$ $2x + 3y = -5$ $3x - y = -2$ $2x + y = 2$

   e. $x + 3y = 0$ **f.** $3x + 3y = 9$ **g.** $2x + 4y = 28$ **h.** $x + 6y = 3$
       $x - 3y = 6$ $3x - y = 1$ $2x + 3y = 24$ $x + y = -2$

4. Use the method of elimination to solve for x and y in the system of equations.
   Hint: See Example 4.

   a. $x - 2y = 1$ **b.** $2x + y = 0$ **c.** $4x - 3y = 1$ **d.** $2x - y = 10$
      $2x + y = 2$ $x + 2y = 3$ $x - 2y = 4$ $x + 3y = 5$

   e. $x + 2y = 10$ **f.** $2x - 5y = 1$ **g.** $7x + 2y = 11$ **h.** $2x + 3y = 5$
      $2x + 5y = 10$ $x - 2y = 3$ $4x + y = 7$ $x + y = 2$

5. Solve the system of equations. Hint: See Example 5.

   a. $2x + 5y = -1$ **b.** $2x + 3y = 29$ **c.** $3x - 2y = 1$ **d.** $10x - 9y = 24$
      $3x + 7y = 1$ $3x + 2y = 16$ $5x - 3y = 3$ $3x - 4y = 15$

Answers to Selected Questions.

1a. $x = 1, y = 3$ **1b.** $x = -3\frac{1}{2}, y = 3.$ **2a.** $x = 2, y = 2$

2b. $x = 1, y = -5$ **3a.** $x = 3, y = 2$ **3b.** $x = 2, y = -3$

3c. $x = -1, y = -1$ **4a.** $x = 1, y = 0$ **4c.** $x = -2, y = -3$

5a. $x = 12, y = -5$ **5c.** $x = 3, y = 4$

REAL WORLD APPLICATIONS - SYSTEM OF EQUATIONS

In algebra, when there are two unknown quantities to be found, two sets of facts must be given from which two equations can be written. The two equations are solved by using any of the methods (graphing method, elimination method, or substitution method) for solving system of equations.

Example 1

The difference of two numbers is 17. If their sum is 29 what are the numbers?

Solution

Step 1: Write the two equations and solve for the variable x or y.

     Let the two numbers be x and y. From the question, the difference of the two numbers is 17, and therefore, $x - y = 17$. The sum of the two numbers is 29, and therefore, $x + y = 29$. So, we can write the two equations together as shown:

$$x - y = 17 \underline{\hspace{8cm}} [A]$$
$$x + y = 29 \underline{\hspace{8cm}} [B]$$
$$\overline{2x + 0 = 46} \qquad \text{Add equations} [A] \text{ and } [B] \text{ to eliminate y, } -y + y = 0.$$

$$2x = 46$$

Divide both sides of the equation 2x = 46 by 2 in order to obtain the value of x as shown:

$$\frac{2x}{2} = \frac{46}{2} \qquad \text{Divide both sides of the equation by 2.}$$

$$\frac{\overset{x}{\cancel{2x}}}{\underset{1}{\cancel{2}}} = \frac{\overset{23}{\cancel{46}}}{\underset{1}{\cancel{2}}}$$

$$x = 23$$

Step 2: Substitute x = 23 into either of the original equations such as x - y = 17 or x + y = 29 in order to find the value of y.

Now substitute x = 23 into x - y = 17 as shown:

$$x - y = 17$$
$$23 - y = 17 \qquad \text{Substitute x = 23.}$$
$$23 - 23 - y = 17 - 23 \qquad \text{Subtract 23 from both sides of the equation 23 - y = 17 in order to obtain the value of -y.}$$
$$-y = -6 \qquad 23 - 23 = 0 \quad 17 - 23 = -6$$

Divide both sides of the equation -y = -6 by -1 in order to obtain the value of y as shown:

$$\frac{-y}{-1} = \frac{-6}{-1} \qquad \text{Divide both sides of the equation -y = -6 by -1.}$$

$$y = 6 \qquad \text{Reminder: A negative number divided by another negative number equals a positive number.}$$

The two numbers are 23 and 6.

Example 2

Six years ago, John was three times as old as Mary. Their combined ages is 24 years. How old are they now?

Solution

Step 1: Write two equations and solve for the variable x or y.

Let John's age now be x years and Mary's be y years. From the question, their combined ages is now 24 years, and therefore:

x + y = 24. _____[A]

Six years ago, John was x - 6 years old, and Mary was y - 6 years old.

But from the question, six years ago, John was three times as old as Mary, and therefore:

x - 6 = 3(y - 6)   An equation should be formed so that the left side of the equation should be equal to the right side of the equation by multiplying (y - 6) by 3.

x - 6 = 3y - 18 _____[B]

$$3(y - 6) = 3y - 6 \times 3 = 3y - 18.$$

x - 6 + 6 = 3y - 18 + 6   Add 6 to both sides of the equation in order to eliminate the 6 at the left side of equation [B] and to obtain the value for x.

x = 3y - 12 _____[C]

$$-6 + 6 = 0 \text{ and } -18 + 6 = -12.$$

x - 3y = 3y - 3y - 12   Subtract 3y from both sides of equation [C] in order to eliminate the 3y at the right side of equation [C], and so that the equation will be in the form for system of equation as shown in equation [D].

x - 3y = -12 _____[D]

$$3y - 3y = 0$$

The two system of equations to be formed are equation [A] and equation [D] as shown:

x + y = 24 _____[A]

x - 3y = -12 _____[D]

x - x + y - (-3y) = 24 - (-12)   Subtract equation [D] from equation [A].

0 + y + 3y = 24 + 12   x - x = 0, - (-3y) = +3y and -(-12) = +12.

4y = 36   y + 3y = 4y and 24 + 12 = 36.

$$\frac{4y}{4} = \frac{36}{4}$$ Divide both sides of the equation 4y = 36 by 4 in order to obtain the value of y.

$$\frac{\overset{1}{\cancel{4y}}}{\underset{1}{\cancel{4}}} = \frac{\overset{9}{\cancel{36}}}{\underset{1}{\cancel{4}}}$$

y = 9

Step 2: Substitute y = 9 into either of the original equations which are x + y = 24 or x - 3y = -12 in order to find the value of x.

Now substitute y = 9 into x + y = 24 in order to find the value of x as shown:

x + y = 24

x + 9 = 24   Substitute y = 9,

281

$$x + 9 - 9 = 24 - 9$$ Subtract 9 from both sides of the equation in order to eliminate the 9 at the left side of the equation, and to obtain the value of x.

$$x + 0 = 15$$ $9 - 9 = 0$ and $24 - 9 = 15$.

$$x = 15$$

Therefore, John is 15 years old and Mary is 9 years old.

Example 3

Five books and 8 binders cost $155.00. Three books and 5 binders cost $70. Find the cost of a book and a binder.

Solution

Step 1: Write two equations and solve for one variable x or y.

Let x = cost of a book and let y = cost of a binder.

From the question, 5 books and 8 binders cost $115.00, and therefore:

$$5x + 8y = \$115 \underline{\hspace{4cm}}[A]$$

From the question, 3 books and 5 binders cost $70, and therefore:

$$3x + 5y = \$70 \underline{\hspace{4cm}}[B]$$

Let us solve equation [A] and equation [B] simultaneously as shown:

$$5x + 8y = 115 \underline{\hspace{4cm}}[A]$$
$$3x + 5y = 70 \underline{\hspace{4cm}}[B]$$

By looking at equations [A] and [B], it can be seen that x or y cannot be found easily by neither elimination nor substition method. Therefore, we have to modify both equations [A] and [B] by multiplying equation [A] by 3 and multiplying equation [B] by 5 so that the coefficient of x in both equations become numerically equal to 15, and so that equation [B] can be subtracted from equation [A] in order to eliminate x as shown:

Equation [A] becomes:

$$3(5x + 8y) = 115 \cdot 3$$ Multiply both sides of equation [A] by 3.
$$3 \cdot 5x + 3 \cdot 8y = 345$$ $115 \cdot 3 = 345$.
$$15x + 24y = 345 \underline{\hspace{3cm}}[C]$$
$3 \cdot 5x = 15x$ and $3 \cdot 8y = 24x$.

Equation [B] becomes:

$$5(3x + 5y) = 70 \cdot 5$$ Multiply both sides of equation [B] by 5.
$$5 \cdot 3x + 5 \cdot 5y = 350$$ $70 \cdot 5 = 350$.
$$15x + 25y = 350 \underline{\hspace{3cm}}[D]$$
$5 \cdot 3x = 15x$ and $5 \cdot 5y = 25y$.

Write equations [C] and [D] together and then subtract equation [D] from equation [C] as shown:

$$15x + 24y = 345 \underline{\hspace{3cm}}[C]$$
$$15x + 25y = 350 \underline{\hspace{3cm}}[D]$$

$$15x - 15x + 24y - 25y = 345 - 350$$ Subtract equation [D] from equation [C].

$$-y = -5 \qquad 15x - 15x = 0,\ 24y - 25y = -y \text{ and } 345 - 350 = -5.$$

$$\frac{-y}{-1} = \frac{-5}{-1} \qquad \text{Divide both sides of the equation by -1 to obtain}$$

the value of y.

$$y = 5 \qquad \text{Reminder: A negative number divided by another}$$

negative number equals a positive number.

Substitute $y = 5$ into either of the original equations to obtain the value of x as shown:

$$5x + 8y = 115$$
$$5x + 8 \cdot 5 = 115 \qquad \text{Substitute } y = 5$$
$$5x + 40 = 115 \underline{\hspace{6cm}} [E]$$
$$8 \cdot 5 = 40.$$

Subtract 40 from both sides of equation $[E]$ in order to isolate 5x as shown:

$$5x + 40 - 40 = 115 - 40$$
$$5x + 0 = 75 \qquad 40 - 40 = 0 \text{ and } 115 - 40 = 75.$$
$$5x = 75$$

$$\frac{5x}{5} = \frac{75}{5} \qquad \text{Divide both sides of the equation } 5x = 75 \text{ by 5}$$

to obtain the value of x.

$$\frac{\overset{x}{\cancel{5}x}}{\underset{1}{\cancel{5}}} = \frac{\overset{15}{\cancel{75}}}{\underset{1}{\cancel{5}}}$$

$$x = 15$$

Therefore, the cost of a book is $15 and the cost of a binder is $5.

Exercises

1. The sum of two numbers is 19 and their difference is 5. Find the numbers. Hint: See Example 1.
2. Samuel's and Joshua's ages add up to 25 years. Eight years ago, Samuel was twice as old as Joshua. How old are they now? Hint: See Example 2.
3. The sum of two numbers is 17 and twice the larger number exceeds three times the smaller number by 4. Find the numbers. Hint: Let the smaller number be y and the larger number be x, and therefore, $2x - 3y = 4$. See also Example 1.
4. The total ages of Rose and Mark is 108 years. Rose is 18 years older than Mark. How old are they? Hint: See Example 1.
5. The sum of the ages of two brothers is 29. If one of the brothers is 3 years older

than the other, how old are they? Hint: Similar to Example 1.

6. Two erasers and 1 pen cost $14.00, two pens and 3 erasers cost $24.00. How much does each pen and eraser cost? Hint: Similar to Example 3.

Answers to Selected Questions
1. 12 and 7   **4.** Rose is 63 and Mark is 45 years old.

Challenge Questions
1. Solve the system of equations for x and y. Hint: If the variables x and y or a and b in both equations are not aligned, first make sure that they are aligned before you proceed. Also, refer to how the examples under the chapter System of Equations are solved.

a. $x + 2y = 14$
$2x + 3y = 24$

b. $x - y = 3$
$x + y = 29$

c. $x + y = 2$
$2x - y = 1$

d. $x + y = 7$
$x - y = 3$

e. $x + y = 3$
$x - y = 1$

f. $2x + 5y = 4$
$3x + 2y = 2$

g. $6x + y = 9$
$4x - y = 11$

h. $2x + 3y = 10$
$3x - 2y = 2$

i. $4x = y + 7$
$3x + 4y + 9 = 0$

j. $2a + 5b + 1 = 0$
$3a + 7b = 1$

k. $5x = 2y - 14$
$5y = x + 12$

l. $5a = 11 + 3b$
$2b + 7a = 3$

m. $-2x + 3y = 19$
$2x + y = 1$

n. $2x - y = 4$
$x + y = 5$

2. The sum of two numbers is 25 and their difference is 5. Find the numbers.

3. The sum of the ages of Elizabeth and Mary is 40 years. Elizabeth is 10 years older than Mary. How old are they?

4. Two years ago, Mr. Brown was six times as old as his daughter. In 18 years he will be twice as old as his daughter. Find their present ages. Hint: Let Mr. Brown's age = x and let his daughter's age = y. Therefore:

the equation for 2 years ago is:
$(x - 2) = 6(y - 2)$,
the equation for 18 years into the future is:
$(x + 18) = 2(y + 18)$.

5. The difference of two numbers is 12. If their sum is 28, find the numbers.

6. Solve the system of equations for x and y.

a. $2x - y = 4$
$x + y = 5$

b. $2x - y = 4$
$x + 2y = -3$

c. $-2x + 3y = 19$
$2x + y = 1$

Answers to Selected Questions
1i. 1, -3   **1j.** 12, -5   **1k.** -2, 2   **1l.** -2, 1   **1m.** x = -2, y = 5   **1n.** x = 3, y = 2

SQUARE ROOTS

The square root of a number x is a number y such that when y is multiplied by itself, equals the original number x. The symbol for square root is $\sqrt{}$.

$$\text{If } x = y \cdot y,$$
$$\text{then } \sqrt{x} = \sqrt{y \cdot y}$$
$$= y$$

Example 1

Find the square root of 4.

Solution

Step 1: To find the square root of 4, find the factors of 4 such that when the factor is multiplied by itself, equals 4. This factor is the square root of 4.

The factors of 4 are: 4×1
$$2 \times 2$$

Step 2: Select the factor that, when multiplied by itself equals 4.

The factors $2 \times 2 = 4$, therefore, the square root of 4 is 2.

We can write the square root of 4 is 2 mathematically as $\sqrt{4} = 2$.

Example 2

Find the $\sqrt{25}$.

Solution

Step 1: To find the $\sqrt{25}$, find the factors of 25 such that the factor multiplied by itself equals 25 is the square root.

The factors of 25 are: 25×1 and 5×5

Step 2: Select the factor that, when multiplied by itself equals 25.

The factor $5 \times 5 = 25$, therefore,
$$\sqrt{25} = \sqrt{5 \times 5}$$
$$= 5$$

Important Rules.

For any number represented by x and y:

Rule 1: If $x = y \cdot y = y^2$, then
$$\sqrt{x} = \sqrt{y \cdot y} = \sqrt{y^2}$$
$$= y$$

Rule 2: If $x = y \cdot y = y^2$, then
$$-\sqrt{x} = -\sqrt{y \cdot y} = -\sqrt{y^2}$$

$$= -y$$

Rule 3: If $x = y \cdot y = y^2$, then

$$\pm\sqrt{x} = \pm\sqrt{y \cdot y} = \pm\sqrt{y^2}$$

Rule 4: $\sqrt{0} = 0$ and $\sqrt{1} = 1$

Example 3

Find the $\sqrt{11^2}$.

Solution

Using Rule 1, $\sqrt{11^2} = 11$

Example 4

Find the $-\sqrt{25}$.

Solution

Using Rule 2, $-\sqrt{25} = -\sqrt{5 \times 5} = -\sqrt{5^2}$

$$= -5$$

Example 5

Find the $\pm\sqrt{100}$.

Solution

Using Rule 3, $\pm\sqrt{100} = \pm\sqrt{10 \times 10} = \pm\sqrt{10^2}$

$$= \pm 10$$

Exercises

1. Describe how you can find the square root of a number.

2. Find the value. Hint: See Examples 1, 2, and Rule 1.

    a. $\sqrt{9}$ **b.** $\sqrt{16}$ **c.** $\sqrt{36}$ **d.** $\sqrt{49}$ **e.** $\sqrt{64}$

3. Find the value. Hint: See Example 3 and Rule 1.

    a. $\sqrt{3^2}$ **b.** $\sqrt{6^2}$ **c.** $\sqrt{p^2}$ **d.** $\sqrt{9^2}$ **e.** $\sqrt{12^2}$

4. Find the value. Hint: See Examples 4.

    a. $-\sqrt{9}$ **b.** $-\sqrt{36}$ **c.** $-\sqrt{4^2}$ **d.** $-\sqrt{81^2}$ **e.** $-\sqrt{100}$

5. Find the value. Hint: See Example 5 and Rule 3.

    a. $\pm\sqrt{25}$ **b.** $\pm\sqrt{25}$ **c.** $\pm\sqrt{25}$ **d.** $\pm\sqrt{25}$ **e.** $\pm\sqrt{25}$

Challenge Questions

6. Find the value.

a. $\sqrt{81}$ b. $-\sqrt{132}$ c. $\pm\sqrt{64}$ d. $\sqrt{100}$ e. $\pm\sqrt{16}$

Notes

1. The symbol $\sqrt{}$ is the square root and it is also called the radial symbol.
2. $\sqrt{2}$ for an example is known as the radical number.
3. $\sqrt{4}$ for an example is read as the positive square root of 4.
4. $-\sqrt{4}$ for an example is read as the negative square root of 4.
5. $\pm\sqrt{4}$ for an example is read as positive or negative square root of 4.
6. The numbers which square roots can be found easily without decimals such as $\sqrt{4} = 2$, $\sqrt{9} = 3$, and $\sqrt{25} = 5$ are called perfect squares. Therefore, any number that is the square of an integer is called a **perfect square**.

How to Solve Expressions Involving the Square Root Symbol

To solve for the expression involving the square root symbol such as $\sqrt{x^2 + y^2}$,

Step 1: Find the square root of each number, and then add the squares of the numbers together. Let's assume that $x^2 + y^2 = z$, then,

$$\sqrt{x^2 + y^2} = \sqrt{z}$$

Step 2: Find the value of $\sqrt{z}$.

Example 6

Find the value of $\sqrt{8^2 + 6^2}$

Solution

Step 1: Find the square of each number and then add the squares of each of the numbers together.

$$\sqrt{8^2 + 6^2} = \sqrt{8 \cdot 8 + 6 \cdot 6}$$
$$= \sqrt{64 + 36}$$
$$= \sqrt{100}$$

Step 2: Find the value of $\sqrt{100}$.

$$\sqrt{100} = \sqrt{10 \cdot 10} = \sqrt{10^2}$$
$$= 10 \qquad \text{Rule 1 is used.}$$

Example 7

Find the value of $\sqrt{3^2 + 1^2 + 1^2 + 2^2 + 1^2}$.

Solution

Step 1: Find the square of each number and then add the squares of the numbers together.

$$\sqrt{3^2 + 1^2 + 1^2 + 2^2 + 1^2} = \sqrt{3 \cdot 3 + 1 \cdot 1 + 1 \cdot 1 + 2 \cdot 2 + 1 \cdot 1}$$
$$= \sqrt{9 + 1 + 1 + 4 + 1}$$
$$= \sqrt{16}$$

Step 2: Find the value of $\sqrt{16}$.

$$\sqrt{16} = \sqrt{4 \cdot 4} = \sqrt{4^2}$$
$$= 4 \qquad\qquad \text{Rule 1 is used.}$$

Exercises

1. Find the values. Hint: See Example 6.

    a. $\sqrt{4^2 + 3^2}$ **b.** $\sqrt{12^2 + 5^2}$ **c.** $\sqrt{6^2 + 8^2}$

2. Find the values. Hint: See Example 7.

    a. $\sqrt{6^2 + 3^2 + 2^2}$ **b.** $\sqrt{2^2 + 1^2 + 4^2 + 2^2}$

REAL WORLD APPLICATIONS - WORD PROBLEMS
Square Root

Example 1

Find the perimeter of a square which has an area of 25 ft^2

Solution

Setup: Area of a square = side × side.

    Therefore, 25 ft^2 = side × side.

    25 ft^2 = s × s   Let a side of the square = s ft.

    25 ft^2 = s^2 _____[A].

Step 1: Find the value of the side or s.

    To find s, find the square root of both sides of equation [A].

$$\sqrt{25 \text{ ft}^2} = \sqrt{s^2}$$
$$\sqrt{5^2 \text{ ft}^2} = \sqrt{s^2}$$
$$5 \text{ ft} = s \qquad\qquad \text{Hint: See Rule 1.}$$
$$\sqrt{5^2 \text{ ft}^2} = 5 \text{ ft and } \sqrt{s^2} = s.$$

    Therefore, the side of the square is 5 ft long.

Step 2: Find the perimeter of the square.

    The perimeter is the distance around the square.

    The square has 4 equal sides therefore:

    Perimeter of the square = 4 × s   where s = length of a side of the square.

$$= 4 \times 5 \text{ ft} \qquad s = 5 \text{ ft}$$
$$= 20 \text{ ft}$$

Exercises - Applications

1. The area of a square is 16 cm². Find the perimeter of the square. Hint: See Example 1.
2. Find the perimeter of a square which has an area of 49 m² Hint: See Example 1.
3. A square swimming pool has an area of 100 m². Find the perimeter of the swimming pool. Hint: See Example 1.
4. Find the perimeter of each of the **square** diagrams.

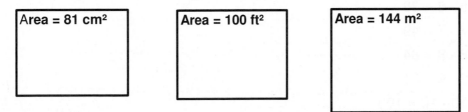

| Area = 81 cm² | Area = 100 ft² | Area = 144 m² |

Note: All the diagrams in this book are not drawn to scale.

   Hint: See Example 1.
5. Find the perimeter of a square which has an area of 36 m². Hint: See Example 1.

Answer to a Selected Question

1. 16 cm.

SQUARE ROOTS OF PERFECT SQUARES

Review

A **perfect square** is a number that has an integer as its square root.

For an example: $\sqrt{25} = \sqrt{5 \times 5} = \sqrt{5^2} = 5$. So 25 is a perfect square. Note that the **square root** of the square of a number is the number itself. (**Integers** are a set of whole numbers including their opposites and zero such as ..., -5, -4, -3, -2, -1, 0, 1, 2, 3, 4, 5, ...) The square root of a perfect square is the factor of a number that can be multiplied by itself to obtain the perfect square.
Some perfect squares are 1, 4, 9, 16, 25, 36, 48, 64, 81, and 100. The factor of each perfect square that can be multiplied by itself to obtain the perfect square are listed as shown:

   25 = 5 · 5, 36 = 6 · 6, 49 = 7 · 7, 64 = 8 · 8, 81 = 9 · 9, and 100 = 10 · 10.
Notice that 1, 4, 9, 16, 25, 36, 48, 64, 81, and 100 are called perfect squares because they are **squares of integers**. Notice also that the opposite of squaring a number is

finding a square root.

Some Factors that are the Square Roots of Perfect Squares

Perfect squares	Factors that are the square roots of perfect squares
1	$1 \cdot 1 = 1$
4	$2 \cdot 2 = 4$
9	$3 \cdot 3 = 9$
16	$4 \cdot 4 = 16$
25	$5 \cdot 5 = 25$
36	$6 \cdot 6 = 36$
49	$7 \cdot 7 = 49$
64	$8 \cdot 8 = 64$
81	$9 \cdot 9 = 81$
100	$10 \cdot 10 = 100$

How to find the Positive and Negative Square Roots of a Number.

The symbol $\sqrt{}$ is used to indicate the positive or principal square root, and the symbol $-\sqrt{}$ is used to indicate the negative square root.

Both the positive and the negative square root may be combined and written as $\pm\sqrt{}$.

Example 1

Find the two square roots of:

a. 25   **b.** 1

Solution

a. $\sqrt{25} = \sqrt{5 \times 5}$ The factors of 25 that can be multiplied by itself to obtain 25 is 5. For an example, $5 \times 5 = 25$.

$\quad\quad = \sqrt{5^2}$ $5 \times 5 = 5^2$

$\quad\quad = 5$ Recall that the square root of the square of a number is the number itself.

Also, $-\sqrt{25} = -\sqrt{5 \times 5}$ $25 = 5 \times 5$

$\quad\quad = -\sqrt{5^2}$ $5 \times 5 = 5^2$

$\quad\quad = -5$ Recall that the square root of the square of a number is the number itself.

Since $5 \times 5 = 25$ and $-5 \times (-5) = 25$, then both 5 and -5 are the two square roots of 25.

b. $\sqrt{1} = \sqrt{1 \cdot 1}$ The factors of 1 that can be multiplied by itself to obtain 1 is 1. For example, $1 \times 1 = 1$.

$\sqrt{1} = \sqrt{1^2}$ $1 \cdot 1 = 1^2$

     $= 1$ Recall that the square root of the square of a number is the number itself.

Also, $-\sqrt{1} = -\sqrt{1 \times 1}$ $1 = 1 \times 1$

      $= -\sqrt{1^2}$ $1 \times 1 = 1^2$

      $= -1$ Recall that the square root of the square of a number is the number itself.

Since $1 \times 1 = 1$ and $-1 \times (-1) = 1$, then both 1 and -1 are the two square roots of 1.

How to Evaluate Expressions Involving Square Roots.

Example 2

Evaluate $3\sqrt{4} - 1$

Solution

$3\sqrt{4} - 1 = 3 \cdot 2 - 1$ Use the order of operations (PERMDAS) to solve this problem. See the section on the Order of Operations. Do the square root first, $\sqrt{4} - 2$.

     $= 6 - 1$ Do the multiplication second. See the section or the chapter on PERMDAS, $3 \cdot 2 = 6$

     $= 5$ Do the subtraction last. See PERMDAS. $6 - 1 = 5$

Example 3

Evaluate $\sqrt{9 + 16} + 3$

Solution

$\sqrt{9 + 16} + 3 = \sqrt{25} + 3$ Do the operation (addition) under the square root first. $\sqrt{9 + 16} = \sqrt{25}$ see PERMDAS.

     $= 5 + 3$ $\sqrt{25} = 5$. Find the square root second.

     $= 8$ $5 + 3 = 8$. Do the addition last.

Example 4

Evaluate $3\sqrt{16 + 9} - 8$

Solution

$3\sqrt{16 + 9} - 8 = 3\sqrt{25} - 8$ Do the operation (addition) under the square root first.

Review the Order of Operations. See PERMDAS.

$= 3 \cdot 5 - 8$ $\sqrt{25} = 5$. Find the square root second, see PERMDAS.

$= 15 - 8$ $3 \cdot 5 = 15$. Do the multiplication third, see PERMDAS.

$= 7$ $15 - 8 = 7$. Do the subtraction last, see PERMDAS.

Example 5

Find the square root of $\dfrac{25}{4}$.

Solution

The square root of $\dfrac{25}{4} = \sqrt{\dfrac{25}{4}}$ Use the square root symbol, $\sqrt{}$.

$= \dfrac{\sqrt{25}}{\sqrt{4}}$ The square root of the numerator and the denominator of a fraction can be found separately if the fraction does not reduce to to a whole number.

$= \dfrac{5}{2}$ Do the square root operation first. $\sqrt{25} = 5$, and $\sqrt{4} = 2$. See PERMDAS.

$= 2\dfrac{1}{2}$ Do the division last. See PERMDAS.

Example 6

Evaluate $3\sqrt{\dfrac{32}{2}} + 12$

Solution

$3\sqrt{\dfrac{32}{2}} + 12 = 3\sqrt{16} + 12$ Note that the square root of the numerator of 32 and the denominator of 2 cannot be found separately and easily, but the fraction $\dfrac{32}{2}$ reduces to a whole number of 16. So we do the operation under the square root first. $\dfrac{32}{2} = 16$. See PERMDAS.

$= 3 \cdot 4 + 12$ Complete the operation involving the square root. $\sqrt{16} = 4$.

$= 12 + 12$ Do the multiplication second. $3 \cdot 4 = 12$.
                      See PERMDAS.

$= 24$ Do the addition last. See PERMDAS, $12 + 12 = 24$.

Example 7
Evaluate $-(\sqrt{81} - \sqrt{16})$.
Solution
$-(\sqrt{81} - \sqrt{16}) = -(9 - 4)$ Do the operations (square roots) in the parenthesis first,

                                     See PERMDAS. $\sqrt{81} = 9$ and $\sqrt{16} = 4$.

           $= -(5)$ Complete doing the operation (subtraction) in the
                            parenthesis. $9 - 4 = 5$. See PERMDAS.

           $= -5$

Example 8
Evaluate $-(\sqrt{9}\,\sqrt{100})$.
Solution
$-(\sqrt{9}\,\sqrt{100}) = -(3 \cdot 10)$ Do the operations (square roots) in the parenthesis first.

                                   See PERMDAS. $\sqrt{9} = 3$ and $\sqrt{100} = 10$.

           $= -(30)$ Complete the operation (multiplication) in the parenthesis
                            next. $3 \cdot 10 = 30$. See PERMDAS.

           $= -30$

REAL WORLD APPLICATIONS - WORD PROBLEMS
Square Root of Perfect Squares

Example 9
A cocoa farm in Ghana is in the form of a square. If the area of the farm is 4 square miles, find how long is a side of the farm.
Solution
The formula for finding the area of the square cocoa farm is:

     Area = Side $\cdot$ Side
     Area = S $\cdot$ S   Let S = Side = Length of a side
     Area = S^2 _____[A]

Substitute Area = 4 square miles into equation [A] as shown:

     $4\ mi^2 = S^2$ _____[B]

Find the square root of both sides of equation [B] as shown:

$$\sqrt{4\ mi^2} = \sqrt{S^2}$$

$$\sqrt{2^2\ mi^2} = \sqrt{S^2} \qquad 4 = 2^2$$

293

$$2 \text{ mi} = S$$

Recall that the square root of the square of a number is the number itself.

Therefore, the side of the squared cocoa farm is 2 miles.

Example 10

A school's swimming pool is in the shape of a square. If a side of the square is 2 kilometers, what is the area of the swimming pool?

Solution

A side of the square swimming pool = 2 km

The formula for the area of the square swimming pool is:

Area = Side · Side

Area = S · S   Let S = Side.

Area = S^2 _____[A]

Substitute S = 2 km in equation [A] as follows:

Area = $(2 \text{ km})^2$

$\quad = 2 \text{ km} \cdot 2 \text{ km}$ $(2 \text{ km})^2 = 2 \text{ km} \cdot 2 \text{ km}$

$\quad = 4 \text{ km}^2$.

Therefore, the area of the squared swimming pool is 4 km².

Example 11

Evaluate: **a.** $\pm\sqrt{16}$ **b.** $\pm\sqrt{36}$

Solution

a. $\pm\sqrt{16} = \pm\sqrt{4^2}$ $16 = 4^2$

$\qquad = \pm 4$ because both the positive and negative roots are indicated. Recall that the square root of the square of a number is the number itself.

b. $\pm\sqrt{36} = \pm\sqrt{6^2}$ $36 = 6^2$

$\qquad = \pm 6$ because both the positive and negative roots are indicated. Recall that the square root of the square of a number is the number itself.

Example 12

Solve each equation.

a. $n^2 = 9$ **b.** $16 = t^2$ **c.** $y^2 = \dfrac{4}{25}$ **d.** $0.16 = w^2$

Solution

a. $n^2 = 9$ Given in the question.

$\sqrt{n^2} = \pm\sqrt{9}$ Equations with squares can be solved by taking the square root of both sides of the equation. This is because the square root of the number that is squared (or raised to the second power) equals the number itself.

$n = \pm 3$ The square root of the number that is squared (or raised to the second power) equals the number itself. So, $\sqrt{n^2} = n$, and $\pm\sqrt{9} = \pm\sqrt{3^2} = \pm 3$. Recall that every positive number has both a positive and a negative square roots.

b. $16 = t^2$ Given in the question.

$\pm\sqrt{16} = \sqrt{t^2}$ Equations with squares can be solved by taking the square root of both sides of the equation. This is because the square root of the number that is squared (or raised to the second power) equals the number itself.

$\pm 4 = t$ The square root of the number that is squared (or raised to the second power) equals the number itself. So, $\sqrt{t^2} = t$, and $\pm\sqrt{16} = \pm 4$. Recall that every positive number has both a positive and a negative square roots.

c. $y^2 = \dfrac{4}{25}$ Given in the question.

$\sqrt{y^2} = \pm\sqrt{\dfrac{4}{25}}$ Equations with squares can be solved by taking the square root of both sides of the equation. This is because the square root of the number that is squared (or raised to the second power) equals the number itself.

$y = \pm\dfrac{2}{5}$ The square root of the number that is squared (or raised to the second power) equals the number itself. So, $\sqrt{y^2} = y$, and $\pm\sqrt{\dfrac{4}{25}} = \pm\sqrt{\dfrac{2^2}{5^2}} = \pm\dfrac{2}{5}$. Recall that every positive number has both a positive and a negative square roots.

d. $0.16 = w^2$ Given

$\pm\sqrt{0.16} = \sqrt{w^2}$ Equations with squares can be solved by taking the square root of both sides of the equation. This is because the square root of the number that is squared (or raised to the second power) equals the number itself.

$\pm 0.4 = w$ The square root of the number that is squared (or raised to the second power) equals the number itself. So, $\sqrt{w^2} = w$, and $\pm\sqrt{0.16} = \pm\sqrt{0.4^2} = \pm 0.4$. We can also find $\sqrt{0.16}$ on the calculator by depressing 2nd $\sqrt{}$ .16 $=$ on the calculator to obtain 0.4. Recall that every positive number has both a positive and a negative square roots. See how to find square roots on page 311.

Exercises

1. Complete the statements:

   a. A perfect square is _____

   b. The opposite of squaring a number is finding a _____

2. Find the two square roots of each number.

   a. 9   **b.** 36   **c.** 81   **d.** 16   **e.** 4

   Hint: See Example 1.

3. Evaluate each expression. Hint: See Example 2.

   a. $2\sqrt{4} + 10$ **b.** $3\sqrt{36} - 4$ **c.** $2\sqrt{100}$

   d. $4\sqrt{81} + 6$ **e.** $2\sqrt{144} - 8$ **f.** $4\sqrt{25} + 11$

4. Evaluate each expression. Hint: See Example 3.

   a. $\sqrt{5 + 20} + 9$ **b.** $\sqrt{6 + 30} - 5$ **c.** $\sqrt{59 + 5} + 9$

   d. $\sqrt{4 + 12} - 3$ **e.** $\sqrt{29 - 4} + 3$ **f.** $\sqrt{92 - 11} - 4$

5. Evaluate each expression. Hint: See Example 4.

   a. $3\sqrt{27 - 2} + 5$ **b.** $2\sqrt{45 - 9} - 8$ **c.** $3\sqrt{17 + 8} + 8$

   d. $2\sqrt{74 + 7} + 12$ **e.** $23\sqrt{1 + 99} + 4$ **f.** $4\sqrt{16 + 20} - 9$

6. Evaluate each expression. Hint: See Example 5.

   a. $\sqrt{\dfrac{36}{16}}$ **b.** $\sqrt{\dfrac{9}{4}}$ **c.** $\sqrt{\dfrac{81}{25}}$ **d.** $\sqrt{\dfrac{81}{16}}$ **e.** $\sqrt{\dfrac{4}{9}}$ **f.** $\sqrt{\dfrac{9}{16}}$

7. Evaluate each expression. Hint: See Example 6.

   a. $4\sqrt{\dfrac{50}{2}} + 10$ **b.** $3\sqrt{\dfrac{72}{2}} + 3$ **c.** $4\sqrt{\dfrac{27}{3}} - 7$ **d.** $5\sqrt{\dfrac{16}{4}} - 8$

8. Evaluate each expression. Hint: See Example 7.

   a. $-(\sqrt{25} - \sqrt{9})$ **b.** $-(\sqrt{36} - \sqrt{25})$ **c.** $-(\sqrt{16} - \sqrt{4})$

   d. $-(\sqrt{81} + \sqrt{25})$ **e.** $-(\sqrt{25} + \sqrt{4})$ **f.** $-(\sqrt{16} - \sqrt{9})$

9. Evaluate each expression. Hint: See Example 8.

   a. $-(\sqrt{4}\,\sqrt{9})$ **b.** $-(\sqrt{81}\,\sqrt{16})$ **c.** $\sqrt{25}\,\sqrt{9}$

   d. $-(\sqrt{25}\,\sqrt{25})$ **e.** $-(\sqrt{4}\,\sqrt{4})$ **f.** $-(\sqrt{36}\,\sqrt{25})$

10. The length of a side of a square classroom is 100 m. Find the area of the classroom.

Hint: See Example 10.

11. A square garden has an area of 81 m². Find the length of a side of the garden.
   Hint: See Example 9.

12. Evaluate:

   a. $\pm\sqrt{4}$ **b.** $\pm\sqrt{49}$ **c.** $\pm\sqrt{100}$ **d.** $\pm\sqrt{81}$
   Hint: See Example 11.

13. Solve each equation.

   a. $t^2 = 4$ **b.** $m^2 = 25$ **c.** $k^2 = 144$ **d.** $36 = p^2$
   Hint: See Examples 12a and 12b.

14. Solve each equation.

   a. $c^2 = \dfrac{9}{25}$ **b.** $p^2 = \dfrac{9}{64}$ **c.** $r^2 = \dfrac{81}{100}$ **d.** $\dfrac{4}{81} = p^2$
   Hint: See Example 12c.

15. Solve each equation.

   a. $y^2 = 0.25$ **b.** $w^2 = 0.36$ **c.** $p^2 = 0.81$ **d.** $0.0121 = k^2$
   Hint: See Example 12d.

Challenge Questions

16. Evaluate each expression.

   a. $4\sqrt{39 - 3} + 4$ **b.** $\sqrt{\dfrac{81}{4}}$ **c.** $6\sqrt{25}$ **d.** $\sqrt{\dfrac{100}{4}}$

   e. $-(\sqrt{4}\sqrt{4})$ **f.** $3\sqrt{13 - 4} + 15$ **g.** $-(\sqrt{64} - \sqrt{36})$ **h.** $4\sqrt{100}$

   i. $\sqrt{26 - 10}$ **j.** $\sqrt{25} - \sqrt{4}$ **k.** $\sqrt{81} + \sqrt{16}$ **l.** $\sqrt{36}\sqrt{9}$

   m. $(\sqrt{81}\sqrt{4})$

17. Evaluate:

   a. $\pm\sqrt{9}$ **b.** $\pm\sqrt{64}$ **c.** $\pm\sqrt{25}$ **d.** $\pm\sqrt{144}$

Answers to Selected Questions

2a. 3 and -3   **3a.** 14   **4a.** 14   **5a.** 30

6a. $1\dfrac{1}{2}$ **7a.** 30   **8a.** -2   **9a.** -6

12a. ±2 **13a.** ±2 **14a.** $\pm\dfrac{3}{5}$ **15a.** ±0.5

Special Properties of Square Roots
The square roots have the following properties:

   a. $\sqrt{a} \cdot \sqrt{a} = a$, **where** $a \geq 0$.

   b. $(-\sqrt{a})(-\sqrt{a}) = a$, **where** $a \geq 0$.

Example 12

a. Show that $\sqrt{9} \cdot \sqrt{9} = 9$.

b. Show that $(-\sqrt{25})(-\sqrt{25}) = 25$.

Solution

a. $\sqrt{9} \cdot \sqrt{9} = \sqrt{3^2} \cdot \sqrt{3^2}$ $9 = 3^2$

$= 3 \cdot 3$ Recall that the square root of the square of a number is the number itself.

$= 9$ This is the required answer.

b. $(-\sqrt{25})(-\sqrt{25}) = (-\sqrt{5^2})(-\sqrt{5^2})$ $25 = 5^2$

$= (-5)(-5)$ $\sqrt{5^2} = 5$, recall that the square root of the square of a number is the number itself.

$= 25$ $(-5)(-5) = 25$
This is the required answer.

Special Note

The solution to Example 12a confirms the special property of square roots, which is:

$$\sqrt{a} \cdot \sqrt{a} = a, \text{ where } a \geq 0.$$

The solution to Example 12b confirms the special property of square roots, which is:

$$(-\sqrt{a})(-\sqrt{a}) = a, \text{ where } a \geq 0.$$

Exercises

Use the following special properties of the square root to answer the exercises.

     a. $\sqrt{a} \cdot \sqrt{a} = a$, **where $a \geq 0$.**

     b. $(-\sqrt{a})(-\sqrt{a}) = a$, **where $a \geq 0$.**

Evaluate:

1. $\sqrt{3} \cdot \sqrt{3}$ **2.** $(-\sqrt{11})(-\sqrt{11})$ **3.** $\sqrt{13} \cdot \sqrt{13}$ **4.** $(-\sqrt{6})(-\sqrt{6})$

5. $\sqrt{10} \cdot \sqrt{10}$ **6.** $(-\sqrt{10})(-\sqrt{10})$ **7.** $\sqrt{101} \cdot \sqrt{101}$ **8.** $(-\sqrt{6558})(-\sqrt{6558})$

Answers to Selected Questions

1. 3   **8.** 6558

How to Add or Subtract Expressions that Contain Radicals

In order to add or subtract expressions that contain radicals, **the number or the expression under the radical sign must be equal**. The number or the expression under the radical sign then becomes the common factor. In this case, we have to find the common factor of the whole expression, and then simplify as needed. (Hint: Review the chapter/section on Common Factors. Recall that the number or the expression under the radical sign is called the **radicand**.)

Example 1

Simplify.

a. $3\sqrt{10} + 2\sqrt{10}$ **b.** $7\sqrt{3} - 4\sqrt{3}$

Solution

a. $3\sqrt{10} + 2\sqrt{10} = (3 + 2)\sqrt{10}$ Notice that $\sqrt{10}$ is a common factor.

$= 5\sqrt{10}$ Simplify, $(3 + 2) = 5$.

b. $7\sqrt{3} - 4\sqrt{3} = (7 - 4)\sqrt{3}$ Notice that $\sqrt{3}$ is a common factor.

$= 3\sqrt{3}$ Simplify, $(7 - 4) = 3$.

Example 2

Simplify.

a. $9\sqrt{3} - 5\sqrt{2} + \sqrt{3} + 7\sqrt{2}$ **b.** $6\sqrt{11} - 9 - 4\sqrt{11} + 13$

Solution

a. $9\sqrt{3} - 5\sqrt{2} + \sqrt{3} + 7\sqrt{2} = 9\sqrt{3} + 1\sqrt{3} + 7\sqrt{2} - 5\sqrt{2}$ Rearrange in order to group the like radicands together. Notice that $\sqrt{3}$ can be written as $1\sqrt{3}$ to make factoring understandable later.

$= (9 + 1)\sqrt{3} + (7 - 5)\sqrt{2}$ Notice that $\sqrt{3}$ and $\sqrt{2}$ are common factors. Hint: Review the chapter/section on factoring.

$= 10\sqrt{3} + 2\sqrt{2}$

b. $6\sqrt{11} - 9 - 4\sqrt{11} + 13 = 6\sqrt{11} - 4\sqrt{11} + 13 - 9$ Rearrange in order to group the like radicands together.

$= (6 - 4)\sqrt{11} + 4$ Notice that $\sqrt{11}$ is a common factor. Hint: Review the chapter/section on factoring. Simplify,

$$= 2\sqrt{11} + 4$$

$$13 - 9 = 4.$$

Simplify, $(6 - 4) = 2$.

Example 3

Simplify.

a. $4\sqrt{27} - 2\sqrt{48}$ **b.** $6\sqrt{18} - 7 - 3\sqrt{98}$

Solution

a. $4\sqrt{27} - 2\sqrt{48} = 4\sqrt{9 \times 3} - 2\sqrt{16 \times 3}$ The **radicands** are not equal, so we cannot factor.
In this case, we should make sure that no factors of the **radicands** are perfect squares other than 1.
$27 = 9 \times 3$, and 9 is a perfect square.
$48 = 16 \times 3$, and 16 is a perfect square.

$$= 4\sqrt{9}\sqrt{3} - 2\sqrt{16}\sqrt{3}$$

$\sqrt{9 \times 3}$ can be written as $\sqrt{9}\sqrt{3}$ so that we can find the square root of the perfect square of 9.
$\sqrt{16 \times 3}$ can be written as $\sqrt{16}\sqrt{3}$ so that we can find the square root of the perfect square of 16.

$$= 4 \times 3\sqrt{3} - 2 \times 4\sqrt{3}$$

$\sqrt{9} = 3$, and the square root of $\sqrt{16} = 4$.

$$= 12\sqrt{3} - 8\sqrt{3}$$

Simplify, $4 \times 3 = 12$, and $2 \times 4 = 8$.

$$= (12 - 8)\sqrt{3}$$

Notice that $\sqrt{3}$ is a common factor.

$$= 4\sqrt{3}$$

Simplify, $(12 - 8) = 4$.

Special Note: Notice that in the solution to Example 3a,

$$\sqrt{27} = \sqrt{9 \cdot 3} = \sqrt{9}\sqrt{3} = 3\sqrt{3}$$

$3\sqrt{3}$ is known as the simplest radical form of $\sqrt{27}$.

$$\sqrt{48} = \sqrt{16 \cdot 3} = \sqrt{16}\sqrt{3} = 4\sqrt{3}$$

$4\sqrt{3}$ is known as the simplest radical form of $\sqrt{48}$.

b. $6\sqrt{18} - 7 - 3\sqrt{98} = 6\sqrt{9 \times 2} - 7 - 3\sqrt{49 \times 2}$ The **radicands** are not equal, so we cannot factor.
In this case, we should make sure that no factors of the **radicands** are

perfect squares other than 1.

18 = 9 × 2, and 9 is a perfect square.

98 = 49 × 2, and 49 is a perfect square.

$= 6\sqrt{9}\sqrt{2} - 7 - 3\sqrt{49}\sqrt{2}$	$\sqrt{9 \times 2}$ can be written as $\sqrt{9}\sqrt{2}$ so that we can find the square root of the perfect square of 9.
	$\sqrt{49 \times 2}$ can be written as $\sqrt{49}\sqrt{2}$ so that we can find the square root of the perfect square of 49.

$= 6 \times 3\sqrt{2} - 7 - 3 \times 7\sqrt{2}$	$\sqrt{9} = 3$, and $\sqrt{49} = 7$.
$= 18\sqrt{2} - 7 - 21\sqrt{2}$	Simplify, $6 \times 3 = 18$, and $3 \times 7 = 21$.
$= 18\sqrt{2} - 21\sqrt{2} - 7$	$\sqrt{2}$ is a common factor, rearrange the terms so that we can factor $\sqrt{2}$.
$= (18 - 21)\sqrt{2} - 7$	Notice that $\sqrt{2}$ is a factor.
$= -3\sqrt{2} - 7$	Simplify, $(18 - 21) = 3$.

Example 4

Simplify.

$2\sqrt{90y} - 3\sqrt{10y} + \sqrt{40y}$

Solution

$2\sqrt{90y} - 3\sqrt{10y} + \sqrt{40y} = 2\sqrt{9 \times 10y} - 3\sqrt{10y} + \sqrt{4 \times 10y}$

The **radicands** are not equal, so we cannot factor.

In this case, we should make sure that no factors of the **radicands** are perfect squares other than 1.

90y = 9 × 10y, and 9 is a perfect square.

40y = 4 × 10y, and 4 is a perfect square.

$= 2\sqrt{9}\sqrt{10y} - 3\sqrt{10y} + \sqrt{4}\sqrt{10y}$

$\sqrt{9 \times 10y}$ can be written as $\sqrt{9}\sqrt{10y}$ so that we can find the square root of the perfect square of 9.

$\sqrt{4 \times 10y}$ can be written as $\sqrt{4}\sqrt{10y}$ so that we can find the square root of the perfect square of 4.

$$= 2 \times 3\sqrt{10y} - 3\sqrt{10y} + 2\sqrt{10y}$$

$$\sqrt{9} = 3, \text{ and } \sqrt{4}.$$

$$= 6\sqrt{10y} - 3\sqrt{10y} + 2\sqrt{10y}$$

Simplify, $2 \times 3 = 6$.

$$= (6 - 3 + 2)\sqrt{10y}$$ Notice that $\sqrt{10y}$ is a factor.

$$= 5\sqrt{10y}$$ Simplify, $(6 - 3 + 2) = 5$

Example 5

Simplify.

$$3x\sqrt{45xy^2} - \sqrt{80x^3y^2}$$

Solution

$$3x\sqrt{45xy^2} - \sqrt{80x^3y^2} = 3x\sqrt{9 \cdot 5xy^2} - \sqrt{16 \cdot 5x^3y^2}$$

The **radicands** are not equal, so we cannot factor.
In this case, we should make sure that no factors of the **radicands** are perfect squares other than 1.
$45 = 9 \cdot 5$, and 9 is a perfect square.
$80 = 16 \cdot 5$, and 16 is a perfect square.

$$= 3x\sqrt{9}\sqrt{5x}\sqrt{y^2} - \sqrt{16 \cdot 5x \, x^2y^2} \qquad x^3 = x\, x^2$$

$$= 3x\sqrt{9}\sqrt{5x}\sqrt{y^2} - \sqrt{16}\sqrt{5x}\sqrt{x^2}\sqrt{y^2}$$

$$\sqrt{16 \cdot 5x \, x^2y^2} = \sqrt{16}\sqrt{5x}\sqrt{x^2}\sqrt{y^2}$$

$$= 3x \cdot 3\sqrt{5x} \cdot y - 4\sqrt{5x} \cdot xy$$

$$\sqrt{9} = 3, \sqrt{y^2} = y, \sqrt{16} = 4,$$
$$\sqrt{x^2} = x, \text{ and } \sqrt{y^2} = y$$

$$= 9xy\sqrt{5x} - 4xy\sqrt{5x}$$

Simplify: $3x \cdot 3 \cdot y = 9xy$, and $4 \cdot x \cdot y = 4xy$

$$= (9xy - 4xy)\sqrt{5x}$$ Notice that $\sqrt{5x}$ is a factor.

$$= 5xy\sqrt{5x}$$ Simplify: $(9xy - 4xy) = 5xy$.

Example 6

Use a shortcut method to solve Example 5. Example 5 shows the detailed method of solving the problem in order to provide understanding. Once the detailed method is understood, the student can use shortcut method in solving homework and during tests.

Simplify.

$$3x\sqrt{45xy^2} - \sqrt{80x^3y^2}$$

Solution

$$3x\sqrt{45xy^2} - \sqrt{80x^3y^2} = 3x\sqrt{9 \cdot 5xy^2} - \sqrt{16 \cdot 5x^3y^2}$$
$$= 3x \cdot 3y\sqrt{5x} - 4xy\sqrt{5x}$$
$$= 9xy\sqrt{5x} - 4xy\sqrt{5x}$$
$$= (9xy - 4xy)\sqrt{5x}$$
$$= 5xy\sqrt{5x}$$

Special Note: Shortcut method can be used to solve Examples 3 and 4, which should be similar to Example 6.

Exercises

1. Simplify:

   a. $5\sqrt{5} + 6\sqrt{5}$ **b.** $8\sqrt{11} - 4\sqrt{11}$ **c.** $4\sqrt{10} - 2\sqrt{10}$

   d. $10\sqrt{3} - 4\sqrt{3}$ **e.** $3\sqrt{7} + 2\sqrt{7}$ **f.** $2\sqrt{2} + 7\sqrt{2}$

   Hint: See Example 1.

2. Simplify:

   a. $4\sqrt{5} - 7\sqrt{2} + 2\sqrt{5} + 10\sqrt{2}$ **b.** $5\sqrt{3} - 4 + 2\sqrt{3} + 6$

   c. $12\sqrt{7} + 9 - 3\sqrt{7} - 6$ **d.** $8 + 9\sqrt{11} - 5\sqrt{11} + 2$

   Hint: See Example 2.

3. Express in simplest radical form:

   a. $\sqrt{27}$ **b.** $\sqrt{48}$ **c.** $\sqrt{12}$

   d. $\sqrt{18}$ **e.** $\sqrt{300}$ **f.** $\sqrt{200}$

   Hint: See the Special Note for the solution to Example 3a.

4. Simplify:

   a. $10\sqrt{27} - 3\sqrt{48}$ **b.** $2\sqrt{20} + 3\sqrt{80}$ **c.** $\sqrt{40} + 2\sqrt{10}$

   d. $8\sqrt{90} - 3\sqrt{10}$ **e.** $\sqrt{45} - 2\sqrt{20}$ **f.** $\sqrt{98} + 2\sqrt{18}$

   g. $4\sqrt{48} - 15 - 2\sqrt{27}$

   Hint: See Example 3.

5. Simplify:

    a. $3\sqrt{40y} + 2\sqrt{10y} + 2\sqrt{90y}$ **b.** $2\sqrt{20x} + 4\sqrt{45x} - \sqrt{80x}$

    c. $3\sqrt{80y} - \sqrt{20y} + 2\sqrt{45y}$ **d.** $2\sqrt{12x} + 3\sqrt{27x} - \sqrt{48x}$

    e. $3\sqrt{27y} - 6\sqrt{48y} - 2\sqrt{27y}$

    Hint: See Example 4.

6. Simplify:

    a. $4x\sqrt{45x^3y^2} - \sqrt{80x^3y^2}$ **b.** $3\sqrt{80x^3y^2} + 2\sqrt{20x^3y^2}$

    c. $6x\sqrt{20x^2y^3} - 2\sqrt{45x^2y^3}$ **d.** $5x\sqrt{20x^3y^2} - \sqrt{45x^3y^2} + \sqrt{80x^3y^2}$

    Hint: See Example 5.

7. Use the shortcut method to solve Exercises 5 and 6.

    Hint: See Example 6.

Answers to Selected Questions

1a. $11\sqrt{5}$ **2a.** $6\sqrt{5} + 3\sqrt{2}$ **3a.** $3\sqrt{3}$ **4a.** $18\sqrt{3}$

Multiplication Property of Square Roots

The multiplication property of square roots states,

$$\sqrt{ab} = \sqrt{a}\,\sqrt{b}, \text{ where } a \geq 0 \text{ and } b \geq 0.$$

How to write radical expressions in the simplest radical form:

1. Look for perfect-square factors in each radicand.
2. Apply the Multiplication Property of Square Roots.

$$\sqrt{ab} = \sqrt{a}\,\sqrt{b}, \text{ where } a \geq 0 \text{ and } b \geq 0.$$

3. Find the square roots of the perfect squares.
4. Leave the non-perfect factors in the radical form.

Example 1

Simplify:

a. $\sqrt{6}\,\sqrt{3}$ **b.** $\sqrt{7}\,\sqrt{14}$ **c.** $(\sqrt{5})^2$

Solutions

a. $\sqrt{6}\,\sqrt{3} = \sqrt{6 \cdot 3}$ The Multiplication Property of Square Roots permit us to multiply separate radicals.

$$\sqrt{ab} = \sqrt{a}\,\sqrt{b}, \text{ where } a \geq 0 \text{ and } b \geq 0$$

    $= \sqrt{18}$ Simplify: $6 \cdot 3 = 18$

    $= \sqrt{9 \cdot 2}$ $18 = 9 \cdot 2$, notice that 9 is a factor.

    $= \sqrt{9}\,\sqrt{2}$ No factor of the radicand should be a perfect square other than 1. Notice that 9 is both a factor and a perfect square.

$= 3\sqrt{2}$

$\sqrt{9} = \sqrt{3 \cdot 3} = \sqrt{3^2} = 3$ Notice that 2 is left in the radical form because it is not a perfect square.

The square root of any number to the second power equals the number itself. $\sqrt{a^2} = a$, where $a \geq 0$

b. $\sqrt{7} \sqrt{14} = \sqrt{7} \sqrt{7 \cdot 2}$ $14 = 7 \cdot 2$ (factor 14 into 7 and 2)

$= \sqrt{7} \sqrt{7} \sqrt{2}$ $\sqrt{7 \cdot 2} = \sqrt{7} \sqrt{2}$ because the Multiplication Property of Square Roots permit us to multiply separate radicals.

$\sqrt{ab} = \sqrt{a} \sqrt{b}$, where $a \geq 0$ and $b \geq 0$

$= 7\sqrt{2}$ $\sqrt{7} \sqrt{7} = \sqrt{7 \cdot 7} = \sqrt{7^2} = 7$

The square root of any number to the second power is the number itself. $\sqrt{a^2} = a$, where $a \geq 0$.

Notice that 7^2 forms a perfect square.

c. $(\sqrt{5})^2 = (\sqrt{5})(\sqrt{5})$ The second power means the product of two identical factors. Hint: See the section/chapter on exponents.

$= \sqrt{5 \cdot 5}$ $(\sqrt{5})(\sqrt{5}) = \sqrt{5} \sqrt{5} = \sqrt{5 \cdot 5}$

The Multiplication Property of Square Roots permit us to multiply separate radicals.

$\sqrt{ab} = \sqrt{a} \sqrt{b}$, where $a \geq 0$ and $b \geq 0$

$= \sqrt{5^2}$ $5 \cdot 5 = 5^2$ Notice that 5^2 forms a perfect square.

$= 5$ The square root of any number to the second power is the number itself. $\sqrt{a^2} = a$, where $a \geq 0$

Example 2

Simplify: $(3\sqrt{6})^2$

Solution

$(3\sqrt{6})^2 = (3\sqrt{6})(3\sqrt{6})$ The second power means the product of two identical factors. Hint: See the section/chapter on exponents.

$= (3 \cdot 3)\sqrt{6} \sqrt{6}$ Rearrange the factors.

$= 9\sqrt{6 \cdot 6}$ $3 \cdot 3 = 9$, and $\sqrt{6} \sqrt{6} = \sqrt{6 \cdot 6}$

The Multiplication Property of Square Roots permit us to multiply separate radicals.

$\sqrt{ab} = \sqrt{a} \sqrt{b}$, where $a \geq 0$ and $b \geq 0$

$$= 9\sqrt{6^2}$$ $6 \cdot 6 = 6^2$ Notice that 6^2 forms a perfect square.

$$= 9 \cdot 6$$ The square root of any number to the second power

equals the number itself. $\sqrt{a^2} = a$, where $a \geq 0$

$$= 54$$ $9 \cdot 6 = 54$

Example 3
Simplify:

$$\sqrt{2}\,(3 + \sqrt{8}\,)$$

Solution

$$\sqrt{2}\,(3 + \sqrt{8}\,) = \sqrt{2} \cdot 3 + \sqrt{2}\,\sqrt{8}$$ Multiply $\sqrt{2}$ by the numbers in the parenthesis.
Hint: Review Distributive Property.

$$= \sqrt{2} \cdot 3 + \sqrt{2}\,\sqrt{4 \cdot 2}$$ $8 = 4 \cdot 2$

$$= \sqrt{2} \cdot 3 + \sqrt{2}\,\sqrt{4}\,\sqrt{2}$$ $\sqrt{4 \cdot 2} = \sqrt{4}\,\sqrt{2}$

The Multiplication Property of Square Roots permit us to multiply separate radicals.
$\sqrt{ab} = \sqrt{a}\,\sqrt{b}$, where $a \geq 0$ and $b \geq 0$.

$$= \sqrt{2} \cdot 3 + \sqrt{2}\,\sqrt{2}\,\sqrt{4}$$ Rearrange: $\sqrt{2}\,\sqrt{4}\,\sqrt{2} = \sqrt{2}\,\sqrt{2}\,\sqrt{4}$

$$= \sqrt{2} \cdot 3 + \sqrt{2 \cdot 2}\,\sqrt{4}$$ $\sqrt{2}\,\sqrt{2} = \sqrt{2 \cdot 2}$

The Multiplication Property of Square Roots permit us to multiply separate radicals.
$\sqrt{ab} = \sqrt{a}\,\sqrt{b}$, where $a \geq 0$ and $b \geq 0$.

$$= \sqrt{2} \cdot 3 + \sqrt{4}\,\sqrt{4}$$ $2 \cdot 2 = 4$

$$= \sqrt{2} \cdot 3 + \sqrt{2^2}\,\sqrt{2^2}$$ $4 = 2^2$

$$= \sqrt{2} \cdot 3 + 2 \cdot 2$$ $\sqrt{2^2} = 2$ Notice that 2^2 forms a perfect square.
The square root of any number to the second power equals the number itself. $\sqrt{a^2} = a$, where $a \geq 0$.

$$= 3\sqrt{2} + 4$$ Rearrange: $\sqrt{2} \cdot 3 = 3\sqrt{2}$, and $2 \cdot 2$.

Special Note: Square-Root Expression Simplification Conditions
In order to simplify a square-root expression, the following three conditions must be met:
   1. **No factor of the radicand should be a perfect square other than 1**.
   2. **No radical should be in the denominator of a fraction**.
   3. **The radicand must contain no fraction**.
Notice that all the examples under the section, Multiplication Property of Square Roots, satisfy the three Square-Root Expression Simplification Conditions.

Example 4

Simplify:

$(5 - \sqrt{2})(4 + \sqrt{2})$

Solution

$(5 - \sqrt{2})(4 + \sqrt{2}) = 5 \cdot 4 + 5 \cdot \sqrt{2} - \sqrt{2} \cdot 4 - \sqrt{2}\sqrt{2}$

> Multiply each number in the first parenthesis by each number in the second parenthesis. Hint: Review Distributive Property.

$= 20 + 5\sqrt{2} - 4\sqrt{2} - \sqrt{2}\sqrt{2}$ Simplify

$= 20 + 5\sqrt{2} - 4\sqrt{2} - \sqrt{2 \cdot 2}$

> $\sqrt{2}\sqrt{2} = \sqrt{2 \cdot 2}$
>
> The Multiplication Property of Square Roots permit us to multiply separate radicals.
> $\sqrt{ab} = \sqrt{a}\sqrt{b}$, where $a \geq 0$ and $b \geq 0$.

$= 20 + 5\sqrt{2} - 4\sqrt{2} - \sqrt{2^2}$ $2 \cdot 2 = 2^2$

$= 20 + 5\sqrt{2} - 4\sqrt{2} - 2$ $\sqrt{2^2} = 2$

> The square root of any number to the second power equals the number itself. $\sqrt{a^2} = a$, where $a \geq 0$.
> Notice that 2^2 forms a perfect square.

$= 20 - 2 + (5 - 4)\sqrt{2}$ Rearrange the numbers. Notice that $\sqrt{2}$ is a common factor for $5\sqrt{2}$ and $4\sqrt{2}$.

$= 18 + \sqrt{2}$ Simplify: $20 - 2 = 18$, and $5 - 4 = 1$.

$1\sqrt{2} = \sqrt{2}$

Exercises

1. State the multiplication property of square roots.

2. Mary said, "The square root of any number to the second power equals the number itself. $\sqrt{a^2} = a$, where $a \geq 0$." Is her statement correct?

3. Simplify:

  a. $\sqrt{5}\sqrt{5}$ **b.** $\sqrt{3}\sqrt{6}$ **c.** $\sqrt{5}\sqrt{15}$ **d.** $\sqrt{2}\sqrt{8}$ **e.** $\sqrt{32}\sqrt{2}$

  f. $\sqrt{3}\sqrt{24}$ **g.** $\sqrt{18}\sqrt{2}$ **h.** $(\sqrt{7})^2$ **i.** $(\sqrt{11})^2$ **j.** $\sqrt{3}\sqrt{12}$

  Hint: See Example 1.

4. Simplify:

  a. $(2\sqrt{8})^2$ **b.** $(3\sqrt{8})^2$ **c.** $(6\sqrt{5})^2$ **d.** $(x\sqrt{7})^2$ **e.** $2\sqrt{3} \cdot 4\sqrt{3}$

f. $3\sqrt{6y} \cdot 4\sqrt{6y}$　　　　　　　**g.** $\sqrt{3} \cdot 3\sqrt{3}$　　**h.** $(2\sqrt{2})^2$　　　**i.** $(2\sqrt{11})^2$
Hint: See Example 2.

5. Simplify:

　　a. $\sqrt{2}(4 + \sqrt{8})$　　**b.** $\sqrt{3}(2 + \sqrt{12})$　　**c.** $3\sqrt{2}(3\sqrt{2} - \sqrt{6})$　　**d.** $2\sqrt{3}(\sqrt{3} + 2\sqrt{12})$
Hint: See Example 3.

6. What are the three square-root expression simplification conditions?

7. Simplify:

　　a. $(6 + \sqrt{3})(6 + \sqrt{3})$　　　　　　　**b.** $(\sqrt{3} - 4)(\sqrt{3} + 6)$

　　c. $(4 - \sqrt{2})(4 + \sqrt{2})$　　　　　　　**d.** $(3\sqrt{2} + 4\sqrt{3})(3\sqrt{2} - 4\sqrt{3})$

　　e. $(2\sqrt{5} + 2\sqrt{2})(\sqrt{5} - \sqrt{2})$　　　　**f.** $(2\sqrt{2} - \sqrt{12})(5\sqrt{2} - 3\sqrt{12})$
Hint: See Example 4.

Answers to Selected Questions

3a. 5　　　　　　**4a.** 32　　　　　　**5a.** $4\sqrt{2} + 4$

Division Property of Square Roots

The Division Property of Square Roots states:

$$\sqrt{\frac{a}{b}} = \frac{\sqrt{a}}{\sqrt{b}}, \text{ where } a \geq 0, \text{ and } b \geq 0.$$

Example 1

Simplify:

a. $\sqrt{\dfrac{9}{16}}$　　　　　　**b.** $\sqrt{\dfrac{5}{36}}$　　　　　　**c.** $\sqrt{\dfrac{9}{7}}$

Solution

a. $\sqrt{\dfrac{9}{16}} = \dfrac{\sqrt{9}}{\sqrt{16}}$　　　　The Division Property of Square Roots permits us to

separate square roots. $\sqrt{\dfrac{a}{b}} = \dfrac{\sqrt{a}}{\sqrt{b}}$, **where $a \geq 0$, and $b \geq 0$.**

　　$= \dfrac{3}{4}$　　　　Simplify the numerator and the denominator: $\sqrt{9} = 3$, and

　　　　　　　　$\sqrt{16} = 4$.

b. $\sqrt{\dfrac{5}{36}} = \dfrac{\sqrt{5}}{\sqrt{36}}$　　　　The Division Property of Square Roots permits us to

308

separate square roots. $\sqrt{\dfrac{a}{b}} = \dfrac{\sqrt{a}}{\sqrt{b}}$, **where a ≥ 0, and b ≥ 0.**

$= \dfrac{\sqrt{5}}{6}$ We cannot simplify the numerator. Simplify the denominator.

$\sqrt{36} = 6$

c. $\sqrt{\dfrac{9}{7}} = \dfrac{\sqrt{9}}{\sqrt{7}}$ The Division Property of Square Roots permits us to

separate square roots. $\sqrt{\dfrac{a}{b}} = \dfrac{\sqrt{a}}{\sqrt{b}}$, **where a ≥ 0, and b ≥ 0.**

$= \dfrac{3}{\sqrt{7}}$ Simplify the numerator, $\sqrt{9} = 3$. Notice that the denominator

cannot be easily simplified. Notice also that a radical remains
in the denominator of $\sqrt{7}$. Recall from the three conditions
for a square-root expressions to be in the simplest radical
form, one of the conditions is no radical should be in the
denominator of a fraction.

$= \dfrac{3}{\sqrt{7}} \cdot \dfrac{\sqrt{7}}{\sqrt{7}}$ $\dfrac{3}{\sqrt{7}}$ can be changed to the simplest radical form by

multiplying by $\dfrac{\sqrt{7}}{\sqrt{7}}$, which is equivalent to multiplying by 1.

This process of removing a radical expression from the
denominator is known as **rationalizing the denominator.**

$= \dfrac{3\sqrt{7}}{7}$ Simplify: $3 \cdot \sqrt{7} = 3\sqrt{7}$, and $\sqrt{7} \cdot \sqrt{7} = 7$

Exercises
1a. State the Division Property of Square Roots.
1b. Explain what is meant by **rationalizing the denominator.**
2. Simplify:

   a. $\sqrt{\dfrac{4}{9}}$ **b.** $\sqrt{\dfrac{4}{25}}$ **c.** $\sqrt{\dfrac{9}{25}}$ **d.** $\sqrt{\dfrac{49}{64}}$

   Hint: See Example 1a.
3. Simplify:

   a. $\sqrt{\dfrac{2}{9}}$ **b.** $\sqrt{\dfrac{3}{25}}$ **c.** $\sqrt{\dfrac{3}{16}}$ **d.** $\sqrt{\dfrac{7}{25}}$

   Hint: See Example 1b.

4. Simplify:

a. $\sqrt{\dfrac{9}{2}}$　　　　b. $\sqrt{\dfrac{4}{5}}$　　　　c. $\sqrt{\dfrac{16}{11}}$　　　　d. $\sqrt{\dfrac{25}{6}}$

Hint: See Example 1c.

Answers to Selected Questions

2a. $\dfrac{2}{3}$　　　　3a. $\dfrac{\sqrt{2}}{3}$　　　　4a. $\dfrac{3\sqrt{2}}{2}$

SQUARE ROOTS OF NON-PERFECT SQUARES

How to Estimate the Square Roots of Non-perfect Squares.
One way to estimate the square root of non-perfect squares is to find two perfect squares which are closest to the non-perfect number such that one of the perfect squares should be greater than the non-perfect number and the other perfect square should be less than the non-perfect number. The square root of the non-perfect number is between the two factors of the two perfect squares such that if the factor of the greater perfect square is multiplied by itself, the product will give the perfect square of the larger perfect square. Similarly, if the factor of the smaller perfect square is multiplied by itself, the product will give the perfect square of the smaller perfect square.

Example 1
a. Find the two integers that $\sqrt{5}$ is between.

b. Find the **best whole number estimate** of $\sqrt{5}$.
Solution
a. Think of two perfect squares that are closest to $\sqrt{5}$ such that one of the perfect squares is greater than 5 and the other perfect square is less than 5 as shown:
$3^2 = 9$　　　　　$9 > 5$
$2^2 = 4$　　　　　$4 < 5$
Therefore, $\sqrt{5}$ is between 2 and 3,
or $9 > 5 > 4$ _____[A]
Find the square root of equation [A] as shown:
$\sqrt{9} > \sqrt{5} > \sqrt{4} = 3 > \sqrt{5} > 2$
Therefore, $\sqrt{5}$ is between 2 and 3.
b. From Equation [A], since 5 is closer to 4 than 9, the **best whole number estimate (or the nearest whole number estimate)** for $\sqrt{5}$ is 2.

Example 2

Find the two integers that $-\sqrt{29}$ is between.

Solution

Think of the two perfect squares that are closest to $-\sqrt{29}$ such that one of the perfect squares is greater than 29 and the other perfect square is less than 29 as shown:

$(-5)^2 = 25$ $25 < 29$
$(-6)^2 = 36$ $36 > 29$

Therefore, $-\sqrt{29}$ is between -5 and -6,

or $25 < 29 < 36$ _____[A]

Find the square root of equation $[A]$ as shown:

$\pm\sqrt{25} < \pm\sqrt{29} < \pm\sqrt{36}$

$-5 < -\sqrt{29} < -6$ The question involves only the negative square root.

                    Note: The square root of any positive number can be + or -.

Therefore, $-\sqrt{29}$ is between -5 and -6.

How to Use the Calculator to Estimate the Value of a Square Root

Note: Different calculators use different methods in finding square roots. Refer to your calculator manual for the correct method that your calculator uses. For example, to find $\sqrt{4}$, the method can be: Press $\sqrt{}$ 4 =, Press 2nd $\sqrt{}$ 4 =, or Press 4 $\sqrt{}$ = on your calculator, depending on the type of calculator.

Example 3

Use a calculator to estimate $\sqrt{17}$. Round your answer to the nearest tenth.

Solution

$\sqrt{17} \approx 4.1231056...$ Press 17 $\sqrt{}$ on your calculator.

$\sqrt{17} \approx 4.1$ Rounded to the nearest tenth. Hint: Review decimal fractions.

Example 4

Use a calculator to find $\sqrt{108}$. Round your answer to the nearest tenth.

Solution

$\sqrt{108} \approx 10.392304...$ Press 108 $\sqrt{}$ on your calculator.

       ≈ 10.4 Rounded to the nearest tenth. Note that the hundredth position digit is 9 which is greater than 5, and therefore, the tenth position digit which is 3 is rounded up to 4. Hint: Review Decimal Fractions.

Example 5

Use a calculator to find $\sqrt{300.95}$. Round your answer to the nearest tenth.

Solution

$\sqrt{300.95} \approx 17.34791...$ Press 300.95 $\sqrt{}$ on your calculator.

≈ 17.3   Rounded to the nearest tenth.
                Hint: Review decimal fractions (rounding of numbers).

Example 6
Evaluate the expression. Round your answer to two decimal places.

$\sqrt{10} \cdot (-\sqrt{36})$

Solution

$\sqrt{10} \cdot (-\sqrt{36}) = \sqrt{10} \cdot -6$ Do the operation in the parenthesis first.
                                                        See the chapter on the Order of Operations.

    ≈ -18.9736...   Depress $10\sqrt{x} \times 6 =$ on your calculator in order to
                                          obtain 1.8 9736..., and then attach the negative sign
                                          which is attached to 6 to obtain -1.89736...
                                          Note: Some calculators may have just $\sqrt{}$ instead of
                                          $\sqrt{x}$ as the symbol for square root.

    ≈ -18.97   Rounded to 2 decimal places.

Example 7
Find the values of $\sqrt{2}$, $\sqrt{3}$, and π. Round each number to the nearest tenth.

Indicate $\sqrt{3}$ and π on a number line.

Solution

$\sqrt{2} \approx 1.4142135...$ Depress $2\sqrt{} =$ on your calculator to obtain 1.4142135...

    ≈ 1.4   Rounded to the nearest tenth. (Review "Place Values").

$\sqrt{3} \approx 1.7320508...$ Depress $3\sqrt{} =$ on your calculator to obtain 1.7320508...

    ≈ 1.7   Round to the nearest tenth. (Review "Place Values").

$\pi = \dfrac{22}{7}$ The standard value of π is $\dfrac{22}{7}$.

  = 3.1428571...   Depress $22 \div 7 =$ on the calculator to obtain 3.1428571...

  = 3.1   Rounded to the nearest tenth.

Locate 1.4, 1.7, and 3.1 on a number line as shown:

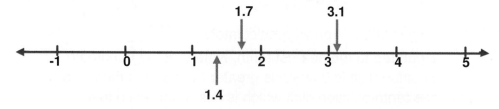

Exercises
1. Find the two integers that each square root number is between.
    Find the best estimate to the nearest whole number.
    Hint: See Example 1.

a. $\sqrt{6}$ **b.** $\sqrt{55}$ **c.** $\sqrt{98}$ **d.** $\sqrt{120}$

2. Find the integers that each square root number is between. Hint: See Example 2.

   a. $-\sqrt{6}$ **b.** $-\sqrt{13}$ **c.** $-\sqrt{27}$ **d.** $-\sqrt{99}$

3. Use a calculator to estimate each square root number. Round your answer to the nearest tenth. Hint: See Example 3.

   a. $\sqrt{11}$ **b.** $\sqrt{51}$ **c.** $\sqrt{91}$ **d.** $\sqrt{101}$

4. Use the calculator to find the value of each square root number.
   Hint: See Example 4. Round your answer to the nearest tenth.

   a. $\sqrt{79}$ **b.** $\sqrt{24}$ **c.** $\sqrt{62}$ **d.** $\sqrt{112}$

5. Use the calculator to find the value of each square root number.
   Hint: See Example 5.
   Round your answer to the nearest tenth.

   a. $\sqrt{400.8}$ **b.** $\sqrt{92}$ **c.** $\sqrt{37}$ **d.** $\sqrt{15}$

6. Evaluate each expression. Round your answer to 2 decimal places.
   Hint: See Example 6.

   a. $\sqrt{8} \cdot (-\sqrt{9})$ **b.** $\sqrt{7} \cdot (-\sqrt{16})$ **c.** $\sqrt{10} \cdot (-\sqrt{64})$ **d.** $\sqrt{8} \cdot \sqrt{100}$

7. Find the values of $\sqrt{5}$, $\sqrt{11}$, and $\sqrt{13}$. Round your answers to the nearest tenth.
   Locate your answers on a number line. Hint: See Example 7.

Challenge Questions

8. use a calculator to find the value of each square root number.
   Round your answer to the nearest tenth.

   a. $\sqrt{9}$ **b.** $\sqrt{89.4}$ **c.** $\sqrt{5}$ **d.** $\sqrt{39}$ **e.** $\sqrt{40}$

9. Locate $\sqrt{7}$, $\sqrt{12}$, and $\sqrt{17}$ on a number line. Round each number to the nearest tenth.

10. Evaluate each expression. Round your answer to the nearest tenth.

   a. $\sqrt{10} \cdot (-\sqrt{49})$ **b.** $\sqrt{17} \cdot (-\sqrt{9})$ **c.** $\sqrt{7} \cdot \sqrt{36}$

11. Find the two integers that each square root number is between.

   a. $\sqrt{10}$ **b.** $\sqrt{67}$ **c.** $\sqrt{101}$ **d.** $\sqrt{120}$

Answers to Selected Questions

1a. 2 and 3   **2a.** -2 and -3   **3a.** 3.3
4a. 8.9   **5a.** 20.0   **6a.** 6.90

CHAPTER 11

REAL NUMBERS

New Terms
real numbers, **rational numbers**, **irrational numbers**, **and integers**.

Real Numbers: A set of real numbers is made up of the set of rational numbers and the set of irrational numbers.

Rational Numbers: Rational numbers can be expressed as fractions in the form $\frac{a}{b}$ where **a** and **b** are integers and **b** $\neq$ 0, and the rational numbers can also be written as decimals that either terminate or repeat. Repeating decimals do not end, but rather at some point they continuously repeat a pattern of digits to the right of the decimal. Therefore, a bar is used above the repeating digits to indicate a repeating decimal. For example, $\frac{4}{11}$ = .36363636, is written as $.\overline{36}$ which indicates repeating of 36. Similarly, $\frac{7}{9}$ = .77777777..., is written as $.\overline{7}$, which indicates repeating of 7.

The terminating decimals simply end at a point, for example $\frac{1}{2}$ = .5, similarly $\frac{3}{4}$ = .75. Some examples of rational numbers are:

1. Proper fractions: $\frac{1}{2}$, $\frac{3}{5}$, $\frac{2}{3}$,...

2. Improper fractions: $\frac{5}{2}$, $\frac{14}{3}$, $\frac{31}{23}$,...

3. Mixed numbers: $1\frac{1}{3} = \frac{4}{3}$, $3\frac{1}{8} = \frac{25}{8}$, $1\frac{1}{9} = \frac{10}{9}$,...

4. Integers: $0 = \frac{0}{1}$, $1 = \frac{1}{1}$, $-8 = \frac{-8}{1}$,...

5. Terminating decimals: -4.86, $.5 = \frac{5}{10}$, $1.2 = \sqrt{1.44}$, ...

6. Repeating or recurring decimals: $.\overline{7} = \frac{7}{9}$, $.\overline{27} = \frac{3}{11}$, $.58\overline{3} = \frac{7}{12}$,...

Irrational numbers: Irrational numbers can be written only as decimals that do not terminate or repeat. The square root of prime numbers are irrational numbers. For example, since the prime numbers are 2, 3, 5, 7, 11, 13, 19, 23,..., then the irrational numbers are $\sqrt{2}$, $\sqrt{3}$, $\sqrt{5}$, $\sqrt{7}$, $\sqrt{11}$, $\sqrt{13}$, $\sqrt{19}$, $\sqrt{23}$,... For example, $\sqrt{2} \approx 1.41421356...$ which does not terminate. π is $\frac{22}{7}$ = 3.1428571...which does not terminate, and therefore, π is an irrational number.

Integers: Integers are the set of whole numbers and their opposites including zero. Therefore, the set of integers is ...-5, -4, -3, -2, -1, 0, 1, 2, 3, 4, 5, ...

Group Work (Refer to the manual of your calculator to know the method used for finding square root.)

Use the calculator to show that $\sqrt{5}$, $\sqrt{7}$, $\sqrt{11}$, $\sqrt{13}$, $\sqrt{19}$, and $\sqrt{23}$ do not terminate, and therefore, they are irrational numbers by depressing the button for each prime number, and then depressing the button $\sqrt{}$ on the calculator in order to obtain the square root of each number.

Whole Numbers: The set of whole numbers is w = 0, 1, 2, 3, 4, ...

Natural or Counting numbers: The set of natural or counting numbers are n = 1, 2, 3, 4, 5, ...
Note that the set of whole numbers is the natural or counting numbers together with the number zero.

Classification of Real Numbers

(Classification of Real Numbers is shown on the next page.)

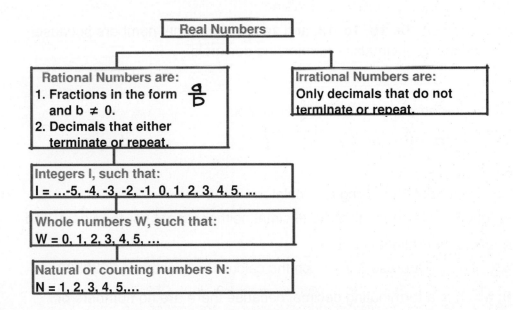

(Classification of Real Numbers is shown above.)

Example 1.
Write each fraction in the decimal form and indicate whether the number is a terminating decimal or a repeating decimal.

a. $\dfrac{6}{11}$ **b.** $\dfrac{3}{5}$ **c.** $\dfrac{5}{12}$ **d.** $\dfrac{2}{3}$ **e.** $\dfrac{24}{100}$

Solution

Use a calculator to divide each fraction.

a. $\dfrac{6}{11}$ = .54545454... = $.\overline{54}$ is a repeating decimal because 54 repeats.

(Depress 6 ÷ 11 = on the calculator to obtain .54545454).

b. $\dfrac{3}{5}$ = .6 is a terminating decimal because there are no numbers after 6.

(Depress 3 ÷ 5 = on the calculator to obtain .6).

c. $\dfrac{5}{12}$ = .41666666... = $.41\overline{6}$ is a repeating decimal because 6 repeats.

(Depress 5 ÷ 12 = on the calculator to obtain .4166666...).

d. $\dfrac{2}{3}$ = .6666666.... = $.\overline{6}$ is a repeating decimal because 6 repeats.

(Depress 2 ÷ 3 = on the calculator to obtain .6666666...).

e. $\dfrac{24}{100}$ = .24 is a terminating decimal because there are no numbers or digits after 4.

(Depress 24 ÷ 100 = on the calculator to obtain .24).

Example 2

Explain why the fractions in examples **1a**, **1b**, **1c**, **1d**, and **1e** are all rational numbers.

Solution

The fractions in example **1a**, **1b**, **1c**, **1d**, and **1e** are all rational numbers because they are either repeating decimals or terminating decimals.

Example 3

Determine which numbers are rational and irrational.

a. $\sqrt{3}$ **b.** $-\dfrac{4}{15}$ **c.** $\sqrt{10}$ **d.** $-\sqrt{9}$

Solution

a. Find the square root of 3 by using a calculator.

$\sqrt{3}$ = 1.7320508...; the digits after the decimal neither repeat nor terminate, and therefore, $\sqrt{3}$ is an irrational number.

(Depress 3 $\sqrt{}$ = on the calculator to obtain 1.7320508...).

b. $-\dfrac{4}{5}$ = -0.8; which is a terminating decimal because there are no numbers or

digits after 8, so $-\dfrac{4}{5}$ is a rational number.

(Depress 4 ÷ 5 = on the calculator to obtain 0.8, and then attach the negative symbol to obtain -0.8).

c. Find the square root of 10 by using a calculator.

$\sqrt{10} = 3.1622776...$, the digits after the decimal neither repeat nor terminate, and therefore, $\sqrt{10}$ is an irrational number.

(Depress 10 $\sqrt{}$ = on the calculator to obtain 3.1622776...).

d. $\sqrt{9} = \sqrt{3 \times 3} = \sqrt{3^2} = 3$ which can be written as $\dfrac{3}{1}$, and therefore, $\sqrt{9}$ is a rational number. (Note that $\sqrt{3^2} = 3$ because the square root of any number raised to the second power equals the number or the square root of the square of a number is the number itself).

Example 4

Write all the names that apply to each number.

a. -7.481   **b.** $\sqrt{5}$ **c.** $\dfrac{\sqrt{25}}{5}$

Solution

a. -7.481 is a terminating decimal, and therefore, -7.481 is a rational and a real number.

b. Use the calculator to find the square root of 5.

$\sqrt{5} = 2.360679...$; which is neither terminating nor repeating decimal, and therefore, $\sqrt{5}$ is an irrational and a real number.

(Depress 5 $\sqrt{}$ = on the calculator to obtain 2.360679).

c. $\dfrac{\sqrt{25}}{5} = \dfrac{\sqrt{5 \times 5}}{5} = \dfrac{\sqrt{5^2}}{5} = \dfrac{5}{5} = 1$

Therefore, the number $\dfrac{\sqrt{25}}{5}$ is a whole number, integer, rational, and a real number.

(Note that $\sqrt{5^2} = 5$ because the square root of the square of a number is the number itself.)

Example 5

Determine if the number is rational, irrational, or not a real number.

a. $\sqrt{-7}$ **b.** $-\sqrt{-7}$ **c.** $\sqrt{\dfrac{9}{-25}}$ **d.** $\dfrac{0}{0}$ **e.** $-\sqrt{\dfrac{0}{16}}$

Hint: It is impossible to find the square root of a negative number.

Solution

a. $\sqrt{-7}$ is not a number and so not a real number because $\sqrt{-7}$ is neither a rational nor an irrational number. A negative number has no real square roots.

b. $-\sqrt{-7}$ is not a number and so not a real number because $\sqrt{-7}$ is neither a rational nor irrational number. A negative number has no real square roots.

c. $\sqrt{\dfrac{9}{-25}}$ is not a number and so not a real number because $\sqrt{\dfrac{9}{-25}}$ is neither a

rational nor an irrational number. A negative number has no real square roots.

d. $\dfrac{0}{0}$ is undefined or is not a number because a numerator should not be

divided by zero, and therefore, $\dfrac{0}{0}$ is neither a rational nor irrational number

and so $\dfrac{0}{0}$ is not a real number.

e. $-\sqrt{\dfrac{0}{16}} = -\sqrt{0} = -0 = 0$. Therefore, $-\sqrt{\dfrac{0}{16}}$ is a rational number.

Exercises

1. A real number is made of _____numbers and _____numbers.

2. Explain what is meant by rational numbers.

3. Explain what is meant by irrational numbers.

4. Integers are _____

5. Terminating decimals are _____

6. Explain what is meant by repeating or recurring decimals.

7. Write each fraction in the decimal form and indicate whether the number is a terminating decimal or a repeating decimal.
Hint: See Example 1.

    a. $\dfrac{7}{12}$ **b.** $\dfrac{4}{5}$ **c.** $\dfrac{11}{12}$ **d.** $\dfrac{7}{10}$ **e.** $\dfrac{17}{100}$

8. Explain why all the numbers in Exercise 7 are rational numbers.
Hint: See Example 2.

9. Determine which numbers are rational or irrational. Hint: See Example 3, also note that you can easily find the square roots of 16 and 25.

    a. $\sqrt{11}$ **b.** $\sqrt{15}$ **c.** $-\dfrac{5}{9}$ **d.** $-\sqrt{16}$ **e.** $-\sqrt{25}$

10. Write all the names that apply to each number. Hint: See Example 4.

    a. -9.3941   **b.** $\sqrt{11}$ **c.** $\dfrac{\sqrt{16}}{4}$ **d.** $\dfrac{\sqrt{16}}{3}$

    e. 0.3442   **f.** 9   **g.** 30   **h.** $\dfrac{\sqrt{9}}{3}$

11. Determine if the square root number is rational, irrational, or not a real number. Hint: See Example 5.

    a. $\sqrt{-8}$ **b.** $\sqrt{\dfrac{12}{-5}}$ **c.** $\dfrac{14}{0}$ **d.** $\sqrt{\dfrac{0}{6}}$ **e.** $\sqrt{-5}$

Challenge Questions

12. Write all the names that apply to each number.

     a. $\dfrac{0}{2}$ **b.** $\dfrac{3}{0}$ **c.** $\sqrt{\dfrac{3}{16}}$ **d.** $\sqrt{8}$ **e.** $\sqrt{17}$

     f. $\sqrt{-2}$ **g.** $-\sqrt{3}$ **h.** $-\sqrt{\dfrac{25}{2}}$ **i.** $\sqrt{\dfrac{0}{2}}$ **j.** $\sqrt{\dfrac{2}{0}}$

Answer to Selected Questions.

10f. Whole number, integer, and real number.

CUBE ROOT

$\sqrt[3]{b}$ is called the "cube root of b". If $\sqrt[3]{b} = k$, it means that $b = k \cdot k \cdot k = k^3$.

Substitute k^3 for b in the expression $\sqrt[3]{b}$.

$$\sqrt[3]{b} = \sqrt[3]{k^3} = k$$

In general, $\sqrt[n]{b}$, the "n^{th} root of b" is k such that $k \cdot k \cdot k......k = b$.   (n factors of k).

$$\sqrt[n]{b} = \sqrt[n]{k^n} = k$$

Since we have shown that $\sqrt[3]{k^3} = k$, we can conclude that the cube root of any number raised to the third power is the number itself. Similarly, the nth root of any number raised to the nth power is the number itself.

Example 1

Find $\sqrt[3]{8}$.

Solution

$\sqrt[3]{8} = 2$ because $2 \cdot 2 \cdot 2 = 8$, such that $\sqrt[3]{8} = \sqrt[3]{2 \cdot 2 \cdot 2} = \sqrt[3]{2^3} = 2$.

$\sqrt[3]{2^3} = 2$ because the cube root of any number raised to the third power is the number itself.

Example 2

Find $\sqrt[3]{64}$.

Solution

Find the factor of 64 that can be multiplied by itself three times in order to obtain 64 by using the factor tree as shown:

319

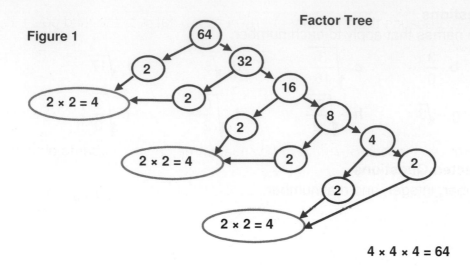

Figure 1

Factor Tree

4 × 4 × 4 = 64

From the factor tree, 4 · 4 · 4 = 64. (Hint: Review the topic on factorization and simply multiply each factor by itself three times until you get a factor that can be multiplied by itself three times to give 64, and this factor is the cube root of 64.)

Therefore, $\sqrt[3]{64} = \sqrt[3]{4 \cdot 4 \cdot 4} = \sqrt[3]{4^3} = 4$ (The cube root of any number which is to the third power is the number itself.)

Example 3

Find $\sqrt[3]{-125}$.

Solution

Find the factor of -125 that can be multiplied by itself three times in order to obtain -125 by using the factor tree as shown:

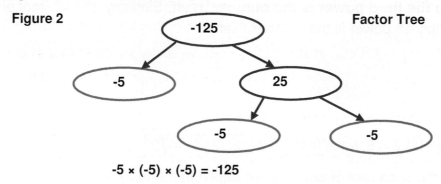

Figure 2

Factor Tree

-5 × (-5) × (-5) = -125

From the factor tree, -5 · (-5) · (-5) = -125. (Hint: Review the topic on factorization and simply multiply each factor by itself three times until you get a factor that can be multiplied by itself three times to give -125, and this factor is the cube root of -125.)

Therefore, $\sqrt[3]{-125} = \sqrt[3]{-5 \cdot (-5) \cdot (-5)} = \sqrt[3]{-5^3} = -5$ (The cube root of any number which is to the third power is the number itself.)

Note: $\sqrt[3]{(-5)^3} = -5$ because the cube root of any number that is to the third power is the number itself.

Example 4
Find $-\sqrt[3]{-27}$

Solution
Find the factor of -27 that can be multiplied by itself three times in order to obtain -27 by using the factor tree as shown:

Figure 3   **Factor Tree**

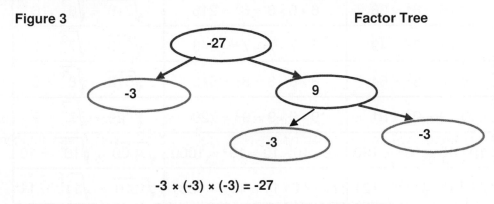

$$-3 \times (-3) \times (-3) = -27$$

From the factor tree, $(-3) \cdot (-3) \cdot (-3) = -27$. (Hint: Review the topic on factoring and simply multiplying each factor by itself three times until you get a factor that can be multiplied by itself three times to give -125, and this factor is the cube root of -27.)

Therefore, $\sqrt[3]{-27} = \sqrt[3]{(-3) \cdot (-3) \cdot (-3)} = \sqrt[3]{(-3)^3} = -3$ (The cube root of any number which is to the third power is the number itself.)

Therefore $-\sqrt[3]{-27} = -(-3)$ **Note:** $\sqrt[3]{-27} = -3$.

$\qquad\qquad = 3$ Answer.   **Note:** $-(- = +$, therefore, $-(-3) = +3 = 3$.

Note: $\sqrt[3]{(-3)^3} = -3$ because the cube root of any number that is to the third power is the number itself.

Table of Powers Involving Square and Cube.
The table 1 of powers involving **square** and **cube** of numbers may provide more understanding of the structure of the factors and powers of numbers.

321

Table 1   Powers Involving Square and Cube of Numbers

Number	Square	Cube	Cube Root
2	$2 \cdot 2 = 2^2 = 4$	$2 \cdot 2 \cdot 2 = 2^3 = 8$	$\sqrt[3]{8} = \sqrt[3]{2^3} = 2$
3	$3 \cdot 3 = 3^2 = 9$	$3 \cdot 3 \cdot 3 = 3^3 = 27$	$\sqrt[3]{27} = \sqrt[3]{3^3} = 3$
4	$4 \cdot 4 = 4^2 = 16$	$4 \cdot 4 \cdot 4 = 4^3 = 64$	$\sqrt[3]{64} = \sqrt[3]{4^3} = 4$
5	$5 \cdot 5 = 5^2 = 25$	$5 \cdot 5 \cdot 5 = 5^3 = 125$	$\sqrt[3]{125} = \sqrt[3]{5^3} = 5$
6	$6 \cdot 6 = 6^2 = 36$	$6 \cdot 6 \cdot 6 = 6^3 = 216$	$\sqrt[3]{216} = \sqrt[3]{6^3} = 6$
7	$7 \cdot 7 = 7^2 = 49$	$7 \cdot 7 \cdot 7 = 7^3 = 343$	$\sqrt[3]{343} = \sqrt[3]{7^3} = 7$
8	$8 \cdot 8 = 8^2 = 64$	$8 \cdot 8 \cdot 8 = 8^3 = 512$	$\sqrt[3]{512} = \sqrt[3]{8^3} = 8$
9	$9 \cdot 9 = 9^2 = 81$	$9 \cdot 9 \cdot 9 = 9^3 = 729$	$\sqrt[3]{729} = \sqrt[3]{9^3} = 9$
10	$10 \cdot 10 = 10^2 = 100$	$10 \cdot 10 \cdot 10 = 10^3 = 1000$	$\sqrt[3]{1000} = \sqrt[3]{10^3} = 10$
11	$11 \cdot 11 = 11^2 = 121$	$11 \cdot 11 \cdot 11 = 11^3 = 1331$	$\sqrt[3]{1331} = \sqrt[3]{11^3} = 11$
12	$12 \cdot 12 = 12^2 = 144$	$12 \cdot 12 \cdot 12 = 12^3 = 1728$	$\sqrt[3]{1728} = \sqrt[3]{12^3} = 12$

Note carefully that Table 1 can be read forward and backward. For example, 2 cubed is 8 but the cube root of 8 is 2.

Exercises

1. Find: **a.** $\sqrt[3]{27}$ **b.** $\sqrt[3]{125}$ **c.** $\sqrt[3]{216}$

   Hint: Use the method in Example 1 or Example 2.

2. Using Example 1, find $\sqrt[3]{1000}$.

3. Find the following cube roots. Hint: See Example 3.

   a. $\sqrt[3]{-27}$ **b.** $\sqrt[3]{-64}$ **c.** $\sqrt[3]{-8}$ **d.** $\sqrt[3]{-216}$

4. Evaluate the following. Hint: See Example 4.

   a. $-\sqrt[3]{-64}$ **b.** $-\sqrt[3]{-125}$ **c.** $-\sqrt[3]{-8}$ **d.** $-\sqrt[3]{-216}$

Answers to Selected Questions.

1a. 3   **3a.** -3   **4a.** 4

Volume of a Cube

The cube of any number is the number to the third power. Therefore, the cube of 5 is 5^3. The cube also refers to a solid figure that has equal length, width, and height.

The formula for finding the volume of a cube is:

Volume = Length × Width × Height

But all the sides of a cube figure are **equal** and if we let a side of the cube be S, then the volume of the cube becomes:

Volume = S × S × S
$$= \mathbf{S^3}$$

Therefore, the cube of any number may be considered as the volume of a cube if the number were to be the sides of a cube.

 This figure is a cube with all the sides equal.

Example 5

The length of a side of a cube is 10 cm. Find the volume of the cube.

Solution

The formula for finding the volume of a cube is:

$$\text{Volume} = \mathbf{S^3}$$
$$= (10 \text{ cm})^3 \qquad\qquad S = 10 \text{ cm.}$$
$$= 10 \text{ cm} \times 10 \text{ cm} \times 10 \text{ cm}$$
$$= 1000 \text{ cm}^3.$$

Example 6

Find the length of a side of a cube which has a volume of 8 m³.

Solution

The formula for the volume of a cube is:

$$\text{Volume} = \mathbf{S^3} \qquad\qquad S \text{ is the length of a side of the cube.}$$
$$8 \text{ m}^3 = S^3 \underline{\hspace{10cm}}\text{[A]}$$

It is given in the problem that the volume is 8 m³.

Find the cube root of both sides of the equation [A] in order to obtain the value of S as shown:

$$\sqrt[3]{8 \text{ m}^3} = \sqrt[3]{S^3}$$

$$\sqrt[3]{2 \text{ m} \times 2 \text{ m} \times 2 \text{ m}} = \sqrt[3]{S^3} \qquad 8 \text{ m}^3 = 2 \text{ m} \times 2 \text{ m} \times 2 \text{ m}$$

$$\sqrt[3]{(2 \text{ m})^3} = \sqrt[3]{S^3} \qquad 2 \text{ m} \times 2 \text{ m} \times 2 \text{ m} = (2 \text{ m})^3$$

$$2 \text{ m} = S \qquad \text{The cube root of any number to the third power is the number itself.}$$

323

Exercises

1. Find the volume of a cube which has a length of a side of 2 m. Hint: See Example 5.
2. Find the volume of each cube which has a length of a side as shown:
   Hint: See Example 1.
   a. 3 m   **b.** 5 cm   **c.** 4 ft
3. Find the length of a side of each cube which has the following volumes.
   Hint: See Example 6.
   a. 64 m^3 **b.** 27 ft^3 **c.** 125 cm^3

Answers to Selected Questions.

   2a. 27 m^3 **3a.** 4 m

RATIOS

Kofi and Ama have 12 pencils. They have agreed to divide the pencils such that Kofi will have 8 pencils and Ama will have the remaining 4 pencils. To find out how many times more pencils Kofi has than Ama, divide 8 by 4.

$$8 \div 4 = 2$$

Therefore, Kofi has twice as many pencils as Ama. In the above statement we are comparing two quantities which are the number of Kofi's pencils and the number of Ama's pencils by division. Similarly, **a ratio is the comparison of two quantities by division**. The ratio of the number of Kofi's pencils to Ama's pencils can be expressed in three ways as shown:

   1). Using "to" method (8 to 4).

   2). Using fraction method ($\frac{8}{4}$).

   3). Using a colon(:) method (8 : 4).

The ratio $\frac{8}{4}$ can be reduced to the simplest form as $\frac{2}{1}$ by dividing both the numerator and the denominator by 4. **Note** carefully that a ratio should always have a denominator, and therefore, if the denominator is 1, we must always write the denominator as 1.

Rule 1: To find the ratio of one number to another number, write the first number as the numerator and the second number as a denominator and then reduce to the lowest terms if possible. For example, the ratio of x to y is $\frac{x}{y}$ or x : y and y is a non-zero number.

More Ratio Concepts.

Recall from the section on fractions that reducing a fraction to the lowest terms, the value of the fraction is not changed, and similarly, reducing a ratio to the lowest terms does not change the value of the ratio.

REAL WORLD APPLICATIONS - WORD PROBLEMS
Ratios

Example 1

A class consists of 13 girls and 12 boys.

(a) What is the ratio of the girls to the boys?

(b) What is the ratio of the boys to the girls?

(c) What is the ratio of the boys to the whole class?

(d) What is the ratio of the girls to the whole class?

(e) What is the ratio of the total class to the number of girls?

(f). What is the ratio of the total class to the number of boys?

Solution

(a) The number of girls = 13

   The number of boys = 12

   Using Rule 1, which states, "To find the ratio of one number to another number, write the first number as the numerator and the second number as the denominator and then reduce to the lowest terms if possible," the ratio of the girls to the boys is:

$$\frac{\text{Number of girls}}{\text{Number of boys}} = \frac{13}{12} \text{ or } 13:12$$

(b) Using Rule 1, the ratio of the boys to the girls is:

$$\frac{\text{Number of boys}}{\text{Number of girls}} = \frac{12}{13} \text{ or } 12:13$$

(c) The total number of students in the whole class = 12 + 13 = 25

   Using Rule 1, the ratio of the number of boys to the whole class is:

$$\frac{\text{Number of boys}}{\text{Total number of students}} = \frac{12}{25} \text{ or } 12:25$$

(d) The total number of students in the whole class = 12 + 13 = 25.

   Using Rule 1, the ratio of the number of the girls to the whole class is:

$$\frac{\text{Number of girls}}{\text{Total number of students}} = \frac{13}{25} \text{ or } 13:25$$

(e) The total number of students in the whole class is 12 + 13 = 25.

Using Rule 1, the ratio of the whole class to the number of girls is:

$$\frac{\text{Total number of students}}{\text{Number of girls}} = \frac{25}{13} \quad \text{or} \quad 25 : 13$$

(f). The total number of students in the whole class is 12 + 13 = 25.

Using Rule 1, the ratio of the whole class to the number of boys is:

$$\frac{\text{Total number of students}}{\text{Number of boys}} = \frac{25}{12} \quad \text{or} \quad 25 : 12$$

Example 2

The ratio of animals to birds in a small zoo is 7 : 3.

If the total population of the animals and the birds at the zoo is 30,

(a) how many animals are in the zoo?

(b) how many birds are in the zoo?

Solution

Step 1: Find the total ratio.

Total ratio $= 7 + 3 = 10$

Step 2: Find the fractions of the animals and the birds.

$$\text{The fraction of the animals} = \frac{\text{The ratio of the animals}}{\text{Total ratio}} = \frac{7}{10}$$

$$\text{The fraction of the birds} = \frac{\text{The ratio of the birds}}{\text{Total ratio}} = \frac{3}{10}$$

(a)

Step 3: To find the number of animals in the zoo, multiply the fraction for the animals by the total population of the zoo.

Therefore, the number of animals at the zoo $= \dfrac{7}{10} \times 30$

$$= \frac{7}{\cancel{10}_{1}} \times \cancel{30}^{3} \quad \text{Divide the numerator and the denominator by 10.}$$

$$= 7 \times 3 = 21 \text{ animals}$$

(b)

Step 4: To find the number of birds at the zoo, multiply the fraction for birds by the total population of the zoo.

Therefore, the number of birds at the zoo $= \dfrac{3}{10} \times 30$

$= \dfrac{\overset{3}{\cancel{3}}}{\underset{1}{\cancel{10}}} \times \cancel{30}$ $= 9$ birds.   Divide the numerator and the denominator by 10.

$= 3 \times 3 = 9$ birds

Example 3

Mr. Jones is 45 years old. His son is 10 years old.
What is the ratio of Mr. Jones' age to his son's age?

Solution

Using Rule 1, the ratio of Mr. Jones' age to his son's age is:

$\dfrac{45}{10}$ or $45 : 10$

$= \dfrac{\overset{9}{\cancel{45}}}{\underset{2}{\cancel{10}}}$ Reduce $\dfrac{45}{10}$ to the lowest term by dividing by 5.

$= \dfrac{9}{2}$

Therefore, the ratio of Mr. Jones' age to his son's age is $\dfrac{9}{2}$ or $9 : 2$

Example 4

What is the ratio of 7 days to 3 weeks?

Solution

Before a ratio can be written, make sure that both the numerator and the denominator of the ratio have the same unit. In this example, the units are days and weeks. We cannot express days as a ratio of weeks. Convert 7 days to 1 week by dividing 7 days by 7 because 7 days = 1 week .

Solution

Using Rule 1, the ratio of 7days to 3 weeks is :

$$\dfrac{7 \text{ days}}{3 \text{ weeks}} = \dfrac{1 \text{ week}}{3 \text{ weeks}}$$

$$= \frac{1 \text{ week}}{3 \text{ weeks}}$$

$$= \frac{1}{3} \text{ or } 1:3$$

Therefore, the ratio of 7 days to 3 weeks $= \frac{1}{3}$ or $1:3$

Note: A ratio also compares more than two numbers by division as shown in Example 5.

Rule 2: To find a number which is equivalent to a ratio when the total number is given, multiply the fraction of the ratio by the total number.

Example 5

John, Eric, and Janet had a joint business, and they shared the profit of the business which was $150.00 in the ratio $2:3:5$ respectively.

(a) What are the fractions of the shares of John, Eric and Janet in the profit?

(b) What is John's share of the profit?

(c) What is Eric's share of the profit?

(d) What is Janet's share of the profit?

Solution

(a) The word "respectively " in the problem means that the ratios are matched with the names John, Eric and Janet in order.

Since the total ratio $= 2 + 3 + 5 = 10$, and the ratio parts are 2, 3, and 5, the ratio $2:3:5$ can also be written as a fraction as $\frac{2}{10}, \frac{3}{10},$ and $\frac{5}{10}$.

(b) The total ratio $= 2 + 3 + 5 = 10$

Using Rule 2 , John's share of the profit $= \frac{2}{10} \times \$150$

$$= \frac{2}{\overset{1}{\underset{1}{10}}} \times \$150 \overset{15}{\quad} \qquad \text{Divide by 10}$$

$$= 2 \times \$15 = \$30$$

Using Rule 2, Eric's share of the profit $= \frac{3}{10} \times \$150$

$$= \frac{3}{\cancelto{1}{10}} \times \cancelto{15}{\$150} \quad \text{Divide by 10}$$

$$= 3 \times \$15 = \$45$$

Using Rule 2, Janet's share of the profit $= \dfrac{5}{10} \times \$150$

$$= \frac{5}{\cancelto{1}{10}} \times \cancelto{15}{\$150} \qquad \text{Divide by 10}$$

$$= 5 \times \$15 = \$75$$

Exercises

1. Explain what is meant by the ratio of two numbers.
2. Change each expression to a ratio in a fraction form, and reduce to the lowest terms if possible. Hint: See Examples 1(a) and 1(b).

   (a) 4 to 7   (b) 5 to 8   (c) 3 to 9   (d) 5 to 20
   (e) 15 : 25   (f) 12 : 4   (g) 16 : 4   (h) 27 : 3
   (i) 49 : 7   (j) 3 to 36   (k) 18 to 3   (l) 24 : 4
   (m). 25 : 75   (n) 75 :35   (0). 11 : 99   (p) 64 : 8

3. A class consists of 10 boys and 13 girls.
   (a) What is the ratio of the number of boys to the number of girls? Hint: See Examples 1(a) and 1(b).
   (b) What is the ratio of the number of girls to the number of boys? Hint: See Examples 1(a) and 1(b).
4. A company has 50 employees. The ratio of the number of the men to the number of women is 2 : 3, find:
   (a) the number of men working for the company. Hint: See Example 2.
   (b) the number of women working for the company. Hint: See Example 2 .
5. A clinic has 3 male nurses and 7 female nurses. What is the ratio of the
   (a) male nurses to the female nurses?
   (b) female nurses to the male nurses?
   (c) female nurses to the total number of nurses at the clinic?
   (d) male nurses to the total number of nurses at the clinic?
   (e) total number of nurses to the male nurses?
   (f) total number of nurses to the female nurses?
      Hint: See Example 1.
6. Judith scored 100% on a test, John scored 95% on the same test. What is the ratio of the test score of Judith to that of John? Reduce your answer to the lowest

terms. Hint: See Example 3.

7. What is the ratio of 10 minutes to 1 hour? Hint: The units of a ratio must be the same, 60 minutes = 1 hour, see Example 4.

8. What is the ratio of 2 feet to 6 inches? Hint: The unit of a ratio must be the same, 12 inches = 1 foot, see Example 4.

9. What is the ratio of 3 weeks to 3 months? Hint: The unit of a ratio must be the same, 4 weeks = 1 month, see Example 4 .

10 Nick, Jones, and George shared $250 in the ratio 5 : 12 : 8, respectively.
   (a) What is the total ratio?
   (b) What is the fraction of the money that Nick received?
   (c) What is the fraction of the money that Jones received?
   (d) What is the fraction of the money that George received?
   (e) What is the money that Nick received?
   (f) What is the money that Jones received?
   (g) What is the money that George received?
   Hint: See Example 5.

Challenge Questions

1. What is the ratio of 2 hours to 30 minutes?
2. What is the ratio of 6 feet to 10 inches?
3. A woman is 35 years old and her son is 5 years old. What is the ratio of the woman's age to the son's age?
4. There are 600 students in a certain school. The ratio of the girls to the boys at the school is 6 : 4.
   (a) Find the fraction of the student population that are girls?
   (b) Find the fraction of the student population that are boys?
   (c) How many students are girls in the school?
   (d) How many students are boys in the school?
5. What is the ratio of 2 weeks to 2 months?
6. Three students shared $100.00 in the ratio 6 : 3 : 1. How much did each student receive?
7. What is the ratio of 6 inches to 2 feet?

EQUIVALENT RATIOS

Equivalent ratios are ratios that represent the same thing or the same value. For example the ratios $\frac{1}{2}$, $\frac{2}{4}$, and $\frac{4}{8}$ are equivalent ratios because all of them represent

the same value of $\frac{1}{2}$ when all the ratios are reduced to the lowest terms.

Understanding the Concept of Equivalent Ratios

The concept of the equivalent ratios can further be explained by observing the equal areas of the squares of figure 1, figure 2, and figure 3. In figure 1, the square is divided into two parts and the area of the triangle BCD represents $\frac{1}{2}$ of the area of the square ABCD. The square ABCD in figure 2 is divided into 4 parts and the same area triangle BCD is now represented by 2 parts(areas of triangles BCE and CDE) which can be written as $\frac{2}{4}$ parts of the same square ABCD which can be reduced to the lowest terms to obtain $\frac{1}{2}$. The square ABCD in figure 3 is divided into 8 parts and the same triangle BCD is now represented by 4 parts which can be written as $\frac{4}{8}$ parts of the same square ABCD which can be reduced to the lowest terms to obtain $\frac{1}{2}$.

figure 1   figure 2   figure3

The logic is the fact that the same area of triangle BCE is represented as $\frac{1}{2}$ in figure 1 and it is represented as $\frac{2}{4}$ in Figure 2 and it is represented as $\frac{4}{8}$ in Figure 3, and therefore, all the ratios of $\frac{1}{2}$, $\frac{2}{4}$, and $\frac{4}{8}$ represent the same area of the triangle BCD, similarly equivalent ratios are ratios that represent the same thing or value. Equivalent ratios can be expressed or written as equivalent fractions. Cross products of equivalent fractions are equal and this will help us to solve many problems as illustrated in the following examples.

Rule 1: Equivalent ratios can be expressed or written as equivalent fractions and the cross products of equivalent fractions are equal.

Example 1

a). There are 205 animals and 37 birds at a certain zoo. Write the ratio of the number of the birds to the number of the animals in 3 different ways.

b). Complete to get equivalent or equal ratios: $\dfrac{3}{2} = \dfrac{12}{?}$

c). Complete to get equivalent or equal ratios: 4 : 1 and ? : 4

Solution

The number of birds = 37, the number of animals = 205.

Ratios can be written in three different ways by using "to," fraction bar or a colon.

The ratio of the birds to the animals is: 37 to 205, $\dfrac{37}{205}$, or 37 : 205.

b). There are two methods to solve this problem. They are by "cross products," or by inspection.

Cross Products Method:

$\dfrac{3}{2} = \dfrac{12}{?}$ can be written as $\dfrac{3}{2} = \dfrac{12}{y}$ so that we can solve for y.

Cross products of equivalent ratios or fractions are equal, and therefore,

$$\dfrac{3}{2} \diagup\hspace{-0.9em}\diagdown \dfrac{12}{y} \quad \text{is } 3 \times y = 2 \times 12$$

$$3y = 24 \qquad\qquad\qquad\qquad [A]$$

Divide each side of equation $[A]$ by 3 to obtain y as follows:

$$\dfrac{3y}{3} = \dfrac{24}{3}$$

$$\dfrac{\overset{y}{\cancel{3y}}}{\underset{1}{\cancel{3}}} = \dfrac{\overset{8}{\cancel{24}}}{\underset{1}{\cancel{3}}}$$

$$y = 8$$

Therefore, the equivalent ratios of $\dfrac{3}{2} = \dfrac{12}{?}$ are $\dfrac{3}{2} = \dfrac{12}{8}$.

Inspection Method:

Let us inspect the ratio $\dfrac{3}{2}$ and $\dfrac{12}{?}$ and find out how the numerator 3 can be changed to the numerator 12. We should find that the numerator 3 is multiplied by 4 to obtain the numerator of 12 and similarly we have to multiply the denominator of 2 by the same number 4 to give us a denominator of 8.

$$\overset{\displaystyle \diagup \text{multiply by the same number.}}{\dfrac{3}{2} = \dfrac{3 \times ?}{2 \times ?} = \dfrac{3 \times 4}{2 \times 4} = \dfrac{12}{8}}$$

$$\underset{\displaystyle \diagdown \text{multiply by the same number.}}{}$$

Therefore, the equivalent ratio $\dfrac{3}{2} = \dfrac{12}{?}$ should be $\dfrac{3}{2} = \dfrac{12}{8}$

c). In order for 4 : 1 and ? : 4 to be equal ratios , then 4 : 1 = ? : 4 and the ratio

can be written in a fraction form as $\dfrac{4}{1} = \dfrac{?}{4}$

There are two methods to solve this problem which is by " cross products " or by inspection.

Cross Products Method

The cross product of equivalent ratios or fractions are equal, and therefore:

$$\dfrac{4}{1} \diagdown\hspace{-1em}\diagup \dfrac{?}{4} \quad \text{is } 4 \times 4 = 1 \times \, ?$$

$$16 = \, ?$$

Therefore, the equivalent ratio of $\dfrac{4}{1} = \dfrac{?}{4}$ is $\dfrac{4}{1} = \dfrac{16}{4}$

Inspection Method

Let us inspect the equivalent ratio $\dfrac{4}{1} = \dfrac{?}{4}$ to find out how the denominator 1 in the

first ratio changes to the denominator 4 in the second ratio. The denominator 1 is multiplied by 4 to get the denominator 4 in the second ratio and similarly, the numerator 4 of the first ratio should be multiplied by the same number 4 to obtain the numerator of 16 in the second ratio as shown:

/ multiply by the same number.

$$\dfrac{4}{1} = \dfrac{?}{4} \quad , \qquad \dfrac{4}{1} = \dfrac{4 \times \,?}{1 \times \,?} = \dfrac{4 \times 4}{1 \times 4} = \dfrac{16}{4}$$

↑   ↑   \ multiply by the same number.

1st ratio   2nd ratio

Therefore, the equivalent ratio is $\dfrac{4}{1} = \dfrac{16}{4}$.

Example 2

a). State four ways to show that one ratio is equivalent to the other?

b). Show that $\dfrac{2}{4}$ and $\dfrac{4}{8}$ are equivalent ratios.

Solution

a). The four ways to show that one ratio is equivalent to another ratio are:

by multiplying each term in the smaller ratio by the same number that will be equal to the bigger ratio, by dividing each term of the bigger ratio by the same number that will be equal to the smaller ratio, by reducing each ratio to the lowest terms or by finding the cross products of the ratios. The cross products of equivalent ratios are equal.

b). Let us use each of the four methods in solution (a) to solve the problem.

Method 1:

What same number can multiply the terms of the smaller ratio (the smaller ratio is $\frac{2}{4}$) in order to obtain the bigger ratio (the bigger ratio is $\frac{4}{8}$)? This can be expressed as shown:

what number that can multiply 2 to obtain 4?

$$\frac{2}{4} = \frac{2 \times ?}{4 \times ?} = \frac{4}{8}$$

smaller ratio ↗   ↘ bigger ratio

what number can multiply 4 to obtain 8?

Since the terms of the smaller ratio can be multiplied by the same number, which is 2 to obtain the bigger ratio, the two ratios are equivalent.

Note: Recall that when the terms of a ratio are multiplied by the same number, the value of the ratio does not change, and that equivalent ratios have equivalent fractions.

Method 2:

What same number can divide the terms of the bigger ratio (the bigger ratio is $\frac{4}{8}$) in order to obtain the smaller ratio. This can be expressed as shown:

what number can divide 4 to obtain 2?

$$\frac{4}{8} = \frac{4 \div ?}{8 \div ?} = \frac{2}{4}$$ smaller ratio

bigger ratio ↗   ↘ what number can divide 8 to obtain 4?

$$\frac{4}{8} = \frac{4 \div 2}{8 \div 2} = \frac{2}{4}$$

Since the terms of the bigger ratio can be divided by the same number, which is 2 to obtain the smaller ratio, the two ratios are equivalent.

Note: Recall that when the terms of a ratio are divided by the same number, the value of the ratio does not change, and that equivalent ratios have equivalent fractions.

Method 3:

Reduce each ratio to the lowest terms, and if the lowest terms are equal, then the ratios are equivalent.

Reduce $\dfrac{2}{4}$ to the lowest terms by dividing the terms by 2 .

Therefore, $\dfrac{2}{4} = \dfrac{\overset{1}{2}}{\underset{2}{4}} = \dfrac{1}{2}$

Reduce $\dfrac{4}{8}$ to the lowest terms by dividing the terms by 4.

Therefore, $\dfrac{4}{8} = \dfrac{\overset{1}{4}}{\underset{2}{8}} = \dfrac{1}{2}$

Since $\dfrac{2}{4} = \dfrac{1}{2}$ and $\dfrac{4}{8} = \dfrac{1}{2}$, both ratios are equivalent.

Method 4:

The cross products of equivalent fractions are equal, therefore,

$$2 \times 8 = 16$$
$$4 \times 4 = 16$$

Since the cross products of the fractions are equal, the fractions are equivalent fractions, and therefore, the ratios are equivalent ratios.

Example 3

It is a fact that equivalent ratios can be written as equivalent fractions. Show that the ratio 15 : 6 is equivalent to 5 : 2.

Solution

The ratios 15 : 6 and 5 : 2 can be written as fractions as follows:

$$15 : 6 = \dfrac{15}{6} \text{ and } 5 : 2 = \dfrac{5}{2}$$

The fractions $\dfrac{15}{6}$ and $\dfrac{5}{2}$ are equivalent because the terms in $\dfrac{15}{6}$ can be divided by 3 to obtain $\dfrac{5}{2}$ as shown :

$$\frac{\frac{15}{6}}{2} = \frac{5}{2} \quad \text{or} \quad \frac{15}{6} = \frac{15 \div ?}{6 \div ?} = \frac{5}{2}$$

Therefore, the ratio 15 : 6 is equivalent to 5 : 2. Note that the style of the solution to Example 2(b) Method 2 is used to solve this problem.

Alternative method:

This problem can simply be solved by using Rule 1, which states that the equivalent ratios can be written as equivalent fractions and the cross products of equivalent fractions are equal.

Let us check if the cross products of the equivalent fractions are equal or not, as shown:

$$\frac{15}{6} = \frac{5}{2}, \text{ and the cross products are:}$$

$$\frac{15}{6} \bowtie \frac{5}{2}$$

Therefore, $15 \times 2 = 30, \ 6 \times 5 = 30$
Since the cross products are equal the ratios are equivalent.

Example 4

Are the ratios $\frac{1}{6}$ and $\frac{5}{31}$ equivalent?

Solution

The ratios $\frac{1}{6}$ and $\frac{5}{31}$ are already written in the fraction form, and therefore, let us find out if the two fractions $\frac{1}{6}$ and $\frac{5}{31}$ are equivalent or not. We should find what same number that can multiply the terms of $\frac{1}{6}$ in order to obtain the ratio $\frac{5}{31}$ as shown:

$$1 \times 5 = 5$$
$$\frac{1}{6} = \frac{1 \times ?}{6 \times ?} = \frac{5}{31}$$
$$6 \times 5 = 30. \text{ Note that 30 is not 31.}$$

Since 5 can not be multiplied by the terms of $\frac{1}{6}$ which are 1 and 6 in order to obtain 5 and 31, $\dfrac{1}{6}$ and $\dfrac{5}{31}$ are not equivalent fractions, and therefore, the ratios $\dfrac{1}{6}$ and $\dfrac{5}{31}$, are not equivalent ratios.

Alternative Method:

This problem can be solved simply by using Rule 1 which states that " Equivalent ratios can be written as equivalent fractions and the cross products of equivalent fractions are equal." Let us check if the cross products of the equivalent fractions are equal or not, as shown:

$$\frac{1}{6} = \frac{5}{31}$$

$$\frac{1}{6} \diagdown\!\!\!\!\diagup \frac{5}{31}$$

$1 \times 31 = 31$

$6 \times 5 = 30$ Note that 30 is not equal to 31.

Since the cross products are 31 and 30, and $31 \neq 30$, the ratios $\dfrac{1}{6}$ and $\dfrac{5}{31}$ are not equivalent. Note that the symbol $\neq$ means "is not equal to."

Example 5

Find a ratio that is equivalent to $\dfrac{6}{9}$ and explain your reasons.

Solution

There are two ways to solve this problem. One way is to divide the numerator and the denominator of $\dfrac{6}{9}$ by the same number and the quotient will give us the solution to the problem as follows:

$$\frac{6}{9} = \frac{6 \div 3}{9 \div 3} = \frac{2}{3}$$

Therefore, the equivalent of $\dfrac{6}{9}$ is $\dfrac{2}{3}$

Alternative Method:

Another way to solve the problem is to multiply the numerator and the denominator of $\dfrac{6}{9}$ by the same number as follows:

$$\frac{6}{9} = \frac{6 \times ?}{9 \times ?} = \frac{6 \times 2}{9 \times 2} = \frac{12}{18}$$

Note: Both the numerator and the denominator are multiplied by the same number 2.

Therefore, the equivalent of $\dfrac{6}{9}$ is $\dfrac{12}{18}$

Exercises

1. Ratios can be written in three ways using "to," "colon," and fractions. Write each of the following ratio statements in three ways. Hint: See Example 1.
   (a) A class consists of 11 boys and 13 girls. What is the ratio of boys to girls?
   (b) There are 2 oranges and 6 apples in the room. What is the ratio of apples to oranges?
   (c) There are 4 vans and 9 cars at the school. What is the ratio of the vans to the cars?

2. State the four ways by which it can be shown that one ratio is equivalent to another ratio. Hint: See Example 2(a).

3. Complete the following statement:
   Equivalent ratios can be written as ———————————— Hint: See Rule 1.

4. Explain what is meant by equivalent ratios?

5. Explain what is meant by equivalent fractions?

6. Show that the following ratios are equivalent, use the cross products method. Hint: See Examples 2 and 3.
   (a) 1 : 2 and 2 : 4   (b) 2 : 4 and 4 : 8   (c) 2 : 4 and 8 : 16

   (d) 3 : 6 and 9 : 18   (e) 3 : 9 and 9 : 27   (f) 6 : 12 and 12 : 24

   (g) $\dfrac{9}{15}$ and $\dfrac{3}{5}$ (h) $\dfrac{3}{5}$ and $\dfrac{12}{20}$ (i) $\dfrac{1}{6}$ and $\dfrac{2}{12}$

   (j) $\dfrac{3}{4}$ and $\dfrac{9}{12}$ (k) $\dfrac{12}{16}$ and $\dfrac{3}{4}$ (l) $\dfrac{5}{15}$ and $\dfrac{10}{30}$

7. Are the ratios $\dfrac{1}{2}$ and $\dfrac{2}{5}$ equivalent? Hint: See Example 4.

8. Determine if the following ratios are equivalent or not? Hint: See Examples 3 and 4.
   (a) $\dfrac{1}{2}$ and $\dfrac{8}{16}$ (b) $\dfrac{1}{3}$ and $\dfrac{3}{8}$ (c) $\dfrac{3}{2}$ and $\dfrac{9}{6}$

   (d) 6 : 2 and 12 : 4   (e) 1 : 3 and 2 : 6   (f) 2 :3 and 5 : 6

   (g) 1 : 5 and 2 : 10   (h) 4 : 1 and 16 : 3   (i) 4 : 2 and 8 : 4

   (j) $\dfrac{2}{3}$ and $\dfrac{4}{6}$ (k) $\dfrac{5}{2}$ and $\dfrac{25}{10}$ (l) $\dfrac{7}{2}$ and $\dfrac{21}{3}$

Challenge Questions

9. A class has 6 girls and 5 boys.
    (a) What is the ratio of the boys to the girls?
    (b) What is the ratio of the girls to the boys?
    (c) What is the ratio of the boys to the number of students in the whole class?

10. Show that the following ratios are equivalent:

   (a) $\dfrac{5}{1}$ and $\dfrac{25}{5}$ (b) $\dfrac{1}{4}$ and $\dfrac{4}{16}$ (c) $\dfrac{2}{7}$ and $\dfrac{6}{21}$

   (d) $8:2$ and $16:4$ (e) $3:7$ and $9:21$ (f) $\dfrac{4}{3}$ and $\dfrac{12}{9}$

11. Determine which ratios are equivalent or not:

   (a) $\dfrac{1}{3}$ and $\dfrac{2}{7}$ (b) $\dfrac{8}{1}$ and $\dfrac{64}{8}$ (c) $\dfrac{2}{3}$ and $\dfrac{1}{2}$

   (d) $\dfrac{2}{9}$ and $\dfrac{6}{27}$ (e) $4:3$ and $12:9$ (f) $2:1$ and $6:3$

12. Complete to get equivalent or equal ratios

   (a) $\dfrac{2}{4}=\dfrac{?}{8}$ (b) $\dfrac{4}{3}=\dfrac{8}{?}$ (c) $\dfrac{?}{2}=\dfrac{5}{6}$

   (d) $\dfrac{3}{8}=\dfrac{9}{?}$ (e) $\dfrac{4}{?}=\dfrac{12}{15}$ (f) $\dfrac{1}{3}=\dfrac{?}{9}$

PROPORTION

A proportion is an equation stating that two ratios are equal.

For example, $\dfrac{30}{10}=\dfrac{15}{5}$ is a proportion because when each ratio $\dfrac{30}{10}$ and $\dfrac{15}{5}$ are reduced to the lowest term, it can be seen that both ratios are equal as follows:

$$\dfrac{30}{10}=\dfrac{\overset{3}{\cancel{30}}}{\underset{1}{\cancel{10}}}=3,\text{ the ratio }\dfrac{30}{10}\text{ is reduced to the lowest term by dividing by 10.}$$

$$\frac{15}{5} = \frac{\overset{3}{\cancel{15}}}{\underset{1}{\cancel{5}}} = 3, \quad \text{the ratio } \frac{15}{5} \text{ is reduced to the lowest term by dividing by 5.}$$

By reducing $\frac{30}{10}$ and $\frac{15}{5}$ to the lowest term, it can be seen that each ratio is equal

to 3, and therefore, both ratios are equal and we can then conclude that $\frac{30}{10} = \frac{15}{5}$ is a

proportion. In fact we have written a proportion by writing that $\frac{30}{10} = \frac{15}{5}$ or

30 : 15 = 15 : 5, and in each equation we are showing that the relationship of the numbers 30 to 10 is the same as the relationship of the numbers 15 to 5.
Note that the ratio 30 : 10 has the same value as the ratio 15 : 5 because when ratios are reduced to the lowest terms, their values are not changed.

Property of Proportion

Rule 1: The cross products of a proportion are equal, such that if $\frac{a}{b} = \frac{c}{d}$, then ad = bc,

and that b and d are non-zero numbers.

If $\frac{a}{b} = \frac{c}{d}$, then the cross product is shown as shown:

$$\frac{a}{b} \diagdown \frac{c}{d} \qquad \begin{array}{l} \text{which is ad = bc and b} \neq 0 \text{ and d} \neq 0 \\ \text{where} \neq \text{means "not equal to".} \end{array}$$

Cross product means to multiply diagonally as shown above.
Note: To make sure that ratios are equal, or are a proportion, we multiply the cross products and compare the value of each cross product, and if the cross products are equal, then the ratios are equal or are a proportion. We can also show that two ratios are equal by reducing each ratio to the lowest term.

Example 1

Are the ratios $\frac{2}{3} = \frac{3}{4}$ a proportion?

Solution

Using the rule, the cross products of a proportion are equal.
The cross products are shown as shown:

$$\frac{2}{3} \diagdown \frac{3}{4}$$

$$2 \times 4 \neq 3 \times 3$$
$$8 \neq 9 \quad \text{The sign} \neq \text{means not equal to.}$$

Since 8 is not equal to 9, the ratio $\frac{2}{3} = \frac{3}{4}$ is not a proportion.

Example 2

Mr. Johnson drove 60 miles in 2 hours. On the next day, he drove 90 miles in 3 hours. Write a proportion and determine if the proportion is true or false.

Solution

The proportion can be written as:

$$60 : 2 = 90 : 3 \text{ or } \frac{60}{2} = \frac{90}{3}$$

Using Rule 1, the cross products of a proportion are equal, and therefore, we can use cross products to determine if the proportion is true or false.

$$\frac{60}{2} = \frac{90}{3}$$

$$60 \times 3 = 2 \times 90$$
$$180 = 180$$

Since the cross products of the ratios are equal, the proportion is true.

Example 3

Last year, Blengo Middle School was cleaned by 6 people in 10 days. This year, the school was cleaned by 4 people in 12 days working at the same rate as that of last year. Write a proportion and determine if the proportion is true or false.

Solution

The proportion can be written as:

$$6 \text{ people} : 10 \text{ days} = 4 \text{ people} : 12 \text{ days or } \frac{6}{10} = \frac{4}{12}$$

Using the Rule 1, the cross product of a proportion are equal, determine if the proportion is true or false.

$$\frac{6}{10} = \frac{4}{12}$$

$$6 \times 12 \neq 10 \times 4 \quad (\neq \text{ means not equal}).$$
$$72 \neq 40$$

Since the cross products are not equal, the proportion is false.

Rule 2

To find a missing number (y) in a proportion, find the cross products, and then divide as needed.

Example 4

Find the value of y in the proportion $\dfrac{y}{4} = \dfrac{5}{2}$

Solution

Using Rule 2, which states that, "to find a missing number (y) in a proportion, find the cross products, and then divide as needed," solve the problem as shown:

$$\frac{y}{4} \times = \frac{5}{2} \qquad \text{or } y \times 2 = 4 \times 5$$

$$2y = 20 \quad\text{————————} [A]$$

Divide each side of equation $[A]$ by 2 to obtain y.

$$\frac{2y}{2} = \frac{20}{2}$$

$$\frac{\overset{y}{\cancel{2y}}}{\underset{1}{\cancel{2}}} = \frac{\overset{10}{\cancel{20}}}{\underset{1}{\cancel{2}}} \qquad \text{Divide by 2.}$$

$$y = 10$$

Example 5
Solve the proportions:

(a) $\dfrac{2}{5} = \dfrac{y}{100}$ (b) $\dfrac{2}{1.8} = \dfrac{4}{y}$

Solution

(a) Using Rule 2,

$$\frac{2}{5} \times = \frac{y}{100} \qquad \text{or } 2 \times 100 = 5 \times y$$

$$200 = 5y \quad\text{————————} [A]$$

Divide each side of equation $[A]$ by 5 to obtain y.

$$\frac{200}{5} = \frac{5y}{5}$$

$$\frac{\overset{40}{\cancel{200}}}{\underset{1}{\cancel{5}}} = \frac{\overset{y}{\cancel{5y}}}{\underset{1}{\cancel{5}}}$$

$$40 = y, \text{ or } y = 40.$$

(b) Using Rule 2,

$$\frac{2}{1.8} \times \frac{4}{y} \qquad \text{or } 2 \times y = 1.8 \times 4$$

$$2y = 7.2 \quad \underline{\hspace{2cm}} [B]$$

Divide each side of equation $[B]$ by 2 in order to obtain the value of y.

$$\frac{2y}{2} = \frac{7.2}{2}$$

$$\frac{\overset{y}{\cancel{2y}}}{\underset{1}{\cancel{2}}} = \frac{\overset{3.6}{\cancel{7.2}}}{\underset{1}{\cancel{2}}}$$

$$y = 3.6$$

Example 6

Solve the proportions:

(a) $\dfrac{y+2}{5} = \dfrac{y}{4}$ (a) $\dfrac{y+3}{y} = \dfrac{8}{6}$

Solution
(a) Using Rule 2,

$$\frac{y+2}{5} \underset{\nearrow}{\overset{\searrow}{\times}} \frac{y}{4} \qquad \text{or} \quad (y+2) \times 4 = 5 \times y$$

$$y \times 4 + 2 \times 4 = 5 \times y$$
$$4y + 8 = 5y \quad \underline{\hspace{1.5cm}} [A]$$

Subtract 4y from each side of equation $[A]$ in order to obtain the value of y as shown:

$$4y + 8 - 4y = 5y - 4y$$
$$8 = y \qquad \text{(Note: } 4y - 4y = 0, \ 5y - 4y = y)$$
$$y = 8$$

(b) Using Rule 2,

$$\frac{y+3}{y} \underset{\nearrow}{\overset{\searrow}{\times}} \frac{8}{6} \qquad \text{or} \quad (y+3) \times 6 = y \times 8$$

$$y \times 6 + 3 \times 6 = y \times 8$$
$$6y + 18 = 8y \quad \underline{\hspace{1.5cm}} [B]$$

Subtract 6y from each side of equation $[B]$ in order to eliminate the 6y at the left side of the equation $[B]$ as shown:

$$6y + 18 - 6y = 8y - 6y \qquad \text{(Note: } 6y - 6y = 0, \text{ and } 8y - 6y = 2y)$$
$$18 = 2y \quad \underline{\hspace{3cm}} [C]$$

Divide each side of equation $[C]$ by 2 to obtain the value of y as shown:

343

$$\frac{18}{2} = \frac{2y}{2}$$

$$\frac{\overset{9}{\cancel{18}}}{\underset{1}{\cancel{2}}} = \frac{\overset{y}{\cancel{2y}}}{\underset{1}{\cancel{2}}}$$

$$9 = y, \text{ or } y = 9$$

Example 7

Find the value of y in the following proportions.

(a) $\dfrac{4}{y - 2} = \dfrac{5}{y + 5}$

(b) $\dfrac{y - 6}{y + 8} = \dfrac{2}{3}$

Solution

(a) Using Rule 2,

$$\frac{4}{y - 2} \times \frac{5}{y + 5} \qquad \text{or} \quad 4 \times (y + 5) = (y - 2) \times 5$$

$$4 \times y + 4 \times 5 = y \times 5 - 2 \times 5$$

$$4y + 20 = 5y - 10 \quad \text{———— } [A]$$

Subtract from each side of the equation $[A]$ in order to eliminate 4y from the left side of equation $[A]$ as shown:

$$4y + 20 - 4y = 5y - 10 - 4y \quad \text{(Note: } 4y - 4y = 0 , 5y - 4y = y)$$

$$20 = y - 10 \text{———————— } [B]$$

Add 10 to each side of equation $[B]$ in order to obtain y at the right side of equation $[B]$ as shown:

$$20 + 10 = y - 10 + 10 \qquad \text{(Note: } -10 + 10 = 0)$$

$$30 = y, \text{ or } y = 30$$

(b) Using Rule 2,

$$\frac{y - 6}{y + 8} \times \frac{2}{3} \qquad \text{or} \quad (y - 6) \times 3 = (y + 8) \times 2$$

$$y \times 3 - 6 \times 3 = y \times 2 + 8 \times 2 \qquad \text{Multiply}$$

$$3y - 18 = 2y + 16 \quad \text{———— } [C]$$

Add 18 to each side of equation $[C]$ in order to eliminate 18 from the left side of equation $[C]$ as shown:

$$3y - 18 + 18 = 2y + 16 + 18 \qquad \text{(Note : } -18 + 18 = 0)$$

$$3y = 2y + 34 \quad \text{——————————————— } [D]$$

Subtract 2y from each side of equation $[D]$ in order to eliminate 2y at the right side of equation $[D]$ as shown:

$$3y - 2y = 2y + 34 - 2y \qquad \text{(Note: } 3y - 2y = y, \ 2y - 2y = 0\text{)}$$
$$y = 34$$

Exercises

1. What is a ratio?
2. What is a proportion?
3. Comparing a ratio and a proportion, what is the difference between a ratio and a proportion?
4. Write a ratio that forms a proportion, and then write another ratio that does not form a proportion, and explain your reasoning. Hint: See Examples 1 to 3.
5. Determine which proportions are true or false: Hint: See Examples 1 to 3.

(a) $\dfrac{1}{2} = \dfrac{3}{7}$ (b) $\dfrac{1}{3} = \dfrac{1}{4}$ (c) $\dfrac{1}{2} = \dfrac{3}{6}$ (d) $\dfrac{1}{3} = \dfrac{4}{12}$

6. Solve each proportion for the missing number. Hint: See Examples 4 and 5.

(a) $\dfrac{y}{2} = \dfrac{3}{4}$ (b) $\dfrac{2}{y} = \dfrac{1}{8}$ (c) $\dfrac{2}{3} = \dfrac{y}{6}$ (d) $\dfrac{5}{y} = \dfrac{3}{6}$

(e) $\dfrac{6}{y} = \dfrac{2}{7}$ (f) $\dfrac{3}{4} = \dfrac{y}{8}$ (g) $\dfrac{3}{2} = \dfrac{5}{y}$ (h) $\dfrac{2.5}{5} = \dfrac{y}{3}$

(i) $\dfrac{3}{y} = \dfrac{2.1}{1}$ (j) $\dfrac{4}{y} = \dfrac{4}{7}$ (k) $\dfrac{2}{7} = \dfrac{?}{49}$ (l) $\dfrac{2}{c} = \dfrac{20}{48}$

(m) $2 : 5 = n : 4$ (n) $4 : 3 = 5 : a$ (o) $y : 8 = 1 : 32$ (p) $c : 2 = 3.6 : 6$

7. Solve the proportions. Hint: See Example 6a.

(a) $\dfrac{y+1}{2} = \dfrac{y}{4}$ (b) $\dfrac{2+y}{3} = \dfrac{y}{6}$ (c) $\dfrac{y+3}{4} = \dfrac{y}{2}$

(d) $\dfrac{3+y}{4} = \dfrac{y}{8}$ (e) $\dfrac{y+2}{3} = \dfrac{y}{6}$ (f) $\dfrac{4+y}{4} = \dfrac{y}{3}$

8. Find y in the proportion. Hint: See Example 6b.

(a) $\dfrac{y+2}{y} = \dfrac{2}{3}$ (b) $\dfrac{y+1}{y} = \dfrac{2}{3}$ (c) $\dfrac{y+3}{y} = \dfrac{1}{4}$

(d) $\dfrac{y+4}{y} = \dfrac{4}{3}$ (e) $\dfrac{y+4}{y} = \dfrac{3}{4}$ (f) $\dfrac{y+2}{y} = \dfrac{2}{4}$

9. Solve the proportion. Hint: See Example 7a.

(a) $\dfrac{3}{y-2} = \dfrac{5}{y+5}$ (b) $\dfrac{2}{y-2} = \dfrac{3}{y+1}$ (c) $\dfrac{2}{y-1} = \dfrac{4}{y+2}$

(d) $\dfrac{1}{y-1} = \dfrac{2}{y+2}$ (e) $\dfrac{4}{y-3} = \dfrac{2}{y+3}$ (f) $\dfrac{1}{y-1} = \dfrac{3}{y+4}$

10. Find y in the proportions. Hint: See Example 7b.

(a) $\dfrac{y-1}{y+2} = \dfrac{1}{4}$ (b) $\dfrac{y-2}{y+4} = \dfrac{3}{4}$ (c) $\dfrac{y-2}{y+5} = \dfrac{1}{5}$

(d) $\dfrac{y-3}{y+5} = \dfrac{2}{5}$ (e) $\dfrac{y-5}{y+4} = \dfrac{5}{2}$ (f) $\dfrac{4+y}{y+3} = \dfrac{2}{3}$

Challenge Questions.

11. Find the value of y in the proportions.

(a) $\dfrac{y-5}{y+2} = \dfrac{1}{4}$ (b) $\dfrac{6}{y-3} = \dfrac{3}{y+6}$ (c) $\dfrac{y+4}{y} = \dfrac{3}{4}$

(d) $\dfrac{6+y}{6} = \dfrac{y}{4}$ (e) $2 : 7 = 4 : y$ (f) $\dfrac{y}{4} = \dfrac{1}{16}$

(g) $\dfrac{3}{y} = \dfrac{3}{4}$ (h) $\dfrac{3}{16} = \dfrac{y}{32}$ (i) $y : 6 = 3 : 18$

12. Find the missing number.

(a) $\dfrac{2}{3} = \dfrac{\$10}{?}$ (b) $\dfrac{\$15}{y} = \dfrac{3}{4}$ (c) $\dfrac{6 \text{ feet}}{y} = \dfrac{4}{6}$ (d) $\dfrac{12}{3} = \dfrac{y}{4 \text{ days}}$

General Order of a Proportion for Solving Word Problems

Recall that a proportion is an equation stating that two ratios are equal, and in solving word problems, **it is critical to set the terms of the two ratios in order**, otherwise the solution of the problem will not be correct. For example, let us write the proportion for the following information. If 3 packages of pencils cost $8, what is the cost of 7 packages of pencils. The required proportion can be written as shown:

First ratio   Second ratio

3 packages : $8 = 7 packages : y

First term   Second term   First term   Second term

Let y be the cost of 7 packages of pencils. The general order of the above proportion

346

can be written as shown:

$$\text{packages} : \$ = \text{packages} : \$ \quad \text{————————} [A]$$

Note that the left side of the ratio of equation [A] has "packages" followed by the $ symbol and the **same order** "packages" followed by the $ symbol occurs at the right side of equation [A]. In order to solve word problems in proportion, the **ratios must be written in the same order.**

Note carefully, that if the two ratios are written as a proportion without the correct order of the terms of the ratios as shown:

$$\text{packages} : \$ = \$: \text{packages}.$$

the proportion will not be correct, and therefore, the answer will not be correct. **It is strongly suggested that in order to solve word problems involving proportions, the terms of the ratios must be written in the correct order.**

REAL WORLD APPLICATIONS - WORD PROBLEMS
Proportion

Example 1

Mr. Johnson drove 60 miles in 2 hours. How long will he take to travel 180 miles if he is traveling at the same speed?

Solution

The proportion can be written as:

$$60 \text{ miles} : 2 \text{ hours} = 180 \text{ miles} : y \quad \text{or} \quad \frac{60 \text{ miles}}{2} = \frac{180 \text{ miles}}{y} \quad \text{where } y \text{ is}$$

the time taken to travel 180 miles.

Using Rule 2, which states that, "to find a missing number (y) in a proportion, **find the cross products and divide as needed,**" solve the proportion as shown:

$$\frac{60}{2} \diagdown \diagup \frac{180}{y} \qquad \text{or} \quad 60 \times y = 2 \times 180$$

$$60y = 360 \quad \text{————————} [A]$$

Divide each side of equation [A] by 60 to obtain the value of y as shown:

$$\frac{60y}{60} = \frac{360}{60}$$

$$\frac{y}{\cancel{60}^{1}} \quad \frac{6}{\cancel{60}^{1}}$$

$$\frac{60y}{60} = \frac{360}{60}$$

$$\frac{y}{1} = \frac{6}{1} \text{, or } y = 6 \text{ hours}$$

Therefore, it takes 6 hours to travel 180 miles.

Example 2

If 2 packages of pens cost $6.40, how many packages can be bought for $38.40?

Solution

Let y be the number of the packages of pens that can be bought for $38.40.
The proportion can be written as:

$$2 \text{ packages} : \$6.40 = y : \$38.40 \quad \text{or} \quad \frac{2 \text{ packages}}{\$6.40} = \frac{y \text{ packages}}{\$38.40}$$

Using Rule 2, **find the cross product**, **and solve the proportion** as shown:

$$\frac{2}{6.40} \quad \diagdown \quad \frac{y}{38.40} \qquad \text{or } 2 \times 38.40 = 6.40 \times y$$

$$2 \times 38.40 = 6.40 \times y \quad\text{———}[A]$$

Divide each side of equation $[A]$ by 6.40 in order to obtain the value of y as shown:

$$\frac{2 \times 38.40}{6.40} = \frac{6.40 \times y}{6.40}$$

$$\frac{2 \times 38.40}{6.40} = \frac{\cancel{6.40}^{1} \times y}{\cancel{6.40}_{1}}$$

$$\frac{2 \times \overset{6}{\cancel{38.40}}}{\cancel{6.40}_{1}} = y \qquad \text{You may use a calculator to divide by 6.40.}$$

$$2 \times 6 = y$$
$$12 = y$$

Therefore, 12 packages of the pens can be bought for $38.40.

Example 3

Three shirts cost $10 and 7 shirts cost $25. Is this proportion false or true?

Solution

The proportion can be written as:

$$3 \text{ shirts} : \$10 = 7 \text{ shirts} : \$25 \quad \text{or} \quad \frac{3}{10} = \frac{7}{25}$$

Using Rule 2, find the cross products, and note that **the cross products of a proportion are equal**, therefore,

$$\frac{3}{10} \diagup \diagdown \frac{7}{25} \qquad \text{or} \quad 3 \times 25 \neq 10 \times 7$$

$$75 \neq 70,$$

$\neq$ means not equal to. Since $75 \neq 70$, the cross products are not equal, and therefore, the proportion is false.

Example 4

A store sold 7 oranges for $3, how many similar oranges would be bought for $5.14? Give your answer to the nearest whole number.

Solution

The proportion can be written as:

$$7 \text{ oranges} : \$3 = y : \$5.14 \quad \text{or} \quad \frac{7 \text{ oranges}}{\$3} = \frac{y}{\$5.14}$$

Let y be the number of oranges that can be bought for $5.14.
Using Rule 2, the **cross products of a proportion are equal**, and solve the proportion as shown:

$$\frac{7 \text{ oranges}}{\$3} \diagup \diagdown \frac{y}{\$5.14} \qquad \text{or} \quad 7 \text{ oranges} \times \$5.14 = \$3 \times y$$

$$7 \text{ oranges} \times \$5.14 = \$3 \times y \quad \text{————————} \quad [A]$$

Divide each side of equation $[A]$ by $3 in order to obtain the value of y as shown:

$$\frac{7 \text{ oranges} \times \$5.14}{\$3} = \frac{\$3 \times y}{\$3}$$

$$\frac{7 \text{ oranges} \times \$5.14}{\$3} = \frac{\overset{1}{\$3} \times y}{\underset{1}{\$3}}$$

$$\frac{35.98 \text{ oranges}}{3} = y \qquad \text{Divide by 3}$$

$$11.9 \text{ oranges} = y$$

Therefore, 12 oranges (to the nearest whole number) can be bought for $5.14.

349

Example 5

Red peppers are on sale for $.72 a dozen. What is the price of 32 peppers?

Solution

The proportion can be written as:

$$\text{peppers} : \$ = \text{peppers} : \$ \qquad \text{(general order of the proportion.)}$$
$$12 \text{ peppers} : \$.72 = 32 \text{ peppers} : y \qquad \text{(a dozen} = 12)$$

or

$$\frac{12 \text{ peppers}}{\$.72} = \frac{32 \text{ peppers}}{y}$$

Let y be the cost of 32 peppers.

Using Rule 2, **find the cross products and divide as needed**, and solve the proportion as shown:

$$\frac{12 \text{ peppers}}{\$0.72} \underset{\times}{\rightleftarrows} \frac{32 \text{ peppers}}{y} \qquad \text{or } 12 \text{ peppers} \times y = \$.72 \times 32 \text{ peppers}$$

$$12 \text{ peppers} \times y = \$.72 \times 32 \text{ peppers} \quad \underline{\hspace{6cm}} \quad [A]$$

Divide each side of the equation $[A]$ by 12 peppers in order to obtain the value of y as shown:

$$\frac{\overset{1}{\cancel{12 \text{ peppers}}} \times y}{\underset{1}{\cancel{12 \text{ peppers}}}} = \frac{\$.72 \times \overset{\$.06}{\cancel{32 \text{ peppers}}}}{\underset{1}{\cancel{12 \text{ peppers}}}} \qquad \text{You may use a calculator.}$$

$$y = \$.06 \times 32 = \$1.92$$

Therefore, 32 peppers will cost $1.92.

Example 6

If some special peanuts are priced at $1.80 per kg., how many kg. of the same type of the peanut can be bought for $12.60?

Solution

The proportion can be written as:

$$\$: \text{kg.} = \$: \text{kg} \qquad \text{(general order of the proportion)}.$$

$$\$1.80 : 1\text{kg} = \$12.60 : y \quad \text{or} \quad \frac{\$1.80}{1\text{kg}} = \frac{\$12.60}{y}$$

Let y be the number of kg. that will cost $12.60.

Using Rule 2, **find the cross products and then divide as needed**. Solve the proportion as shown:

$$\frac{\$1.80}{1 \text{ kg.}} \overset{\longrightarrow}{\underset{\longrightarrow}{\times}} \frac{\$12.60}{y} \qquad \text{or} \quad \$1.80 \times y = 1 \text{ kg.} \times \$12.60.$$

$$\$1.80 \times y = 1 \text{kg} \times \$12.60 \text{ ———————— } [A]$$

Divide each side of equation $[A]$ by $1.80 in order to obtain the value of y as shown:

$$\frac{\overset{1}{\cancel{\$1.80}} \times y}{\underset{1}{\cancel{\$1.80}}} = \frac{1\text{kg} \times \overset{7}{\cancel{\$12.60}}}{\underset{1}{\cancel{\$1.80}}} \qquad \text{You may use a calculator to divide.}$$

$$y = 1\text{kg} \times 7 = 7\text{kg}.$$

Therefore, 7 kg will cost $12.60.

Example 7

Elizabeth earned $20 for 4 hours of baby-sitting. At this rate, what would she earn for 3 hours of baby-sitting?

Solution

The proportion can be written as:

$$\$: \text{hours} = \$: \text{hours} \quad \text{(general order of the proportion)}.$$

$$\$20 : 4 \text{ hours} = y : 3 \text{ hours} \qquad \text{or} \quad \frac{\$20}{4} = \frac{y}{3}$$

Let y be the amount earned in 3 hours.

Using Rule 2, **find the cross products, then divide as needed,** and solve the proportion as shown:

$$\frac{\$20}{4 \text{ hrs.}} \overset{\longrightarrow}{\underset{\longrightarrow}{\times}} \frac{y}{3 \text{ hrs.}} \qquad \text{or} \quad \$20 \times 3 \text{ hrs.} = 4 \text{ hrs.} \times y$$

$$\$20 \times 3\text{hrs} = 4\text{hrs} \times y \text{ ———————— } [A]$$

Divide each side of equation $[A]$ by 4 hrs in order to obtain the value of y as shown:

$$\frac{\overset{\$5}{\cancel{\$20}} \times 3\text{hrs}}{\underset{1}{\cancel{4 \text{ hrs}}}} = \frac{\overset{1}{\cancel{4 \text{ hrs}}} \times y}{\underset{1}{\cancel{4 \text{ hrs}}}}$$

$$\$5 \times 3 = y \qquad \text{or} \quad y = \$15$$

Therefore, Elizabeth will earn $15 in 3 hours.

Example 8

A certain machine can print 3000 pages in 2 hours. At this rate, how many minutes would it take to print 600 pages?

Solution

The proportion can be written as:

pages : hours = pages : hours   (general order of the proportion)

$$3000 \text{ pages} : 2 \text{ hours} = 600 \text{ pages} : y \quad \text{or} \quad \frac{3000 \text{ pages}}{2 \text{ hrs}} = \frac{600 \text{ pages}}{y}$$

Let y be the time taken to print 600 pages.

Using Rule 2, **find the cross products and then divide as needed**. Solve the proportion as shown:

$$3000 \text{ pages} \times y = 600 \text{ pages} \times 2 \text{ hrs} \text{ ———————— } [A]$$

Divide each side of equation $[A]$ by 3000 pages in order to obtain the value of y as shown:

$$\frac{\overset{1}{\cancel{3000 \text{ pages}}} \times y}{\underset{1}{\cancel{3000 \text{ pages}}}} = \frac{600 \text{ pages} \times 2 \text{ hrs}}{3000 \text{ pages}}$$

$$y = \frac{600 \text{ pages} \times 2 \text{ hrs}}{3000 \text{ pages}}$$

$$y = \frac{600 \text{ pages} \times 120 \text{ minutes}}{3000 \text{ pages}} \qquad \begin{array}{l} (\ 60 \text{ minutes} = 1 \text{ hr} \\ 2 \text{ hrs} = 60 \times 2 = 120 \text{ minutes}) \end{array}$$

$$y = \frac{\overset{\overset{1}{6}}{\cancel{600 \text{ pages}}} \times 120 \text{ minutes}}{\underset{\underset{5}{30}}{\cancel{3000 \text{ pages}}}} \qquad \text{(Divide by 100, and then by 6)}$$

352

$$y = \frac{1 \times 120 \text{ minutes}}{5} = 24 \text{ minutes.}$$

Therefore, it will take 24 minutes to print 600 pages.

Example 9

Grace hit 6 home runs in 97 times at bat. At this rate, how many times at bat would she need to hit 9 home runs? Round your answer to the nearest whole number.

Solution

The proportion can be written as :

home runs : # of times at bat = home runs : # of times at bat   (General order)

6 home runs : 97 times at bat = 9 home runs : y,

or

$$\frac{6 \text{ home runs}}{97 \text{ times at bat}} = \frac{9 \text{ home runs}}{y}$$

Let y be the number of times at bat that would be needed to produce 9 home runs. Using Rule 2, **find the cross products and then divide as needed.** Solve the proportion as shown:

$$\frac{6 \text{ home runs}}{97 \text{ times at bat}} \times \frac{9 \text{ home runs}}{y}$$

or 6 home runs $\times$ y = 97 times at bat $\times$ 9 home runs   ————————————— [A]

Divide each side of equation [A] by 6 home runs in order to obtain the value of y as shown:

$$\frac{6 \text{ home runs} \times y}{6 \text{ home runs}} = \frac{97 \text{ times at bat} \times 9 \text{ home runs}}{6 \text{ home runs}}$$

$$\frac{\overset{1}{\cancel{6 \text{ home runs}}} \times y}{\underset{1}{\cancel{6 \text{ home runs}}}} = \frac{97 \text{ times at bat} \times 9 \text{ home runs}}{6 \text{ home runs}}$$

$$y = \frac{97 \text{ times at bat} \times \overset{3}{\cancel{9 \text{ home runs}}}}{\underset{2}{\cancel{6 \text{ home runs}}}} \qquad \text{(Divide by 3)}$$

$$y = \frac{97 \text{ times at bat} \times 3}{2} = \frac{291 \text{ times at bat}}{2} \qquad (97 \times 3 = 291)$$

$y = 145.5$ times at bat   (Review Decimal Fractions).
$y = 146$ times at bat to the nearest whole number. (Review Decimal Fractions).

Therefore, 146 times at bat would be needed to hit 9 home runs.

Exercises

1. Eric drove 45 miles in 3 hours. How long will he take to travel 135 miles if he travels at the same rate? Hint: See Example 1.
2. If 3 packages of candy cost $12.00, how many packages can be bought for $28.00. Hint: See Example 2.
3. Determine which proportions are false and which are true. Hint: See Example 3.

   (a) $\dfrac{2}{3} = \dfrac{6}{9}$ (b) $\dfrac{2}{3} = \dfrac{4}{7}$ (c) $\dfrac{3}{5} = \dfrac{1}{4}$ (d) $\dfrac{1}{2} = \dfrac{6}{12}$

4. A store sold 5 mangoes for $4.00, how many similar mangoes can be bought for $24.00? Hint: See Example 4.
5. Oranges are on sale for $1.60 per dozen. What is the price of 4 oranges? Hint: See Example 5.
6. Red peppers are on sale for $.64 a dozen. What is the price of 30 peppers? Hint: See Example 5.
7. If some special apples are priced at $1.20 per pound, how many pounds of the same type of the of the apples can be bought for $3.00? Hint: See Example 6.
8. Mary earned $63.00 for 7 hours of baby-sitting. At this rate, what would she earn for 2 hours of baby-sitting? Hint: See Example 7.
9. A special machine can print 250 pages in 2 hours. At this rate, how many minutes would it take to print 95 pages? Hint: See Example 8.
10. Judith hit 2 home runs in 13 times at bat. At this rate, how many times at bat will she need to hit 5 home runs? Round off your answer to the nearest whole number. Hint: See Example 9.

Challenge Questions

11. A train covers 80 miles in 2 hours. How long will it take the train to travel 240 miles at the same speed?
12. Five oranges cost $2.00 and three of the same type of oranges cost $4.00. Is the proportion true or false?
13. John earned $30.00 for 5 hours of baby-sitting. At this rate, how much will he earn for 7 hours of baby-sitting?

Answers to Selected Questions

1. 9 hours   6. $1.60

RATES

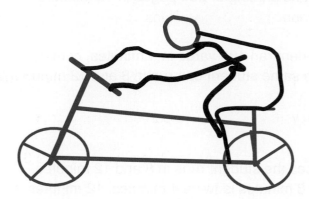

Joshua can ride 5 miles in 2 hours on his bicycle. The 5 miles in 2 hours can be written as a ratio as shown:

$$\frac{5 \text{ miles}}{2 \text{ hours}}$$

Note that the ratio above **compares two quantities** which are 5 and 2 which are **measured in two different units** which are miles and hours.

Ratios that compare two quantities measured in different units are called rates.

Group Exercise

The class should be divided into four groups. Each group should select 3 students who can represent them in running 100 yards. Each group should have their own stop watch. Each group should time and record how long it takes each of the selected 3 students to run the 100 yards. Each group should complete the chart that follows and also find the speed of each student in 100 yards per __ minutes.

Chart

Group 1, 2, 3, or 4.

Student #	Distance	Time to run 100 yards	Speed = $\dfrac{\text{Distance}}{\text{Time}}$
1	100 yards	_____ minutes	$\dfrac{100 \text{ yards}}{\text{____ minutes}}$
2	100 yards	_____ minutes	$\dfrac{100 \text{ yards}}{\text{____ minutes}}$
3	100 yards	_____ minutes	$\dfrac{100 \text{ yards}}{\text{____ minutes}}$

Each group should report out to the whole class about their best speed. Note that the speed which compares distance to time is a rate, and this can be expressed as yards per minute or miles per hour. Similarly, rates can also be expressed as 100 miles in 6 hours, 8 mangoes for $6.00, and printing of 200 pages in 15 minutes.

Complete the Table
Suppose from the group exercise, a student ran 100 yards in 4 minutes, complete the table below that predicts how far the same student can run in 8 and 12 minutes if the student runs at the same rate.

Time in minutes	4	8	12
Distance in yards	100	?	?

Explain how you can predict the distances the student runs in 8 and 12 minutes. The prediction is based on the fact that 8 minutes is twice 4 minutes, 12 minutes is 3 times 4 minutes such that the following rates can be written as shown in (a) and (b).

(a) 4 is multiplied by 2 to obtain 8, therefore, 100 should also be multiplied by 2 to obtain 200.

$$\frac{100}{4} : \frac{?}{8} = \frac{100}{4} : \frac{200}{8}$$

(b) 4 is multiplied by 3 to obtain 12, therefore, 100 should also be multiplied by 3 to obtain 300.

$$\frac{100}{4} : \frac{?}{12} = \frac{100}{4} : \frac{300}{12}$$

The table becomes:

Time in minutes	4	8	12
Distance in yards	100	200	300

The table that we have created is obtained by using the idea of equivalent ratios. **Equivalent ratios are ratios which have equivalent fractions**.
Equivalent fractions means fractions that are the same in value or equal and equivalent ratios means ratios that are the same in value or equal.
For example,

$$\frac{100 \text{ yards}}{4 \text{ minutes}} \text{ is equivalent to } \frac{200 \text{ yards}}{8 \text{ minutes}} \text{ because each term of}$$

$$\frac{200 \text{ yards}}{8 \text{ minutes}} \text{ can be divided by 2 to obtain } \frac{100 \text{ yards}}{4 \text{ minutes}}.$$

Similarly, $\frac{100 \text{ yards}}{4 \text{ minutes}}$ is equivalent to $\frac{300 \text{ yards}}{12 \text{ minutes}}$ because the terms of

$$\frac{300 \text{ yards}}{12 \text{ minutes}} \text{ can be divided by 3 to obtain } \frac{100 \text{ yards}}{4 \text{ minutes}}.$$

Rule 1:
Equivalent ratios can be written as equivalent fractions and the cross product of equivalent fractions are equal.

Distance-Time Graph
A distance-time graph is a graph that shows the distance on the y axis and the time on the x-axis. From the distance-time graph, we can tell the time it takes to cover a certain distance and also, we can tell the distance covered in a certain time as shown in Example 1.

Example 1
Using the distance-time graph of a man who is walking slowly,
a. Find the distance walked in 2 hours.
b. How long does it take to walk 3.5 miles?

c. What is the distance walked in $3\frac{1}{2}$ hours?

d. How long did it take to walk 3 miles? Select one of the answers.

(Answers: **1.** 6 hr   **2.** 4 hr   **3.** $5\frac{1}{5}$ hr)

e. What distance did he walk in 1 hr?

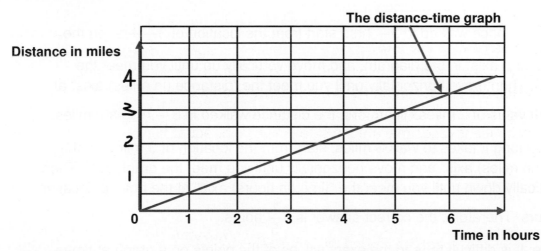

The distance-time graph

Distance in miles

Time in hours

Solution
The important features of the distance-time graph are as follow and this features will help us in understanding how to solve the problem.

357

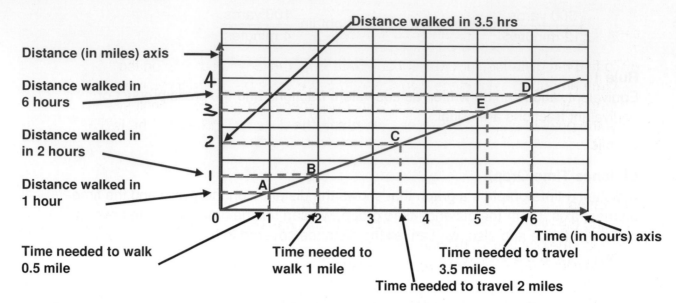

Distance walked in 3.5 hrs

Distance (in miles) axis

Distance walked in 6 hours

Distance walked in in 2 hours

Distance walked in 1 hour

Time needed to walk 0.5 mile

Time needed to walk 1 mile

Time needed to travel 3.5 miles

Time needed to travel 2 miles

Time (in hours) axis

a. To find the distance walked in 2 hrs., start from the location of 2 hrs. on the "time (in hours) axis" in the diagram, and move vertically up until you meet the graph at point A. Then move horizontally to the "distance (in miles) axis" to meet the "distance (in miles) axis" at the point of value of 1 mile. Therefore, the distance walked in 2 hrs. is 1 mile.

b. To find how long it takes to walk 3.5 miles, start from the location of 3.5 miles on the "distance (in miles) axis" in the diagram, and move horizontally until you meet the graph at point D. Then move vertically down until you meet the "time (in hours) axis" at the point of value of 6 hrs. Therefore, the time needed to walk 3.5 miles 6 hrs.

c. To find the distance walked in $3\frac{1}{2}$ hrs., start from the location of $3\frac{1}{2}$ hrs. on the "time (in hours) axis" in the diagram, and move vertically up until you meet the graph at C. Then move horizontally until you meet the "distance (in miles) axis" at the point of value of 2 miles. Therefore, the distance walked in $3\frac{1}{2}$ hrs. is 2 miles.

d. To find how long it takes to walk 3 miles, start from the location of 3 miles on the "distance (in miles) axis" and move horizontally until you meet the graph at E. Then move vertically down until you meet the "time (in hours) axis" at the point of location of $5\frac{1}{5}$ hours. Therefore, the correct answer is $5\frac{1}{5}$ hours.

Special note: It is difficult to read the exact values of the points on a graph at times. Therefore, we should estimate the values of the points on the graph as the required answers at times as best as we can. For example, the best answer that we obtained in Example 1d is $5\frac{1}{5}$ hr., but $5\frac{1}{5}$ hrs. may not be the exact answer, but luckily in this case, $5\frac{1}{5}$ hrs. is one of the answers provided.

e. To find the distance walked in 1 hour, start from the location of 1 hr on the "time (in hours) axis" in the diagram, and move vertically up until you meet the graph at A. Then move horizontally until you meet the "distance (in miles) axis" at the point of value of 0.5 miles. Therefore, the distance walked in 1 hr. is 0.5 mile.

Exercises

1. Using the distance-time graph of a woman who was walking slowly,
   a. Find the distance walked in 2 hours.
   b. How long does it take to walk 6.5 miles?
   c. What is the distance walked in 1 hour?
   d. How long did it take to walk 7 miles? Select one of the answers.

   (Answers: **1.** $4\frac{1}{3}$ hr   **2.** 4 hr   **3.** 6 hr)

   e. What distance did she walk in 3.5 hrs.?

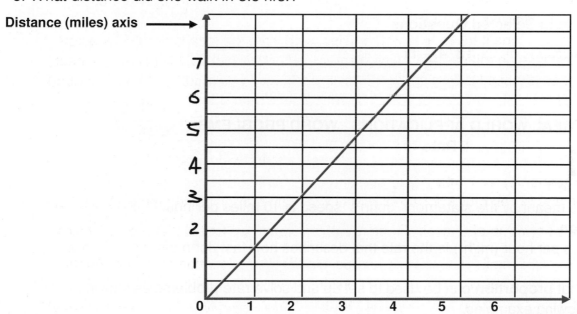

Distance (miles) axis ⟶

Time (in hours) axis

Challenge Question

2. Using the distance-time graph of a girl who was walking slowly,
   a. Find the distance walked in 3 hours.
   b. How long does it take to walk 2 miles?
   c. What is the distance walked in 4 hour?
   d. How long did it take to walk 5 miles? Select one of the answers.

   (Answers: **1.** $4\frac{1}{3}$ hr   **2.** $2\frac{1}{2}$ hr   **3.** 4 hr)

359

e. What distance did she walk in 1 hr.?

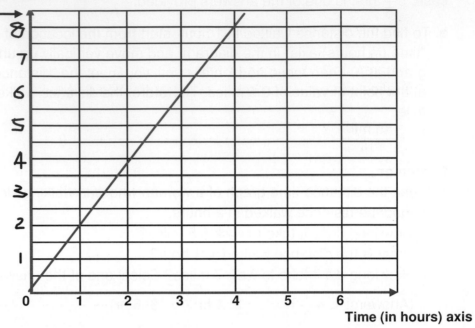

Distance (miles) axis

Time (in hours) axis

Answers to Selected Questions

1a. 3 miles.   **1d.** $4\frac{1}{3}$ hr

REAL WORLD APPLICATIONS - WORD PROBLEMS
Rate

Example 1
What is meant by the statement "John's speed is 10 miles per hour?"
Solution
10 miles per hour (mi/hr) is the rate that describes how fast John can travel in one hour.

Note that **proportion** can be used to set up and solve rate problems as shown in the following examples.

Example 2
Joshua drove his car at a speed of 45 miles per hour.
(a) How far did he travel in 3 hours at that rate?
(b) If he traveled 225 miles at that rate, how many hours did he take to complete the trip.
Solution
(a) We are given in the problem that Joshua traveled 45 miles in every 1 hour, and we are required to find how long did he take to travel 225 miles. We can use a

360

proportion to set up the solution and solve the problem as shown:

45 miles : 1 hour = n miles : 3 hours,

where n is the distance traveled in 3 hours.
The ratios can be written in the form of a fraction as shown:

$$\frac{45 \text{ miles}}{1 \text{ hour}} = \frac{n}{3 \text{ hours}} \quad\text{———————————} [A]$$

The cross products of equivalent ratios are equal, and therefore, equation $[A]$ then becomes:

$$\frac{45 \text{ miles}}{1 \text{ hour}} \quad \underset{\times}{-} \quad \frac{n}{3 \text{ hours}}$$

$$45 \text{ miles} \times 3 \text{ hours} = 1 \text{ hour} \times n \text{ miles} \quad\text{———————} [B]$$

Divide each side of equation $[B]$ by 1 hour in order to obtain the value of n as shown:

$$\frac{45 \text{ miles} \times 3 \text{ hours}}{1 \text{ hour}} = \frac{1 \text{ hour} \times n}{1 \text{ hour}}$$

$$\frac{45 \text{ miles} \times 3 \text{ hours}}{1 \text{ hour}} = \frac{1 \text{ hour} \times n}{1 \text{ hour}}$$

$$45 \text{ miles} \times 3 = n$$
$$135 \text{ miles} = n$$

Therefore, Joshua traveled 135 miles in 3 hours.

(b) We are given in the problem that Joshua traveled 45 miles in every hour and we are required to find how many hours did he take to travel 225 miles. We can use proportion to set up the solution and solve the problem as shown:

45 miles : 1 hour = 225 miles : n

where n is the number of hours taken to travel 225 miles. The ratios can be written in the form of fractions as shown:

$$\frac{45 \text{ miles}}{1 \text{ hour}} = \frac{225 \text{ miles}}{n} \quad\text{—————————} [C]$$

The cross products of equivalent ratios are equal, and therefore, equation $[C]$ then becomes:

$$\frac{45 \text{ miles}}{1 \text{ hour}} \underset{\nearrow}{\overset{\searrow}{=}} \frac{225 \text{ miles}}{1 \text{ hour}}$$

$$45 \text{ miles} \times n = 1 \text{ hour} \times 225 \text{ miles} \quad \text{———————} [D]$$

Divide each side of equation $[D]$ by 45 miles in order to obtain the value of n as shown:

$$\frac{45 \text{ miles} \times n}{45 \text{ miles}} = \frac{1 \text{ hour} \times 225 \text{ miles}}{45 \text{ miles}}$$

$$\frac{\overset{1}{\cancel{45 \text{ miles}}} \times n}{\underset{1}{\cancel{45 \text{ miles}}}} = \frac{1 \text{ hour} \times \overset{\overset{5}{\cancel{45}}}{\cancel{225 \text{ miles}}}}{\underset{\underset{1}{9}}{\cancel{45 \text{ miles}}}} \qquad \text{Divide by 5 and then by 9}$$

↑

Divide by 45

$$n = 1 \text{ hour} \times 5$$
$$= 5 \text{ hours}$$

Therefore, Joshua used 5 hours to travel 225 miles.

Example 3
If Eric paid $6.24 for 3 gallons of gasoline, at this price,
(a) how much will he pay for 5 gallons of gasoline?
(b) how many gallons can he buy for $12.48?
(c) how much would 7 gallons cost?

Solution
(a) A proportion can be used to set up the solution as follows:

$6.24 : 3 gallons = ? : 5 gallons

where ? represents the cost for 5 gallons of gasoline.

(Always remember to set the terms of a proportion in order.)

The proportion can be written in a fraction form as shown:

$$\frac{\$6.24}{3 \text{ gallons}} = \frac{?}{5 \text{ gallons}}$$

Cross products of equivalent ratios are equal, and therefore:

$$\frac{\$6.24}{3 \text{ gallons}} \underset{\nearrow}{\overset{\searrow}{=}} \frac{?}{5 \text{ gallons}}$$

$$\$6.24 \times 5 \text{ gallons} = 3 \text{ gallons} \times ? \quad \text{———————} [A]$$

362

Divide each side of equation [A] by 3 gallons in order to obtain the value for?
Equation [A] then becomes:

$$\frac{\$6.24 \times 5 \text{ gallons}}{3 \text{ gallons}} = \frac{3 \text{ gallons} \times ?}{3 \text{ gallons}}$$

$$\frac{\overset{\$2.08}{\cancel{\$6.24} \times 5 \cancel{\text{ gallons}}}}{\underset{1}{\cancel{3 \text{ gallons}}}} = \frac{\overset{1}{\cancel{3 \text{ gallons}} \times ?}}{\underset{1}{\cancel{3 \text{ gallons}}}}$$

$$\$2.08 \times 5 = ?$$
$$\$10.40 = ?$$

Therefore, 5 gallons of gasoline = $10.40

(b) Proportion can be used to set up the solution as:

$6.24 : 3 \text{ gallons} = \$12.48 : n \text{ gallons}$ ───────────── [B]

where n represents the number of gallons of gasoline that can be bought with
$12.48. Equation [B] can be written in a fraction form as shown:

$$\frac{\$6.24}{3 \text{ gallons}} = \frac{\$12.48}{n}$$

Cross products of equivalent ratios are equal, and therefore:

$$\frac{\$6.24}{3 \text{ gallons}} \begin{smallmatrix}\searrow\\\nearrow\end{smallmatrix} \frac{\$12.48}{n}$$

Therefore, $6.24 $\times n = 3$ gallons $\times$ $12.48 ───────────── [C]

Divide each side of equation [C] by $6.24 in order to obtain the value for n
gallons of gasoline as shown:

$$\frac{\$6.24 \times n}{\$6.24} = \frac{3 \text{ gallons} \times \$12.48}{\$6.24}$$

$$\frac{\overset{1}{\cancel{\$6.24} \times n}}{\underset{1}{\cancel{\$6.24}}} = \frac{3 \text{ gallons} \times \overset{2}{\cancel{\$12.48}}}{\underset{1}{\cancel{\$6.24}}}$$

$$n = 3 \text{ gallons} \times 2$$
$$n = 6 \text{ gallons}$$

Therefore, 6 gallons can be bought for $12.48.

(c) A proportion can be used to set up the solution as shown:

$$\$6.24 : 3 \text{ gallons} = n : 7 \text{ gallons}$$

where n is the cost for 7 gallons of gasoline.
The ratios can be written in the form of a fraction as shown:

$$\frac{\$6.24}{3 \text{ gallons}} = \frac{n}{7 \text{ gallon}} \qquad\qquad\qquad\qquad [D]$$

The cross products of equivalent ratios are equal, and therefore, equation $[D]$ becomes:

$$\frac{\$6.24}{3 \text{ gallons}} = \frac{n}{7 \text{ gallons}}$$

$$\$6.24 \times 7 \text{ gallons} = 3 \text{ gallons} \times n \qquad\qquad\qquad [E]$$

Divide each side of equation $[E]$ by 3 gallons in order to obtain the value of n as shown:

$$\frac{\overset{\$2.08}{\cancel{\$6.24}} \div 7 \text{ gallons}}{\underset{1}{3 \text{ gallons}}} = \frac{\overset{1}{\cancel{3 \text{ gallons}}} \times n}{\underset{1}{\cancel{3 \text{ gallons}}}}$$

$$\$2.08 \times 7 = n$$
$$\$14.56 = n$$

Therefore, 7 gallons of gasoline will cost $14.56.

Example 4
During the first 2 days of her vacation, Elizabeth spent $5.12 on breakfast.
At this rate,
(a) how much did she spend on breakfast for 7 days?
(b) how many days of breakfast could she buy for $23.04?

Solution
(a) We are given in the problem that in 2 days Elizabeth spent $5.12 on breakfast and we are requested to find how much she spent on breakfast in 7 days. We an use a proportion to set up and solve the problem as shown:

$$2 \text{ days} : \$5 : 12 = 7 \text{ days} : n$$

where n is how much money Elizabeth spent on the breakfast for 7 days. The ratios can be written in the form of a fraction as shown:

$$\frac{2\ days}{\$5.12} = \frac{7\ days}{n} \text{ —————————— } [A]$$

The cross products of equivalent ratios are equal, and therefore, equation $[A]$ then becomes:

$$\frac{2\ days}{\$5.12} \diagdown\!\!\!\!\diagup \frac{7\ days}{n}$$

$$2\ days \times n = \$5.12 \times 7\ days \text{ ————————— } [B]$$

Divide each side of equation $[B]$ by 2 days in order to obtain the value of n as shown:

$$\frac{2\ days \times n}{2\ days} = \frac{\$5.12 \times 7\ days}{2\ days}$$

$$\frac{\overset{1}{\cancel{2\ days}} \times n}{\underset{1}{\cancel{2\ days}}} = \frac{\$5.12 \times 7\ \cancel{days}}{\cancel{2\ days}}$$

$$n = \frac{\$5.12 \times 7}{2} = \frac{\$35.84}{2}$$

$$= \$17.92$$

(b) We are given in the problem that in 2 days Elizabeth spent $5.12 on breakfast and we are requested to find how many days of breakfast she could buy for $23.04. We can use a proportion to set up and solve the problem as shown:

$$2\ days : \$5.12 = n : \$23.04$$

where n represents the number of days of breakfast that could be bought with $23.04. The ratios can be written in the form of fractions as shown:

$$\frac{2\ days}{\$5.12} = \frac{n}{\$23.04} \text{ —————————— } [C]$$

The cross products of equivalent ratios are equal, and therefore, equation $[C]$ then becomes:

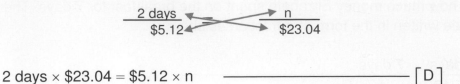

$$2 \text{ days} \times \$23.04 = \$5.12 \times n \quad \text{————————————} \left[D\right]$$

Divide each side of equation $\left[D\right]$ by $5.12 in order to obtain the value of n as shown:

$$\frac{2 \text{ days} \times \$23.04}{\$5.12} = \frac{\$5.12 \times n}{\$5.12}$$

$$\frac{2 \text{ days} \times \$23.04}{\$5.12} = \frac{\overset{1}{\cancel{\$5.12}} \times n}{\underset{1}{\cancel{\$5.12}}}$$

$$\frac{2 \text{ days} \times \$23.04}{\$5.12} = n \qquad \text{(You may use a calculator)}.$$

$$9 \text{ days} = n$$

Therefore, Elizabeth can buy breakfast for 9 days with $23.04.

Exercise

1. Explain what is meant by a rate.
2. Explain the statement that Eric's car uses a gallon of gasoline per 18 miles.
   Hint: See Example 1.
3. A bus covers 60 miles in 3 hours, and at this rate:
   (a) How many miles will the bus cover in 10 hours?
   (b) How many hours will the bus take to cover 100 miles?
   (c) How many hours will the bus take to cover 45 miles?
   Hint: See Example 2, you may use a calculator. Round your answer to 2 decimal places.
4. Judith can walk 5 miles in 3 hours, and at this rate:
   (a) How long does she take to walk 15 miles?
   (b) How long does she take to walk 25 miles?
   (c) How many miles can she walk in 10 hours?
   (d) How many miles can she walk in 12 hours?
   Hint: See Example 2. Round your answer to 1 decimal place.
5. Hope bought 3 oranges for $.90.
   (a) How many oranges could she buy for $3.60?
   (b) How much will she pay for 9 oranges?

(c) How much will she pay for 12 oranges?
Hint: See Example 4.

Challenge Questions
6. Samuel bought 6 apples for $1.00.
  (a) How many apples could he buy for $3.50?
  (b) How many apples could he buy for $2.25?
  (c) How much will he pay for 10 apples?
  (d) How much will he pay for 24 apples?
  (e) How much will he pay for 36 apples?
  (f) How many apples could he buy for $4.00?
7. Given that Joseph can run 5 miles in 2 hours and at that rate:
  (a) How long does he take to run 20 miles?
  (b) How many miles does he cover in 8 hours?
  (c) How long does he take to run 12 miles?
  (d) How many miles does he cover in 14 hours?
  (e) How long does he take to run 50 miles?

Answers to Selected Questions
3a. 200 miles   **4a**. 9 hrs.

CHAPTER 18

DIRECT VARIATION

In a direct variation, two variables are related proportionally by a constant positive ratio. The constant positive ratio is called the constant of proportionality.
If Joshua can travel 5 miles in every 1 hour, then we expect that his speed which is $\dfrac{distance}{time}$ can be represented as shown:

$$Speed = \frac{distance}{time} = \frac{5\ mi}{1\ hr} = \frac{10\ mi}{2\ hr} = \frac{15\ mi}{3\ hr} = \frac{20\ mi}{4hr} = 5\ mph$$
$$= \text{a constant positive ratio.}$$

The distance traveled by Joshua varies directly with the time and it can be represented by the equation $y = kx$, where the constant ratio k is 5.

In general: **If y varies directly as x then y = kx or $\dfrac{y}{x}$ = k, where k is the constant**.

How to Determine Whether a Data Set Varies Directly
Example 1

Determine whether the data set shows direct variation in (**a**) table 1 and (**b**) table 2 by using a graph, and then using algebra.

Table 1

Time (hr)	1	2	3	4
Distance (mi)	5	10	15	20

Table 2

Time (hr)	1	2	3	4
Distance (mi)	3	5	2	8

Solution

(a). Considering Table 1

Graphical Method

Make a graph that shows the relationship between the time and the distance by plotting the data given in table 1 on graph paper as shown:

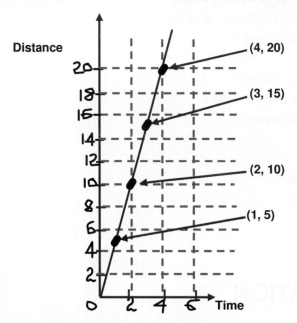

From the graph, the points lie in a straight line, and so the graph is linear and it passes through the point (0, 0). **A graph that is linear and passes through the point (0, 0) shows direct variation**.

Algebraic Method

Compare the ratios of the data in Table 1 to see if a direct variation occurs or not as shown:

$$\frac{5}{1} = \frac{10}{2} = \frac{15}{3} = \frac{20}{4} = 5 = \text{constant value.}$$

The ratios give a constant value of 5, and therefore, the relationship is a direct variation. Note also that the ratios are proportional and for any direct variation, the cross products of any of the ratios is equal as shown:

$$\frac{5}{1} = \frac{10}{2}$$

A proportion is an equation that states that two ratios are equal.

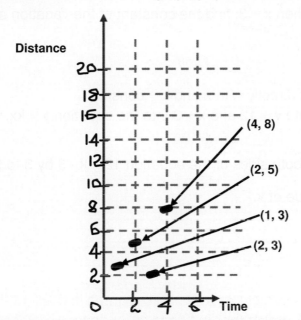

Cross multiply

5 · 2 = 1 · 10   In a proportion, the cross product of ratios are equal.
10 = 10   Confirms cross products of ratios are equal because the left side of the equation equals to the right side of the equation.

(b). Considering Table 2

Graphical Method

Make a graph that shows the relationship between the time and the distance by plotting the data in Table 2 on graph paper as shown:

From the graph, the points do not lie in a straight line, and therefore, the graph is not linear. **A graph that is not linear does not show direct variation**.

Algebraic Method

Compare the ratios of the data in table 2 to see if a direct variation occurs or not as shown:

$$\frac{3}{1} \neq \frac{5}{2} \neq \frac{2}{3} \neq \frac{8}{4} \neq \text{a constant value.}$$ The symbol ≠ means not equal to.

The ratios do not give a constant value, and therefore, the relationship is not a direct variation. Note also that the ratios are not proportional, and therefore, the cross products of any of the two ratios are not equal as shown:

$$\frac{3}{1} \neq \frac{5}{2}$$

369

Cross multiplication of unequal ratios.

$3 \cdot 2 \neq 5 \cdot 1$ The cross products are not equal .

$6 \neq 5$ Confirms cross products of the ratios are not equal because the left side of the equation $6 = 5$ is not equal to the right side of the equation.

How to Find the Constant of Variation and How to Write an Equation of Direct Variation

Example 2

If y varies directly as x and y = 12 when x = 3, find the constant of the variation and write an equation of direct variation.

Solution

Step 1: Find the value of k.

$y = kx$ y varies directly with x and k = constant.

$12 = k \cdot 3$ Substitute y = 12 and x = 3 into the equation y = kx.

$$\frac{12}{3} = \frac{k \cdot 3}{3}$$ Divide both sides of the equation 12 = k · 3 by 3 to find the value of k.

$$\frac{\overset{4}{\cancel{12}}}{\underset{1}{\cancel{3}}} = \frac{\overset{k}{\cancel{k \cdot 3}}}{\underset{1}{\cancel{3}}}$$

$4 = k$ and k is the constant.

Step 2: Write the equation of the direct variation.

From step 1, k = 4.

Substitute k = 4 into the original equation y = kx to obtain the equation of the direct variation as follows:

$y = kx$

$y = 4x$ Substitute k = 4.

Therefore, the equation of the direction variation is y = 4x.

Example 3

Find the equation of the direct variation given that y varies directly with x and x = 4 when y = 18.

Solution

Step 1: Find the value of k.

$$y = kx$$ y varies directly with x, where k is the constant.

$$18 = k \cdot 4$$ Substitute y = 18 and x = 4 into the equation y = kx.

$$\frac{18}{4} = \frac{k \cdot 4}{4}$$ Divide both sides of the equation 18 = k · 4 by 4 in order to obtain the value of k.

$$\frac{\overset{9}{\cancel{18}}}{4} = \frac{k \cdot \cancel{4}}{\cancel{4}}$$

$$\frac{9}{2} = k$$

Step 2: Write the equation of the direct variation.

From step 1, $k = \dfrac{9}{2}$

Substitute $k = \dfrac{9}{2}$ into the original equation y = kx to obtain the equation of the direct variation as shown:

$$y = kx$$

$$y = \frac{9}{2}x$$ Substitute $k = \dfrac{9}{2}$ into the equation y = kx.

Therefore, the equation of the direct variation is $y = \dfrac{9}{2}x$.

How to Find the Unknown Variable in Direct Variations

Example 4
If y varies directly as x and y = 25 when x = 10, find x when y = 75.
Solution

In direct variations, all the ratios or all the values of $\dfrac{y}{x}$ are equal to a certain

constant, k. Therefore, all the ratios or all the values of $\dfrac{y}{x}$ must be equal. We can

therefore, setup and solve a proportion to find x as follows:

$$\frac{y_1}{x_1} = \frac{y_2}{x_2}$$ A proportion is a statement showing that 2 ratios are equal.

$$\frac{25}{10} = \frac{75}{x}$$ Substitute $y_1 = 25$, $x_1 = 10$, $y_2 = 75$, and $x_2 = x$.

$\frac{25}{10} \diagdown \diagup \frac{75}{x}$ **Cross multiply because the cross products of a proportion are equal.**

$25 \cdot x = 10 \cdot 75$ Cross product of a proportion are equal.

$\frac{25 \cdot x}{25} = \frac{10 \cdot 75}{25}$ Divide both sides of the equation $25 \cdot x = 10 \cdot 75$

by 25 in order to obtain the value of x.

$$\frac{\overset{x}{\cancel{25}} \cdot x}{\underset{1}{\cancel{25}}} = \frac{10 \cdot \overset{3}{\cancel{75}}}{\underset{1}{\cancel{25}}}$$

$x = 10 \cdot 3$

$x = 30$

Example 5

If y varies directly as x and y = 9 when x = 4 find y when x = 28.

Solution

In direct variations, all the ratios or all the values of $\frac{y}{x}$ are equal to a certain constant, k.

Therefore, all the ratios or all the values of $\frac{y}{x}$ must be equal. We can therefore, set up

and solve a proportion to find y as shown:

$\frac{y_1}{x_1} = \frac{y_2}{x_2}$ A proportion is a statement showing that two ratios are equal.

$\frac{9}{4} = \frac{y}{28}$ Substitute $y_1 = 9$, $x_1 = 4$, $y_2 = y$, and $x_2 = 28$.

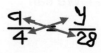 **Cross multiply because the cross products of a proportion are equal.**

$4 \cdot y = 9 \cdot 28$ Cross products of a proportion are equal.

$\frac{4 \cdot y}{4} = \frac{9 \cdot 28}{4}$ Divide both sides of the equation $4 \cdot y = 9 \cdot 28$ by 4 to obtain the value of y.

$$\frac{\overset{1}{\cancel{4}} \cdot y}{\underset{1}{\cancel{4}}} = \frac{9 \cdot \overset{7}{\cancel{28}}}{\underset{1}{\cancel{4}}}$$

$$y = 9 \cdot 7$$
$$y = 63.$$

Exercises

1. Explain a direct variation.

2. Explain in one sentence how you could tell from a graph that:
   a. a data set is a direct variation.
   b. a data set is not a direct variation.
      Hint: See Example 1.

3. Explain in one sentence how you could tell from a table using algebra that a data set is:
   a. a direct variation.
   b. not a direct variation.
      Hint: See Example 1.

4. The table shows the distance covered per hour by Mrs. Brown.

Time (hr)	1	2	3	4	5
Distance (mi)	2	4	6	8	10

   a. Explain graphically that the data set is a direct variation.
   b. Using algebra, explain why the data set is a direct variation.
      Hint: See Example 1.

5. Find each constant and each equation of direct variation, given that y varies directly with x. Hint: See Example 1.
   a. y is 14 when x is 7.   **b.** y is 93 when x is 3.   **c.** y is 84 when x is 12.
   d. y is 10 when x is 50.   **e.** y is 3 when x is 24 f.   **f.** y is 3 when x is 21.
   g. y is 128 when x is 2.   **h.** y is 100 when x is 10.   **i.** y is 15 when x is 12.
   j. y is 4 when x is 15   **k.** y is 4 when x is 48.   **l.** y is 3 when x is 63.

6. For each of the following values of x and y, y varies directly as x. Find the value of x. Hint; See Example 4.
   a. y is 15 when x is 3. Find x when y is 75
   b. y is 56 when x is 16. Find x when y = 7
   c. y is 16 when x is 36. Find x when y = 4
   d. y is 24 when x is 8. Find x when y = 4
   e. y is 3 when x is 7. Find x when y = 36
   f. y is 18 when x is 24. Find x when y = 6.

7. For each of the following values of x and y, y varies directly as x. Find the value of y.

Hint: See Example 5.

    a. y is 5 when x is 8. Find y when x is 32.

    b. y is 64 when x is 4. Find y when x is 1.

    c. y is 100 when x is 5. Find y when x is 20.

    d. y is 21 when x is 35. Find y when x is 7.

    e. y is 4 when x is 28. Find y when x is 7.

    f. y is 7 when x is 3. Find y when x is 24.

Answers to Selected Questions

5a. Constant is 2 and the equation of the direct variation is y = 2x.

6a. x = 15   **7a.** y = 20.

CHAPTER 19

INVERSE VARIATION

In the direct variation, the variables x and y either increase together or decrease together. **In the inverse variation, as one variable quantity increases, the other variable quantity decreases**. This is written as $y = \dfrac{k}{x}$ or yx = k where k is a constant of the variation, $k \neq 0$ and $x \neq 0$. Note that a constant is a number that will not change for a specific relation. **It is important to note that in the inverse variation, the product of the variables is a constant**.

If it takes 50 days to build a new soccer stadium with 200 people, then if we increase the number of workers, then the number of days to complete a similar new stadium will decrease. Therefore, as the number of the workers increases, the number of days needed to build the new stadium decreases. This is an example of inverse variation.

How to Tell if Each Relationship From a Table is an Inverse or Not, and How to Write an Equation of the Relation

Example 1

The table shows the number of days needed to drive new cars from lot A to lot B based on the size of the work crew.

    a. Tell whether each relationship is an inverse variation.

    b. Write the equation of the relationship.

Crew size	10	20	25	40	50
Days of driving	100	50	40	25	20

Solution

a. Let the "crew size" be the variable y.

Let the "days of driving" be the variable x.

For an **inverse variation**, the product of the variables is a constant, therefore:

xy = k where k is a constant or a constant number.

Let us find the value of k in each relation to see if the value of k is the same or constant as shown:

xy = k, 10 · 100 = 1000, 20 · 50 = 1000, 25 · 40 = 1000

40 · 25 = 1000, 50 · 20 = 1000.

Since the products of the variables are always the same, which is 1000, the relation is an inverse variation, and therefore, k = 1000.

b. From the solution of Example **1a**, k = 1000. From the solution of Example **1a**, the relation is an inverse variation, and therefore, the products of the variations are constant as shown:

$$xy = k \underline{\hspace{3cm}} [A]$$

$$\frac{xy}{x} = \frac{k}{x} \qquad \text{Divide both sides of the equation } [A] \text{ by x to obtain the value of y.}$$

$$\frac{\overset{y}{\cancel{xy}}}{\underset{1}{\cancel{x}}} = \frac{k}{x}$$

$$y = \frac{k}{x} \underline{\hspace{3cm}} [B]$$

$$y = \frac{1000}{x} \qquad \text{Substitute k = 1000 into equation } [B].$$

Therefore, the equation of the relation is $y = \dfrac{1000}{x}$.

Example 2

The table shows the number of toys produced in a given amount of time. Tell whether the relation is an inverse variation.

Toys produced	28	36	48	55	60
Time (hr)	2	3	4	5	6

Solution

Let the number of the toys produced be the variable x.

Let the number of hours required to produce the toys be the variable y.

In an inverse variation, the product of the variables is a constant or a constant number.

Therefore, if the relation is an inverse variation, then xy = k where k is a constant or a constant number, so let us check if the products of the variables are constants or constant numbers as shown:

$$xy = k, \quad 28 \cdot 2 = 56, \quad 36 \cdot 3 = 108.$$

The product is not the same, and therefore, the relation is not an inverse variation.

How to Write an Equation That Shows How y is Related to x When Given That y Varies Inversely as x and the Values of x and y are Given.

Example 3

If y varies inversely as x and $y = 5$ when $x = 10$ write an equation that shows how y is related to x.

Solution

Step 1: Find k.

$y = 5$ when $x = 10$.

The equation for an inverse variation can also be written as:

$y = \dfrac{k}{x}$ _____[A]   where k is a constant.

$5 = \dfrac{k}{10}$ _____[B]   Substitute $y = 5$ and $x = 10$ into the equation [A].

$10 \cdot 5 = \dfrac{k}{10} \cdot 10$ Multiply both sides of the equation [B] by 10 in order to eliminate the denominator 10 at the right side of the equation [B] to obtain the value of k.

$$50 = \dfrac{k}{\overset{\displaystyle 1}{\cancel{10}}} \times \overset{\displaystyle 1}{\cancel{10}}$$

$$50 = k$$

Step 2: Write an equation to show how y is related to x.

It is already given in the question that y varies inversely as x, so let us use the equation for inverse variation to write the equation that relates y to x as shown:

$y = \dfrac{k}{x}$ _____[C]   Equation for inverse variation.

$y = \dfrac{50}{x}$ Substitute $k = 50$ in equation [C].

376

The equation that relates y to x is:

$$y = \frac{50}{x}$$

How to Graph Inverse Variation Functions

Example 4

a. Graph the inverse variation function of $f(x) = \frac{1}{x}$.

b. What are the special features of the graph $f(x) = \frac{1}{x}$?

c. What value of x makes the function or the graph undefined? Explain why the graph did not cross neither the x-axis nor the y-axis.

d. Label the graph with the four quadrants.

Solution

Step 1: Create a table for x and y.

Create a table for x and y by assigning numbers to x and finding the corresponding values of y as shown:

(The table is on the next page.)

x	$y = f(x) = \dfrac{1}{x}$	y	(x, y)
-4	$y = f(-4) = \dfrac{1}{-4} = -\dfrac{1}{4}$	$-\dfrac{1}{4}$	$(-4, -\dfrac{1}{4})$
-3	$y = f(-3) = \dfrac{1}{-3} = -\dfrac{1}{3}$	$-\dfrac{1}{3}$	$(-3, -\dfrac{1}{3})$
-2	$y = f(-2) = \dfrac{1}{-2} = -\dfrac{1}{2}$	$-\dfrac{1}{2}$	$(-2, -\dfrac{1}{2})$
-1	$y = f(-1) = \dfrac{1}{-1} = -1$	-1	(-1,-1)
$-\dfrac{1}{2}$	$y = f(-\dfrac{1}{2}) = \dfrac{1}{-\dfrac{1}{2}} = 1 \times (\dfrac{-2}{1}) = -2$	-2	$(-\dfrac{1}{2}, -2)$
0	$y = f(0) = \dfrac{1}{0} = $ Not defined	Not defined	(0, Not defined)
$\dfrac{1}{2}$	$y = f(\dfrac{1}{2}) = \dfrac{1}{\dfrac{1}{2}} = 1 \times \dfrac{2}{1} = 2$	2	$(\dfrac{1}{2}, 2)$
1	$y = f(1) = \dfrac{1}{1} = 1$	1	(1, 1)
2	$y = f(2) = \dfrac{1}{2}$	$\dfrac{1}{2}$	$(2, \dfrac{1}{2})$
3	$y = f(3) = \dfrac{1}{3}$	$\dfrac{1}{3}$	$(3, \dfrac{1}{3})$
4	$y = f(4) = \dfrac{1}{4}$	$\dfrac{1}{4}$	$(4, \dfrac{1}{4})$

Step 2: Plot the points (x, y) in the table on graph paper and connect the points with a smooth curve as shown:

(The graph is shown on the next page.)

378

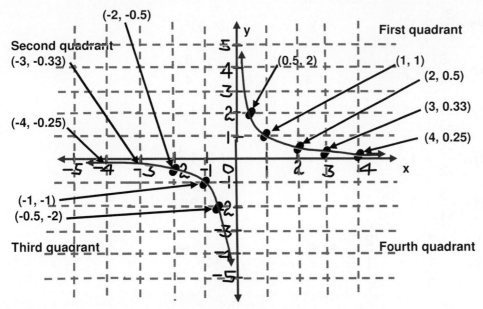

Note that on the graph, $0.5 = \dfrac{1}{2}$, $-0.5 = -\dfrac{1}{2}$, $0.25 = \dfrac{1}{4}$, $-0.25 = -\dfrac{1}{4}$,

$$0.33 = \dfrac{1}{3}, \text{ and } -0.33 = -\dfrac{1}{3}.$$

b. The function $f(x) = \dfrac{1}{x}$ creates two graphs. One graph is in the first quadrant and the other graph is in the third quadrant. Both graphs cross neither the x-axis nor the y-axis.

c. When $x = 0$, the function $f(x) = \dfrac{1}{x} =$ becomes $f(0) = \dfrac{1}{0} =$ undefined, and this is the reason why the graphs could not cross neither the x-axis nor the y-axis.

d. The four quadrants are shown on the graph.

Example 5

a. Graph the inverse variation function $f(x) = \dfrac{-3}{x}$.

b. What are the special features of the graph of $f(x) = \dfrac{-3}{x}$?

c. What value of x makes the function or the graph undefined? Explain why the graph did not cross neither the x-axis nor the y-axis.

Solution

a. Step 1: Create a table for x and y.

Create a table for x and y by assigning numbers to x and then finding the corresponding values of y as shown:

379

x	$y = f(x) = \dfrac{-3}{x}$	y	(x, y)
-4	$y = f(-4) = \dfrac{-3}{-4} = \dfrac{3}{4}$	$\dfrac{3}{4}$	$(-4, \dfrac{3}{4})$
-3	$y = f(-3) = \dfrac{-3}{-3} = 1$	1	(-3, 1)
-2	$y = f(-2) = \dfrac{-3}{-2} = 1\dfrac{1}{2}$	$1\dfrac{1}{2}$	$(-2, 1\dfrac{1}{2})$
-1	$y = f(-1) = \dfrac{-3}{-1} = 3$	3	(-1, 3)
$-\dfrac{1}{2}$	$y = f(-\dfrac{1}{2}) = \dfrac{-3}{-\dfrac{1}{2}} = -3(-\dfrac{2}{1}) = 6$	6	$(-\dfrac{1}{2}, 6)$
0	$y = f(0) = \dfrac{-3}{0} = $ Not defined	Not defined	(0, Not defined)
$\dfrac{1}{2}$	$y = f(\dfrac{1}{2}) = \dfrac{-3}{\dfrac{1}{2}} = -3(\dfrac{2}{1}) = -6$	-6	$(\dfrac{1}{2}, -6)$
1	$y = f(1) = \dfrac{-3}{1} = -3$	-3	(1, -3)
2	$y = f(2) = \dfrac{-3}{2} = -\dfrac{3}{2} = -1\dfrac{1}{2}$	$-1\dfrac{1}{2}$	$(2, -1\dfrac{1}{2})$
3	$y = f(3) = \dfrac{-3}{3} = -1$	-1	(3, -1)
4	$y = f(4) = \dfrac{-3}{4} = -\dfrac{3}{4}$	$-\dfrac{3}{4}$	$(4, -\dfrac{3}{4})$

Step 2: Plot the points (x, y) in the table on graph paper and connect the points with a smooth curve as shown:

(The graph is shown on the next page.)

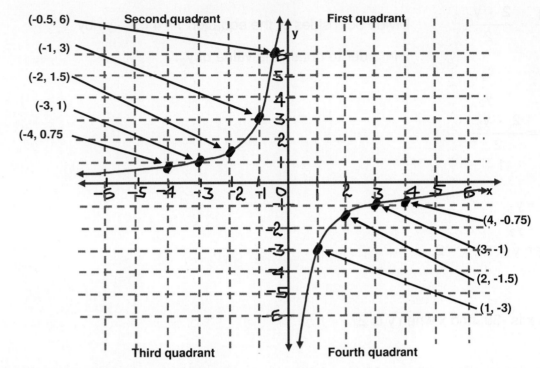

Notice on the graph that $0.75 = \dfrac{3}{4}$, $1.5 = 1\dfrac{1}{2}$, $-0.5 = -\dfrac{1}{2}$, $-1.5 = -1\dfrac{1}{2}$, and $-0.75 = -\dfrac{3}{4}$.

b. The function $f(x) = \dfrac{-3}{x}$ creates two graphs. One graph is in the second quadrant and the other graph is in the fourth quadrant. Both graphs cross neither the x-axis nor the y-axis.

c. When $x = 0$, the function $f(x) = \dfrac{-3}{x}$ becomes $f(0) = \dfrac{-3}{0} =$ undefined, and this is the reason why the graphs could not cross neither the x-axis nor the y-axis.

How to Find x or y in an Inverse Variation

Example 6
If y is 4 when x is 7 and y varies inversely as x, explain how to find y when x is 2. Find y when x is 2.

Solution
In an inverse variation, the product of the variables is a constant. This means that:

$xy = k$ Where x and y are variables and k is a constant.

$xy = \text{constant}$

Therefore, $x_1 y_1 = x_2 y_2$ Where $x_1 = 7$, $y_1 = 4$, $x_2 = 2$, and y_2 is the unknown.

$7 \cdot 4 = 2 \cdot y_2$ Substitute $x_1 = 7$, $y_1 = 4$, $x_2 = 2$, and y_2 into the equation $x_1 y_1 = x_2 y_2$.

$$\frac{7 \cdot 4}{2} = \frac{2 \cdot y_2}{2}$$

Divide both sides of the equation $7 \cdot 4 = 2 \cdot y_2$ by 2 in order to obtain the value of y_2.

$$\frac{7 \cdot \overset{2}{\cancel{4}}}{\underset{1}{\cancel{2}}} = \frac{\cancel{2} \cdot y_2}{\underset{1}{\cancel{2}}}$$

$$7 \cdot 2 = y_2$$
$$14 = y_2$$

Therefore, when $y = 14$, $x = 2$.

Example 7

If y is $\dfrac{2}{5}$ when x is -30, find x when y is 2.

Solution

In an inverse variation, the products of the variables is a constant. This means that:

$$xy = k \qquad \text{Where } x \text{ and } y \text{ are variables and } k \text{ is a constant.}$$
$$xy = \text{constant}$$

Therefore, $x_1 y_1 = x_2 y_2$ Where $x_1 = -30$, $y_1 = \dfrac{2}{5}$, $x_2 =$ unknown and $y_2 = 2$.

$$(-30) \cdot \frac{2}{5} = x_2 \cdot 2$$

Substitute $x_1 = -30$, $y_1 = \dfrac{2}{5}$, $x_2 =$ unknown and $y_2 = 2$ into the equation $x_1 y_1 = x_2 y_2$.

$$\frac{(-30) \cdot \dfrac{2}{5}}{2} = \frac{x_2 \cdot 2}{2}$$

Divide both sides of the equation $(-30) \cdot \dfrac{2}{5} = x_2 \cdot 2$ by 2 in order to obtain the value of x_2.

$$\frac{\overset{-6}{\cancel{(-30)}}}{\underset{1}{\cancel{2}}} \cdot \frac{\overset{1}{\cancel{2}}}{\underset{1}{5}} = \frac{x_2 \cdot \cancel{2}}{\underset{1}{\cancel{2}}}$$

Rewrite the left side of the equation and then divide as shown.

$$-3 \cdot 2 = x_2$$
$$-6 = x_2$$

Therefore, when $y = 2$, $x = -6$.

Exercises

1. Explain what is meant by inverse variation. Hint: See the preceding explanations.

2. What is the difference between direct variation and inverse variation?
   Hint: See the preceding explanations.

3. In each table, tell whether x varies inversely as y. Write the equation of the
   relationship. Hint: See Example 1.

a.
x	y
1	36
2	18
4	9
6	6

b.
x	y
1	12
2	6
3	4
4	3

c.
x	y
2	12
3	8
4	6

d.
x	8	10	20	40	80
y	5	4	2	1	0.5

4. The table shows the cleaning time of a school based on the number of workers.
   a. Tell whether the relationship is an inverse variation.
   b. Write the equation of the relationship. Hint: See Example 1.

Time (hr)	6	3	10	5	10
Number of workers	5	10	3	6	3

5. In each table, tell whether x varies inversely as y. Hint: See Example 2.

a.
x	y
1	8
2	10
3	4
4	6

b.
x	y
1	4
2	10
3	8
4	9

c.
x	y
2	22
3	34
5	40
7	14

6. The table shows the distance covered by a student in a given time. Tell whether
   the relationship is an inverse variation. Hint: See Example 2.

Distance (mi)	1	2	3	4	5	6
Time (min)	12	25	30	38	42	56

7. Find each constant of each inverse variation equation, given that x and y vary
   inversely. Hint: See Example 3.
   a. $y = 10$ when $x = 2$ **b.** $y = 3$ when $x = 4$ **c.** $y = 12$ when $x = 5$
   d. $y = 11$ when $x = 8$ **e.** $y = 7$ when $x = 3$ **f.** $y = 2$ when $x = 3$
   g. $y = 16$ when $x = 3$ **h.** $y = 6$ when $x = 11$

8. Graph each inverse variation function. What are the special features of the graph?
   Explain why the graph did not cross neither the x-axis nor the y-axis.
   Hint: See Example 4.

   a. $f(x) = \dfrac{1}{2x}$ **b.** $f(x) = \dfrac{1}{3x}$ **c.** $f(x) = \dfrac{2}{x}$

9. Graph each inverse variation function.
   What are the special features of the graph?
   What value of x makes the function or the graph undefined?

Explain why the graph did not cross neither the x-axis nor the y-axis.
Hint: See Example 5.

    a. $f(x) = -\dfrac{1}{x}$ **b.** $f(x) = -\dfrac{2}{x}$ **c.** $f(x) = -\dfrac{1}{2x}$

10. If y is 4 when x is 12 and y varies inversely as x, explain how to find y when x is 3. Find y when x is 3. Hint: See Example 6.

11. Given that y varies inversely as x;
    a. If y is 6 when x is 8, find y when x is 3.
    b. If y is 4 when x is 10, find y when x is 5.
    c. If y is 7 when x is 12, find y when x is 3.
    d. If y is 16 when x is 12, find x when y is 8.
    e. If y is 3 when x is 32, find x when y is 4.
    f. If y is 6 when x is 11, find y when x is 3.
    Hint: See Example 6.

12. Given that y varies inversely as x:
    a. If y is 6 when x is -11, find x when y is 2.

    b. If y is $\dfrac{3}{4}$ when x is -24, find y when x is 4.

    c. If y is 3 when x is -8, find x when y is -4.

    d. If y is $\dfrac{2}{5}$ when x is -40, find y when x is 4.

    e. If y is $\dfrac{5}{6}$ when x is 24, find y when x is 12.

    f. If y is $\dfrac{3}{4}$ when x is 24, find y when x is 27.

    Hint: See Example 7.

Challenge Questions

13. If y varies inversely as x, write an equation that shows y is related to x for each situation.
    a. y is 8 when x is 2.   **b.** y is 12 when x is 36.
    c. y is 3 when x is 9   **d.** y is 3 when x is 7.

14. Given that y varies inversely as x,
    a. If y is 7 when x is -12, find x when y is 35.
    b. If y is 15 when x is 4, find y when x is 3.

15. If y varies inversely with x and y = 27 when x = 9, find the constant of variation.

Answers to Selected Questions

7a. constant is 20 and $y = \dfrac{20}{x}$ **11a.** y = 16   **12a.** x = -33.

REAL WORLD APPLICATIONS OF VARIATIONS - WORD PROBLEMS

Example 1

The height of a triangle with an area 60 cm^2 varies inversely with the length of its base. If the base = 30 cm when the height = 4 cm, find the base when the height = 10 cm.

Solution

Let the length of the base = b and let the height = h. It is given in the question that the height of the triangle varies inversely with the length of the base. In the inverse variation, the product of the variables is a constant. Therefore, b · h = k where k is a constant. Since b · h = k for any set of b and h we can write:

$$b_1 h_1 = b_2 h_2$$ where b_1 = 30 cm, h_1 = 4 cm, b_2 = unknown length of the base, and h_2 = 10 cm.

$$30 \cdot 40 = b_2 \cdot 10 \underline{\hspace{3cm}}[A]$$

Substitute b_1 = 30 cm, h_1 = 4 cm, and h_2 = 10 cm into the equation $b_1 h_1 = b_2 h_2$.

Divide both sides of the equation [A] by 10 in order to obtain the value of b_2 as shown:

$$\frac{30 \cdot 4}{10} = \frac{b_2 \cdot 10}{10}$$

$$\frac{\overset{3}{\cancel{30}} \cdot 4}{\underset{1}{\cancel{10}}} = \frac{b_2 \cdot \overset{1}{\cancel{10}}}{\underset{1}{\cancel{10}}}$$

$$3 \cdot 4 = b_2$$
$$12 = b_2$$

Therefore, when the height is 10 cm the base is 12 cm.

Boyle's Law

Physics is a higher level science subject. In physics, Bolye's law shows that when the volume of a gas decreases, the pressure increases. The relationship between the volume and the pressure is an inverse variation, where the variables are volume and pressure. Since the product of the variables of an inverse relation is a constant, we can write:

VP = K where V = volume, P = pressure, and K = a constant.

Therefore, for any set of variables of volume and pressure, we can write:

$V_1 P_1 = V_2 P_2 = V_3 P_3 = V_4 P_4 =...$, and this is known as the Boyle's Law.

Example 2

Using Boyle's law, when the volume of a gas decreases the pressure increases.

a. Find the inverse variation function of the data in the table.

b. Use the inverse variation function to find the pressure of the gas if the volume is decreased to 4 liters.

Volume (L)	5	6	10	12	15
Pressure (atm)	12	10	6	5	4

Solution

a. Step 1: Find K.

In an inverse variation, the product of the variables is a constant.

Therefore, we can write:

$VP = K$ Where V = volume, P = pressure and K = a constant.

Therefore: $5 \cdot 12 = K$ Substitute a set of the data from the table, for example, V = 5 L and P = 12 atm into the equation $VP = K$.

$60 = K$

Step 2: Write the inverse variation function.

In general, the inverse function of two variables x and y is written as shown:

$$y = \frac{K}{x} \text{ and } f(x) = \frac{K}{x} \text{ where } f(x) \text{ is the function form of } y.$$

Similarly:

$$f(V) = \frac{K}{V} \qquad \text{where f(v) is the function.}$$

$$f(V) = \frac{60}{V} \qquad \text{Substitute K = 60 into the equation } f(V) = \frac{K}{V}.$$

From step 1, K = 60.

Therefore, the inverse variation function of the data is $f(V) = \frac{60}{V}$.

b. The inverse variation function is:

$$f(V) = \frac{60}{V}$$

Therefore, if V = 4 L, then,

$$f(4) = \frac{60}{4} \qquad \text{Substitute V = 4 L into the equation } f(V) = \frac{60}{V}.$$

$$f(4) = \frac{\overset{15}{\cancel{60}}}{\underset{1}{\cancel{4}}}$$

$$f(4) = 15$$

Therefore, the pressure of the gas if the volume is decreased to 4 liters is 15 atm.

Exercises

1. The height of a triangle varies inversely with the length of its base. If the length of the base = 45 cm when the height is 5 cm, find the length of the base when the height is 9 cm. Hint: See Example 1.

2. When the volume of a gas decreases, the pressure increases.
   a. Find the inverse variation function of the data in the table.
   b. Use the inverse variation function to find the pressure of the gas when the volume is 2 liters.
   Hint: See Example 2.

Volume (L)	3	6	9	10
Pressure (atm)	30	15	10	9

3. The mass of an object varies inversely with its acceleration if a constant force of 60 N is applied to it. Using the table:
   a. Write an inverse variation function.
   b. What is the mass of an object if its acceleration is 20 m/s^2?
   Hint: See Example 2.

Mass (kg)	2	4	5	6	10
Acceleration (m/s^2)	30	15	12	10	6

Challenge Questions

4. The table shows the number of weeks needed to clean a hospital based on the size of the work crew.

Work crew size	2	3	4	10
Weeks of cleaning	45	30	22.5	9

   a. Write an inverse variation function
   b. What is the size of the work crew needed to clean the hospital in 8 weeks?

INTEGERS

Cumulative Review

1. 44 + 17 =	**2.** 33 - 4 =	**3.** 54 + 8 =	**4.** 16 - 7 =
5. 23 - 17 =	**6.** 12 ÷ 4 =	**7.** 18 × 2 =	**8.** 15 ÷ 3 =

9. 12
　　× 3

10. 9
　　× 3

11. 72 ÷ 3 =

12. 7 + 8 =

13. 15 + 8 =

14. 18 ÷ 3 =

15. 16 - 8 =

16. 9 × 2 =

17. 35 ÷ 5 =

18. 21 - 15 =

19. 30 ÷ 6 =

20. 17 - 8 =

21. 25
　　× 3

22. 18
　　+ 19

23. 37
　　- 13

24. 17
　　× 4

25. 42 ÷ 3 =

26. 24 ÷ 8 =

27. 12 + 38 =

28. 44 - 18 =

New Terms: **integer, negative integer, positive integer, opposites, and absolute**
　　　　　　values.

An **integer** is any negative or positive whole number or zero. We can show integers
on the number line as shown:

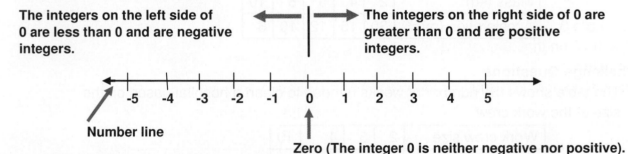

**The integers on the left side of
0 are less than 0 and are negative
integers.**

**The integers on the right side of 0 are
greater than 0 and are positive
integers.**

-5　-4　-3　-2　-1　0　1　2　3　4　5

Number line

Zero (The integer 0 is neither negative nor positive).

Negative integers are always written with a – sign, however, positive integers can
be written with or without a + sign. Positive and negative integers can be used to
represent actual life situations as shown:
a. The temperature 40 degrees below zero can be written as –40⁰F.
b. The temperature 52 degrees above zero can be written as +52⁰F or 52⁰F.

Example 1
a. Express twenty feet below sea level using integers.
b. Express thirty feet above sea level using integers.
Solution
Hint: The sea level is at 0 ft. such that any measurement above the sea level is a
positive number and any measurement below the sea level is a negative number.
a. Twenty feet below sea level can be written as –20 ft.
b. Thirty feet above sea level can be written as +30 ft or 30 ft.

Team Project

The class should be divided into four teams and each team should write about two situations that negative or positive integers could be used such as scoring a football game by losing 10 yards or gaining 12 yards. Each team should report to the class about their real life situations with integers.

Graph Integers

Integers can be graphed on a number line by drawing a dot.

Example 2

Graph –4 on the number line.

Solution

Draw a number line and then draw a dot at the position of –4.

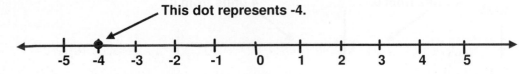

This dot represents -4.

Example 3

Graph +3 on the number line.

Solution

Draw a number line and then draw a dot at the position of +3.

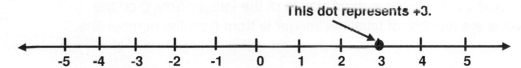

This dot represents +3.

Opposite Integers

The opposite of saving $4.00 in the bank is withdrawing $4.00 from the bank. In both cases, the same amount of $4.00 is involved. Every integer has an opposite and **opposite integers** are at the same distances from 0 on a number line, but in opposite directions.

Example 4

Write the opposite of +3.

Solution

The opposite integers are at the same distance from 0 on a number line, but in the opposite direction as shown:

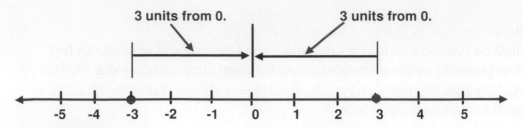

The opposite of +3 is –3.

Example 5

Write the opposite of –4.

Solution

The opposite integers are at the same distance from 0 on a number line, but in the opposite direction.

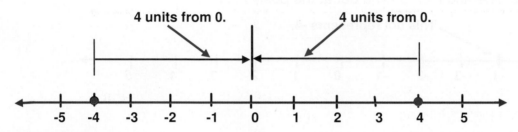

The opposite of –4 is +4 or 4.

Absolute Value

The **absolute value** of an integer is the distance of the integer from 0 on the number line or it is the number of units the integer is from 0 on the number line.

Example 6

Find the absolute value of –4. Find the absolute value of +4.

Solution

The absolute value of an integer is the distance of the integer from 0 on the number line or the number of units the integer is from 0 on the number line. The absolute value of –4 is at a distance of 4 units from, 0 and therefore, the absolute value of –4 is +4 or 4.

The absolute value of +4 which is the same as 4 is at a distance of 4 units from 0, and therefore, the absolute value of +4 is 4.

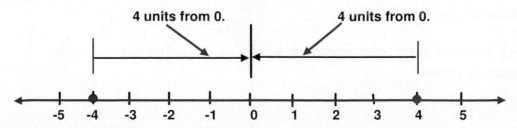

390

Example 7

Find the absolute value of +3. Find the absolute value of -3.

Solution

The absolute value of an integer is the distance of the integer from 0 on the number line or it is the number of units the integer is from 0. The absolute value of +3 which is the same as 3 is at a distance of 3 units from 0 on the number line, and therefore, the absolute value of +3 is 3.

The absolute value of -3 is at a distance of 3 units from 0 on the number line, and therefore, the absolute value of -3 is 3.

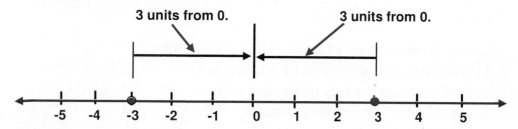

Conclusion

The absolute value of any number **is the same number without any sign in front of the number** as follows:

a. The absolute value of –4 is 4.

b. The absolute value of +4 is 4.

c. The absolute value of –3 is 3.

d. The absolute value of +3 is 3.

| | is the symbol for the absolute value.

|–6| means the absolute value of –6 which is 6.

|–2| means the absolute value of –2 which is 2.

We can conclude that the absolute value of any number is the same number without any sign in front of the number.

Example 8

Find |–5|

Solution

The absolute value of any number is the value of the same number without any sign in front of the number. Therefore, |–5| = 5.

Example 9

Find |–10| + |–8| + |+2|

Solution

The absolute value of any number is the value of the same number without any sign in front of the number. Therefore, |–10| + |– 8| + |+2|

$$= 10 + 8 + 2 \qquad (|–10| = 10, \ |–8| = 8, \ |+2| = 2$$
$$= 20$$

Example 10

Evaluate: $|+2| - |-9| + 4 + |+2| - |-1|$

Solution

The absolute value of any number is the same number without any sign in front of number. Therefore,

$$|+2| - |-9| + 4 + |+2| - |-1|$$
$$= 2 - 9 + 4 + 2 - 1 \qquad (|+2| = 2, |-9| = 9, |+2| = 2, |-1| = 1$$
$$= -2 \qquad\qquad (2 - 9 = -7, -7 + 4 = -3, -3 + 2 = -1, -1 -1 = -2)$$

Exercises

1. Express the following statements as integers. Hint: See Example 1.

   a. The school football team gained 5 yards for a first down.

   b. The school football team lost 4 yards on the last play.

   c. John withdrew $10.00 from his checking account.

   d. Mary deposited $20.00 in her checking account.

2. Graph the following on a number line. Hint: See Examples 2 and 3.

   a. −2   **b.** +5   **c.** −6   **d.** +1   **e.** −1

3. Identify the integers graphed. Hint: See Examples 1, 2, and 3.

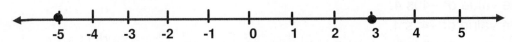

4. Write an integer to represent each situation. Hint: See Example 1.

   a. 90 degrees above 0.   **b.** a lost of 8 yards.

   c. a deposit of $50.00.   **d.** a withdrawal of $100. 00.

5. Graph the opposite of each integer on a number line. Hint: See Examples 4 and 5.

   a. −1   **b.** +2   **c.** −6   **d.** +5   **e.** −5

6. Write the opposite of each integer. Hint: See Examples 4 and 5. Do not indicate your answer on the number line.

   a. −0   **b.** +12   **c.** −20   **d.** +15

   e. −200   **f.** +400   **g.** −1,340   **h.** +5,000

7. Write an integer to represent each situation. Hint: See Example 1.

   a. a gain of 2 pounds.   **b.** 10 feet below sea level.

   c. 10 feet underground.   **d.** 10 feet below ground.

   e. a growth of 7 inches.   **f.** 6 points ahead.

8. What is the absolute value of a number?

9. Graph the absolute values of the following numbers on a number line. Hint: See Examples 6 and 7.

   a. −1   **b.** −7   **c.** +5   **d.** +6   **e.** −3   **f.** +8

10. Write each absolute value. Hint: See Example 8.

   a. $|-11|$ **b.** $|-24|$ **c.** $|+200|$ **d.** $|-64|$ **e.** $|-1|$

   f. $|0|$ **g.** $|+36|$ **h.** $|-36|$ **i.** $|-89|$ **j.** $|20|$

11. Evaluate the following. Hint: See Example 9.

    a. $|-2| + |-10| =$ **b.** $|+4| + |-1| =$ **c.** $|+12| - |+2| =$

    d. $|-3| + |+4| - |-1| =$ **e.** $|20| - |-4| + |-2| - |5| =$

    f. $|-44| - |+6| - |+18| =$ **g.** $|+2| - |-3| + |-10| - |4| =$

12. Evaluate the following. Hint: See Example 10.

    a. $|-26| + |-1| + |-16| =$ **b.** $|+30| - |-15| - |+15| =$

    c. $|-18| - |-11| + |+6| - |+2| =$ **d.** $|-64| - |+64| =$

Challenge Questions

13. Evaluate the following.

    a. $|-100| - |-100| =$ **b.** $|+58| - |+48| =$ **c.** $16 + |-16| =$

14. Graph the opposite of 10.

15. Graph –7, –8, 0, 2, and 6 on the same number line.

16. Write an integer to describe each situation.

    a. a helicopter rises 100 feet.

    b. a submarine is 20 feet below the surface of the water.

Answers to Selected Questions

10a. 11   **11a.** 12   **12a.** 43   **16a.** +100ft or 100ft

Compare and Order Integers

A time line can be used to show the events of the day. For example, a student's daily time line may include the following:

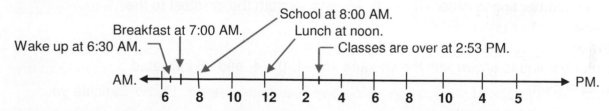

On the above number line, the student wakes up at 6:30 A.M. before having breakfast at 7:00 A.M., Similarly, you can use number lines to compare and order numbers. The numbers to the right on a number line are always greater than the numbers to the left. Alternatively, the numbers to the left on a number line are always less than the numbers to the right. Notice that on the number line that follows, –4 is to the left of 0, therefore, –4 is less than 0, and also, 0 is greater than –4 since 0 is to the right of –4 on the number line.

Team Exercise

The class should be divided in to teams and each team should make a typical

Monday time line for a student within the team starting from the time the student wakes up to the time that the student goes to bed. The time line should include dinner time, play time, and homework time. Each team should report their time line to the whole class.

1. From your time line, could you say that a time line can help you to order events?
2. Each team should make a time line for a typical Thanksgiving Day, and then report the time line to the whole class.

Example 1
Use the number line to order –4, +3, –5, +4, and –2 from the least to the greatest.
Solution
The number line is drawn with the integers –4, +3, –5, +4, and –2 indicated on it as follows:

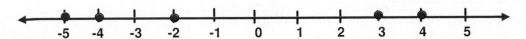

The number to the left on the number line is always less than the number to the right, and therefore, using the number line, the order of the numbers from the least to the greatest is:

$$-5, -4, -2, 3, \text{ and } 4.$$

Example 2
Use the number line to order +5, –1, 0, –4, and +3 from the greatest to the smallest.
Solution
The number line is drawn with the integers +5, –1, 0, –4, and +3 indicated on it as shown:

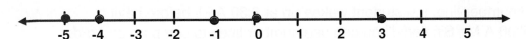

The number to the right on the number line are always greater than the numbers on the left, and therefore, using the number line, the order of the numbers from the greatest to the least is:

$$+3, 0, -1, -4, \text{ and } -5.$$

Using "greater than" and "less than" symbols
The symbol > means greater than.
The symbol < means less than.

Example 3
Using the number line, replace ? with <, >, or =.

a. −3 ? −1   **b.** 0 ? −3   **c.** +1 ? −1
Solution
a. Graph -3 and −1 on a number line.

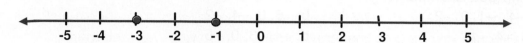

          −3 is to the left of −1 on the number line, so −3 < −1
b. Graph 0 and −3 on a number line.

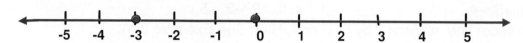

          0 is to the right of −3 on the number line, so 0 > −3.
c. Graph +1 and −1 on a number line.

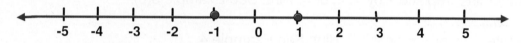

          +1 is to the right of −1, so +1 > −1.

Example 4

Compare. Write < , >, or = for each ?
a. |−3| ? +3   **b.** |−4| ? −5   **c.** |−2| ? + 4
Solution

$|-3| = 3$ Review absolute numbers.
  Therefore, |−3| ? +3
          = 3 ? +3
       3 = 3   The two values are equal.
b. $|-4| = 4$ Review absolute numbers.
  Therefore, |−4| ? −5
      = 4 ? −5
Graph 4 and −5 on a number line.

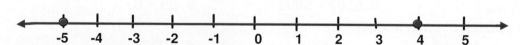

    4 is on the right side of −5 on the number line, so 4 > −5
c. $|-2| = 2$ Review absolute numbers.
  Therefore, |−2| ? +4
      = 2 ? +4
Graph 2 and +4 on the number line.

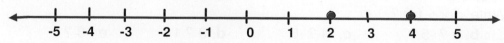

    2 is to the left of +4 on the number line, so 2 < +4.

Exercises

1. Use the number line to order the following numbers from the least to the greatest. Hint: See Example 1.
   a. −3, +5, −4, −1, 0, +2
   b. +6, 0, −4, −2,
   c. −1, 0, −6, +4, +1,
   d. +4, −3, 0, +5

2. Use the number line to order the following number from the greatest to the least. Hint: See Example 2.
   a. −6, 0, +4, −2
   b. +5, −1, 0, +2
   c. −1, +1, 0, +5, −4
   d. 0, +2, −2, +5

3. Using the number line, replace ? by >, <, or =. Hint: See Example 3(a).
   −5 ? −4

4. Using a number line, replace ? by >, <, or =. Hint: See Example 3(b).
   0 ? −1

5. Using a number line, replace ? by >, <, or =. Hint: See Example 3(c).
   + 4 ? − 3

6. Compare. Write >, <, or = for each ?. Hint: See Example 4.
   a. |−5| ? +4
   b. |−1| ? −6
   c. |+2| ? −4

Challenge Questions

Compare. Write >, <, or = for each?
7. a. |−3| ? |+3|
   b. |−2| ? −2
   c. 0 ? −1
8. Which number has the least value: 0, −4, +8, −1, or −10?
9. Which number has the greatest value: −14, −2, +9, +100, or −200?
10. What is the absolute value of −1000?

Mixed Review

1. 20% of $100.00 =

2. $\frac{2}{3}$ of 18 =

3. $\frac{1}{6} \times \frac{18}{25}$ =

4. The inverse of $\frac{3}{4}$ =

5. The opposite of −6 =

6. Absolute of -7 =

7. $2 + 4 \div 2 − 1 =$

8. $6901 − 5999 =$

9. $25 \times 6 =$

10. Write the opposite of each integer.
    a. -99
    b. +12
    c. -1
    d. +32

11. Graph each integer and its opposite on a number line.
    a. -4
    b. +5
    c. -6
    d. +6

12. Name a positive or a negative number to represent each situation.
    a. 13 feet above sea level
    b. Earning $10
    c. 15^0 below 0
    d. A decrease of 5 points

13. Compare. Write < or > for ?.
    a. -8 ? 8
    b. 0 ? -5
    c. -4 ? -6
    d. 9 ? 14
    e. -8 ? 1

14. Order the integers in each set from least to greatest.

396

a. 4, -1, 0, -4   **b.** -5, 8, -2, 3   **c.** -4, 7, -11, 0   **d.** 23, -33, 55, -2

ADDITION OF INTEGERS

I can solve the problems too if only
I understand the concepts.

New Term
Zero pair

Playing a Board Game - Group Exercises

Example 1
John and Mary decide to play a board game.
- John starts at 0 and rolls a 4.
- The fourth square tells him to roll again. His token lands on a square that tells him to move back 4 spaces.

How many spaces from the start is John's token?

Solution
Use red counters to represent negative integers and blue counters to represent positive integers.

Let (-) represent red counters, which then represent negative integers.
Let (+) represent blue counters, which then represent positive integers.

Step 1: Use 4 positive (blue) counters to represent John's first roll which can be represented as +4. Place all of the counters on a table.

(+) (+) (+) (+)

Step 2: Use 4 negative (red) counters to represent John's 4 spaces backwards. Place the 4 negative (red) counters on the table with the 4 positives (blue) counters from step 1.

(+) (+) (+) (+)
(-) (-) (-) (-)   = +4 + (-4)

Step 3: Make as many pairs of one positive and one negative counters. The sum of each pair is zero, and so remove each **zero pair** since it does not change the value on the table.

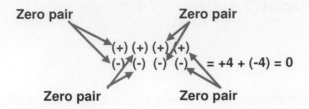

Zero pair   Zero pair

$$(+)\ (+)\ (+)\ (+)$$
$$(-)\ (-)\ (-)\ (-) = +4 + (-4) = 0$$

Zero pair   Zero pair

There are no counters left on the table. John's token is 0 spaces from the start which means that John is back to the starting point.

Let us establish an integer addition rule for adding a negative integer to a positive integer. From Example 1, note that +4 + (-4) = 0 is possible if + (- **becomes** - such that +4 + (-4) can be written as +4 - 4 = 0. It is important to note that + (- **becomes** -. We can use absolute values to establish an integer addition rule for adding a negative integer to a positive integer as follows:

> **Adding a negative integer to a positive integer** (or adding a positive integer to a negative integer), **subtract the smaller absolute value from the larger, and then use the sign of the number with larger absolute value as the sign of the sum. If the two integers are equal, their sum is zero.**

The absolute value of a number is the number itself when the number is positive or zero, and the absolute value of a number is the opposite of the number when the number is negative. (Review the chapter/section on Absolute Values.)

Example 1 can be written as: +4 + (-4) = 0. The absolute of +4 is 4 and the absolute of -4 is 4 (the opposite of -4 is 4), so that 4 - 4 = 0.

Hint: See how Example 1 is solved using a shortcut method in Example 6.

Zero pairs means equal numbers of positive and negative integers such that the addition of each pair is zero.

Example 2

Use counters to find -5 + (-2)

Solution

Use red counters to represent negative integers.

Let (-) represent red counters, which then represent negative integers.

Step 1: Place 5 negative counters on the table to represent -5.
Place 2 more negative counters on the same table to represent adding -2.

(-) (-) (-) (-) (-)
(-) (-)

Step 2: There are no positive counters and therefore we cannot remove any zero pairs. Count the total number of counters on the table.

Step 3: There are a total of 7 negative counters on the table and this represents -7.
Therefore, -5 + (-2) = -7.

Let us establish an integer addition rule for adding two negative integers. From

Example 2, note that -5 + (-2) = -7 is possible if + (- **becomes** - such that -5 + (-2) can be written as -5 - 2 = -7. We can use absolute values to establish an integer addition rule for adding a negative integer to a positive integer as follows:

Adding two negative numbers, add the absolute values of the numbers, and then attach a negative sign to their sum.

The absolute value of a number is the number itself when the number is positive or zero, and the absolute value of a number is the opposite of the number when the number is negative. (Review the chapter/section on Absolute Values.)

Example 2 can be written as: -5 + (-2) =. The absolute of -5 is 5 (the opposite of -5 is 5), and the absolute of -2 is 2 (the opposite of -2 is 2), so that 5 + 2 = 7. Using the rule, attach a negative sign to this sum, so that the sum becomes -7. Therefore, -5 + (-2) = -7.

Hint: See how Example 2 is solved using a shortcut method in Example 7.

Example 3

Use counters to find -3 + (+4)

Solution

Use red counters to represent negative integers and blue counters to represent positive integers.

Let (+) represent blue counters, which then represent positive integers.
Let (-) represent red counters, which then represent negative integers.

Step 1: Place 3 negative counters on a table
Place 4 positive counters on the same table representing adding +4.

(-) (-) (-)
(+) (+) (+) (+)

Step 2: Make as many pairs of the positive and negative counters. The sum of each pair is zero and so remove each zero pair since it does not change the value on the table.

Zero pair   **Zero pair**

(-) (-) (-)
(+)(+)(+)(+)   = -3 + (+4) = +1 = 1

Zero pair

Count the total number of counters left on the table.

Step 3: There is 1 positive counter left on the table. Therefore, -3 + (+4) = +1 = 1.

Let us establish an integer addition rule for adding a negative integer to a positive integer. From Example 3, note that -3 + (+4) = +1 is possible if + (+ **becomes** + such that -3 + (+4) = +1 can be written as -3 + 4 = +1 = 1. In mathematics, positive signs are not generally attached to a number to indicate that the number is positive, so +1 is written as 1. We can use absolute values to establish an integer addition rule for adding a positive integer to a negative integer as shown:

Adding a positive integer to a negative integer (or adding a negative integer to a positive integer), subtract the smaller absolute value from the larger, and then use the sign of the number with larger absolute value as the sign of the sum. If the two integers are equal, their sum is zero.

The absolute value of a number is the number itself when the number is positive or zero, and the absolute value of a number is the opposite of the number when the number is negative. (Review the chapter/section on Absolute Values.)

Example 3 can be written as: -3 + (+4) =. The absolute of -3 is 3 (the opposite of -3 is 3) and the absolute of +4 is 4 (the absolute value of a number is the number itself when the number is positive), so that 4 - 3 = 1. Using the rule, use the sign of the number with larger absolute value as the sign of the sum, and in this case, the larger absolute number is 4, and the sign of 4 is positive. In general, we do not attach a positive sign to an answer, so that 4 - 3 = +1 = 1.

Hint: See how Example 3 is solved using a shortcut method in Example 8.

Example 4

Use counters to find +1 + (+4)

Solution

Use blue counters to represent positive integers.

Let (+) represent blue counters, which then represent positive integers.

Step 1: Place 1 positive counter on the table to represent +1
Place 4 positive counters on the table to represent +4

(+)
(+) (+) (+) (+)

Step 2: Since there are no negative counters, we cannot remove any zero pair number.

Step 3: Count the total number of counters on the table, which is +5.
Therefore, +1 + (+4) = +5

Let us establish an integer addition rule for adding two positive integers.

From Example 4, note that +1 + (+4) = +5 is possible if + (+ **becomes** + such that +1 + (+4) = +5 can be written as +1 + 4 = 5.

From Example 4, note that +1 + (+4) = +5 means that **to add any two positive integers, add the two integers and attach the positive sign after the addition, which is called the sum**. In this particular case, add 1 to 4 which is 5, and then attach a positive sign to the 5 which is +5. In mathematics, positive signs are not generally attached to a number to indicate that the number is positive, so +5 is written as 5. The rule for adding two positive integers is as follows:

To add any two positive integers, add the two integers and attach the

positive sign after the addition, which is called the sum.
Hint: See how Example 4 is solved using a shortcut method in Example 9.

Example 5
Find -6 + (+4)
Solution
Use red counters to represent negative integers and blue counters to represent positive integers.

Let (+) represent blue counters, which then represent positive integers.
Let (-) represent red counters, which then represent negative integers.

Step 1: Place 6 negative counters on the table to represent -6.
Place 4 positive counters on the table to represent +4.

(-) (-) (-) (-) (-) (-)
(+) (+) (+) (+)

Step 2: Make as many pairs of one positive and one negative counters. The sum of each pair is zero, and so remove each zero pair since it does not change the value on the table.

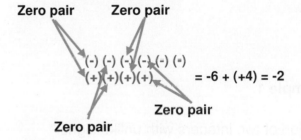

Count the total number of counters left on the table. There are a total of 2 negative counters left on the table, therefore: -6 + (+4) = -2
Let us establish a rule for integer addition of positive and negative integers.
From Example 5, note that -6 + (+4) = -2 is possible if + (+ **becomes** + such that
-6 + (+4) = -2 can be written as -6 + 4 = -2.
Notice how the negative sign is attached to the final answer because 6 (not -6) is larger than 4, and 6 has the negative sign. Notice also that, if the question were to be -3 + 4 = , the solution is -3 + 4 = +1 = 1. In this case, there is no negative sign attached to 1 because 3 is less then 4, and although 3 has a negative sign. Notice that the absolute value of -6 is 6 (-6 is the opposite of 6), and the absolute value of +4 is 4, so that 6 - 4 = 2. In Example 5, the larger absolute value is 6 and the smaller absolute value is 4, so that 6 - 4 = 2, and the sign of the larger absolute number is -, so that -6 + 4 = -2. We can use absolute values to establish an integer addition rule for adding a positive integer to a negative integer as shown:

Adding a positive integer to a negative integer (or adding a negative integer to a positive integer), subtract the smaller absolute value from the larger,

and then use the sign of the number with larger absolute value as the sign of the sum. **If the two integers are equal, their sum is zero**.

Hint: See how Example 5 is solved using a shortcut method in Example 10.

Summary of the Steps or Rules for Adding Integers

1. Addition of two integers with like signs

   a. Find the absolute values of the integers.

   b. Find the sum of the absolute values.

   c. Attach the sign common to both integers to the answer.

2. Addition of two integers with unlike signs.

   a. Find the absolute values of the integers.

   b. Find the difference of the absolute values.

   c. Attach the sign of the integer with the greater absolute value to the answer.

     If the absolute values of both integers are the same, then their sum is zero.

Let us Use the information Under the Section "Summary of the Steps or Rules for Adding Integers" to Solve Examples 1 to 5.

Example 6

Find the sum.

+4 + (-4)   **This is the same as Example 1.**

Solution

Find the absolute values of +4 and -4. See "Addition of two integers with unlike signs."

      $|+4| = 4$

      $|-4| = 4$

Find the **difference** of the absolute values. Hint: Find the **difference** of the absolute values of the integers with **unlike signs**

     $4 - 4 = 0$ Since the two integers have unlike signs, and their absolute values are the same, their sum is zero. Hint: "See Addition of Two Integers With Unlike Signs."

Example 7

Find the sum.

-5 + (-2)   **This is the same as Example 2.**

Solution

Find the absolute values of -5 and -2. See "Addition of Two Integers With Like Signs."

      $|-5| = 5$

      $|-2| = 2$

Find the **sum** of the absolute values. Hint: Find the **sum** of the absolute values of the integers with **like signs**. See "Addition of Two Integers With Like Signs."

$$5 + 2 = 7$$

Attach the sign common to both integers to the answer. So,

$$-5 + (-2) = -7$$ **Note**: The - sign is common to both 5 and 2.

Hint: See the information under the section "Addition of Two Integers With Like Signs."

Example 8

Find the sum.

$-3 + (+4)$ **This is the same as Example 3**.

Solution

Find the absolute values of -3 and +4. See "Addition of two integers with unlike signs."

$$|-3| = 3$$
$$|+4| = 4$$

Find the **difference** of the absolute values. Hint: Find the **difference** of the absolute values of the integers with **unlike signs**. **Subtract the smaller absolute integer from the larger absolute integer**.

$$4 - 3 = 1$$

Attach the sign of the integer with the greater absolute value to the answer. So,

$$-3 + (+4) = +1 = 1$$ **Note**: +1 is the same as 1.

Hint: "See Addition of Two Integers With Unlike Signs."

Example 9

Find the sum.

$+1 + (+4)$ **This is the same as Example 4**.

Solution

Find the absolute values of +1 and +4. See "Addition of Two Integers With Like Signs."

$$|+1| = 1$$
$$|+4| = 4$$

Find the **sum** of the absolute values. Hint: Find the **sum** of the absolute values of the integers with **like signs**. See "Addition of Two Integers With Like Signs."

$$1 + 4 = 5$$

Attach the sign common to both integers to the answer. So,

$$+1 + (+4) = +5 = 5$$ Note: The + sign is common to both 1 and 4.

Hint: See the information under the section "Addition of Two Integers With Like Signs."

Example 10

Find the sum.

$-6 + (+4)$ **This is the same as Example 5**.

Solution

Find the absolute values of -6 and +4. See "Addition of two integers with unlike signs."

$$|-6| = 6$$
$$|+4| = 4$$

Find the **difference** of the absolute values. Hint: Find the **difference** of the absolute values of the integers with **unlike signs**. **Subtract the smaller absolute integer from the larger absolute integer**.

$$6 - 4 = 2$$

Attach the sign of the integer with the larger absolute value to the answer. So,

$$-6 + (+4) = -2$$ Notice that the integer with the larger absolute value is 6. The 6 has a - sign, so attach a - sign to the answer. Hint: "See Addition of Two Integers With Unlike Signs."

The notes and the generous worked examples have provided me with conceptual understanding and computational fluency to do my homework.

Exercises

1. Explain what is meant by zero pairs.

2. Group Exercise:

Mary and John decided to play a board game. Mary started at 0 and rolled 5. The fifth square tells her to roll again. Her token lands on a square that tells her to move back 3 spaces. How many spaces back is Mary's token? Hint: See Examples 1 and 6. You may use the integer addition rule for Examples 1 and 6.

3. Group exercise:

Use counters to find the following: Hint: See Examples 2.

    a. -3 + (-2) =   **b**. -7 + (-2) =   **c**. -1 + (-1) =

    d. -10 + (-7) =   **e**. -5 + (-4) =   **f**. -6 + (-4) =

    g. -3 + (-5) =   **h**. -5 + (-4) =   **i**. -7 + (-7) =

4. Solve Exercise 3 without using counters. Use the rule for adding integers. Hint: See the rule for Examples 2 and 7. Note that + (- is -.

5. Use counters to find the following: Hint: See Example 3.

    a.-4 + (+8) =   **b**. -7 + (+2) =   **c**. -1 + (+1) =

    d.-2 + (+6) =   **e**. -9 + (+1) =   **f**. -6 + (+4) =

    g.-4 + (+8) =   **h**. -5 + (+6) =   **j**. -7 + (+7) =

6. Solve Exercise 5 without using counters. Use the rule for adding integers. Hint: See Examples 3 and 8. Note that + (+ is +.

7. Use counters to find the following: Hint: See Example 4.

    a. +2 + (+6) =   **b**. +1 + (+9) =   **c**. +7 + (+3) =

    d. +4 + (+7) =   **e**. +8 + (+4) =   **f**. +3 + (+11) =

    g. +6 + (+5) =   **h**. +5 + (+8) =   **j**. +3 + (+7) =

8. Solve Exercise 7 without using counters. Use the rule for adding integers in Examples 4 and 9.

    Hint: See Example 4.

9. Use counters to solve the following. Hint: See Example 5.

    a. -5 + (+4) =   **b.** -6 + (+2) =   **c.** -6 + (+1) =   **d.** -8 + (+4) =

    e. -7 + (+5) =   **f.** -5 + (+2) =   **g.** -4 + (+3) =   **h.** -2 + (+1) =

10. Solve Exercise 9 without using counters. Use the rule for adding integers in Examples 5 and 10. Hint: See Example 5.

Challenge Questions

11 Solve the following problems.

    a. +6 + (-4) =   **b.** -3 + (-5) =   **c.** -4 + (+) 2 =   **d.** -6 + 0 =

    e. -7 + (-7) =   **f.** +4 + (-6) =   **g.** +7 + (+) 3 =   **h.** +2 - 6 =

12 Compare and write <, >, or = for ? Hint: Use Examples 1 to 5 to simplify first before comparing. To solve **a**, simplify +2 + (-4) as -2 first, and then compare -2 to -3. Since -2 is greater than -3, the correct answer to **a** is +2 + (-4) > -3.

    a. +2 + (-4) ? -3   **b.** -2 + (+8) ? +5   **c.** +4 + (-5) ? +2

    d. +4 + (-3) ? +2   **e.** -4 + (-7) ? +2   **f.** -3 + (-7) ? +3

Answers to Selected Questions

3a. -5	**3b.** -7	**5a.** 4	**5b.** -5
7a. 8	**7b.** 10	**9a.** -1	**9b.** 4

Why Do We Need to Know How to Use the Rules For Addition of Integers?
It is useful to know and use the rules for integer addition especially when the integers are large instead of using counters. For example, it will be difficult to use counters to add integers involving 300 and -450.
It is possible to use the rules for integer addition or a number line to add integers when the integers are large, as shown in the following examples.

Example 13

Using the rule for adding integers, find +261 + (-200)

Solution

+ (- becomes -, and so that, +261 + (-200) = +261 - 200 = +61 = 61. Notice that +261 - 200 = +61 = 61, when the rule for integer addition for adding a negative integer to a positive integer is used as in Example 3. Recall that absolute values are used in the rule.

Example 14

Using the rule for adding integers, find -261 + (-300).

Solution

From the solution of Example 2, +(- becomes -, therefore,
-261 + (-300) = -261 - 300 = -561. Notice that -261 - 300 = -561, when the rule
for adding a negative integer to another negative integer is used as in Example 2.
Recall that absolute values are used in the rule.

Example 15

Use the number line to find the sum of 300 + (-450).

Solution

Step 1: Draw a number line, and start at 0 and go 300 units in the positive direction
(right) as shown.

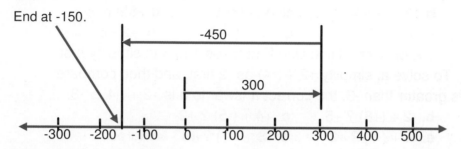

Step 2: From point 300 go 450 in the negative direction (left) as shown.
You end at -150, making, 300 + (-450) = -150.

The notes and the generous worked examples
have provided me with conceptual understanding
and computational fluency to do my homework.

Exercise

1. Use the rule to find the following sums. Hint: See Example 13.

    a. +340 + (-329) =   **b**. -450 + (+200) =   **c**. -701 + (+204) =

    d. +528 + (-224) =   **e**. -178 + (+464) =   **f**. +379 + (-580) =

2. Use the rule to find the following sums. Hint: See Example 14.

    a. -492 + (-321) =   **b**. -209 + (-164) =   **c**. -342 + (-201) =

    d. -239 + (-101) =   **e**. -341 + (-244) =   **f**. -464 + (-100) =

3 Use a number line to find the sum of the following numbers.
Hint: See Example 15.

    a. 250 + (-200) =   **b**. 100 + (-400) =   **c**. 381 + (-250) =

    d. 98 + (-164) =   **e**. 88 + (-238) =   **f**. 238 + (-108) =

Challenge Questions

4. Find the sum of the following numbers.

    a. 340 + (-264) =   **b**. -277 + (-341)   **c**. +516 + (-201) =

    d. -168 + (-295) =   **e**. 255 + (-179) =   **f**. +209 + (-304) =

Answers to Selected Questions
1a. 11   **2a**. 750   **3a**. 50

SUBTRACTING INTEGERS

The subtraction problems can be solved by using counters as shown in example 1.

Example 1

Find 5 - 2

Solution

Step 1: Place 5 positive counters on a mat.

⊕ ⊕ ⊕ ⊕ ⊕

Step 2: Since subtraction is the opposite of addition, remove 2 of the positive counters from the mat to represent subtracting 2.

Remove 2 of the positive counters.

⁄⁄

⊕ ⊕ ⊕ ⊕ ⊕ = 5 - 2

Step 3: Count the positive counters remaining on the mat.

⊕ ⊕ ⊕   = 5 - 2 = 3

There are 3 positive counters left on the mat and meaning, 5 - 2 = 3.

Rule 1: **To subtract a smaller positive number from a bigger positive number, subtract the smaller number from the bigger number**.

Example 2

Find 2 - 6.

Solution

Step 1: Place 2 positive counters on a mat.

⊕ ⊕ = 2

Step 2: To subtract 6, we must remove 6 positive counters. But we cannot remove 6 positive counters because there are not 6 positive counters on the mat. We must add 6 zero pairs to the mat, and then we can remove 6 positive counters.

⊕ ⊕

⊖ ⊖ ⊖ ⊖ ⊖ ⊖   (6 negative and 6 positive counters form 6 zero pairs.)

⊕ ⊕ ⊕ ⊕ ⊕ ⊕   ← Remove these 6 positive counters.

Step 3: Pair the positive and negative counters. Remove all zero pairs.

$\oplus \oplus$

$\ominus \ominus \ominus \ominus \ominus \ominus$ = -4

Step 4: The number of the negative counters that remains on the mat is 4, therefore,
2 - 6 = -4

Rule 2: Considering Examples 1 and 2, **to subtract one positive number from another positive number, subtract the smaller absolute value of the numbers from the bigger absolute value, and then attach the sign of the bigger absolute value number**.

In Example 2, the bigger absolute value number is 6 and the smaller absolute value number is 2. Using the rule, 2 - 6 becomes 6 - 2 = 4, and then a negative sign is attached to the 4 because the sign of the bigger absolute value number is -. So we can write 2 - 6 = -4.

Example 3

Use counters to find -5 - 3

Solution

Step 1: Place 5 negative counters on the mat to represent -5.

$\ominus \ominus \ominus \ominus \ominus$ = -5

Step 2: To subtract 3 we must remove 3 positive counters, but we cannot remove 3 positive counters because there are none on the mat. Therefore, we must add 3 zero pairs to the mat. We can now remove 3 positive counters. Note that we cannot remove something that we do not have.

$\ominus \ominus \ominus \ominus \ominus = \ominus \ominus \ominus \ominus \ominus$

$\ominus \ominus \ominus$ $= \ominus \ominus \ominus$

$\oplus \oplus \oplus$ ← Remove these 3 positive counters.

Step 3: There are 8 negative counters remaining on the mat and this represents -8. Therefore, -5 - 3 = -8.

Rule 3: Considering the answer for Example 3, **to subtract a positive number 3 from a negative number -5, add the absolute values of the numbers together (5 + 3 = 8) and attach negative sign the sum**, for example -8. Note that it is sometimes necessary to add zero pairs in order to subtract. When zero pairs are added, the value of the integers on the mat does not change. Note also that the absolute value of -5 is 5 and the absolute value of 3 is 3.

Example 4 (Subtraction problems involving two negative integers).
Use counters to find -6 - (-2).

Solution

Step 1: Place 6 negative counters on the mat to represent -6.

$\ominus \ominus \ominus \ominus \ominus \ominus$ = -6

Step 2: Remove 2 negative counters from the mat to represent subtracting -2.

Remove these 2 negative counters.

⊖ ⊖ ⊖ ⊖ ⊖ ⊖ = ⊖ ⊖ ⊖ ⊖ = -4

Step 3: There are 4 negative counters left on the mat and this represents -4.

Therefore, -6 - (-2) = -4.

Notice that -6 - (-2) = -4 is possible only when - (- becomes +, so that
-6 - (-2) becomes -6 + 2 = -4

Rule 4: Considering Example 4, **to subtract one negative number from another,
subtract the smaller absolute value number (2) from the bigger absolute
value number (6) and attach the sign of the bigger absolute value
number (6) to the subtraction or difference (-4).**

Considering example 4, the absolute value of -6 is 6 and the absolute value
of -2 is 2.

The notes and the generous worked examples
have provided me with conceptual understanding
and computational fluency to do my homework.

Exercise

1. Find the difference. You may use counters.
Hint: See Example 1 or Rule 1.

a. 6 - 2   **b.** 5 - 3   **c.** 7 - 4   **d.** 6 - 2

2. Find the difference. You may use counters.
Hint: See Example 2 or Rule 2.

a. 2 - 4   **b.** 3 - 5   **c.** 3 - 7   **d.** 1 - 5

3. Use counters to find the following.
Hint: See Example 3 or Rule 3.

a. -4 - 2 =   **b.** -6 - 4 =   **c.** -5 - 4 =   **d.** -2 - 3 =
e. -1 - 2 =   **f.** -4 - 4 =   **g.** -7 - 3 =   **h.** -2 - 1 =

4. Use counters to find the following:
Hint:See Example 4 or Rule 4.

a. -1 - (-4) =   **b.** -7 - (-3) =   **c.** -2 - (-5) =   **d.** -8 - (-2)=   **e.** -8 - (-5) =
f. -3 - (-4) =   **g.** -3 - (-3) =   **h.** -10 - (-10) =   **i.** -8 - (-9) =

Challenge Questions

5. Find the difference.

a. 3 - 5 =   **b.** 3 - (-5) =   **c.** -4 - (-8) =   **d.** -8 - (-8) =   **e.** 6 - 4 =
f. -6 - 8 =   **g.** 0 - (-6) =   **h.** 7 - (-3) =   **i.** -5 - (-7) =   **j.** -6 - 6 =
k. 4 - (-4) =   **l.** 1 - 7 =   **m.** -3 - (-4) =   **n.** -5 - (-6) =   **o.** -2 - (-2) =

Answers to Selected Questions

REAL WORLD APPLICATIONS - WORD PROBLEMS
Subtracting Integers

Example 1
The temperature in New York at 7:00 A.M. was -2^0F and at 2:00 P.M, the temperature was 5^0F. Find the change in the temperature.
Solution
To find the change in the temperature, subtract the starting temperature $(-2^0$F) from the ending temperature $(5^0$F) as follows:

$$5 - (-2) = 5 + 2 \qquad\qquad \text{Note: } - (- = +$$
$$= 7^0\text{F}$$

Therefore the change in the temperature $= 7^0$F.

―――――――――――――――― The notes and the generous worked examples have provided me with conceptual understanding and computational fluency to do my homework.

Exercises
1. On December 25 at 6:00 A.M. the temperature was -8^0F and at 12:30 P.M, the temperature was 10^0F. What is the change in temperature?
Hint: See Example 1.
2. On December 24, 2004 the temperature of a certain city was -1^0F and 8 hours later, the temperature was -7^0F. What was the change in the temperature? Hint: Set up as follow: Change in temperature $= -7 - (-1)$ and also see Example 1.

Challenge Questions
3. At 12:00 P.M. on January 6, 2005 the temperature was -2^0F, and at 7:00 P.M. the temperature was -3^0F. What is the change in the temperature?
4. The temperature of a certain village on December 28,1997 was -6^0F and about 10 hours later, the temperature was -3^0F. What is the change in the temperature?

MULTIPLYING INTEGERS

What is multiplication? Multiplication is repeated addition. The symbol for multiplication is $\times$. For example, 6×3 means $3 + 3 + 3 + 3 + 3 + 3$.

Example 1
Model the multiplication of 6×3 using counters.
Step 1: 6×3 means 6 sets of 3 positive counters. Put these counters on the mat.

$\quad\quad \oplus \oplus \oplus \quad \oplus \oplus \oplus \quad \oplus \oplus \oplus$
$\quad\quad \oplus \oplus \oplus \quad \oplus \oplus \oplus \quad \oplus \oplus \oplus$

Step 2: Find the number of counters on the mat. There are 18 positive counters on the mat. Therefore, $6 \times 3 = 18$.
Rule 1: **To multiply a positive number by another positive number, just multiply the two numbers together as in Example 1.**

Example 2
Use counters to find $5 \times (-2)$
Solution
Step 1: $5 \times (-2)$ means 5 sets of 2 negative counters as shown on the mat.

$\quad\quad \ominus \ominus \quad \ominus \ominus \quad \ominus \ominus \quad \ominus \ominus \quad \ominus \ominus$

Step 2: There are 10 negative counters on the mat, making $5 \times (-2) = -10$
Rule 2: **To multiply a positive number by a negative number just multiply the two numbers together and attach a negative sign to the product as shown in Example 2, Step 2. Note** also that $\times$ (- becomes a multiplication with a negative symbol attach to the product as in Example 2, Step 2.

Example 3
Use counters to find -2×4
Solution
Step 1: Using the fact that -2 is the opposite of 2, -2×4 means to remove 2 sets of 4 positive counters. However, we cannot remove 2 sets of 4 positive counters because there are none to remove. We must first add 2 sets of 4 zero pairs and then we can remove 2 sets of 4 positive counters.

Two sets of 4
zero pairs of counters

Remove 2 sets of 4
positive counters.

↓   ↓   ↑   ↑

⊕⊖   ⊕⊖   ⊕⊖   ⊕⊖   ⊖   ⊖

⊕⊖   ⊕⊖ = ⊕⊖   ⊕⊖ = ⊖   ⊖

⊕⊖   ⊕⊖   ⊕⊖   ⊕⊖   ⊖   ⊖

⊕⊖   ⊕⊖   ⊕⊖   ⊕⊖   ⊖   ⊖

Step 2: Find the number of the counters remaining on the mat. There are 8 negative counters remaining on the mat and this represents -8. Therefore, $-2 \times 4 = -8$.

Rule 3: **To multiply a negative number by a positive number, just multiply the two numbers and attach a negative symbol to the product as in Example 3, Step 2**.

Special note: To multiply a negative integer by another integer, remove as many sets of positive counters as possible as in Example 3, Step 1.

Example 4

Use counters to find -3(-2).

Solution

Step 1: Using the fact that -3 is the opposite of 3, -3(-2) means to remove 3 sets of 2 negative counters but there are none to remove. Therefore, we must first add 3 sets of 2 zero pairs and then we can remove 3 sets of 2 negative counters.

Remove 3 sets of
2 negative counters.

↑   ↑   ↑

⊕⊖   ⊕⊖   ⊕⊖   ⊕⊖   ⊕⊖   ⊕⊖   ⊕   ⊕   ⊕

⊕⊖   ⊕⊖   ⊕⊖ = ⊕⊖   ⊕⊖   ⊕⊖ = ⊕   ⊕   ⊕

3 sets of 2 zero pairs   6 positive counters
of counters   remain

Step 2: Find the number of the remaining counters on the mat. There are 6 positive counters that remain on the mat, and this represents +6 or 6, and therefore, $-3(-2) = 6$.

Rule 4: **To multiply one negative number by another negative number, just multiply the two numbers together and their product must be positive as shown in Example 4, Step 2**.

Summary of the Signs of the Rules for Multiplying Integers

Considering examples 1 to 4, when multiplying two numbers that have the same signs, the sign of the product of the numbers is positive. For example, $-2(-3) = +6 = 6$, and

$2(3) = +6 = 6$.

Considering examples 1 to 4, when multiplying two numbers that have different signs, the sign of the product of the numbers is negative. For example, $-2(3) = -6$, and $2(-3) = -6$.

The notes and the generous worked examples have provided me with conceptual understanding and computational fluency to do my homework.

Exercises

1. Explain what is meant by multiplication.

2. Use counters to multiply the following. Hint: See Example 1. You may use Rule 1.

    a. 3×2 **b.** 4×3 **c.** 2×5 **d.** 5×4

3. Use counters to find the following. Hint: See Example 2. You may use Rule 2.

    a. $3 \times (-2)$ **b.** $4 \times (-3)$ **c.** $3 \times (-5)$ **d.** $4 \times (-2)$

4. Use counters to find the following. Hint: See Example 3. You may Use Rule 3.

    a. -3×4 **b.** -2×5 **c.** -4×3 **d.** -5×2

    e. -3×3 **f.** -5×6 **g.** -2×6 **h.** -6×3

5. Use counters to find the following. Hint: See Example 4. You may use Rule 4.

    a. $-2(-4)$ **b.** $-4(-4)$ **c.** $-3(-3)$ **d.** $-5(-3)$

    e. $-4(-2)$ **f.** $-3(-2)$ **g.** $-4(-5)$ **h.** $-2(-5)$

6. Solve questions 2 to 5 using just the rules.

Challenge Questions

7. Find the following products using the rules of multiplications.

    a. $-6(-6) =$ **b.** $-8 \times 6 =$ **c.** $7 \times (-3) =$ **d.** $9 \times 4 =$

    e. $-5(-5) =$ **f.** $7 \times 3 =$ **g.** $-3 \times 8 =$ **h.** $(-7) =$

    i. $3 \times (-7) =$ **j.** $-3 \times (-7) =$ **k.** $-3(5) =$ **l.** $-4 \times (-9) =$

Answers to Selected Questions.

2a. 6   **3a.** -6   **4a.** -12   **5a.** 8   **7k.** 21

Cumulative Review

Find each product, sum or difference.

1. $-6 + 10 =$ **2.** $-8 - (-3) =$ **3.** $-3 + (-4) =$

4. $7 - (-4) =$ **5.** $-7 \times 3 =$ **6.** $-4 - (-3) =$

7. $8 - (-2) =$ **8.** $-5 \times (-2) =$ **9.** $6(-3) =$

10. Replace each ? with $=$, $<$, or $>$ to make a true statement. Review the chapter/section on Number Line.

    a. $4 ? -2$ **b.** $-4 ? -3$ **c.** $-3 ? 0$

d. -1 ? -1   **e**. -2 ? -1   **f**. 0 ? -1

11. Which problem does not have -4 as its answer?
    A. 8 - 12
    B. -1 + (-3)
    C. 2 - 6
    D. -2(-2)
    E. 2(-2)

Answer to Selected Questions

10a. 4 > -2   **10c**. -3 < 0   **10d**. -1 = -1

DIVIDING INTEGERS

What is division? Division is separating a quantity into equal-sized groups. For example, 3 girls want to share 9 apples equally, how can this be done?

Step 1: Put 9 counters on a mat, and let 9 counters represent the 9 apples.

⊕ ⊕ ⊕ ⊕ ⊕ ⊕ ⊕ ⊕ ⊕

Step 2: Separate the 9 counter into 3 equal-sized groups.

⊕ ⊕ ⊕
⊕ ⊕ ⊕
⊕ ⊕ ⊕

There are 3 equal groups of 3 positive counters each and therefore, $9 \div 3 = 3$. Each girl will receive 3 apples.

Example 1
Use counters to find $-12 \div 4$
Solution
Step 1: Put 12 negative counters on the mat to represent -12.

⊖ ⊖ ⊖ ⊖ ⊖ ⊖ ⊖ ⊖ ⊖ ⊖ ⊖ ⊖

Step 2: Separate the 12 counters into 4 equal-sized groups.

⊖ ⊖ ⊖ ⊖
⊖ ⊖ ⊖ ⊖
⊖ ⊖ ⊖ ⊖
 4 equal-sized groups.

There are 4 equal-sized groups of 3 negative counters each and meaning
     $-12 \div 4 = -3$

414

Rule 1: From Example 1, **when a negative integer is divided by a positive integer, the quotient is negative**.

Working backward to solve division problems.
Multiplication is the opposite of division. We can therefore work backward by using multiplication to solve division problems by using the logic of "**what number multiplied by the divisor equals to the dividend**". Examples 2 to 5 will explain how we can divide integers by working backward. Review the section on multiplication of integers and knowing the multiplication tables will be helpful.

Example 2
Find 12 ÷ 3.
Solution
To find 12 ÷ 3, think of what number times 3 equals to 12?

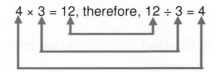

4 × 3 = 12, therefore, 12 ÷ 3 = 4

Rule 2: From Example 2, **when a positive integer is divided by a positive integer the quotient is positive**.

Example 3
Find -8 ÷ (-2).
Solution
To find -8 ÷ (-2), think of what number times -2 equals to -8?

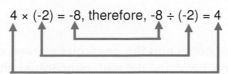

4 × (-2) = -8, therefore, -8 ÷ (-2) = 4

Rule 3: From Example 3, **when a negative integer is divided by a negative integer the quotient is positive**.

Example 4
Find -15 ÷ 3.
Solution
To find -15 ÷ 3, think of what number multiplied by 3 equals to -15?

415

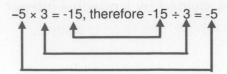

−5 × 3 = −15, therefore −15 ÷ 3 = −5

Rule 4: From Example 4, **when a negative integer is divided by a positive integer, the quotient is negative**.

Example 5
Find 15 ÷ (−3).
Solution
To find 15 ÷ (−3), think of what number multiplied by −3 equals to 15?

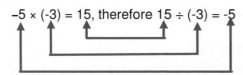

−5 × (−3) = 15, therefore 15 ÷ (−3) = −5

Rule 5: From Example 5, **when a positive integer is divided by a negative integer the quotient is negative**.

Summary of the Signs of the Rules for Dividing Integers
Considering examples 1 to 5, when dividing an integer by another integer, that have the same signs, the sign of the quotient (answer) is positive. For example, −6 ÷ −2 = 3, and 6 ÷ 2 = 3.
Considering examples 1 to 5, when dividing an integer by another integer, that have different signs, the sign of the quotient (answer) is negative. For example, −6 ÷ 2 = −3, and 6 ÷ (−2) = −3.

The notes and the generous worked examples have provided me with conceptual understanding and computational fluency to do my homework.

Exercises
1. Division is the opposite of multipli_____.
2. Use counters to find the following. Hint: See Example 1. **You may use Rule 1.**

    a. −9 ÷ 3 =   **b.** −10 ÷ 2 =   **c.** −4 ÷ 2 =   **d.** −6 ÷ 3 =
    e. −15 ÷ 5 =   **f.** −18 ÷ 3 =   **g.** −24 ÷ 8 =   **i.** 36 ÷ 6 =
    k. −28 ÷ 4 =   **l.** −50 ÷ 10 =   **m.** −44 ÷ 11 =   **n.** −14 ÷ 7 =

3. Work backward by using multiplication to solve the following division problems. Hint: See Example 2. **You may use Rule 2.**

    a. 15 ÷ 5 =   **b.** 12 ÷ 6 =   **c.** 28 ÷ 4 =   **d.** 16 ÷ 4 =

e. 18 ÷ 9 =   **f.** 21 ÷ 3 =   **g.** 24 ÷ 3 =   **h.** 48 ÷ 6 =

4. Work backward by using multiplication to solve the following division problems.
   Hint: See Example 3. **You may use Rule 3**.
   a. -12 ÷ (-2) =   **b.** -8 ÷ (-4) =   **c.** -10 ÷ (-5) =   **d.** -21 ÷ (-3) =
   e. -30 ÷ (-6) =   **f.** -18 ÷ (-3) =   **g.** -28 ÷ (-4) =   **h.** -9 ÷ (-3) =

5. Work backward by using multiplication to solve the following division problems.
   Hint: See Example 4. **You may use Rule 4**.
   a. -4 ÷ 2 =   **b.** -6 ÷ 3 =   **c.** -9 ÷ 3 =   **d.** -16 ÷ 4 =
   e. -20 ÷ 5 =   **f.** -21 ÷ 7 =   **g.** -36 ÷ 3 =   **h.** -12 ÷ 6 =

6. Work backward by using multiplication to solve the following division problems.
   Hint: See Example 5. **You may use Rule 5**.
   a. 21 ÷ (-3) =   **b.** 12 ÷ (-4.) =   **c.** 28 ÷ (-4) =   **d.** 16 ÷ (-4) =
   e. 36 ÷ (-6) =   **f.** 18 ÷ (-3) =   **g.** 10 ÷ (-2) =   **h.** 14 ÷ (-7) =

Answers to Selected Questions.
2a. -3   **2b.** -5   **3a.** 3   **3b.** 2   **4a.** 6
4b. 2   **5a.** -2   **5b.** -2   **6a.** -7   **6b.** -3

Challenge Questions
7 Find each quotient.
   a. -32 ÷ 4 =   **b.** 21 ÷ (-3) =   **c.** -33 ÷ (-11) =   **d.** 24 ÷ 8 =
   e. -15 ÷ 3 =   **f.** -6 ÷ (-6) =   **g.** -36 ÷ (-4) =   **h.** 35 ÷ (-7) =

8 Find the value of a ÷ b if a = -2 and b = -1. Hint: Substitute a = -2 and b = -1 in the expression a ÷ b, and then divide.

Cumulative Review Exercises.
1. Solve the following problems.
   a. -5 + (-4) =   **b.** -3 + (+3) =   **c.** +2 + 6 =   **d.** -4 ÷ (-2) =
   e. 8 ÷ (-4) =   **f.** 27 + (-7) =   **g.** -3 + 8 =   **h.** -6 - (-3) =
   i. -3 - 4 =   **j.** 4 × (-3) =   **k.** -2 × 7 =   **l.** -1 + (-1) =
   m. 4 - 6 =   **n.** -4(-2) =   **o.** -5 - 3 =   **p.** -2 × (-3) =
   q. -8 - (-2) =   **r.** -16 ÷ 4 =   **s.** -16 ÷ (-4) =   **t.** 10 - (-4) =

6. Compare and write <, >, or = for ?
   a. +3 + (-2) ? -3   **b.** -1 + (+7) ? 6   **c.** -1 + (-1) ? 0   **d.** +3 + (-3) ? +1

METRIC AND CUSTOMARY SYSTEMS OF UNITS

Understanding Measures

When the early humans changed from hunters to farmers, they needed to measure the size of their farms. The first units of length were based on the human body parts such as the length of the palm and the length of a finger. For example, the people of Ghana in West Africa use the distance from the tip of the left middle finger to the tip of the right middle finger of an adult as approximately 6 feet or 2 yards.
(3 feet = 1 yard). People do not have the same body size, and therefore each of the measures using body parts differed considerably. In order to avoid confusion, measures were made standard so that everybody would use the same standards.

The National Bureau of Standards in Washington D.C. determines the units on rulers or measuring tapes. When you measure something with a ruler or a tape measure, you are actually comparing it with these standard units.

The two main systems of measurements are the Customary and the Metric systems. The Customary system is also known as the English system. The metric system is used in most countries and the metric system is also known as SI which stands for System International.

METRIC SYSTEM

Metric Length

The metric unit is named after the unit of length, the meter, because the metric units of length are based on the meter. The diagram shows a part of the metric length of a ruler in centimeters. The distance between any small division = 1 millimeter (mm) and 10 millimeters (mm) = 1 centimeter (cm). Note carefully that when you take a ruler, the type of the units at any edge of the ruler is indicated such as centimeter (cm) or inch (in.).

Let us measure the length of an eraser as shown in the diagram.

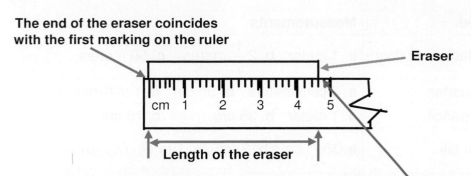

The end of the eraser coincides with the first marking on the ruler

Eraser

Length of the eraser

The end of the eraser coincides with a marking on the ruler

The length of the ruler is **4 centimeters and 6 millimeters**.

To measure the length of an eraser or any object, one of the edges of the eraser or the object should coincide with the first marking on the ruler, and then read the marking on the ruler that coincides with the other edge of the eraser or the object. This method of measuring the length of any object is very useful in solving many exercises later.

Benchmark

A benchmark is an object whose measure is already known and we can then use the object to estimate the lengths of other objects. For example if we know the length of your mathematics textbook, we can then use the textbook as a benchmark to measure the length of the top of your desk at school. We should then record the length of your desk in "mathematics textbook lengths."

Team Exercise

1. Use a ruler to measure the length of your mathematics textbook to the nearest millimeter (for example, the measurement could be 10 centimeters and 4 millimeters.)
2. Now use the length of the mathematics textbook to estimate the length of the top of your desk.
3. Record the length of the top of your desk in "mathematics textbook lengths."

   For example, your record could be $3\frac{1}{3}$ mathematics textbook lengths.

4. Now use a ruler to measure the length of the top of your desk.
5. Which unit is more convenient to use in measuring the length of the top of your desk? (Length of the mathematics textbook or using a ruler.) Explain your answer.

Team Exercise

Each team should measure the following objects and then select the most appropriate measure. (Hint: It is more convenient to use a measuring tape to measure longer distances or objects.)

Object to be measured.	Measurements
1. The length of your classroom door.	**a.** 1 meter **b.** $2\frac{1}{2}$ meters **c.** 50 meters
2. The thickness of a quarter.	**a.** 2 centimeters **b.** 35 cm **c.** 1 millimeters
3. The length of a new pencil.	**a.** 1 meter **b.** 35 cm **c.** 19 cm
4. The length of a dollar bill.	**a.** $15\frac{1}{2}$ cm **b.** 2 cm **c.** 1 m
5. The width of a dollar bill.	**a.** $2\frac{1}{2}$ m **b.** $6\frac{1}{2}$ cm **c.** 12 cm

6. Track events are measured in meters. Each team should record two track events in meters.

7. Each team should use a measuring tape to measure the length and width of the classroom. What unit would be the most appropriate for measuring the length and the width of the classroom? (a) meters (b) centimeters (c) millimeters.
   Hint: The largest feasible unit is the correct answer.

8. What unit would be the most appropriate for measuring the length of a postage stamp?
   (a) meters (b) centimeters (c) millimeters. Hint: The largest feasible unit is the correct answer.

9. Explain why the length of the chalkboard should be expressed in meters instead of millimeters?

10. Select the correct answer
    a. Your classroom door is about 92 cm, 92 m, or 92 km wide.
    b. The thickness of a dime is about 1 kg, 1 cm, or 1 mm.
    c. The width of an index fingernail is about 1 mm, or 1 cm or 1 km.
    d. The height of a kitchen counter is about 90 km, 90 m, or 90 cm.
    e. The width of a quarter is about 1 mm, 1 cm, or 1 m

Each team should report their answers to the whole class.

====================

The notes and the generous worked examples have provided me with conceptual understanding and computational fluency to do my homework.

Group Exercises/Exercises
Use the method of measuring the length of the eraser to measure the length of each line with a ruler. Record your answers in centimeters and milliliters.
(Group Exercises: 1 - 4, Exercises: 5 - 10)

1 ——————————————— = ? cm and ? mm

2 ————————————— = ? cm and ? mm

3 ——————————————————— = ? cm and ? mm

4 —— = ? cm and ? mm

5 ——————— = ? cm and ? mm

6 ————————————————— = ? cm and ? mm

7 ——————————————————————— = ? cm ? mm

8 ———————————————————————— = ? cm and ? mm

9 —————————————————————— = ? cm and ? mm

10 ———————————————— = ? cm and ? mm

Metric Units of Length
10 millimeters (mm) = 1 centimeter (cm)
100 centimeters (cm) = 1 meter (m)
1,000 meters (m) = 1 kilometer (km)

Look at the metric equations involving millimeters, centimeters, meters, and kilometers.
Note that the metric system is easy to use because the units of measurements are related by the powers of 10. For example, to change different size units you just divide or multiply by 10, 100, or 1,000. The prefixes **milli**-, **centi**-, **deci**-, **deka**-, **hecto**-, and **Kilo**- shows how the measures are related to the basic unit which is the meter.
For example;

a. **milli** - means "thousandth" therefore, 1 **milli**meter is .001 or $\frac{1}{1000}$ of a meter.

b. **Centi** - means "hundredth" therefore, 1 **centi**meter is .01 or $\frac{1}{100}$ of a meter.

c. **Kilo** - means "one thousand " and therefore, 1 Kilometer means 1000 meters.

Table of Metric Prefixes - Based on the Meter

Prefix	Meaning
milli-	one thousandth or .001 or $\dfrac{1}{1000}$
centi-	one hundredth or .01 or $\dfrac{1}{100}$
deci-	one tenth or .1 or $\dfrac{1}{10}$
basic unit (meter)	1
dcka	ten or 10
hecto-	one hundred or 100
kilo-	one thousand or 1000

The prefixes that are in the bold type are most commonly used units of measurement.

Table of Metric Units

Unit	Abbreviation	Equivalent
millimeter	**mm**	**.001 m**, .01 dm, **.1 cm**
centimeter	**cm**	**.01 m**, .1 dm, **10 mm**
decimeter	dm	.1m, 10 cm, 100 mm
meter	**m**	10 dm, **100 cm**, **1,000 mm**, .1 dam, .01 hm, .001 km
dekameter	dam	10 m, .1 hm, .01 km
hectometer	hm	100 m, 10 dam, .1 km
kilometer	**km**	**1,000 m**, 100 dam, 10 hm

The prefixes that are in the bold type are most commonly used units of measurement.

Converting between the Metric Units

There are two ways to convert between the metric units as follows:
(a). by multiplying by .001, .01, .1, 10, 100, or 1,000 as applicable.
(b). by multiplying or dividing by 10, 100, or 1000 as applicable.

Rule 1: To change a smaller unit to a larger unit follow the following two steps:
Step 1: Find how many smaller units are contained in one unit of the larger unit.
Step 2: **Divide** the given number of smaller units by the number you have determined in step 1.

Rule 2: To change a larger unit to a smaller unit follow the following two steps:
Step 1: Find how many smaller units are **contained** in one unit of the larger unit.

Step 2: **Multiply** the given number of larger units by the number you have determined in Step 1.

Example 1

How many centimeters are there in 200 millimeters?

Solution

We are converting from millimeters to centimeters and therefore, we are converting from a smaller unit to a larger unit. Therefore, we can use **Rule 1** as shown:

Step 1: 10 mm = 1 cm

Step 2: Therefore, 200 mm = 200 mm ÷ 10 mm = $\dfrac{200}{10} = \dfrac{\overset{20}{\cancel{200}}}{\underset{1}{\cancel{10}}} = 20$ cm.

Example 2

Solve: 25 cm = ? mm

Solution

We are converting from centimeters to millimeters, and therefore, we are converting from a larger unit to a smaller unit. Therefore, we can use **Rule 2** as follows:

Step 1: l cm = 10 mm

Step 2: Therefore, 25 cm = 25 × 10 mm = 250 mm.

Example 3

Solve: 15 m = ? cm.

Solution

We are converting from meters to centimeters, and therefore, we are converting from a larger unit to a smaller unit. Therefore, we can use **Rule 2** as follows:

Step 1: 1 m = 100 cm.

Step 2: Therefore, 15 m = 15 × 100 cm = 1500 cm.

Example 4

Solve: ? m = 250 cm.

Solution

We are converting from centimeters to meters, and therefore, we are converting from a smaller unit to a larger unit. Therefore, we can use **Rule 1** as shown:

Step 1: 1m = 100 cm

Step 2: Therefore, $\dfrac{250}{100}$ m = 250 cm.

$$\dfrac{250}{100} \text{ m} = 250 \text{ cm.}$$

$$\frac{250}{100} \text{ m} = 250 \text{ cm.}$$

$$2.5\text{m} = 250 \text{ cm.} \qquad \frac{250}{100} = 2.5 \text{ by moving the decimal}$$

point two places to the left.

Example 5
Solve: 8 km = ? m.
Solution
We are converting from kilometers to meters, and therefore, we are converting from a larger unit to a smaller unit. Therefore, we can use **Rule 2** as follows:
Step 1: 1 km = 1000 m.
Step 2: Therefore, 8 km = 8 × 1000 m = 8,000 m.

Example 6
Solve: 300 m = ? km.
Solution
We are converting from meters to kilometers and therefore, we are converting from a smaller unit to a larger unit. Therefore, we can use **Rule 1** as follows:
Step 1: 1 km = 1000 m.

Step 2: Therefore, 300 m = $\dfrac{300}{1000}$ km.

$$= \frac{300}{1000} \text{ km.}$$

$$= \frac{3}{10} \text{ km.} \qquad (\frac{300}{1000} = \frac{3}{10} \text{ by dividing by 100)}$$

$$= .3 \text{ km.}$$

Example 7
Solve: 5 km = ? cm.
Solution
We are converting kilometers to centimeters, and therefore, we are converting from a larger unit to a smaller unit. Therefore, we can use **Rule 2** as shown:
Step 1: 1 km = 100,000 cm.
Step 2: Therefore, 5 km = 5 × 100,000 cm = 500,000 cm.

Example 8
Solve: 250,000 cm = ? km.
Solution

We are converting centimeters to kilometers and therefore we are converting from a smaller unit to a larger unit. Therefore, we can use **Rule 1** as shown:

Step 1: 1 km = 100,000 cm.

Step 2: Therefore, 250,000 cm = $\dfrac{250,000}{100,000}$ km.

$$= \frac{25}{10} \text{ km.} \qquad (\frac{250,000}{100,000} = \frac{25}{10} \text{ by dividing by 10,000.})$$

$$= 2.5 \text{ km.} \qquad (\frac{25}{10} = 2.5 \text{ by moving the decimal point}$$
one place to the left.)

Summary

1. In order to convert a smaller unit to a larger unit, **divide** by moving the decimal point to the **left** as needed.
2. In order to convert a larger unit to a smaller unit, **multiply** by moving the decimal point to the **right** as needed.

The notes and the generous worked examples have provided me with conceptual understanding and computational fluency to do my homework.

Exercises

1. How many centimeters are there in 300 millimeters? Hint: See Example 1.
2. How many centimeters are there in the following? Hint: See Example 1.
   a. 150 mm   **b.** 500 mm   **c.** 520 mm   **d.** 80 mm
3. Solve the following: Hint: See Example 2.
   a. 100 cm = ? mm   **b.** 60 cm. = ? mm   **c.** 15 cm. = ? mm
   d. 5 cm. = ? mm   **e.** 8 cm = ? mm   **f.** 18 cm = ? mm
4. Solve the following: Hint :See Example 3.
   a. 10 m = ? cm   **b.** 13 m = ? cm   **c.** 18 m = ? mm
   d. 5 m. = ? cm   **e.** 17 m. = ? cm   **f.** 22 m = ? mm
5. Solve the following: Hint: See Example 4.
   a. ? m = 270 cm   **b.** ? m = 300 cm   **c.** ? m = 150 cm
   d. ? m = 200 cm   **e.** ? m = 90 cm   **f.** ? m = 180 cm
6. Solve the following: Hint: See Example 5.
   a. 10 km = ? m   **b.** 5 km = ? m   **c.** 20 km = ? m
   d. 6 km = ? m   **e.** 2 km = ? m   **f.** 11 km = ? m
7. Solve the following: Hint: See Example 6.
   a. 200 m = ? km   **b.** 2500 m = ? km   **c.** 20 km = ? km

d. 900 m = ? m   **e.** 2 km = ? m   **f.** 560 m = ? km

8. Solve the following: Hint: See Example 7.

     a. 6 km = ? cm   **b.** 12 km = ? cm   **c.** 16 km = ? cm

     d. 2 km = ? cm   **e.** 8 km = ? cm   **f.** 3 km = ? cm

9. Solve the following: Hint: See Example 8.

     a. 150,000 cm = ? km   **b.** 200,000 cm = ? km   **c.** 100,000 cm = ? km

Challenge Questions

10. Solve the following:

     a. 9 m = ? cm   **b.** 3 km = ? m   **c.** 95 cm = ? mm

     d. 450 mm = ? cm   **e** 1500 m = ? km   **f.** 160,000 cm = ? km

Answers to Selected Questions

1. 30 cm   **2a.** 15 cm   **3a.** 1000 mm   **4a.** 1000 cm

REAL WORLD APPLICATIONS - WORD PROBLEMS
METRIC UNITS OF LENGTH

Example 1

John runs 4.2 kilometers every day. How many meters does he run in a week?

Solution

Setup: There are 7 days in a week, therefore, multiply 4.2 kilometers by 7 to obtain the total number of kilometers that John runs in a week. Then, change the total number of kilometers that John runs in a week to meters.

Step 1:Find the total number of kilometers that John runs every week as shown:

In 1 day John runs 4.2 km.

In 7 days (1 week) John will run 7 × 4.2 km = 29.4 km.

Step 2: Change the 29.4 km into meters as shown:

1 km = 1000 m (See the section on "Metric units of Length,")

therefore, 29.4 km = 29.4 × 1000 m = 29,400 m.   Review Decimal Multiplication.

Therefore, John runs 29,400 m. in a week.

Example 2

How many meters are in $\frac{4}{5}$ kilometer?

Solution

Setup: Change the common fraction $\frac{4}{5}$ to a decimal fraction. Then find the number of meters that are contained in the decimal fraction of the kilometer.

Step 1: Change the common fraction $\frac{4}{5}$ to a decimal fraction as shown:

$$\frac{4}{5} = 5\overline{)\begin{array}{r} 0.8 \\ 40 \\ -\,40 \\ \hline 00 \end{array}} = .8$$

Step 2: Find the number of meters that are contained in .8 km as shown:

1 km = 1000 m (See the section on "Metric Units of Length")

Therefore, .8 × 1000 m = 800 m.   (Review Decimal Multiplication).

Example 3

Mary has a wire that measures .8 meters long. If her school project requires many lengths of a wire measuring 20 millimeters, how many lengths of 20 millimeters can she cut from the .8 meter long wire?

Solution

Setup: Change the .8 meters to millimeters, and then **divide** by 20 millimeters.

Step 1: Change the .8 meters to millimeters as shown:

1 m = 1000 mm (See the section on "Metric units of Length.")

Therefore, .8 m = .8 × 1000 mm = 800 mm. (Review decimal multiplication.)

Step 2: Find the number of 20 mm that are contain in 800 mm as shown:

Divide 800 mm by 20 mm to obtain the number of 20 mm that are contained in 800 mm as shown:

$$800 \div 20 = \frac{800}{20}$$

$$= \frac{80\cancel{0}}{2\cancel{0}} \qquad \text{Cancel out the zero by dividing by 10.}$$

$$= \frac{\overset{40}{\cancel{80}}}{\underset{1}{\cancel{2}}} \qquad \text{Divide by 2.}$$

$$= 40$$

Therefore, 40 lengths of 20 mm can be cut from the .8 m of the wire.

Example 4

Given that the scale on a map is 10 mm = 78 km, how many kilometers are represented by 5.5 cm?

Solution

427

Setup: Change 5.5 cm to millimeters, and then find how many 10 mm
   (10 mm = 1 cm) are contained in 5.5 cm. Finally, multiply 78 km by the
   number of 10 mm in 5.5 cm.
Step 1: Change the 5.5 cm to millimeters as shown:
   1 cm =10 mm (See the section on "Metric units of Length.")
   Therefore, 5.5 cm = 5.5 × 10 mm = 55 mm.   (Review decimal multiplication.)
Step 2: Find the number of 10 mm that are contained in the 55 mm as shown:

$$\textbf{Divide } 55 \text{ mm by } 10 = 55 \div 10 = \frac{55}{10} = 5.5$$

Step 3: Find the kilometers represented by 5.5 cm on the map as shown:
   Multiply 78 km by 55 = 78 km × 55 = 429 km.
Therefore, 5.5 cm on the map represents 429 km.

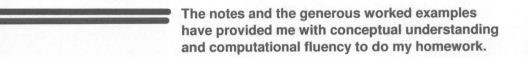

The notes and the generous worked examples have provided me with conceptual understanding and computational fluency to do my homework.

Exercises

1. Eric runs 3.8 kilometers every day. How many meters does he run in a week?
   Hint: See Example 1.

2. How many meters are contained in $\frac{3}{5}$ kilometers? Hint: See Example 2.

3. Susan has a wire that measures .95 meters long. If her school project requires many
   lengths of the wire measuring 30 millimeters, how many lengths can she cut from
   the .95 meter long wire. Hint: See Example 3.

4. Given that the scale on a certain map is 5 mm = 74 km, how many kilometers are
   represented by 7.2 cm? Hint: See Example 3.

Challenge Question

5. How many meters are contained in $\frac{2}{5}$ km?

Add and Subtract Measurements
Example 1
Copy and complete.
2 m + 150 cm = ? cm
Solution
Change the 2 m to centimeters by multiplying 2 m by 100 because 1 m = 100 cm
(See the section on "Metric Units of Length") and then add as shown:
2 m × 100 + 150 cm = ? cm
200 cm + 150 cm = 350 cm

Example 2

Copy and complete.

3 m + 400 cm = ? m

Solution

Change the 400 cm to meters by dividing 400 cm by 100 because 1 m = 100 cm (See the section on "Metric units of Length") and then add as shown:

$3 \text{ m} + \dfrac{400}{100} \text{ m} = ? \text{ m}$

$3 \text{ m} + \dfrac{\overset{4}{\cancel{400}}}{\underset{1}{\cancel{100}}} \text{ m} = ? \text{ m}$

3 m + 4 m = 7 m

Example 3

Copy and complete.

2 cm + 8 mm + 7 mm + 1 cm =

Solution

Step 1: Add the like units together as shown:

2 cm + 1 cm + 8 mm + 7 mm =
3 cm + 15 mm =

Step 2: Change 15 mm to centimeters and millimeters by dividing 15 mm by 10 because 1 cm = 10 mm (See the section on "Metric units of Length,") such that 15 mm ÷ 10 = 1 remainder 5 and the 1 has a unit of cm and the 5 has a unit of mm as shown:

3 cm + 1 cm + 5 mm = 4 cm + 5 mm
= 4 cm 5 mm

Example 4

Solve: 10 km   600 m
          - 2 km   900 m
          _____

Solution

Step 1: We cannot subtract 900 m from 600 m, therefore, we have to borrow 1 km from the 10 km. The borrowed 1 km = 1000 m (See the section on "Metric units of Length") and add the 1000 m to the 600 m to obtain 1600 m as shown:

```
     9      1600
    1̶0̶ km   6̶0̶0̶ m
  -  2 km   900 m
```

Step 2: Do the subtraction now as shown:

```
      9      1600
     1̶0̶ km   6̶0̶0̶ m
   -  2 km    900 m
   ─────────────────
      7 km    700 m
```

Example 5

Solve: 6 cm 3 mm - 2 cm 8 mm =

Solution

Step 1: Rewrite the question as shown:

```
      6 cm  3 mm
    - 2 cm  8 mm
```

Step 2: We cannot subtract 8 mm from 3 mm, and therefore, we have to borrow 1 cm from 6 cm and then change the 1 cm to millimeters, 1 cm = 10 mm (See the section on "Metric units of Length,") then add the 10 mm to the 3 mm to obtain 13 mm as shown:

```
      5      13
      6̶ cm   3̶ mm
    - 2 cm   8 mm
```

Step 3: Do the subtraction now as shown:

```
      5      13
      6̶ cm   3̶ mm
    - 2 cm   8 mm
    ──────────────
      3 cm   5 mm
```

Example 6

Solve: 12 m 9 cm
        - 8 m 5 cm

Solution

Do the subtraction as shown:

```
  12 m   9 cm
-  8 m   5 cm
─────────────
   4 m   4 cm
```

─────────────────────────────────

The notes and the generous worked examples have provided me with conceptual understanding and computational fluency to do my homework.

Exercises

1. Copy and complete. Hint: See Example 1.

    a. 4 m + 125 cm =? cm   **b.** 1 m + 85 cm = ? cm

    c. 6 m + 201 cm = ? cm   **d.** 3 m + 111 cm = ? cm

2. Copy and complete. Hint: See Example 2.

    a. 4 m + 300 cm = ? m   **b.** 1 m + 100 cm = ? m

    c. 2 m + 500 cm = ? m   **d.** 3 m + 200 cm = ? m

3. Copy and complete. Hint: See Example 3.

    a. 3 cm + 4 mm + 12 mm + 2 cm =

    b. 7 mm + 1 cm + 3 mm + 4 cm =

    c. 10 cm + 6 mm + 4 cm + 12 mm =

    d. 12 mm + 5 cm + 5 mm + 2 cm =

4. Solve: See Example 4.

```
a.    4 km   200 m          b.    3 km   700 m          c.    5 km    98 m
     -1 km   400 m               - 2 km   800 m             - 3 km   100 m
```

5. Solve: Hint: See Example 5.

    a. 3 cm 4 mm - 1 cm 6 mm =

    b. 2 cm 5 mm - 1 cm 7 mm =

    c. 6 cm 8 mm - 2 cm 9 mm =

    d. 12 cm 6 mm - 9 cm 7 mm =

6. Solve: Hint: See Example 6.

```
a.   10 m   8 cm          b.    2 m   5 cm          c.    4 m   7 cm
    - 5 m   3 cm               - 1 m   2 cm              - 2 m   5 cm
```

Challenge Questions

7. Copy and complete.

    a. 9 cm + 4 mm + 2 cm + 8 mm =

    b. 4 cm 3 mm - 2 cm 9 mm =

    c. 6 cm 7 mm - 5 cm 5 mm =

    d. 3 m + 600 cm = ? m

e. 10 m + 150 cm = ? cm

8. Solve:

a.	12 km	700 m	**b.**	2 cm	9 mm	**c.**	6 m + 700 cm = ? m
	- 2 km	800 m		+ 5 cm	5 mm		

Answers to Selected Questions

1a. 525 cm   **2a.** 7 m   **3a.** 6 cm 6 mm   **4a.** 2 km 800 m

CUSTOMARY UNITS OF LENGTH

The Customary unit of length are the inch, foot, yard, and mile.

        12 inches (in.) = 1 foot (ft)
                3 feet (ft) = 1 yard (yd)
        5,280 feet (ft) = 1 mile (mi)
            1,760 yards = 1 mile

Detailed Customary Units of Length table

Unit	Abbreviation	Equivalence
inch	in.	12 in. = 1 foot
foot	ft	1 ft = 12 in., 3 ft = 1 yard, 5,280 ft = 1 mile
yard	yd	1 yd = 3 ft, 1 yd = 36 in., 1,760 yd = 1 mile

Example 1

How many inches are in 5 feet?

Solution

We are to find 5 feet = how many inches.

Note: **To change from a larger unit (for example feet) to a smaller unit, (for example inches), multiply as shown**:

Number of feet × Number of inches in 1 foot = Number of inches.

Number of feet × Number of inches in 1 foot = Number of inches

        5   ×   12   =   60 inches.

There are 60 inches in 5 feet.

Example 2

How many feet are in 48 inches?

Solution

We are to find 48 inches = how many feet.

Note: **To change from a smaller unit (such as inches) to a larger unit (such as feet), divide.**

Number of inches ÷ Number of inches in 1 foot = Number of feet.

Number of inches	÷	Number of inches in 1 foot	=	Number of feet.
48	÷	12	=	4 feet

There are 4 feet in 48 inches.

Example 3

An electric wire is 72 yards long. How many feet does the wire contain?

Solution

We are to find 72 yards = how many feet.

Note: **To change from a larger unit (yard) to a smaller unit (feet), multiply.**

Number of yards × Number of feet in 1 yard = Number of feet.

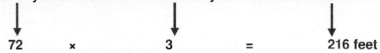

Number of yards	×	Number of feet In 1 yard	=	Number of feet.
72	×	3	=	216 feet

There are 216 feet in 72 yards.

Example 4

One of the school's hallways is 99 feet long. How long is the hallway in yards?

Solution

We are to find 99 feet = how many yards.

Note: **To change from a smaller unit (feet) to a larger unit (yard), divide.**

Number of feet ÷ Number of feet in 1 yard = Number of yards.

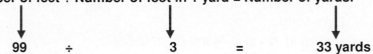

Number of feet	÷	Number of feet in 1 yard	=	Number of yards.
99	÷	3	=	33 yards

There are 33 yards in 99 feet.

Example 5

Find 3 ft 5 in + 6ft 11 in.

Solution

Step 1: Rewrite the question and add the like units as follows:

```
    3 ft    5 in.
  + 6 ft   11 in.
  _____
    9 ft   16 in.
```

Step 2: Change 16 in. into feet and inches as follows:

16 in. is more than 1 foot because 12 in. = 1 ft, therefore, rename 16 in. as 1 ft + 4 in (16 in. ÷ 12 = 1 ft remainder 4 in.).

(Note that from the customary unit of length, 12 inches = 1 foot).

Therefore, the 9 ft 16 in. = 9 ft + (1 ft + 4 in.).

Step 3: Combine the like units as shown:

$$9 \text{ ft} + (1 \text{ ft} + 4 \text{ in.}) = 9 \text{ ft} + 1 \text{ ft} + 4 \text{ in.}$$
$$= 10 \text{ ft} \ 4 \text{ in.}$$

Example 6

Solve:
```
    8 yd    1 ft
  - 3 yd    2 ft
```

Solution

Step 1: 2 ft cannot be subtracted from 1 ft because 2 ft is greater than 1 ft and therefore, we have to borrow 1 yd from 8 yd and this 1 yd = 3 ft (See customary unit of length.) Add the 3 ft to 1 ft to become 4 ft and rewrite the question as shown:

```
    7        4
    8 yd    1 ft
  - 3 yd    2 ft
```

Step 2: Do the subtraction as shown:

```
    7        4
    8 yd    1 ft
  - 3 yd    2 ft
  _____
    4 yd    2 ft
```

Example 7

Solve:
```
    5 yd    2 ft
  - 2 yd    1 ft
```

Solution

Do the subtraction as shown:

434

```
  5 yd   2 ft
- 2 yd   1 ft
  3 yd   1 ft
```

The notes and the generous worked examples have provided me with conceptual understanding and computational fluency to do my homework.

Exercises

1. What are the customary units of length?

2. How many inches are in the following lengths? Hint: See Example 1.

    a. 10 ft   **b**. 4 ft   **c**. 8 ft   **d**. 2 ft

3. How many feet are in the following lengths? Hint See Example 2.

    a. 24 in.   **b**. 60 in.   **c**. 36 in.   **d**. 72 in.

4. A fence is 144 yards long. How long is the fence in feet?
    Hint: See Example 3.

5. A swimming pool is 39 ft long. How long is the swimming pool in yards?
    Hint: See Example 4.

6. Solve: Hint: See Example 5.

    a. 4 ft 8 in. + 7 ft 6 in. =   **b**. 2 ft 7 in. + 3 ft 8 in. =

    c. 12 ft 5 in. + 2 ft 8 in. =   **c**. 1 f 9 in. + 8 ft 6 in. =

7. Solve: Hint: See Example 6.

    a.
```
  6 yd   1 ft
- 4 yd   2 ft
```
    b.
```
  9 yd   1 ft
- 6 yd   2 ft
```
    c.
```
  5 yd   0 ft
- 3 yd   1 ft
```

Challenge Questions

8. Copy and complete

    a. 72 in. = ? ft   **b**. 6 yd = ? ft   **c**. 9 ft = ? in.

    d. 36 ft = ? yd   **e**. 15 yd = ? ft   **f**. 9ft = ? yd

Answers to Selected Questions

2a. 120 in.   **3a**. 2 ft   **6a**. 12 ft 2 in.

CUSTOMARY UNITS OF SQUARE MEASURE

The basic customary units of square measures are square inches, square foot, square yard, acre and square miles. These basic customary units of square measure are shown in the table.

Table

Unit	Equivalence	Abbreviation
Square inch (in.²)	144 in.² = 1 ft² 1,296 in.² = 1 yd²	in.²
Square foot (ft²)	1 ft² = 144 in.² 9 ft² = 1 yd²	ft²
Square yard (yd²)	1 yd² = 9 ft² 1 yd² = 1,296 in² 4,840 yd² = 1 A.	yd²
Acre	1 A. = 43,560 ft² 1 A. = 4,840 yd² 640 A. = 1 mi.²	A.
Square mile (mi.²)	1 mi.² = 640 A.	mi.²

Although the basic customary units of the square measure are given in the table, we will only discuss two most important ones as follows:

$$1 \text{ ft}^2 = 144 \text{ in.}^2$$
$$1 \text{ yd}^2 = 9 \text{ ft}^2$$

It is important to know that the rules for changing units of square measurement are the same as the rules for the linear measurements as shown:

First, find how many smaller units are contained in one unit of the bigger unit, and then;

1. **To change a smaller unit to a bigger unit, divide by the number that you have found**.
2. **To change a bigger unit to a smaller unit, multiply by the number that you have found**.

Example 1

Change 288 in.² to square feet.

Solution

When we compare inches to feet, the smaller unit is inches. Using the rule, to change from smaller unit to bigger unit, we must divide.

$$144 \text{ in.}^2 = 1 \text{ ft}^2 \qquad \text{See the table.}$$

Therefore, $288 \text{ in.}^2 = 288 \text{ in.}^2 \div 144 \text{ in.}^2 = 2 \text{ ft}^2$ Using the rule, we must divide.

$$
\begin{array}{r}
2 \\
144\overline{)288} \\
-288 \\
\hline
000
\end{array}
$$

Example 2
Change 2 ft^2 to square inches.
Solution
When we compare feet to inches, the feet is a bigger unit. Using the rule, to change a bigger unit to a smaller unit, we must multiply.

$$1 \text{ ft}^2 = 144 \text{ in.}^2 \qquad \text{See table}$$

Therefore, $2 \text{ ft}^2 = 2 \times 144 \qquad$ Using the rule, we must multiply.
$$= 288 \text{ in.}^2$$

Example 3
Change 4 yd^2 to square feet.
Solution
When we compare yards to feet, the yard is a bigger unit. Using the rule, to change a bigger unit to a smaller unit, we must multiply.

$$1 \text{ yd}^2 = 9 \text{ ft}^2 \qquad \text{See the table.}$$

Therefore, $4 \text{ yd}^2 = 4 \times 9 \qquad$ Using the rule, we must multiply.
$$= 36 \text{ ft}^2$$

Example 4
Change $5\frac{2}{3}$ yd^2 to square feet

Solution
When we compare yards to feet, the yard is a bigger unit. Using the rule, to change a bigger unit to a smaller unit, we must multiply.

$$1 \text{ yd}^2 = 9 \text{ ft}^2 \qquad \text{See the table.}$$

Therefore, $5\frac{2}{3} \text{ yd}^2 = 5\frac{2}{3} \times 9 \text{ ft}^2 \qquad$ Using the rule, must multiply.

$$= \frac{17}{3} \times 9 \text{ ft}^2 \qquad \text{Review fractions.}$$

$$= \frac{17}{\overset{}{\underset{1}{3}}} \times \overset{3}{9} \text{ ft}^2 \qquad \text{Divide by 3.}$$

$$= 17 \times 3 \text{ ft}^2$$
$$= 51 \text{ ft}^2$$

Example 5
Change 63 square feet to square yards.
Solution
When we compare feet and yard, feet is the smaller unit. Using the rule, changing

from the smaller unit to the bigger unit, we must divide.

$$9 \text{ ft}^2 = 1 \text{ yd}^2 \quad\quad \text{See the table.}$$
$$\text{Therefore, } 63 \text{ ft}^2 = 63 \div 9 \quad\quad \text{Using the rule, we must divide.}$$
$$= 7 \text{ yd}^2$$

Exercises
1. Change the following square inches to square feet. Hint: See Example 1.
   a. 432 in.²   **b**. 720 in.²
2. Change the following square feet to square inches. Hint: See Example 2.
   a. 3 ft²   **b**. 8 ft²   **c**. 10 ft²   **d**. 12 ft²
3. Change the following square yards to square feet. Hint: See Example 3.
   a. 3 yd²   **b**. 7 yd²   **c**. 10 yd²   **d**. 6 yd²
4. Change the following square yards to square feet. Hint: See Example 4.
   a. $4\frac{1}{3}$ yd²   **b**. $6\frac{2}{3}$ yd²   **c**. $7\frac{1}{3}$ yd²   **d**. $3\frac{2}{3}$ yd²
5. Change the following square feet to square yards. Hint: See Example 5.
   a. 18 ft²   **b**. 90 ft²   **c**. 45 ft²   **d**. 72 ft²

Challenge Questions
5. Change the following square yards to square feet
   a. $2\frac{2}{3}$ yd²   **b**. 1 yd²   **c**. 11 yd²
6. Change the following square inches to square feet.
   a. 144 in²   **b**. 576 in²
7. Change the following square feet to square inches.
   a. 4 ft²   **b**. 7 ft²   **c**. 8 ft²
8. Change the following square feet to square yards.
   a. 27 ft²   **b**. 36 ft²   **c**. 45 ft²   **d**. 9 ft²

Answers to Selected Questions.
   1a. 3 ft²   **2a**. 432 in²   **3a**. 27 ft²

REAL WORLD APPLICATIONS - WORD PROBLEMS
CUSTOMARY UNITS OF SQUARE MEASURES

Example 1
A room has 99 square feet of floor space. How many square yards of tiles is needed for the floor assuming that there will be no waste of the tiles.

Solution

When we compare feet to yard, the yard is a bigger unit. Using the rule, to change from smaller unit to bigger unit, we must divide.

$$9 \text{ ft}^2 = 1 \text{ yd}^2 \qquad \text{See the table.}$$

Therefore, $99 \text{ ft}^2 = 99 \div 9 \qquad \text{Using the rule, we must divide.}$

$$= 11 \text{ yd}^2$$

Exercise

A room has 72 square feet of floor space. How many square yards of tiles is needed for the floor assuming that there will be no waste of the tiles.
Hint: See Example 1.

METRIC MASS AND CUSTOMARY WEIGHT

Metric Mass

Recall that the units of the metric length are based on the meter, similarly the units of the metric mass are based on the gram. A benchmark for 1 gram is the mass of a large paper clip.

Team Work

Each team should do a research at a super market and list the names and the weights of 4 different packages of cookies in grams. The weights are already written on the packages. Can you compare the mass of a large paper clip, which is 1 gram to the mass of each package of cookie?

Metric Prefixes

Prefix	Meaning	Abbreviations
milli-	one thousandth, (0.001) or $\dfrac{1}{1000}$	mg for milligram
kilo-	one thousand, (1,000)	kg for kilogram

The prefix for gram is g.

Metric Mass Units

1 milligram (mg) = .001 g or $\dfrac{1}{1000}$ g

1 gram (g) = 1,000 mg, .001 kg or $\dfrac{1}{1000}$ kg

439

1 kilogram (kg) = 1,000, .001 metric ton or $\dfrac{1}{1000}$ metric tons.

1 metric ton (t) = 1,000 kg, 1,000,000 g.

Rule 1: To change smaller units to larger units **divide**.
Rule 2: To change larger units to smaller units **multiply**.

Example 1
How many grams are there in 5 kilograms?
Solution
The question may be rewritten as shown:
5 kilograms = ? grams.
To change larger units to smaller units multiply.

Number of kilograms × Number of grams in 1 kilogram = Number of grams.

↓	↓	↓
5	**× 1,000**	**= 5,000 gram.**

There are 5,000 grams in 5 kilograms.

Example 2
If glucophage 1000 mg tablet is one of the medications that Nick takes daily, what is the mass of 1 tablet of the glucophage in grams?
Solution
The question may be rewritten as shown:
1000 mg = ? g
To change from smaller units (for example mg) to larger units (for example g) divide as shown:

Number of mg ÷ Number of mg in 1 g = Number of grams.

↓	↓	↓
1,000	**÷ 1,000**	**= 1 gram**

Therefore the mass of 1 tablet of glucophage is 1 gram.

Example 3
Replace ? with the number that makes the statement true.
6 g = ? mg
Solution
To change from larger units (for example g) to smaller units (for example mg) multiply as shown:

Number of grams × Number of milligrams in 1 gram = Number of milligrams.

$$6 \quad \times \quad 1{,}000 \quad = \quad 6{,}000 \text{ milligrams}$$

Therefore, 6 g = 6,000 mg.

Example 4
Solve: 3.6 kg = ? g.
Solution
To change from larger units (for example kg) to smaller units (for example g) multiply as shown:

Number of kilograms × Number of grams in 1 kilogram = Number of grams.

$$3.6 \quad \times \quad 1{,}000 \quad = \quad 3{,}600$$

Therefore, 3.6 kg = 3, 600 grams.   (Review decimal multiplication).

Example 5
Solve: 7500 kg = ? metric ton
Solution
To change from smaller units (for example kg) to larger units (for example metric tons) divide as shown:

Number of kilograms ÷ Number of kilograms in 1 metric ton = Number of metric tons.

$$7{,}500 \quad \div \quad 1{,}000 \quad = \quad \frac{7500}{1000}$$

$$= \quad \frac{75\cancel{0}\cancel{0}}{10\cancel{0}\cancel{0}}$$

$$= \quad 7.5$$

Therefore, 7,500 kg = 7.5 metric tons

Example 6
Compare and write =, < or > for ?
3 metric tons ? 2,500,000 g
Solution
Setup: The first step in comparing numbers is to change the numbers to the same

units before comparing.

Step 1: Change 3 metric tons to grams. To change from larger units (for example metric tons) to smaller units (for example grams) multiply as shown:

Number of metric tons × Number of grams in 1 metric tons = Number of grams.

3   ×   1,000,000   =   3,000,000 g

Therefore, 3 metric tons = 3,000,000 g.
But 3,000,000 g is greater than 2,500,00 g. Therefore, 3 metric tons > 2,500,000 g.

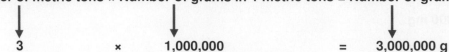

The notes and the generous worked examples have provided me with conceptual understanding and computational fluency to do my homework.

Exercises

1. Select the correct answer. The metric mass is based on:

    a. inches   **b**. meter   **c**. gram   **d**. kilogram

2. How many grams are there in the following? Hint: See Example 1.

    a. 6 kg   **b**. 2 kg   **c**. 1.5 kg   **d**. 3 kg

3. If the mass of 1 tablet of a medication is 500 mg, what is the weight of the tablet in grams? Hint: See Example 2.

4. Replace ? with the number that makes the statement true. Hint: See Example 3.

    a. 2 g = ? mg   **b**. 4 g = ? mg   **c**. 3 g = ? mg

5. Solve the following: Hint: See Example 4.

    a. 4.2 kg = ? g   **b**. 2.3 kg = ? g   **c**. 1.5 kg = ? g

6. Solve: Hint: See Example 5.

    a. 2,500 kg = ? metric tons   **b**. 3,300 kg = ? metric tons
    c. 1,100 kg = ? metric tons   **d**. 6,200 kg = ? metric tons

7. Compare and write =, < or > for ? Hint: See Example 6.

    a. 2 metric tons ? 2,000,000 g   **b**. 4 metric tons ? 3,900,000 g
    c. 3 metric tons ? 3,100,000 g   **d**. 5 kg ? 4,900 g

Challenge Questions

8. Solve:

    a. 4 metric tons = ? kg   **b**. 8 g = ? mg   **c**. 5000 g = ? kg.
    d. 3,000,000g =? metric tons   **e**. 4,500 mg = ? g.

CUSTOMARY UNITS OF WEIGHT

The basic unit of mass in the Customary System is the pound.

16 ounces (oz) =1 pound (lb)

2,000 pounds =1 ton (T)

Example 1

Solve: 40 oz = ? lb

To change from smaller units (for example, ounces) to larger units (for example pound), divide as shown:

Number of ounces ÷ Number of ounces in 1 pound = Number of pounds.

$$40 \quad ÷ \quad 16 \quad = \quad \frac{40}{16}$$

$$= \quad \frac{\overset{5}{\cancel{40}}}{\underset{2}{\cancel{16}}}$$

$$= \quad \frac{5}{2}$$

Therefore, 40 oz = $2\frac{1}{2}$ lb.

Example 2

Solve: 4lb = ? oz.

Solution

To change from larger units (for example, pounds) to smaller units (for example ounces), multiply as shown:

Number of pounds × Number of ounces in 1 pound = Number of ounces.

$$4 \quad × \quad 16 \quad = 64 \text{ ounces.}$$

Therefore, 4 lb = 64 oz.

Example 3

Solve: 6,000 lb = ? T

Solution

443

To change from smaller units (for example, pounds) to larger units (for example tons), divide as shown:

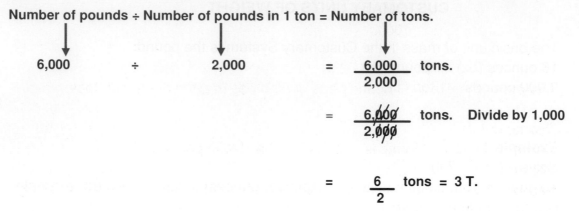

Number of pounds ÷ Number of pounds in 1 ton = Number of tons.

$$6,000 \quad ÷ \quad 2,000 \quad = \quad \frac{6,000}{2,000} \text{ tons.}$$

$$= \quad \frac{6,\cancel{000}}{2,\cancel{000}} \text{ tons.} \quad \text{Divide by 1,000}$$

$$= \quad \frac{6}{2} \text{ tons} = 3 \text{ T.}$$

Therefore, 6,000 lb = 3 T

Example 4
Solve: 4 T = ? lb
Solution
To change from larger units (for example, tons) to smaller units (for example pounds), multiply as shown:

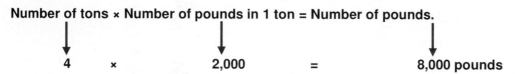

Number of tons × Number of pounds in 1 ton = Number of pounds.

$$4 \quad × \quad 2,000 \quad = \quad 8,000 \text{ pounds}$$

Therefore, 4 T = 8,000 lb.

REAL WORLD APPLICATION - WORD PROBLEMS
CUSTOMARY UNITS OF WEIGHT

Example 5
How many 100-pound bags of potatoes can be obtained from a ton of potatoes?
Solution
Setup: Change a ton of potatoes to pounds of potatoes and then divide by 100 pounds.
To change from larger units (for example, tons) to smaller units (for example pounds), multiply as shown:

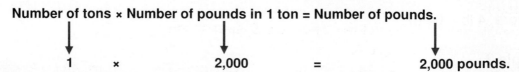

Number of tons × Number of pounds in 1 ton = Number of pounds.

$$1 \quad × \quad 2,000 \quad = \quad 2,000 \text{ pounds.}$$

Therefore, there are 2000 lb in 1 ton.
To find how many 100-pound bags of potatoes are contained in the 2000 lb of

potatoes, divide 2000 lb by 100 lb as shown:

$$\frac{2{,}000 \text{ lb}}{100 \text{ lb}} = \frac{2{,}000 \text{ lb}}{100 \text{ lb}}$$

Divide by 100.

$$= 20$$

Therefore, there are 20-pound bags of potatoes in a ton of the potatoes.

Example 6
How much would 48 ounces of candy cost at $4.00 per pound?
Solution
Setup: Let us find how many pounds are there in 48 ounces, and then multiply the number of pounds in 48 ounces by $4.00 to obtain the cost of 48 ounces of the candy as shown:
To change from smaller units (for example, ounces) to larger units (for example pounds), divide as shown:

Number of ounces ÷ Number of ounces in 1 pound = Number of pounds.

$$48 \qquad \div \qquad 16 \qquad = \qquad \frac{48}{16} \text{ pounds}$$

$$= \frac{\cancel{48}\,\cancel{12}\,3}{\cancel{16}\,\cancel{4}\,1}$$

$$= 3 \text{ (Divide by 4 and by 4 again).}$$

Therefore, there are 3 pounds in 48 ounces.
If 1 lb of the candy costs $4.00, then 3 lb of the candy will cost 3 × $4.00 = $12.00.

The notes and the generous worked examples have provided me with conceptual understanding and computational fluency to do my homework.

Exercises
1. The basic unit of mass in the Customary System is the_____.
2. Solve: Hint: See Example 1.

   a. 32 oz = ? lb   **b**. 24 oz = ? lb   **c**. 8 oz = ? lb   **d**. 48 oz = ? lb

3. Solve: Hit: See Example 2.

a. 2 lb = ? oz   **b**. 5 lb = ? oz   **c**.10 lb = ? oz   **d**. 7 lb = ? oz

4. Solve: Hint: See Example 3.

    a. 2000 lb = ? T   **b**. 1000 lb = ? T   **c**. 4000lb = ? T   **d**. 8000 lb = ? T

5. Solve: Hint: See Example 6.

    a. 2 T = ? lb   **b**. 6 T = ? lb   **c**. 3 T = ? lb   **d**. 5 T = ? lb

6. Solve: Hint: See Example 5.

How many 50-pound bags of rice can be obtained from 2 tons of rice?

7. Solve: Hint: See Example 6.

How much would 32 ounces of candy cost at $3.00 per pound?

Challenge Questions

8. Solve: **a**. 6 lb = ? oz   **b**. 40 oz = ? lb   **c**. 10 T = ? lb   **d**. 5000 lb = ? t

Answers to Selected Questions

2a. 2 lb   **3a**. 32 oz   **4a**. 1 T   **5a**. 4000 lb

METRIC CAPACITY AND CUSTOMARY CAPACITY

METRIC CAPACITY

The basic unit in measuring liquid is the liter. The metric units of capacity are:

1,000 millimeters (ml) = 1 liter (L)

250 milliliters = 1 metric cup

4 metric cups = 1 liter

1,000 liters = 1 kilometer (KL)

Team Project

The class should be divided into four teams. (Each team should bring the big, bigger and the biggest empty containers of milk, orange juice and soda drink from the super market to the class.) Each team should sketch and complete the chart using the labels on the containers.

Table 1

Product Name	Big size/Sketch	Bigger size/Sketch	Biggest size/Sketch
Milk containers	Capacity = ?	Capacity = ?	capacity = 3.78 L
Orange juice container	Sketch = ? Capacity = ?	Sketch = ? Capacity = ?	Sketch = ? Capacity = ?
Soda drink container	Sketch = ? Capacity = ?	Sketch = ? Capacity = ?	Sketch = ? Capacity = ?

a. What size and what capacity of milk is used most in each team member's family?

b. What size and what capacity of orange juice is used the least in each member's family?

c. What size and what capacity of the soda drink is used the most in each team member's family?

Example 1

Explain when you would multiply or divide in order to change one unit to another unit.

Solution

In order to change from lower units such as milliliters to higher units such as liters we should **divide** because the final answer we are looking for should be less than the number of the lower unit. For example, 1,000 milliliters = 1 liter. Therefore, to change 1,000 milliliters to liters, we have to **divide** 1,000 milliliters by 1,000 to obtain the number of liters that are contained in 1,000 milliliters.

In order to change from higher units such as liters to metric cups, we should **multiply** because the final answer that we are looking for should be more than the number of the higher units. For example, 4 metric cups = 1 liter and to change 1 liter to metric cups we have to **multiply** the 1 liter by 4.

Example 2

Solve: 8 metric cups = ? liters.

Solution

To change smaller units (metric cups) to bigger units (liters) we **divide** as shown:

447

Number of metric cups ÷ Number of metric cups in 1 liter = Number of liters.

8	÷ 4	= 2

There are 2 liters in 8 metric cups.

Example 3

a. Change 22 liters to milliliters.

b. Change 164 milliliters to liters.

Solution

a. To change from larger units (such as liters) to smaller units (such as milliliters), we should **multiply** as shown:

Number of liters × Number of milliliters in 1 liter = Number of milliliters.

22	× 1,000	= 22,000 milliliters.

Therefore, there are 22,000 milliliters in 22 liters.

b. To change from smaller units (such as milliliters) to larger units (such as liters), we should **divide** as shown:

Number of milliliters ÷ Number of milliliters in 1 liter = Number of liters

$$164 \div 1{,}000 = \frac{164}{1{,}000}$$

$$= .164$$

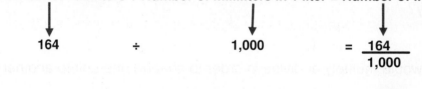

We are dividing by 1,000 which has three zeros and therefore, we have to move the decimal point three places or three digits to the left.

Therefore, there are .164 liters in 164 milliliters.

Example 4

Solve: ? milliliters = 10 metric cups

Solution

To change from larger units (such as metric cups) to smaller units (such as milliliters) we multiply as shown:

Number of metric cups × Number of milliliters in 1 mtric cup = Number of milliliters.

10	× 250	= 2,500 milliliters

Therefore, there are 2500 milliliters in 10 metric cups.

Example 5

Compare. Write $<$, $>$ or $=$ for ? in the question.

a. 4,000 L ? 3 kL

b. 2 L ? 9 metric cups

Solution

a. In order to compare two quantities, we must change both quantities to the **same units** first before comparing. In this case, let us change kL to L first as follows: To change from larger units (such as kL) to smaller units (such as L), multiply as shown:

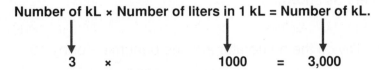

Number of kL × Number of liters in 1 kL = Number of kL.

$$3 \quad \times \quad 1000 \quad = \quad 3,000$$

Therefore, there are 3,000 liters in 3 kL.

We can now compare the 4,000 L and the 3,000 L because 3,000 L and 4,000 L have the same units. Since 4,000 L is greater than 3,000 L, we can write: 4,000 L > 3,000 L, and therefore, 4,000 L > 3 kL.

(Note: We have already showed that 3kL = 3,000 L.)

b. In order to compare two quantities, we must change both quantities to the same units first before comparing them. In this case, let us change 2L to metric cups first as shown:

To change from larger units (such as liters) to smaller units (such as metric cups) we multiply as shown:

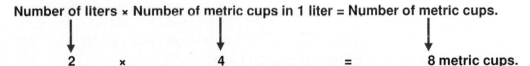

Number of liters × Number of metric cups in 1 liter = Number of metric cups.

$$2 \quad \times \quad 4 \quad = \quad 8 \text{ metric cups.}$$

Therefore, there are 8 metric cups in 2 L.

Now, we can compare the 8 metric cups and the 9 metric cups because the 8 metric cups and the 9 metric cups have the same units. Since 8 metric cups is less than 9 metric cups we can write:

8 metric cups < 9 metric cups. Therefore, we can write:

2 L < 9 metric cups (Note: We have already showed that 2 L = 8 metric cups).

REAL WORLD APPLICATIONS - WORD PROBLEMS
METRIC CAPACITY

Example 6

How many bottles each holding 150 milliliters of orange juice can be filled from a plastic container that holds 4.5 liters of the orange juice?

Solution

Change the 150 milliliters and 4.5 liters to the same unit, and then divide 4.5 liters by 150 milliliters. Let us change 4.5 liters to milliliters as shown:

Number of liters × Number of milliliters in 1 liter = Number of milliliters.

$$4.5 \quad \times \quad 1,000 \quad = \quad 4500.0 \text{ milliliters.}$$

Therefore, there are 4,500 milliliters in 4.5 liters.

Let us find how many 150 milliliters are contained in 4,500 milliliters by dividing 4,500 milliliters by 150 milliliters as shown:

$$\frac{4,500}{150} = \frac{4,500}{150} \qquad \text{Divide the numerator and the denominator by 10.}$$

$$= \frac{\overset{90}{\cancel{450}}}{\underset{3}{\cancel{15}}} \qquad \text{Divide the numerator and the denominator by 5.}$$

$$= \frac{\overset{30}{\cancel{90}}}{\underset{1}{\cancel{3}}} \qquad \text{Divide the numerator and the denominator by 3.}$$

$$= 30$$

Therefore, 30 bottles each holding 150 milliliters of orange juice can be filled from a plastic container that holds 4.5 liters of orange juice.

Example 7

Five engineers drank a total of 4 L of water. If each engineer drank an equal amount of water, how many milliliters did each engineer drink?

Solution

Step 1: Change 4 L to milliliters as shown:

To change from larger units (such as liters) to smaller units (such as milliliters) we should multiply as shown:

Number of liters × Number of milliliters in 1 liter = Number of milliliters.

$$4 \quad \times \quad 1,000 \quad = \quad 4000 \text{ milliliters.}$$

Therefore, there are 4000 milliliters in 4 liters.

Step 2: To find the amount of water that each engineer drank, find the average amount of water that each engineer drank by dividing 4000 milliliters by 5 engineers as shown:

$$\frac{4{,}000}{5} = \frac{\overset{800}{\cancel{4{,}000}}}{\underset{1}{\cancel{5}}}$$

= 800 milliliters of water.

Therefore, each engineer drank 800 milliliters of water.

The notes and the generous worked examples have provided me with conceptual understanding and computational fluency to do my homework.

Exercises

1. When do we divide and when do we multiply if we want to convert one unit to another? Hint: See Example 1.
2. Solve: (Hint: See Example 2).
    a. 12 metric cups = ? liters   **b**. 4 metric cups = ? liters
    c. 16 metric cups = ? liters   **d**. 2 metric cups = ? liters
3a. Change 8 liters to milliliters. Hint: See Example **3a**.
3b. Change 158 milliliters to liters. Hint: See Example **3b**.
4. Solve: Hint: See example 4.
    a. ? milliliters = 8 metric cups.   **b**. ? milliliters = 5 metric cups.
    c. ? milliliters = 3 metric cups.   **d**. ? milliliters = 4 metric cups
5. Compare. Write <, > or = for ? in the questions. Hint: See example **5a**.
    a. 2000 L ? 4 kL   **b**. 2500 L ? 2 kL   **c**. 3000 L ? 3 kL   **d**. 5000 L ? 4 kL
6. Compare. Write <, > or = for ? in the questions. Hint: See Example **5b**.
    a. 2 L ? 8 metric cups   **b**. 3L ? 12 metric cups
    c. 16 metric cups ? 4 L   **d**. 8 metric cups ? 3 L
7. How many bottles each holding 100 milliliters can be filled from a plastic container that holds:
    a. 1 liter?   **b**. 2 liters?   **c**. 3 liters?   (Hint: See Example 6.)
8. How many bottles each holding 250 milliliters of apple juice can be filled from a plastic container that holds:
    a. 1 liter of the apple juice?   **b**. 2 liters of the apple juice?
    c. 3 liters of the apple juice?
    Hint: See Example 6.
9. Four nurses drank a total of 2 L of water. If each nurse drank an equal amount of water, how many milliliters did each nurse drink? Hint: See Example **7**.

Challenge Questions

10. Solve: **a**. ? milliliters = 6 metric cups   **b**. ? milliliters = 7 metric cups
11. Solve: **a**. 6 metric cups = ? liters   **b**. 10 metric cups = ? liters
12. How many bottles each holding 200 milliliters can be filled from a plastic container that holds:
  a. 1 liter?   **b**. 4 liters?
14. Compare. Write <, > or = for ? in the questions.
  a. 3 L ? 12 metric cups   **b**. 5000 L ? 4 kL

Answers to Selected Questions

2a. 3 L   **3a**. 8,000 ml   **4a**. 2000 ml   **5a**. <

CUSTOMARY CAPACITY

The basic unit in measuring liquids in the Customary system is the gallon.
The Customary units of capacity are as shown:

$$8 \text{ fluid ounces (fl oz)} = 1 \text{ cup (c)}$$
$$2 \text{ cups} = 1 \text{ pint (pt)}$$
$$2 \text{ pints} = 1 \text{ quart (qt)}$$
$$4 \text{ cups} = 1 \text{ quart (qt)}$$
$$4 \text{ quarts} = 1 \text{ gallon (gal)}$$

Group Exercise
The class should be divided into four groups.
a. Each group should list four liquid products that can be seen at the supermarket with their corresponding measurements involving capacity. For example, a container of milk at the supermarket may have a capacity of one gallon or half a gallon.
b. Sketch the container of each product.
c. Compare the lists with the corresponding capacities from the other groups and list the products in increasing order of their capacity.

Example 1
In the Customary system the basic unit in measuring liquids is the gallon, true or false? Hint: See notes.
Solution
The student is to find the answer to example 1 by reading the notes/text in this book.

Example 2
Solve: 12 quarts = ? pints

Solution

To change larger units (such as quarts) to smaller units (such as pints) **multiply** as shown:

Number of quarts × Number of pints in 1 quart = Number of pints.

| 12 | × | 2 | = | 24 pints |

Example 3

Solve: 20 quarts = ? gal

Solution

To change smaller units (such as quarts) to larger units (such as gallons) **divide** as shown:

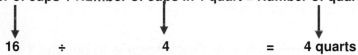

Number of quarts ÷ Number of quarts in 1 gallon = Number of gallons.

| 20 | ÷ | 4 | = 5 gallons. |

Example 4

Solve: 16 c = ? qt

Solution

To change smaller units (such as cups) to larger units (such as quarts) **divide** as shown:

Number of cups ÷ Number of cups in 1 quart = Number of quarts.

| 16 | ÷ | 4 | = | 4 quarts |

Example 5

Solve: 6 gal = ? c

Solution

Setup: This is a two step solution.

Step 1: Change the gallons to quarts.

To change from larger units (such as gallons) to smaller units (such as quarts), **multiply** as shown:

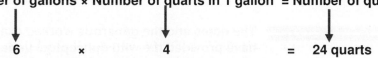

Number of gallons × Number of quarts in 1 gallon = Number of quarts.

| 6 | × | 4 | = | 24 quarts |

Step 2: Change the 24 quarts to cups.

To change from larger units (such as quarts) to smaller units (such as cups), **multiply** as shown:

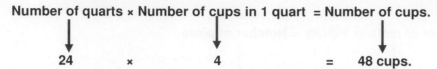

Number of quarts × Number of cups in 1 quart = Number of cups.

| 24 | × | 4 | = | 48 cups. |

Example 6
Solve: 7 c = ? ft oz

To change larger units (such as cups) to smaller units (such as fluid ounces) **multiply** as shown:

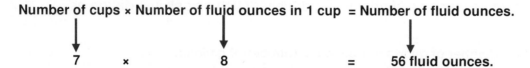

Number of cups × Number of fluid ounces in 1 cup = Number of fluid ounces.

| 7 | × | 8 | = | 56 fluid ounces. |

Therefore, there are 56 fluid ounces in 7 cups.

REAL WORLD APPLICATIONS - WORD PROBLEMS
CUSTOMARY CAPACITY

Example 7
Given that 1 gallon of a certain ice cream is on sale for $3.95 and two 1-quart containers of the same ice cream are on sale for $2.25. If Mary needs 1 gallon of ice cream for her birthday party, which is a better buy?

Solution

Setup: The better buy will be the least expensive buy. One choice is to buy the 1 gallon ice cream for $3.95 and the other choice is to buy four 1-quart containers of the same ice cream because 4 quarts makes 1 gallon.

Step 1: Find the cost of four 1-quart containers of the same ice cream.
Two 1–quart containers of ice cream = $2.25
Four 1–quart containers of ice cream = 2.25 × 2 = $4.50.

Step 2: Decide which size of the ice cream is a better buy.
Since $3.95 < $4.50, the 1 gallon of ice cream which is on sale for $3.95 is a better buy.

_____

The notes and the generous worked examples have provided me with conceptual understanding and computational fluency to do my homework.

Exercises

1. In the customary system the basic unit for measuring liquid is _____
Hint: See Example 1

2. Solve: (See Example 2).

    a. 10 quarts = ? pints   **b.** 4 quarts = ? pints
    c. 2 quarts = ? pints   **d.** 12 quarts = ? pints

3. Solve: (See Example 3).

    a. 12 quarts = ? gal   **b.** 8 quarts = ? gal
    c. 16 quarts = ? gal   **d.** 4 quarts = ? gal

4. Solve: (See Example 4).

    a. 4 c = ? qt   **b.** 12 c = ? qt
    c. 20 c = ? qt   **d.** 10 c = ? qt

5. Solve: (See Example 5).

    a. 4 gal = ? c   **b.** 10 gal = ? c
    c. 8 gal = ? c   **d.** 3 gal = ? c

6. Solve: (See Example 6).

    a. 6 c = ? ft oz   **b.** 3 c = ? ft oz
    c. 2 c = ? ft oz   **d.** 5 c = ? ft oz

7. If 1 gallon of type A ice cream costs \$2.85 and 4 cups of type B ice cream costs \$.50, which type of the ice cream is cheaper? Hint: See Example 7.

Challenge Questions

8. Solve:
    a. 7 gal = ? c   **b.** 16 c = ? qt   **c.** 24 c = ? qt
    d. 10 quarts = ? gal   **e.** 6 qt = ? qt   **f.** 4 gal = ? c

Cumulative Review

1. 15 ÷ (-3) =   **2.** -15 ÷ (-3) =   **3.** -24 ÷ 6 =   **4.** $\dfrac{3}{4} \div \dfrac{3}{8} =$

TIME

Review of How to Tell the Time

The time is 12: 20

The time is 9:55

Measuring time is measuring the interval of time between two separate events. An example of two separate events is when John started to eat and when John finished eating. We should be able to determine the length of the interval between two given times. There are 24 hours that make up a day and this 24 hours is divided into two periods, the A.M. (which is before noon) hours from 12 o'clock midnight to 12 o'clock noon and the P.M. (which is after noon) hours from 12 o'clock noon to 12 o'clock midnight.

Rule 1: To find the length of the time interval between two given times that are both A.M. or both P.M., subtract the hours and the minutes of the earlier time from the later time.

Rule 2: To find the length of the time interval between two given times when one is A.M. and the other is P.M., use the fact that 12:00 o'clock is the time that separates A.M. from P.M. hours, and therefore, we first find how far each of the given times is from 12:00 o'clock and secondly, we add the two results.

Table 1

The units of time are as follows:	
60 seconds (sec) = 1 minute (min)	
60 minutes	= 1 hour (hr)
24 hours	= 1 day (da)
7 days	= 1 week (wk)
4 weeks	= 1 month (mo)
52 weeks	= 1 year (yr)
365 days	= 1 year (yr)
366 days	= 1 leap year
10 years	= 1 decade
100 years	= 1 century
1,000 years	= 1 millennium

Example 1

What is the length of time between 7:15 A.M. and 10:50 A.M.?

Solution

Use Rule 1 to solve the question as shown:

```
    10 hr    50 min
  -  7 hr    15 min
  ─────────────────
     3 hr    35 min
```

Therefore, the length of time between 7:15 A.M. and 10:50 A.M. is 3 hr and 35 minutes.

Example 2

Find the length of time between 2:50 P.M. and 10:23 P.M.

Solution

Use Rule 1 to solve the question as shown:

```
    10 hr    23 min
  -  2 hr    50 min
```

We cannot subtract 50 minutes from 23 minutes, and therefore, we have to borrow 1 hr from 10 hr and this 1 hr becomes 60 minutes (see Table 1), and we then add the 60 minutes to the 23 minutes to obtain 83 minutes, and the 10 hours is therefore reduced to 9 hours, and then subtract as shown:

```
     9       83
    10 hr    23 min
  -  2 hr    50 min
  ─────────────────
     7 hr    33 min
```

Therefore, the length of the time between 2:50 P.M. and 10:23 P.M. is 7 hr 33 min.

Example 3

The school day of the Accra Middle School starts at 8:10 A.M and ends at 2:51 P.M. How long is the school day?

Solution

Use Rule 2 to solve the question as shown:

Step 1: Subtract to find the length of the time from 8:10 A.M. to 12:00 noon.

```
    12 hr    00 min
  -  8 hr    10 min
  ─────────────────
```

457

We cannot subtract 10 minutes from 00 minutes, and therefore, we have to borrow 1 hour from 12 hours, and this 1 hr is 60 minutes (see Table 1), and we then add the 60 minutes to the 00 minutes to become 60 minutes and the 12 hours is therefore, reduced to 11 hours, and then we subtract as shown:

$$
\begin{array}{rr}
11 & 60 \\
\cancel{12} \text{ hr} & \cancel{00} \text{ min} \\
- 8 \text{ hr} & 10 \text{ min} \\
\hline
3 \text{ hr} & 50 \text{ min}
\end{array}
$$

Step 2: 2:51 P.M. is 2 hours and 51 minutes after 12:00 noon.

Step 3: Add the two intervals found in Steps 1 and 2 as shown:

$$
\begin{array}{rr}
3 \text{ hr} & 50 \text{ min} \\
+ 2 \text{ hr} & 51 \text{ min} \\
\hline
5 \text{ hr} & 101 \text{ min}
\end{array}
$$

Note that 101 minutes is more than 60 minutes and 60 minutes is equal to one hour. Divide 101 minutes by 60 to obtain the hours and minutes that are contained in 101 minutes as shown:

$$
\begin{array}{r}
1 \text{ hr remainder 41 minutes} \\
60 \overline{)101 \text{ minutes}} \\
\underline{- 60} \\
41
\end{array}
$$

Therefore, 5 hr 101 min can be written as:

$$
\begin{array}{rr}
5 \text{ hr} & \\
+ 1 \text{ hr} & 41 \text{ min} \\
\hline
6 \text{ hr} & 41 \text{ min}
\end{array}
$$

Therefore, the school day is 6 hours and 41 minutes.

Example 4

Find the length of the interval between 9:45 P.M and 4:10 A.M.

Solution

Use Rule 2 to solve the question as shown:

Step 1: Subtract to find the length of the time from 9:45 P.M to 12:00 midnight.

$$
\begin{array}{rr}
12 \text{ hr} & 00 \text{ min} \\
- 9 \text{ hr} & 45 \text{ min} \\
\hline
\end{array}
$$

We cannot subtract 45 minutes from 00 minutes, and therefore, we borrow 1 hour from 12 hours and this 1 hour is 60 minutes and we add the 60 minutes to 00 minutes to obtain 60 minutes and the 12 hours is reduced to 11 hours and we then subtract as shown:

$$
\begin{array}{rr}
11 & 60 \\
12\ hr & 00\ min \\
-\ 9\ hr & 45\ min \\
\hline
2\ hr & 15\ min
\end{array}
$$

Step 2: 4:10 A.M. is 4 hours and 10 minutes after 12 midnight.

Step 3: Add the two intervals found in steps 1 and 2 as shown:

$$
\begin{array}{rr}
2\ hr & 15\ min \\
+\ 4\ hr & 10\ min \\
\hline
6\ hr & 25\ min
\end{array}
$$

Therefore, the interval between 9:45 P.M and 4:10 A.M is 6 hr 25 min.

Example 5

How many hours are in 3 days?

Solution

To change from larger units such as days to smaller units such as hours, multiply as shown:

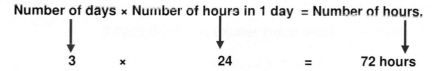

Number of days × Number of hours in 1 day = Number of hours.

$$3 \quad \times \quad 24 \quad = \quad 72\ hours$$

Therefore, there are 72 hours in 3 days.

Example 6

How many weeks are in 28 days?

Solution

To change from smaller units such as days to larger units such as weeks, divide as shown:

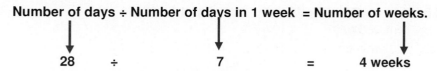

Number of days ÷ Number of days in 1 week = Number of weeks.

$$28 \quad \div \quad 7 \quad = \quad 4\ weeks$$

Therefore, there are 4 weeks in 28 days.

The notes and the generous worked examples have provided me with conceptual understanding and computational fluency to do my homework.

Exercises

1. State the rule that is used in finding the length of the time interval between two given times that are both A.M. or both P.M. Hint:See Rule 1.

2. State the rule that is used in finding the length of the time interval between two given times when one is A.M. and the other is P.M. Hint: See Rule 2.

3. Find the length of the interval between the two given times. Hint: See Example 1.
   a. 7:30 A.M. to 11:46 A.M.   b. 6:14 A.M. to 10:34 A.M.
   c. 9:47 A.M. to 10:59 A.M.   d. 10:01 A.M. to 11:09 A.M.

4. Find the length of the interval between the two given times. Hint: See Example 2.
   a. 6:30 P.M. to 9:40 P.M   b. 4:10 P.M. to 8:30 P.M.
   c. 7:20 A.M. to 10:45 A.M   d. 8:15 A.M. to 11:35 A.M

5. Find the length of the interval between the two given times. Hint: See Example 3.
   a. 10:30 A.M to 3:15 P.M   b. 9:00 A.M. to 2:30 P.M.
   c. 7:40 A.M. to 2:45 P.M.   d. 8:07 A.M. to 5:45 P.M.

6. Find the length of the interval between the two given times. Hint: See Example 4.
   a. 10:30 P.M to 2:30 A.M   b. 7:00 P.M. to 4:00 A.M
   c. 8:18 P.M. to 8:19 A.M   d. 11:20 P.M. to 1:40 A.M

7. Solve: (Hint: See Example 5).
   a. How many hours are in 6 days?   b. How many hours are in 2 days?

8. Solve: (Hint: See Example 6).
   a. How many weeks are in 21 days?   b. How many weeks are in 35 days?

Challenge Questions

9. Find the length of the interval between the two given times.
   a. 11:15 P.M. to 3:00 A.M.   b. 5:20 A.M. to 10:30 A.M.
   c. 7:48 A.M. to 11:57 A.M.   d. 1:31 P.M. to 9:20 P.M.
   e. 7:25 A.M. to 4:15 P.M.   f. 9:00 A.M. to 11:30 A.M.
   g. 6:18 A.M. to 11:30 A.M.   h. 2:40 P.M. to 3:15 A.M.

Answers to Selected Questions

3a. 4 hr 16 min   **4a.** 3 hr 10 min   **5a.** 4 hr 45 min.   **6a.** 4 hr 0 min

460

PROBABILITY

Cumulative Review

1. $8 + 9 =$ 2. $12 + 9 =$ 3. $11 - 8 =$ 4. $7 \times 2 =$

5. $12 \div 3 =$ 6. $23 - 14 =$ 7. $24 \div 6 =$ 8. $13 - 7 =$

9. $\begin{array}{r} 11 \\ \times\ \ 2 \\ \hline \end{array}$ 10. $\begin{array}{r} 26 \\ +\ \ 25 \\ \hline \end{array}$ 11. $\begin{array}{r} 31 \\ -\ 13 \\ \hline \end{array}$ 12. $\begin{array}{r} 8 \\ \times\ 4 \\ \hline \end{array}$

13. $18 \div 6 =$ 14. $24 \div 3 =$ 15. $12 + 8 =$ 16. $19 - 12 =$

17. $\begin{array}{r} 27 \\ \times\ \ 3 \\ \hline \end{array}$ 18. $\begin{array}{r} 17 \\ +\ 18 \\ \hline \end{array}$ 19. $\begin{array}{r} 39 \\ -\ 13 \\ \hline \end{array}$ 20. $\begin{array}{r} 18 \\ \times\ \ 4 \\ \hline \end{array}$

21. $48 \div 3 =$ 22. $24 \div 8 =$ 23. $12 + 38 =$ 24. $36 - 17 =$

25. $\begin{array}{r} 14 \\ \times\ \ 5 \\ \hline \end{array}$ 26. $\begin{array}{r} 23 \\ +\ 27 \\ \hline \end{array}$ 27. $\begin{array}{r} 19 \\ -\ 15 \\ \hline \end{array}$ 28. $\begin{array}{r} 12 \\ \times\ 3 \\ \hline \end{array}$

29. $48 - 17 =$ 30. $20 \div 4 =$ 31. $16 + 38 =$ 32. $28 - 16 =$

New Terms: probability, outcome, experiment

Probability is sometimes used in decision making. For example, if two friends want to go to either a movie or a football game together, but they are not sure if they should go to the movie first or the football game, then they may use coin flipping for decision making. There must be established rules before the coin is flipped, such as, if a head appears, they should go to the movie first and if a tail appears, they should go to the football game first.

Class Exercise

1. Give reasons why you think that coin flipping for decision making is not fair.
2. Give reasons why you think that coin flipping for decision making is fair
.

Group Exercise

In a soccer game, a coin toss is used to decide which team gets to select on which direction of the field it wants to play towards on the first play of the game.
Let us divide the class into two soccer teams of Team A and Team B. Each team should toss a coin 10 times and record the results using the tally table as

shown:

Team A and Team B Sample Chart

Trials	Heads tally	Tails tally
1st trial		
2nd trial		
3rd trial		
4th trial		
5th trial		
6th trial		
7th trial		
8th trial		
9th trial		
10th trial		
Total trials		
Fraction	$\dfrac{\text{Number of Heads}}{\text{Sum of total trials of heads and tails}} = \dfrac{?}{10}$	

Add up the results for the heads and tails. Find the fraction of the heads by using the formula :

$$\text{Fraction of the heads} = \frac{\text{Number of heads}}{\text{Number of trials}} = \frac{?}{10}$$

Find the fraction of the tails by using the formula:

$$\text{Fraction of the tails} = \frac{\text{Number of tails}}{\text{Number of trials}} = \frac{?}{10}$$

Conclusions of the Group Exercise
1. The group exercise is an example of an **experiment**. Therefore, the toss of a coin is an experiment.
2. The result of the experiment is the **outcome**. Therefore, the results of the number of heads and tails during the toss of the coin is the outcome.
3. The fraction of heads is actually the chances of obtaining a head when the coin is tossed 10 times, and this is known as the **probability** of obtaining a head.
4. The fraction of tails is actually the chances of obtaining a tail when the coin is tossed 10 times, and this is known as the **probability** of obtaining a tail.
5. From the group exercise, what is the fraction of heads? What is the probability of obtaining a head?
6. From the group exercise, what is the fraction of tails? What is the probability of obtaining a tail?
7. The outcomes of Team A and Team B should not necessarily be the same.

8. Note that the probability that Team A and Team B have found are fractions, for example, $\frac{?}{10}$. However, the probability can be expressed in **decimal** and **percent** also. Each group should change the fractional probability to decimal and percent probability (review the section on Decimal and Percent.)
9. When a coin was tossed, it was equally likely for either a head or a tail to occur. When outcomes have the same chance of occurring, they are said to be **equally likely**.
10. In the group exercise, we tossed the coin 10 times. It is possible to toss the coin more than 10 times, such as 20, 40, 100, or 200 times. Note that **the more we repeat the experiment, the closer we are to the true value of the probability**.

Experimental Probability

Experimental probability can be found by repeating an experiment many times and observing the results, as we did with the group exercise.

The formula for finding the experimental probability is given as shown:

$$\text{Experimental probability (outcome)} = \frac{\text{number of outcomes}}{\text{number of times the experiment was repeated}}$$

The experimental probability is sometimes called the **relative frequency**.

Example 1

A coin was tossed 45 times and 25 heads occurred.
(a) What is the experimental probability of obtaining heads? Express your answer as a fraction, a decimal, and a percent. Round your answer to the nearest hundredth.
(b) What is the experimental probability of obtaining tails? Express your answer as a fraction, a decimal, and a percent. Round your answer to two decimal places.

Solution

The number of times the coin was tossed = 45
The number of times the heads occurred = 25

$$\text{Experimental probability of heads} = \frac{\text{number of times heads occurred}}{\text{number of times the coin was tossed}}$$

$$= \frac{25}{45} \quad \text{This is the fractional form.}$$

$$= \frac{\overset{5}{\cancel{25}}}{\underset{9}{\cancel{45}}} \quad \text{Reduce to the lowest term by dividing by 5.}$$

$= \dfrac{5}{9}$ This is the probability in the fractional form,

reduced to the lowest terms.

To change the probability of $\dfrac{5}{9}$ to decimal, divide 5 by 9 as shown:

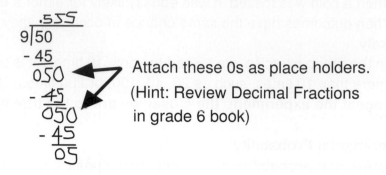

Attach these 0s as place holders.

(Hint: Review Decimal Fractions

in grade 6 book)

The decimal probability is .56 to the nearest hundredth. (Review the section on decimal fractions.)

The decimal probability of .56 can be changed to a percent form by moving the decimal point in .56 two decimal places or two digits to the right which is the same as multiplying .56 by 100 as shown:

$$.56 = .56. = 56\%$$

Move the decimal point two decimal places to the right.

Decimal
↓

Therefore, the probability of $\dfrac{5}{9}$ = .56 = 56%.

↑   ↑
Fraction   Percent

(b) The coin was tossed 45 times and the outcome in each toss was either a head or a tail. Since the heads occurred 25 times, then the number of tails is 45 − 25 = 20.

Experimental probability of tails = $\dfrac{\text{Number of times tails occurred}}{\text{Number of times the coin was tossed.}}$

$= \dfrac{20}{45}$ This is the fractional form.

464

$$= \frac{\overset{4}{\cancel{20}}}{\underset{9}{\cancel{45}}}$$ Reducing to the lowest term by dividing by 5.

$$= \frac{4}{9}$$ This is the probability in the fractional form,

reduced to the lowest terms.

To change the probability of $\frac{4}{9}$ to a decimal form, divide 4 by 9 as shown:

$$
\begin{array}{r}
.444 \\
9\overline{)40} \\
-36 \\
\hline
40 \\
-36 \\
\hline
40 \\
-36 \\
\hline
4
\end{array}
$$

The decimal probability = .44 to the nearest hundredth.
The decimal probability of .44 can be changed to a percent by moving the decimal point in .44 two decimal places or two digits to the right which is the same as multiplying .44 by 100 as shown:

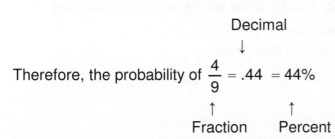

$$.44 = .44 = 44\%$$

Move the decimal point two places to the right.

Decimal
↓

Therefore, the probability of $\frac{4}{9}$ = .44 = 44%

    ↑   ↑
Fraction Percent

Example 2
What is the probability of getting a tail when a coin is tossed?
Solution
We can use the tree diagram to solve the problem as follows with H representing a head and T representing a tail when a coin is tossed once.

a head and T representing a tail when a coin is tossed once.

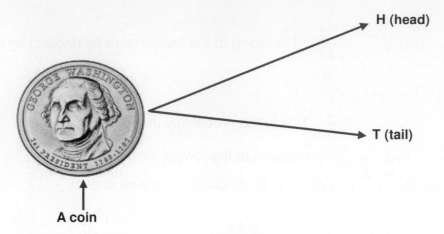

A coin

There is one successful outcome of a tail or a T out of two possible outcomes of H or T as shown in the diagram. There are two possible outcomes, which are a head or a tail when a coin is tossed.

The probability of getting a tail when a coin is tossed

$$= \frac{\text{Number of successful outcomes}}{\text{Number of possible outcomes}} = \frac{1}{2}$$

Special Note: The probability of getting a tail is $\frac{1}{2}$ and this can also be expressed in a decimal form as .5 and in percent form as 50%. This means that the probability of getting a head $=100\% - 50\% = 50\%$ (The total probability = 100% or 1). We can then say that there is a **fifty-fifty chance** of getting a head or a tail when a coin is tossed.

Example 3
(a) Using T_1 and T_2 for tails and H_1 and H_2 for heads, show all the possible outcomes of tossing a coin twice by drawing a tree diagram.
(b) How is the tree diagram read? Write the possible outcomes.
(c) Explain the possible outcomes in terms of probability.
Solution
(a) The tree diagram is shown as shown:

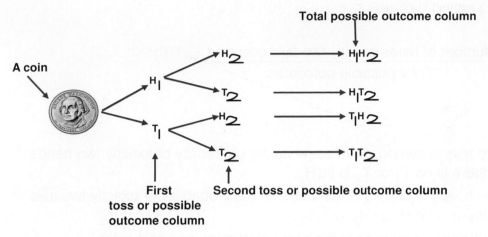

Total possible outcome column

A coin

H_1
H_2 → H_1H_2
T_2 → H_1T_2

T_1
H_2 → T_1H_2
T_2 → T_1T_2

First toss or possible outcome column

Second toss or possible outcome column

(b) The tree diagram is read by following each branch from left to right. Using this idea and starting from the top of the tree diagram, the possible outcomes are: H_1H_2, H_1T_2, T_1H_2, and T_1T_2.

(c) There are 4 possible outcomes which are H_1H_2, H_1T_2, T_1H_2, and T_1T_2.

Exactly two heads or H_1H_2 occurred one time out of the 4 outcomes, and therefore the probability of obtaining exactly two heads

$$= \frac{\text{Number of times } H_1H_2 \text{ occurred}}{\text{Total possible outcomes}}$$

$$= \frac{1}{4}$$

The probability that at least one head occurred is 3 times in H_1H_2, H_1T_2, and T_1H_2 out of 4 possible outcomes of H_1H_2, H_1T_2, T_1H_2, and T_1T_2 is:

$$= \frac{\text{Number of times that at least one head occurred}}{\text{Total possible outcomes}}$$

$$= \frac{3}{4} \quad \text{(At least one head occurred 3 times in } H_1H_2, H_1T_2, \text{ and } T_1H_2).$$

The probability that at least one tail occurred 3 times in H_1T_2, T_1H_2, and T_1T_2 out of 4 possible outcomes of H_1H_2, H_1T_2, T_1H_2, and T_1T_2

$$= \frac{\text{Number of times at least one tail occurred}}{\text{Total possible outcomes}}$$

$$= \frac{3}{4}$$

The probability of exactly two tails or T_1T_2 occurred one time out of the 4 possible outcomes of H_1H_2, H_1T_2, T_1H_2, and T_1T_2

$$= \frac{\text{Number of times exactly two tails occurred}}{\text{Total possible outcomes}}$$

$$= \frac{1}{4}$$

The probability of no tails occurring is the same as the probability of exactly two heads occurring because there is no T_1 or T_2 in H_1H_2.

The probability of no heads occurring is the same as the probability of exactly two tails occurring because there is no H_1 or H_2 in T_1T_2.

Special Note: Tossing two coins once is the same as tossing one coin twice.

Group Exercise

Recall that experimental probability is sometimes called relative frequency. Let us find out how we can use relative frequency to find the probability. The class should select one person as the recorder to record the month in which every student in the class was born on a frequency table as shown:

Months	Jan	Feb	Mar	Apr	May	June	July	Aug	Sept	Oct	Nov	Dec
Frequency												

Frequency here means how many students are born in each month.
Sum of the frequencies = Total number of students in the class.
Let us answer a few questions.
(a) What is the fraction of the students who were born in January?

$$\text{The fraction of the students who were born in January} = \frac{\text{Frequency for January}}{\text{Sum of the frequencies}}$$

$$= \frac{\text{No. of students born in January}}{\text{Total number of students}}$$

Using your frequency table, find the fraction of the students who were born in January. How do you think that we can interpret this fraction? We can interpret this fraction by stating that the probability of selecting a student at random from the class that was born in January.

(b) Similarly, we can find the probability of selecting a student at random that was born in August as shown:
Probability of selecting a student at random that was born in August =

$$\frac{\text{Frequency of students born in August}}{\text{Sum of the frequencies}} = \frac{\text{No. of students born in August}}{\text{Total number of students in the class}}$$

Using your frequency table, find the probability that if a student is selected at random from the class, that student was born in August.

(c) Similarly using your frequency table, find the probability that if a student is selected at random, the student was born in: (1) June, (2) December, (3) April, (4) October.

Note: **Random** selection means that the selection is from a population without being biased. Population means a group, such as a group of students in a class or the total number of students is a population of students.

Example 4

A coin is tossed three times.

(a) Show the outcomes by using a tree diagram.

(b) Find the probability of getting no heads.

(c) Find the probability of getting exactly one head.

(d) Find the probability of getting at least one head.

(e) Find the probability of getting no tails.

(f) Find the probability of getting at least 2 tails.

Solution

(a) The outcomes using the tree diagram are shown below:

Heads are represented by H_1, H_2, and H_3. Tails are represented by T_1, T_2, and T_3.

(The diagram is on the next page.)

Third toss or possible outcome column.

Total possible outcome column.

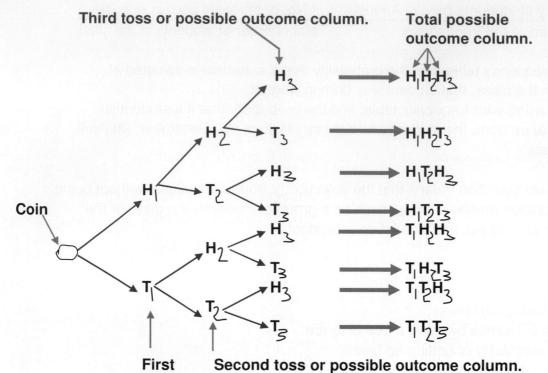

Coin

First toss or possible outcome column.

Second toss or possible outcome column.

(b) There are 8 total possible outcomes and they are:
$H_1H_2H_3$, $H_1H_2T_3$, $H_1T_2H_3$, $H_1T_2T_3$, $T_1H_2H_3$, $T_1H_2T_3$, $T_1T_2H_3$, and $T_1T_2T_3$
No heads occurred once, as shown in $T_1T_2T_3$, out of the possible 8 outcomes.
Therefore, the probability of getting no heads

$$= \frac{\text{Number of outcomes with no heads}}{\text{Total number of possible outcomes}}$$

$$= \frac{1}{8}$$

(c) A head is represented by H_1, H_2, or H_3 and therefore, exactly one head means that at most one of H_1, H_2, or H_3 should be in the total possible outcome list.
Exactly one head appears in the following total possible outcomes as shown:
$H_1T_2T_3$, $T_1H_2T_3$, $T_1T_2H_3$.
Therefore, exactly 1 head occurred 3 times out of 8 total possible outcomes and the probability of getting exactly 1 head

$$= \frac{\text{Number of outcomes with exactly 1 head}}{\text{Total number of possible outcomes}}$$

$$= \frac{3}{8}$$

470

The probability of obtaining exactly 1 head $= \dfrac{3}{8}$

(d) Getting at least one head means getting one or more heads in the total possible outcomes. A head is represented by H_1, H_2, or H_3, and therefore, getting one or more heads is shown in the following total possible outcomes:

$H_1H_2H_3$, $H_1H_2T_3$, $H_1T_2H_3$, $H_1T_2T_3$, $T_1H_2H_3$, $T_1H_2T_3$, and $T_1T_2H_3$.

Getting at least one head occurred 7 times out of 8 possible outcomes. Therefore,

probability of getting at least one head $= \dfrac{\text{Number of outcomes with at least 1 head}}{\text{Total number of possible outcomes}}$

$$= \frac{7}{8}$$

(e) A tail is represented by T_1, T_2, or T_3.

Out of 8 total possible outcomes of $H_1H_2H_3$, $H_1H_2T_3$, $H_1T_2H_3$, $H_1T_2T_3$, $T_1H_2H_3$, $T_1H_2T_3$, $T_1T_2H_3$, and $T_1T_2T_3$ no tails occurred once in $H_1H_2H_3$.

Therefore, probability of obtaining no tails $= \dfrac{\text{Number of outcomes with no tails}}{\text{Total number of possible outcomes}}$

$$= \frac{1}{8}$$

(f) A tail is represented by T_1, T_2, or T_3.

Getting at least 2 tails means getting 2 or more tails. Two or more tails occurred in 4 out of the total 8 outcomes as follows:

$H_1T_2T_3$, $T_1H_2T_3$, $T_1T_2H_3$, and $T_1T_2T_3$.

At least 2 tails occurred 4 times out of 8 outcomes, and therefore, the

probability of obtaining at least 2 tails $= \dfrac{\text{Number of outcomes with at least 2 tails}}{\text{Total number of possible outcomes}}$

$$= \frac{4}{8}$$

$$= \frac{\overset{1}{\cancel{4}}}{\underset{2}{\cancel{8}}} \qquad \text{Reduce to the lowest term by dividing by 4.}$$

$$= \frac{1}{2}$$

Special Note: 1. Tossing one coin three times is the same as tossing three coins once.

471

2. If a coin is tossed fairly n times, the number of possible outcomes is 2^n.
3. If three coins are tossed fairly once then the number of possible outcomes is $2^3 = 8$.
4. To solve any coin tossing problem, use the tree diagram and find the set of possible outcomes.

Example 5

The frequency distribution table shows the ages of the students in a club.

Ages in years	12	13	14	15	16	17	18
Frequency	1	2	1	6	4	5	1

Find the probability that a student selected at random from the club is:
(a) 13 years old.
(b) less than 16 years old.
(c) greater than 14 years old.
(d) between 13 and 17 years old.

Solution

The frequency is the number of times that students are in a certain age group.

Total number of students = Sum of the frequency
$$= 1 + 2 + 1 + 6 + 4 + 5 + 1$$
$$= 20 \text{ students}$$

(a) Probability of a student selected, is 13 years old
$$= \frac{\text{No. of students who are 13 years old}}{\text{Total number of students}}$$

$$= \frac{2}{20} \quad \text{From the table, 2 students are 13 years old.}$$

$$= \frac{\overset{1}{\cancel{2}}}{\underset{10}{\cancel{20}}} \quad \text{Reduce to the lowest term by dividing by 2.}$$

$$= \frac{1}{10}$$

The probability of a student selected is 13 years old $= \dfrac{1}{10}$

(b) From the table, the number of students who are less than 16 years old
= Sum of the frequencies of students who are 12 to 15 years old
$$= 1 + 2 + 1 + 6 = 10 \text{ students.}$$

Probability that a student selected is less than 16 years old

$$= \frac{\text{No. of students who are less than 16 years old}}{\text{Total number of students}}$$

$$= \frac{10}{20}$$

$$= \frac{\overset{1}{\cancel{10}}}{\underset{2}{\cancel{20}}} \qquad \text{Reduce to the lowest term by dividing by 10}$$

The probability of a student selected is less than 16 years old $= \dfrac{1}{2}$

(c) Number of students whose ages are greater than 14 years old
   = Sum of the frequencies of the students who are 15 to 18 years old.
   $= 6 + 4 + 5 + 1$
   = 16 students.
Probability that a student selected is more than 14 years old

$$= \frac{\text{No. of students who are more than 14 years old}}{\text{Total number of students}}$$

$$= \frac{16}{20}$$

$$= \frac{\overset{4}{\cancel{16}}}{\underset{5}{\cancel{20}}} \qquad \text{Reduce to the lowest terms by dividing by 4}$$

$$= \frac{4}{5}$$

(d) Number of students who are between 13 years and 16 years old.
   = Sum of the frequencies of the students who are 13 to 16 years old.
   $= 2 + 1 + 6 + 4$
   = 13 students
Probability of a student selected is between 13 and 16 years old

$$= \frac{\text{No. of students between the ages of 13 and 16 years old}}{\text{Total number of students.}}$$

$$= \frac{13}{20}$$

Example 6

(**Note**: The solutions to this example may be considered by some students as being too long, however, the purpose of this Example 6 is to provide a very useful tool in comparing logical solution methods.)

The frequency table shows the number of boys and girls in a class who studied chemistry and biology.

Students	Chemistry	Biology	Total
Girls	13	15	28
Boys	10	12	22
Total	23	27	50

(a) If a student is selected at random from the class, find the probability that the student is:

(i) a boy   (ii) a girl   (iii) studying chemistry   (iv) studying biology

(v) a boy and studying chemistry   (vi) a boy and studying biology

(vii) a girl and studying chemistry   (viii) a girl and studying biology

(b) If a girl is chosen at random, find the probability that she is:

(i) studying chemistry   (ii) studying biology

(c) If a boy is chosen at random, find the probability that he is:

(i) studying chemistry   (ii) studying biology

(d) If a student is studying chemistry, find the probability that the student is:

(i) a boy   (ii) a girl

Solution

(a) If a student is selected at random from the class, then:

(i) The probability that the student is a boy $= \dfrac{\text{Total number of boys}}{\text{Total number of students}}$

$$= \frac{22}{50}$$

$$= \frac{\overset{11}{\cancel{22}}}{\underset{25}{\cancel{50}}} \quad \text{Reduce to lowest term by dividing by 2.}$$

$$= \frac{11}{25}$$

The probability that the student is a boy $= \dfrac{11}{25}$.

(ii) The probability that the student is a girl $= \dfrac{\text{Total number of girls}}{\text{Total number of students}}$

474

$$= \frac{28}{50}$$

$$= \frac{\overset{14}{\cancel{28}}}{\underset{25}{\cancel{50}}} \quad \text{Reduce to the lowest term by dividing by 2.}$$

$$= \frac{14}{25}$$

The probability that the student is a girl $= \dfrac{14}{25}$

(iii) The probability that the student is studying chemistry

$$= \frac{\text{Total number of students studying chemistry}}{\text{Total number of students}}$$

$$= \frac{23}{50}$$

The probability that the student is studying chemistry is $\dfrac{23}{50}$

(iv) The probability that the student is studying biology

$$= \frac{\text{Total number of students studying biology}}{\text{Total number of students}}$$

$$= \frac{27}{50}$$

The probability that the student is studying Biology $= \dfrac{27}{50}$.

(v) The probability that the student is a boy and studying chemistry

$$= \frac{\text{Number of boys studying chemistry}}{\text{Total number of students}}$$

$$= \frac{10}{50}$$

$$= \frac{\overset{1}{\cancel{10}}}{\underset{5}{\cancel{50}}} \quad \text{Reduce to the lowest term by dividing by 10.}$$

$$= \frac{1}{5}$$

The probability that a student is a boy and studying chemistry $= \frac{1}{5}$

(vi) The probability that a student is a boy and studying biology

$$= \frac{\text{Number of boys studying biology}}{\text{Total number of students}}$$

$$= \frac{12}{50}$$

$$= \frac{\overset{6}{\cancel{12}}}{\underset{25}{\cancel{50}}} \quad \text{Reduce to the lowest term by dividing by 2}$$

$$= \frac{6}{25}$$

The probability that a student is a boy studying biology $= \frac{6}{25}$

(vii) The probability that a student is a girl and studying chemistry

$$= \frac{\text{Number of girls studying chemistry}}{\text{Total number of students}}$$

$$= \frac{13}{50}$$

The probability that a student is a girl and studying chemistry $= \frac{13}{50}$

(viii) The probability that the student is a girl and studying biology

$$= \frac{\text{Number of girls studying biology}}{\text{Total number of students.}}$$

$$= \frac{15}{50}$$

$$= \frac{\overset{3}{\cancel{15}}}{\underset{10}{\cancel{50}}} \quad \text{Reduce to the lowest term by dividing by 5.}$$

$$= \frac{3}{10}$$

The probability that the student is a girl and studying biology $= \dfrac{3}{10}$

(b) If a girl is chosen at random, the problem changes from the style of the solution (a) because the boys' section of the frequency table will not be considered for the solution as follows:

(i) If a girl is chosen at random, the probability that she is studying chemistry

$$= \frac{\text{Number of girls studying chemistry}}{\text{Total number of girls.}}$$

$$= \frac{13}{28}$$

If a girl is chosen at random, the probability that she is studying chemistry $= \dfrac{13}{28}$

(ii) If a girl is chosen at random, the probability that she is studying biology

$$= \frac{\text{Number of girls studying biology}}{\text{Total number of girls.}}$$

$$= \frac{15}{18}$$

$$= \frac{\overset{5}{\cancel{15}}}{\underset{6}{\cancel{18}}} \quad \text{Reduce to the lowest term by dividing by 3.}$$

$$= \frac{5}{6}$$

If a girl is chosen at random, the probability that she is studying biology $= \dfrac{5}{6}$

(c) If a boy is chosen at random, the solution of the problem changes from the style of the solution (b) because the girls' section of the frequency table will not be considered for the solution as follows:

(i) If a boy is chosen at random, the probability that he is studying chemistry

$$= \frac{\text{Number of boys studying chemistry}}{\text{Total number of boys}}$$

$$= \frac{10}{22}$$

$$= \frac{\cancel{10}^{5}}{\cancel{22}_{11}}$$ Reduce to the lowest term by dividing by 2.

$$= \frac{5}{11}$$

If a boy is chosen at random, the probability that he is studying chemistry $= \dfrac{5}{11}$

(ii) If a boy is chosen at random, the probability that he is studying biology

$$= \frac{\text{Number of boys studying biology}}{\text{Total number of boys}}$$

$$= \frac{12}{22}$$

$$= \frac{\cancel{12}^{6}}{\cancel{22}_{11}}$$ Reduce to the lowest term by dividing by 2.

$$= \frac{6}{11}$$

If a boy is chosen at random, the probability that he is studying biology $= \dfrac{6}{11}$

(d) If a student is studying chemistry, the solution of the problem changes from the style of solution (c) because the biology section of the frequency table is not being considered in solving the problem as shown:

(i) If a student is studying chemistry, the probability that the student is a boy

$$= \frac{\text{Number of boys studying chemistry}}{\text{Total number of students studying chemistry}}$$

$$= \frac{10}{23}$$

If a student is studying chemistry, the probability that the student is a boy $= \dfrac{10}{23}$

If a student is studying chemistry, the probability that the student is a girl

$$= \frac{\text{Number of girls studying chemistry}}{\text{Total number of students studying chemistry}}$$

$$= \frac{13}{23}$$

If a student is studying chemistry, the probability that the student is a girl $= \dfrac{13}{23}$

Special Notes in Solving Example 6.
1. The solution of 6(a) involves all of the students or the students population.
2. The solution of 6(b) involves the girls only or the girls population only.
3. The solution of 6(c) involves the boys only or the boys population only.
4. The solution of 6(d) involves the students studying chemistry only or the chemistry student population only.

Example 7

The table below shows the distribution of ages of the students who belong to the Physics Club.

Age in years	13	14	15	16
Number of students	2	4	1	3

(a) What is the number of students who belong to the Physics Club?
(b) What is the average age of the Physics Club members?
(c) What is the modal age?
(d) If a student is selected at random what is the probability that his age is
   (i) At least 15 years.
   (ii) At most 15 years.

Solution

(a) The sum of the number of the students will be the total number of the students who belong to the Physics Club which is $= 2 + 4 + 1 + 3 = 10$ students.

(b) Total ages of the students $= 13 \times 2 + 14 \times 4 + 15 \times 1 + 16 \times 3$
$$= 26 + 56 + 15 + 48$$
$$= 145 \text{ years}$$

$$\text{Average age of students} = \frac{\text{Total ages of the students}}{\text{Number of students}}$$

$$= \frac{145}{10} = 14.\,5 \text{ years} \qquad \text{(Divide by 10).}$$

(c) The modal age is the age which has the highest frequency.
The age of 14 years has the highest frequency of 4, and therefore, the modal age is 14 years. (You may read more about mode in the section under Mode).

(d)(i) The ages of the students that are at least 15 years means the students who are 15 years and older. Therefore, using the table, the number of students who are at least 15 years $= 1 + 3 = 4$ students.
Probability of selecting a student whose age is at least 15 years

$$= \frac{\text{Number of students whose age is at least 15 years}}{\text{Total number of students}}$$

$$= \frac{4}{10}$$

$$= \frac{\overset{2}{\cancel{4}}}{\underset{5}{\cancel{10}}} \qquad \text{Reduce to the lowest term by dividing by 2.}$$

$$= \frac{4}{5}$$

(ii) The ages of the students that are at most 15 years means the students ages that are 15 years and younger, which are, 15 years, 14 years and 13 years. The frequency of 15 years, 14 years and 13 years are 1, 4 and 2. The sum of the frequencies is $1 + 4 + 2 = 7$.
The probability of selecting a student whose age is at most 15 years

$$= \frac{\text{Number of students whose ages are at most 15 years}}{\text{Total number of students}}$$

$$= \frac{7}{10}$$

Exercises
1. Explain what is meant by probability.
2. Explain what is meant by an experiment and an outcome of an experiment.
3. Explain what is meant by the probability of obtaining a head.
4. Explain what is meant by "an outcome is equally likely."
5. The more we repeat the experiment, the closer we are to the true value of the probability. True or False?
6. What is the formula for finding experimental probability?
7. The experimental probability is sometimes called relative frequency. True or False?
8. A coin was tossed 10 times and 3 heads occurred.
  (a) What is the experimental probability of obtaining a head? Express your answer in a fraction, a decimal, and a percent forms. Hint: See Example **1**.
  (b) What is the experimental probability of obtaining a tail? Express your answer in a fraction, a decimal, and a percent forms. Hint: See Example 1.
9. A coin was tossed 15 times and 5 tails occurred.
  (a) What is the probability of obtaining a tail? Express your answer in a fraction, a decimal, and a percent forms. Hint: See Example **1**.
  (b) What is the probability of obtaining a head? Express your answer in a fraction,

a decimal and a percent forms. Hint: See Example **1**.

10. Explain why a coin is tossed, there is a fifty-fifty chance of obtaining a head or a tail? Hint: See Example **2**.

11. Draw a tree diagram when a coin is tossed twice.
    (a) From your diagram, what are the possible outcomes?
    (b) What is the probability of obtaining exactly 2 tails?
    (c) What is the probability of obtaining exactly 2 heads?
    Hint: See Example **3**.

12. Tossing one coin twice is the same as tossing two coins once. True or False?

13. A coin is tossed three times, show the outcome by using a tree diagram and
    (a) find the probability of obtaining exactly 3 heads.
    (b) find the probability of obtaining no heads.
    (c) find the probability of getting at least 2 heads.
    (d) find the probability of getting 2 heads.
    Hint: See Example **4**.

14. The frequency distribution table shows the ages of the students in a club. Hint: See Example **5**.

Ages	9	10	11	12	13
Frequency	2	1	3	4	2

Find the probability that a student selected at random from the club is
(a) 12 years old .
(b) less than 11 years old.
(c) greater than 10 years old.
(d) between 10 and 12 years old.

15. The frequency distribution table shows the ages of the students in a Chemistry Club. Hint: See Example **5**.

Ages in years	8	9	10	11	12
Frequency	2	1	3	1	2

Find the probability that a student selected at random from the club is:
(a) 10 years old.
(b) less than 9 years old.
(c) more than 10 years old
(d) between 9 years and 11 years old.

16. The frequency table shows the number of boys and girls in a class who studied physics and chemistry. Hint: See Example **6**.

Students	Physics	Chemistry	Total
Girls	12	7	19
Boys	8	10	18
Total	20	17	37

(a) If a student is selected at random from the class, find the probability that the student is:

(i) a boy   (ii) a girl   iii) studying chemistry   (iv) studying biology

(v) a girl and studying chemistry   (vi) a boy and studying chemistry

(vii) a girl and studying physics   (viii) a boy and studying physics

(b) If a girl is chosen at random, find the probability that she is :

(i) studying chemistry   (ii) studying physics

(c) If a boy is chosen at random, find the probability that he is:

(i) studying physics   (ii) studying chemistry

(d) If a student is studying biology, find the probability that the student is:

(i) a boy   (ii) a girl

17. The table below shows the distribution of the ages of the students who belong to the Science Club. Hint: See Example **7**.

Age in years	11	12	13	14
Number of students	3	4	2	5

(a) What is the number of students who belong to the Science Club?

(b) What is the average age of the Science Club members?

(c) What is the modal age?

(d) If a student is selected at random, what is the probability that his age is:

(i) at least 14 years old?   (ii) at most 15 years old?

Challenge Questions

18. The frequency distribution table shows the ages of patients visiting a doctor's office.

Ages in years	24	28	36	40
Frequency	2	1	3	4

Find the probability that a patient selected at random is:

(a) between 28 years and 40 years old.

(b) more than 36 years.

(c) less than 40 years old.

(d) 24 years old.

19. The frequency table shows the number of boys and girls in a class who studied history and geography.

Students	History	Geography	Total
Boys	6	10	16
Girls	8	9	17
Total	14	19	33

(a) If a student is selected at random from the class, find the probability that the student is:

(i) a boy   (ii) a girl and studying geography

(iii) a boy and studying history.

(b) If a boy is chosen at random, find the probability that he is studying geography.

(c) If a girl is chosen at random, find the probability that she is studying History.
(d) If a student is studying geography, find the probability that the student is a
   (i) a girl   (ii) a boy

THEORETICAL PROBABILITY

Theoretical probability is when the probability of an event is found without doing an experiment.
A set of outcomes for a particular experiment is known as an **event**.

$$\text{Theoretical probability of an event} = \frac{\text{Number of outcomes in the event}}{\text{Total number of possible outcomes}}$$

Example 1
What is the theoretical probability that in the spinner below, the pointer will:
(a) land on 2?   (b) land on an even number?
(c) land on an odd number?   (d) land on a prime number?

Solution
(a) There is one outcome of 2 out of a total of 4 possible outcomes of 1, 2, 3, and 4 when the pointer lands on 2. Therefore, the theoretical probability that the spinner

$$\text{will land on 2} = \frac{\text{Number of the number 2 outcomes}}{\text{Total number of possible outcomes}}$$

$$= \frac{1}{4}$$

(b) The even numbers on the spinner are 2 and 4, and that means, there will be two outcomes of even numbers out of a possible of 4 outcomes of 1, 2, 3, and 4. Therefore, the theoretical probability that the spinner will land on an even number

$$= \frac{\text{Number of even number outcomes}}{\text{Total number of possible outcomes}}$$

$$= \frac{2}{4}$$

$$= \frac{\frac{2}{4}}{2} \quad \text{Reduce to the lowest term by dividing by 2.}$$

$$= \frac{1}{2}$$

(c) The odd numbers on the spinner are 1 and 3, that means, there will be two outcomes of odd numbers out of a total of 4 possible outcomes of 1, 2, 3, and 4. Therefore, the theoretical probability that the spinner will land on an odd number

$$= \frac{\text{Number of odd number outcomes}}{\text{Total number of possible outcomes}}$$

$$= \frac{2}{4}$$

$$= \frac{\frac{2}{4}}{2} \quad \text{Reduce to the lowest term by dividing by 2.}$$

$$= \frac{1}{2}$$

(d) A prime number is a number that has exactly two factors, which are 1 and the number itself. Out of the numbers 1, 2, 3, and 4 on the spinner, only 2 and 3 are prime numbers. Therefore, two out of four numbers are prime numbers. Therefore, there will be two outcomes of prime numbers out of the possible 4 outcomes of 1, 2, 3, and 4.

$$\text{Theoretical probability of a prime number} = \frac{\text{Number of prime number outcomes}}{\text{Total number of possible outcomes}}$$

$$= \frac{2}{4}$$

$$= \frac{\frac{2}{4}}{2} \quad \text{Reduce to the lowest term by dividing by 2}$$

$$= \frac{1}{2}$$

Example 2

Find the theoretical probability of each event .

(a) The spinner stops on C.

(b) The spinner stops on a vowel.

Solution

(a) There is one letter which is C out of a possible 8 letters.

$$\text{The theoretical probability of event C} = \frac{\text{Number of outcomes of C}}{\text{Total number of possible outcomes}}$$

$$= \frac{1}{8}$$

(b) All the vowels in the English language are a, e, i, o, and u. The vowels on the spinner are A, O and U, therefore, there are 3 vowels out of the 8 possible letters on the spinner.

The theoretical probability that the spinner stops on a vowel

$$= \frac{\text{Number of outcomes of a vowel}}{\text{Total number of possible outcomes}}$$

$$= \frac{3}{8}$$

0 and 1 Probability Values

A probability of 0 is an event that cannot happen, and it is, therefore, an **impossible event**. A probability of 1 is an event that must happen, and it is, therefore, a **certain event**. Some events are either impossible or certain. For example, if a bag contains only 10 green apples, the probability of drawing a green apple is $\frac{10}{10}$ which is 1.

The event of drawing a green apple is certain to occur because no other types of apples are in the bag and therefore, no other result is possible. An event which is certain to occur has a probability of 1.

Using the same bag of green apples, the event of drawing a red apple is impossible because the bag contains no red apples. Therefore, the probability of drawing a red apple is $\frac{0}{10} = 0$. An **impossible event has a probability of 0**.

Some more examples of impossible events are:

(a) obtaining an outcome of 7 from a single roll of a die because the maximum number on a die is 6, and so the outcome of a 7 will never occur. The number of outcomes of a 7 is 0 out of the possible outcomes of 6. Therefore, the probability of obtaining a 7 is $\frac{0}{6}$ = 0. Obtaining an outcome of a 7 is impossible.

(b) A spinner has the numbers 1, 2, 3, 4, and 5. The probability of obtaining an outcome of a 9 out of 5 possible outcomes is 0 because there is no 9 on the spinner. Obtaining an outcome of a 9 is impossible.

Group Exercise
Decide if the following events are impossible or certain:

(a) A spinner has the numbers 1, 2, 3, 4, 5, 6, 7, and 8. What is the probability of the pointer stopping on 10?

(b) A bag has 6 black pens. What is the probability of drawing a red pen? What is the probability of drawing a black pen?

(c) The probability of obtaining a 10 from the roll of a single die.

Extreme Values of Probability
The extreme values of probability are 0 and 1 where an impossible event is 0 and an event certain to happen is 1. The probability of all other events is between 0 and 1. The extreme values of probability means the minimum and the maximum values of probability.

Example 3
Plot the probability of an impossible event, certain event, a 50-50 chance event, an equally likely event, 0% chance of an event and 100% chance of an event.

Solution
Since the extreme values of probability are 0 and 1, probabilities can be plotted on the part of a number line between 0 and 1 as shown:

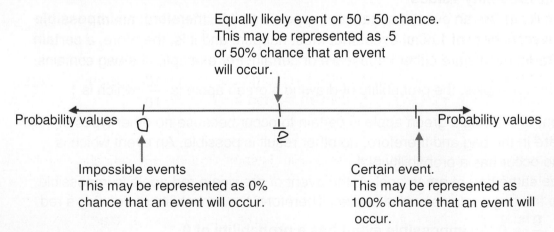

486

Comparing the Values of Probability

Since an event which is certain to happen has a probability of 1 and an impossible event has a probability of 0, an event which has a probability value close to 1 has a better chance of occurring than an event that has a probability value that is close to 0.

Rule: Given the probability values of many events, the event that has the highest probability value has the best chance of occurring and the event that has the lowest probability value has the least chance of occurring.

If the value of an event is close to 0, it is likely that the **event will not occur**.
If the value of an event is close to 1, it is likely that the **event will occur**.

Group Exercise

1. Using the rule, select the event which has the best chance of occurring and the least chance of occurring and explain your choices.

(a) Event A has the probability of .4 of occurring, event B has the probability of .2 of occurring and event C has the probability of .9 of occurring.

(b) Event A has the probability of $\frac{3}{4}$ of occurring, event B has the probability of $\frac{1}{4}$ of occurring and event C has the probability of $\frac{4}{4}$ of occurring.

(c) Event A has the probability of $\frac{1}{2}$ of occurring, event B has the probability of $\frac{1}{4}$ of occurring and event C has the probability of $\frac{1}{3}$ of occurring. Hint: Change all the fractions of the probabilities to have the **same** least common denominator (LCD), and then you will be able to compare the fractions (numerators). (Hint: Refer to the sections/chapter on fractions.) You may also change all the fractions to decimals and then compare the decimals. (Hint: Refer to the section/chapter on decimals.)

(d) Event A has an 80% chance of occurring, event B has a 20% chance of occurring, and event C has a 100% chance of occurring.

2. Discuss five examples of impossible events and five examples of certain events in everyday life. The class should be divided into 8 groups for the discussion and each group should record their five examples and report them to the class.

Example 4

A spinner is divided into 8 sections. If the pointer is spun, find the theoretical probability that it will land on:

(a) a number 3   (b) an even number   (c) an odd number
(d) a prime number   (e) a number 9   (f) a number greater than 8
(g) a number which is not a 6   (h) a number less than 5
(i) a number greater than 3
Indicate the probabilities of the events on a number line.

Solution

These solutions may be considered by some students to be long, but this example is designed to show the students various ways to solve the problem and also to enable the students to logically compare many solution methods.

(a) There is only one number 3 out of the total number of 8. Therefore, the probability of landing on the number 3 out of 8 numbers can be represented as shown:

$$\text{The the theoretical probability of landing on 3} = \frac{\text{Number of outcomes of 3}}{\text{Total number of possible outcomes}}$$

$$= \frac{1}{8}$$

(b) An even number is a number that can be divided by 2. The spinner has 4 even numbers which are 2, 4, 6, and 8 out of a total of 8 numbers on the spinner. Therefore, the probability of landing on an even number can be represented as shown:

The theoretical probability of landing on an even number

$$= \frac{\text{Number of even number outcomes}}{\text{Total number of possible outcomes}}$$

$$= \frac{4}{8}$$

$$= \frac{\overset{1}{\cancel{4}}}{\underset{2}{\cancel{8}}} \quad \text{Reduce to the lowest term by dividing by 4}$$

$$= \frac{1}{2}$$

(c) An odd number is a number that cannot be divided by 2. The spinner has 4 odd numbers which are 1, 3, 5, and 7 out of a total of 8 numbers on the spinner. Therefore, the probability of landing on an odd number can be represented as shown:

The theoretical probability of landing on an odd number

$$= \frac{\text{Number of odd number outcomes}}{\text{Total number of possible outcomes}}$$

$$= \frac{4}{8}$$

$$= \frac{\overset{1}{\cancel{4}}}{\underset{2}{\cancel{8}}} \quad \text{Reducing to lowest term by dividing by 4.}$$

$$= \frac{1}{2}$$

(d) A prime number is a number that has exactly two factors, which are 1 and the number itself. There are four prime numbers on the spinner, which are 2, 3, 5, and 7 out of the total of 8 numbers on the spinner. Therefore, the probability of landing on a prime number can be represented as shown:
Theoretical probability of landing on a prime number

$$= \frac{\text{Number of outcomes of a prime number}}{\text{Total number of possible outcomes}}$$

$$= \frac{4}{8}$$

$$= \frac{\overset{1}{\cancel{4}}}{\underset{2}{\cancel{8}}} \quad \text{Reduce to the lowest term by dividing by 4.}$$

$$= \frac{1}{2}$$

(e) There is no number 9 on the spinner, so it is impossible for the pointer to land on number 9. The impossible events have the probability of 0.

(f) There is no number greater than 8, so it is impossible for the pointer to land on a number greater than 8. The impossible events have the probability of 0.

(g) The total number of numbers on the spinner is 8. If the pointer will not land on 6, then the pointer will land on the other 7 remaining numbers of 1, 2, 3, 4, 5, 7, and 8 out of the total number of 8 on the spinner. The probability that the pointer will not land on the number 6 can be represented as:

$$\text{Theoretical probability of not landing on 6} = \frac{\text{Number of outcomes of not landing on 6}}{\text{Total possible outcomes}}$$

$$= \frac{7}{8}$$

(h) The numbers on the spinner which are less than 5 are 1, 2, 3, and 4. Therefore, there are 4 numbers that are less than 5 out of the total number of 8 numbers on the spinner. The probability that the pointer will land on a number less than 5 can be represented as:

Theoretical probability of landing on a number less than 5

$$= \frac{\text{Number of outcomes that are less than 5}}{\text{Total possible outcomes}}$$

$$= \frac{4}{8}$$

$$= \frac{\overset{1}{\cancel{4}}}{\underset{2}{\cancel{8}}} \qquad \text{Reduce to the lowest term by dividing by 4.}$$

$$= \frac{1}{2}$$

(i) The numbers on the spinner which are greater than 3 are 4, 5, 6, 7, and 8. There are a total of five numbers that are greater than 3 out of the total number of 8 on the spinner.

Theoretical probability of landing on a number which is greater than 3

$$= \frac{\text{Number of outcomes} > 3}{\text{Total possible outcomes}}$$

$$= \frac{5}{8}$$

The probabilities of the events are indicated on the number line using assigned solution numbers.

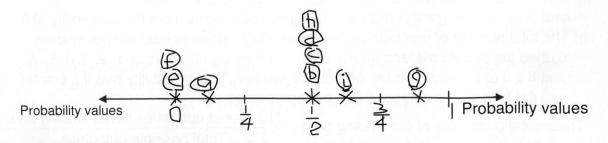

490

Example 5

(a) Find the theoretical probability of the outcome of B. Give your answer in a fraction, a decimal, and a percent form.
(b) Find the experimental probability of the outcome of B.
(c) Find the experimental probability of the outcome of A.
(d) Find the experimental probability of the outcome of C.
(e) Find the experimental probability of the outcome of D.

This diagram is used to find the theoretical probability because the data on the spinner is obtained without conducting any experiment.

Outcome	Number of spins
A	8
B	2
C	7
D	3
Total	20

This diagram is used to find the experimental probability because the data in the diagram is got from conducting the experiment.

Solution

(a) The spinner is divided into 4 equal sections labelled A, B, C, and D. Section B is 1 out of the 4 equal parts of the spinner.

$$\text{Theoretical probability of outcome of B} = \frac{\text{Number of outcomes of B}}{\text{Total number of possible outcomes}}$$

$$-\frac{1}{4} \text{ (Fraction form of the probability)}.$$

The decimal form of the theoretical probability of $\frac{1}{4}$ can be obtained by dividing 1 by 4 as shown:

$$\begin{array}{r} .25 \\ 4\overline{)10} \\ -8 \\ \hline 20 \\ -20 \\ \hline 00 \end{array}$$

The decimal form of the theoretical probability of $\frac{1}{4}$ = .25

The decimal form of the theoretical probability of .25 can be changed to a percent by moving the decimal point 2 places or two digits to the right, and attaching the percent sign (%), which is the same as multiplying by 100 as shown:

$$.25 = .25. = 25\%$$

Therefore, the theoretical probability of $\dfrac{1}{4}$ = .25 = 25%

(b) The number of spins that give the outcomes of B are 2 out of the total of 20 spins.

Experimental probability of outcome of B = $\dfrac{\text{Number of spins that give outcomes of B}}{\text{Total number of possible spins}}$

$$= \frac{2}{20}$$

$$= \frac{\overset{1}{\cancel{2}}}{\underset{10}{\cancel{20}}} \quad \text{Reduce to the lowest term by dividing by 2.}$$

$$= \frac{1}{10}$$

(c) The number of spins that give the outcomes of A are 8 out of the total of 20 spins.

Experimental probability of outcome of A = $\dfrac{\text{Number of spins that give outcomes of A}}{\text{Total number of possible spins}}$

$$= \frac{8}{20}$$

$$= \frac{\overset{2}{\cancel{8}}}{\underset{5}{\cancel{20}}} \quad \text{Reduce to the lowest term by dividing by 4.}$$

$$= \frac{2}{5}$$

(d) The number of spins that give the outcomes of C are 7 out of the total of 20 spins.

Experimental probability of outcome of C = $\dfrac{\text{Number of spins that give outcomes of C}}{\text{Total number of possible spins}}$

$$= \frac{7}{20}$$

(e) The number of spins that give the outcomes of D are 3 out of the total of 20 spins.

Experimental probability of outcome of D = $\dfrac{\text{Number of spins that give outcomes of D}}{\text{Total number of possible spins}}$

$$= \frac{3}{20}$$

Example 6

A die is a small solid cube marked on each face from one to six spots or dots.

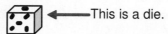 ←———This is a die.

A die was rolled 10 times. On 2 of the rolls, the outcome was three dots on the die.

(a) What is the experimental probability of rolling a three?
Give your answer as a fraction, a decimal, and a percent.

(b) How many rolls was the outcome not showing the side with three dots? What is the experimental probability of not rolling the side with three dots?

(c) Based on the experimental probabilities that you have found, and suppose the die is rolled 100 times, about how many times do you expect to roll a side:
(i) with three dots?
(ii) without three dots?

Solution

Note that this is an experimental probability because the event was repeated, for example, it was repeated 10 times.

(a) The outcome of the three dots on the die is 2 out of 10 total possible rolls.
Experimental probability of the outcome of rolling a three

$$= \frac{\text{Number of outcomes of rolling a three on a side}}{\text{Total number of possible rolls or outcomes}}$$

$$= \frac{2}{10}$$

$$= \frac{\overset{1}{\cancel{2}}}{\underset{5}{\cancel{10}}} \qquad \text{Reduce to the lowest term by dividing by 2.}$$

$$= \frac{1}{5}$$

The experimental probability of $\frac{1}{5}$ can be expressed as a decimal by dividing 1 by 5 as shown:

$$\begin{array}{r} .2 \\ 5\overline{)10} \\ -\underline{10} \\ 00 \end{array}$$

Therefore, the decimal form of the experimental probability of $\frac{1}{5} = .2$

The decimal form of the experimental probability of .2 can be expressed as a percent by moving the decimal point two places or two digits to the right and attaching the percent sign (%) which is the same as multiplying by 100 as follows:

Write a zero here as a place holder.

$$.2 = .20 = 20\%$$

Therefore, the experimental probability of $\frac{1}{5} = .2 = 20\%$

(b) The die was rolled 10 times. The outcome of the side with three dots was 2 and therefore, the number of rolls that the outcomes were not the side with three dots

$= 10$ rolls - 2 rolls

$= 8$ rolls

Experimental probability of not rolling the side with three dots

$$= \frac{\text{Number of outcomes with not rolling a three}}{\text{Total number of possible rolls or outcomes}}$$

$$= \frac{8}{10}$$

$$= \frac{\overset{4}{\cancel{8}}}{\underset{5}{\cancel{10}}} \qquad \text{Reduce to the lowest term by dividing by 2.}$$

$$= \frac{4}{5}$$

(c)(i) From Example 6(c), the number of possible rolls $= 100$.

Let the number of outcomes with three dots when the die is rolled 100 times $= x$. The experimental probability of the outcomes with the three dots when the die is rolled 100 times

$$= \frac{\text{Number of outcomes with a three when the die is rolled 100 times}}{\text{Number of possible rolls}}$$

$$= \frac{x}{100} \qquad\rule{7cm}{0.4pt}[A]$$

From the solution of Example 6(a), the experimental probability of the outcome

494

of the side with the three dots $= \dfrac{1}{5}$ ─────────────────────────[B]

Equation [A] and equation [B] are equal because $\dfrac{x}{100}$ and $\dfrac{1}{5}$ are equivalent

fractions or equivalent ratios, therefore,

$$\dfrac{x}{100} = \dfrac{1}{5}$$ ─────────────────────[C]

(Review the section on Equivalent Fractions or Equivalent Ratios).
The cross products of equivalent fractions or ratios are equal, so

$$\dfrac{x}{100} \diagdown\diagup \dfrac{1}{5}$$

Therefore, $5 \times x = 100 \times 1$

$\quad\quad\quad 5x = 100$ ─────────────────────────[D]

Divide each side of equation [D] by 5 in order to obtain the value of x as shown:

$$\dfrac{\overset{x}{\cancel{5x}}}{\underset{1}{\cancel{5}}} = \dfrac{\overset{20}{\cancel{100}}}{\underset{1}{\cancel{5}}}$$

$x = 20$ outcomes of three dots.

(ii) From Example 6(c), the number of possible rolls = 100.

Let $y =$ "the number of times of outcomes with no side with three dots out of 100 possible rolls."

The experimental probability of not rolling the side with three dots out of 100 possible outcomes

$= \dfrac{\text{Number of outcomes with no three dots when the die is rolled 100 times}}{\text{Total number of possible rolls}}$

$= \dfrac{y}{100}$ ─────────────────────────[E]

From solution of Example 6(b), the experimental probability of not rolling the side

with three dots $= \dfrac{4}{5}$ ─────────────────────────[F]

Equation [E] and equation [F] are equal because $\dfrac{y}{100}$ and $\dfrac{4}{5}$ are equivalent

fractions or ratios, and therefore,

$$\dfrac{y}{100} = \dfrac{4}{5}$$

(Review the section on Equivalent Fractions and Equivalent Ratios.)
The cross products of equivalent fractions or ratios are equal, so

$$\frac{y}{100} \diagup\!\!\!\!\diagdown \frac{4}{5}$$

Therefore, $= 5 \times y = 4 \times 100$

$$5y = 400 \quad\rule{7cm}{0.4pt}\quad [G]$$

Divide each side of equation $[G]$ by 5 in order to obtain the value of y as shown:

$$\frac{5y}{5} = \frac{400}{5}$$

$$\frac{\overset{y}{\cancel{5y}}}{\underset{1}{\cancel{5}}} = \frac{\overset{80}{\cancel{400}}}{\underset{1}{\cancel{5}}} \quad \text{Divide each side of the equation by 5.}$$

$$y = 80 \text{ outcomes of not rolling a side with three dots.}$$

Example 7

(Example 7 is intentionally designed to be long to provide the student with critical and logical methods of solving diverse problems.)
A die was thrown once.
(a) List the possible outcomes.

From your possible outcomes in (a), what is the theoretical probability of rolling:

(b) an even number.   (c) an odd number.   (d) a number greater than 2.
(e) a number between 2 and 5.   (f) a multiple of 3.   (g) not a multiple of 3.
(h) a prime number.   (i) not a prime number.

Solution

(a) A die has six sides and the sides are numbered from 1 to 6. When the die is thrown, any of the six sides can show up, so there are six possible outcomes, which are 1, 2, 3, 4, 5, and 6.

(b) The even numbers out of the total possible outcomes of 1, 2, 3, 4, 5, and 6 are 2, 4, and 6. There are three even numbers out of the total of 6 possible outcomes. The theoretical probability of obtaining an even number

$$= \frac{\text{Number of outcomes of an even number}}{\text{Total number of possible outcomes}}$$

$$= \frac{3}{6}$$

$$= \frac{\frac{1}{3}}{\frac{6}{2}}$$ Reduce to the lowest term by dividing by 3.

$$= \frac{1}{2}$$

(c) The odd numbers out of the total possible outcomes of 1, 2, 3, 4, 5, and 6 are
1, 3 and 5. Therefore, there are three odd numbers out of the total of 6 possible
outcomes.

The theoretical probability of obtaining an odd number

$$= \frac{\text{Number of outcomes of an odd number}}{\text{Total number of possible outcomes}}$$

$$= \frac{3}{6}$$

$$= \frac{\frac{1}{3}}{\frac{6}{3}}$$ Reduce to the lowest term by dividing by 3.

$$= \frac{1}{2}$$

(d) The outcome of the numbers that are greater than 2 out of the total possible
outcomes of 1, 2, 3, 4, 5, and 6 are 3, 4, 5, and 6. There are four numbers,
which are greater than 2 out of the total possible outcome of 6 numbers.
The theoretical probability of obtaining a number greater than 2

$$= \frac{\text{Number of outcomes greater than 2}}{\text{Total number of possible outcomes}}$$

$$= \frac{4}{6}$$

$$= \frac{\frac{2}{4}}{\frac{6}{3}}$$ Reduce to the lowest term by dividing by 2.

$$= \frac{2}{3}$$

(e) The numbers between 2 and 5 are 3 and 4 out of the total possible outcomes of 1, 2, 3, 4, 5, and 6. There are two numbers between 2 and 5 out of the total possible outcome of 6 numbers.

The theoretical probability of obtaining a number between 2 and 5

$$= \frac{\text{Number of outcomes of a number between 2 and 5}}{\text{Total number of possible outcomes}}$$

$$= \frac{2}{6}$$

$$= \frac{\overset{1}{\cancel{2}}}{\underset{3}{\cancel{6}}} \qquad \text{Reduce to the lowest term by dividing by 2.}$$

$$= \frac{1}{3}$$

(f) The multiples of 3 out of the total numbers of possible outcomes of 1, 2, 3, 4, 5, and 6 are 3 and 6. There are two numbers (3 and 6) that are multiples of 3 out of the total of the 6 possible outcomes of 1, 2, 3, 4, 5, and 6.

The theoretical probability of obtaining a multiple of 3

$$= \frac{\text{Number of outcomes of a multiple of 3}}{\text{Total number of possible outcomes}}$$

$$= \frac{3}{6}$$

$$= \frac{\overset{1}{\cancel{3}}}{\underset{3}{\cancel{6}}} \quad \text{Reduce to the lowest term by dividing by 2..}$$

$$= \frac{1}{3}$$

(g) The numbers that are not multiples of 3 out of the total outcomes of 1, 2, 3, 4, 5, and 6 are 1, 2, 4, and 5. There are 4 numbers (1, 2, 4, and 5) that are not multiples of 3 out of a total of 6 possible outcomes.

The theoretical probability of obtaining a number that is not a multiple of 3

$$= \frac{\text{Number of outcomes that are not multiples of 3}}{\text{Total number of possible outcomes}}$$

$$= \frac{4}{6}$$

$$= \frac{\overset{2}{\cancel{4}}}{\underset{3}{\cancel{6}}} \qquad \text{Reduce to the lowest term by dividing by 2}$$

$$= \frac{2}{3}$$

(h) A prime number has exactly two factors which are 1 and the number itself. The prime numbers out of the total possible outcomes of 1, 2, 3, 4, 5, and 6 are 2, 3, and 5. There are 3 prime numbers (2, 3, and 5) out of the total possible outcomes of 6 numbers.

The theoretical probability of obtaining a prime number

$$= \frac{\text{Number of outcomes of a prime number}}{\text{Total number of possible outcomes}}$$

$$= \frac{3}{6}$$

$$= \frac{\overset{1}{\cancel{3}}}{\underset{2}{\cancel{6}}} \qquad \text{Reduce to the lowest term by dividing by 3.}$$

$$= \frac{1}{2}$$

(i) The numbers which are not prime numbers out of the total possible outcome of 1, 2, 3, 4, 5, and 6 are 1, 4, and 6.There are 3 numbers (1, 4, and 6), which are not prime numbers out of a total possible outcomes of 6 numbers.

The theoretical probability of not getting a prime number

$$= \frac{\text{Number of outcomes which are not a prime number}}{\text{Total number of possible outcomes}}$$

$$= \frac{3}{6}$$

$$= \frac{\overset{1}{\cancel{3}}}{\underset{2}{\cancel{6}}} \text{ Reduce to the lowest term by dividing by 3.}$$

$$= \frac{1}{2}$$

Example 8

A coin is tossed once and a die is thrown once.

(a) Construct a tree diagram showing all the possible outcomes.

(b) What is the theoretical probability that a head showed on the coin and an odd number showed up on the die?

(c) What is the theoretical probability of obtaining a tail and a 6?

Solution

(a) The tree diagram shows all the possible outcomes is shown.

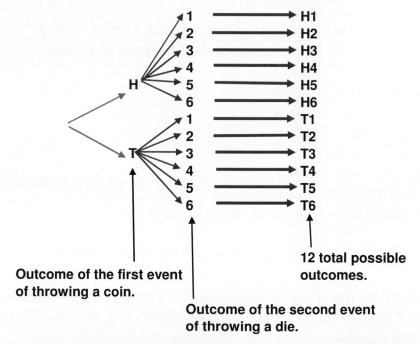

(b) From the 12 possible outcomes shown in the solution of Example 8(a), the outcomes showing a head on the coin and an odd number on the die are H1, H3, and H5. Therefore, there are 3 outcomes of a head and an odd number (H1, H3, and H5) out of the 12 total possible outcomes of H1, H2, H3, H4, H5, H6, T1, T2, T3, T4, T5, and T6.

Therefore, the theoretical probability of obtaining an outcome of a head and an odd number

500

$$= \frac{\text{Number of outcomes of a head and an odd number}}{\text{Total number of possible outcomes}}$$

$$= \frac{3}{12}$$

$$= \frac{\overset{1}{\cancel{3}}}{\underset{4}{\cancel{12}}} \qquad \text{Reduce to the lowest term by dividing by 3.}$$

$$= \frac{1}{4}$$

(c) From the solution of example 8(a), a tail and a 6 occurred once as T6 out of the total of 12 possible outcomes of H1, H2, H3, H4, H5, H6, T1, T2, T3, T4, T5, and T6. Therefore, the theoretical probability of obtaining an outcome of a tail and a 6

$$= \frac{\text{Number of outcomes of a tail and a 6}}{\text{Total number of possible outcomes}}$$

$$= \frac{1}{12}$$

Example 9

Two dice A and B are tossed simultaneously.
(a) (i) List all the pairs of possible outcomes.
    (ii) What are the total possible outcomes?
(b) What is the probability that:
    (i) the sum of the outcomes of a pair of the dice is 7?
    (ii) the sum of the outcomes of a pair of the dice is more than 9?
    (iii) the sum of the outcomes of a pair of the dice is less than 6?

Solution

(a) (i) The total pairs of the possible outcomes are shown in the table below.

B A	1	2	3	4	5	6
1	1, 1	1, 2	1, 3	1, 4	1, 5	1, 6
2	2, 1	2, 2	2, 3	2, 4	2, 5	2, 6
3	3, 1	3, 2	3, 3	3, 4	3, 5	3, 6
4	4, 1	4, 2	4, 3	4, 4	4, 5	4, 6
5	5, 1	5, 2	5, 3	5, 4	5, 5	5, 6
6	6, 1	6, 2	6, 3	6, 4	6, 5	6, 6

(ii) From the total pairs of the possible outcomes in the solution of Example 9(a)(i), the sum of the total pairs of the possible outcomes are found and listed in the table as shown:

B \ A	1	2	3	4	5	6
1	2	3	4	5	6	7
2	3	4	5	6	7	8
3	4	5	6	7	8	9
4	5	6	7	8	9	10
5	6	7	8	9	10	11
6	7	8	9	10	11	12

b(i) From the table, the total number of the possible outcomes is 36.
(Do not count the numbers in column B and row A.)
From the table, the pairs of numbers that have a sum of 7 is 6.
Therefore, the probability that the sum of pairs of numbers is 7

$$= \frac{\text{Number of the pairs of outcomes which have a sum of 7}}{\text{Total number of possible outcomes}}$$

$$= \frac{6}{36}$$

$$= \frac{\overset{1}{\cancel{6}}}{\underset{6}{\cancel{36}}} \qquad \text{Reduce to the lowest term by dividing by 6.}$$

$$= \frac{1}{6}$$

(ii) From the table, the total number of the possible outcomes is 36.
From the table, the number of the sum of the pairs of the outcomes that is greater than 9 is 6.
Therefore, the probability that the number of the sum of the pairs of the outcomes that is greater than 9

$$= \frac{\text{Number of pairs of the outcomes which have sums greater than 9}}{\text{Total number of possible outcomes}}$$

$$= \frac{6}{36}$$

$$= \frac{\frac{1}{6}}{\frac{36}{6}} \qquad \text{Reduce to the lowest term by dividing by 6.}$$

$$= \frac{1}{6}$$

(iii) From the table, the total number of the possible outcomes is 36.

From the table, the number of the outcomes of a pair of the dice, which have a sum less than 6 is 10.

Therefore, the probability that the sum of the outcome of the dice is less than 6

$$= \frac{\text{Number of the pairs of outcomes which have a sum less than 6}}{\text{Total number of possible outcomes}}$$

$$= \frac{10}{36}$$

$$= \frac{\frac{5}{10}}{\frac{36}{18}} \qquad \text{Reduce to the lowest term by dividing by 2}$$

$$= \frac{5}{18}$$

Group Exercise – Application of Experimental Probability

The class should be divided into two teams, Team A and Team B.

 (a) Team A should be given 10 red pens and 10 blue pens and a bag. Team A has a total of 20 pens.

(b) Team B should be given 18 red pens and 2 blue pens and a bag. Team B has a total of 20 pens.

(c) Team A should put all the 20 pens into the bag.

Team A's bag containing 10 red pens and 10 blue pens.

Team B's bag containing 18 red pens and 2 blue pens.

(d) Each member of team A should take turns in picking a pen from the bag, one at a time, without looking into the bag. Each time a member from team A picks a pen from the bag, the color of the pen should be recorded on a tally table as shown. The pen should be put back into the bag, and the bag should be shaken for 1 minute.

Pen Type	Tally
Red pen	\\\
Blue pen	\\

(e) Repeat part (d) 49 more times.

(f) Team B should also do parts (c), (d), and (e).

(g) Let us compare the tally tables of Team A and Team B.

  (i) How many times was a red pen picked out of the 50 trials by Team A and Team B?

  (ii) How many times was a blue pen picked out of the 50 trials by team A and Team B?

  (iii) Why do you think that the number of times that a red pen was picked by Team A is very different from that of Team B?

(h) Team A and Team B should find the experimental probability of drawing a red pen by using their respective tally table.

The experimental probability of drawing a red pen is as shown:

Experimental probability of drawing a red pen

$$= \frac{\text{Number of times a red pen was drawn}}{\text{Total number of trials}}$$

(i) Is the experimental probability of drawing a red pen different for Team A and Team B? Give reasons for the difference. Do you think that the number of red pens in the bag compared to the number of blue pens in the bag can affect the outcome of the experimental probability of drawing a red pen?

(j) Repeat part (h) to find the experimental probability of drawing a blue pen and also apply part (i) to the blue pen.

Analysis of the Group Exercise

1. Team A was given 10 red pens and 10 blue pens and therefore, the probability of drawing a red pen or a blue pen are equal because the quantity of the red pens and the blue pens are equal. True or False?

2. Team B was given 18 red pens and 2 blue pens, and therefore, the probability of drawing:
   (a) a red pen is higher than the probability of drawing a blue pen. True or False?
   (b) a blue pen is lower than the probability of drawing a red pen. True or False?

3. What did you learn from this group exercise?

Example 10

There are 20 red pens and 10 blue pens in a bag. Find the probability of picking at random:

      (a) a red pen

      (b) a blue pen

Solution

(a) Total number of pens = 20 + 10 = 30

$$\text{Probability of picking a red pen} = \frac{\text{Number of red pens}}{\text{Total number of pens}}$$

$$= \frac{20}{30}$$

$$= \frac{\overset{2}{\cancel{20}}}{\underset{3}{\cancel{30}}} \quad \text{Reduce to the lowest term by dividing by 10.}$$

$$= \frac{2}{3}$$

(b) $\text{Probability of picking a blue pen} = \dfrac{\text{Number of blue pens}}{\text{Total number of pens}}$

$$= \frac{10}{30}$$

$$= \frac{\overset{1}{\cancel{10}}}{\underset{3}{\cancel{30}}} \quad \text{Reduce to the lowest term by dividing.}$$

$$= \frac{1}{3}$$

Example 11

A bag has 8 red, 4 blue and 3 green marbles. James pulls out one marble without looking. What is the probability that it is not:

(a) blue   (b) red   (c) green

Solution

(a) The probability that it is not blue means that it could be red or green.

    Total number of red and green marbles = 8 + 3 = 11

    Total number of marbles in the bag = 8 + 4 + 3 = 15

The probability that the marble pulled is not blue

$$= \frac{\text{Number of red and green marbles in the bag.}}{\text{Total number of marbles in the bag.}}$$

$$= \frac{11}{15}$$

The probability of not pulling a blue marble $= \dfrac{11}{15}$

(b) The probability that it is not red means that it could be blue or green.
Total number of blue and green marbles $= 4 + 3 = 7$
Total number of marbles in the bag $= 8 + 4 + 3 = 15$

The probability that the marble pulled is not red

$$= \frac{\text{Number of blue and green marbles in the bag}}{\text{Total number of marbles in the bag}}$$

$$= \frac{7}{15}$$

The probability of not pulling a red marble $= \dfrac{7}{15}$

(c) The probability that the marble pulled is not green means that it could be red or blue.
Total number of red and blue marbles $= 8 + 4 = 12$
Total number of marbles in the bag $= 8 + 4 + 3 = 15$

The probability that the marble pulled is not green

$$= \frac{\text{Number of red and blue marbles in the bag}}{\text{Total number of marbles in the bag}}$$

$$= \frac{12}{15}$$

$$= \frac{\overset{4}{\cancel{12}}}{\underset{5}{\cancel{15}}} \qquad \text{Reduce to the lowest term by dividing by 3.}$$

$$= \frac{4}{5}$$

The probability of not pulling a green marble $= \dfrac{4}{5}$

Without Replacement Problem
Example 12
A bag contains 3 red and 4 blue pens. What is the probability that if two pens are picked from the bag at random **without replacement**, the:
(a) first pen picked is blue?
(b) second pen picked is red?
Solution
(a) The total number of pens in the bag $= 3 + 4 = 7$
   The number of blue pens $= 4$
   Probability that the first pen picked is blue

$$= \dfrac{\text{Number of blue pens in the bag}}{\text{Total number of pens in the bag}}$$

$$= \dfrac{4}{7}$$

The probability that the first pen is blue is $= \dfrac{4}{7}$

(b) The number of red pens $= 3$
   Total number of pens in the bag $= 3 + 4 = 7$
   But when the first pen was picked without replacement, then the remaining total number of pens in the bag $= 7 - 1 = 6$.
   Probability that the second pen is red

$$= \dfrac{\text{Number of red pens in the bag}}{\text{Total remaining pens in the bag}}$$

$$= \dfrac{3}{6}$$

$$= \dfrac{\overset{1}{\cancel{3}}}{\underset{2}{\cancel{6}}} \qquad \text{Reduce to the lowest term by dividing by 3}$$

$$= \dfrac{1}{2}$$

The probability that the second pen is red is $\dfrac{1}{2}$

507

Exercises

1. Explain what is meant by (a) theoretical probability, (b) an event.
2. How do you find the theoretical probability of an event?
3. What is the theoretical probability that if you spin the spinner:

      (a). The pointer will land on 3?
      (b). The pointer will land on an even number?
      (c). The pointer will land on an odd number?
      (d). The pointer will land on a prime number?
      Hint: See example 1.

4. Find the theoretical probability of each event:

      (a). The spinner will stop on E.
      (b). The spinnerwill stop on a vowel.
      Hint: See example 2.

5. Explain (a) an impossible event, (b) equally likely event, (c) certain event.
    Hint: See Example 3.
6. The probability of an event A occurring is .6, B occurring is .9, C occurring is .5, and D occurring is .2. By comparing the probability values, which event is most likely to occur and which event is least likely to occur? Hint: See the section under "Comparing the Values of Probability."
7. Find the theoretical probability that the pointer will land on:

      (a). a number 10.
      (b). a number 0.
      (c). an odd number.
      (d). an even number.
      (e). a number less than 3.
      (f) . a prime number.
      Indicate the probabilities on a number line.
      Hint: See example 4.

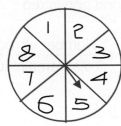

8. (a) Find the theoretical probability of outcome of Y.
      Give your answer as a fraction, a decimal, and a percent.
   (b) Find the experimental probability of the outcome of W.
   (c) Find the experimental probability of the outcome of Z.
   (d) Find the experimental probability of the outcome of Y.
   (e) Find the experimental probability of the outcome of X.
      Hint: See Example **5**.

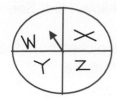

Outcome	Number of spins
W	3
X	6
Y	8
X	4

9. A die was rolled 20 times. On 4 of the rolls the outcome was a 2.
   (a) What is the experimental probability of rolling a 2?
      Give your answer as a fraction, a decimal, and a percent.
   (b) How many rolls was the outcome not showing a 2? What is the experimental probability of not rolling a 2?
   (c) Based on the experimental probabilities that you have found and suppose the die is rolled 100 times, about how many times do you expect to roll a side:
      (i) with a 2?
      (ii) without a 2?
   Hint: See Example **6**.

10. A die was thrown once.
   (a) List the possible outcomes.
      From your possible outcomes in (a), what is the theoretical probability of obtaining:
   (b) an odd number?   (c) an even number?
   (d) a number greater than 4?   (e) a number between 3 and 6?
   (f) a multiple of 2?   (g) not a multiple of 2?
   (h) a prime number?   (i) not a prime number?
   Hint: See Example **7**.

11. A coin is tossed once and a die is thrown once.
   (a) Construct a tree diagram showing all the possible outcomes.
   (b) What is the theoretical probability that:
      (i) a head showed up on the coin and an odd number showed up on the die?
      (ii) a tail showed up on the coin and an even number showed up on the die?
   (c) What is the theoretical probability of obtaining a head and a 4?
      Hint: See Example **8**

12. Two dice A and B are tossed simultaneously,
   (a) (i) List all the pairs of possible outcomes.
      (ii) What is the total possible outcome?
   (b) What is the theoretical probability that:
      (i) the sum of the outcomes of a pair of the dice is 8?
      (ii) the sum of the outcomes of a pair of the dice is more than 6?
      (iii) the sum of the outcomes of a pair of the dice is less than 5?
      Hint: See Example **9**.

13 There are 7 red and 3 blue marbles in a bag. Find the probability of picking at random: (a) a blue marble (b) a red marble. Hint: See Example **10**.

14. A bag has 5 green, 3 blue and 4 yellow pens. James picks a pen without looking.

What is the probability it is not: (a) blue, (b) green (c) yellow. Hint: See
Example **11**

15. A bag contains 6 blue and 4 black pens. If two pens are picked from the bag
at random, without replacement, what is the probability that the:
(a) first pen picked is blue?
(b) second pen picked is black?
Hint: See Example **12**.

Challenge Questions

16. Using the spinner, what is the probability in a fraction, a decimal and a
percent of:

(a). Obtaining a number less than 30.
(b). Obtaining a number between 15 and 35.
(c). Obtaining an even number?
(d). Obtaining an odd number?
(e). Obtaining a number greater than 60.

17. A bag contains 3 green balls and 7 yellow balls. If a ball is selected at random,
what is the probability that the ball is: (a) green, (b) yellow, (c) not green,
and (d) not yellow?

18. A box contains 6 yellow apples and 4 green apples. What is the probability that
if two apples are picked at random without replacement, the:
(a) first apple picked is green?
(b) second apple picked is yellow?

PROBABILITY AND PREDICTIONS

Experimental probability can be used to predict future events. This means that
once we know the probability from an experiment, based on that probability, we
can predict future events.

Group Project

1. Explain what is meant by the statement, "There is a 60% chance of rainfall today."
2. Write three paragraphs about how the meteorologist predicts that there will be a
60% chance of snow on a certain day. Report your research to the class.
Hint: You may contact your local weather station for assistance on this project.
Let us examine the following examples about how experimental probability can help
us in predicting future events.

510

Example 1

The soccer team won 5 out of 12 games. Based on these results, how many times can the team expect to win in the next 24 games?

Solution

Let us find the experimental probability based on the games already played.

$$\text{Experimental probability of winning} = \frac{\text{Number of wins}}{\text{Total number of games played}}$$

$$= \frac{5}{12}$$

There are two methods by which we can predict the winnings in the next 20 games.

Method 1

Prediction of winning in the next 20 games.

= Experimental probability × number of games to be played.

$$= \frac{5}{12} \times 24$$

$$= \frac{5}{12} \times \frac{24}{1}$$

$$= \frac{5}{\underset{1}{12}} \times \frac{\overset{2}{24}}{1}$$

$$= 5 \times 2 = 10 \text{ wins}$$

The team can expect to win 10 of the next 24 games.

Method 2

We can predict the winnings in the next 24 games by using the fact that equivalent fractions or ratios are equal. (Review the section on Fractions and Ratios.)
Let us first find the probability of winnings in the next 24 games as shown:
Let y be the number of the games that can be won out of the next 24 games.
Therefore, the probability of winning y games out of 24 games

$$= \frac{\text{Number of wins}}{\text{Total number of games played}}$$

$$= \frac{y}{24} \quad\text{―――――――――――――}[A].$$

We have already shown that the experimental probability of winning based on the 24

games already played $= \dfrac{5}{12}$ ――――――――――――――――――― $[B]$.

$\dfrac{y}{24}$ and $\dfrac{5}{12}$ are equivalent fractions or ratios and since equivalent fractions or ratios are

equal, we can write:

$$\frac{y}{24} = \frac{5}{12} \quad\text{――――――――――――――――――}[C].$$

The cross products of equivalent fractions or ratios are equal, and therefore,

$$\frac{y}{24} \times\!\!\!\!\!\diagdown\!\!\!\!\!\times \frac{5}{12} \qquad \text{becomes } y \times 12 = 24 \times 5$$

$y \times 12 = 24 \times 5$ ――――――――――――――――――――― $[D]$

Divide each side of equation $[D]$ by 12 in order to obtain the value of y as shown:

$$\frac{y \times 12}{12} = \frac{24 \times 5}{12}$$

$$\frac{y \times \overset{1}{12}}{\underset{1}{12}} = \frac{\overset{2}{24} \times 5}{\underset{1}{12}}$$

$$y = 2 \times 5$$
$$y = 10$$

Therefore, 10 games out of 24 games can be won

Note: Method 1 or Method 2 may be used to solve or predict similar experimental probability questions.

Example 2

The experimental probability of a basketball team winning a game is $\dfrac{7}{10}$.

Predict the number of wins for the team out of 100 games.

Solution

Prediction of winning in the next 100 games

$\qquad\qquad$ = Experimental probability $\times$ number of games to be played

$$= \frac{7}{10} \times 100$$

$$= \frac{7}{\underset{1}{10}} \times \frac{\overset{10}{100}}{1}$$ Reduce to the lowest terms by dividing by 10.

$$= 70$$

The team can expect to win 70 out of 100 games.

Exercises

1. Given that the experimental probability of team A winning a game is $\frac{3}{20}$, predict

   the number of winnings:
   (a) in 40 games   (b) in 120 games   (c) in 60 games
   (d) in 80 games   (e) in 30 games   (f) in 20 games
   Hint: See Example 2.

2. The baseball team won 3 out of 10 games. Predict the winnings of the team:
   (a) in 30 games   (b) in 40 games   (c) in 60 games
   (d) in 90 games   (e) in 100 games   (f) in 180 games
   Hint: See Example 1.

3. Eric obtained 2 heads out of 8 tosses of a coin. Predict how many heads he
   will obtain:
   (a) in 18 tosses   (b) in 24 tosses   (c) in 32 tosses
   (d) in 64 tosses   (e) in 16 tosses   (f) in 72 tosses
   Hint: See Example 1.

4. Mary drew 3 green pens in 15 trials. Predict the number of green pens that she
   will draw:
   (a) in 30 trials   (b) in 45 trials   (c) in 60 trials
   Hint: See Example 1.

Challenge Questions

5. The experimental probability of winning a soccer game is $\frac{2}{7}$. Predict the number

   of winnings:
   (a) in 21 games   (b) in 35 games   (c) in 49 games

6. Judith won 2 out of 9 games. Predict the number of her winnings:
   (a) in 18 games   (b) in 27 games   (c) in 36 games
   (d) in 45 games   (e) in 54 games   (f) in 72 games

INDEPENDENT AND DEPENDENT EVENTS

Quick Review

(1) 1999
    + 2248

(2) What is the reciprocal of 9?

(3) $-2 \times (-44) =$

(4) 65% of 120 =

(5) $\sqrt{25} =$

(6) $\sqrt{100}$

(7) $\sqrt{3^2 + 4^2} =$

(8) $\sqrt{6^2 + 8^2} =$

(9) $\dfrac{3}{4} \div \dfrac{1}{8} =$

(10) The area of a square is 49 m^2, find the perimeter of the square. Hint: First find the length of a side of the square.

(11) What are the similarities between a rhombus and a square with respect to their sides.

(12) Solve for x.   (a) 6(4 - x) + 2x = -12   (b) 8.5 = x + 0.45

(13) What is the reciprocal of $\dfrac{23}{24}$.

(14) To divide by a fraction, multiply by the reciprocal of the fraction. True or false?

(15) The prime factorization of 48 is _____

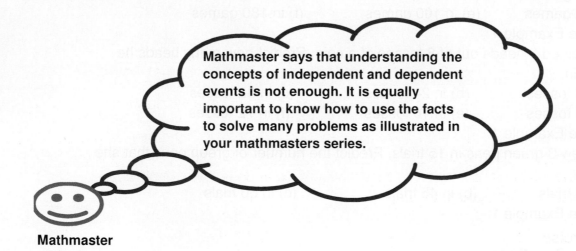

Mathmaster says that understanding the concepts of independent and dependent events is not enough. It is equally important to know how to use the facts to solve many problems as illustrated in your mathmasters series.

Mathmaster

Independent Events

New Term: independent events

Independent Events are events in which the occurrence of one event does not affect the probability of the occurrence of the other.

Example 1

a) A die is rolled twice. Event A = rolling a five on the first roll and Event B = rolling a five on the second roll. Determine if event A and event B are independent events

514

or not.

b) Use drawing balls from the same bag **with replacement** to explain independent events.

Solution

a) The occurrence of event A does not affect the probability of the occurrence of the event B. Therefore event A and event B are **independent events**.

b) Drawing from the same bag with replacement is an independent event because the sample space or the total number of the items in the bag is the same after the first draw. For an example, if a bag contains 2 green balls and 5 blue balls and a ball is drawn from the bag at random, and then replaced before the second ball is drawn, the result of the second draw does not depend on the first draw. The words **"with replacement"** should indicate to the student that the question involves an **independent event**.

The probability that the first ball drawn is green is

$$= \frac{\text{Number of green balls in the bag}}{\text{Total number of balls in the bag}} = \frac{2}{2+5} = \frac{2}{7}$$

The probability that the second ball drawn is green is still

$$= \frac{\text{Number of green balls in the bag}}{\text{Total number of balls in the bag}} = \frac{2}{2+5} = \frac{2}{7}$$

The probability that the second ball drawn is green is still $\frac{2}{7}$ because drawing the first ball did not change the sample space of the second drawing. The **sample space is the same for both drawings**. The sample space is the same as the total possible outcomes or in this particular case, the sample space is the total number of balls in the bag.

Group Exercise

The class may be divided into four teams, Team A, Team B, Team C and Team D. Each team should list four examples of a pair of independent events in life and give reasons why they are independent. One member from each team should report the list of the pairs of independent events to the whole class. Hint: The occurrence of the second event should not depend on the outcome of the first event.

To Find the Probability of Independent Events

The key equations or rules which are used to solve questions involving the **probability** of **independent events** are listed below. The students will know how the equations are used when the students read through the examples that shown.

(1) **Rule 1**: If X and Y are independent events, then

$$P(X \textbf{ and } Y) = \textbf{P(X)} \cdot \textbf{P(Y)} \quad\quad\quad\quad\quad\quad\quad\quad\quad\quad\quad\quad [A]$$

P(X and Y) may be written also as P(X, Y). Note that the "and" in bold means multiplication.

Equation [A] means the probability of X and Y occurring is equal to the probability of X occurring multiplied by the probability of Y occurring. This relation is known as the **multiplication law of probability**. It is also useful to know that the multiplication law can be used to solve questions if the questions contain the words "**both ... and ...**" Rule 1 can be stated as "If two events are independent, the probability of the first event followed by the second event is the **product of the probabilities of the first and second events**."

(2) **Rule 2**: Similarly, for three independent events X, Y and Z, then,

$$P(X \textbf{ and } Y \textbf{ and } Z) = \textbf{P(X)} \cdot \textbf{P(Y)} \cdot \textbf{P(Z)} \quad\quad\quad\quad\quad\quad [B]$$

P(X **and** Y **and** Z) may be written also as P(X, Y, Z).

Note that the "and" in bold in item (2) means multiplication.

(3). **Rule 3**: The simplest method of solving the "**at least one** ..." type of question is P(**at least one** ...) = **1** - **P(none of them** ...). You will see how this is used in many examples later.

(4) **Rule 4**: The word "**or**" in probability means **addition**, the word "**and**" means **multiplication**.

(5) **Rule 5**: In general, **P(A occurs)** + **P(A did not occur)** = **1**. You will see how this is used in many examples later.

Example 2

X and Y are two independent events. The probability of event X occurring is .4 and the probability of the event Y occurring is .2, find the probability of both the event X and the event Y occurring.

Solution

The probability of both X **and** Y occurring is:

P(X **and** Y) = **P(X)** · **P(Y)**   **Rule 1 is used**.

       = .4 × .2   From the question, P(X) = .4 and P(Y) = .2

       = .08   .4 × .2 = .08

Therefore the probability of both X and Y occurring is .08.

Example 3

If A and B are two independent events and the probability of A occurring is $\frac{1}{3}$ and the

probability of B occurring is $\frac{3}{5}$, find the probability of both A and B occurring.

Solution

The probability of both A and B occurring is:

P(A **and** B) = **P(A)** · **P(B)**   **Rule 1 is used**. ———————————[C]

$$= \frac{1}{3} \times \frac{3}{5}$$

From the question, $P(A) = \frac{1}{3}$ and $P(B) = \frac{3}{5}$,

substitute $P(A) = \frac{1}{3}$ and $P(B) = \frac{3}{5}$ into equation $[C]$.

$$= \frac{1}{\underset{1}{\cancel{3}}} \times \frac{\overset{1}{\cancel{3}}}{5}$$

Divide by 3

$$= \frac{1}{5}$$

Therefore, the probability of both events A and B occurring is $\frac{1}{5}$.

Example 4

A and B are two independent events such that $P(A) = \frac{4}{9}$ and $P(A \text{ and } B) = \frac{1}{8}$.

Find $P(B)$.

Solution

If A and B are two independent events then the probability that both events will occur is:

$P(A \text{ and } B) = P(A) \cdot P(B)$ **Rule 1 is used.** —————————————$[D]$

$$\frac{1}{8} = \frac{4}{9} \times P(B) \text{ ———————} [E]. \text{ From the question, } P(A \text{ and } B) = \frac{1}{8} \text{ and}$$

$$P(A) = \frac{4}{9}. \text{ Substitute } P(A \text{ and } B) = \frac{1}{8} \text{ and}$$

$$P(A) = \frac{4}{9} \text{ into equation } [D].$$

$$\frac{\frac{1}{8}}{\frac{4}{9}} = \frac{\frac{4}{9}}{\frac{4}{9}} \cdot P(B) \quad \text{Divide each side of the equation } [E] \text{ by } \frac{4}{9} \text{ to obtain the value of } P(B).$$

$$\frac{1}{8} \times \frac{9}{4} = \frac{4}{9} \times \frac{9}{4} \cdot P(B) \quad \text{To divide by a fraction is the same as multiplying by the}$$

reciprocal of the fraction. The reciprocal of $\frac{4}{9}$ is $\frac{1}{\frac{4}{9}} = \frac{9}{4}$

517

$$\frac{1}{8} \times \frac{9}{4} = \frac{\overset{1}{\cancel{4}}}{\cancel{9}} \times \frac{\overset{1}{\cancel{9}}}{\underset{1}{\cancel{4}}} \cdot P(B)$$ Divide the numerator and the denominator by 4 and 9.

$$\frac{9}{32} = P(B)$$

Therefore $P(B) = \dfrac{9}{32}$

Example 5

Bag A contains 3 yellow balls and 2 blue balls. Bag B contains 6 green balls and 5 blue balls. If a ball is selected at random from each box, find the probability that :

(a) one is green and the other is yellow.

(b) they are both of the same color.

Solution

Since the bags are separate, the events are independent.

Bag A: Number of yellow balls = 3, number of blue balls = 2 and the total number of balls = 3 + 2 = 5.

Bag B: Number of green balls = 6, number of blue balls = 5 and the total number of balls = 6 + 5 = 11

(a) P(one ball is green **and** the other is yellow)

     = P(green ball from bag B) · P(yellow ball from bag A).   **Rule 1 is used.** ———[F]

Let us find P(green ball from bag B) as shown:

$$P(\text{green ball from bag B}) = \frac{\text{Number of green balls in bag B}}{\text{Total number of balls in bag B}}$$

$$= \frac{6}{11}$$ The number of green balls in bag B is 6 and the total number of balls in bag B is 11.

Let us find P(yellow ball from bag A) as shown:

$$P(\text{yellow ball from bag A}) = \frac{\text{Number of yellow balls in bag A}}{\text{Total number of balls in bag A}}$$

$$= \frac{3}{5}$$

Substitute $P(\text{green ball from bag B}) = \dfrac{6}{11}$ and P(yellow ball from bag A) into equation [F] as follows:

P(one ball is green **and** the other is yellow) $= \dfrac{6}{11} \times \dfrac{3}{5}$

$$= \dfrac{18}{55}$$

(b) P(they are **both** the same color)

= P(blue ball from bag A **and** blue ball from bag B)

= P(blue ball from bag A) · P(blue ball from bag B) ⎯⎯⎯⎯⎯⎯⎯⎯⎯ [G]

Rule 1 is used.

Note that the only same color of balls in both bag A and bag B is blue.

Let us find P(blue ball from bag A) as follows:

P(blue ball from bag A) $= \dfrac{\text{Number of blue balls in bag A}}{\text{Total number of balls in bag A}}$

$$= \dfrac{2}{5}$$ The number of blue balls in bag A = 2 and the

total number of balls in bag A is 5.

Let us find P(blue ball from bag B) as shown:

P(blue ball from bag B) $= \dfrac{\text{Number of blue balls in bag B}}{\text{Total number of balls in bag B}}$

$$= \dfrac{5}{11}$$ The number of blue balls in bag B is 5 and

the total number of balls in bag B is 11.

Substitute P(blue ball from bag A) $= \dfrac{2}{5}$ and P(blue ball from bag B) $= \dfrac{5}{11}$ into

equation [G] as shown:

P(they are **both** of the same color) $= \dfrac{2}{5} \times \dfrac{5}{11}$

$$= \dfrac{2}{\cancel{5}} \times \dfrac{\cancel{5}}{11} \quad \text{Divide by 5.}$$

$$= \dfrac{2}{11}$$

Example 6

A bag contains 3 blue balls and 5 red balls. If two balls are selected at random,

one after the other, with replacement, what is the probability that:
(a) both are red?
(b) both are of the same color?

Solution

The number of blue balls = 3, the number of red balls = 5 and the total number of balls in the bag = 3 + 5 = 8.

(a) P(both are red) = P(first ball drawn is red **and** the second ball drawn is red).

$$= \text{P(first ball drawn is red)} \cdot \text{P(second ball drawn is red)} \quad \text{———}[H].$$

Rule 1 is used.

Let us find P(first ball drawn is red) as shown:

$$\text{P(first ball is red)} = \frac{\text{Number of red balls in the bag}}{\text{Total number of balls in the bag}}$$

$$= \frac{5}{8} \qquad \text{The number of red balls in the bag is 5 and the total}$$

number of balls in the bag is 8.

Let us find P(second ball drawn is red) as shown:

$$\text{P(second ball drawn is red)} = \frac{\text{Number of red balls in the bag after the replacement}}{\text{Total number of balls in the bag.}}$$

$$= \frac{5}{8}$$

Substitute P(first ball drawn is red) $= \frac{5}{8}$ and P(second ball drawn is red) $= \frac{5}{8}$ into equation $[H]$ as shown:

$$\text{P(\textbf{both} are red)} = \frac{5}{8} \times \frac{5}{8}$$

$$= \frac{25}{64}$$

(b) P(**both** are of the same color) = P(both are blue) **or** P(both are red).

$$= \text{P(both are blue)} + \text{P(both are red)} \quad \text{———————}[I]$$

(Note that "or" changes to "+" and **this is rule 4**.)

Let us find P(both are blue) as shown:

$$\text{P(first ball drawn is blue)} = \frac{\text{Number of blue balls}}{\text{Total number of balls}} = \frac{3}{8}$$

$$\text{P(second ball drawn is blue)} = \frac{\text{Number of blue balls after replacement}}{\text{Total number of balls after replacement}}$$

$$= \frac{3}{8}$$

P(both are blue) = P(first ball drawn is blue **and** second ball drawn is blue)

= P(first ball drawn is blue) · P(second ball drawn is blue).

Rule 1 is used.

$$= \frac{3}{8} \times \frac{3}{8} = \frac{9}{64}$$

Let us find P(both are red) as shown:

It has been shown in solution (a) that P(**both** are red) = $\frac{25}{64}$.

Let us find P(both are of the same color) as shown:

Substitute P(**both** are blue) = $\frac{9}{64}$ and P(both are red) = $\frac{25}{64}$ into equation $[1]$ as shown:

P(**both** are of the same color) = $\frac{9}{64} + \frac{25}{64}$

$$= \frac{34}{64}$$

$$= \frac{\overset{17}{\cancel{34}}}{\underset{32}{\cancel{64}}} \qquad \text{Reduce to the lowest term by dividing by 2.}$$

$$= \frac{17}{32}$$

Example 7

The probability that an event A occurs is $\frac{1}{6}$ and the probability that an event B occurs

is $\frac{2}{3}$. Assuming that the two events are independent, find the probability that:

(a) A **and** B occur.

(b) **neither** events occur.

(c) **at least one** of the events occurs.

Solution

(a) P(A **and** B occur) = **P(A) · P(B)**   **Rule 1 is used**.

$$= \frac{1}{6} \times \frac{2}{3}$$

$$= \frac{1}{6} \times \frac{2}{3} \overset{1}{\underset{3}{}}$$

Divide by 2

$$= \frac{1}{9}$$

(b) P(**neither** events occur) = **P(A did not occur)** · **P(B did not occur)** ————[J]

Rule 1 is used.

Let us find P(A did not occur) as shown:

P(A did not occur) = 1 - P(A occurs).

Rule 5 is P(A occurs) + P(A did not occur) = 1

$$= 1 - \frac{1}{6}$$ P(A occurs) is the same as P(A) = $\frac{1}{6}$, given in the question.

$$= \frac{5}{6}$$

Let us find P(B did not occur) as shown:

P(B did not occur) = 1 - P(B occurs)   Use rule 5: P(B occurs) + P(B did not occur) = 1

$$= 1 - \frac{2}{3}$$ P(B occurs) is the same as P(B) = $\frac{2}{3}$, given in the question.

$$= \frac{1}{3}$$

Substitute P(A did not occur) = $\frac{5}{6}$ and P(B did not occur) = $\frac{1}{3}$ into equation [J] as

shown:

$$P(\text{neither events occur}) = \frac{5}{6} \times \frac{1}{3}$$

$$= \frac{5}{18}$$

(c) P(at least one of the events occurs) = 1 - P(neither of the events occurs)

Rule 3 is used.

$$= 1 - \frac{5}{18}$$ From solution(b), P(neither

events occur) = $\frac{5}{18}$.

$$= \frac{13}{18}$$

Example 8

The probabilities that three students A, B, and C did their homework are $\frac{1}{6}$, $\frac{1}{8}$, and $\frac{1}{3}$

respectively. Calculate the probability that:

(a) none of them did the homework

(b) at least one of them did the homework.

(c) only one of them did the homework.

Solution

Let $P(A)$ = Probability that student A did the homework and

$P(\overline{A})$ = Probability that student A did not do the homework.

Let $P(B)$ = Probability that student B did the homework and

$P(\overline{B})$ = Probability that student B did not do the homework.

Let $P(C)$ = Probability that student C did the homework and

$P(\overline{C})$ = Probability that student C did not do the homework.

Therefore:

$P(A) = \dfrac{1}{6}$ and $P(\overline{A}) = 1 - \dfrac{1}{6} = \dfrac{5}{6}$ $P(A) + P(\overline{A}) = 1$, **see Rule 5.**

$P(B) = \dfrac{1}{8}$ and $P(\overline{B}) = 1 - \dfrac{1}{8} = \dfrac{7}{8}$ $P(B) + P(\overline{B}) = 1$, **see Rule 5.**

$P(C) = \dfrac{1}{3}$ and $P(\overline{C}) = 1 - \dfrac{1}{3} = \dfrac{2}{3}$ $P(C) + P(\overline{C}) = 1$, **see Rule 5.**

The events are independent because the occurrence of any one of them did not affect the occurrence of the others.

(a) P(**none of them** did the homework) = $\mathbf{P(\overline{A} \text{ and } \overline{B} \text{ and } \overline{C})}$

$$= P(\overline{A}) \cdot P(\overline{B}) \cdot P(\overline{C}) \qquad \textbf{Rule 2 is used.}$$

$$= \frac{5}{6} \times \frac{7}{8} \times \frac{2}{3} \qquad \text{Substitute } P(\overline{A}) = \frac{5}{6},$$

$$P(\overline{B}) = \frac{7}{8} \text{ and } P(\overline{C}) = \frac{2}{3}$$

$$= \frac{5}{6} \times \frac{7}{\overset{1}{\underset{4}{8}}} \times \frac{\overset{1}{2}}{3} \qquad \text{Divide by 2.}$$

$$= \frac{35}{72}$$

(b) P(**at least one** of them did the homework)

$$= \mathbf{1 - P(\textbf{none of them did the homework})} \qquad \textbf{Rule 3 is used.}$$

$$= 1 - \frac{35}{72} \qquad \text{From solution (a), P(none of them did the homework)} = \frac{35}{72}$$

$$= \frac{37}{72}$$

(c) The probability equation for P(only one of them did the homework) is setup using the fact that out of the three students A, B, and C, only one did the homework and the other two students did not do the homework as shown:

P(only one of them did the homework)

$= P(A \text{ and } \overline{B} \text{ and } \overline{C}) \text{ or } P(\overline{A} \text{ and } B \text{ and } \overline{C}) \text{ or } P(\overline{A} \text{ and } \overline{B} \text{ and } C)$

$= P(A) \cdot P(\overline{B}) \cdot P(\overline{C}) + P(\overline{A}) \cdot P(B) \cdot P(\overline{C}) + P(\overline{A}) \cdot P(\overline{B}) \cdot P(C)$ ────[K]

Note that "or" changes to +, **Rules 2 and 4 are used**.

$= (\frac{1}{6} \times \frac{7}{8} \times \frac{2}{3}) + (\frac{5}{6} \times \frac{1}{8} \times \frac{2}{3}) + (\frac{5}{6} \times \frac{7}{8} \times \frac{1}{3})$ Substitute $P(A) = \frac{1}{6}$, $P(\overline{A}) = \frac{5}{6}$,

$$P(B) = \frac{1}{8}, P(\overline{B}) = \frac{7}{8},$$

$$P(C) = \frac{1}{3}, P(\overline{C}) = \frac{2}{3}$$

into equation [K].

$$= \frac{14}{144} + \frac{10}{144} + \frac{35}{144}$$

$$= \frac{59}{144}$$

Example 9

The probability that Mary went to school on a certain day is $\frac{1}{6}$ and the probability that John went to school on the same day is $\frac{3}{4}$. What is the probability that:

(a) both were absent?
(b) at least one was present?
(c) exactly one of them was present?

Solution

Let M = the event that Mary went to school, P(M) is the probability that Mary went to school and P($\overline{M}$) is the probability that Mary did not go to school.

Let J = the event that John went to school, P(J) is the probability that John went to school and P($\overline{J}$) is the probability that John did not go to school.

$P(M) = \frac{1}{6}$ and $P(\overline{M}) = 1 - \frac{1}{6} = \frac{5}{6}$ $P(M) + P(\overline{M}) = 1$, **Rule 5 is used**.

$P(J) = \frac{3}{4}$ and $P(\overline{J}) = 1 - \frac{3}{4} = \frac{1}{4}$ $P(J) + P(\overline{J}) = 1$, **Rule 5 is used**.

(a) P(**both** were absent) = P($\overline{\text{M}}$ **and** $\overline{\text{J}}$)

$\quad\quad\quad\quad\quad\quad$ = **P($\overline{\text{M}}$) · P($\overline{\text{J}}$)** ———————————————[L]

$\quad\quad\quad\quad\quad\quad\quad\quad\quad\quad\quad\quad\quad\quad\quad\quad\quad\quad$ **Rule 1 is used.**

$\quad\quad\quad\quad\quad\quad$ = $\dfrac{5}{6} \times \dfrac{1}{4}$ $\quad$ Substitute P($\overline{\text{M}}$) = $\dfrac{5}{6}$ and P($\overline{\text{J}}$) = $\dfrac{1}{4}$ into equation [L].

$\quad\quad\quad\quad\quad\quad$ = $\dfrac{5}{24}$

(b) P(**at least one** was present) = **1 - P(both were absent)** $\quad\quad$ **Rule 3 is used.**

$\quad\quad\quad\quad\quad\quad\quad\quad$ = 1 - $\dfrac{5}{24}$ $\quad$ From solution (a) P(both were absent) = $\dfrac{5}{24}$

$\quad\quad\quad\quad\quad\quad\quad\quad$ = $\dfrac{19}{24}$

(c) P(**exactly one** of them was present) means that only one person should be present
and the other person should be absent in the equation as shown:

P(**exactly one** of them was present)

$\quad\quad$ = P(M **and** $\overline{\text{J}}$) **or** P($\overline{\text{M}}$ **and** J)

$\quad\quad$ = **P(M) · P($\overline{\text{J}}$) + P($\overline{\text{M}}$) · P(J)** ———————————————[M].

$\quad\quad\quad\quad\quad\quad\quad\quad\quad\quad\quad\quad\quad$ Rules 1 and 4 are used and "or" changes to +.

$\quad\quad$ = ($\dfrac{1}{6} \times \dfrac{1}{4}$) + ($\dfrac{5}{6} \times \dfrac{3}{4}$) $\quad$ Substitute P(M) = $\dfrac{1}{6}$, P($\overline{\text{J}}$) = $\dfrac{1}{4}$, P($\overline{\text{M}}$) = $\dfrac{5}{6}$

$\quad\quad\quad\quad\quad\quad\quad\quad\quad\quad\quad\quad$ and P(J) = $\dfrac{3}{4}$ into equation [M].

$\quad\quad$ = $\dfrac{1}{24} + \dfrac{15}{24}$

$\quad\quad$ = $\dfrac{16}{24}$

$\quad\quad$ = $\dfrac{\overset{2}{16}}{\underset{3}{24}}$ $\quad\quad\quad\quad\quad\quad\quad$ Reduce to the lowest term by dividing by 8.

$\quad\quad$ = $\dfrac{2}{3}$

Example 10

The outcome of each spin of a spinner is equally likely. An experiment consists of spinning the spinner 3 times. What is the probability of spinning a 2 all 3 times?

Solution

Since the result of each spin does not affect the results of the other spins, the spin results are independent.

$$\text{The probability of spinning a } 2 = P(2) = \frac{\text{Number of outcomes of a 2}}{\text{Total number of possible outcomes}}$$

$$= \frac{1}{4} \qquad \text{There is one outcome of a 2 out of the total possible outcomes of 4.}$$

The probability of spinning a 2 all 3 times
$$= P(2 \textbf{ and } 2 \textbf{ and } 2)$$
$$= \textbf{P(2)} \cdot \textbf{P(2)} \cdot \textbf{P(2)} \qquad\qquad\qquad\qquad [\text{N}].$$

Hint: **Rule 2 is used**.

$$= \frac{1}{4} \times \frac{1}{4} \times \frac{1}{4} \qquad \text{Substitute } P(2) = \frac{1}{4} \text{ into equation } [\text{N}].$$

$$= \frac{1}{64}$$

Example 11

All the outcomes of spinning a spinner are equally likely. A spinner was spun two times.
(a) What is the probability of spinning an even number both times?
(b) What is the probability of spinning a 3 at least once?

Solution

(a) The probability of spinning an even number is:

$$P(\text{even}) = \frac{\text{Number of outcomes of an even number}}{\text{Total number of possible outcomes}}$$

$$= \frac{2}{4} \qquad\qquad \text{The spinner has 2 and 4 as even numbers out of the total possible of 4 numbers which are 1, 2, 3, and 4.}$$

$$= \dfrac{\dfrac{1}{2}}{\dfrac{4}{2}}$$ Reduce to the lowest term by dividing by 2.

$$= \dfrac{1}{2}$$

The probability of spinning an even number both times is:

P(even and even) = P(even) · P(even) ————————————————————[O].

Hint: Rule 1 is used.

$$= \dfrac{1}{2} \times \dfrac{1}{2}$$ Substitute P(even) = $\dfrac{1}{2}$ into equation [O].

$$= \dfrac{1}{4}$$

(b) The probability of spinning a 3 at least once is

P(at least one 3) = 1 - P(not 3 for first spin and not 3 for second spin)

Hint: Rule 3 is used.
Note: P(at least one 3) +
P(not 3 and not 3) = 1.

= 1 - P(not 3) · P(not 3) ————————————————————[P].

Let us find P(not 3)

P(not 3) – $\dfrac{\text{Number of outcomes of not 3}}{\text{Total number of possible outcomes}}$

$$= \dfrac{3}{4}$$ There are three outcomes of 1, 2, and 4 which are not 3 out of a total possible outcomes of 4 which are 1, 2, 3, and 4.

Substitute P(not 3) = $\dfrac{3}{4}$ into equation [P] as shown:

P(at least one 3) = 1 - ($\dfrac{3}{4} \times \dfrac{3}{4}$)

$$= 1 - \dfrac{9}{16}$$

$$= \dfrac{7}{16}$$

Example 12

A die is rolled and then a coin is tossed. Find:

(a) P(4, T)   (b) P(less than 5, H)   (c) P(not 4, H)

(d) P(odd number,T)   (e) P(more than 3, H).

Solutions

The rolling of the die does not affect the occurrence of the probability of tossing the coin, and therefore, the two events are independent.

(a) $P(4, T) = P(4) \cdot P(T)$ ——————————————————————————[Q].

Hint: **Rule 1 is used**.

P(4, T) is the probability of tossing a 4, and then rolling a T where T is a tail of the coin.

Let us find P(4)

The sample space or the total possible outcomes of rolling a die are 1, 2, 3, 4, 5, and 6 which is a total of 6 possible outcomes. A 4 occurs only once out of the possible outcomes of 6, and therefore:

$$P(4) = \frac{\text{Number of outcomes of a 4}}{\text{Total possible number of outcomes}} = \frac{1}{6}$$

Let us find P(T)

The sample space or the total possible outcomes of tossing a coin are H and T which is a total possible outcomes of 2. T occurs only once out of a total possible outcomes of 2, and therefore:

$$P(T) = \frac{\text{Number of outcomes of a T}}{\text{Total possible number of outcomes}} = \frac{1}{2}$$

Let us find P(4, T)

Substitute $P(4) = \frac{1}{6}$ and $P(T) = \frac{1}{2}$ into equation $[Q]$ as shown:

$$P(4, T) = \frac{1}{6} \times \frac{1}{2}$$

$$= \frac{1}{12}$$

(b) $P(\text{less than 5, H}) = P(\text{less than 5}) \cdot P(H)$ ——————————————————-[R].

Hint: **Rule 1 is used**

P(less than 5, H) is the probability of rolling a die and the outcomes are numbers less than 5 and then obtaining an H when a coin is tossed.

Let us find P(less than 5)

The sample space or the total possible outcomes of rolling a die are 1, 2, 3, 4, 5, and 6 which is a total of 6 possible outcomes. From the sample space, the outcomes that are less than 5 are 1, 2, 3, and 4 which shows that 4 out of 6 outcomes are less than 5, and therefore:

$$P(\text{less than 5}) = \frac{\text{Number of outcomes less than 5}}{\text{Total possible number of outcomes}} = \frac{4}{6}$$

$$= \frac{\overset{2}{\cancel{4}}}{\underset{3}{\cancel{6}}} \qquad \text{Reduce to the lowest}$$

term by dividing by 2.

$$= \frac{2}{3}$$

Let us find P(H)

The sample space or the total possible outcomes of tossing a coin are H and T which is a total possible outcomes of 2. H occurs only once out of the total possible outcomes of 2, and therefore:

$$P(H) = \frac{\text{Number of outcomes of H}}{\text{Total possible number of outcomes}} = \frac{1}{2}$$

Let us find P(less than 5, H)

Substitute $P(\text{less than 5}) = \frac{2}{3}$ and $P(H) = \frac{1}{2}$ into equation $[R]$ as shown:

$$P(\text{less than 5, H}) = \frac{2}{3} \times \frac{1}{2}$$

$$= \frac{2}{6}$$

$$= \frac{\overset{1}{\cancel{2}}}{\underset{3}{\cancel{6}}} \qquad \text{Reduce to the lowest term by dividing by 2.}$$

$$= \frac{1}{3}$$

(c) $P(\text{not 4, H}) = P(\text{not 4}) \cdot P(H)$ ────────────────── $[S]$

Hint: **Rule 1 is used**.

P(not 4, H) is the probability of rolling a die and obtaining an outcome which is not 4 and tossing a coin and obtaining H.

Let us find P(not 4)

The sample space or the total possible outcomes of rolling a die are 1, 2, 3, 4, 5, and 6 which are 6 total possible outcomes. Therefore, the outcomes that are not a 4 are 1, 2, 3, 5, and 6 which are 5 outcomes out of 6 outcomes that are not 4, and therefore:

$$P(\text{not } 4) = \frac{\text{Number of outcomes which are not } 4}{\text{Total possible number of outcomes}} = \frac{5}{6}$$

Let us find P(H)

We already showed in solution (b) that $P(H) = \dfrac{1}{2}$

Let us find P(not 4, H)

Substitute $P(\text{not } 4) = \dfrac{5}{6}$ and $P(H) = \dfrac{1}{2}$ into equation $[S]$ as shown:

$$P(\text{not } 4, H) = \frac{5}{6} \times \frac{1}{2}$$

$$= \frac{5}{12}$$

(d) $P(\text{odd number, } T) = P(\text{odd number}) \cdot P(T)$ ⎯⎯⎯⎯⎯⎯⎯$[T]$

Hint: **Rule 1 is used.**

$P(\text{odd number, } T)$ is the probability that when a die is rolled, the outcome is an odd number and when a coin is tossed, the outcome is T.

Let us find P(odd number)

The sample space or the total possible outcomes of rolling a die are 1, 2, 3, 4, 5 and 6 which is a total of 6 possible outcomes. The odd numbers in the sample space are 1, 3, and 5 which is 3 outcomes of odd numbers out of a total possible outcomes of 6, and therefore:

$$P(\text{odd number}) = \frac{\text{Number of outcomes of odd numbers}}{\text{Total possible number of outcomes}}$$

$$= \frac{3}{6}$$

$$= \frac{\overset{1}{3}}{\underset{2}{6}} \qquad \text{Reduce to the lowest term by dividing by 3.}$$

$$= \frac{1}{2}$$

Let us find P(T)

We have already found in solution (a) that $P(T) = \dfrac{1}{2}$

Let us find P(odd number, T)

Substitute P(odd number) = $\frac{1}{2}$ and P(T) = $\frac{1}{2}$ into equation $[T]$ as shown:

$$P(\text{odd number, T}) = \frac{1}{2} \times \frac{1}{2}$$

$$= \frac{1}{4}$$

(e) P(more than 3, H) = P(more than 3) · P(H) ——————————————$[U]$

Hint: **See Rule 1**

P(more than 3, H) is the probability that when the die is rolled the outcome is a number greater than 3, and when a coin is tossed, the outcome is H.

Let us find P(more than 3)

The sample space or the total number of possible outcomes of rolling a die are 1, 2, 3, 4, 5, and 6 which is a total of 6 possible outcomes. The outcomes of 4, 5, and 6 are more than 3, and there are 3 outcomes out of a total of 6 that are more than 3, and therefore:

$$P(\text{more than 3}) = \frac{\text{Number of outcomes that are more than 3}}{\text{Total possible number of outcomes}}$$

$$= \frac{3}{6}$$

Let us find P(H)

We have already shown from solution (b) that P(H) = $\frac{1}{2}$.

Let us find P(more than 3, H)

Substitute P(more than 3) = $\frac{1}{2}$ and P(H) = $\frac{1}{2}$ into equation $[U]$ as shown:

$$P(\text{more than 3, H}) = \frac{1}{2} \times \frac{1}{2}$$

$$= \frac{1}{4}$$

Example 13

A coin is tossed 3 times. What is the probability of getting either all heads or all tails?

Solution

P(either all 3 heads **or** all 3 tails) = P(all 3 heads) **or** P(all 3 tails)

= P(all 3 heads) + P(all 3 tails)   **Rule 4 is used**, the "or" becomes +.

= P(H, H, H) + P(T, T, T)

$$= P(H) \cdot P(H) \cdot P(H) + P(T) \cdot P(T) \cdot P(T) \quad \text{——}[V].$$

Rule 2 is used.

Let us find P(H) and P(T)

The sample space or the total possible number of outcomes when a coin is tossed are H and T, which is a total of 2 outcomes. From the sample space, H occurs once out of a possible outcomes of 2, and T occurs once out of the possible outcomes of 2, and therefore:

$$P(H) = \frac{\text{Number of outcomes of H}}{\text{Total possible number of outcomes}} = \frac{1}{2}$$

$$P(T) = \frac{\text{Number of outcomes of T}}{\text{Total possible number of outcomes}} = \frac{1}{2}$$

Let us find P(either all 3 heads or all 3 tails)

Substitute $P(H) = \dfrac{1}{2}$ and $P(T) = \dfrac{1}{2}$ into equation $[V]$ as shown:

$$P(\textbf{either} \text{ all 3 heads or all 3 tails}) = \frac{1}{2} \times \frac{1}{2} \times \frac{1}{2} + \frac{1}{2} \times \frac{1}{2} \times \frac{1}{2}$$

$$= \frac{1}{8} + \frac{1}{8}$$

$$= \frac{2}{8}$$

$$= \frac{\overset{1}{\cancel{2}}}{\underset{4}{\cancel{8}}} \qquad \text{Reduce to the lowest term, divide by 2.}$$

$$= \frac{1}{4}$$

Example 14

A coin is tossed 3 times. What is the probability that the outcome is three 3 heads?

Solution

$$P(3 \text{ heads}) = P(H \text{ and } H \text{ and } H) = P(H) \cdot P(H) \cdot P(H) \quad \text{——————}[W].$$

Rule 2 is used.

Let us find P(H)

The sample space or the total possible number of outcomes when a coin is tossed are H and T, which is a total of 2 outcomes. From the sample space, H occurs once out of possible outcomes of 2, and therefore:

532

$$P(H) = \frac{\text{Number of outcomes of H}}{\text{Total possible number of outcomes}} = \frac{1}{2}$$

Let us find P(3 heads)

Substitute $P(H) = \frac{1}{2}$ into equation $[W]$ as shown:

$$P(3 \text{ heads}) = P(H \text{ and } H \text{ and } H) = \frac{1}{2} \times \frac{1}{2} \times \frac{1}{2}$$

$$= \frac{1}{8}$$

Exercises

1. What is an independent event?
2. Explain the statement that when a coin is tossed twice, the first and the second tosses are independent events? Hint: See Example **1(a)**.
3. Use drawing balls from the same bag, with replacement, to explain independent events. Hint: See Example **1(b)**.
4 (a) Event A and event B are two independent events. If the probability of event A occurring is .3 and the probability of event B occurring is .5, find the probability that both of the events occurred. Hint: See Example **2**.

(b) If P and Q are two independent events and the probability of P occurring is $\frac{1}{4}$

and the probability of Q occurring is $\frac{1}{2}$, find the probability of both P and Q

occurring. Hint: See Example **3**.
5. Complete the following probability equations:
(a) If W and Y are independent events, then P(W and Y) = ?
Hint: See Rule 1.
(b) If A, B, and C are independent events, then P(A and B and C) = ?
Hint: See Rule 2.
(c) P(at least one ...) = ?
Hint: See Rule 3.
(d) In probability, the word "or" means _____ and the word "and" means _____
Hint: See Rule 4.

6. If A and B are two independent events and the probability of A occurring is $\frac{2}{7}$ and

the probability of B occurring is $\frac{1}{4}$, find the probability of both A and B occurring.

Hint: See Example **3**.

7. X and Y are two independent events such that $P(X) = \frac{3}{5}$ and $P(X \text{ and } Y) = \frac{1}{6}$.

Find P(Y). Hint: See Example **4**.

8. A and B are two independent events. P(A) = $\frac{3}{4}$ and P(A and B) = $\frac{1}{5}$. Find P(B).

   Hint: See Example **4**.

9. X and Y are two independent events and the probability of X occurring is $\frac{1}{3}$ and the

   probability of Y occurring is $\frac{1}{5}$, find the probability of both X and Y occurring.

   Hint: See Example **3**.

10. Bag X contains 2 green marbles and 3 red marbles. Bag Y contains 4 black marbles and 5 red marbles. If a marble is selected at random from each bag, find the probability that:

(a) one is green and the other is black

(b) they are both of the same color.

   Hint: See Example **5**.

11. A box contains 4 black marbles and 6 green marbles. If two marbles are selected one after the other with replacement, what is the probability that:

   (a) both are green?

   (b) they are both of the same color?

   Hint: See Example **6**.

12. The probability that an event X occurs is $\frac{1}{3}$ and the probability that an event Y

   occurs is $\frac{2}{5}$. Assume that the two events are independent, find the probability that:

   (a) X and Y occur.

   (b) neither events occur

   (c) at least one of the events occurs.

   Hint: See Example **7**.

13. The probabilities that three students X, Y, and Z passed their tests are $\frac{2}{3}$, $\frac{1}{4}$,

   and $\frac{3}{4}$ respectively. Calculate the probability that:

   (a) none of them passed the test.

   (b) at least one of them passed the test.

   (c) only one of them passed the test.

   Hint: See Example **8**.

14. The probability that Judith got a baby-sitting job on a certain day is $\frac{1}{4}$ and the

   probability that Eric got a baby-sitting job on the same day is $\frac{2}{3}$. Given that the two

   events are independent, what is the probability that:

   (a) **both** did not get the job?

534

(b) **at least one** of them got the job?

(c) **exactly one** of them got the job.

Hint: See Example **9**.

15. The outcomes for each spin of a spinner are equally likely. An experiment consists of spinning the spinner 3 times. What is the probability of spinning a 7 three times?

Hint: See Example **10** and note that $P(7) = \dfrac{\text{Number of outcomes of a 7}}{\text{Total number of possible outcomes}} = \dfrac{1}{8}$.

16. All the outcomes of spinning a spinner are equally likely. A spinner was spun 2 times.

(a) What is the probability of spinning an odd number both times?

(b) What is the probability of spinning a 4 at least once?

Hint: See Example **11**

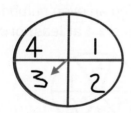

17. A die is rolled, and then a coin is tossed. What is the probability of:

(a) P(5, H)?

(b) P(less than 4, T)?

(c) P(not 2, T)?

(d) P(odd number, H)?

(e) P(more than 4, H)?

Hint: See Example **12**.

18. A coin was tossed 4 times. What is the probability of getting either all tails or all heads? Hint See Example **13**.

19. A coin is tossed 4 times. What is the probability that the outcome is 4 tails? Hint: See Example **14**.

Challenge Questions

20. A and B are two independent events. $P(B) = \dfrac{3}{5}$ and $P(A \text{ and } B) = \dfrac{1}{3}$. Find $P(A)$.

21. The probability that event X occurs is $\dfrac{1}{4}$ and the probability that event Y occurs is $\dfrac{1}{3}$. Assuming that the two events are independent, find the probability that:

   (a) X **and** Y occur.

   (b) **neither** events occur.

   (c) **at least one** of the events occurs.

22. A bag contains 3 black pens and 5 green pens. If two pens are selected one after the other, with replacement, what is the probability that:

   (a). **both** are green?

   (b). they are both the **same color**?

23. The probabilities that three students A, B, and C went to school are $\dfrac{1}{5}, \dfrac{1}{3}$, and $\dfrac{1}{4}$ respectively. Calculate the probability that:

   (a). **none of them** went to school.

   (b). **at least one** of them went to school.

   (c). **only one** of them went to school.

24. All the outcomes of spinning a spinner are equally likely. A spinner was spun three times.

   (a). What is the probability of spinning an even number **all three times**?

   (b). What is the probability of spinning a 4 **at least once**?

25. If X, Y, and Z are independent events, then:

   (a). $P(X \text{ and } Y \text{ and } Z) =$

   (b). $P(\overline{X} \text{ and } \overline{Y} \text{ and } \overline{Z}) =$

c). The outcomes for each spin of a spinner are equally likely. An experiment consists of spinning the spinner 2 times. What is the probability of spinning a 6 both times?

26. A die is rolled, and then a coin is tossed. What is the probability of:

   (a). P(1, H)   (b). P(less than 3, H)   (c). P(not 5, T)

   (d). P(even number, T)   (e). P(more than 2, H)   (f). P(less than 5, T)

27. A coin is tossed 2 times. What is the probability of getting either all heads or all tails?
28. A coin is tossed 2 times. What is the probability that the outcome is 2 tails?
29. A marble is tossed on the square. It lands at random on one of the colored squares. Find the probability that it lands on a specific colored square as shown:
    a. P(blue)   b. P(white)   c. P(green)   d. P(red)
    e. P(not blue)   f. P(not green)   g. P(red or white)   h. P(blue or green)

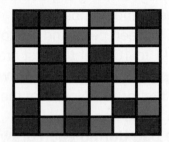

 Hint: Find the total number of the colored squares. The total number of the colored squares is the same as the total number of outcomes. Find the total number of each type of the colored squares. This question is similar to the examples involving spinning of a spinner.

PROBABILITY OF DEPENDENT EVENTS

New Term: dependent event

The 3 important steps in calculating the probability of two dependent events are:
1). calculate the probability of the first event.
2). calculate the probability that the second event will occur if only the first event has occurred.
3). Multiply the two probabilities in (1) and (2).

Rule 5: If X and Y are dependent events, then P(X **and** Y) = P(X) · P(Y after X occurs).
Rule 6: If X, Y, and Z are dependent events, then P(X **and** Y **and** Z) = P(X) · P(Z after Y occurs).

Example 1
There are 5 black pens and 6 green pens in a bag. Given that:
a). 1 pen was drawn, find the probability of drawing a green pen in the first draw.
b). Explain how the probability of the first draw **without replacement** affects the probability of the occurrence of the second draw.

c). Find the probability of drawing a green pen in the second draw.

Solution

a). On the first draw,

$$P(\text{green}) = \frac{\text{Number of green pens}}{\text{Total number of pens in the bag}}$$

$$= \frac{6}{5+6} = \frac{6}{11} \qquad \text{(There are 5 black pens and 6 green pens.)}$$

P(green) means the probability of selecting a green pen.

b). Since the first green pen was drawn without a replacement, the number of the green pens has reduced from a total of 6 green pens to 5 green pens and the total number of pens in the bag has therefore reduced from 11 to 10 after the first draw. Therefore, the **sample space for the second draw depends on the first draw**. The sample space has changed from 11 to 10 after the first draw. (Note that the sample space of an experiment is the set of all possible outcomes.)

The sample space is the total number of pens in the bag during each draw.

c). If the first draw was a green pen, then the probability of the second draw being a green pen is:

$$P(\text{green after the first draw}) = \frac{\text{Number of green pens left after the first draw}}{\text{Total number of pens in the bag after the first draw}}$$

$$= \frac{6-1}{5+6-1} \qquad \text{(6 - 1 = number of pens left after first draw.)}$$

$$(5 + 6 - 1 = \text{number of total pens in the bag after the first draw.})$$

$$= \frac{5}{10}$$

$$= \frac{5}{10} = \frac{1}{2} \qquad \text{(Reduce to the lowest term by dividing by 5.)}$$

P(First green **and** second green) = P(First green) · P(second green after first green)

$$= \frac{6}{11} \cdot \frac{1}{2} \qquad (\frac{6}{11} \text{ is the probability of selecting the first green pen.})$$

$$= \frac{\overset{3}{\cancel{6}}}{11} \times \frac{1}{\underset{1}{\cancel{2}}}$$

$$= \frac{3}{11}$$

Example 2

A bag contains 6 red marbles and 11 green marbles. A marble is drawn at random from the bag and is not replaced. A second marble is then drawn at random. Find the probability that:

(a) both marbles are red.

(b) both marbles are of the same color.

(c) the first marble selected is green and the second is red.

Solution

(a) Let R denote the event of drawing a red marble and G denote the event of drawing a green marble.

P(both red) = P(first red **and** second red) = P(first red) · P(second red)_____$[X]$

See Rule 1

Let us find P(first red)

P(first red) is the probability that the first marble drawn is red.

$$P(\text{first red}) = \frac{\text{Number of red marbles}}{\text{Total number of marbles}} = \frac{6}{6+11} = \frac{6}{17}$$

Let us find P(second red)

P(second red) is the probability that the second marble drawn is also red.

Since the first marble drawn is red and it is not replaced, the number of red marbles in the bag is reduced from 6 to 5, and therefore, the total number of marbles in the bag is reduced from 17 to 16. Therefore:

$$P(\text{second red}) = \frac{\text{Number of red marbles after the first draw}}{\text{Total number of marbles after the first draw}} = \frac{6-1}{17-1} = \frac{5}{16}$$

Substitute $P(\text{first red}) = \frac{6}{17}$ and $P(\text{second red}) = \frac{5}{16}$ into equation $[X]$ as shown:

$$P(\text{both red}) = P(\text{first red and second red}) = \frac{6}{17} \times \frac{5}{16} = \frac{30}{272}$$

$$= \frac{30}{272}$$

$$= \frac{\overset{15}{\cancel{30}}}{\underset{136}{\cancel{272}}}$$ Reduce to the lowest term by dividing by 2.

$$= \frac{15}{136}$$

b). Both marbles drawn are of the same color means that either the 2 marbles are both red **or** the 2 marbles are both green. Therefore:

P(**both** are of the same color) = P(**both** are red) **or** P(**both** are green)

= P(first red **and** second red) **or** P(first green **and** second green).

= P(first red) · P(second red) + P(first green) · P(second green) _____ [Y]

See **Rule 1** and **Rule 4**, "**or**" changes to "**addition**".

Let us find P(first red) · P(second red)

From the solution (a), P(first red) · P(second red) = $\frac{15}{136}$

Let us find P(first green) · P(second green)

P(first green) = $\dfrac{\text{Number of green marbles}}{\text{Total number of marbles}} = \dfrac{11}{17}$

P(second green) = $\dfrac{\text{Number of green marbles after first drawing}}{\text{Total number of marbles after first drawing}}$

$$= \frac{11 - 1}{17 - 1}$$

$$= \frac{10}{16} = \frac{5}{8}$$ (Reduce to the lowest term by dividing by 2.)

(Note that after the first drawing of the green marble, without replacement, the number of green marbles reduces from 11 to 10, so the total number of marbles after the first drawing reduces from 17 to 16.)

P(first green) · P(second green) = $\dfrac{11}{17} \times \dfrac{5}{8}$

$$= \frac{55}{136}$$

Substitute P(first red) · P(second red) = $\dfrac{15}{136}$ and

P(first green) · P(second green) = $\frac{55}{136}$ into equation [Y] as shown:

P(both are of the same color) = $\frac{15}{136} + \frac{55}{136}$

$$= \frac{70}{136}$$

$$= \frac{\overset{35}{\cancel{70}}}{\underset{68}{\cancel{136}}}$$ Reduce to the lowest term by dividing by 2.

$$= \frac{35}{68}$$

c). P(first green **and** second red) = P(first green) · P(second red) ——————[Z]

See Rule 1.

Let us find P(first green) :
P(first green) is the probability of drawing a green marble on the first draw.

$$P(\text{first green}) = \frac{\text{Number of green marbles}}{\text{Total number of marbles}} = \frac{11}{17}$$

Let us find P(second red.)
P(second red) is the probability that after the first green marble is drawn, without replacement, the second marble drawn is red. Note that after the first green marble is selected without replacement the number of the red marbles is still 6, but the total number of marbles in the bag is reduced from 17 to 16.
Therefore,

P(second red)

$$= \frac{\text{Number of red marbles}}{\text{Total number of marbles after the first red marble is drawn without replacement}}$$

$$= \frac{6}{17 - 1}$$

$$= \frac{6}{16}$$

$$= \frac{6 \div 2}{16 \div 2}$$ Reduce to the lowest term by dividing by 2.

$$= \frac{3}{8}$$

Substitute P(first green) $= \frac{11}{17}$ and P(second red) $= \frac{3}{8}$ into equation $[Z]$ as shown:

P(first green **and** second red) $= \frac{11}{17} \times \frac{3}{8} = \frac{33}{136}$

Example 3

The marbles numbered from 1 to 8 are identical in shape and are shuffled and spread out facedown. If a marble is drawn, **without replacement**, and the second marble is drawn, find:
(a) P(6, odd)   (b) P(odd, even)   (c) P(even, even)

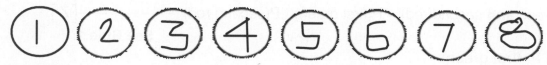

Solution
(a) P(6, odd) = P(6) · P(odd after drawing a 6)_____$[AI]$.

See Rule 5.

Let us find P(6):
P(6) is the probability of selecting a 6.

$$P(6) = \frac{\text{Number of a 6}}{\text{Total number of the marbles}} = \frac{1}{8}$$

Let us find P(odd after drawing a 6):
P(odd after drawing a 6) without a replacement is the probability of drawing an odd number after drawing a 6 without replacement.

$$P(\text{odd after drawing a 6}) = \frac{\text{Number of odd marbles}}{\text{Total number of the marbles after drawing a 6}}$$

(The odd numbers are 1, 3, 5, and 7.)
(Total number of the marbles left after drawing a 6 = 8 - 1 = 7.)

$$= \frac{4}{8 - 1}$$

$$= \frac{4}{7}$$

Note that the total number of the marbles is reduced from 8 to 7 because of drawing an odd number marble, without replacement.

Substitute $P(6) = \frac{1}{8}$ and P(odd after drawing a 6) $= \frac{4}{7}$ into equation [AI] as shown:

$$P(6, \text{odd}) = \frac{1}{8} \times \frac{4}{7}$$

$$= \frac{1}{\overset{}{\underset{2}{8}}} \times \frac{\overset{1}{4}}{7} \qquad\qquad \text{Divide by 4.}$$

$$= \frac{1}{14}$$

b). P(odd, even) = P(odd) · P(even after drawing an odd) _____[B1]

See **Rule 5**.

Lets us find P(odd):
P(odd) is the probability of drawing an odd numbered marble.

$$P(\text{odd}) = \frac{\text{Number of odd numbered marbles}}{\text{Total number of the marbles}} = \frac{4}{8}$$

(The four odd numbers are 1, 3, 5, and 7.)

$$= \frac{1}{2} \quad \text{Reduce to the lowest term by dividing by 4.}$$

Lets us find P(even after drawing an odd.)
P(even after drawing an odd) is the probability of drawing an even numbered marble after an odd numbered marble is drawn.

$$P(\text{even after drawing an odd}) = \frac{\text{Number of even numbered marbles}}{\text{Total number of marbles after drawing an odd number}}$$

$$= \frac{4}{8 - 1} = \frac{4}{7}$$

(The four even numbers are 2, 4, 6, and 8.
Note that the total number of marbles is reduced from 8 to 7 because an odd

numbered marble was drawn **without replacement**.)

Substitute P(odd) = $\frac{1}{2}$ and P(even after drawing an odd) = $\frac{4}{7}$ into equation [BI] as shown:

$$P(\text{odd, even}) = \frac{1}{2} \times \frac{4}{7}$$

$$= \frac{4}{14}$$

$$= \frac{\overset{2}{4}}{\underset{7}{14}} \qquad \text{Reduce to the lowest term by dividing by 2.}$$

$$= \frac{2}{7}$$

(c). P(even, even) = P(even) · P(even after drawing an even)

Let us find P(even):

P(even) is the probability of drawing an even numbered marble.

$$P(\text{even}) = \frac{\text{Number of even numbered marbles}}{\text{Total number of the marbles}}$$

$$= \frac{4}{8} \qquad \text{(The four even numbered marbles are 2, 4, 6, and 8.)}$$

$$= \frac{\overset{1}{4}}{\underset{2}{8}} \qquad \text{(Reduce to the lowest term by dividing by 4.)}$$

$$= \frac{1}{2}$$

Let us find P(even after drawing even.)

P(even after drawing an even) is the probability of drawing an even numbered marble after another even numbered marble had already been drawn, **without replacement**. Therefore:

P(even after drawing an even)

544

$$= \frac{\text{Number of even numbered marbles after drawing an even numbered marble}}{\text{Total marbles after drawing an even numbered marble}}$$

$$= \frac{4 - 1}{8 - 1}$$

(Both the even numbered marbles and the total marbles are reduced by 1 each after drawing an even numbered marble, **without replacement**.)

$$= \frac{3}{7}$$

Substitute $P(\text{even}) = \frac{1}{2}$ and $P(\text{even after drawing an even}) = \frac{3}{7}$ into equation [C1] as shown:

$$P(\text{even, even}) = \frac{1}{2} \times \frac{3}{7}$$

$$= \frac{3}{14}$$

Example 4

The marbles A to J were shuffled and spread out facedown. The marbles were drawn one after the other, **without replacement**. Find P(B, E, H).

Solution

P(B, E, H) = P(B) · P(E after drawing B) · P(H after drawing E).

Let us find P(B):

P(B) is the probability of drawing the marble B out of a total of 10 marbles. Therefore:

$$P(B) = \frac{\text{Number of marble B}}{\text{Total number of marbles}} = \frac{1}{10}$$

Let us find P(E after drawing B):

P(E after drawing B) is the probability of drawing the marble E after drawing marble B **without replacement**. Therefore:

P(E after drawing B)

$$= \frac{\text{Number of marble E}}{\text{Total number of marbles after drawing B \textbf{without replacement}}}$$

$= \dfrac{1}{10 - 1}$ The total number of the marbles is reduced by 1, **without replacement**.

$= \dfrac{1}{9}$

Let us find P(H after drawing E.)

P(H after drawing E) is the probability of drawing the marble H after drawing marble E **without replacement**. Therefore,

P(H after drawing E)

$$= \dfrac{\text{Number of marble H}}{\text{Total number of marbles after drawing E \textbf{without replacement}}}$$

$= \dfrac{1}{9 - 1} = \dfrac{1}{8}$ (Note that the total number of marbles left after drawing marble B is 9 and the total number of marbles left after drawing E is 9 - 1 = 8).

Substitute $P(B) = \dfrac{1}{10}$, P(E after drawing B) $= \dfrac{1}{9}$ and P(H after drawing E) $= \dfrac{1}{8}$ into equation [D1] as shown:

$$P(B, E, H) = \dfrac{1}{10} \times \dfrac{1}{9} \times \dfrac{1}{8}$$

$$= \dfrac{1}{720}$$

Exercises

1. A and B are dependent events. Complete the statement:
   P(A and B) =? Hint: See Rule 5.
2. If A, B, and C are dependent events, then P(A and B and C) =? Hint: See Rule 6.
3. There are 3 green marbles and 4 red marbles in a bag.
   a) Given that 1 marble was drawn, find the probability that the marble drawn first is red. See Example **1**.
   b) Explain how the probability of the first draw **without a replacement** affects the probability of the occurrence of the second draw. Hint: See Example **1**.
   c) If the first red marble was drawn **without a replacement**, find the probability of drawing a red marble in the second draw. Hint: See Example **1**.
4. A box contains 5 blue pens and 8 red pens. A pen is drawn at random **without replacement**. A second pen is then drawn at random. Find the probability that:
   (a) both pens are blue.
   (b) both pens are of the same color.
   (c) the first pen drawn is red and the second pen is red.
   Hint: See Example **2**

5. The marbles numbered from 1 to 6 are shuffled and spread out facedown. If a marble is drawn, **without replacement**, and the second marble is drawn find:
   (a) P(2, odd)   (b) P(even, odd)   (c) P(even, even)

Hint: See Example 3

6. The marbles A to G were shuffled and spread out face down. The marbles were drawn one after the other **without replacement**. Find P(A, C, F).

Hint: See Example **4**

Challenge Questions

1. If P, Q and R are dependent events, then P(P, Q, R) = ?
   Note that P(P, Q, R) is the same as P(P and Q and R).

2. A bag contains 7 green shirts and 5 yellow shirts. A shirt is drawn at random without replacement. A second shirt is then drawn at random. Find the probability that:
   (a) both shirts are green
   (b) both shirts are of the same color.
   (c) the first shirt drawn is yellow and the second shirt drawn is also yellow.

3. The marbles numbered from 1 to 9 are shuffled and spread out facedown. If a marble is drawn without replacement and the second marble is then drawn, find:
   (a) P(odd, odd)   (b) P(7, even)   (c) P(even, odd).

4. The marbles A to F were shuffled and spread out facedown. The marbles were drawn one after the other without replacement. Find P(C, D, F).

5. There are 5 green pens and 4 blue pens in a bag.
   (a) Given that 1 pen is drawn, find the probability that the pen is green.
   (b) If the first green pen was drawn without a replacement, find the probability of drawing a green pen in the second draw.

RELATIVE FREQUENCY

The relative frequency is how frequently a value appears relative to the total data set. The relative frequency can therefore be represented as percent of frequency or probability. The relative frequency table is a frequency table that has a column that shows how frequently a value appears relative to the total data set. The relative frequency column is a percent of frequency or probability. The formula for relative frequency is:

$$\text{Relative frequency} = \frac{\text{each frequency}}{\text{sum of all frequencies}}$$

Example 1

The table shows the result of the survey of the favorite month of the year of some students.

a. Make a relative frequency table for the data.

b. What is the least popular month of the year?

c. How many more people choose December rather than November?

d. How many people took part in the survey?

e. If 2 more students choose December, how many total people would have chosen December?

f. Which month had the highest relative frequency and what is the value of the relative frequency?

g. What month had the least relative frequency, and what is the value of the relative frequency?

h. What is the probability that a randomly selected student will choose November as a favorite month?

i. Find the probability that a student selected at random had February, September, or November as a favorite month.

j. How many more people chose November rather than February?

(The table is on the next page.)

548

Month	Number of students
January	4
February	2
March	3
April	5
May	1
June	2
July	4
August	5
September	4
October	4
November	6
December	20

Solution

a. The relative frequency table includes a column that shows how frequently each month appears relative to the total number of times that all the months appear as shown in the table:

(The Relative Frequency Table is Shown on the Next Page.)

Month	Number of Students	Relative frequency
January	4	$\dfrac{\text{Frequency}}{\text{Total frequency}} = \dfrac{4}{60} = 0.0\overline{6} = 6.\overline{6}\%$
February	2	$\dfrac{\text{Frequency}}{\text{Total frequency}} = \dfrac{2}{60} = 0.0\overline{3} = 3.\overline{3}\%$
March	3	$\dfrac{\text{Frequency}}{\text{Total frequency}} = \dfrac{3}{60} = 0.05 = 5\%$
April	5	$\dfrac{\text{Frequency}}{\text{Total frequency}} = \dfrac{5}{60} = 0.08\overline{3} = 8.\overline{3}\%$
May	1	$\dfrac{\text{Frequency}}{\text{Total frequency}} = \dfrac{1}{60} = 0.01\overline{6} = 1.\overline{6}\%$
June	2	$\dfrac{\text{Frequency}}{\text{Total frequency}} = \dfrac{2}{60} = 0.0\overline{3} = 3.\overline{3}\%$
July	4	$\dfrac{\text{Frequency}}{\text{Total frequency}} = \dfrac{4}{60} = 0.0\overline{6} = 6.\overline{6}\%$
August	5	$\dfrac{\text{Frequency}}{\text{Total frequency}} = \dfrac{5}{60} = 0.08\overline{3} = 8.\overline{3}\%$
September	4	$\dfrac{\text{Frequency}}{\text{Total frequency}} = \dfrac{4}{60} = 0.0\overline{6} = 6.\overline{6}\%$
October	4	$\dfrac{\text{Frequency}}{\text{Total frequency}} = \dfrac{4}{60} = 0.0\overline{6} = 6.\overline{6}\%$
November	6	$\dfrac{\text{Frequency}}{\text{Total frequency}} = \dfrac{6}{60} = 0.1 = 10\%$
December	20	$\dfrac{\text{Frequency}}{\text{Total frequency}} = \dfrac{20}{60} = 0.\overline{3} = 33.\overline{3}\%$
Total	60	

(The Relative Frequency Table is Shown Above.)

b. The least popular month is May because May had the least frequency of 1 or the least relative frequency of $0.01\overline{6}$.

c. There are 20 - 6 = 14 more people that chose December than November.

d. The number of the people that took part in the survey is the sum of the frequencies which is 60.

e. The number of students that chose December is 20 and if 2 more people chose December, the new total for December would be 20 + 2 = 22 people.

f. The month that has the highest relative frequency is December and the value of this relative frequency is $0.\overline{3}$.

g. May has the least relative frequency of $0.01\overline{6}$.

h. The relative frequency for November is 0.1, and therefore, there is a 0.1 probability that a randomly selected student will pick November as his favorite month.

i. Let event A = February as favorite month, let event B = September as favorite month, let event C = November as favorite month. Assume that events A, B, and C are mutually exclusive. (Hint: Review the MathMasters Series on mutually exclusive events).

P(A or B or C) = P(A) + P(B) + P(C)
$\qquad\qquad\qquad$ = 0.03 + 0.06 + 0.1 $\qquad$ Where P(A) = 0.03, P(B) = 0.06 and P(C) = 0.1.
$\qquad\qquad\qquad$ ≈ 0.19

The probability that a student had randomly selected February, September or November as a favorite month is approximately 0.19.

Note that P(A) is the probability of event A occurring, P(B) is the probability of event B occurring and P(C) is the probability of event C occurring. Hint: Review the chapter on probability in the MathMasters Series.

j. Number of students that chose November = 6 and the number of students that chose February = 2. Therefore, 6 - 2 = 4 more people chose November than February.

Special Note
Example 1 is long but it is intentionally designed to show the students the possible types of questions that could be asked involving relative frequency.

Example 2
The table shows the result of students' survey. The survey shows how many hours students stayed at the library in a week.

Hours	Frequency
1	2
2	5
3	11
4	6
5	5
6	1

a. Make a relative frequency table for the data.
b. Use the relative frequencies obtained in Example 2a to find the probability that a randomly selected student will stay in the library for 6 hours.
c. Use the relative frequencies obtained in the solution of Example 2a to estimate the probability that a randomly selected student will stay in the library for 4 or more hours.

Solution
a. The relative frequency table is shown as shown:

Hours	Frequency	Relative Frequency		
1	2	Relative Frequency $= \dfrac{\text{Frequency}}{\text{Total Frequency}}$	$= \dfrac{2}{30}$	$= 0.0\overline{6}$ or $6.\overline{6}\%$
2	5	Relative Frequency $= \dfrac{\text{Frequency}}{\text{Total Frequency}}$	$= \dfrac{5}{30}$	$= 0.1\overline{6}$ or $16.\overline{6}\%$
3	11	Relative Frequency $= \dfrac{\text{Frequency}}{\text{Total Frequency}}$	$= \dfrac{11}{30}$	$= 0.3\overline{6}$ or $36.\overline{6}\%$
4	6	Relative Frequency $= \dfrac{\text{Frequency}}{\text{Total Frequency}}$	$= \dfrac{6}{30}$	$= 0.2$ or 20%
5	5	Relative Frequency $= \dfrac{\text{Frequency}}{\text{Total Frequency}}$	$= \dfrac{5}{30}$	$= 0.1\overline{6}$ or $16.\overline{6}\%$
6	1	Relative Frequency $= \dfrac{\text{Frequency}}{\text{Total Frequency}}$	$= \dfrac{1}{30}$	$= 0.0\overline{3}$ or $3.\overline{3}\%$
Total	30			

b. From the solution of Example 2a, the relative frequency for a student staying in the library for 6 hours is $0.0\overline{3}$ or $3.\overline{3}\%$ and therefore, the probability that a randomly selected student will stay in the library for 6 hours is $0.0\overline{3}$ or $3.\overline{3}\%$.

c. Let event A = 4 hours, event B = 5 hours and event C = 6 hours. Assume that events A, B, and C are mutually exclusive. (Hint: Review the section on mutually exclusive events under probability in the MathMasters Series). Note that from the question, staying in the library 4 or more hours means that we have to consider the events involving 4, 5, or 6 hours.

P(A or B or C) = P(A) + P(B) + P(C)

$= 0.2 + 0.1\overline{6} + 0.0\overline{3}$ Where P(A) = 0.2, P(B) = $0.1\overline{6}$, and P(C) = $0.0\overline{3}$.

≈ 0.39

The probability that a student selected at random stayed in the library for 4 or more hours is approximately 0.39 or about 39%.

Exercises

1. Explain relative frequency.
2. The table shows the survey of students involving their favorite animals.
   Hint: See Example 1.

Animals	Number of students
Lion	3
Dog	10
Elephant	1
Gorilla	2
Zebra	4

   a. Make a relative frequency table for the data.

b. How many students took part in the survey?

c. What is the least popular animal?

d. Which animal has the highest relative frequency?

e. How many more students like the dog than the zebra?

f. Which animal had the least relative frequency?

g. What is the probability that a randomly selected student will choose a dog as a favorite animal?

h. Find the probability that a student selected at random will choose a lion, an elephant or a zebra as a favorite animal?

3. Find the relative frequency of each set of data or each set of table. Hint: See Examples 1 and 2.

Favorite days

a.

Day	Number of students
Monday	1
Tuesday	3
Wednesday	2
Thursday	2
Friday	6
Saturday	11
Sunday	5

Favorite animals

b.

Animals	Number of students
Lion	2
Zebra	8
Tiger	1
Gorilla	5
Elephant	2
Flamingo	3

Test scores

c.

Marks	Number of students
50 - 60	2
61 - 70	5
71 - 80	12
81 - 90	4
91 - 100	3

Challenge Questions

4. The table shows the list of the majors of the students in the Supporters Club. Find the probability that a randomly selected student is an engineering major or undecided.

Major	Number of students
English	8
Biology	12
Engineering	10
Chemistry	7
Undecided	9

CUMULATIVE AND RELATIVE CUMULATIVE FREQUENCY

New Terms: **Cumulative frequency** and **relative cumulative frequency**

Cumulative frequency is the sum of all the frequencies of all the data values that are less than a given value. The cumulative frequency for a class is the sum of all the frequencies for that class and all the previous classes.

Relative cumulative frequency is the cumulative frequency divided by the total number of the data values or the total sum of the frequencies.

$$\text{Relative cumulative frequency} = \frac{\text{Cumulative frequency}}{\text{Sum of all the frequencies}}$$

How to find cumulative frequencies.

Table 1 shows that the cumulative frequency is obtained by writing the first original frequency of 3 in the first column of the cumulative frequency, the second cumulative frequency of 7 is obtained by adding the first and the second frequencies together $(3 + 4 = 7)$, the third cumulative frequency of 16 is obtained by adding the first, the second and the third frequencies together $(3 + 4 + 9 = 16)$, and so on.

Table 1

Time (s)	Frequency	Cumulative Frequency
5 - 14	3	3
15 - 24	4	$3 + 4 = 7$
25 - 34	9	$3 + 4 + 9 = 16$
35 - 44	8	$3 + 4 + 9 + 8 = 24$
45 - 54	1	$3 + 4 + 9 + 8 + 1 = 25$
55 - 64	6	$3 + 4 + 9 + 8 + 1 + 6 = 31$

Example 1

The table shows how long a number of balloons stayed on a post.

a. Create a cumulative frequency table.

b. How many balloons stayed on the post no more than 64 seconds?

Time (s)	Frequency
25 - 34	5
35 - 44	2
45 - 44	7
55 - 64	6
65 - 74	3

Solution

a. Create a cumulative frequency table as shown below.

Time (s)	Frequency	Cumulative frequency
25 - 34	5	5
35 - 44	2	5 + 2 = 7
45 - 54	7	5 + 2 + 7 = 14
55 - 64	6	5 + 2 + 7+ 6 = 20
65 - 74	3	5 + 2 + 7 + 6 + 3 = 23

b. The cumulative frequency table shows, 20 balloons stayed on the post no more than 64 seconds or 20 balloons stayed on the post for 64 seconds or less.

Example 2

The table shows the range of students' test scores with the associated number of students who scored in that range or frequency.

a. Find the relative frequency of the test scores in the 81 - 85 range.

b. What is the cumulative frequency of the test scores less than 76?

c. Find the relative cumulative frequency of test scores less than 81.

Test scores	61 - 65	66 - 70	71 - 75	76 - 80	81 - 85	86 - 90	91 - 95	96 - 100
Frequency	2	4	8	6	5	9	2	3

Solution

a. The formula for relative frequency is:

$$\text{Relative frequency} = \frac{\text{Each frequency}}{\text{Sum of all frequencies}} \quad\quad [A]$$

The sum of all the frequencies = 2 + 4 + 8 + 6 + 5 + 9 + 2 = 39.

The frequency for the range of 81 - 85 test score is 5.

Substitute "each frequency" = 5 and sum of all the frequencies = 39 into equation

[A] as shown:

$$\text{Relative frequency} = \frac{\text{Each frequency}}{\text{Sum of all frequencies}}$$

$$= \frac{5}{39}$$

Each frequency or frequency for the range of

81 - 85 = 5 and the sum of all the frequencies = 39.

$$\approx 0.14$$

b. To find the cumulative frequency of the test scores less than 76, add the frequencies of all the test scores less than 76 as shown:

$$2 + 4 + 8 = 14$$

Recall that the cumulative frequency is the sum of all the frequencies of all the data values that are less than a given value.

c. Relative cumulative frequency of the test scores less than 81

$$= \frac{\text{Cumulative frequency of the test scores less than 81}}{\text{Sum of all frequencies}}$$

$$= \frac{2 + 4 + 8 + 6}{2 + 4 + 8 + 6 + 5 + 9 + 2 + 3}$$

$$= \frac{20}{39}$$

$$\approx 0.51$$

Exercises

1. Explain cumulative frequency.
2. Describe how you could find the cumulative frequency.
3. Create a cumulative frequency table for each of the tables. Hint: See Example 1.

a.

Age (years)	Frequency
15 - 24	2
25 - 34	1
35 - 44	5
45 - 54	4
55 - 64	3
65 - 74	8

b.

Test scores	Frequency
55 - 64	3
65 - 74	2
75 - 84	1
85 - 94	8
95 - 100	6

Test scores	Frequency
10 - 19	2
20 - 29	4
30 - 39	7
40 - 49	1
50 - 59	3
60 - 69	2

c.

4. The frequency table shows the frequency of each range of height of students selected at random for a survey.

   a. What is the cumulative frequency of the students' heights less than 5 ft 6 in?
      Hint: See Example 1b and Example 2b.

   b. What is the cumulative frequency of the students' height less than 6 ft?
      Hint: See Example 1b and Example 2b.

   c. What is the relative frequency of the students' height in the 5 ft 6 in. - 5 ft 11 in. range? Hint: See Example 2a.

   d. What is the relative frequency of the students' heights in the 4 ft 6 in. - 4 ft 11 in. range? Hint: See Example 2a.

   e. Find the relative cumulative frequency of the students' heights less than 6 ft.
      Hint: See Example 2c.

   f. What is the relative cumulative frequency of the students' height less than 5 ft?
      Hint: See Example 2c.

Students' heights	Frequency
4 ft - 4 ft 5 in.	3
4 ft 6 in. - 4 ft 11 in.	5
5 ft - 5 ft 5 in.	7
5 ft 6 in. - 5 ft 11 in.	3
6 ft - 6 ft 5 in.	2

Challenge Question

5. The table shows the test scores for students who are randomly selected for a survey.

Test score	61 - 65	66 - 70	71 - 75	76 - 80	81 - 85	86 - 90	91 - 95	96 - 100
Frequency	1	3	5	4	2	6	8	2

   a. What is the relative frequency of the students' test scores in the 86 - 90 range?

   b. What is the cumulative frequency of the students' test scores less than 91?

   c. What is the cumulative frequency of the students' test scores less than 81?

   d. What is the relative frequency of the students' test scores in the 76 - 80 range?

   e. Find the relative cumulative frequency of the students' test scores less than 96.

   f. Find the relative cumulative frequency of the students' test scores less than 76.

Answers to Selected Questions

4a. Cumulative frequency less than 5 ft 6 in. = 3 + 5 + 7 = 15.

CHAPTER 25

GRAPHS

Cumulative Review

1. 13 + 17 =   **2**. 18 ÷ 6 =   **3**. 42 - 8 =   **4**. 8 × 8 =

5. 45 ÷ 5 =   **6**. 41 - 12 =   **7**. 30 ÷ 6 =   **8**. 44 - 8 =

9. 24   **10**.   14   **11**.   35   **12**.   19
     × 4   + 18   - 16   × 5

13. 48 ÷ 3 =   **14**. 24 ÷ 8 =   **15**. 12 + 38 =   **16**. 36 - 17 =

17. 2.9 + 3.7 =   **18**. 5.6 × 4 =   **19**. 2.5 × 3.4 =   **20**. 24.7 - 1.6 =

21. $\dfrac{2}{3} \times \dfrac{2}{5} =$ **22**. $\dfrac{2}{3} \div \dfrac{2}{5} =$ **23**. $\dfrac{3}{4} - \dfrac{3}{5} =$ **24**. $4\dfrac{2}{3} + 3\dfrac{3}{4} =$

New Terms: **frequency table**, **at least**, **at most**, **fewer than**, **relative frequency**

Interpreting Data

Frequency Table

A **frequency table** is a table that shows the number of times each event occurs.

> Note that in the tally column in example 1, the 5th time of an event is indicated by crossing the previous 4 events as shown: ~~1111~~.

Example 1

The frequency table shows the number of subjects studied by students in grade 11 at the Peki Secondary school in Ghana.

Number of subjects studied by students		
Number of subjects studied	Number of students. Tally	Number of students. Frequency
9	1111	4
8	~~1111~~ ~~1111~~ 11	12
7	~~1111~~ 1	6
6	111	3
5	11	2

a. How many students studied 8 subjects?

b. How many students studied at least 7 subjects?

c. How many students studied 6 or more subjects?

d. How many students studied at most 7 subjects?

e. How many students were in the survey?

f. What percent of the students studied 6 subjects?

g. What percent of the students studied fewer than 6 subjects?

h. What percent of the students studied at least 7 subjects?

i. What percent of the students studied at most 7 subjects?

j. What is the relative frequency of the students that studied 5 subjects?

k. If a student is selected at random, what is the probability that the student studied 9 subjects?

Solution

a. The frequency column shows that 12 students studied 8 subjects.

b. "**At least 7 subjects**" means 7 or more subjects. Therefore, the number of students that studied at least 7 subjects is the sum of the frequencies of the students that studied 7, 8, and 9 subjects which – 6 + 12 + 4 = 22 students.

c. The number of students that studied 6 or more subjects is the sum of the frequencies of the students that studied 6, 7, 8, and 9 subjects which = 3 + 6 + 12 + 4 = 25 students.

d. "**At most 7 subjects**" means 7 or less subjects. Therefore, the number of students that studied at most 7 subjects is the sum of the frequencies of the students that studied 7, 6, and 5 subjects which = 6 + 3 + 2 = 11 students.

e. The number of the students in the survey is the sum of the total frequency which = 4 + 12 + 6 + 3 + 2 = 27 students.

f. Percent of students that studied 6 subjects

$$= \frac{\text{Number that studied 6 subjects}}{\text{Total number of students}} \times 100 \quad \text{(Hint: Review the section on percent.)}$$

$$= \frac{3}{27} \times 100 \qquad (\frac{\text{Part}}{\text{Total}} \times 100 = \text{Percent of the total.})$$

$= \dfrac{\dfrac{3}{27}}{9} \times 100$ Divide by 3.

$= \dfrac{100}{9} = 11\dfrac{1}{9}\%$ Divide by 9.

g. Those who studied **fewer than** 6 subjects means those who studied 5 subjects.
The number of students that studied 5 subjects = 2

h. Percent of the students that studied **at least** 7 subjects

$= \dfrac{\text{Number that studied at least 7 subjects}}{\text{Total number of students}} \times 100$ (Review the section on Percent).

$= \dfrac{22}{27} \times 100$ (From solution (b) 22 students studied at least 7 subjects)

                  $(\dfrac{\text{part}}{\text{Total}} \times 100 = \text{percent of total})$.

$= 81.48\%$ You may use a calender.

i. Percent of students that studied **at most** 7 subjects

$= \dfrac{\text{Number of students that studied at most 7 subjects}}{\text{Total number of students}} \times 100$

                                   Review the section on Percent.

$= \dfrac{11}{27} \times 100$ $(\dfrac{\text{Part}}{\text{Total}} \times 100 = \text{Percent of the total})$.

                     (From solution **d**, the number of the students that
                     studied at most 7 subjects is 11).

$= 40.74\%$ You may use a calculator.

j. The relative frequency of an event

$= \dfrac{\text{Frequency of the event.}}{\text{Total frequencies}}$, therefore,

the **relative frequency** of the students that studied 5 subjects

$= \dfrac{\text{Frequency of the students that studied 5 subjects}}{\text{Total frequencies}}$

$$= \frac{2}{27}$$

k. Probability that a student selected studied 9 subjects

$$= \frac{\text{Number of students that studied 9 subjects}}{\text{Total number of students}}$$

(Review the section on probability).

$$= \frac{4}{27}$$

Bar Graph

A bar graph is a graph in which the height of the vertical bars represent the frequencies or values assigned to each activity. The bars are spaced evenly and they may be drawn vertically or horizontally. A bar graph is drawn from a frequency table.

Example 2

Use the bar graph to answer the following question:

Students' test scores in percent.

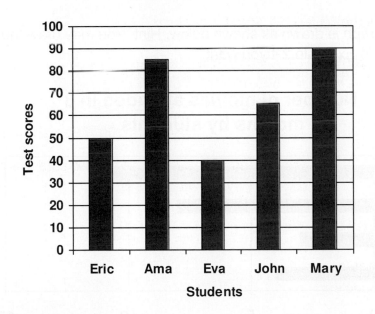

a. Who did the best in the test?

b. Who did the poorest in the test?

c. How many more marks did Mary have than Erica?

d. Who scored 10% more marks than Eva?

e. What is the range of the scores?

Solution

a. Mary had the highest score of 90%, and therefore, Mary did the best in the test.

b. Eva had the lowest score of 40%, and therefore Eva did poorest in the test.

c. Mary's score was 90%, and Eric's score was 50%, and therefore, Mary has 40% or (90% - 50%) more marks than Eric.

d. Eric scored 50%, and Eva scored 40%, and therefore, Eric scored 10% or (50% - 40%) more marks than Eva.

e. The range of the scores:

$$= \text{Greatest score - Least score}$$
$$= 90\% - 40\%$$
$$= 50\%$$

Example 3

Use the frequency table to draw a bar graph on graph paper. Hint: Recall that the bar graph is spaced evenly and may be drawn vertically or horizontally.

Number of movies attended in 3 months by students		
Number of movies	Number of students. Tally	Number of students. Frequency
3	̶1̶1̶1̶1̶ ̶1̶1̶1̶1̶ 1	11
2	̶1̶1̶1̶1̶ 111	8
1	111	3
0	1111	4

Solution

The horizontal bar graph is drawn as shown below. Hint: You may draw the vertical bar graph as shown in Example **2** if you want.

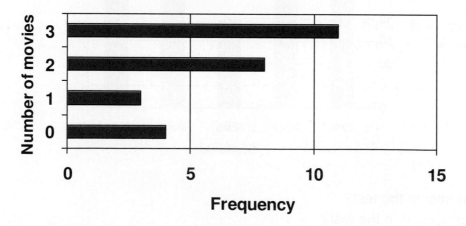

Number of movies attended in 3 months by students.

Hint: It is best to draw graphs on a graph or grid paper.

Multiple Bar Graph

A multiple bar graph consists of two or more component bar columns or graphs which are evenly spaced and the heights of the component bars represent the frequencies or values assigned to each activity. Like a bar graph, the multiple bar graph can be vertical or horizontal.

Test scores of two schools in percent		
Year	School A	School B
2000	95	80
2001	85	90
2002	95	95

a. Which school had the better score in 2000?

b. In which year were the performance of schools A and B the same?

Solution

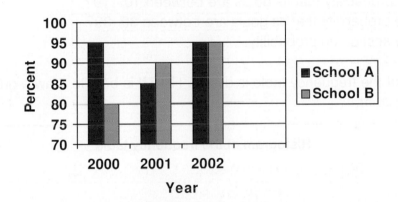

The graph shows a vertical multiple bar graph. The component bar column or graph are evenly spaced and the heights of the component bar columns represent the frequencies or values assigned to each activity.

a. School A had a better score than school B because school A had a higher score of 95% in 2000 whereas school B has a score of 80%.

b. The performance of the schools A and B were the same in 2002 because both schools had the same score of 95%. Hint: It is best to draw graphs on graph paper or grid paper.

Histogram

A histogram is a bar graph which does not have any space between the bars. Like the bar graph, a histogram can be vertical or horizontal.

Example 5

Some school districts in Ghana were surveyed to find the number of goals scored by the soccer teams during the year. A frequency table is made with intervals of 10 goals.

Goals	Frequency of the school district
0 - 9	3
10 - 19	4
20 - 29	2
30 - 39	0
40 - 49	1
50 - 59	3

a. Draw a histogram of the frequency table.

b. From the survey, how many school districts scored the highest number of goals?

c. How many school districts took part in the survey?

d. How many school districts scored the least number of goals?

e. If a school district is selected at random,

　　(i) what is the probability that its goals are between 10 - 19?

　　(ii) what is the probability that its goals are between 30 -39?

　Hint: Review the section on probability.

Solution

a. The histogram of the frequency table is drawn. Hint: It is best to draw a graph on a paper or grid paper.

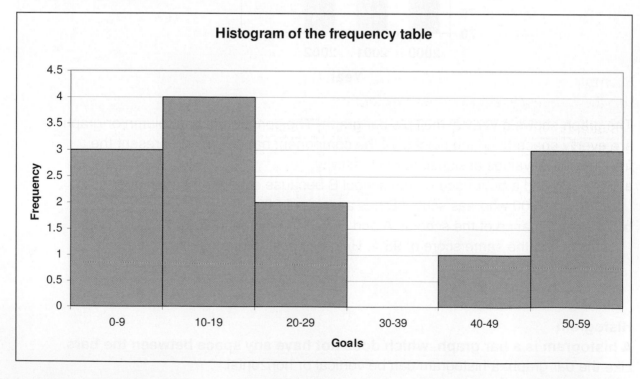

564

b. Three schools scored the highest number of goals between 50 - 59 goals.

c. The number of the school districts that took part in the survey

$$= \text{sum of the frequencies}$$
$$= 3 + 4 + 2 + 0 + 1 + 3$$
$$= 13 \text{ school districts.}$$

d. Three schools scored the least goals in the interval of 0 - 9 goals.

e(i). The number of school districts that have goals between 10 - 19 is 4. The total number of school districts that took part in the survey is the sum of the frequencies which is $(3 + 4 + 2 + 0 + 1 + 3 = 13)$.

The probability of selecting a school district that has goals between 10 - 19

$$= \frac{\text{Number of school districts that have goals between 10 - 19}}{\text{Total number of schools}}.$$

$$= \frac{4}{13}$$

e(ii). The number of school districts that have goals between 30 - 39 is 0. The total number of school districts that took part in the survey is the sum of the frequencies which is $(3 + 4 + 2 + 0 + 1 + 3 = 13)$. Therefore, the number of school districts that has goals between 30 - 39

$$= \frac{\text{Number of school districts that have goals between 30 - 39}}{\text{Total number of school districts}}$$

$$= \frac{0}{13} = 0$$

Example 6

Use the frequency table to draw a histogram.

Students	Joe	Mary	Eric	Ben	Eli
Ages in years	6	7	10	9	8

Solution

The histogram of the frequency table is drawn. Hint: It is best to draw graphs on graph paper or grid paper.

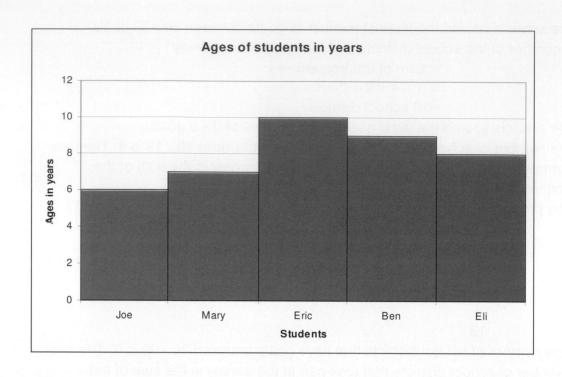

Ages of students in years

Line Graphs

Line graphs are ordered pairs from a data in a table and the ordered pairs are plotted on a grid or graph paper and the points of the plotted ordered pairs are connected with lines. What is the line graph used for? **The line graph is used to find or estimate one of the ordered pairs if the other ordered pair is known**.

Example 7

Make a line graph of the given data.

Months	1	2	3	4	5	6	7
Savings in dollars	10	15	10	8	5	20	30

Solution

Use the ordered pairs of the data to plot each point, for example, the first set of the data is the savings in the first month which is $10 which may be written as a pair of data as (months, dollars) or (1,10) where 1 is the first month's savings and 10 is $10 saved in the first month. Similarly, the other sets of data or ordered pairs of data are (2, 15), (3, 10), (4, 8), (5, 5), (6, 20), and (7, 30). To plot the points using the ordered pairs of data, first draw the axis for the savings for the months horizontally and draw the axis for the savings vertically and then for the first ordered pair of data (1,10), locate 1 which represents the first month on the horizontal axis and locate the 10 which represent the $10 on the vertical axis. Where (1,10) meet is the required point to be plotted. Similarly, you can plot the points of the remaining ordered pairs of data. (Hint: See how to plot points under the chapter on "Coordinate Geometry.") Connect the points with lines to form a line

566

graph as shown.

When a line in a line graph goes up from left to right, it shows that there is **an increase in the data**. When a line in a line graph goes down from left to right, it shows that there is **a decrease in the data**. When a line in a line graph is horizontal (for example between two points,) it shows that there is **no change in the data**. The **trend** in the data is the increase or decrease in the data.

Example 8
Use the line graph to answer each question (**a** to **d**.)

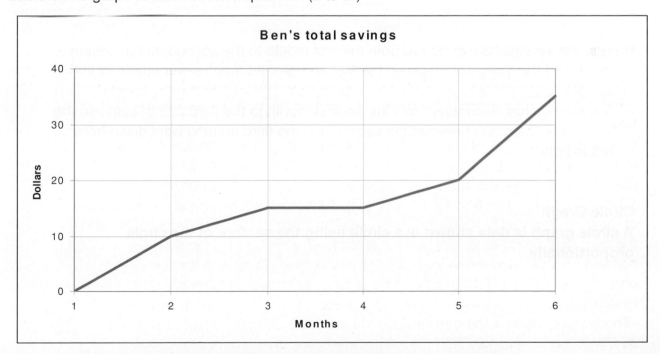

a. During which month did Ben not save any money? Explain your answer.

b. During which month did Ben save most? Give reasons for your answer.

c. If Ben is saving his money to buy a calculator which costs $70, what percent of the money did he save at the end of the fifth week?

d. Did the savings increase from the first month to the second month? Explain your answer.

e. In Example 7, did the savings increase or decrease from the second month to the third month? Explain your answer.

Solution

a. Ben did not save any money during the third month because the line graph during the third month is horizontal which means that there was no increment of savings in the third month.

b. Ben saved most in the fifth month because the line graph during the fifth month is the steepest which shows the greatest savings of $35 - $20 = $15.

c. The total money saved at the end of the fifth month is $35. Therefore, the percent of the amount saved is:

$$= \frac{35}{70} \times 100 \qquad (\frac{\text{Part}}{\text{Total}} \times 100 = \text{Percent of the total}).$$

$$= \frac{\overset{5}{\cancel{35}}}{\underset{\underset{1}{7}}{\cancel{70}}} \times 100 \qquad \text{Divide by 10 and 7.}$$

$$= 5 \times 10 = 50\%$$

d. Yes, the savings has increased from the first month to the second month because, the line of the line graph between the first and second months went up from left to right.

e. The savings has decreased from the second month to the third month because the line of the line graph between the second and the third months went down from left to right.

Circle Graph

A circle graph is data shown in a circle using the sectors of the circle proportionally.

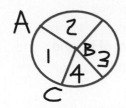

In this circle graph, the areas 1, 2, 3, and 4 represent sectors. For example, the sector ABC is represented by area 1.

Example 9

If Mary spends her monthly income according to the circle graph, find:

a. How much she spends on rent?

b. How much she spends on food?

c. How much more does she spend on the rent than food monthly?

d. On which item does she spend the least amount of money?

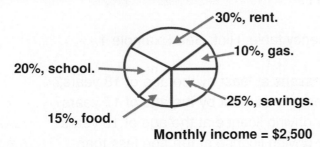

30%, rent.

10%, gas.

20%, school.

25%, savings.

15%, food.

Monthly income = $2,500

Solution

a. She spent 30% of $2,500 on rent,

$$= \frac{30}{100} \times \$2,500$$ (Express 30% as $\frac{30}{100}$ and "of" is the same as

multiplication). Hint: Review the section on percent.

$$= \frac{30}{\cancel{100}} \times \$2,\cancel{500}^{\,25}$$ Divide by 100 by canceling the two zeros.

$$= 30 \times \$25$$
$$= \$750.$$

b. She spends 15% of $2,500 on food,

$$= \frac{15}{100} \times \$2,500$$ (Express 15% as $\frac{15}{100}$ and "of" is the same as

multiplication.) Hint: Review the section on percent.

$$= \frac{15}{100} \times \$2,500$$ Divide by 100 by canceling the zeros

569

$$= 15 \times \$25 = \$375$$

c. From the solution of **a**, she spends $750 on rent, from the solution of **b**, she spends $375 on food, and therefore, she spends

$750 - $375 more on rent than food.

$$= \$375$$

d. She spends the least amount of money on gas because the percent of gas is the lowest percent among the items that she spends money on.

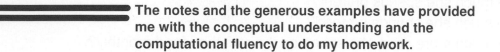 The notes and the generous examples have provided me with the conceptual understanding and the computational fluency to do my homework.

Exercises

1. Answer the questions by using the frequency table. Hint: See Example 1.
  a. How many students were surveyed?
  b. How many students had their driving lessons at least by the age of 18 years?
  c. How many students had their driving lessons at most by the age of 17 years?
  d. What percent of the students had their driving license at the age of 18 years?
  e. What percent of the students had their driving license at the age less than 18 years?
  f. What percent of the students had their driving license at the age of at least 17 least?
  g. What is the relative frequency of the students who had their driving license at the age of 19 years.
  h. If a student is selected at random, what is the probability that the student is 16 years old?

Student's age of obtaining a license.		
Age	Tally	Frequency
16	~~1111~~ ~~1111~~ 11	12
17	~~1111~~ 111	8
18	~~1111~~	5
19	111	3

2. Describe a bar graph.
3. Use the bar graph to answer the following questions:
  a. Who did the best in the test?
  b. Who did the poorest on the test?
  c. How many more marks did student D have than student A?
  d. Which student had 25% more marks than student A?
  e. What is the range of scores?
  Hint: See Example **2**.

570

Test scores of students A, B, C, and D in percent.

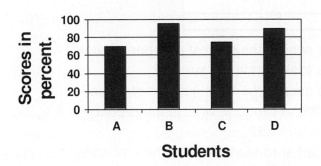

4. Use the frequency table to draw a bar graph on a graph paper.
   Hint: See Example **3**.

Number of movies attended in 3 months by students		
Number of movies.	Number of students. Tally	Number of students. Frequency
4	~~1111~~ 11	7
3	1111	4
2	~~1111~~ 111	8
1	~~1111~~	5
0	11	2

5. Describe a multiple bar graph.
6. Use the table to draw a multiple bar graph.

Year	Test scores of two schools A and B in percent.	
	School A	School B
2002	88	92
2003	79	80
2004	95	95
2005	98	97

(**a**) Which school had the better score in 2004?

(**b**) In which year were the scores of schools A and B the same?

Hint: See Example **4**.

7. Describe a histogram.
8. Use the data in the table to draw a histogram.

Goals (soccer)	Frequency of schools.
0 - 9	2
10 - 19	5
20 - 29	3
30 - 39	0
40 - 49	4
50 - 59	7
60 - 69	1

a. How many schools scored the highest number of goals?

b. How many schools took part in the survey?

c. How many schools scored the least number of goals?

d. If a school is selected at random, what is the probability that the school's goals were between 50 - 59?

e. If a school is selected at random, what is the probability that the school's goals were between 20 - 29?

f. If a school is selected at random, what is the probability that the school's goals were between 30 - 39?

Hint: See Example **5**.

9. Use the frequency table to draw a histogram.

Students	Nick	Rose	Josh	Sam	Eric
Ages in years.	12	14	10	15	8

Hint: See Example **6**.

10. Describe a line graph. What is a **trend** in a line graph?

11. Make a line graph of the given data.

Weeks	1	2	3	4	5	6
Savings in dollars.	12	8	13	9	10	11

Hint: See Example **7**.

12. Use the line graph to answer each question.

(The line graph is on the next page.)

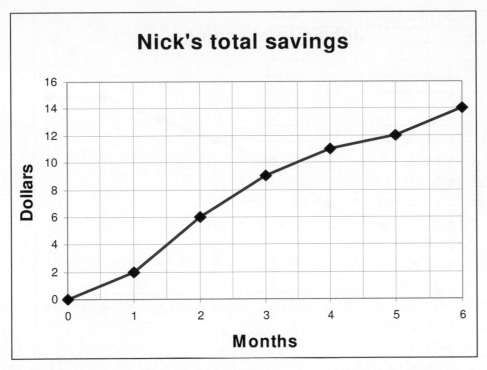

Nick's total savings

a. During which month did Nick not save any money? Explain your answer.

b. During which month did Nick save the most?
   Explain you answer.

c. If Nick is saving his money to buy a calculator which costs $21, what percent of the money did he save by the end of the sixth month?
   Hint: See Example **8**.

13. Describe a circle graph.

14. If Nick spends his monthly income according to the circle graph, find:

   a. How much he spent on insurance?

   b. How much he spent on school?

   c. How much more does he spend on school than on insurance monthly?

   d. On which item does he spend the least amount of money?

   Hint: See Example **9**.

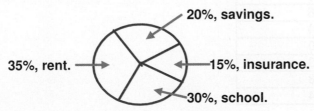

20%, savings.

35%, rent.

15%, insurance.

30%, school.

Challenge Questions

15. Use the line graph to answer each question.

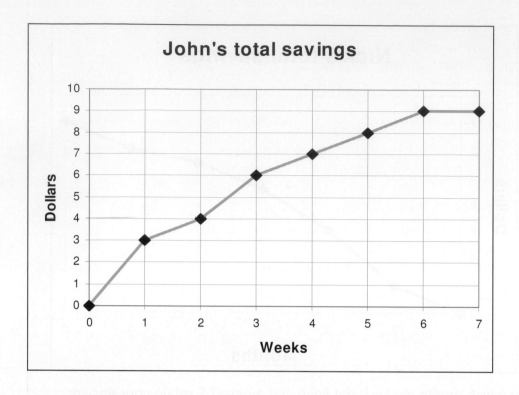

John's total savings

(**a**) If John is saving his money to buy a toy that costs $12.00, what percent of the money did he save by the end of the seventh week?

(**b**) During which week did he save most?
Explain your answer.

(**c**) During which week did he not save any money? Explain your answer?

16. Make a line graph of the given data.

Weeks	1	2	3	4	5	6	7
Savings in dollars.	5	8	4	10	9	7	5

17. Use the data in the table to draw a histogram.

Goals (soccer)	Frequency of schools.
0 - 9	7
10 - 19	5
20 - 29	6
30 - 39	4
40 - 49	0
50 - 59	3
60 - 69	8
70 - 79	4

a. If a school is selected at random, what is the probability that the school scored between 50 - 59 goals?

b. How many schools scored the most goals?

c. If a school is selected at random, what is the probability that the school scored between 40 - 49 goals?

18. If the circle graph shows how a bookstore spent $2000 on books for specific subjects, find:

a. the amount spent on math books.

b. the amount spent on history books.

c. the greatest amount spent on history books.

d. which subject is the least money spent on?

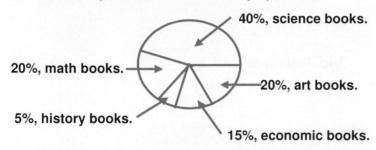

19. Use the bar graph to answer the following questions.

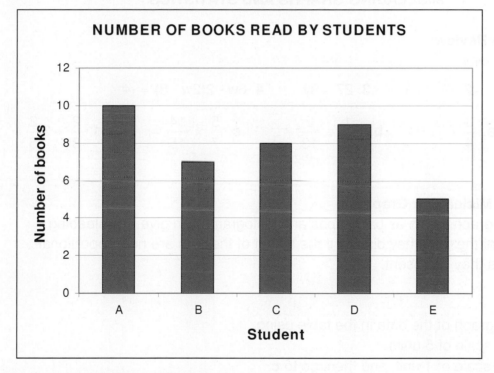

a. Which student read the most books?

b. What is the range of the number of books read?

c. How many more books did student A read than student E?

d. What fraction of the total books in the survey was read by student D?

Hint: Fraction of books read by student D = $\dfrac{\text{Number of books read by student D}}{\text{Total number of books}}$

e. What percent of the books was read by student D?

Hint: Percent of books read by student D = $\dfrac{\text{Number of books read by student D}}{\text{Total number of books.}} \times 100$

Answers to Selected Questions.

1a. 28 students   **1h.** $\dfrac{3}{7}$ **6b.** 2004

8f. 0   **12c.** $66\dfrac{2}{3}\%$ **14d.** Insurance

MISLEADING GRAPHS AND STATISTICS

Cumulative Review:
Solve or simplify:

1. $3x = 18$ **2.** $\dfrac{3x}{4} = 9$ **3.** $27 = 9y$ **4.** $6w - 2(2w - 8) = -4$

5. Simplify **a.** $\dfrac{3}{4} - \dfrac{3}{8} =$ **b.** $4\dfrac{1}{3} \div \dfrac{2}{13} =$ **c.** $\dfrac{5}{7} \times \dfrac{14}{15} =$ **d.** $\dfrac{2}{3} + 3\dfrac{2}{5} =$

Identifying Misleading Graphs.
Sometimes graphs such as bar graphs and histograms can give a misleading impression of the data they display if the height of the bars are not proportional to the values they represent.

Example 1
Draw a line graph of the data in the table using:
a. a vertical scale of 5 units.
b. a vertical scale of 1 unit, and then, go to **c.**
c. compare line graph **a** and **b**. What is your conclusion?
   The savings is in dollars.

Week	1	2	3	4	5
Savings	2	3	5	8	9

Solution
a. A line graph with a vertical scale of 5 units is shown below.

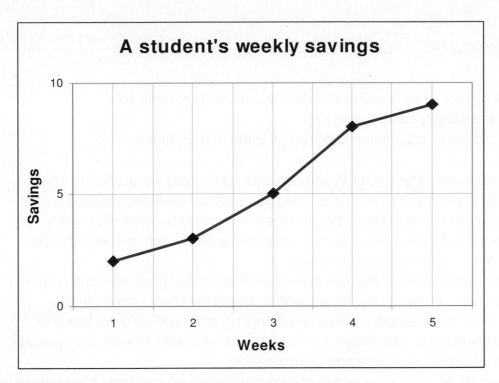

b. A line graph with a vertical scale of 1 unit is shown below.

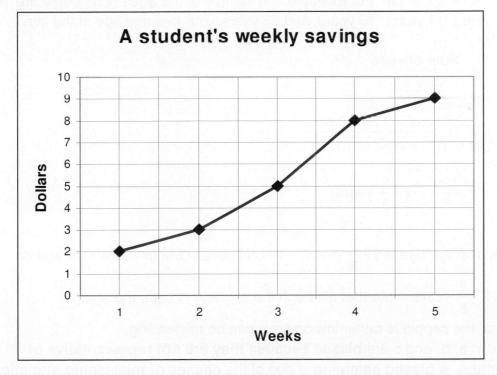

c. By changing the vertical scale of the line graph from 5 units as in **a**, to 1 unit as in **b**, the data values seem large in **b**. It can be concluded that the vertical scale of a line graph can be changed or adjusted to make the data values seem larger or smaller.

Statistics

Example 2

Some of the factors of misleading statistics are: **a**. small sample size,
b. period of the sample, and **c**. average.
Explain the factors of misleading statistics as listed in **a**, **b**, and **c**.

Solution

a. Small sample size: The bigger the sample size, the closer we are to the true value of the statistics. For example, if two students are selected randomly, and both of them had an A in chemistry, it does not necessarily mean that every student in the school had an A in chemistry, because the school has over 800 students whose grades we do not know.

b. The period of the sample: For example, the weather may affect the outcome of a sampling if one sampling is done in the Winter and the other is done in the Summer. Another example is when one sampling is done during the low sale season and the other sampling is done during the high sale season. The period or season of certain sampling can be misleading.

c. When average is used: An average does not show the true picture of the individual data that form the sample. For example, the sample of the ages of 5 people are 10 years, 12 years, 11 years, 10 years, and 95 years. The average age of the five people is

$$= \frac{\text{Sum of ages}}{\text{Total ages}}$$

$$= \frac{10 + 12 + 11 + 10 + 95}{5}$$

$$= \frac{138}{5} = 27\frac{2}{5} \text{ years.}$$

Although the average age is $27\frac{2}{5}$ years, only one person out of five whose age is greater than $27\frac{2}{5}$ years. Note that although the average is high, the age of the majority of the people is rather low and this can be misleading.

The samples in **a**, **b**, and **c** are **biased because they are not representative of each population**. A **biased sampling** is one of the **causes of misleading statistics**.

Example 3

A business had 6 employees with the following salaries: $14,000, $15,000, $13,000, $14,000, $120,000 (owner), $10,000. "Employment available, average salary

$31,000" was the owner's advertisement . It is therefore, not likely that the salary of a new employee would be $31,000. The advertisement is misleading noting that only the owner had a huge salary of $120, 000.

Example 4
If the total revenue of market A during the three months in the summer was $400,000 and the total revenue of market B in the winter was $800,000,
a. Will it be misleading to compare the revenues of markets A and B?
b. What is the correct method of comparing the revenues of markets A and B?
Solution
a. Yes, it is misleading to compare the revenues of markets A and B because the revenues were measured at two different seasons of the year which are winter and summer and that during the busy shopping season of winter, the revenue of market B is greater than the revenue of market A in the summer.
b. The correct method of comparing the revenues of markets A and B is to measure the revenue for both markets at the same season.

Example 5
a. If a car dealership claims that out of a survey of 10 customers, 5 of them are satisfied with their cars, and the dealership's ad states: "5 out of 10 customers are satisfied with their cars", is this ad misleading?
b. What is the correct way of doing the survey?
Solution
a. Yes, the ad is misleading because the sample size of 10 customers is too small. The sample size of 10 customers is not representative of the population of the customers who bought cars from the dealership. The dealership has many more customers than 10.
b. The correct method of doing the survey is to include all the customers who bought vehicles from the dealership in the survey and that will enable the dealership to know the total number of people who are satisfied with their vehicles.

Exercises
1. It can be concluded that the vertical scale of a line graph can be changed or adjusted to make changes in the data values seem larger or smaller.
   True or false? Explain. Hint: See Example 1.
2. "Five out of seven students scored 90% in the math test".
a. How many students are in the sample?
b. Can you say that the number of students in the sample is representative of the student population?

c. Is the statement misleading? Hint: See Examples **2a** and **5**.

3. A school newspaper is comparing the total revenue of two stores, P-mart and J-Mart. If the total revenue of P-Mart from May 1st to August 1st is compared to the total revenue for J-Mart from October 1st to January 1st, do you think that the comparison is misleading? Explain your answer. Hint: See Examples 2b and 4.

Challenge Questions

4. A biased sampling is one of the causes of misleading statistics. True or false? Explain.

5. Comparing the total summer revenue of one super market to the total winter revenue of another super market is misleading statistics. True or false? Explain.

6. Explain how the average revenue for twelve months of a supermarket could be misleading statistics.

7. Explain how a vertical scale of a line graph can be adjusted to make changes in a data value seem larger or smaller.

CHAPTER 26

COORDINATE SYSTEM

INTRODUCTION
New Terms: **coordinate system**, **coordinate plane**, **x-axis**, **y-axis**, **origin**, **quadrants**, **ordered pair**, **x-coordinate**, **y-coordinate**.

The **coordinate system** or the **coordinate plane** is formed by two perpendicular and intersecting number lines called the x-axis and the y-axis. The horizontal number line is called the x-axis and the vertical number line is called the y-axis. The point where the two number lines intersect is called the **origin** and the origin has a coordinate of (**0**, **0**). The coordinate of a point is an **ordered pair of numbers** such that the first number is related to a point on the x-axis and the second number is related to a point on the y-axis. The x-axis, y-axis, and the origin are shown in the diagram.

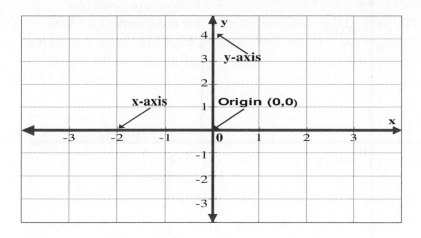

Example 1

Describe how to find the coordinates of the ordered pair of point A.

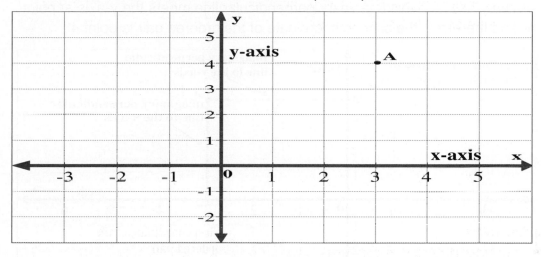

Solution

Step 1: Find the x-coordinate first. From point A, imagine a perpendicular line on the x-axis and this imaginary perpendicular line meets the x-axis at point 3, and therefore, the first coordinate of the ordered pair is 3.

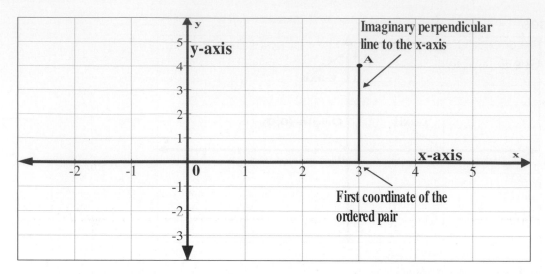

Step 2: Find the y-coordinate second. From point A, imagine a perpendicular line on the y-axis and this imaginary perpendicular line meets the y-axis at point 4, and therefore, the second coordinate of the ordered pair is point 4.

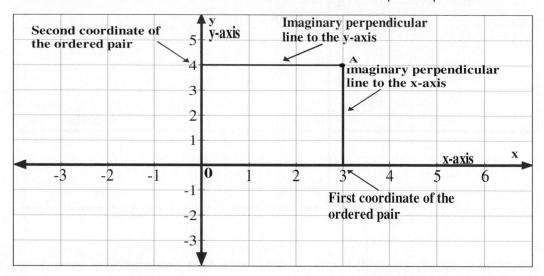

Step 3: Combine the first coordinate of the ordered pair which is 3 with the second coordinate of the ordered pair which is 4 to form the **coordinates of the ordered pair of the point A as (3, 4)**.

Special notes
1. In general, the coordinates of the ordered pair of any point may be written as (x, y) where x, which is always the first pair refers to a number on the x-axis and y which is always the second pair refers to a number on the y-axis.
2. How can the coordinates of a point be read? The coordinates of a point can be read by moving along the x-axis to read the first coordinate and then moving along the y-axis to read the second coordinate.

Exercises

1. Find the coordinates of the ordered pair of point B in the diagram.
Hint: See Example **1**.

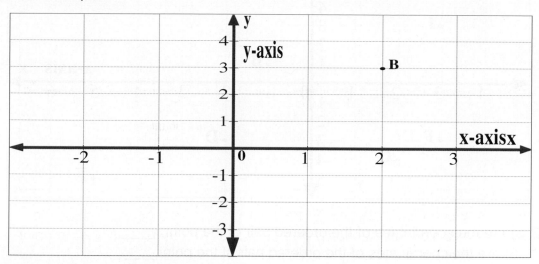

2. Find the coordinates of the ordered pair of the point C in the diagram.
Hint: See Example 1.

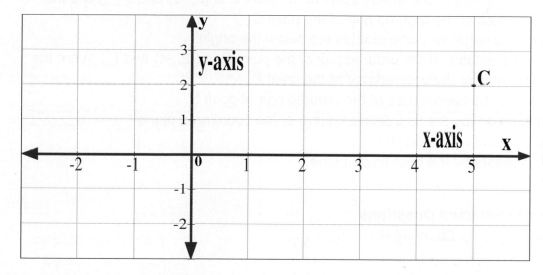

3. Using the diagram, copy and complete the sentences.
Hint: See Example **1**, Step **3**.

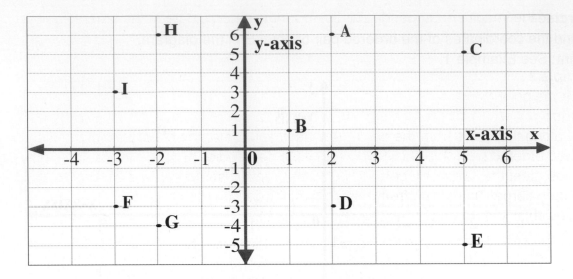

a. (2, 6) are the coordinates of the ordered pair of the point _____.

b. (-2, 6) are the coordinates of the ordered pair of the point _____.
   Hint: The negative x-coordinates are at the left side of the origin.

c. (_, _) are the coordinates of the ordered pair of point C.

d. The coordinate of the ordered pair of the point E is (5, -5) and (_, _) are the coordinates of the ordered pair of the point D.
   Hint: The negative y-coordinates are below the origin.

e. The coordinates of the ordered pair of the point G is (-2, -4) and (_, _) are the coordinates of the ordered pair of the point F.

f. (1, 1) are the coordinates of the ordered pair of point B.

4. What is meant by the coordinate system or the coordinate plane?

5. What is meant by the origin?

6. What is meant by the coordinate plane.

Answers to Selected Questions

1. (2, 3)   **3b.** point H

Critical thinking: What is the importance of the coordinates of a point? The coordinates of a point show how far and in which direction to move horizontally along the x-axis and then vertically along the y-axis on the coordinate plane.

Graphing on the Coordinate Plane
We can graph the coordinates of the ordered pair of any point by moving along the x-axis until we are at the x-coordinate of the required ordered pair. Then we continue by moving perpendicularly to the x-axis until we meet the imaginary perpendicular line from the y-coordinate of the ordered pair which is on the y-axis. The point where the imaginary perpendicular line from the x-coordinate of the ordered

pair meet the imaginary perpendicular line from the y-coordinate of the ordered pair is the point or the graph of the point.

Example 1
Graph the point (3, 5).
Solution
Move along the x-axis from the origin (0, 0) until you are at the coordinate of the first required ordered pair which is 3, then you move perpendicular to the x-axis (imaginary) until you meet the imaginary perpendicular line from point 5 on the y-axis. Where the imaginary perpendicular line from the x-axis coincide with the imaginary perpendicular line from the y-axis is the point (3, 5).

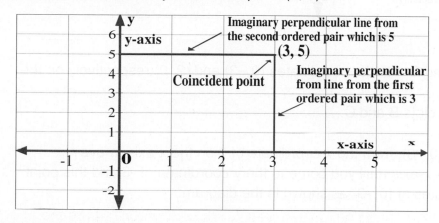

Importance of the Sign of the Coordinates
1. If the first coordinate is negative, then move along the x-axis is toward the left side of the origin (0, 0), but if the sign is positive, then the move is towards the right of the origin (0, 0).
2. If the second coordinate is negative, then move along the y-axis is below the origin (0, 0)

Example 2
Graph the point (-3, 4).
Solution
Move along the x-axis from the origin (0, 0) until you are at the x-coordinate of -3 and then move perpendicularly to the x-axis until you coincide with the imaginary perpendicular line from the point 4 on the y-axis. Where the imaginary perpendicular lines from the x-coordinate of -3 and the y-coordinate of 4 meet is the coordinate of the ordered pair of the point (-3, 4) or the graph of the point.

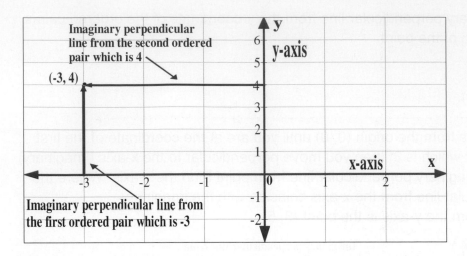

Example 3

a. Graph the points B and C with the coordinates (0, -3) and (2, 0) respectively on the same diagram.

b. Draw a line through points B and C.

Solution

a. To graph the point B(0, -3), from the x-coordinate of 0 on the x-axis, move perpendicularly to the x-axis until you come to the y-coordinate of -3 and this point will have the coordinates of (0, -3) as shown in the diagram.

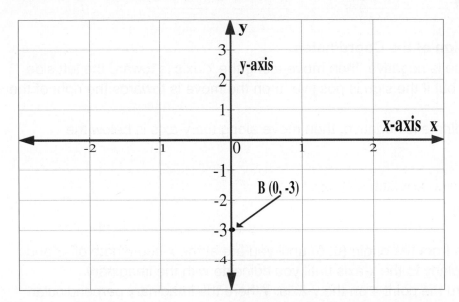

To graph the point C(2, 0), move along the x-axis from the origin (0, 0) until you are at the x-coordinates of 2 but y = 0 on the x-axis and this mean that the y-coordinate of 0 is on the x-axis therefore, the point (2, 0) is the graph of point C as shown in the diagram.

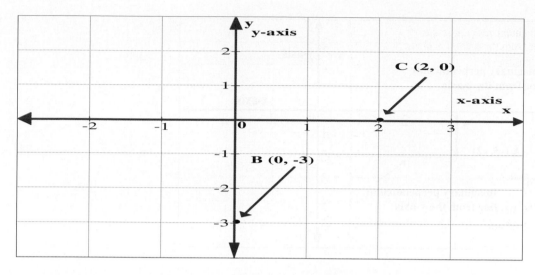

b. Draw a line through the points B(0, -3) and C(2, 0).

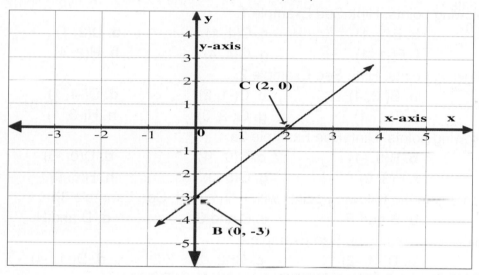

Example 4

Graph the point A with coordinates (-3, -2).

Solution

Move along the x-axis from the origin (0, 0) until you are at the x-coordinate of the ordered pair which is -3 and then move perpendicularly to the x-axis until you meet the imaginary perpendicular line from the point -2 on the y-axis. This meeting point are the coordinates of the ordered pair (-3,-2) or the graph of the point (-3, -2).

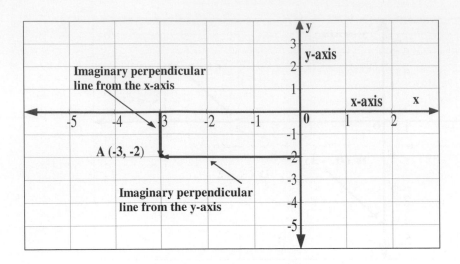

Exercises

1. Graph the following points. Hint: See Example **1**.

a. A(2, 1)   **b**. B(3, 1)   **c**. C(4, 1)   **d**. D(2, 1)

e. E(2, 2)   **f**. F(-1, 1)   **g**. G(4, 4)   **h**. H(2, 4)

2. Graph the following points. Hint: See Example **2**.

a. A(-2, 1)   **b**. B(-3, 4)   **c**. C(-1, 2)   **d**. D(-4, 1)

e. E(-2, 2)   **f**. F(-1, 1)   **g**. G(-2, 3)   **h**. H(-3, 1)

3. Graph the following points. Hint: See Example **3a**.

a. A(0, -2)   **b**. B(0, -1)   **c**. C(0, -4)   **d**. D(0, -5)

e. E(1, 0)   **f**. F(3, 0)   **g**. G(5, 0)   **h**. H(6, 0)

4. Using question 3, join the following points with a line. Hint: See Example **3b**.

a. A and E   **b**. B and F   **c**. C and G   **d**. D and H

5. Graph the following points. Hint: See Example **4**.

a. A(-1, -1)   **b**. B(-3, -2)   **c**. C(-2, -3)   **d**. D(-1, -4)

Challenge Questions

6. Graph the following points.

a. A(0, 4)   **b**. B(1, 4)   **c**. C(0, -6)   **d**. D(-3, -3)

7. Graph the three points (1, 2), (3, 1), and (1, 3).

Join the three points to form a triangle.

Quadrants

Quadrants are the four areas that the x-axis and the y-axis divide the coordinate system into as shown in Figure 1.

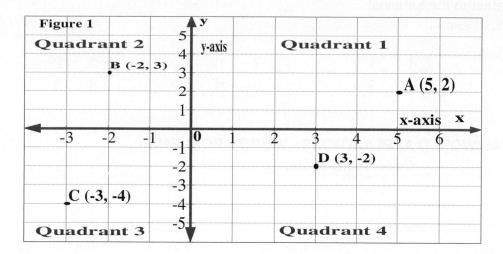

Critical Thinking

Using Figure 1:

1. The coordinates of the point A are (5, 2) which are positive and the point A is located in the quadrant 1, and therefore, any point that has both positive x-coordinate and y-coordinates is in quadrant 1.

2. The coordinates of the point B are (-2, 3) which shows that the x-coordinate is negative and the y-coordinate is positive and the point B is located in the quadrant 2. Therefore, any point that has a negative x-coordinate and a positive y-coordinate is located in the quadrant 2.

3. The coordinates of the point C are (-3, -4) which shows that both the x-coordinate and the y-coordinate are negative and the point C is located in the quadrant 3. Therefore, any point that has a negative x-coordinate and a negative y-coordinate is located in the quadrant 3.

4. The coordinates of the point D are (3, -2) which shows that the x-coordinate is positive and the y-coordinate is negative and the point D is located in the quadrant 4. Therefore, any point that has a positive x-coordinate and a negative y-coordinate is located in the quadrant 4.

Team Exercises

Using the notes under "Critical Thinking,"

1. In which quadrant is the graph of the following ordered pairs located?
   a. (-1, -3)   **b.** (3, -1)   **c.** (-2, 3)   **d.** (4, 3).
2. in which quadrant is a graph of the ordered pair located when both coordinates are negative?
3. in which quadrant is a graph of the ordered pair located when both coordinates are positive?

Cumulative Review

1. Draw a number line and use dots to locate the integers on it. Then list the integers

from the greatest to the smallest.

10, 2, -3, -8, 6, 0, and -1

2. Solve:

a. $\dfrac{2}{3} \div \dfrac{1}{6} =$ **b.** $2\dfrac{1}{4} - 1\dfrac{1}{2} =$ **c.** $\dfrac{7}{9} \times \dfrac{12}{4} =$ **d.** $\dfrac{3}{4} + \dfrac{2}{3} =$

REAL WORLD APPLICATIONS - WORD PROBLEMS
Coordinate System

Example 1

Mary started walking from the origin (0, 0). If she went 4 units to the right on the x-axis and then went 3 units down what are the coordinates of the final location of Mary?

Solution

Mary walked 4 units from the origin (0, 0) to the right on the x-axis, and therefore, her location is 4 units to the right. She then went 3 units down and her position on the y-axis is -3. The coordinates of her location are (4, -3) as shown in the diagram.

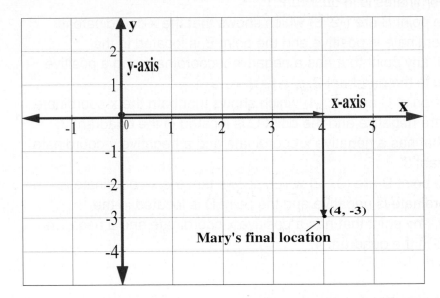

Example 2

John started walking from the origin. If he moved 6 units to the left and then 5 units up what are the coordinates of John?

Solution

John moved 6 units to the left from the origin, and therefore the x-coordinate of his location is -6. He then moved 5 units up, and therefore, his y-coordinate is 5. The coordinates of his location are (-6, 5) as shown in the diagram.

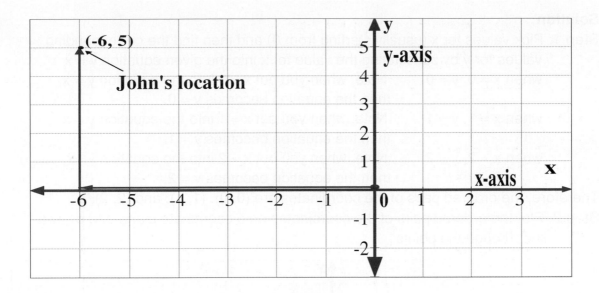

Exercises

1. Eric started at the origin and moved 5 units to the right and then 5 units down.
   What are the coordinates of Eric? Hint: See Example 1.
2. Start at the origin, move 1 unit to the left and then 4 units up.
   What are the coordinates of the location? Hint: See Example 2.

Graphing of Equations

An equation is a mathematics statement which indicates that one expression is equivalent to another expression. An example of an equation is $y = 2x + 2$.

How Can We Graph An Equation?

1. In the previous section under "Graphing on the coordinate plane" we learned that we can graph a point if we know the x and the y coordinates.
2. Similarly in order to graph an equation of a line, we need to find at least two sets of the values of the x and y coordinates of the equation by giving a value to x (usually starting from 0 and finding the corresponding value of y as shown in Example 1.
3. Using the values of the x and y coordinates, we can write the ordered pairs to be graphed.
4. Make the graph by:
   a. Plotting each ordered pair on a coordinate plane
   b. Connect all the points by using a straight line
   c. Put arrows at both ends of the line to show that the line continues in both directions.

Example 1

Graph the equation $y = x$ on a coordinate plane.

Solution

Step 1: Pick values for x (usually starting from 0) and then find the corresponding values for y by substituting the value for x into the given equation y = x.

    when x = 0, y = 0   Note, when you put x = 0 into the equation y = x, then the equation becomes y = 0.

    when x = 1, y = 1   Note, when you put x = 1 into the equation y = x, then the equation becomes y = 1.

    when x = 2, y = 2   Note, when you put x = 2 into the equation y= x, then the equation becomes y = 2.

Therefore, the ordered pairs of the coordinates are (0, 0), (1, 1), and (2, 2).

Step 2: Plot the ordered pairs of the coordinates on a coordinate plane and draw a line through the points.

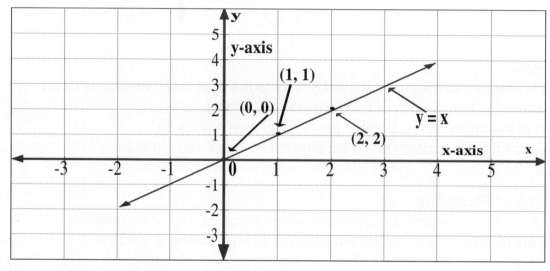

The graph shows the equation y = x.

Example 2

Graph the equation y = x + 1 on a coordinate plane.

Solution

Step 1: Pick values for x (usually starting from 0) and then find the corresponding values for y by substituting the values for x in the given equation y = x + 1.

    When x = 0, y = 0 + 1 = 1.   Note, when you put x = 0 into the equation y = x + 1, the equation becomes y = 0 + 1 = 1. Therefore, when x = 0, y = 1.

    When x = 1, y = 1 + 1 = 2   Note, when you put x = 1 into the equation y = x + 1, the equation becomes y = 1 + 1 = 2. Therefore, when x = 1, y = 2.

    When x = 2, y = 2 + 1 = 3   Note, when you put x = 2 into the equation y = x + 1, the equation becomes y = 2 + 1 = 3. Therefore, when x = 1, y = 3.

Therefore, the ordered pairs of the coordinates are (0, 1), (1, 2), and (2, 3).

Step 2: Plot the ordered pairs on a coordinate plane and draw a line through the points.

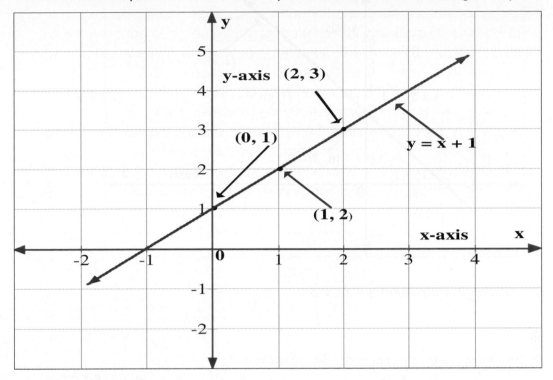

The graph shows the equation y = x + 1.

Example 3

Graph the equation y = 2x + 3.

Solution

Step 1: Pick values for x (usually starting from 0), and then find the corresponding values for y.

When x = 0, y = 2 × 0 + 3 = 3   Note, when you put x = 0 into the equation y = 2x + 3, the equation becomes y = 2 × 0 + 3 = 3. Therefore, when x = 0, y = 3.

When x = 1, y = 2 × 1 + 3 = 5   Note, when you put x = 1 into the equation y = 2x + 3, the equation becomes y = 2 × 1 + 3 = 5. So, when x = 1, y = 5.

When x = 2, y = 2 × 2 + 3 = 7   Note, when you put x = 2 into the equation y = 2x + 3, the equation becomes y = 2 × 2 + 3 = 7. Therefore, when x = 2, y = 7.

Therefore, the ordered pair of the coordinates are (0, 3), (1, 5), and (2, 7).

Step 2: Plot the ordered pairs of the coordinates on a coordinate plane and draw a line through the points.

593

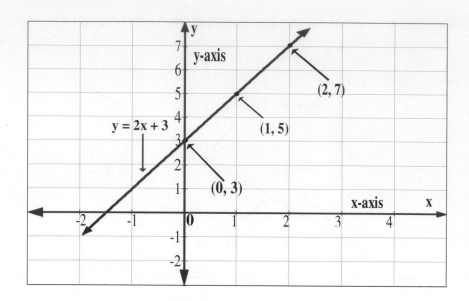

The graph shows the equation y = 2x + 3

Exercises
1 Graph the following equations Hint: See Example **1**.
   a. y = 2x   **b.** y = 3x   **c.** y = 4x   **d.** y = 5x
2. Graph the following equations. Hint: See Example **2**.
   a. y = x + 2   **b.** y = x + 3   **c.** y = x + 5   **d.** y = x + 4
3. Graph the following equations. Hint: See Example **3**.
   a. y = 2x + 2   **b.** y = 3x + 1   **c.** y = 4x + 1   **d.** y = 2x - 1

Challenge Questions
4. Graph the following equations.
   a. y = 3x - 1   **b.** y = 2x + 3   **c.** y = 3x + 2   **d.** y = 2x - 2
5. A real world application of the ordered pair of numbers may be the temperature corresponding to each day as shown in the table.

Day	1	2	3	4	5	6
Temperature (°F)	4	-2	6	0	-3	2

Let the day be on the x-coordinate and the temperature be on the y-coordinate and graph each ordered point. Hint: the first coordinate may be written as (1, 4).

Mixed Review
1. The sum of the measures of two angles of a triangle is 101°. What is the measure of the third angle?
2. The sum of the measures of three angles of a quadrilateral is 300°. What is the measure of the fourth angle?
3. The sum of the angles on a line except an angle labelled A is 155°. What is the

594

measure of angle A?

4. Solve for x:

    a. $5x - 3 = 3x + 7$ **b.** $\dfrac{3x}{8} = \dfrac{3}{4}$ **c.** $90^0 + 3x = 180^0$

5. Find 20% of $200

6. What is the reciprocal of $\dfrac{2}{5}$?

7. A square swimming pool has an area of 100 m². Find the perimeter of the swimming pool.

8. Simplify:

    a. $\dfrac{4}{5} \div \dfrac{3}{20}$ **b.** $\dfrac{5 \times 3 \times 4 \times 2}{3 \times 20 \times 2 \times 3}$ **c.** $20 \div 4 - 2$ **d.** $20 - 4 \div 2$

SLOPE OF A LINE

The slope of a line is the ratio: $\dfrac{\text{Vertical change}}{\text{Horizontal change}} = \dfrac{\text{Change in y distance}}{\text{Change in x distance}} = \dfrac{\text{rise}}{\text{run}}$

where the "rise" is the number of units moved up or down and the "run" is the number of units moved to the left or right.

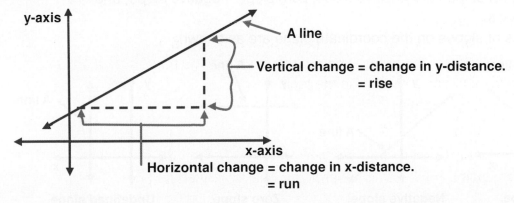

Types of Slopes.

The four types of slopes are positive, zero, negative, and undefined slopes.

The four types of slopes may be described as shown:

a. An upward slope (↗) has a positive slope.

b. A horizontal slope (→) has a zero slope.

c. A downward slope (↘) has a negative slope.

d. A vertical slope (↓) has an undefined slope.

Students may be able to remember the four types of slopes if they can recall the slopes sketch below. Let us call this slopes sketch the "Aggor slopes sketch."

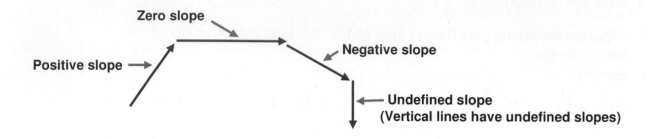

Hint: Example 3 explained mathematically positive, zero, negative, and undefined slopes.

Example 1

a. Name the four types of slopes.

b. Sketch the four types of slopes on a coordinate plane.

c. Describe a line with a positive slope.

d. Describe a line with a negative slope.

e. Describe a line with q zero slope.

f. Describe a line with an undefined slope.

Solution

a. The four types of slopes are positive slope, zero slope, negative slope, and undefined slopes.

b. The four types of slopes on the coordinate plane are as shown:

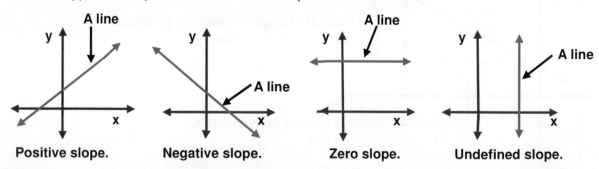

Positive slope.   Negative slope.   Zero slope.   Undefined slope.

c. A line with a positive slope goes up in the direction from left to right. Hint: See the positive slope diagram in the Solution **b**.

d. A line with a negative slope goes down from the direction of left to right. Hint: See the negative slope diagram in the Solution **b**.

e. A line with a zero slope is parallel to the horizontal or the x axis. Hint: See the diagram of the line with a zero slope in the Solution **b**.

f. A line with an undefined slope is parallel to the y axis or it is vertical. Hint: See the diagram of the line with the undefined slope in the Solution **b**.

Example 2

What is the slope of the line that passes through the points $(x_1, y_1,)$ and (x_2, y_2)?

Solution

The line is sketched with the points as shown below.

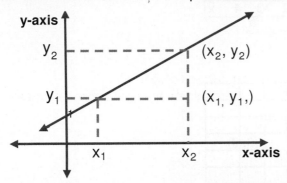

The slope of a line is the ratio: $\dfrac{\text{Vertical change}}{\text{Horizontal change}} = \dfrac{\text{change in y-distance}}{\text{change in x-distance}}$

$$= \frac{\text{rise}}{\text{run}} = \frac{y_2 - y_1}{x_2 - x_1}$$

Note: The formula for finding the slope of a line is:

$$\textbf{Slope} = \frac{\textbf{Vertical change}}{\textbf{Horizontal change}} = \frac{\textbf{change in y-distance}}{\textbf{change in x-distance}} = \frac{\textbf{rise}}{\textbf{run}} = \frac{y_2 - y_1}{x_2 - x_1}$$

Example 3

Using slope $= \dfrac{y_2 - y_1}{x_2 - x_1}$, show that:

a. Figure 1 has a positive slope.

b. Figure 2 has a negative slope.

c. Figure 3 has a zero slope.

d. Figure 4 has an undefined slope.

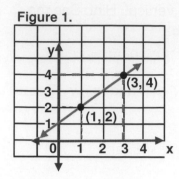

Figure 1.

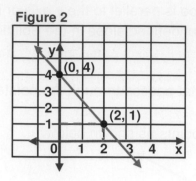

Figure 2

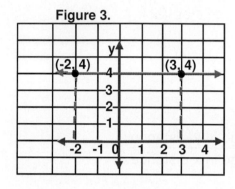

Figure 3.

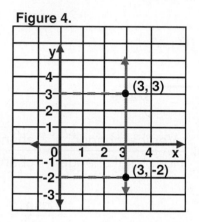

Figure 4.

Solution

a. Let (x_1, y_1) be (1, 2) and let (x_2, y_2) be (3, 4).

$$\text{Slope} = \frac{y_2 - y_1}{x_2 - x_1} = \frac{4 - 2}{3 - 1}$$ Substitute 4 for y_2, 2 for y_1, 3 for x_2, and 1 for x_1.

$$= \frac{2}{2}$$ $4 - 2 = 2, 3 - 1 = 2$

$$= 1$$

The slope is positive because the sign in front of the slope, which is 1 is positive, although a positive symbol is not written in front of the slope 1. (The slope is positive because 1 is a positive number.)

b. Let (x_1, y_1) be (2, 1) and let (x_2, y_2) be (0, 4).

$$\text{Slope} = \frac{y_2 - y_1}{x_2 - x_1} = \frac{4 - 1}{0 - 2}$$ Substitute 4 for y_2 1 for y_1 0 for x_2, and 2 for x_1.

$$= \frac{3}{-2}$$ $4 - 1 = 3, 0 - 2 = -2$

$$= -1\frac{1}{2}$$

The slope is negative because there is a negative symbol in front of the slope as $-1\frac{1}{2}$. (The slope is negative because $-1\frac{1}{2}$ is a negative number.)

c. Let (x_1, y_1) be (-2, 4) and let (x_2, y_2) be (3, 4).

$$\text{Slope} = \frac{y_2 - y_1}{x_2 - x_1} = \frac{4 - 4}{3 - (-2)}$$ Substitute 4 for y_2, 4 for y_1, x_2 for 3, and x_1 for -2.

$$= \frac{0}{3 + 2}$$ $4 - 4 = 0$, $3 - (-2) = 3 + 2$. Note that -(-2 becomes +2.

$$= \frac{0}{5}$$ $3 + 2 = 5$

$$= 0$$ Zero divided by any number is zero.

The slope is 0 because the value of the slope is 0

d. Let (x_1, y_1) be (3, -2) and let (x_2, y_2) be (3, 3).

$$\text{Slope} = \frac{y_2 - y_1}{x_2 - x_1} = \frac{3 - (-2)}{3 - 3}$$ Substitute 3 for y_2 -2 for y_1, 3 for x_2, and 3 for x_1.

$$= \frac{3 + 2}{0}$$ $3 - (-2) = 3 + 2$, $3 - 3 = 0$. Note that -(-2 becomes +2.

$$= \frac{5}{0}$$ A number divided by 0, the result is undefined.

$$= \text{undefined slope. A number divided by 0, the result is undefined.}$$

How to Find the Slope When Two Points are Given

Example 4

Find the slope of the line that passes through (3, 6) and (5, 2).

Solution

The formula for the slope of a line that passes through the points (x_1, y_1) and (x_2, y_2) is:

$$\text{Slope} = \frac{y_2 - y_1}{x_2 - x_1}$$

To find the slope of a line when two ordered pairs of points (x_1, x_2) and (y_1, y_2) are given, use the formula:

$$\text{Slope} = \frac{y_2 - y_1}{x_2 - x_1}$$

Let (x_1, y_1) be (3, 6) ad let (x_2, y_2) be (5, 2).

$$\text{Slope} = \frac{y_2 - y_1}{x_2 - x_1} = \frac{2 - 6}{5 - 3}$$ Substitute 2 for y_2, 6 for y_1, 5 for x_2, and 3 for x_1.

$$= \frac{-4}{2}$$ $2 - 6 = -4$, $5 - 3 = 2$

$$= -2$$ $-4 \div 2 = -2$

The slope of the line is -2.

Example 5

Find the slope of the line that passes through (-3, -2) and (0, 4).

Solution

The formula for the slope of a line that passes through the points (x_1, y_1) and (x_2, y_2) is:

$$\text{Slope} = \frac{y_2 - y_1}{x_2 - x_1}$$

Let (x_1, y_1) be (-3, -2) and let (x_2, y_2) be (0, 4).

$$\text{Slope} = \frac{y_2 - y_1}{x_2 - x_1} = \frac{4 - (-2)}{0 - (-3)}$$ Substitute 4 for y_2, -2 for y_1, 0 for x_2, and -3 for x_1.

$$= \frac{4 + 2}{0 + 3}$$ $-(-2) = +2$, and $-(-3) = +3$.

$$= \frac{6}{3}$$ $4 + 2 = 6$ and $0 + 3 = 3$

$$= 2$$ $6 \div 3 = 2$.

The slope of the line is 2.

How to Find the Slope From a Graph

Example 6

Use the graph to find the slope of the line by:

a. Using the formula, Slope $= \dfrac{y_2 - y_1}{x_2 - x_1}$

b. Using the formula, Slope $= \dfrac{\text{rise}}{\text{run}}$

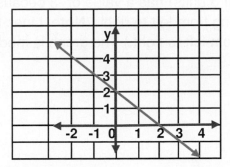

Solution

a. Select two points on the line and then use the slope formula to find the slope as follows:

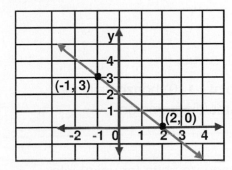

Let the two points selected on the line be (2, 0) and (-1, 3).
Let (x_1, y_1) be (-1, 3) and let (x_2, y_2) be (2, 0).

Slope $= \dfrac{y_2 - y_1}{x_2 - x_1} = \dfrac{0 - 3}{2 - (-1)}$ Substitute 0 for y_2, 3 for y_1, 2 for x_2, and -1 for x_1.

$= \dfrac{0 - 3}{2 + 1}$ Note: - (- = +, so 2 - (-1) = 2 + 1

Hint: See the chapter on "Subtraction of Integers."

$= \dfrac{-3}{3}$ $-3 \div 3 = -1$

$= -1$ $-3 \div 3 = -1$

b. Use the same graph as in the solution of Example 6a. Select the same two points

601

on the line as in the graph of the solution of Example 6a.

To find the slope by using the formula, Slope $= \dfrac{\text{rise}}{\text{run}}$, we have to count square

units (or units) on the graph that represent "rise" and "run."
We can count 3 square units (or 3 units) down on the graph from the point (-1, 3)
to the x-axis as the rise. This 3 square units (or 3 units) has a value of -3 because
the y value of the line on the graph is decreasing from left to right. (**Note**: Lines that
have negative slopes go down as you move from left to right.) The graph is modified
to show the rise and the run.

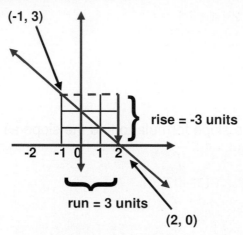

We can also count 3 square units (or units) from the point (-1, 0) horizontally to
the point (2, 0) as the run. (Hint: See the preceding notes/diagrams on

Slope $= \dfrac{\text{rise}}{\text{run}}$.)

Substitute rise = -3 square units (or units) and run = 3 square units (or units) into
the equation:

$$\text{Slope} = \dfrac{\text{rise}}{\text{run}} \text{ to obtain the slope as shown:}$$

$$\text{Slope} = \dfrac{\text{rise}}{\text{run}} = \dfrac{-3}{3}$$

$$= -1 \qquad\qquad\qquad -3 \div 3 = -1$$

How to Identify Parallel Lines by Using Other Slopes

Note: Parallel lines have equal slopes.

Example 7
Is the line AB that passes through the points (1, 1) and (-2, 2) parallel to the line
DC that passes through the points (1, 3) and (-2, 4)?

(The line AB can be written as $\overleftrightarrow{AB}$, and the line DC can also be written as $\overleftrightarrow{DC}$.)

Solution

If the line AB is parallel to the line DC, then the line AB and the line DC must have the same slope because parallel lines have equal slopes. For line AB, let (x_1, y_1) be (1, 1) and (x_2, y_2) be (-2, 2).

Slope of the line AB $= \dfrac{y_2 - y_1}{x_2 - x_1} = \dfrac{2 - 1}{-2 - 1}$ Substitute 2 for y_2, 1 for y_1, -2 for x_2,

and 1 for x_1.

$$= \dfrac{1}{-3} \qquad 2 - 1 = 1, -2 - 1 = -3$$

$$= -\dfrac{1}{3}$$

For the line DC, let (x_1, y_1) be (1, 3) and (x_2, y_2) be (-2, 4).

Slope of the line DC $= \dfrac{y_2 - y_1}{x_2 - x_1} = \dfrac{4 - 3}{-2 - 1}$ Substitute 4 for y_2, 3 for y_1, -2 for x_2,

and 1 for x_1.

$$= \dfrac{1}{-3} \qquad 4 - 3 = 1, -2 - 1 = -3$$

$$= -\dfrac{1}{3}$$

Since the lines AB and DC have the same slope of $-\dfrac{1}{3}$, they are parallel.

Example 8

Determine if the line AB that passes through the points (4, 2) and (7, -1) and the line DC that passes through the points (5, 3) and (4, 3) are parallel or not.

Solution

If the line AB is parallel to the line DC, then their slopes must be equal. Let us find if their slopes are equal or not.

For the line AB, let (x_1, y_1) be (4, 2) and let (x_2, y_2) be (7, -1).

For the line DC, let (x_1, y_1) be (5, 3) and let (x_2, y_2) be (4, 3).

Slope of the line AB $= \dfrac{y_2 - y_1}{x_2 - x_1} = \dfrac{-1 - 2}{7 - 4}$ Substitute -1 for y_2, 2 for y_1, 7 for

x_2, and 4 for x_1.

$$= \dfrac{-3}{3} \qquad -1 - 2 = -3, 7 - 4 = 3$$

$$= -1$$
$$-3 \div 3 = -1$$

Slope of the line $DC = \dfrac{y_2 - y_1}{x_2 - x_1} = \dfrac{3 - 3}{4 - 5}$

Substitute 3 for y_2, 3 for y_1, 4 for x_2, and 5 for x_1.

$$= \dfrac{0}{-1}$$

$3 - 3 = 0$, $4 - 5 = -1$

$$= 0$$

0 divided by any number is 0.

The slope of the line AB is -1 and the slope of line DC is 0. Since the slopes of the line AB and the line DC are not equal, then the line AB and the line DC are not parallel.

How to Identify Perpendicular Lines by Using Their Slopes

Two lines are perpendicular to each other if the product of their slopes is **-1**, and that is, their slopes are negative reciprocals of each other. For an example, if two lines are **perpendicular**, and the slope of the first line is **m**, then the slope of the second line should be $-\dfrac{1}{m}$.

Note that the product of the two slopes $= m \times (-\dfrac{1}{m})$

$$1$$
$$= \not{m} \times (-\dfrac{1}{\not{m}})$$
Divide.
$$1$$

$$= 1 \times (-\dfrac{1}{1})$$

$$= 1 \times (-1)$$
$$-\dfrac{1}{1} = -1$$

$$= -1$$

Example 9

Determine if the line AB that passes through the points (1, 1) and (4, 0) is perpendicular to the line DC that passes through the points (1, 1) and (2, 4).

Solution

Two lines are perpendicular to each other if the product of their slopes is -1, and that is their slopes are negative reciprocals of each other. Let us find the slopes of the line AB and the line DC, and then check if the product of their slopes is -1 or not.

For the line AB, let (x_1, y_1) be (1, 1) and let (x_2, y_2) be (4, 0).

Slope of the line AB $= \dfrac{y_2 - y_1}{x_2 - x_1} = \dfrac{0 - 1}{4 - 1}$ Substitute 0 for y_2, 1 for y_1, 4 for

x_2 and 1 for x_1.

$$= \dfrac{-1}{3}$$ $0 - 1 = -1,\ 4 - 1 = 3$

$$= -\dfrac{1}{3}$$

For the line DC, let (x_1, y_1) be $(1, 1)$ and let (x_2, y_2) be $(2, 4)$.

Slope of the line DC $= \dfrac{y_2 - y_1}{x_2 - x_1} = \dfrac{4 - 1}{2 - 1}$ Substitute 4 for y_2, 1 for y_1, 2 for

x_2, and 1 for x_1.

$$= \dfrac{3}{1}$$ $4 - 1 = 3,\ 2 - 1 = 1$

$$= 3$$

The slope of the line AB $= -\dfrac{1}{3}$ and the slope of the line DC is 3. Note that $-\dfrac{1}{3}$ and 3

are negative reciprocal of each other and therefore the line AB and the line DC are
perpendicular to each other.

Additionally, the product of the slopes of the line AB and the line DC is -1 as shown
below.

$$= -\dfrac{1}{3} \times 3$$

$$= -\dfrac{1}{3} \times 3 = -\dfrac{3}{3} = -1$$

Since the product of the slopes of the line AB and the line DC is -1, then the line AB
is perpendicular to the line DC.

Example 10

Show that the line AB that passes through the points $(6, 2)$ and $(4, 1)$ and the line DC
that passes through the points $(4, 8)$ and $(9, 3)$ are not perpendicular to each other.

Solution

To show that the line AB is not perpendicular to the line DC, we need to show that the
slopes of the line AB and the line DC are not negative reciprocal of each other, and
that means the product of their slopes is not equal to -1.

For the line AB, let (x_1, y_1) be $(6, 2)$ and let (x_2, y_2) be $(4, 1)$.

Slope of the line AB $= \dfrac{y_2 - y_1}{x_2 - x_1} = \dfrac{1 - 2}{4 - 6}$ Substitute 1 for y_2, 2 for y_1, 4 for

x_2, and 6 for x_1.

$= \dfrac{-1}{-2}$ $1 - 2 = -1$, $4 - 6 = -2$

$= \dfrac{1}{2}$ $\dfrac{-1}{-2} = \dfrac{1}{2}$, the negative symbols cancel out.

Considering the line DC, let (x_1, y_1) be $(4, 8)$ and let (x_2, y_2) be $(9, 3)$.

Slope of the line DC $= \dfrac{y_2 - y_1}{x_2 - x_1} = \dfrac{3 - 8}{9 - 4}$ Substitute 3 for y_2, 8 for y, 9 for x_2, and

4 for x_1.

$= \dfrac{-5}{5}$ $3 - 8 = -5$, $9 - 4 = 5$

$= -1$ $-5 \div 5 = -1$

The slope of the line AB is $\dfrac{1}{2}$ and the slope of the line DC $= -1$. Since the slope of the

line AB is not a negative reciprocal of the slope of the line DC, then the line AB is not perpendicular to the line DC.

Or we can state that since the product of the slopes of the line AB and the line DC

(which is $\dfrac{1}{2} \times -1 = -\dfrac{1}{2}$) is not equal to -1, then the line AB and the line DC are not

perpendicular to each other.

Example 11

Sketch (a) parallel lines (b) perpendicular lines.

Solution

The parallel lines and the perpendicular lines are sketched as shown.

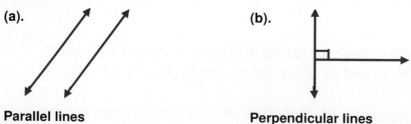

(a).   (b).

Parallel lines   **Perpendicular lines**

Exercises

1. What is the slope of a line? Hint: See the notes.

2. What are the four types of slopes? Hint: See Example 1.

3a. Sketch the four types of slopes. Hint: See Example 1.

3b. Label each slope of the line as undefined, zero, positive, and negative.
Hint: See the notes.

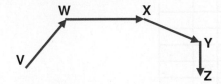

4. The slope of a line $= \dfrac{y_2 - y_1}{x_2 - x_1}$. Is this true or false? Hint: See Example 2

5. a. Vertical change = change in y distance = rise. True or false?
   b. Horizontal change = change in x distance = run. True or false?
   c. Rise is the number of units moved up or d_____.
   d. Run is the number of units moved to the left or r_____.
   e The slope of a line is the ratio:

$$\frac{\text{Vertical change}}{\text{horizontal change}} = \frac{\text{Change in y distance}}{\text{Change in x distance}} = \frac{\text{rise}}{\text{run}}, \text{ true or false?}$$

Hint: See the notes.

6. Describe the slope of the line x at the top of the mountain and the slopes of the two lines Y and Z at the sides of the mountain. Hint: See the notes.

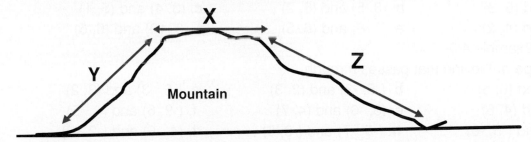

Mountain

7. Do the following slopes appear to be zero, positive, negative or undefined?
   Hint: See Example 1.

a.   b.   c.   d.

8. Using slope $= \dfrac{y_2 - y_1}{x_2 - x_1}$ show that:

   a. figure 1 has a positive slope
   b. figure 2 has a negative slope.
   c. figure 3 has a zero slope.
   d. figure 4 has an undefined slope.

Hint: See Example 3.

Figure 1.

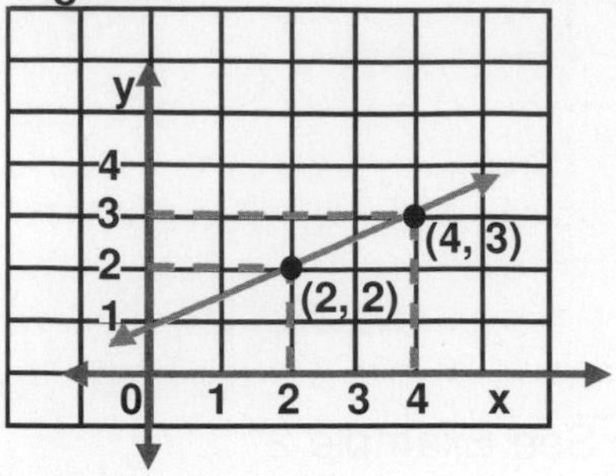

Figure 2

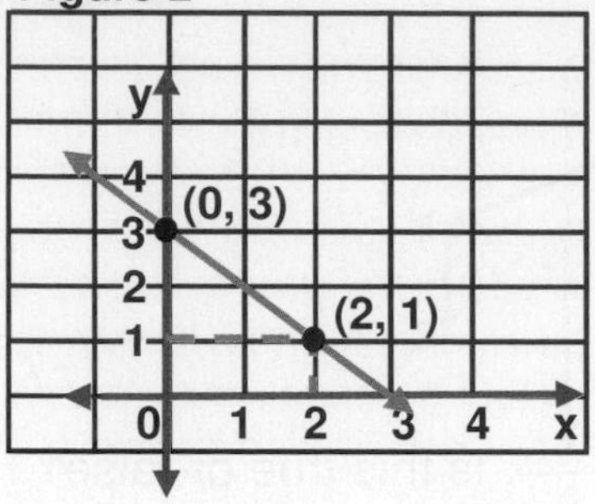

Figure 3.

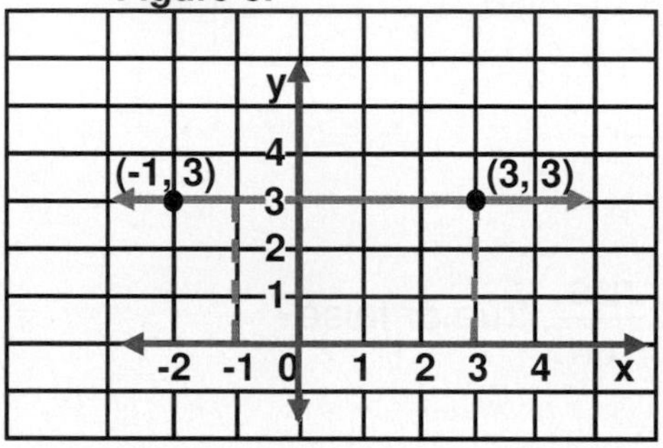

Figure 4.

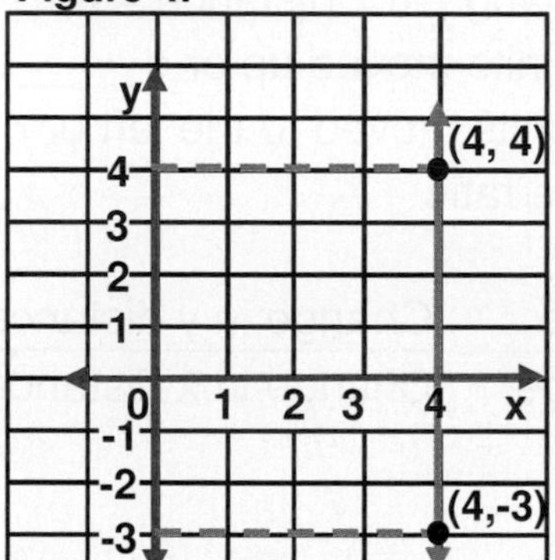

9. Find the slope of the line that passes through:

   a. (2, 4) and (6, 3)   **b**. (3, 5) and (5, 2)   **c**. (3, 4) and (5, 1)
   d. (5, 6) and (4, 2)   **e**. (7, 8) and (6, 5)   **f**. (8, 10) and (6, 5)
   Hint: See Example 4

10. Find the slope of the line that passes through:

   a. (-4, -2) and (0, 5)   **b**. (-5, -3) and (2, 3)   **c**. (-6, -3) and (3, 2)
   d. (-8, 5) and (4, 6)   **e**. (8, -6) and (4, 7)   **f**. (-9, 6) and (4, -5)
   g. (-7, -3) and (-5, -6)   **h**. (-5, -7) and (-8, 6)   **i**. (4, -6) and (-2, -3)
   Hint: See Example 5.

11. Use the graphs to find the slope of each line. Hint: See Example 6.

(The graphs are on the next page.)

a.

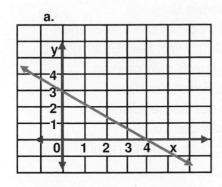

b.

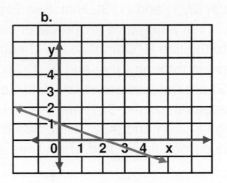

c.

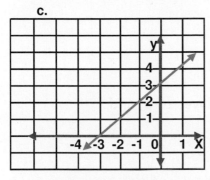

12. Complete the statement. Parallel lines have the s_____ slopes.
    Hint: See the notes.

13. Complete the statement. If line X is parallel to line Y, then line X and line Y must
    have the same s____ because parallel lines have eq_____- slopes.
    Hint: See Example 7.

14. Lines that are parallel have the same slope. True or false? Hint: See Example 7.

15. Determine if line A that passes through (4, 9) and (-3, -5) is parallel to line B that
    passes through (1, 9) and (-1, 5). Hint: See Example 7.

16. Determine if line X that passes through (-2, 0) and (1, 3) is parallel to line Z that
    passes through (-1, -2) and (3, 2). Hint: See Example 7.

17. Determine if line A that passes through (0, 0) and (1, 2) is parallel to the line that
    passes through (1, 0) and (2, 2). Hint: See Example 7.

18. If the slope of the line X and the line Z are not equal, then the line X and the line Z
    are not parallel. True or false? Hint: See Example 8.

19. Determine if line A that passes through (1, 1) and (2, -1) is parallel to line B that
    passes through (-4, 0) and (2, -2). Hint: See Example 8.

20. Determine if the line A that passes through (1, 2) and (4, 6) is parallel to the line B
    that passes through the points (2, 3) and (-3, 1). Hint: See Example 8.

21. Two lines are perpendicular to each other if the products of their slopes is _____,
    and that their slopes are n_____ reciprocals of each other. Complete the
    statement. Hint: See Example 9.

22. Determine if line P that passes through (1, 3) and (1, 1) is perpendicular to line
    that passes through (-2, 1) and (1, 1). Hint: See Example 9.

23. Determine if the line A that passes through (2, 2) and (0, 0) is perpendicular to the

line B that passes through (3, 1) and (1, 3). Hint: See Example 9.

24. If the slope of the line A is not a negative reciprocal of the slope of the line B, then line A is not p———— to the line B. Complete the statement. Hint: See Example 10.

25. Show that line A that passes through (3, 4) and (6, 1) and line B that passes through (-2, -2) and (2, 2) are not perpendicular. Hint: See Example 10.

26. Show that line Y that passes through (-3, 1) and (-1, 4) is not perpendicular to line X that passes through (-1, -1) and (4, 3). Hint: See Example 10.

27. Which lines appear to be perpendicular and which lines appear to be parallel?

a.

b.

Challenge Questions

28. In the diagram, which lines appear to have undefined, positive, zero, and negative slopes?

29. In the diagram, which lines appear to be parallel and which lines appear to be perpendicular?

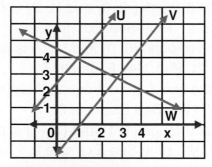

30. Find the slope of the line that passes through:
   a. (5, 7) and (9, 2)   b. (2, 7) and (9, 5)   c. (-5, -3) and (2, 4)
   d. (-7, 3) and (4, -6)   e. (-2, -4) and (-3, -1) f. (-4, 7) and (0, 0)
   g. (-4, -3) and (-6, -2) h. (-5, 0) and (-1, -3)   i. (0, 0) and (-1, -3)

31. Use the graph to find the slope of each line.

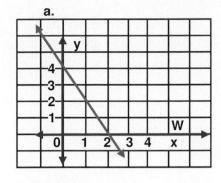

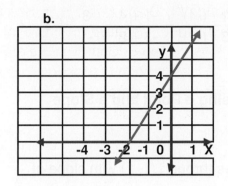

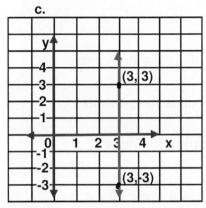

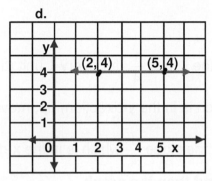

32. Determine if line A that passes through (1, 3) and (-2, 0) is parallel to line B that passes through (2, 2) and (-3, -3).

33. Determine if line Y that passes through (1, 2) and (-2, -4) is parallel to line X which passes through (2, 1) and (-1, -5).

34. Determine if line P that passes through (2, -4) and (3, 6) is parallel to line Q which passes through (1, 7) and (-3, 5).

35. Determine if line A that passes through (-4, 2) and (5, 3) is perpendicular to line that passes through (4, 0) and (3, 4).

36. Determine if line P that passes through (-3, 3) and (0, 0) is perpendicular to line Q that passes through (2, 2) and (-3, -3).

Answers to Selected Questions

8d. $\text{slope} = \dfrac{y_2 - y_1}{x_2 - x_1} = \dfrac{4 - (-3)}{4 - 4} = \dfrac{4 + 3}{0} = \dfrac{7}{0} = \text{undefined.}$

9a. $\text{slope} = \dfrac{y_2 - y_1}{x_2 - x_1} = \dfrac{3 - 4}{6 - 2} = \dfrac{-1}{4} = -\dfrac{1}{4}$

10a. $\text{slope} = \dfrac{y_2 - y_1}{x_2 - x_1} = \dfrac{5 - (-2)}{0 - (-4)} = \dfrac{5 + 2}{4} = \dfrac{7}{4} = 1\dfrac{3}{4}$

30e. slope $= \dfrac{y_2 - y_1}{x_2 - x_1} = \dfrac{-1 - (-4)}{-3 - (-2)} = \dfrac{-1 + 4}{-3 + 2} = \dfrac{3}{-1} = -3$

How to Graph a Line Using a Point and a Slope

Example 12

Graph the line that passes through (1, 1) with slope of $\dfrac{1}{4}$

Solution
Step 1: Slope analysis

Since the slope of the line is $\dfrac{1}{4}$, for every 1 unit (this 1 unit is the numerator

of the slope $\dfrac{1}{4}$ which is in the y-direction) up, move four units (this 4 units is

the denominator of the slope $\dfrac{1}{4}$ which is in the x-direction) to the right.

Step 2: Plot the points and then the graph.

Plot the given point (1, 1). Then from the point (1, 1), move 4 units (this 4

units represent the denominator of the slope of $\dfrac{1}{4}$ which is in the x-direction)

to the right and then move 1 unit (this 1 unit represents the numerator of the

slope of $\dfrac{1}{4}$ which is in the y-direction) up and then plot the point (5, 2). Note

that (1 + 4, 1 + 1) = (5, 2). Use a ruler to connect the two points (1, 1) and
(5, 2) which is the graph of the required line. Hint: See diagram.

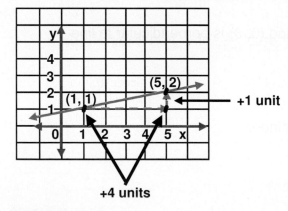

Example 13

Graph the line that passes through (2, 3) with a slope of $-\dfrac{1}{4}$.

Solution
Step 1: Slope analysis

Since the slope of the line is $-\frac{1}{4}$, for every 1 unit movement down, 4 units should be moved to the right, or, for every 1 unit movement up, move 4 units to the left. (Compare the Step 1 in Example 12 to the Step 1 in Example 13 and note the effect of the negative symbol in front of the slope in Step 1 of Example 13.)

Step 2: **Plot the points and then the graph**.

Plot the given point (2, 3). Then from the point (2, 3), move 4 units (this 4 units represent the positive denominator of the slope of $-\frac{1}{4}$) to the right and then move 1 unit (this 1 unit represents the negative numerator of the slope of $-\frac{1}{4}$) down and then plot the point (6, 2). Note that (2 + 4, 3 - 1) = (6, 2). Use a ruler to connect the two points (2, 3) and (6, 2) which is the graph of the required line. Hint: See diagram.

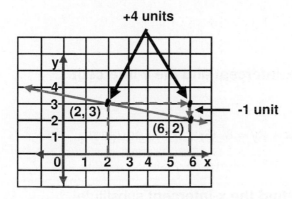

Exercises

1. Graph the line that passes through (3, 5) with a slope of $\frac{1}{3}$. Hint: See Example 12.

2. Graph the line that passes through (1, 3) with a slope of $-\frac{1}{4}$. Hint: See Example 13.

Challenge Questions

3. Graph the line that passes through (2, 6) with a slope of $\frac{1}{5}$.

4. Graph the line with a slope of $-\frac{1}{2}$ and passes through (-4, 3).

SLOPE-INTERCEPT FORM

New Terms: x-axis, y-axis, and slope-intercept form

How to Find the x-intercept and the y-intercept.

The **x-intercept** of a line is the value of x at the point where the line crosses the **x-axis**. **Note** that where the line crosses the x-axis, y = 0. The **y-intercept** of a line is the value of y at where the line crosses the **y-axis**. **Note** that where the line crosses the y-axis, x = 0. The diagram shows the x-intercept and the y-intercept.

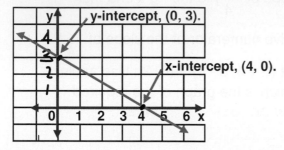

How to Graph Linear Equations by Finding the x-intercept and the y-intercept.

Example 1

Find the x-intercept and the y-intercept of the line 2x + 2y = 8. Graph the equation.

Solution

Step 1: **Find the x-intercept and the y-intercept.**

Recall that at the x-axis, y = 0, therefore, **to find the x-intercept** substitute y = 0 into the equation of the line which is 2x + 2y = 8 as shown:

When y = 0, 2x + 2y = 8 becomes 2x + 2(0) = 8

2x + 0 = 8   2(0) = 0

2x = 8

$$\frac{2x}{2} = \frac{8}{2}$$ Divide each side of the equation by 2 in order to obtain the value of x.

$$\frac{\overset{x}{\cancel{2x}}}{\cancel{2}} = \frac{\overset{4}{\cancel{8}}}{\cancel{2}}$$

x = 4

So, the x-intercept is 4 and the coordinates of the x-intercept are (4, 0). At the x-intercept, y = 0. (See the graph in Step 2.)

Recall that at the y-axis, x = 0, (See the graph in Step 2.) so, **to find the y-intercept**

substitute x = 0 into the equation of the line which is 2x + 2y = 8 as shown:
When x = 0, 2x + 2y = 8 becomes 2(0) + 2y = 8

$$0 + 2y = 8 \qquad\qquad\qquad\qquad\qquad\qquad 2(0) = 0$$
$$2y = 8$$

$$\frac{2x}{2} = \frac{8}{2} \qquad \text{Divide each side of the equation by 2 in order to obtain the value of x.}$$

$$\begin{array}{cc} x & 4 \\ \dfrac{2x}{2} & \dfrac{8}{2} \\ 1 & 1 \end{array}$$

$$x = 4$$

The y-intercept is 4 and the coordinates of the y-intercept are (0, 4). At the y-intercept, x = 0. (See the graph in Step 2.)

Step 2: Use the intercepts to graph the equation.

Plot the x-intercept of 4 and y-intercept of 4 on a graph and use a ruler to draw a line through the x-intercept and the y-intercept. This line is the required graph of the line 2x + 2y = 8.

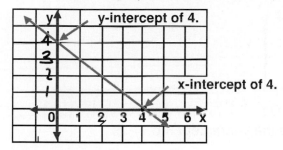

Slope-Intercept Form.

The equation of a line can be written in the standard slope-intercept form which is **y = mx + b** where m is the slope and b is the y-intercept

Example 2

Use the **slope-intercept form** to find the slope and the y-intercept of the equation of the line:

    a. y = 8x + 3   **b.** y = -7x + 1   **c.** y = 3x - 5

Solution

a. If we compare y = 8x + 3 to the slope-intercept form of y = mx + b, we can conclude that y = 8x + 3 is already in the slope-intercept form and we can therefore, find the corresponding values for m and b as shown:

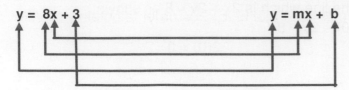

By comparing or matching the two equations above, m = 8 and b = 3. So the slope = m = 8 and the y-intercept = b = 3.

b. If we compare y = -7x + 1 to the slope-intercept form of y = mx + b, we can conclude that y = -7x + 1 is already in the slope-intercept form and we can therefore find the corresponding values for m and b as shown:

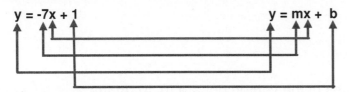

By comparing or matching the two equations above,
m = -7 and b = 1 therefore the slope = m = -7 and the y-intercept = b = 1.

c. If we compare y = 3x - 5 to the slope intercept form of y = mx + b, we can conclude that y = 3x - 5 is already in the slope-intercept form and we can therefore find the corresponding values for m and b as shown:

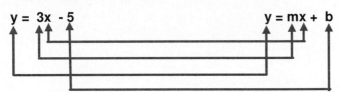

By comparing or matching the two equations above,
m = 3 and b = -5 therefore the slope = m = 3 and the y-intercept = b = - 5.

Example 3

The equation of the line in Example 1 is 2x + 2y = 8.

a. Write the equation of the line 2x + 2y = 8 in the slope-intercept form.

b. Find the slope of the line and the y-intercept.

Solution

a. The slope-intercept form is y = mx + b where m is the slope and b is the y-intercept. We need to write the equation 2x + 2y = 8 in the slope-intercept form such that y will have no number attached to it as a coefficient. We want y to be by itself at the left side of the equation as shown:

2x + 2y = 8

2x - 2x + 2y = 8 - 2x   Subtract 2x from both sides of the equation such that 2y will remain at the left side of the equation.

2x - 2x + 2y = -2x + 8

2y = -2x + 8   2x - 2x = 0

616

$$\frac{2y}{2} = \frac{-2x+8}{2}$$ Divide each side of the equation by 2 in order to obtain y by itself.

$y = -x + 4$ $\frac{2y}{2} = y$ and $\frac{-2x+8}{2} = -x + 4$

$y = -1x + 4$ which is in the slope-intercept form of $y = mx + b$. Note that $-x = -1x$.

b. From the solution of **a**, $y = -1x + 4$ which is in the slope-intercept form of
$y = mx + b$, where $m = -1$ and $b = 4$ by comparing the equation $y = -1x + 4$ to the
slope-intercept form of $y = mx + b$ as shown:

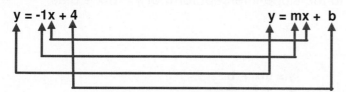

The slope of the line $= m = -1$ and the y-intercept of the line $= b = 4$.

Example 4
Using the slope-intercept form, find the slope and the y-intercept of:

a. $y = x$

b. $2x = 3y$

Solution

a. Rewrite the equation $y = x$ to show similar parts of the slope-intercept form of
$y = mx + b$ as shown:

$y = x$ becomes $y = 1x + 0$ 1 is in the place of m and 0 is in the place of b.

Note that $x = 1x$.

We can now compare or match $y = 1x + 0$ with the slope-intercept form as shown:

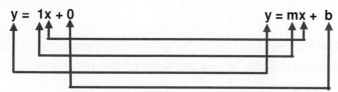

By comparing or matching the two equations above, the slope $= m = 1$ and the
intercept on the y-axis$= b = 0$

b. Rewrite the equation $2x = 3y$ to show similar parts of the slope-intercept form, so
you can compare the equation of the formula $y = mx + b$ to the given equation.

$2x = 3y$

$3y = 2x$ Reverse the equation so that y will be on the left side of the equation.

$$\frac{3y}{3} = \frac{2x}{3}$$ Divide both sides of the equation by 3 in order to obtain the value for y.

$$\frac{\overset{y}{\cancel{3y}}}{\underset{1}{\cancel{3}}} = \frac{2x}{3}$$ Divide by 3.

$$y = \frac{2}{3}x$$

$$y = \frac{2}{3}x + 0$$ Add the 0 to obtain the slope-intercept form of $y = mx + b$.

We can now compare $y = \frac{2}{3}x + 0$ to the slope-intercept form of $y = mx + b$ as

shown:

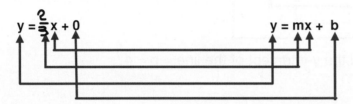

By comparing or matching the two equations above, the slope $= m = \frac{2}{3}$ and the

y-intercept $= b = 0$.

Example 5
Write the equation $-2y - 4x = 4$ in the slope-intercept form, and then find the slope and the y-intercept.
Solution
Rewrite the equation $-2y - 4x = 4$ to show the similar parts of the slope-intercept form as shown:

$-2y - 4x = 4$

$-2y - 4x + 4x = 4x + 4$ Add 4x to both sides of the equation in order to
                                 eliminate the -4x at the left side of the equation.

$-2y + 0 = 4x + 4$ $-4x + 4x = 0$

$-2y = 4x + 4$

$$\frac{-2y}{-2} = \frac{4x}{-2} + \frac{4}{-2}$$ Divide both sides of the equation by -2 in order to obtain the value of y.

$$\frac{\overset{y}{\cancel{-2y}}}{\underset{1}{\cancel{-2}}} = \frac{\overset{-2x}{\cancel{4x}}}{\underset{1}{\cancel{-2}}} + \frac{\overset{-2}{\cancel{4}}}{\underset{1}{\cancel{-2}}}$$

$y = -2x - 2$ $4x \div (-2) = -2x$ and $4 \div (-2) = -2$

618

We can now compare or match the equation y = - 2x - 2 to the slope-intercept form of y = mx + b as shown:

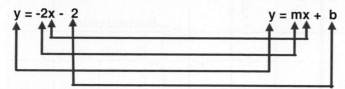

By comparing or matching the two equations above, the slope = m = -2 and the y-intercept = b = -2.

How to Use the Slope-intercept Form to Construct the Graph of an Equation.

Example 5a

Use the slope-intercept form to construct a graph of each equation

a. $y = 2x + 5$.   **b.** $y = \dfrac{2x}{3} + 3$

Solution

a. Step 1: Find the rise, run, and the y-intercept.

The slope-intercept form is y = mx + b

$$-(\dfrac{\text{rise}}{\text{run}})x + b \qquad\qquad\qquad [A].$$

$$\text{Recall that slope} = m = \dfrac{\text{rise}}{\text{run}}, \text{ substitute } m = \dfrac{\text{rise}}{\text{run}}.$$

The equation y = 2x + 5 can be written in the form of equation [A] as shown:

$$y = (\dfrac{2}{1})x + 5 \qquad\qquad\qquad\qquad [B],$$

$$\text{where } \dfrac{2}{1} = \dfrac{\text{rise}}{\text{run}}. \text{ Note: } \dfrac{2}{1} = 2 \text{ such that m is not changed}$$

Equation [B] shows that the rise = 2, the run = 1, and the y-intercept = b = 5. This y-intercept should be the first point on the graph. Locate the y-intercept on graph paper, and draw the **run** and the **rise** to locate the second point.

Since the y-intercept or b is 5, measure or count 5 units up from the origin (0, 0) on the y-axis and graph a point. This point has coordinates of (0, 5), see Figure 1.

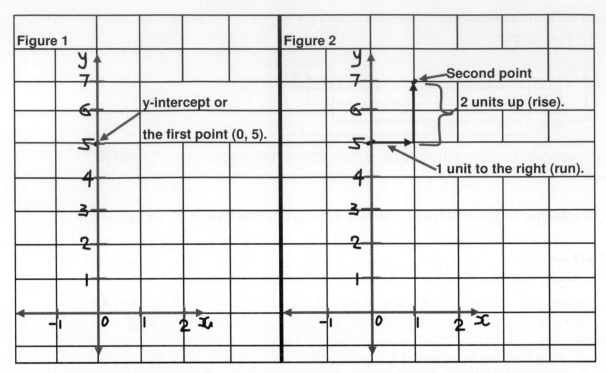

Since the run is 1, from this initial point of (0, 5), draw 1 unit to the right and since the rise is 2, draw 2 units up and then graph the second point, see Figure 2.

Step 3: Draw a line through the y-intercept which is the first point and the second point to obtain the graph of y = 2x + 5 as shown in Figure 3.

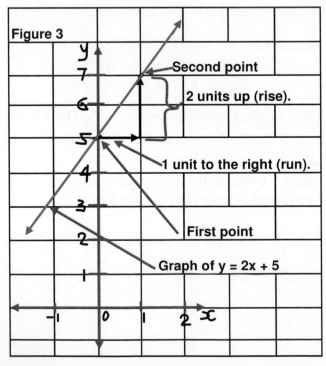

b. **Step 1**: Find the rise, run and the intercept.

The slope-intercept form is y = mx + b

$$= (\frac{rise}{run})x + b \underline{\hspace{5cm}} [C]$$

Recall that slope = m = $\frac{rise}{run}$, substitute m = $\frac{rise}{run}$.

Similarly, the equation y = $\frac{2x}{3}$ + 3 can be written in the form of equation [C] as shown:

$$y = (\frac{2}{3})x + 3 \underline{\hspace{4cm}} [D], \text{ where } \frac{2}{3} = \frac{rise}{run} = m.$$

Equation [D] shows that the rise = 2, the run = 3, and the y-intercept is 3 and this y-intercept should be the first point drawn on the graph.

Step 2: Locate the y-intercept on graph paper, draw the run and the rise to locate the second point.

Since the y-intercept or b is 3, measure or count 3 units up from the origin (0, 0) on the y-axis and graph a point and this point has coordinates of (0, 3) as shown in Figure 4.

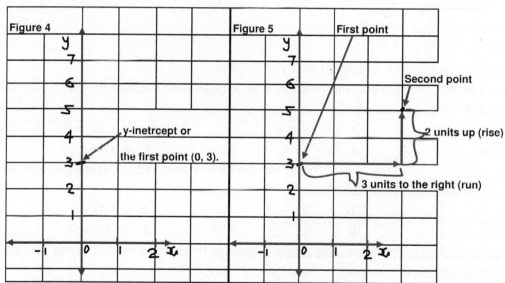

Since the run = 3, from this initial point of (0, 3) draw 3 units to the right and since the rise is 2, draw 2 units up, and then draw the second point as shown in Figure 5.

Step 3: Draw a line through the first and the second points. This line is the graph

of y = $\frac{2}{3}$x + 3 as shown in Figure 6.

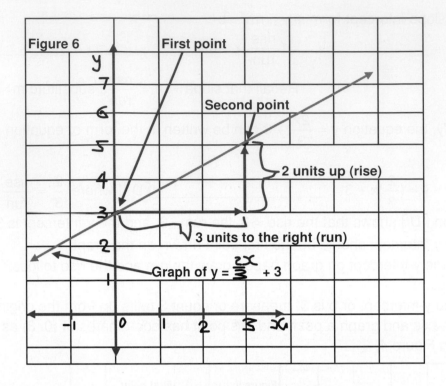

Figure 6

First point

Second point

2 units up (rise)

3 units to the right (run)

Graph of $y = \frac{2x}{3} + 3$

Exercises

1. Explain what is meant by x-intercept and y-intercept.

2. Find the x-intercept and y-intercept of each line. Graph each equation. Hint: See Example 1.

    a. $2x + y = 3$ **b.** $x + 2y = 4$ **c.** $2x + 2y = 3$

    d. $2x + 3y = 4$ **e.** $2x + 2y = 4$ **f.** $3y + 2x = 4$

3. Use the slope-intercept form to find the slope and the y-intercept of the equation of each line. Hint: See Example 2.

    a. $y = 2x + 4$ **b.** $y = -3x + 2$ **c.** $y = 4x - 3$

    d. $y = 3x - 2$ **e.** $y = -4x + 3$ **f.** $y = 2x + 2$

4. Write the equation of each line in the slope-intercept form, and then find the slope and the y-intercept of each equation. Hint: See Example 3.

    a. $2x + 3y = 4$ **b.** $3x + 2y = 5$ **c.** $2y + x = 4$

    d. $x + y = 2$ **e.** $2x - 4y = 8$ **f.** $-3x + y = 2$

5. Using the slope-intercept form, find the slope and the y-intercept of each equation. Hint: See Example 4.

    a. $y = 2x$ **b.** $2y = x$ **c.** $3y = 2x$

    d. $2y = 2x$ **e.** $3y = x$ **d.** $2y = 3x$

6. Write each equation in the slope-intercept form and then find the slope and the y-intercept. Hint: See Example 5.

    a. $-2y - 3x = 4$ **b.** $-2y - 2x = 3$ **c.** $-2y + 3x = 3$

    d. $-y - 2x = 3$ **e.** $-2x + 3y = 4$ **f.** $-3y - 2x = 6$

7. Construct the graph of each equation by using the slope and the y-intercept.

Hint: See Example 5a.

a. $y = 2x + 3$　　　　　**b.** $y = \dfrac{3}{4}x + 2$　　　　　**c.** $y = \dfrac{4}{3}x + 2$

d. $y = 3x - 3$　　　　　**e.** $y = 3x - 1$　　　　　**f.** $y = 2x + 5$

Challenge Questions

8. Identify the x-intercept and the y-intercept. Use the intercepts to draw each line.
   a. $y = 3x + 4$　　　　　**b.** $y = 6x - 1$　　　　　**c.** $y = -2x + 3$
   d. $y = 8x - 5$　　　　　**e.** $y = -4x + 3$　　　　　**f.** $y = -3x + 4$

9. Construct the graph of each equation by using the slope and the y-intercept.
   Hint: See Example 5a.

   a. $y = 2x + 4$　　　　　**b.** $y = \dfrac{3}{5}x - 2$　　　　　**c.** $y = 3x + 2$

   d. $y = 4x - 2$　　　　　**e.** $y = \dfrac{3}{2}x + 4$　　　　　**f.** $y = 2x + 1$

10. Write an equation in the slope-intercept form for each line that fits each description.
    a. The line that crosses the y-axis at 2 and has a slope of 3.
       Hint: Where the line crosses the y-axis is the y-intercept.
    b. The line that crosses the y-axis at -2 and has a slope of 4.
       Hint: Where the line crosses the y-axis is the y-intercept.
    c. The line that crosses the y-axis at -3 and has a slope of -5.
       Hint: Where the line crosses the y-axis is the y-intercept.
    d. The line that contains the origin and has a slope of 3.
       Hint: The origin has coordinates of (0, 0), and therefore, the y-intercept = 0.
    e. The line that contains the origin and has a slope $\dfrac{3}{5}$.

       Hint: The origin has coordinates of (0, 0), and therefore, the y-intercept = 0.
    f. The line contains the origin and has a slope of -3.
       Hint: The origin has coordinates of (0, 0), and therefore, the y-intercept = 0

11. Using the slope intercept form, find the slope and the y-intercept of each equation

    a. $y = -3x + 4$　　　　　**b.** $y = -2x$　　　　　**c.** $y = \dfrac{3x}{4} + 1$

    d. $y = -x - 4$　　　　　**e.** $y = -\dfrac{2x}{5}$　　　　　**f.** $y = 2 + 3x$

    g. $y = \dfrac{x}{4} + 5$　　　　　**h.** $y = 7$ (Hint: See the chapter on horizontal lines).

    i. $x = 3$ (Hint: See the chapter on vertical lines)　　　．**j.** $y = 6 - x$.

Answer to Selected Questions (Partial answer)

2a. y-intercept = 3 and x-intercept = $\dfrac{3}{2}$

3a. Slope = 2 and y-intercept = 4

4a. $y = \dfrac{-2x}{3} + \dfrac{4}{3}$

How to Write the Equation of the Line That Passes Through Two Given Points in a Slope-intercept Form

Example 6

Find the equation of the line that passes through (-2, 5) and (3, -4) in the slope-intercept form.

Solution

Step 1: Find the slope. Let this slope be m.

Let (x_1, y_1) be (-2, 5) and let (x_2, y_2) be (3, -4).

$\text{Slope} = m = \dfrac{y_2 - y_1}{x_2 - x_1}$ Slope formula.

$= \dfrac{-4 - 5}{3 - (-2)}$

$= \dfrac{-9}{3 + 2}$ -4 - 5 = -9 and -(-2) = 2.

$= \dfrac{-9}{5}$

Step 2: Find the y-intercept which is b.

Substitute the slope of $\dfrac{-9}{5}$ in step 1 and either the point (-2, 5) or (3, -4) into the slope-intercept form of y = mx + b in order to obtain b as shown:

$y = mx + b$ _____[A]

$5 = \dfrac{-9}{5}(-2) + b$ Substitute (-2, 5) and $m = \dfrac{-9}{5}$ in to equation [A].

$5 = \dfrac{18}{5} + b$ -9(-2) = 18

$5 - \dfrac{18}{5} = \dfrac{18}{5} - \dfrac{18}{5} + b$ Subtract $\dfrac{18}{5}$ from both sides of the equation in order to obtain only b at the right side.

$$5 - \frac{18}{5} = 0 + b \qquad\qquad \frac{18}{5} - \frac{18}{5} = 0$$

$$\frac{5}{1} - \frac{18}{5} = b$$

$$\frac{25 - 18}{5} = b \qquad\qquad\qquad \text{LCD (least common denominator) is 5.}$$

$$\frac{7}{5} = b \qquad\qquad\qquad 25 - 18 = 7$$

We can now write the equation of the line using $\frac{-9}{5}$ for m and $\frac{7}{5}$ for b as shown:

$$y = \frac{-9}{5}m + \frac{7}{5}$$

POINT - SLOPE FORM

The **point-slope form** of an equation of a line enables us to find the equation of a line given one point and the slope. The **point-slope form** of an equation of a line that passes through (x_1, y_1) with a slope m is $\mathbf{y - y_1 = m(x - x_1)}$.

Let us find how we can obtain the piont-slopc form of an equation:
Recall that the slope of a line passing through the points (x_1, y_1) and (x_2, y_2) is:

$$\text{Slope} = \frac{y_2 - y_1}{x_2 - x_1}$$

$$m = \frac{y_2 - y_1}{x_2 - x_1} \qquad\qquad \text{Substitute m for slope.}$$

$$m(x_2 - x_1) = \frac{y_2 - y_1}{x_2 - x_1}(x_2 - x_1) \qquad \text{Multiply both sides of the equation by } (x_2 - x_1) \text{ in}$$

order to eliminate $x_2 - x_1$ as a denominator.

$$m(x_2 - x_1) = \frac{y_2 - y_1}{\overset{}{\underset{1}{x_2 - x_1}}}\overset{1}{(x_2 - x_1)} \qquad \text{Divide by } (x_2 - x_1). \text{ Note: } (x_2 - x_1) \div (x_2 - x_1) = 1$$

$m(x_2 - x_1) = y_2 - y_1$ ────────────────────────────[A]

Reverse equation [A] as follows:

$y_2 - y_1 = m(x_2 - x_1)$ and this equation is in the **point-slope form** of the equation of a line which is $y - y_1 = m(x - x_1)$ where y_2 is replaced by y and x_2 is replaced by x.

It is important to note that the point-slope form of the equation of a line, which is $y - y_1 = m(x - x_1)$, is used to solve many problems.

How to Use the Point-slope Form of the Equation of a Line to Identify the Slope of the Line and the Point the Line Passes Through

Example 1

Use the point-slope form of the equation of a line to identify the slope of the line and the point the line passes through.

$$y - 2 = 3(x + 4)$$

Solution

The equation of the line is $y - 2 = 3(x + 4)$. The equation of the point slope form of a line is $y - y_1 = m(x - x_1)$ where m is the slope and the line passes through the point (x_1, y_1). Compare or match the equation of the line $y - 2 = 3(x + 4)$ with the point-slope form of the equation of the line which is $y - y_1 = m(x - x_1)$ as shown:

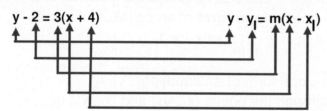

By comparing or matching the two equations as shown above, $-2 = -y_1$, $3 = m$, and $4 = -x_1$.

If $-2 = -y_1$, then $2 = y_1$ Multiply both sides of the equation by -1 in order to eliminate the negative symbol in front of y.
                                             Note: $-2(-1) = 2$ and $(-y)(-1) = y$

If $4 = -x_1$, then $-4 = x_1$ Multiply each side of the equation by -1 in order to eliminate the negative symbol in front of x_1.

The slope of the line $= m = 3$, and the line passes through the point (x_1, y_1) which is (-4, 2).

Example 2

Use the point-slope form of the equation of a line to identify the slope of the line and the point the line passes through.

$$y - 6 = -\frac{4}{5}(x - 12)$$

Solution

The equation of the line is $y - 6 = -\frac{4}{5}(x - 12)$.

The equation of the point-slope form of a line is $y - y_1 = m(x - x_1)$ where m is the slope and the line passes through the point (x_1, y_1). Compare or match the equation of the line $y - 6 = -\frac{4}{5}(x - 12)$ with the point-slop form of the equation of the line which is $y - y_1 = m(x - x_1)$ as shown:

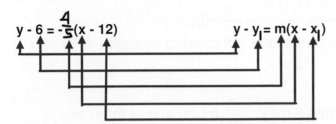

By comparing or matching the two equations as shown above, $-6 = -y_1$, $\frac{-4}{5} = m$, and $-12 = -x_1$.

If $-6 = -y_1$, then $6 = y_1$ Multiply both sides of the equation by -1 in order to eliminate the negative symbol in front of y_1.
                                         Note: $-6(-1) = 6$ and $-y_1(-1) = y_1$

If $-12 = -x_1$ then $12 = x_1$ Multiply each side of the equation by -1 in order to eliminate the negative symbol in front of x_1.
                                         Note: $-12(-1) = 12$ and $-x_1(-1) = x_1$.

The slope of the line $= m = -\frac{4}{5}$, and the line passes through the point (x_1, y_1) which is $(12, 6)$.

How to Write the Point-slope Form of an Equation of a Line That Passes Through a Given Point With a Given Slope.

Example 3

Write the point-slope form of the equation of a line that passes through (3, 2) with a slope of 5.

Solution

The point-slope form of the equation of a line passing through (x_1, y_1) with a slope m is:

$$y - y_1 = m(x - x_1) \ \text{————————————————————-[A]}$$

Therefore, the slope of the equation of a line passing through (3, 2) with a slope of 5 is:

$$y - 2 = 5(x - 3)$$ Substitute 2 for y_1, 3 for x_1, and 5 for m into equation [A].

Example 4
Write the point-slope form of the equation of a line that passes through (-4, 6) with a slope of $-\frac{3}{8}$.

Solution
The point-slope form of the equation of a line passing through (x_1, y_1) with a slope m is:

$$y - y_1 = m(x - x_1)\text{————————————————}[B].$$

Therefore, the point-slope form of the equation of a line passing through (-4, 6) with a slope of $-\frac{3}{8}$ is:

$$y - 6 = -\frac{3}{8}[x - (-4)]$$ Substitute 6 for y_1, $\frac{-3}{8}$ for m, and -4 for x_1 into
equation [B].

$$y - 6 = -\frac{3}{8}(x + 4)$$ **Note**: -(-4) = +4

Exercises
1. The point-slope form of the equation of a line that passes through (x_1, y_1) with a slope m is _____ .
2. Use the point-slope form of each equation to identify the slope of the line and the point the line passes through. Hint: See Examples 1 and 2.

   a. $y - 5 = 3(x - 4)$ **b.** $y - 2 = -4(x - 3)$ **c.** $y - 1 = 9(x + 6)$

   d. $y + 3 = 7(x - 4)$ **e.** $y + 5 = \frac{4}{5}(x + 1)$ **f.** $y - 2 = \frac{-3}{7}(x + 4)$

   g. $y - 3 = \frac{-2}{5}(x - 8)$ **h.** $y - 3 \cdot 5 = -2 \cdot 4(x - 8)$ **i.** $y - 2 = -6(x + 3)$

3. Write the point-slope form of the equation of a line with the given slope that passes through the given points. Hint: See Examples 3 and 4.

   a. slope = 4, point is (2, 7)   **b.** slope = -2, point is (-2, 3)

   c. slope = 1, point is (5, 6)   **d.** slope = $\frac{3}{7}$, point is (6, -3)

   e. slope = $-\frac{1}{9}$, point is (-2, 5)   **f.** slope = 12, point is (7, 2)

Challenge Questions
4. Use the point-slope form of each equation to identify the slope of the line and the point the line passes through.

a. $y - 10 = 4(x - 12)$ **b.** $y + 2 = \dfrac{-7}{8}(x - 4 \cdot 5)$

5. Write the point-slope form of the equation of the line with the given slope that passes through the given points.

   a. slope $= 13$, point is $(3, 16)$ **b.** slope $= -3$, point is $(-2, -5)$

PARALLEL AND PERPENDICULAR LINES

How to Write the Point-slope Form of the Equation of a Line that is Parallel to a Given Line and Passes Through a Given Point

Example 1
Write the point-slope form of the equation of a line that is parallel to $y = 5x - 2$ and passes through $(3, -4)$.

Solution
We need the slope and the point that the line passes through to write the point-slope form of the equation of the line. It is given that the line passes through $(3, -4)$, and therefore, we need to find the slope of the line.

To find the slope of the line:
It is given that the line is parallel to $y = 5x - 2$, and $y - 5x - 2$ is in the **slope-intercept form** of $y = mx + b$ where m is the slope and the y-intercept is b. By comparing or matching the two equations $y = 5x - 2$ and $y = mx + b$, the slope of $y = 5x - 2$ is 5 as shown:

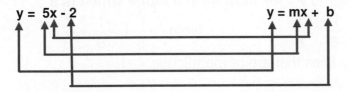

Recall that the line that is parallel to $y = 5x - 2$ **must also have a slope of 5 because parallel lines have the same slope**.

Let us write the equation of a line which has slope of 5 and passes through $(3, -4)$.
Recall that the **point-slope** of an equation of a line with slope m and passes through (x_1, y_1) is:

$$y - y_1 = m(x - x_1). \text{————————————————————}[A]$$

Similarly the point-slope of an equation of a line with slope of 5 and passes through $(3, -4)$ is:

$$y - (-4) = 5(x - 3)$$ Substitute m = 5, x_1 = 3, and y_1 = -4 into equation [A].

$$y + 4 = 5(x - 3)$$ **Note**: -(-4) = 4.

How to Write the Point-slope Form of the Equation of the Line Which is Perpendicular to a Given Line and Passes Through a Given Point.

Example 2

Write the **point-slope form** of the equation of a line that is perpendicular to y = -8x and passes through (-2, -6).

Solution

We need the slope and the point that the line passes through to write the point-slope form of the equation of the line. It is given that the line passes through (-2, -6), and therefore, we need to find the slope of the line.

To find the slope of the line:

It is given that the line is perpendicular to y = -8x, and y = -8x is in the slope-intercept form (if we add zero to the equation, see the diagram.) of y = mx + b where m is the slope and y-intercept is b. By comparing or matching the two equations, y = -8x and y = mx + b, the slope of the line is -8 and the y-intercept = 0 as shown:

Write this zero to obtain the slope intercept form of y = mx + b.

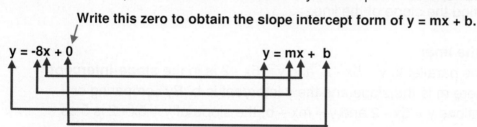

$$y = -8x + 0 \qquad\qquad y = mx + b$$

Recall that the line that is perpendicular to y = -8x must have **a slope which is a negative reciprocal of -8**, which is $-\dfrac{1}{-8} = \dfrac{1}{8}$,   Note: $-\dfrac{1}{-8} = \dfrac{-1}{-8} = \dfrac{1}{8}$.

or the product of the slopes of the two lines that are perpendicular = -1.

For example, $-8 \times \dfrac{1}{8} = \overset{-1}{-\cancel{8}} \times \dfrac{1}{\underset{1}{\cancel{8}}}$ Divide by 8.

     Note: Review Reciprocals.

$$= -1$$

The slope of the line that is perpendicular to y = -8x is $\dfrac{1}{8}$.

Let us write the equation of a line which has a slope of $\dfrac{1}{8}$ and passes

through (-2, -6).

Recall that the point-slope form of an equation of a line with a slope m and passes through (x_1, y_1) is:

$$y - y_1 = m(x - x_1) \text{ ————————————————[B]}$$

Similarly, the point-slope of an equation of a line with a slope $\dfrac{1}{8}$ and passes through

(-2, -6) is:

$$y - (-6) = \frac{1}{8}[x - (-2)]$$

$$y + 6 = \frac{1}{8}(x + 2) \qquad\qquad \text{Note: } -(-6) = 6 \text{ and } -(-2) = 2.$$

Exercises

Write the point-slope form of the equation of each of the lines described:

1. The line parallel to y = 4x + 3 and passes through (3, -5). Hint: See Example 1.
2. The line parallel to y = 5x - 4 and passes through (6, 4). Hint: See Example 1.
3. The line parallel to y = -7x + 2 and passes through (-4, -2). Hint: See Example 1.
4. The line perpendicular to y = -5x + 1 and passes through (-3, -2).
   Hint: See Example 2.
5. The line perpendicular to y = -9x - 4 and passes through (4, 3).
   Hint: See Example 2.
6. The line perpendicular to y = 3x + 10 and passes through (1, -4).
   Hint: See Example 2.

Challenge Questions

Write the point-slope form of the equation of each of the lines described:

7. The line parallel to y = 8x + 4 and passes through (2, -5).
8. The line perpendicular to y = -5x + 8 and passes through (-7, 4).
9. The line parallel to y = -10x - 2 and passes through (-6, 2).
10. The line perpendicular to y = 12x - 7 and passes through (-3, 4).

Answers to selected questions

1. $y + 5 = 4(x - 3)$ 4. $y + 2 = \dfrac{1}{5}(x + 3)$

SCATTER PLOT

New Terms: scatter plot, correlation, positive correlation, negative correlation, no correlation, line of best fit

Scatter plots show relationships between two sets of data.
A correlation is when two variables are related in some way and the correlation describes the type of relationship between the two data sets.

The three major types of the correlations are:
1. Positive correlation
2. Negative correlation
3. No correlation

A positive correlation between two variables is when one variable (for example x) increases as the other variable (for example y) also increases. See Figure 1.
A negative correlation between two variables is when one variable (for example x) decreases as the other variable (for example y) increases. See Figure 2.
A no correlation between two variables is when the changes in one variable (for example x) do not affect the other variable (for example y). See Figure 3.

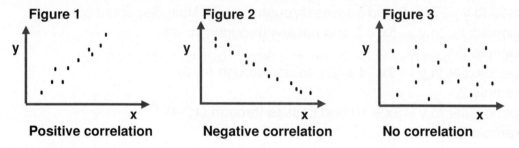

Figure 1 — Positive correlation
Figure 2 — Negative correlation
Figure 3 — No correlation

Examples of three real-world variables that have positive correlations are:
1. Increase in the time (weeks) to exercise, results in increased weight loss. The variables here are time and "weight loss."
2. The more time it takes to snow, the more inches of snow will be on the ground. The variables here are time and "inches of snow."
3. More effective study time results in higher grades. The variables here are time and grades.

Group Exercises
The class may be divided into four teams.
1. Each team should list five real-world variables that have a negative correlation. Does an increase in one variable cause a decrease in the other variable?
2. Each team should list their five variables on the blackboard, and then explain them to the class.

Line of Best Fit
The line of best fit is the line which is drawn on the scatter plot such that the line is the closest to all the points on the scatter plot.

Estimating the line of best fit.

The line of best fit can be estimated by laying a ruler's edge over the scattered plot, and then adjusting the ruler until the ruler appears to be closest to all of the points. Use a pencil to draw the line along the edge of the ruler and this line is the line of best fit. The line of best fit is shown in Figure 4 and Figure 5.

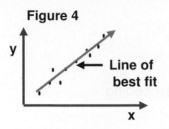

Figure 4

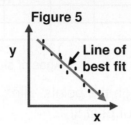

Figure 5

Strong and Weak Correlations

A strong correlation of two variables is when the points on the scatter plot are close together or when the points are close to the line of best fit. Figure 6 shows positive strong correlation and figure 8 shows negative strong correlation.

A weak correlation of two variables is when the points on the scatter plot are wide spread about the line of best fit. Figure 7 shows a weak positive correlation and Figure 9 shows a negative weak correlation.

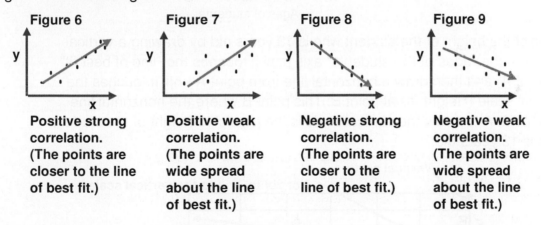

Figure 6	Figure 7	Figure 8	Figure 9
Positive strong correlation. (The points are closer to the line of best fit.)	Positive weak correlation. (The points are wide spread about the line of best fit.)	Negative strong correlation. (The points are closer to the line of best fit.)	Negative weak correlation. (The points are wide spread about the line of best fit.)

Using a Scatter Plot to Make Predictions

Example 1

Use the data to predict the height of a student who is 13 years old.

Heights (ft.)	5.4	5.5	6.0	5.0	5.0	6.4	6.0
Age of students (years)	11	12	14	12	11	14	15

Solution

Step 1: Indicate the ordered pair of the points (11, 5.4), (12, 5.5), (14, 6.0), (12, 5.0), (11, 5.0), and (15, 5.8) on a graph paper as shown. This is the same as making a scatter plot of a data set.

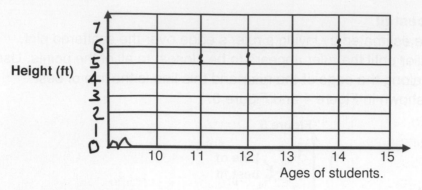

Step 2: Draw the line of best fit through the points. Hint: See the preceding notes on "estimating the line of best fit."

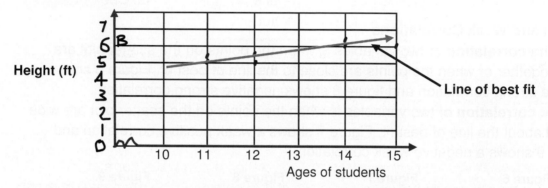

Step 3: Predict the height of the student who is 13 years old by drawing a vertical line from the "ages of the students" axis until it touches the "line of best fit" at point A, and then draw a horizontal line from point A until it touches the vertical scale (Height, ft) at point B. This point B where the horizontal line from point A touches the vertical scale is the predicted height of the student who is 13 years old.

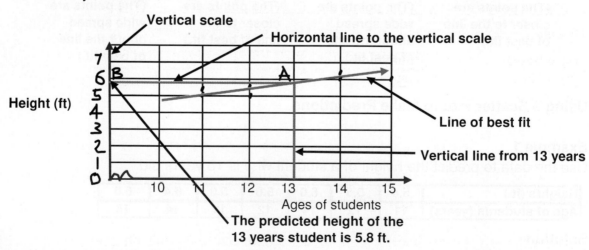

Exercises

1a. What is a correlation?

1b. What are the three major types of correlations?
   Hint: See the preceding notes.

2a. Describe 2 positive correlations using a diagram.

2b. Describe 2 negative correlations using a diagram.

2c. Describe no correlation with a diagram.
   Hint: See the preceding notes.

3a. Describe the "line of best fit".

3b. Describe how to estimate the "line of best fit". Hint: See preceding notes.

4. In your **own words**, explain what is meant by a strong correlation and a weak correlation using a diagram. Hint: See the preceding notes.

5. Explain how a scatter plot can be used to make predictions. Hint: See Example 1.

6. Use the data to predict the test grade for a student who studies:

(a). 8 hours.

(b). 4 hours.

(c). 2 hours

Hint: See Example 1.

Hours studied	10	5	7	6	12
Test grades	98	75	85	80	100

Challenge Questions

7. What is the difference between a strong correlation and a weak correlation?

8. What is the difference between a positive strong correlation and a negative strong correlation?

9. Use the data to predict the apparent temperature at (**a**) 30% humidity
                                                          (**b**) 90% humidity

Temperature due to humidity at room temperature of 70º F.						
Humidity (%).	0	20	40	60	80	100
Apparent temperature (ºF).	62	65	67	70	72	74

10. Use the data to predict the test grade for a student who studies:

(a). 6 hours.

(b). 10 hours.

(c). 7 hours

Hours studied	5	2	3	9	12
Test grades	75	68	78	90	95

LINE OF BEST FIT

(Review the chapter on Coordinate Geometry before reading this chapter.)

The **line of best fit** is the line that is closest to all the points on a scatter plot such that about the same number of points are above the line as they are below the line.

Use of the Line of Best Fit
The line of best fit can be used to make **predictions** as shown in Example 1.

How to Estimate the Equation of a Line of Best Fit.
The steps for estimating the equation of a line of best fit are as follows:
Step 1: Find the means of the x-coordinate and y-coordinates and let the coordinates of the means be (x, y).
Step 2: Draw a line through (x, y) that appears to best fit the data such that about the same number of points are above the line as below the line.
Step 3: Estimate the coordinates of another point on the line.
Step 4: Find the equation of the line by finding the slope and then using the **point-slope form**.

Example 1
a. Plot the data and find the line of best fit.
b. Use the equation of the line of best fit to predict the value of y when x = 100.

x	3	1	2	7	6	8
y	3	2	5	10	6	10

Solution
a. The coordinates (x, y) for (3, 3), (1, 2), (2, 5), (7, 10), (6, 6), and (8,10) are plotted on graph paper as shown:

(See the next page.)

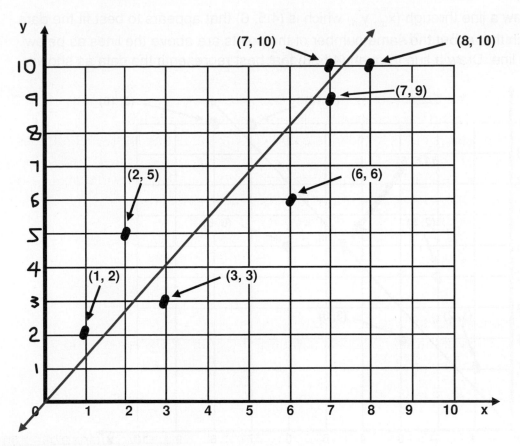

To Find the Line of Best Fit

Step 1: Find the means of the x-coordinates and the y-coordinates.

$$\text{Mean of the x-coordinates} = x_m = \frac{\text{Sum of x-coordinates}}{\text{Total number of x-coordinates.}}$$

$$= \frac{3 + 1 + 2 + 7 + 6 + 8}{6}$$

$$= \frac{27}{6} = 4.5$$

$$\text{Mean of y-coordinates} = y_m = \frac{\text{Sum of y-coordinates}}{\text{Total number of y-coordinates}}$$

$$= \frac{3 + 2 + 5 + 10 + 6 + 10}{6}$$

$$= \frac{36}{6}$$

$$= 6$$

Therefore, $(x_m, y_m) = (4.5, 6)$.

Step 2: Draw a line through (x_m, y_m) which is (4.5, 6) that appears to best fit the data such that about the same number of the points are above the lines as below the line. Draw a line through (4.5, 6) that best represents the data as shown:

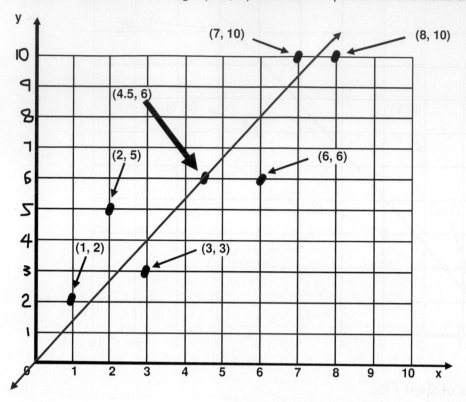

Step 3: Estimate the coordinates of another point on the line and then plot this second point on the line. The coordinates (3, 4) is another point on the line as shown:

(See the next page.)

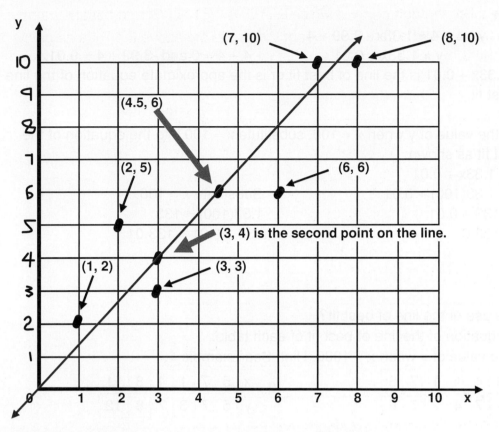

Step 4: Find the equation of the line by finding the slope and then using the point-slope form.

Let us use the two coordinates (3, 4) and (4.5, 6) to find the slope.

$$\text{Slope} = m = \frac{y_2 - y_1}{x_2 - x_1}$$

$$= \frac{6 - 4}{4.5 - 3} \qquad\qquad (x_1, y_1) = (3, 4) \text{ and } (x_2, y_2) = (4.5, 6).$$

$$= \frac{2}{1.5}$$

$$\approx 1.33 \qquad\qquad \text{You may use a calculator.}$$

Let us use the **point-slope form** to find the equation of the line of best fit as shown:

The equation of a line using the **point-slope form** is:

$$y - y_1 = m\,(x - x_1)$$

$$y - 4 \approx 1.33(x - 3) \qquad\qquad x_1 = 3 \quad y_1 = 4 \text{ and } m \approx 1.33$$

$$y - 4 \approx 1.33x - 3 \cdot 1.33$$

$$y - 4 \approx 1.33x - 3.99 \underline{\hspace{5cm}}[A]$$

Add 4 to both sides of equation $[A]$ in order to obtain the value of y as

639

shown:

$$y - 4 + 4 \approx 1.33x - 3.99 + 4$$
$$y \approx 1.33x + 0.01 \qquad -4 + 4 = 0 \text{ and } -3.99 + 4 = 0.01.$$

$y \approx 1.33x + 0.01$ is the line of best fit or is the approximate equation of the line of best fit.

b. To predict the value of y when x = 100, substitute x = 100 into the equation of the line of best fit as shown:

$$y \approx 1.33x + 0.01$$
$$y \approx 1.33(100) + 0.01 \qquad \text{Substitute x = 100.}$$
$$y \approx 133 + 0.01 \qquad\qquad 1.33(100) = 133$$
$$y \approx 133.01 \qquad\qquad\quad 133 + 0.01 = 133.01$$

Exercises

1. What is the use of the line of best fit?

2a. Find the equation of the line of best fit of each table.

2b. Predict the value of y when x = 1000. Hint: See Example 1.

1.

x	3	4	4	1	7	6
y	1	7	4	2	7	6

2.

x	5	7	1	4	8	11
y	5	7	3	7	8	12

3.

x	4	2	6	8	9	3	7	1
y	5	3	7	8	9	5	8	2

4.

x	0	3	5	6	7	8	10
y	3	3	6	9	7	8	11

5.

x	2	7	4	0	2	2
y	3	1	1	6	5	6

6.

x	4	6	9	0	3	7	8	9
y	1	8	11	5	7	3	8	9

Cumulative Review

1. The side of a square is 4 ft. What is the area of the square?

2. An equilateral triangle has a side of 10 cm.

    a. What is the area of the triangle?

    b. What is the perimeter of the triangle?

CONGRUENT TRIANGLES

Cumulative Review

1. Describe how you would write 7.1723×10^6 in the standard notation. Hint: If you cannot solve this exercise, review the chapter on Scientific Notations.

2. Describe how you would write 0.01061 in the scientific notation. Hint: If you cannot solve this exercise, review the chapter on Scientific Notations.

3. Use factoring to find the zeros of each function.

    a. $y = x^2 - 5x + 6$ **b.** $y = x^2 - 2x - 3$ **c.** $y = x^2 + 5x - 14$

    Hint: If you cannot solve these exercises, review the chapter on Quadratic Functions.

4. Factorize each expression.

    a. $x^2 + 7x + 12$ **b.** $n^2 - 8n + 7$ **c.** $x^2 - 3x - 10$

    Hint: If you cannot solve these exercises, review the chapter on Factorization of Quadratic Functions/Expressions/Equations.

5. Describe how you would find the median of each data:

    a. 2, 10, 6, 13, 4   **b.** 4, 6, 3, 7   **c.** 6.6, 2, 8, 4.7, 1, 4.7

    Hint: If you cannot solve these exercises, review the section of the MathMasters Series on median.

Congruent Triangles
New Term: congruent

Two triangles are **congruent** to each other if their corresponding sides and angles are equal. If $\triangle ABC$ and $\triangle XYZ$ are congruent, then the corresponding sides and angles are equal as follows:

Comparing sides

    $\overline{AB}$ corresponds to $\overline{XY}$, therefore $\overline{AB} = \overline{XY}$

    $\overline{BC}$ corresponds to $\overline{YZ}$ therefore $\overline{BC} = \overline{YZ}$

    $\overline{AC}$ corresponds to $\overline{XZ}$ therefore $\overline{AC} = \overline{XZ}$

Comparing angles

    $\angle A$ corresponds to $\angle X$ therefore $\angle A = \angle x$

    $\angle B$ corresponds to $\angle Y$ therefore $\angle B = \angle Y$

    $\angle C$ corresponds to $\angle Z$ therefore $\angle C = \angle Z$

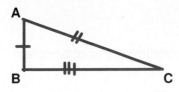
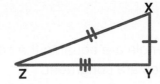

How to Determine the Corresponding Sides and the Corresponding Angles Between Two Triangles.

Example 1

How could you determine the corresponding sides and the corresponding angles between two triangles?

Solutions

In order to determine the corresponding sides and the corresponding angles between two triangles, imagine that one triangle is put over the other triangle to coincide. The pairs of matching sides of both triangles are called a one-to-one correspondence and each pair of the matching sides form a specific corresponding side which are equal to one another. Similarly the pairs of matching angles of both triangles are called one-to-one correspondence and each pair of the matching angles form specific corresponding angles which equal to one another.

For example, $\triangle ABC$ is congruent to $\triangle DEF$, and therefore, if we imagine that we place $\triangle DEF$ over $\triangle ABC$ to coincide, the matching pairs of sides and angles are:

$\overline{AB}$ and $\overline{DE}$, and therefore, $\overline{AB} = \overline{DE}$

$\overline{BC}$ and $\overline{DF}$, and therefore, $\overline{BC} = \overline{DF}$

$\overline{AC}$ and $\overline{EF}$, and therefore, $\overline{AC} = \overline{EF}$

$\angle A$ and $\angle E$, and therefore, $\angle A = \angle E$

$\angle B$ and $\angle D$, and therefore, $\angle B = \angle D$

$\angle C$ and $\angle F$, and therefore, $\angle C = \angle F$

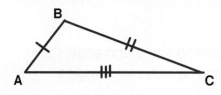 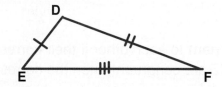

Congruence Postulate

The 3 basic congruence postulates that are used to prove that two triangles are congruent are:

1. SSS (side-side-side) Congruence Postulate

2. SAS (side-angle-side) Congruence Postulate

3. ASA (Angle-side-Angle) Congruence Postulate.

3. Congruence Postulates

1. SSS

If the three sides of one triangle are equal to the corresponding parts of another triangle then the two triangles are congruent.

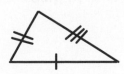 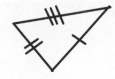

2. SAS

If the two sides and the **included angle** of one triangle are equal to the corresponding parts of another triangle then the two triangles are congruent.

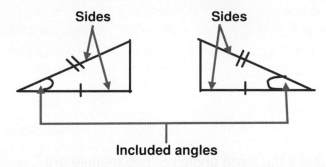

Note that in this particular case, included angle means that the angle is **between the two corresponding sides** of each triangle.

3. ASA

If two angles and the **included sides** of one triangle are equal to the corresponding parts of another triangle, then the triangles are congruent.

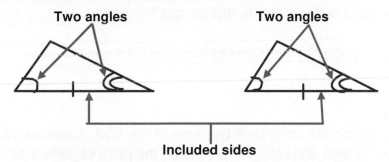

Note that in this particular case, included side means that the side is **between the two corresponding angles** of each triangle.

Critical Exclusions from the Congruence Postulate.
The following are not Congruence Postulate.
1. AAA
2. SAA or AAS

Example 1
Draw a triangle and label its vertices A, B, and C.
a. Which sides include ∠B?
b. Which side of the triangle is included by ∠A and ∠B?

643

c. Which angle is included by sides $\overline{BC}$ and $\overline{AC}$?

d. Which angles include $\overline{AC}$?

Solution

Draw the △ABC.

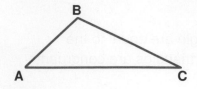

a. $\overline{AB}$ and $\overline{BC}$

b. $\overline{AB}$

c. $\angle C$

d. $\angle A$ and $\angle C$

Example 2

John says that two triangles are congruent if the three angles of one triangle are equal to the corresponding angles of the other. Is this correct?

Solution

No, because there is no AAA congruence postulate.

Example 3

Mary said that two triangles are congruent if two sides and an angle of one triangle are equal to the corresponding parts of the other. Is this correct?

Solution

No, because the angle must be included by the sides to form the SAS congruence postulate.

Example 4

Nick said that the two triangles shown are congruent because of the ASA. congruence postulate. Note that the number of arcs and tick marks indicate the pairs of parts that are equal. Is this correct?

Solution

No, because the sides are not included by the angles.

Example 5

In each pair of triangles, the tick marks and the arcs identify equal parts. Write which congruence postulate that makes any pair of the triangles congruent, otherwise write

644

"not congruent." Explain your answers as needed. The solutions to this example provide the students with useful road map with critical bench marks for solving problems.

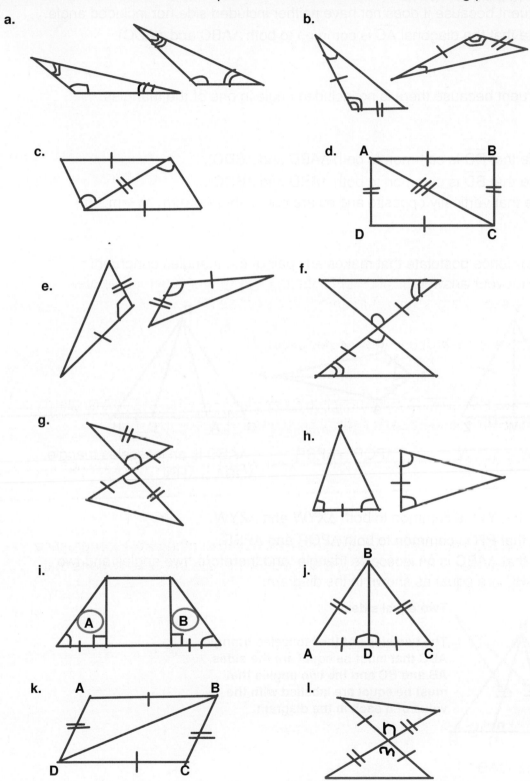

a.

b.

c.

d. A   B

    D   C

e.

f.

g.

h.

i.

    A   B

j.   B

    A   D   C

k.   A   B

    D   C

l.

Solution

5a. Not congruent, there is no AAA congruence postulate.

5b. SAS or ASA.

5c. Not congruent because it does not have neither included side nor included angle.

5d. SSS (**Note** that the diagonal $\overline{AC}$ is common to both △ABC and △ADC).

5e. SAS

5f. ASA

5g. Not congruent because there is no included angle in one of the triangles.

5h. ASA

5i. ASA

5j. SAS (**Note** that $\overline{BD}$ is common to both △ABD and △BDC).

5k. SSS (**Note** that $\overline{BD}$ is common to both △ABD and △BDC).

5l. SAS (**Note** that vertically opposite angles are equal, therefore $m\angle n = m\angle m$)

Example 6

Write the congruence postulate that makes any pair of the triangles congruent. Give reasons for your answer.

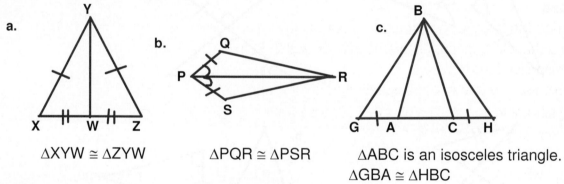

a.

△XYW ≅ △ZYW

b.

△PQR ≅ △PSR

c.

△ABC is an isosceles triangle.
△GBA ≅ △HBC

Solution

a. SSS. Note that $\overline{YW}$ is common to both △XYW and △ZYW.

b. SAS. Note that $\overline{PR}$ is common to both △PQR and △PSR.

c. SAS. Note that △ABC is an isosceles triangle, and therefore, two angles and two sides of △ABC are equal as shown in the diagram:

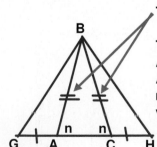

Two equal sides.

The two sides of the isosceles triangle ABC that must be equal are the sides AB and BC and the two angles that must be equal are labelled with the value of n each in the diagram.

How to find $m\angle$ GAB.

Due to the fact that the sum of angles on a straight line is 180^0, then we can write:

646

$$m\angle GAB + n = 180^0 \underline{\hspace{4cm}}[A]$$

$m\angle GAB + n - n = 180 - n$ Subtract n from both sides of equation $[A]$
to obtain the value of $m\angle GAB$.

$$m\angle GAB = 180 - n \qquad n - n = 0$$

How to find $m\angle BCH$.

Due to the fact that the sum of angles on a straight line is 180^0, then we can write:

$$m\angle BCH + n = 180^0 \underline{\hspace{4cm}}[B]$$

$m\angle BCH + n - n = 180 - n$ Subtract n from both sides of equation $[B]$
to obtain the value of $m\angle BCH$.

$$m\angle BCH = 180 - n \qquad n - n = 0$$

Therefore, the $m\angle GAB = 180 - n$ and also the $m\angle BCH = 180 - n$.
Therefore, $m\angle GAB = m\angle BCH$. We can use the SAS postulate to state that $\triangle GBA \cong \triangle HBC$.

Exercises

1. Describe the three Congruence Postulates.
2. Draw a triangle and label its vertices X, Y and Z.
   a. Which sides include $\angle Z$?
   b. Which side of the triangle is included by $\angle X$ and $\angle Y$?
   c. Which angle is included by sides $\overline{XY}$ and $\overline{YZ}$?
   d. Which angles include $\overline{YZ}$?
   Hint: See Example 1.
3. Explain why $\triangle ABC$ and $\triangle XYZ$ are not congruent triangles. Hint: See Example 2.

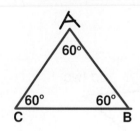 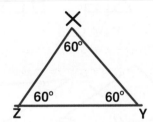

4. Explain why $\triangle ABC$ and $\triangle PQR$ are not congruent triangles. Hint: See Example 3.

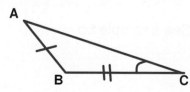 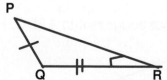

5. Is it correct to say that $\triangle ABC$ and $\triangle RPQ$ are congruent because of AAS?
   Hint: See Example 4.

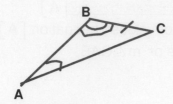 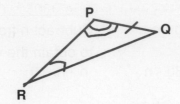

6. In each pair of the triangles the tick marks and arcs identify equal parts. Write the congruence postulate that makes any pair of the triangles congruent, otherwise write "not congruent." Hint: See Example 5.

a.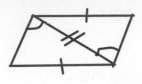

b.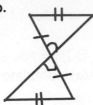

c.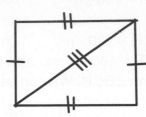

d.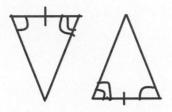

e.

f.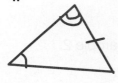

g.

h.

i.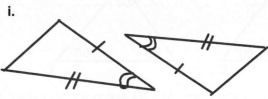

7. Explain why △ABC is not congruent to △ADC. Hint; See Example 6b.

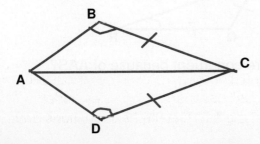

8. Explain why each pair of triangles are congruent. Hint: See Example 6.

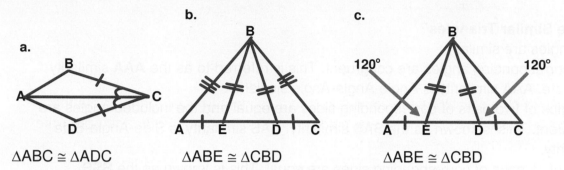

a.

$\triangle ABC \cong \triangle ADC$

b.

$\triangle ABE \cong \triangle CBD$

c.

$\triangle ABE \cong \triangle CBD$

Challenge Questions

10. With the help of diagrams explain the three congruent postulates.

11. Give reasons why the pairs of the triangles are congruent.

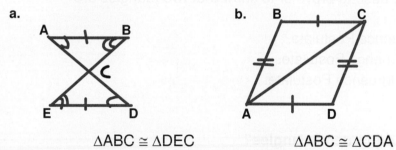

a.

$\triangle ABC \cong \triangle DEC$

b.

$\triangle ABC \cong \triangle CDA$

12. Give reasons why the pairs of the triangles are congruent or not congruent.

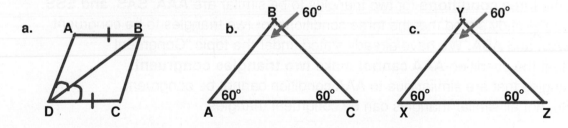

a.

b.

c.

CHAPTER 29

SIMILAR TRIANGLES

New Term: **similar triangles**

It is recommended that the topic on "Congruent Triangles" should be discussed before discussing the topic on "Similar Triangles" because all the rules under "Congruent Triangles" apply to the "Similar Triangles." Detailed explanations and examples for similar triangles will not be given here.

What are Similar Triangles?
Two triangles are similar if:
1. their corresponding angles are congruent. This is referred to as the **AAA** similarity postulate. AAA similarity is Angle-Angle-Angle similarity.
2. the ratios of two pairs of corresponding sides are equal and the included angles are congruent. This is known as the **SAS** similarity. SAS similarity is Side-Angle-Side similarity.
3. ratios of all pairs of corresponding sides are equal. This is known as the **SSS** similarity. SSS similarity is the Side-Side-Side similarity.

What are congruent triangles?
We have already shown under the topic "Congruent Triangles" that the 3 congruence postulates that are used to prove or to show that two triangles are congruent are:
1. **SSS** (side-side-side) Congruence Postulate.
2. **SAS** (side-angle-side) Congruence Postulate.
3. **ASA** (Angle-side-Angle) Congruence Postulate.

Are all similar triangles also congruent triangles?
No, all similar triangles are not necessarily congruent triangles. We have already stated that the three **conditions** for two triangles to be similar are **AAA**, **SAS**, **and SSS**. We have also already stated that the three conditions for two triangles to be congruent are **SSS**, **SAS**, and **ASA**. We have already stated under the topic "Congruent Triangles" that the condition **AAA cannot make two triangles congruent**. Any two triangles that are similar due to AAA condition cannot be congruent triangles. So, not all similar triangles can be congruent triangles.

Caution: Note that **ASA** and **AAS** are not listed as conditions for triangle similarity and therefore, never list them as the conditions for two triangles to be similar.

SIMILAR AND CONGRUENT FIGURES

New Terms: **similar, congruent, corresponding sides, and corresponding angles**.

Similar figures are figures that have the same shape but they do not necessarily have to be the same size. In the diagrams, Figure A is similar to Figure B because they have the **same shape** but they do not have the **same size**. The symbol ∼ means "is similar to".

In the diagram, Figure A is similar to Figure B because they have the same shape but not the same size. Similarly, Figure C is similar to Figure D because they have the same shape but not the same size.

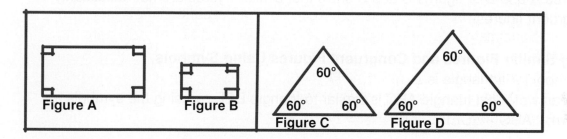

Congruent figures are figures that have the same shape and size. In the diagrams, Figure E is congruent to Figure F because they have the same shape and size. The symbol ≅ means "is congruent to."

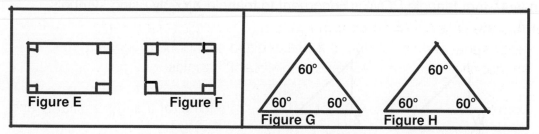

In the diagram, Figure I and Figure J are neither similar nor congruent because they have different shapes and different sizes. Similarly, Figure K and Figure L are neither similar nor congruent because they have different shapes and different sizes.

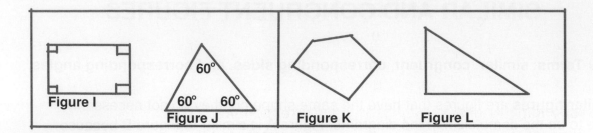

Figure I Figure J Figure K Figure L

Critical Conclusions

1. Figures E and F or figures G and H show that congruent figures are also similar figures.

2. Figures A and B or figures C and D show that similar figures are not necessarily congruent figures.

Writing Similar Figures and Congruent Figures Using Symbols.

The symbol for a triangle is △.

1. We can write that triangle ABC is similar to triangle DEF by using the symbols as shown: △ABC ∼ △DEF

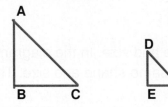

2. We can write that triangle PQW is congruent to triangle XYZ by using symbols as shown: △PQW ≅ △XYZ

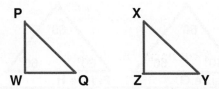

Group Discussion

Triangles ABC and triangles DEF are similar.

Similar polygons have corresponding angles and corresponding sides.

Note that when two figures are similar, for each part of one figure, there is a corresponding part on the other figure. To determine the corresponding angles and the corresponding sides of similar polygons, compare the shape of the polygons and then determine how each pair of angles and each pair of sides form corresponding parts as shown:

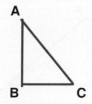

Corresponding Angles

∠A corresponds to ∠D

∠B corresponds to ∠E

∠C corresponds to ∠F

∠ is the symbol for angle.

Corresponding sides

$\overline{AB}$ corresponds to $\overline{DE}$

$\overline{BC}$ corresponds to $\overline{EF}$

$\overline{AC}$ corresponds to $\overline{DF}$

Note that the angles in △ABC are congruent to the corresponding angles in △DEF and the length of the sides of △DEF are about twice the length of the corresponding sides in △ABC.

Conclusion: Note that in similar figures the **corresponding angles are congruent** (the same measure of angles), and the ratio of the lengths of the corresponding sides are **equal**.

Group Exercise

Given that △ABC is similar to △DEF, copy and complete the statements:

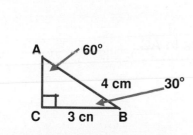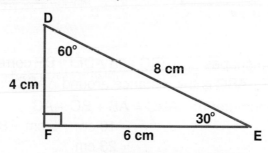

Corresponding Angles

∠A corresponds to ∠D

∠B corresponds to ∠?

∠C corresponds to ?

Corresponding sides

$\overline{AC}$ corresponds to $\overline{DF}$

$\overline{AB}$ corresponds to ?

$\overline{BC}$ corresponds to ?

Example 1

Given that the trapezoid ABCD is similar to the trapezoid EFGH, list all the pairs of the corresponding sides.

653

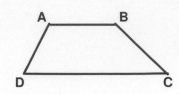
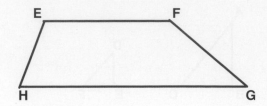

Solution

By comparing the shapes of the trapezoids ABCD and EFGH,

$\overline{AB}$ corresponds to $\overline{EF}$

$\overline{BC}$ corresponds to $\overline{FG}$

$\overline{CD}$ corresponds to $\overline{GH}$

$\overline{DA}$ corresponds to $\overline{HE}$

Example 2

Given that △ABC is congruent to △DEF,

a. What side of △DEF corresponds to side $\overline{AC}$?

b. What is the perimeter of △DEF ?

c. What is the length of $\overline{DF}$?

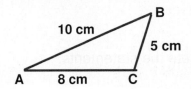
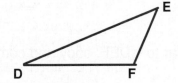

Solution

a. By comparing the shapes of △ABC and △DEF, $\overline{DF}$ corresponds to $\overline{AC}$.

b. The perimeter of △ABC is the distance around △ABC.

Therefore, the perimeter of △ABC = $\overline{AB} + \overline{BC} + \overline{AC}$

$$= 10 \text{ cm} + 5 \text{ cm} + 8 \text{ cm}$$
$$= 23 \text{ cm}$$

Since △ABC and △DEF are congruent, they have the same size and shape. So, the perimeter of △DEF is also 23 cm.

Example 3

Write whether each pair of figures appear to be similar, congruent, both, or neither.

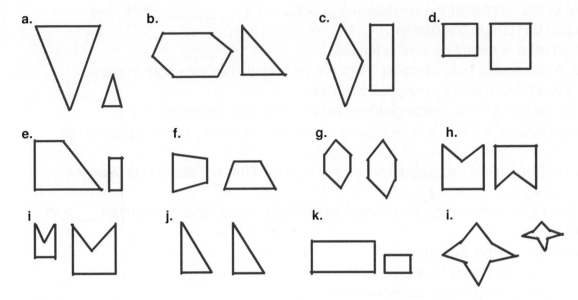

Solution

a. The two triangles appear to be similar because they have the same shape but not the same size.

b. The hexagon and the triangle are neither similar nor congruent because they have neither the same shape nor the same size.

c. The rhombus and the rectangle are neither similar nor congruent because they have neither the same shape nor the same size.

d. The two rectangles appear to be similar because they have the same shape but not the same size.

e. The trapezoid and the rectangle are neither similar nor congruent because they have neither the same shape nor the same size.

f. The two quadrilaterals appear to be similar and congruent because they have the same shape and the same size.

g. The two hexagons appear to be similar because they have the same shape but not the same size.

h. The two figures appear to be similar and congruent because they have the same shape and the same size.

i. The two figures appear to be similar because they have the same shape but not the same size.

j. The two triangles are similar and congruent because they have the same shape and the same size.

k. The two rectangles appear to be similar because they have the same shape but not the same size.

l. The two figures appear to be similar because they have the same shape but not the same size.

Exercise

1. We can say that in similar figures the corresponding angles are c _____ and the ratio of the lengths of the corresponding sides are e _____. Hint: See the section on "Group discussion".

2. **a.** Explain what is meant by similar figures

   b. Sketch two similar right triangles. Hint: A right triangle has one right angle.

3. **a.** Explain what is meant by congruent figures.

   b. Sketch two congruent rectangles and explain why they are congruent.

4. Congruent figures are also similar figures. True or False? Hint: See the preceding notes.

5. Similar figures are not necessarily congruent figures. True or False? Hint: See the preceding pages.

6. Two figures are neither similar nor congruent because they have different sh___ and different si____.

7. **a.** What is the symbol for a triangle?

   b. What is the symbol for "is similar to"?

   c. What is the symbol for (is congruent to"?

   Hint: See the preceding pages.

8. Using symbols, write that:

   a. triangle XYZ is similar to triangle ABC.

   b. triangle ABC is congruent to triangle XYZ.

   Hint: See the preceding pages.

9. Similar polygons have corresponding angles and corresponding sides. True or False? Hint: See the preceding pages.

10. When two figures are similar, for each part of one figure, there is a corresponding p____ on the other figure.

    Hint: See the preceding pages.

11. In similar figures, the corresponding ang___ are congruent (the same measure of angles), and the ratio of the r_____ of the corresponding s____ are equal. Hint: See the preceding pages.

12. Trapezoid WXYZ is similar to trapezoid ABCD. List all the pairs of corresponding sides. Hint: See Example 1.

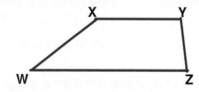 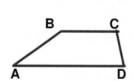

13. Given that △ABC ≅ △XYZ.

    (a) What side of △XYZ corresponds to side $\overline{BC}$?

    (b) What is the perimeter of △XYZ ?

    (c) What is the length of $\overline{XY}$?

    Hint: See Example 2

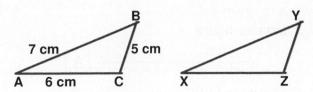

14. Write whether each pair of figures appears to be similar, congruent, both, or neither and give the reason for your choice.
Hint: See Example 3.

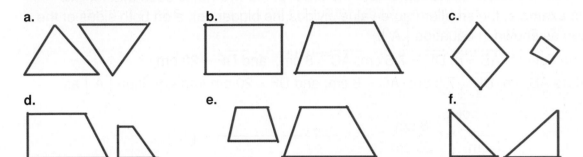

a. b. c.

d. e. f.

How to Use Proportion to Solve Similar Figure Problems.
What is a proportion? A **proportion** is an equation that states that **two ratios are equal**. The **cross products** of a proportion are **equal**. Examples 1, 2, and 3 show and explain how a proportion and the cross products of a proportion can be used to solve similar figure problems.

Example 1
Given that the two figures are similar, write and solve the proportion to find the length of n.

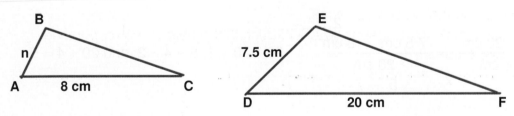

Solution
By observing the shape of the figure,

$\overline{AB}$ corresponds to $\overline{DE}$
$\overline{AC}$ corresponds to $\overline{DF}$

We can find the value of n by using the fact that in similar figures, the ratios of the corresponding sides are equal.
Step 1: We can therefore write two ratios or a proportion as shown:

657

smaller figure

smaller figure

$$\frac{\overline{AB}}{\overline{DE}} = \frac{\overline{AC}}{\overline{DF}} \qquad \text{————————— [A]}$$

bigger figure

bigger figure

(**Note**: It is very important to remember the order of the two ratios such that for this specific example, the smaller figure value divides the bigger value on both sides of the equation as shown in equation [A].)

From the figures, $\overline{AB}$ = n, $\overline{DE}$ = 7.5 cm, $\overline{AC}$ = 8 cm, and $\overline{DF}$ = 20 cm.

Substitute $\overline{AB}$ = n, $\overline{DE}$ = 7.5 cm, $\overline{AC}$ = 8 cm, and $\overline{DF}$ = 20 cm into equation [A] as shown:

$$\frac{n}{7.5 \text{ cm}} = \frac{8 \text{ cm}}{20 \text{ cm}} \qquad \text{————————— [B]}$$

Step 2: Solve the equation [B] or the proportion [B] to obtain the value of n as shown:

$$\frac{n}{7.5 \text{ cm}} \quad \times \quad \frac{8 \text{ cm}}{20 \text{ cm}}$$ **Cross products of proportions are equal.**
Hint: Review the chapter/section on proportion.

$$n \times 20 \text{ cm} = 7.5 \text{ cm} \times 8 \text{ cm} \qquad \text{————————— [C]}$$

Divide each side of the equation [C] by 20 cm in order to obtain the value of n as shown:

$$\frac{n \times 20 \text{ cm}}{20 \text{ cm}} = \frac{7.5 \text{ cm} \times 8 \text{ cm}}{20 \text{ cm}}$$

$$\frac{n \times 20 \overset{1}{\cancel{\text{cm}}}}{\underset{1}{20 \cancel{\text{cm}}}} = \frac{7.5 \text{ cm} \times \overset{2}{\cancel{8 \text{ cm}}}}{\underset{5}{20 \cancel{\text{cm}}}} \qquad 20 \div 20 = 1, 8 \div 4 = 2, \text{ and } 20 \div 4 = 5$$

$$n = \frac{7.5 \text{ cm} \times 2}{5}$$

$$n = \frac{\overset{1.5}{\cancel{7.5 \text{ cm}}} \times 2}{\underset{1}{\cancel{5}}} \qquad \text{Divide by 5, } 7.5 \div 5 = 1.5, 5 \div 5 = 1.$$

$$n = 1.5 \text{ cm} \times 2$$
$$n = 3.0 \text{ cm}$$

Example 2

The two figures are similar. Find the length of n.

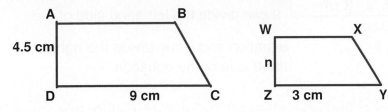

Solution

By observing the shape of the two figures, $\overline{AD}$ corresponds to $\overline{WZ}$ and $\overline{DC}$ corresponds to $\overline{ZY}$. We can find the value of n by using the fact that in similar figures, the ratios of the corresponding sides are equal.

Step 1: We can therefore write two ratios or a proportion as shown:

Bigger figure

Bigger figure

$$\dfrac{\overline{AD}}{\overline{WZ}} = \dfrac{\overline{DC}}{\overline{ZY}} \quad\text{————————— [A]}$$

Smaller figure

Smaller figure

(**Note**: It is very important to remember the order of the two ratios such that for this specific example, the bigger figure value divides the smaller figure value on both sides of the equation [A] as shown.)

From the figures, $\overline{AD}$ = 4.5 cm, $\overline{WZ}$ = n, $\overline{DC}$ = 9 cm, and $\overline{ZY}$ = 3 cm.

Substitute $\overline{AD}$ – 4.5 cm, WZ – n, DC – 9 cm, and ZY = 3 cm into equation [A] as shown:

$$\dfrac{4.5\text{ cm}}{n} = \dfrac{9\text{ cm}}{3\text{ cm}} \quad\text{————————— [B]}$$

Step 2: Solve the equation [B] or the proportion [B] to obtain the value of n as shown:

$$\dfrac{4.5\text{ cm}}{n} \quad \dfrac{9\text{ cm}}{3\text{ cm}}$$

Cross products of a proportion are equal.
Hint: Review the chapter/section on proportion.

$$n \times 9\text{ cm} = 4.5\text{ cm} \times 3\text{ cm} \quad\text{——————— [C]}$$

Divide both sides of equation [C] by 9 cm in order to obtain the value of n as shown:

$$\dfrac{n \times 9\text{ cm}}{9\text{ cm}} = \dfrac{4.5\text{ cm} \times 3\text{ cm}}{9\text{ cm}}$$

$$\frac{n \times \overset{1}{\cancel{9}} \cancel{cm}}{\underset{1}{\cancel{9}} \cancel{cm}} = \frac{4.5 \ cm \times \overset{1}{\cancel{3}} \cancel{cm}}{\underset{3}{\cancel{9}} \cancel{cm}}$$

9 can divide the left hand side of the equation and 3 can divide the right hand side of the equation.

$$n = \frac{4.5 \ cm}{3}$$

$n = 4.5 \div 3 = 1.5$ cm   (You may use a calculator).

$n = 1.5$ cm.

Example 3

The two figures are similar. Find the length of n.

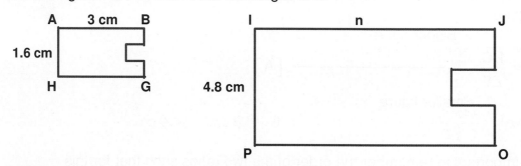

Solution

By observing the shape of the figure,

$\overline{AB}$ corresponds to $\overline{IJ}$

$\overline{AH}$ corresponds to $\overline{IP}$

We can find the value of n by using the fact that in similar figures, the ratios of the corresponding sides are equal.

Step 1: We can therefore write two ratios or a proportion as shown:

Smaller figure

Smaller

$$\frac{\overline{AB}}{\overline{IJ}} = \frac{\overline{AH}}{\overline{IP}} \qquad\qquad\qquad [A]$$

Bigger figure

Bigger figure

(**Note**: It is very important to remember the order of the ratios such that for this specific example, the smaller figure value divides the bigger figure value on both sides of the equation [A] as shown).

From the figures, $\overline{AB} = 3$ cm, $\overline{IJ} = n$, $\overline{AH} = 1.6$ cm, and $\overline{IP} = 4.8$ cm.

Substitute $\overline{AB} = 3$ cm, $\overline{IJ} = n$, $\overline{AH} = 1.6$ cm, and $\overline{IP} = 4.8$ cm into equation [A] as shown:

$$\frac{3 \text{ cm}}{n} = \frac{1.6 \text{ cm}}{4.8 \text{ cm}}$$ ———————————————————— $[B]$

Step 2: Solve equation $[B]$ or the proportion $[B]$ to obtain the value of n as shown:

$$\frac{3 \text{ cm}}{n} \diagdown \diagup \frac{1.6 \text{ cm}}{4.8 \text{ cm}}$$ **Cross products of a proportion are equal.**
Hint: Review the chapter/section on proportion.

$n \times 1.6 \text{ cm} = 3 \text{ cm} \times 4.8 \text{ cm}$ ————————————— $[C]$

Divide both sides of equation $[C]$ by 1.6 cm in order to obtain the value of n as shown:

$$\frac{n \times 1.6 \text{ cm}}{1.6 \text{ cm}} = \frac{3 \text{ cm} \times 4.8 \text{ cm}}{1.6 \text{ cm}}$$

$$\frac{n \times 1.6 \cancel{\text{cm}}}{1.6 \cancel{\text{cm}}} = \frac{3 \text{ cm} \times 4.8 \cancel{\text{cm}}}{1.6 \cancel{\text{cm}}}$$ $1.6 \div 1.6 = 1$

$$n = \frac{14.4 \text{ cm}}{1.6}$$ $3 \times 4.8 \text{ cm} = 14.4 \text{ cm}$

$n = 14.4 \div 1.6 = 9 \text{ cm}$ (You may use a calculator).
$n = 9 \text{ cm}.$

Exercise

1. Each pair of figures are similar. Write and solve the proportion to find the length n.
   Hint: See Example 1.

(a).

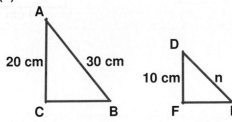

(b).

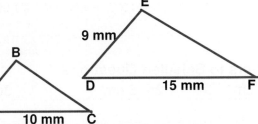

(c).

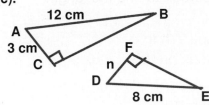

(d).

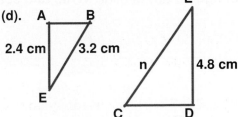

661

2. Each pair of figures are similar. Write and solve the proportion to find the length n.
Hint: See Example 2.

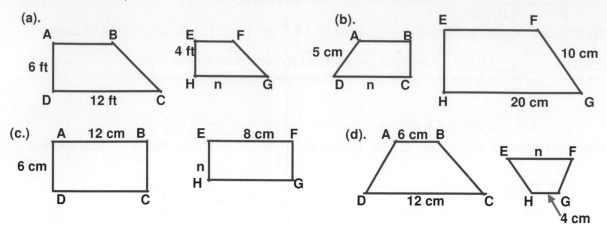

(a).

A — B
6 ft
D — 12 ft — C

E — F
4 ft
H — n — G

(b).

A — B
5 cm
D — n — C

E — F
10 cm
H — 20 cm — G

(c.)

A — 12 cm — B
6 cm
D — C

E — 8 cm — F
n
H — G

(d).

A 6 cm B
D — 12 cm — C

E — n — F
H — G
4 cm

3. Each pair of figures are similar. Write and solve the proportion to find the length n.
Hint: See Example 3.

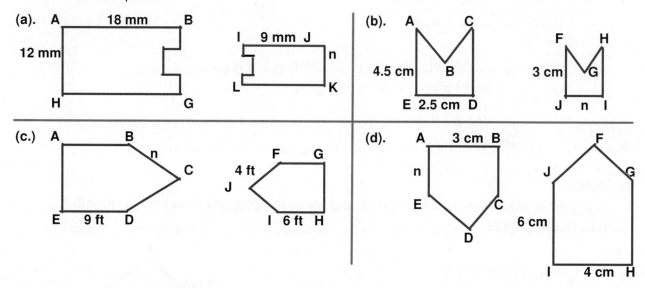

(a).

A — 18 mm — B
12 mm
H — G

I — 9 mm — J
n
L — K

(b).

A — C
4.5 cm — B
E 2.5 cm D

F — H
3 cm — G
J — n — I

(c.)

A — B
n
C
E — 9 ft — D

F — G
4 ft
J
I — 6 ft — H

(d).

A — 3 cm B
n
E
C
D

F
J — G
6 cm
I — 4 cm — H

Answers to Selected Questions

1c. 2 cm   **2d.** 8 cm   **3d.** 4.5 cm

Challenge Questions

4. Each pair of figures are similar. Write and solve the proportion to find the length of n.

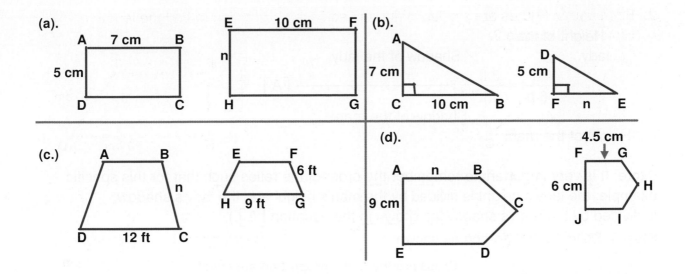

(a).

(b).

(c.)

(d).

REAL WORD APPLICATIONS - WORD PROBLEMS
Similar and Congruent Figures

Example 1

1. A man 6 feet tall casts a 4 foot shadow. A lady who is standing next to the man casts a 3 foot shadow. How tall is the lady?

Solution

We assume that both the man and the lady form right angles with the horizontal floor.
We can then use pairs of similar right triangles to find how tall the lady is as shown:
Let the height of the lady be n

Step 1: Sketch the diagram.

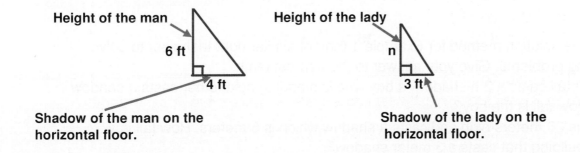

Height of the man

6 ft

4 ft

Shadow of the man on the horizontal floor.

Height of the lady

n

3 ft

Shadow of the lady on the horizontal floor.

Step 2: The right triangles are similar, and therefore, write a ratio relating the shadow of the man and the shadow of the lady, and also write a ratio relating the height of the man and the height of the lady because the ratios of the corresponding sides of similar figures are equal as shown:

Height of the
lady. ↘   ↙ Shadow of the lady.
$$\frac{n}{6\text{ ft}} = \frac{3\text{ ft}}{4\text{ ft}}$$ ——————————————— [A]
↗   ↖ Shadow of the man.
Height of the man.

(**Note**: It is very important to remember the order of the ratios such that for this specific example, the lady's height is divided by the man's height and the lady's shadow is divided by the man's shadow as shown in the equation [A].).

Step 3: Solve the proportion as shown:

$$\frac{n}{6\text{ ft}} \times \frac{3\text{ ft}}{4\text{ ft}}$$ **Cross products of a proportion are equal.**
Hint: Review the chapter/section on proportion.

$$n \times 4\text{ ft} = 6\text{ ft} \times 3\text{ ft}$$ ——————————————— [B]

Divide both sides of equation [B] by 4 ft in order to obtain the value of n as shown:

$$\frac{n \times 4\text{ ft}}{4\text{ ft}} = \frac{6\text{ ft} \times 3\text{ ft}}{4\text{ ft}}$$

$$\frac{n \times \overset{1}{4\text{ ft}}}{\underset{1}{4\text{ ft}}} = \frac{\overset{3}{6\text{ ft}} \times 3\text{ ft}}{\underset{2}{4\text{ ft}}}$$ $(4 \div 4 = 1 , 4 \div 2 = 2 , 6 \div 2 = 3)$

$$n = \frac{3 \times 3\text{ ft}}{2} = \frac{9\text{ ft}}{2} = 4.5\text{ ft.}$$

$$n = 4.5\text{ ft.}$$

Exercises

Hint: Use the solution method for Example 1 (pair of similar right triangles) to solve the following problems. Give your answer to the nearest tenth.

1. A girl 5 ft tall casts a 3 ft shadow, a boy who is standing next to her casts a shadow of 2 ft. How tall is the boy?

2. A tower is 20 meters high and casts a shadow which is 5 meters. How tall is a nearby building that casts a 3 meter shadow?

3. When a tree casts a 6 meter shadow, a man 2 meters tall casts a 1.4 meter shadow. How tall is the tree?

4. When a 2.5 meter sign post casts a 4.2 meter shadow, a man nearby casts a 3.2 meter shadow. How tall is the man?

5. John is 6.2 ft tall and casts a 10 ft shadow. A stop sign post nearby casts a 12 ft shadow. How tall is the stop sign post?

Answer to Selected Questions:
1. 3.3 ft

CHAPTER 31

ANGLES FORMED BY A TRANSVERSAL

A transversal is a line that intersects two or more other lines. A transversal that intersects two parallel lines is shown below:

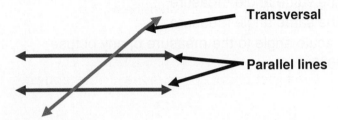

Group Exercise
The angles formed by the transversal that intersects parallel lines have special properties with respect to:
    a. Alternate interior angles.
    b. Alternate exterior angles.
    c. Corresponding angles.

First let us measure the angles formed by the transversal $\overleftrightarrow{XY}$ that intersects the two parallel lines $\overleftrightarrow{AB}$ and $\overleftrightarrow{BC}$, and then record the measurement of each angle in table 1. (Note: Draw your own diagram.) Use a protractor to measure the angles, and note that measuring with a protractor may not give the exact measurements.

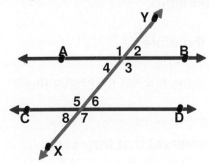

Table 1

Angles	Angle measurements	Acute or supplementary angle
∠1	m∠1	
∠2	m∠2	
∠3	m∠3	
∠4	m∠4	
∠5	m∠5	
∠6	m∠6	
∠7	m∠7	
∠8	m∠8	

Note: ∠ is the symbol for an angle and m∠ is the symbol for "measure of an angle".

1. List the angles that appear to have the same measurements as shown:

∠1, ∠?, ∠?, and ∠? have about the same angle measure.

∠2, ∠?, ∠?, and ∠? have about the same angle measure.

2. When you add the measure of any acute angle to the measure of any obtuse angle, is the sum approximately 180^0?

Critical Conclusion

From your measurements, it can be concluded that:

Rule 1: The even number angles are the acute angles and the measure of their angles are equal, so their angles are congruent to each other.

Rule 2: The odd number angles are the obtuse angles and the measure of their angles are equal and, so their angles are congruent to each other.

Rule 3: Any acute angle is **supplementary** to any **obtuse** angle: (**Note**: The sum of the measures of two angles that add up to 180^0 are said to be **supplementary**. The sum of the measures of two angles that add to 90^0 are **complementary** angles.)

From the group exercise, we can conclude that:

a. the acute angles are congruent to each other, and therefore,

∠2 ≅ m∠4 ≅ m∠6 ≅ m∠8.

b. the obtuse angles are congruent to each other, and therefore,

m∠1 ≅ m∠3 ≅ m∠5 ≅ m∠7.

Note: ≅ is the symbol for "is congruent to." **Congruent** means figures that have the same size and shape.

How to Find the Measure of Angles Formed by a Transversal that Intersects Two or More Parallel Lines.

To find the measure of angles formed by a transversal that intersects two or more parallel lines, use the following two facts:

1. All the acute angles formed by the transversal are congruent to each other, so

we can write in general that the **measure of any acute angle** =
the **measure of any other acute angle**, and then solve the equation as needed.

2. All the obtuse angles formed by the transversal are congruent to each other, so
we can write in general that the **measure of any obtuse angle** =
the **measure of any other obtuse angle**, and then solve the equation as needed.

3. Any acute angle is **supplementary** to any obtuse angle, and therefore, we can then
write that the **sum of the measures of any obtuse angle and any acute angle is
180⁰**, and then solve the equation as needed.

Example 1

In the figure, given that $\overleftrightarrow{PQ}$ is a transversal and $\overleftrightarrow{XY}$ is parallel to $\overleftrightarrow{WZ}$, find the measure of

    a. each obtuse angle.

    b. $\angle 5$.

    c. each acute angle.

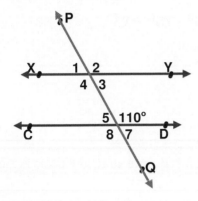

Solution

a. All the obtuse angles are congruent to each other, so

    $m\angle 2 = m\angle 4 = m\angle 8 = 110^0$ Hint: **See Rule 1.**

b. Any acute angle is supplementary to any obtuse angle, so

    $m\angle 5 + 110^0 = 180^0$ $\angle 5$ is supplementary to 110^0.

                                    Hint: **See Rule 3.**

    $m\angle 5 + 110^0 - 110^0 = 180^0 - 110^0$ Subtract 110^0 from both sides of the
                                           equation in order to isolate $m\angle 5$.

                $m\angle 5 = 70^0$ $110^0 - 110^0 = 0$ and $180^0 - 110^0 = 70^0$.

c. $\angle 5$ is an acute angle and all the acute angles are congruent to each other, and
therefore, $m\angle 1 = m\angle 3 = m\angle 5 = m\angle 7 = 70^0$. Hint: **See Rule 2** and also, we have
already shown in the solution of Example 1b that $m\angle 5 = 70^0$.

Example 2

Find x in the diagram. $\overleftrightarrow{XY}$ is parallel to $\overleftrightarrow{CD}$.

667

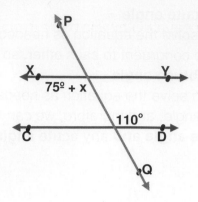

Solution

$$75^0 + x = 100^0$$

Recall from the group exercise that, all the obtuse angles are congruent to each other.

$$75^0 - 75^0 + x = 100^0 - 75^0$$

Subtract 75^0 from both sides of the equation in order to isolate x.

$$x = 25^0$$

$75^0 - 75^0 = 0$ and $100^0 - 75^0 = 25^0$.

Example 3

Find x in the diagram. $\overleftrightarrow{XY}$ is parallel to $\overleftrightarrow{CD}$.

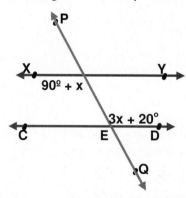

Solution

$$90^0 + x = 3x + 20^0$$

Recall from the group exercise that, all the obtuse angles are congruent.

$$90^0 + x - x = 3x - x + 20^0$$

Subtract x from both sides of the equation in order to eliminate the x on the left side of the equation, and also to gather the unknown terms only at the right side of the equation.

$$90^0 = 2x + 20^0$$

$x - x = 0$ and $3x - x = 2x$.

$$90^0 - 20^0 = 2x + 20^0 - 20^0$$

Subtract 20^0 from both sides of the equation in order to eliminate the 20^0 on the right side of the equation.

$$70^0 = 2x$$

$90^0 - 20^0 = 70^0$ and $20^0 - 20^0 = 0$.

$$\frac{70^0}{2} = \frac{2x}{2}$$

Divide both sides of the equation by 2 in order to obtain the value of x.

$$\overset{35^0}{\underset{1}{\frac{70^0}{2}}} = \overset{x}{\underset{1}{\frac{2x}{2}}}$$

$$35^0 = x$$

The value of x is 35^0.

Example 4

a. Find x in the diagram. $\overleftrightarrow{AB}$ is parallel to $\overleftrightarrow{CD}$.
b. Find $m\angle AEY$.
c. Find $m\angle CFX$.

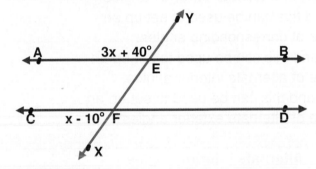

Solution

a. $m\angle AEY + m\angle CFX = 180^0$

Recall from the group exercise that any acute angle is **supplementary** to any obtuse angle.

$3x + 40^0 + x - 10^0 = 180^0$

$m\angle AEY = 3x + 40^0$ and $m\angle CFX = x - 10^0$

$4x + 30^0 = 180^0$

Combine like terms, $3x + x = 4x$ and $40^0 - 10^0 = 30^0$.

$4x + 30^0 - 30^0 = 180^0 - 30^0$

Subtract 4x from each side of the equation in order to isolate 4x.

$4x = 150^0$

$30^0 - 30^0 = 0$ and $180^0 - 30^0 = 150^0$.

$$\frac{4x}{4} = \frac{150^0}{4}$$

Divide both sides of the equation by 4 to isolate x.

$$\overset{x}{\underset{1}{\frac{4x}{4}}} = \frac{150^0}{4}$$

669

$$x = 37.5^0 \qquad\qquad 150 \div 4 = 37\frac{1}{2} = 37.5$$

b. $m\angle AEY = 3x + 40^0$ Given in the diagram.
    $m\angle AEY = 3(37.5^0) + 40^0$ From the solution of Example 4**a**, $x = 37.5^0$.
    $m\angle AEY = 112.5^0 + 40^0$
    $m\angle AEY = 152.5^0$

c. $m\angle CFX = x - 10^0$ Given in the diagram.
    $m\angle CFX = 37.5^0 - 10^0$ From the solution of Example 4**a**, $x = 37.5^0$.
    $m\angle CFX - 27.5^0$

Corresponding, Alternate Interior, and Alternate Exterior Angles

When a transversal intersects two or more parallel lines, the angles formed are classified as **corresponding**, **alternate interior**, or **alternate exterior** angles.

1. Corresponding angles are congruent, and this can be used to set up an equation, and then solve for the measure of corresponding angles.
2. Alternate interior angles are congruent, and this can be used to set up an equation, and then solve for the measure of alternate interior angles.
3. Alternate exterior angles are congruent, and this can be used to set up an equation, and then solve for the measure of alternate exterior angles.

Corresponding angles.   **Alternate Interior angles**
$\angle 1$ corresponding to $\angle 5$ $\angle 4$ is alternate interior to $\angle 6$
$\angle 4$ corresponding to $\angle 8$ $\angle 3$ is alternate interior to $\angle 5$
$\angle 2$ corresponding to $\angle 6$
$\angle 3$ corresponding to $\angle 7$

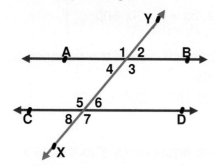 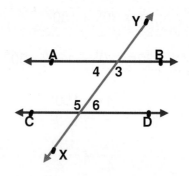

$\overleftrightarrow{AB}$ is parallel to $\overleftrightarrow{CD}$, and this is written as $\overleftrightarrow{AB} \parallel \overleftrightarrow{CD}$. The symbol for "is parallel to" is $\parallel$.

Alternate exterior angles
$\angle 1$ is alternate exterior to $\angle 7$
$\angle 2$ is alternate exterior to $\angle 8$.

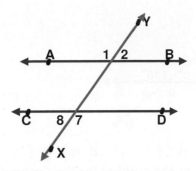

$\overleftrightarrow{AB}$ is parallel to $\overleftrightarrow{CD}$, and this is written as $\overleftrightarrow{AB} \parallel \overleftrightarrow{CD}$. The symbol for "is parallel to" is $\parallel$.

The Conditions for Two Lines to be Parallel
The five conditions for two lines to be parallel are:

1. If any of the corresponding angles are congruent.

2. If any of the alternate interior angles are congruent.

3. If any of the alternate exterior angles are congruent.

4. If the perpendicular distance at any point on the parallel lines are the same.

5. If the two lines will never meet if they are produced indefinitely.

Group Exercise
Try this!!, draw perpendicular lines or 90^0 lines to two parallel lines at different points on the line, and measure the perpendicular distances, and you will find that the perpendicular distances are the same only if the two lines are parallel.

Exercises

1. What is a transversal? What are the conditions for two lines to be parallel?

2. In the figure, $\overleftrightarrow{AB}$ is parallel to $\overleftrightarrow{CD}$.

    a. Which line is the transversal?

    b. List three pairs of supplementary angles. Hint: See Example 1**b**.

    c. List all the angles that are congruent to $\angle 3$. Hint: See Example 1**c**.

    d. List all the angles that are congruent to $\angle 6$. Hint: See Example 1**a**.

    e. If $m\angle 7$ is 125^0, find $m\angle 8$. Hint: See Example 1**b**.

    f. If $m\angle 3$ is 63^0, what is $m\angle 1$? Hint: See Rule 1.

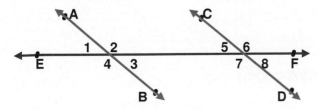

3. Given that in the figure $\overleftrightarrow{AB} \parallel \overleftrightarrow{CD}$, find the measure of each angle. Remember that $\parallel$ is the symbol for "is parallel to."

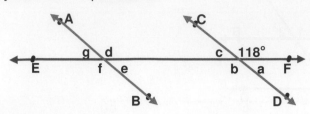

a. m∠d   **b.** m∠b   **c.** m∠f   **d.** m∠g   **e.** m∠c.

Hint: See Example 1. Note that m∠ is the symbol for the "measure of an angle".

4. Given that in the figure, $\overleftrightarrow{AB}$ ∥ $\overleftrightarrow{CD}$,

   a. List all the alternate exterior angles.

   b. List all the alternate interior angles.

   c. List all the corresponding angles.

   Hint: See the notes under "Corresponding, Alternate Interior and Alternate Exterior Angles". Hint: See Example 1.

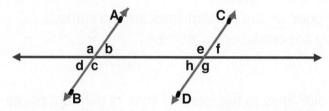

5. $\overleftrightarrow{AB}$ ∥ $\overleftrightarrow{CD}$, find the measure of each obtuse and each acute angle.

   Hint: See Example 1.

a. 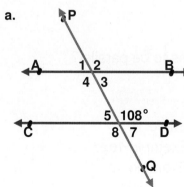   **b.** 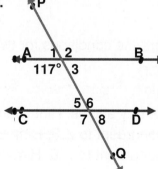   **c.**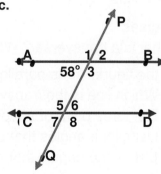

6. $\overleftrightarrow{AB}$ ∥ $\overleftrightarrow{CD}$, find x in each diagram. Hint: See Example 2.

(The diagrams are located on the next page.)

a. P, A, 60° + x, B, 114°, C, D, Q

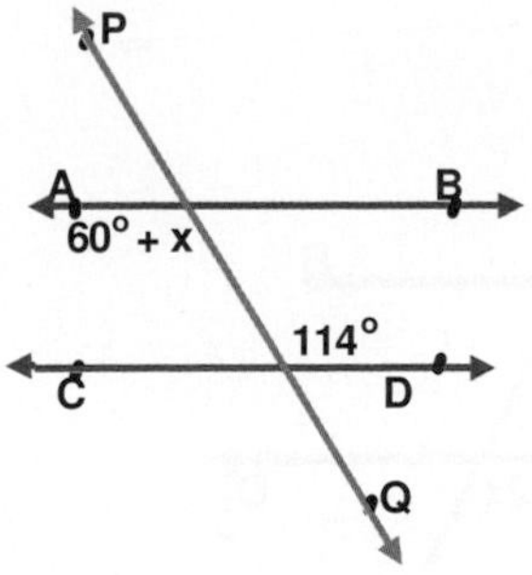

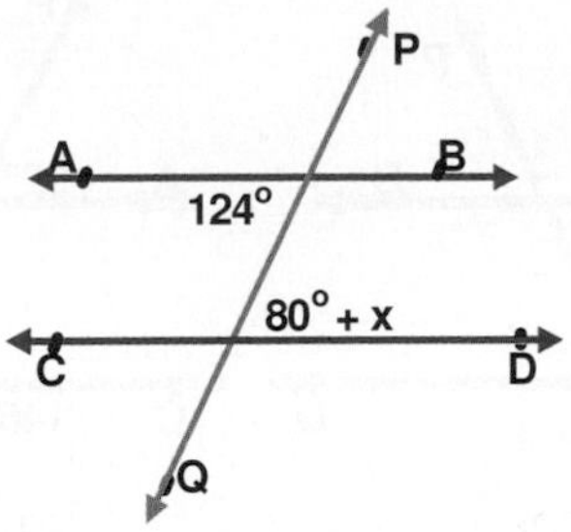

b. P, A, 124°, B, 80° + x, C, D, Q

c. P, A, 84° + x, B, 120°, C, D, Q

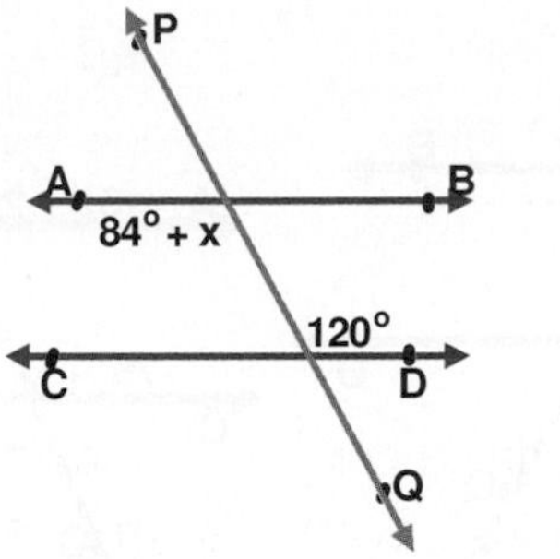

7. Find x. $\overleftrightarrow{AB} \parallel \overleftrightarrow{CD}$. Hint: Round your answer to the nearest tenth. See Example 3.

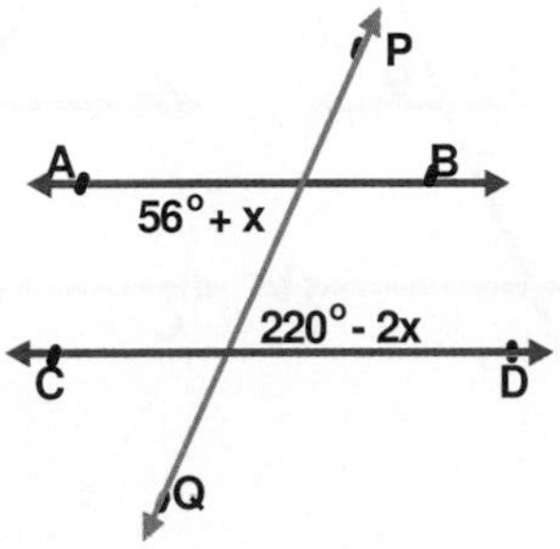

a. P, A, 100° + x, B, 4x + 30°, C, D, Q

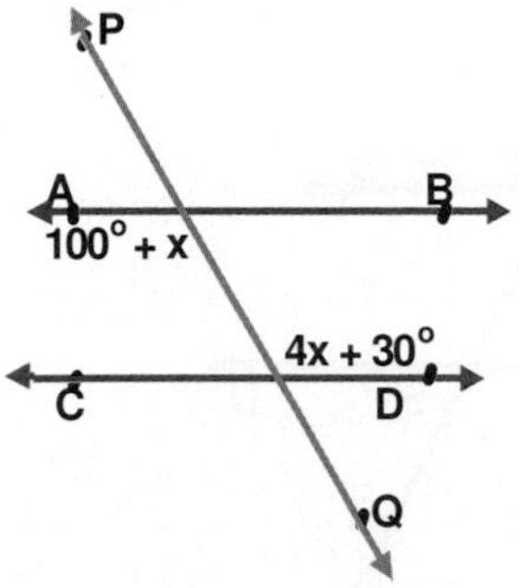

b. P, A, 56° + x, B, 220° - 2x, C, D, Q

c. P, A, 70° + x, B, 224° - 2x, C, D, Q

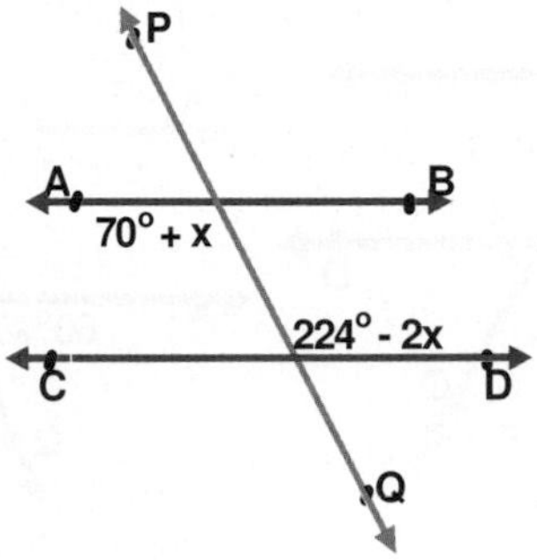

8. $\overleftrightarrow{AB} \parallel \overleftrightarrow{CD}$. In the diagram **a**, find x and also find the m∠PEB and the m∠QFD.
In the diagram **b**, find x and also find the m∠AEP and the m∠PFD.
In the diagram **c**, find x and also find the m∠CFQ.

Hint: See Example 4. Round your answers to the nearest tenth.

a. P, A, 2x + 60°, B, E, C, F, x - 14°, D, Q

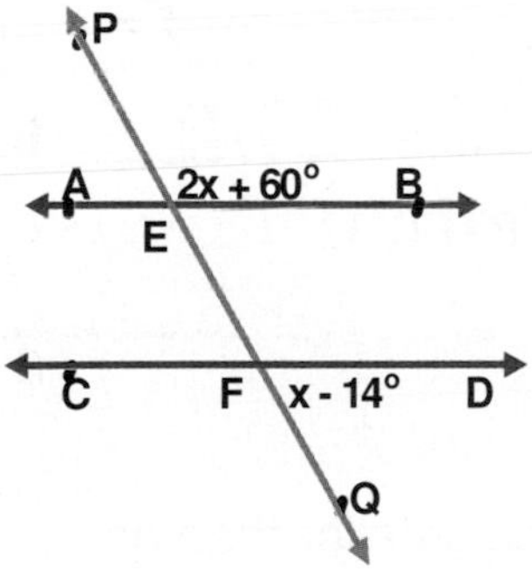

b. P, A, 2x + 50°, B, E, x - 10°, C, F, D, Q

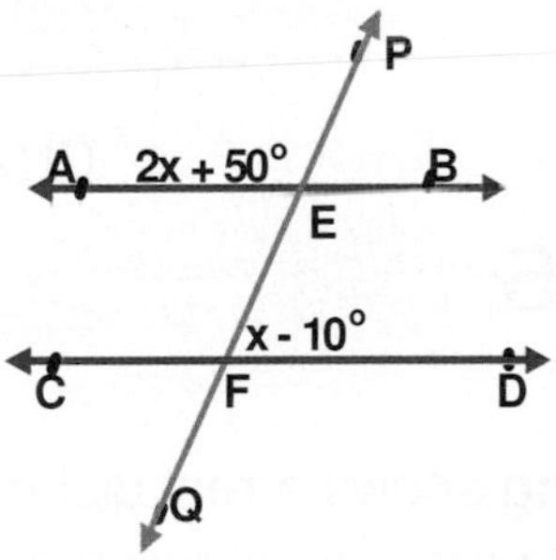

c. P, A, 50°, B, E, F, C, 145° - 2x, D, Q

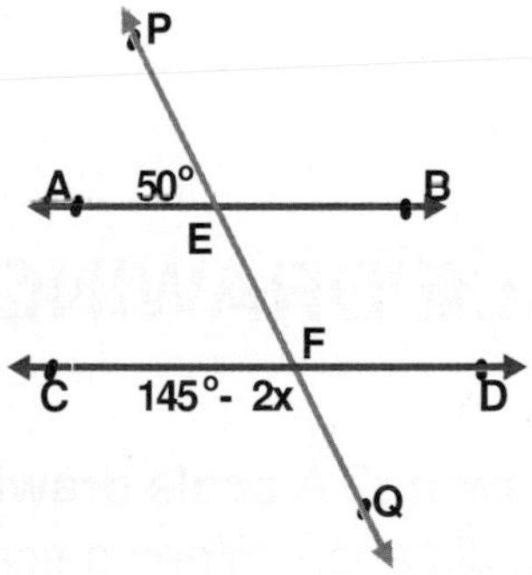

Challenge Questions

9. $\overleftrightarrow{AB} \parallel \overleftrightarrow{CD}$, find the value of x. Round your answer to the nearest tenth.

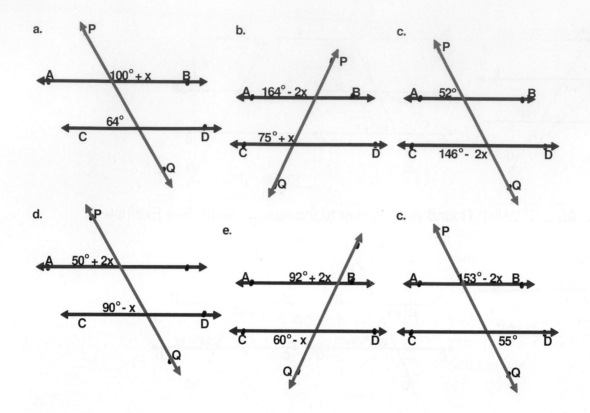

a.

A —— 100° + x —— B

64°

C —— D

P
Q

b.

A. 164° - 2x B

75° + x

C D

P
Q

c.

A. 52° B

C 146° - 2x D

P
Q

d.

A 50° + 2x

90° - x

C D

P
Q

e.

A. 92° + 2x B

C 60° - x D

P
Q

c.

A. 153° - 2x B

C 55° D

P
Q

Answers to Selected Questions

2e. 55^0 **5a.** $m\angle 1 = m\angle 3 = m\angle 5 = m\angle 7 = 72^0$, $m\angle 2 = m\angle 4 = m\angle 8 = 108^0$.

6a. $80°$ **7a.** 23.3^0 **8a.** $x \approx 44.7^0$ $m\angle PEB \approx 149.3^0$ $m\angle QFD \approx 30.7^0$

SCALE DRAWINGS

What is a **scale drawing**? A **scale drawing** shows a real distance smaller than or longer than the real distance. When a scale drawing shows a real distance that is smaller than the real distance, is called a **reduction**. When a scale drawing shows a real distance that is longer than the real distance, is called an **enlargement**. A **map scale** is the ratio that compares the distance on a map to the actual distance.

Team Project 1
Goal of the project: To use a scale drawing and a map scale to find the actual distance between Peki and Hoe by using equivalent ratios.
Method

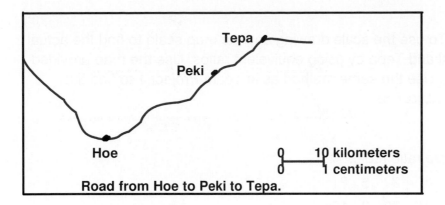

Road from Hoe to Peki to Tepa.

Step 1: **Read the map scale.**

The map shows the scale of 1 cm = 10 km, or $\dfrac{1 \text{ cm}}{10 \text{ km}}$.

Step 2: **Use a string to measure the distance from Peki to Hoe on the map.**

The distance between Peki and Hoe is marked on the string.

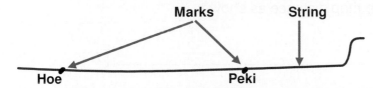

(**Note**: The distance from Hoe to Peki on the string is an approximate distance.)

Step 3: **Use a centimeter ruler to measure the distance between the two marks on the string as shown.**

The distance between the two marks on the string is about 5.2 cm.

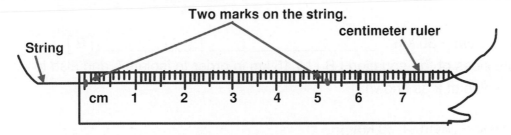

Step 4: **Use equivalent ratios to find the actual distance as shown**:

$$\frac{1}{10} = \frac{5.2}{k}$$

k is the actual distance in kilometers.

Hint: Review the chapter/section on equivalent ratios.

$1 \times k = 10 \times 5.2$ Cross multiply.

$k = 52 \text{ km}$

Therefore, the distance from Peki to Hoe is 52 km.

675

Team Project 2

Goal of the project: To use the scale drawing and the map scale to find the actual distance between Peki and Tepa by using equivalent ratios. Use the map provided under Team Project 1. Use the same method as in Team Project 1 to find the distance between Peki and Tepa.

Example 1

Complete the map scale ratio table.

Map distance (cm)	1	?	5	?
Actual distance (km)	15	30	?	105

Solution

To find the map distance when the actual distance is 30 km.

Step 1: From the table, the map scale is 1 cm = 15 km or $\dfrac{1 \text{ cm}}{15 \text{ km}}$.

Step 2: When the actual distance is 30 km, let the map distance be k.

Step 3: Use equivalent ratios to find the map distance as shown:

$$\frac{1 \text{ cm}}{15 \text{ km}} = \frac{k}{30 \text{ km}} \hspace{4cm} [A]$$

Step 4: Cross multiply equation $[A]$ because **cross products of equivalent ratios are equal** as shown:

$$\frac{1 \text{ cm}}{15 \text{ km}} \times \frac{k}{30 \text{ km}}$$

$$15 \text{ km} \times k = 1 \text{ cm} \times 30 \text{ km} \hspace{3cm} [B]$$

Divide both sides of the equation $[B]$ by 15 km in order to isolate k and also to obtain the value of k as shown:

$$\frac{15 \text{ km} \times k}{15 \text{ km}} = \frac{1 \text{ cm} \times 30 \text{ km}}{15 \text{ km}}$$

$$\frac{\overset{1}{\cancel{15 \text{ km}}} \times k}{\underset{1}{\cancel{15 \text{ km}}}} = \frac{1 \text{ cm} \times \overset{2}{\cancel{30 \text{ km}}}}{\underset{1}{\cancel{15 \text{ km}}}}$$

$$k = 1 \text{ cm} \times 2$$
$$k = 2 \text{ cm}$$

Therefore, when the actual distance = 30 km, the map distance = 2 cm.

To find the actual distance when the map distance is 5 cm.

Step 1: From the table, the map scale is 1 cm = 15 km or $\dfrac{1\ cm}{15\ km}$.

Step 2: When the map distance is 5 cm, let the actual distance be n.

Step 3: Use equivalent ratios to find the actual distance as shown:

$$\frac{1\ cm}{15\ km} = \frac{5\ cm}{n} \hspace{4cm} [C]$$

Step 4: Cross multiply equation [C] because cross products of equivalent ratios are equal as shown:

$$\frac{1\ cm}{15\ km} \bowtie \frac{5\ cm}{n}$$

$$1\ cm \times n = 15\ km \times 5\ cm. \hspace{3cm} [D]$$

Divide both sides of equation [D] by 1 cm in order to obtain the value for n as shown:

$$\frac{1\ cm \times n}{1\ cm} = \frac{15\ km \times 5\ cm}{1\ cm}$$

$$\frac{\overset{1}{\cancel{1\ cm}} \times n}{\underset{1}{\cancel{1\ cm}}} = \frac{15\ km \times \overset{5}{\cancel{5\ cm}}}{\underset{1}{\cancel{1\ cm}}}$$

$$n = 15\ km \times 5$$
$$n = 75\ km$$

Therefore, when the map distance is 5 cm, the actual distance is 75 km.

To Find the Map Distance When the Actual Distance is 105 km

Step 1: From the table, the map scale is 1 cm =15 km or $\dfrac{1\ cm}{15\ km}$.

Step 2: When the map distance is 105 km, let the map distance be w.

Step 3: Use equivalent ratios to find the actual distance as shown:

$$\frac{1\ cm}{15\ km} = \frac{w}{105\ km} \hspace{4cm} [E]$$

Step 4: Cross multiply equation [E] because cross products of equivalent ratios are equal as shown:

$$\frac{1 \text{ cm}}{15 \text{ km}} \underset{105 \text{ km}}{\overset{w}{\bowtie}}$$

$$1 \text{ cm} \times 105 \text{ km} = 15 \text{ km} \times w \underline{\hspace{4cm}}[F]$$

Divide both sides of equation [F] by 15 km in order to isolate w and also to obtain the value of w as shown:

$$\frac{1 \text{ cm} \times 105 \text{ km}}{15 \text{ km}} = \frac{15 \text{ km} \times w}{15 \text{ km}}$$

$$\frac{1 \text{ cm} \times \overset{7}{\cancel{105 \text{ km}}}}{\underset{1}{\cancel{15 \text{ km}}}} = \frac{\overset{1}{\cancel{15 \text{ km}}} \times w}{\underset{1}{\cancel{15 \text{ km}}}}$$

$$1 \text{ cm} \times 7 = w$$
$$7 \text{ cm} = w$$

Therefore, when the actual distance is 105 km, the map distance is 7 cm.

Therefore, the completed table is:

Map Distance (cm)	1	2	5	7
Actual distance (km)	15	30	75	105

Example 2

Using the map, an inch ruler and the map scale, find the distance from Peki to Jawa to the nearest mile. Hint: Assume that the distance between any two cities is a straight line, and therefore, the distance can be measured directly with a ruler to the nearest inch.

(The map is on the next page.)

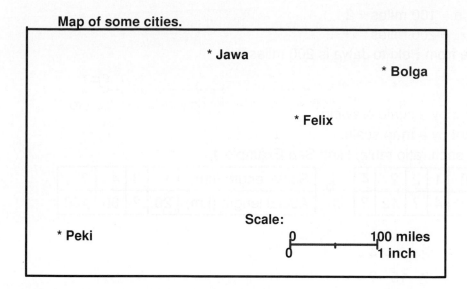

Map of some cities.

* Jawa

* Bolga

* Felix

Scale:

* Peki

0 _____ 100 miles
0 _____ 1 inch

Solution

Step 1: Read the map scale.

The map shows a scale of 1 inch =100 miles or $\dfrac{1 \text{ inch}}{100 \text{ miles}}$.

Step 2: Use an inch ruler to measure the distance from Peki to Jawa on the map.
The distance from Peki to Jawa on the map is approximately 2 inches to the nearest inch.

Step 3: When the map distance from Peki to Jawa is 2 inches, let the actual distance from Peki to Jawa be n.

Step 4: Use equivalent ratios to find the actual distance as shown:

$$\frac{1 \text{ inch}}{100 \text{ miles}} = \frac{2 \text{ inches}}{n} \qquad\qquad\qquad\qquad\qquad [A]$$

Step 5: Cross multiply equation [A] because cross products of equivalent ratios are equal as shown:

$$\frac{1 \text{ in.}}{100 \text{ mi}} \diagdown\diagup \frac{2 \text{ in.}}{n}$$

$$1 \text{ in.} \times n = 100 \text{ miles} \times 2 \text{ in.} \qquad\qquad\qquad\qquad [B]$$

Step 6: Divide both sides of the equation $[B]$ by 1 in. in order to isolate n and also to obtain the value of n as shown:

$$\frac{1 \text{ in.} \times n}{1 \text{ in.}} = \frac{100 \text{ miles} \times 2 \text{ in.}}{1 \text{ in.}}$$

$$\frac{1 \text{ in.} \times n}{1 \text{ in.}} = \frac{100 \text{ miles} \times 2 \text{ in.}}{1 \text{ in.}}$$

679

$$n = 100 \text{ miles} \times 2$$
$$= 200 \text{ miles}$$

Therefore, the distance from Peki to Jawa is 200 miles.

Exercises

1. Explain what is meant by a scale drawing.

2. Explain what is meant by a map scale.

3. Copy and complete each ratio table. Hint: See Example **1**.

a.

Scale length (cm)	1	2	?	4
Actual length (km)	4	?	12	?

b.

Scale length (cm)	1	3	4	?
Actual length (km)	20	?	80	100

c.

Scale length (in.)	1	2	?	4
Actual length (ft)	5	?	15	?

4. Using the map in Example 2, find the:

    a. distance from Peki to Bolga.

    b. distance from Jawa to Bolga.

Hint: See example 2. The map distance should be to the nearest whole number. Assume that the road between any two cities is straight, and therefore, a ruler could be used to measure the map distance.

Challenge Questions

5. Copy and complete the ratio tables.

a.

Scale length (cm)	1	3	?
Actual length (km)	10	?	50

b.

Scale length (in.)	1	3	?	?
Actual length (ft)	4	?	24	48

6. Explain how to find the actual distance between two cities on a map.

CHAPTER 33

MEASUREMENT OF ANGLES

Quick Review

1. In the figure, given that $\overleftrightarrow{PQ}$ is a transversal and $\overleftrightarrow{XY}$ is parallel to $\overleftrightarrow{CD}$, find the measure of:

    a. Each obtuse angle.

    b. $\angle 5$.

    c. Each acute angle.

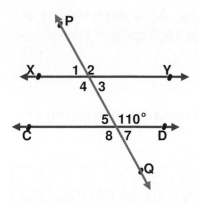

2. Change 125% to a fraction.
3. Find the next three terms of the sequence.

   3, 6, 9, 12, __, __, __.
4. Express the ratio 1 out of 5 as percent.
5. Explain what is meant by the probability of an event is:

   a. 0   **b.** 1   **c.** 50%   **d.** 100%

New Terms: protractor, center of protractor, placement

Example 1

(a) What instrument is used to measure angles?

(b) Describe a protractor.

Solution

(a) The instrument which is used to measure angles is the **protractor**.

(b) A protractor usually consist of a half circle or a half circular shape cut from transparent material or metal. A protractor is drawn below.

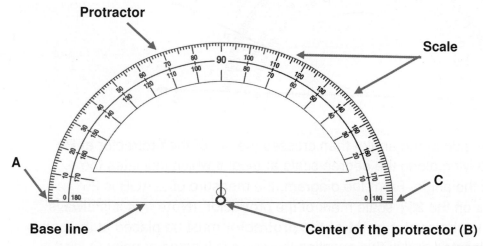

A protractor has a center and this is marked B and AC is the diameter of the protractor. The curved edge is divided and marked off equally in degrees from 0^0 to 180^0 in both clockwise and counterclockwise directions. This curved marked

681

off section of the protractor is the scale of the protractor. AC is the base line of the protractor which is the same as the zero degree or 180⁰ division line of the protractor.

Special Note
There are many styles of the protractors but they are all **used for measuring or drawing angles**.

Example 2
Describe how you would measure ∠AQB in the diagram, and then find the measurement of ∠AQB.

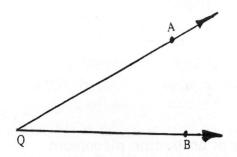

Solution
Place the protractor so that its **center** coincides with Q (which is the vertex of the angle) and its zero line (base line) should be lying along $\overrightarrow{QB}$ as shown in the diagram.

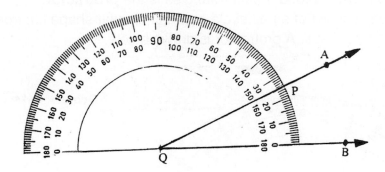

QA (which is the other side of the angle) then crosses the arc of the protractor at P. The ray QA should be lying along the degree scale at a point which indicates the number of degrees in the angle. From the diagram, the measure of ∠AQB is 25⁰ because the ray QA is on the 25⁰ scale mark of the protractor. (**Note** that it is always important to realize that the **center point of the protractor** must be placed at the point at which the angle is located and in this question the angle is located at point Q, and therefore, the protractor center coincided with point Q. The point Q is known as the vertex.)

Example 3

Using a protractor, measure angle BAC in the diagram. Show two methods of **placement** of the protractor on the diagram in order to measure angle BAC.

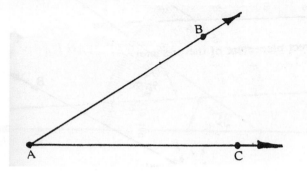

Placement means how to position the protractor on the diagram.

Solution

Method 1: Place the protractor on the diagram so that the center is at A and the base line (the zero degree or 180^0 division line) lies on the ray AC. When measuring an angle with a protractor, it is very important that the base line (0^0 or 180^0 division line lies on one of the rays (for example $\overrightarrow{AC}$) that forms the angle and then the curved edge of the protractor must cross the second ray (for example $\overrightarrow{AB}$) that forms the angle. The two diagrams show the correct placements of the protractor for measuring angle A.

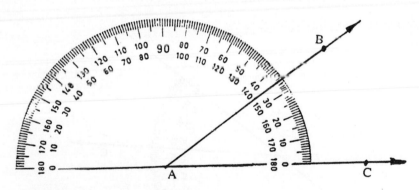

Correct placement of the protractor.
Fig. 1.

From Fig. 1, which is the diagram showing the correct placement of the protractor, read the number of the degrees on the scale which coincides with $\overrightarrow{AB}$. Counting from the base line(zero division line) the reading of the scale which coincides with AB is 35^0. Therefore, the measurement of angle A = 35^0 as shown in the next diagram.

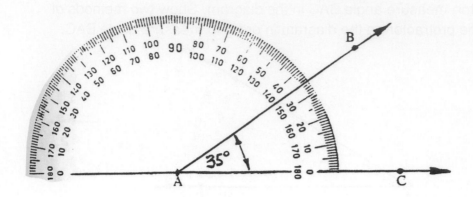

Method 2

Place the protractor on the diagram in the question so that the **center point** of the protractor is at A and the **base line** (0^0 or 180^0 division line) lies on AB. When measuring an angle with a protractor **it is very important that the base line (0^0 or 180^0 division line) lies on one of the rays (for example $\overrightarrow{AB}$) that forms the angle**, and the curved edge of the protractor must cross the second ray (for example $\overrightarrow{AC}$) of the angle.

The Fig. 1 and Fig. 3 of the diagrams show the correct placement of the protractor for measuring angle A.

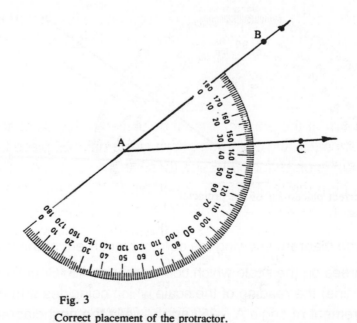

Fig. 3
Correct placement of the protractor.

From Fig. 3 which is the diagram showing the correct placement of the protractor, read the number of degrees on the scale which coincides with ray AC. Counting from the base line (0^0 division line), the reading of the scale that coincides with the ray AC is

35^0. Therefore, the measurement of angle A is 35^0 as shown in the next diagram.

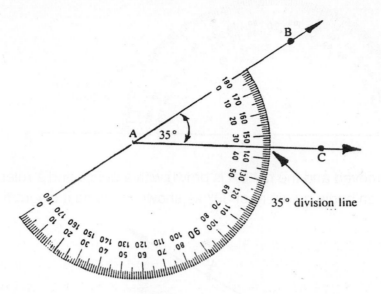

Example 4

Describe how to draw an angle ABC which is 30^0 and then draw the angle ABC.

Solution

Note that when three letters of the alphabets are used to name an angle such as angle ABC or $\angle$ABC, the middle letter (in this case, B) is the vertex of the triangle and the angle is formed at the vertex of the triangle.

Draw a segment and label it BC, and note that the segment starts from B because B is the middle letter and the angle is formed at the middle letter as the vertex.

Note that the **center point** of the protractor must be placed at the point at which the angle is to be drawn. Since the angle is to be drawn at the point B, place the protractor such that its **center point** is on B and its 0^0 line (base line) is on the ray BC. Counting the number of degrees from the ray BC as 0^0, mark a point A on the paper at the desired degree reading on the scale of the protractor. From the question, the desired degree measurement is 30^0, and therefore, mark the point A at the 30^0 reading mark on the protractor scale.

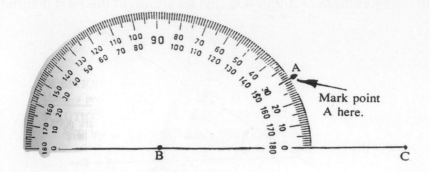

Mark point
A here.

The protractor is removed and the ray BA is drawn with a pencil and a ruler to form
the angle ABC with an angle measure of 30⁰ as shown in the next diagram.

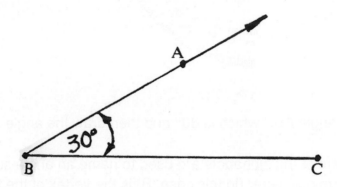

Example 5
Using a protractor, draw an angle BOA which is 60^0.
Solution
Note that when three letters of the alphabets are used to name an angle such as
angle BOA or ∠BOA, the middle letter of the alphabet (in this case, O), is the vertex of
the triangle and the angle is formed at the vertex of the triangle.
Step 1: Draw the ray OA.

        Note that the ray starts from O, because O is the middle letter of the alphabet
        and the angles are formed at the middle letter of the alphabets as the vertex.
Step 2: Put the protractor center on O with the 0^0 division mark of the protractor scale
        on ray OA, mark B at 60^0.

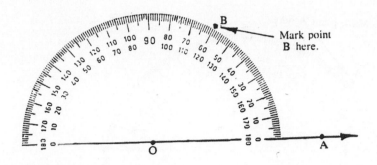

Mark point
B here.

Step 3: Remove the protractor and use a pencil and a ruler to draw the ray OB.
The $m\angle BOA = 60^0$.

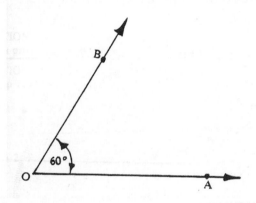

60°

Example 6

Using a protractor, a pencil and a ruler, draw $\angle ABC$ which is 140^0.
Solution

Step 1: Draw the $\overrightarrow{BC}$. Note that the ray starts from B because B is the middle
letter of the alphabets in the $\angle ABC$, and therefore, B is the vertex.

Step 2: Put the protractor **center point** on B with the 0^0 division mark on the
protractor on $\overrightarrow{BC}$ and then mark point A on the paper at 140^0 division scale
marking on the protractor.

687

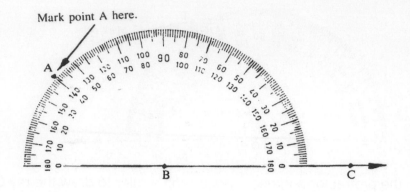

Mark point A here.

Step 3: Remove the protractor and use a pencil and a ruler to draw the $\overrightarrow{BA}$.
$m\angle ABC = 140^0$.

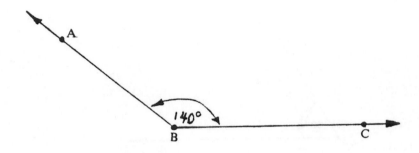

Example 7
Using a protractor draw $\angle XYZ$ which is 75^0.
Solution

Step 1: Draw the $\overrightarrow{YZ}$. Note that the ray starts with Y because Y is the middle letter of the alphabet in the angle XYZ, and therefore, Y is the vertex of the angle XYZ.

Step 2: Put the protractor **center point** on point Y with the 0^0 division mark (base line) on the protractor scale on $\overrightarrow{YZ}$, and then mark the point X on the paper at 75^0 division scale marking.

688

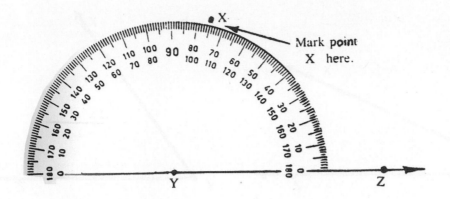

Step 3: Remove the protractor and use a pencil and a ruler to draw $\overrightarrow{YX}$, $m\angle XYZ = 75^0$.

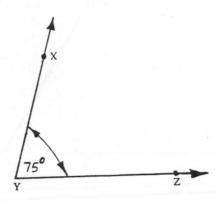

Exercises

1. The maximum scale reading on the protractor is 180^0. True or false? Hint: Look at the picture of the protractor.
2. The minimum scale reading on the protractor is 0^0 True or false? Hint: Look at the picture of the protractor.
3. Describe a protractor. Hint: See the notes.
4. What are protractors used for?
5. Describe how you would measure angle ABC.
6. Use a protractor to measure $\angle XYZ$ in each case.

(The diagrams are on the next page.)

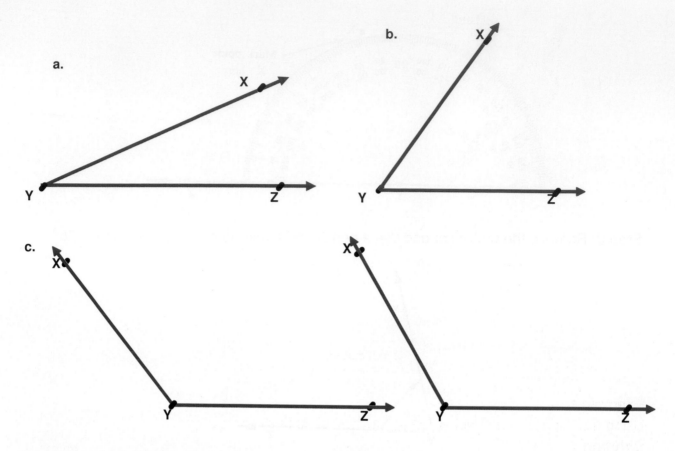

Hint: See Examples 2 and 3.

7. Use a protractor, a pencil, and a ruler to draw the following angles.
   a. 90^0 **b**. 65^0 **c**. 15^0 **d**. 44^0
   e. 38^0 **f**. 77^0 **g**. 21^0 **h**. 88^0
   i. 110^0 **j**. 121^0 **k**. 134^0 **l**. 165^0
   Hint: See Examples 4 to 7.

CHAPTER 34

CONSTRCTION OF ANGLES

Note that a compass is not shown in the construction of angles in this chapter. The picture of the compass is shown on the next page.

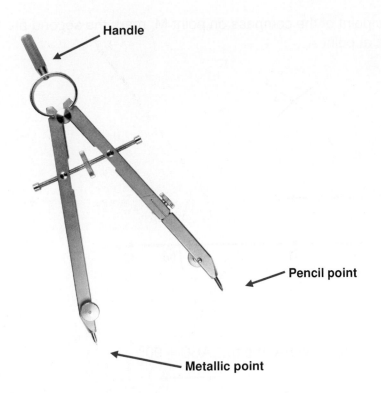

Handle

Pencil point

Metallic point

Example 1
Using a compass, construct an angle ABC which is 90^0.

Solution

Step 1: Draw $\overrightarrow{BC}$ and extend $\overline{CB}$ to E. Note that the ray BC starts with B because B is the letter that is in the middle of the angle ABC, therefore, B is the vertex of the angle ABC.

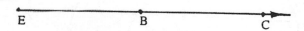

E   B   C

Step 2: Open the compass to about 3 cm and with the metallic point of the compass on point B mark an arc on $\overline{BE}$ at L, and then mark another arc with the same compass opening on $\overrightarrow{BC}$ at M.

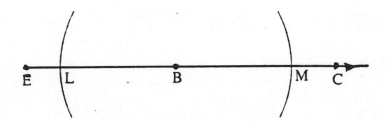

E   L   B   M   C

Step 3: With the metallic point of the compass on point L, and opening the compass beyond point B, mark an arc above point B. With the same compass opening

691

and with the metallic point of the compass on point M, mark the second arc to intersect the first arc at point A.

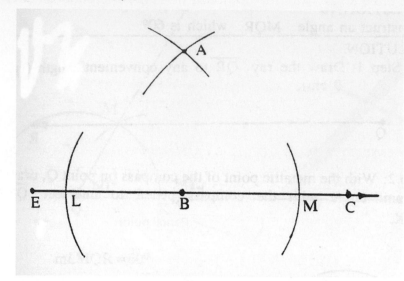

Step 4: Use a pencil and a ruler to draw $\overrightarrow{BA}$, the m$\angle$ABC = 90⁰.

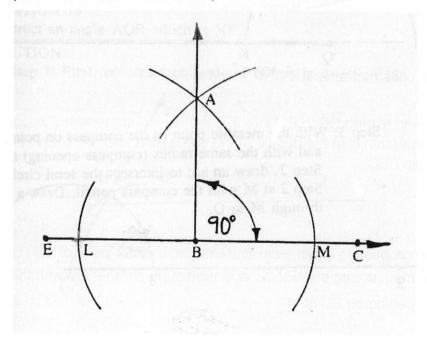

Example 2

Construct $\angle$MQR which should be 60⁰.
Solution

Step 1: Draw $\overrightarrow{QR}$ to any convenient length (for example to about 9 cm).

Step 2: With the metallic point of the compass on the point Q, and with a radius of about 3 cm, draw an arc with the compass pencil to intersect $\overrightarrow{QR}$ at K.

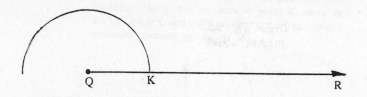

Step 3: With the metallic point of the compass on point K and with the same radius (compass opening) as in Step 2, draw an arc to intersect the semi circle in Step 2 at M with the compass pencil. Using a ruler and a pencil, draw a ray through Q and M.

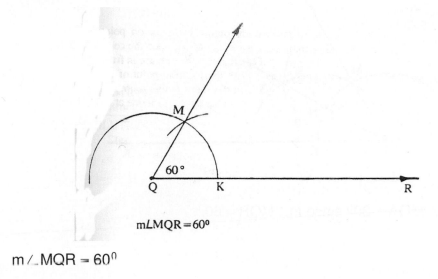

m∠MQR = 60⁰

m∠MQR = 60⁰

Example 3
Construct ∠AQR which is 30⁰.
Solution
Step 1: First construct an angle of 60⁰ as in Example 2.

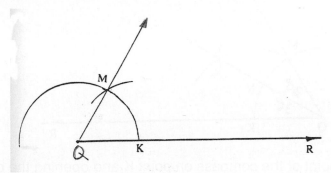

Step 2: With the metallic point of the compass on point K and opening the compass to M (or open the compass more than half of arc MK), draw an arc in front of

693

arc MK, and now with the metallic point of the compass on M and with the same radius (compass opening), draw an arc to intersect the first one at A.

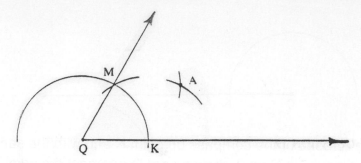

Step 3: Use a pencil and a ruler to draw $\overrightarrow{QA}$

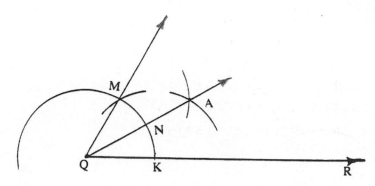

m∠AQR = 30⁰

Note: Also, m∠MQA = 30⁰ since m∠MQR = 60⁰.

Example 4

Construct an angle WQR which is 15⁰.

Solution

Step 1: First construct an angle of 30⁰ as in Example 3.

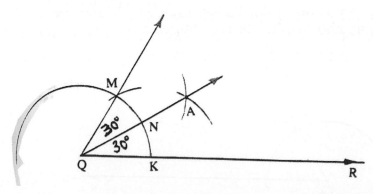

Step 2: With the metallic point of the compass on point K and opening the compass to N, draw an arc in front of the arc NK, use the same compass opening and with the metallic point of the compass on point N, draw another arc to

694

intersect the first arc at point W. (Note: The compass opening can be any convenient length which is more than half the length of arc NK.)

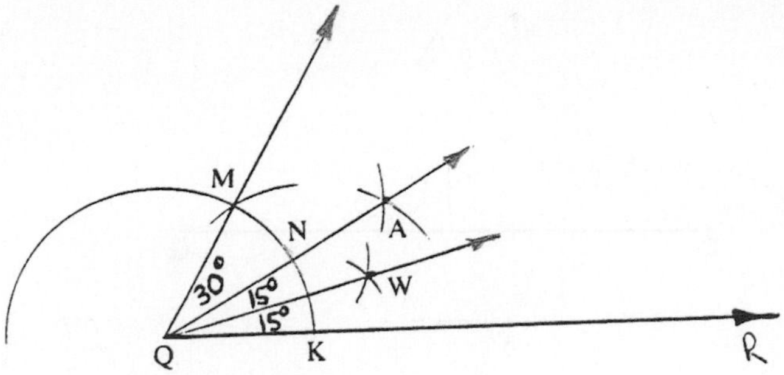

m∠WQR = 15°

$m\angle WQR = 15^0$

Note:

(a) Angle 30^0 can be constructed by bisecting 60^0 angle.

(b) Angle 15^0 can be constructed by bisecting angle 30^0.

(c) Angle $7\frac{1}{2}$ can be constructed by bisecting angle 15^0.

Example 5

Construct $\angle ABC$ which is 45^0.

Solution

Step 1: First construct an angle of 90^0 as shown in Step 1.

(a) Draw a segment DC to any convenient length (for example about 8 cm).

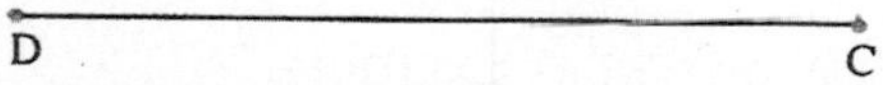

(b) Bisect line DC by putting the metallic point of the compass on D and opening the compass distance more than half the distance of DC, mark an arc above and below line DC with the compass pencil.

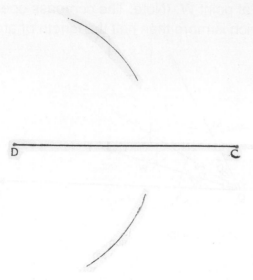

(c) With the metallic point of the compass on point C and keeping the same
    compass opening (distance) as in (b), draw an arc above and below line
    DC to intersect the arcs in (b) at point X and Y. Using a pencil and a ruler,
    draw a line through X and Y to intersect DC at B. m∠XBC is 90⁰.

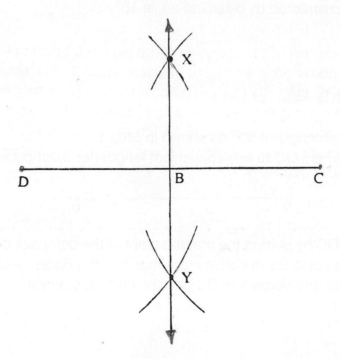

Step 2: With the metallic point of the compass on point B and with a convenient
    radius (for example about 1.5 cm) draw an arc to cut $\overline{BX}$ and $\overline{BC}$ at H and K
    respectively with the compass pencil.

696

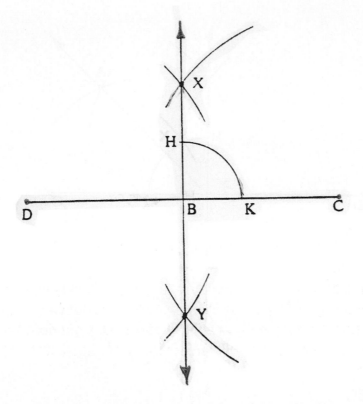

Step 3: With the metallic point of the compass on point H and opening the compass distance to any convenient length (for example about 3 cm), draw an arc in front of the arc HK. With the metallic point of the compass on point K and keeping the same compass distance (3 cm), draw another arc to intersect the first arc at point A. Using a pencil and a ruler, draw the ray BΛ.
(**Note**: The compass opening can be any convenient length which is more than half the length of arc HK.)

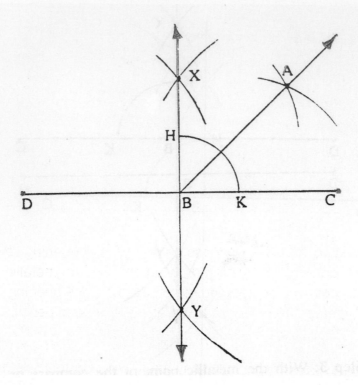

m∠ABC is 45⁰.

Example 6

Bisect ∠ABC which is 75⁰.

Solution

Step 1: Draw ∠ABC which is 75⁰ by using a protractor (See the chapter/section on "Measurement of Angles", Example 7 for the method.)

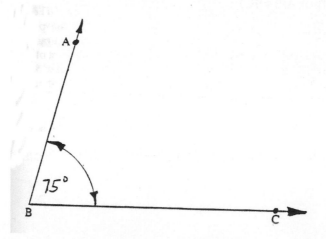

Step 2: With the metallic point of the compass on point B and opening the compass to a convenient length (about 1 cm) draw an arc to cut both $\overrightarrow{BA}$ and $\overrightarrow{BC}$ at T and P respectively.

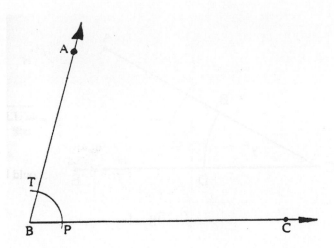

Step 3: With the metallic point of the compass on point T and opening the compass to a convenient radius (about 5 cm), draw an arc. Put the metallic point of the compass on point P and keeping the same compass opening, draw another arc to intersect the first arc at J with the compass pencil. Using a pencil and a ruler, draw the ray BJ. $m\angle ABJ = m\angle JBC = 37\frac{1}{2}^{0}$.

(**Note**:The compass opening can be any length which should be more than half the length of arc TP.)

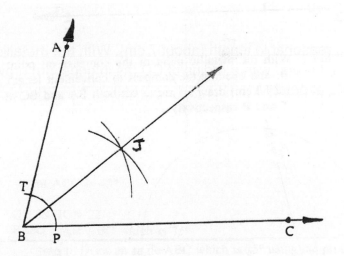

Check: Measure $\angle JBC$ with a protractor which should be $37\frac{1}{2}^{0}$. Note that the $\overrightarrow{BJ}$ bisects $\angle ABC$.

Example 7
Construct an angle with measure $y^0 + z^0$, given that $m\angle ACD = y^0$ and $m\angle FHJ = z^0$. (**Note**: The radii of BC and CD of the arc BD and the radii of GH and HI of the arc GI are equal.)

699

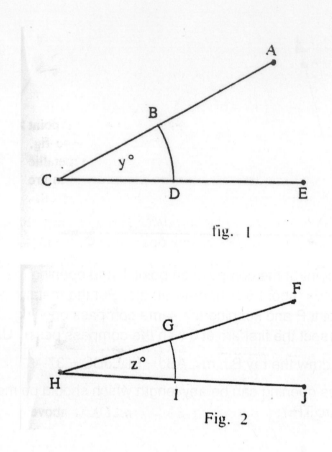

fig. 1

z°

Fig. 2

Solution

Step 1: Draw a $\overrightarrow{KL}$ of a reasonable length (about 7 cm). With the metallic point of the compass on point K and with a radius of CD (as in question) draw an arc to meet the line KL at point M.

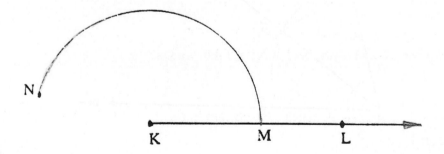

Step 2: Put the metallic point of the compass on point D and open the compass to point B (see Fig. 1), now with this compass on point M, mark an arc to cross the arc MN at O with the compass pencil.

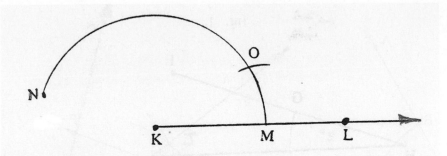

(**Note**: $m\angle BCE = y^0 = m\angle OKM$.)

Step 3: Put the metallic point of the compass on point I and open the compass to point G (see fig. 2), and with this compass opening, put the metallic point of the compass on point O and draw an arc to cross arc MN at P. Using a pencil and a ruler, draw $\overrightarrow{KP}$.

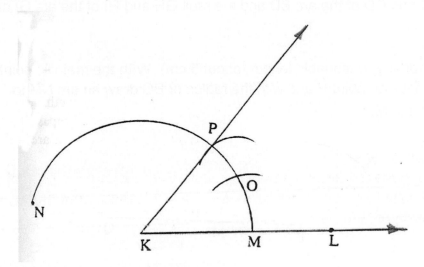

(Note: $m\angle PKO$ is equivalent to Fig. 2.)

Therefore, $m\angle PKM = m\angle BCD + m\angle GHI = y^0 + z^0$.

Example 8

Given angles of measures of y^0 and z^0 as shown in Fig. 1 and Fig. 2, construct an angle with measure $y^0 - z^0$

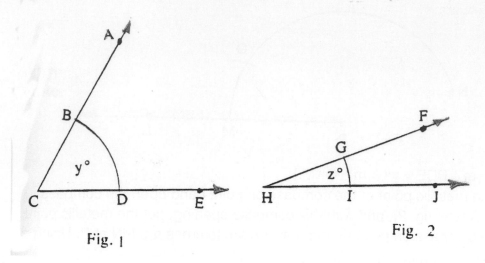

Fig. 1   Fig. 2

(Note: The radii BC and CD of the arc BD and the radii GH and HI of the arc GI are equal.)

Solution

Step 1: Draw a $\overline{PQ}$ of any reasonable length (about 5 cm). With the metallic point of the compass on point P and with the radius of BC draw an arc NM to meet the $\overline{PQ}$ at M.

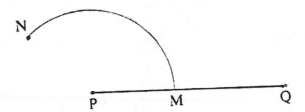

Step 2: Put the metallic point of the compass on point D and open the compass to point B in Fig 1. With this compass opening, put the metallic point of the compass on point M and mark an arc to cross arc MN at O.

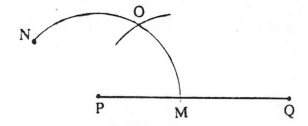

(**Note** that m∠ACE = y^0 = m∠OPM if $\overrightarrow{PO}$ were to be drawn.)

Step 3: Put the metallic point of the compass on point I and open the compass to point G. With this compass opening and with the metallic point of the compass on point O, draw an arc to cross arc MO at K. Using a pencil and

702

a ruler, draw $\overrightarrow{PO}$ and $\overrightarrow{PK}$.

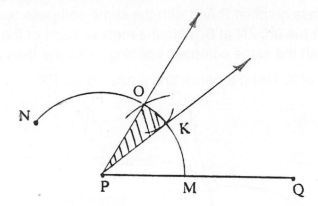

(**Note**: m∠OPK = m∠FHJ). The shaded part is ∠OPK (which is equal to ∠FHJ which is subtracted from ∠OPM (which is equal to ∠ACE). The remaining angle after this subtraction is ∠KPM which is y^0 - z^0.

Example 9
Given an angle of measure of x^0 below, construct an angle of $3x^0$.

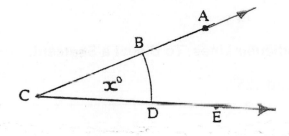

Solution
Step 1: Draw $\overline{PQ}$ with a length of about 5 cm. Put the metallic point of the compass on point C and open the compass to point D. With the same compass opening, put the metallic point of the compass on point P, and then draw an arc to cross the $\overline{PQ}$ at Z.

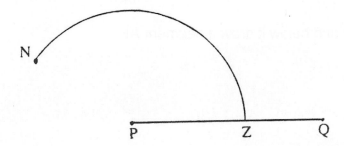

Step 2: Put the metallic point of the compass on point D and open the compass to

703

point B. With this compass opening, put the metallic point of the compass on point Z, and then mark an arc to intersect arc ZN at R. With the metallic point of the compass on point R and with the same compass opening, draw an arc to intercept the arc ZN at S. With the metallic point of the compass on point S, and with the same compass opening, draw the third arc which intercepts arc ZN at X. Using a pencil and a ruler, draw $\overrightarrow{PX}$.

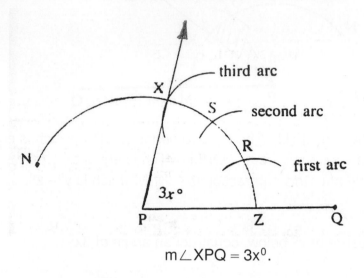

$$m\angle XPQ = 3x^0.$$

Construction of Perpendicular Lines, To Bisect a Segment, Construction of $22\frac{1}{2}^0$ and 135^0.

Example 10
What are perpendicular lines?
Solution
Two lines are perpendicular if they intersect to form a right angle. A right angle is an angle which has a measure of 90^0.

Example 11
Construct a perpendicular line from a point P to the segment AB.
Solution
Step 1: Mark a point P and below it draw a segment AB.

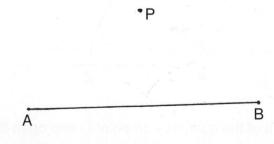

Step 2: With the metallic point of the compass on point P and with a radius of about 5 cm, draw an arc to cross $\overline{AB}$ at points X and Y.

Step 3: With the metallic point of the compass at point X and with the compass opening more than half the length of $\overline{XY}$, draw an arc below $\overline{XY}$. With the same compass opening and with the metallic point of the compass on the point Y, draw the second arc below $\overline{XY}$ to intersect the first arc at point Q.

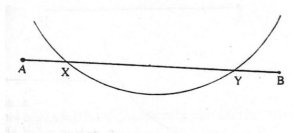

Step 4: Using a pencil and a ruler, draw the ray PQ. PQ is perpendicular to $\overline{AB}$.

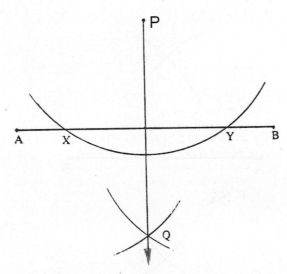

Example 12

Bisect $\overline{AB}$ which is 5 cm.

Solution

Step 1: Using a ruler and pencil, draw $\overline{AB}$ which is 5 cm long. To draw $\overline{AB}$ which is 5 cm long, put the ruler on the paper and draw a segment from the 0 marking along the centimeter scale to the 5 centimeter marking. Label the ends of the segments A and B. With the metallic point of the compass on point A and with the radius of the compass opening more than half of $\overline{AB}$, draw an arc above and below $\overline{AB}$.

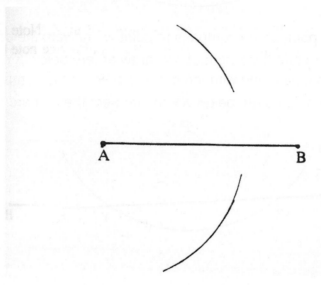

Step 2: With the metallic point of the compass on point B and with the same radius or compass opening as in Step 1, draw an arc above $\overline{AB}$ to cross the arc drawn in Step 1 at point X and also draw an arc below $\overline{AB}$ to cross the arc drawn in Step 1 at point Y.

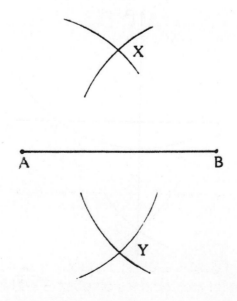

Step 3: Using a pencil and a ruler, draw the line XY to intersect $\overline{AB}$ at Z. Note that the point Z bisects $\overline{AB}$ and therefore $\overline{AZ} = \overline{ZB}$. We can also state that Z is the midpoint of $\overline{AB}$.

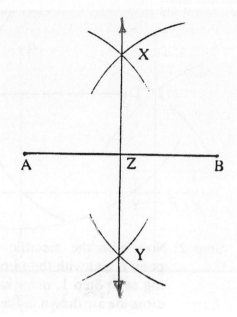

Example 13

Construct an angle of $22\frac{1}{2}^{0}$.

Solution

Step 1: Construct an angle of 90^{0}(See Example 1 for the construction method.)

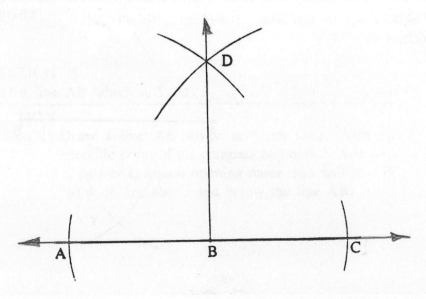

Step 2: Bisect the 90^{0} angle in Step 1 into two equal parts of 45^{0} as shown:
   With the metallic point of the compass on point B and with a radius 5 cm or

compass opening of 5 cm, draw an arc to cross $\overrightarrow{BC}$ at Z. With the same compass opening and still with the metallic point of the compass at point B, draw another arc to cross $\overrightarrow{BD}$ at P.

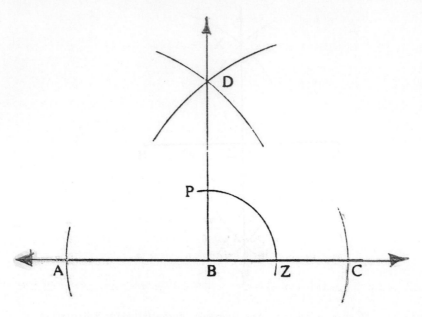

Step 3: With any convenient radius (about 6 cm) or any convenient compass opening, put the metallic point of the compass on point Z and draw an arc and with the same radius or with the same compass opening, put the metallic point of the compass at point P and draw an arc. Both arcs must intersect at point K. Using a pencil and a ruler, draw the ray BK. m∠KBC is 45⁰. Note that the $\overrightarrow{BK}$ crossed the arc PZ at M. (The convenient radius or the compass opening in Step 3 can be any length which is more than half of the length of the arc PZ.)

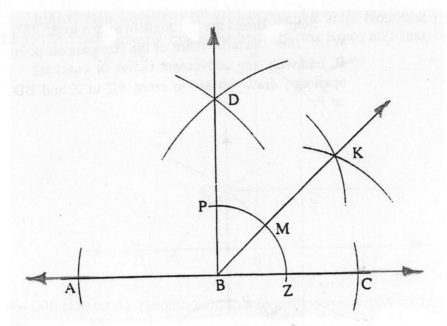

Step 4: Bisect $\angle KBC$ which is 45^0 to get $22\frac{1}{2}^0$. With the metallic point of the compass on point Z and with any convenient radius (about 4 cm) or compass opening, draw an arc, and with the same radius or with the same compass opening, and with the metallic point of the compass at point M, draw an arc. Both arcs must intersect at point G. Using a pencil and a ruler, draw the ray BG. $\angle GBC = 22\frac{1}{2}^0$.

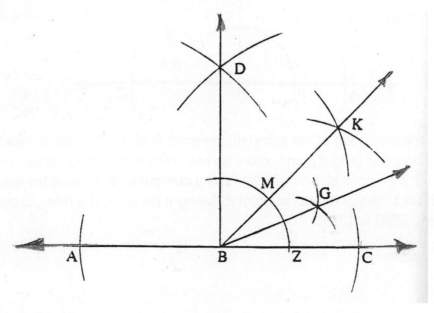

Example 14
Construct an angle of 135^0.

709

Step 1: Construct a 90⁰ angle (See Example 1 for the construction method.)

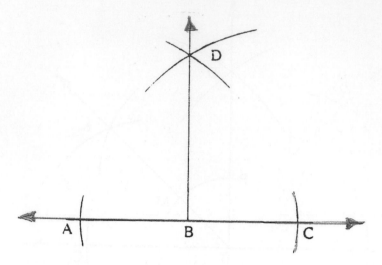

Step 2: Bisect ∠ABD. With the metallic point of the compass on point B and with any convenient radius (about 2 cm), draw an arc to cross $\overrightarrow{BA}$ at P and also to cross $\overrightarrow{BD}$ at K. The bisection of the ∠ABD is continued in Step 3.

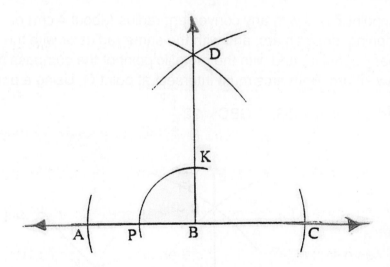

Step 3: With the metallic point of the compass on point P and with a convenient compass opening (about 5 cm), draw an arc. With the metallic point of the compass on point K, and with the same compass opening, draw another arc. Both arcs must intersect at point Z. Using a pencil and a ruler, draw the ray BZ. m∠ZBC is 135⁰.

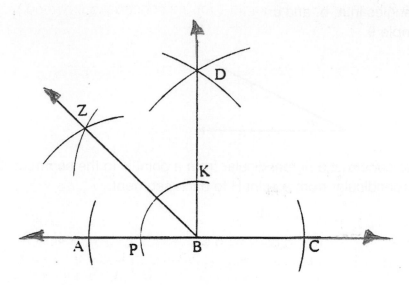

(Note that $m\angle ZBD = 45^0$ and $m\angle KBC = 90^0$ and so,
$m\angle ZBD + m\angle KBC = 45^0 + 90^0 = 135^0$).

Exercises

1. A compass may be used to draw arcs. True or false?
2. Describe how you can construct a 90^0 angle, and then construct a 90^0 angle. Hint: See Example 1.
3. Describe how you can construct a 60^0 angle, and then construct a 60^0 angle. Hint: See Example 2.
4. Describe how you can construct a 30^0 angle, and then construct a 30^0 angle. Hint: See Example 3.
5. Describe how you can construct a 15^0 angle, and then construct a 15^0 angle. Hint: See Example 4.
6. Describe how you can construct a 45^0 angle, and then construct a 45^0 angle. Hint: See Example 5.
7. Describe how you can bisect a 60^0 angle, and then draw a 60^0 angle with a protractor and then bisect the 60^0 angle. Hint: See Example 6.
8. Use a protractor to draw two angles of measures 30^0 and 45^0. (Hint: See the section on how to draw angles with a protractor). Describe how you can construct an angle that contain both the 30^0 and 45^0 angles, and then construct the angle that contains both the 30^0 and the 45^0 angles. Hint: See Example 7.
9. Using the diagrams of the 30^0 and 45^0 angles in Exercise 8, explain how you could construct an angle of 45^0 - 30^0, and then construct an angle of 45^0 - 30^0. Hint: See Example 8.
10. Given an angle of measure x^0, describe how you can construct an angle of measure:

    a. $2x^0$ **b.** $3x^0$ **c.** $4x^0$

Construct the angles in **a**, **b**, and **c**.
Hint: See Example 9.

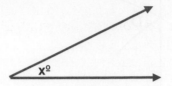

11. Describe how to construct a perpendicular from a point K to the segment XY.
Construct a perpendicular from a point H to each segment.

a.   **b.**

                                                                •H

         •H

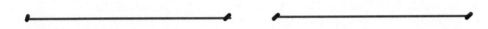

Hint: See Example 11.
12. a. Describe how you can bisect any line.
    b. Explain what is meant by "to bisect a line".
    c. Using a pencil and a ruler, draw a segment that is 6 cm long, and then
       bisect the segment.
    d. Using a pencil and a ruler, draw a segment that is 8 cm long, and then
       bisect the segment.
    Hint: See Example 12.

13. a. Explain how to construct an angle of $22\frac{1}{2}^{0}$.

    b. Construct an angle of $22\frac{1}{2}^{0}$.

    Hint: See Example 13.
14. a. Explain how to construct an angle of 135^{0}.
    b. Construct an angle of 135^{0}.
    Hint: See Example 14

FUNCTIONS

A **function** is a relationship between two sets of numbers such that each **input value** corresponds to exactly one **output value**.

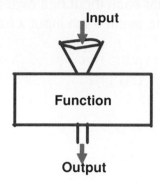

How to Determine if a Relationship is a Function
The condition for a relationship to be a function is that each input must have exactly one output.

Example 1:
Explain why the relationship in figure **a** is a function but the relationship in figure **b** is not a function.

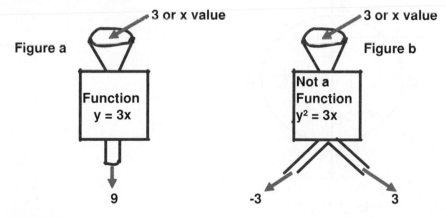

Solution
a. When x = 3, y = 3x becomes y = 3 × 3 = 9. The relationship is a function because each input gives exactly one output.

b. When x = 3, y² = 3x becomes y² = 3 × 3 = 9.

$$y^2 = 9$$

$$\sqrt{y^2} = \sqrt{9}$$ Take the square root of both sides of the equation in order to find the value of y.

$$y = \pm 3$$

So, the relation is not a function because each input gives 2 outputs. In this case, the two outputs are -3 and +3.

Example 2
Determine if y = 2x is a function.
Solution
The condition for a relationship to be a function is that each input has exactly one output. Make an input-output table, and then check to see if each input x has only one output for y.

x (input)	y = 2x (output)
0	2 · 0 = 0
1	2 · 1 = 2
2	2 · 2 = 4
3	2 · 3 = 6
4	2 · 4 = 8

Since each input has exactly one output, the relationship is a function.

Example 3
Observe the diagram and determine if the relationship represents a function.

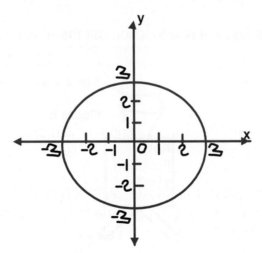

Solution
The relationship is not a function because when the input is x = 0 the output y has two values of 3 and -3. Therefore when x = 0, y = 3 or -3.

A set of ordered pairs
A set of ordered pairs can be represented by using braces to enclose the set as shown: An example of a set of ordered pairs is {(1, 4), (2, 8), (10, 15)}.

Example 4
Determine whether each set of ordered pairs is a function or not.

a. {(2, 5), (4, 3), (4, 6), (5, 6)}   **b.** {(3, 2), (4, 11), (6, 13), (7, 11)}

Solution

a. The ordered pairs (4, 3) and (4, 6) have the same first coordinates, and therefore, this relation is not a function. The condition for a function is that each input must have exactly one output.

b. None of the ordered pairs have the same first coordinates, and therefore, this relation is a function.

Another Condition for a Function.

In a function, all of the first coordinates must be different but some of the second coordinates may be the same.

Example 5

a. A relation is a pairing between two sets of numbers. Explain why in Table 1 the relation is not a function but the relation in Table 2 is a function.

Table 1

x	y
1	6
2	9
3	13
2	8
4	15

Table 2

x	y
6	28
8	48
9	48
12	56
15	69

b. Explain why {(4, 6), (5, 8), (5, 10), (6, 13)} is not a function but {(3, 7), (4, 9), (5, 12), (6, 9)} is a function.

Solution

a. The set of ordered pairs from Table 1 is {(1, 6), (2, 9), (3, 13), (2, 8), (4, 15)}. The relation in Table 1 is not a function because the ordered pairs (2, 9) and (2, 8) have the same first coordinate of 2. In a function all the first coordinates must be different.

The set of ordered pairs in Table 2 is {(6, 28), (8, 48), (9, 48), (12, 56), (15, 69)}. The relation in Table 2 is a function because none of the ordered pairs have the same first coordinate. Considering the ordered pairs (8, 48) and (9, 48), their second coordinates are the same but a function may have the same second coordinates.

b. The relation of the set of ordered pairs {(4, 6), (5, 8), (5, 10), (6, 13)} is not a function because the ordered pairs (5, 8) and (5, 10) have the same first coordinate of 5. The relation of the ordered pairs {(3, 7), (4, 9), (5, 12), (6, 9)} is a function because none of the first coordinates are the same.

Domain and Range

The set of all possible input values is the domain, and therefore, considering ordered pairs (x, y), the first coordinates in the set of ordered pairs are the domain of the relation. The set of all possible output values is the range, and therefore, considering ordered pairs (x, y), the second coordinates are the range of the relation.

So, a **function has a domain and a range**.

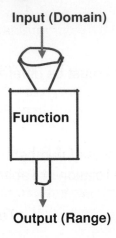

Input (Domain)

Function

Output (Range)

Example 6

Describe the domain and the range of the ordered pairs {(3, 5), (7, 8), (6, 9)}.

Solution

The first coordinates in the set of ordered pairs are the domain of the relation, and therefore, the domain of the ordered pair is {3, 7, 6}. The second coordinates in the set of ordered pairs are the range, and therefore, the range of the ordered pairs is {5, 8, 9,}.

Example 7

Find the domain and the range of the set of each relation.

a. {(2, 4), (2, 7), (4, 9), (7, 9)}

b. {(3, 10), (4, 12), (7, 10), (9, 14)}

c.

x	y
2	8
3	12
5	16
9	19

d.

x	y
5	1
6	4
8	10
9	14
2	-1

Solution

a. The first coordinates in the set of ordered pairs are the domain of the relation, and therefore, the domain of the ordered pair is {2, 4, 7}. Notice that the ordered pairs (2, 4) and (2, 7) have the same first coordinates of 2, however the 2 is not repeated in the domain.

The second coordinates in the set of ordered pairs are the range of the relation, and therefore, the range of the ordered pair is {4, 7, 9}. Notice that the ordered pairs (4, 9) and (7, 9) have the same second coordinate of 9 however the 9 is not repeated in the range.

b. The first coordinates in the set of ordered pairs are the domain of the relation, and therefore, the domain of the ordered pair is {3, 4, 7, 9}.

The second coordinates in the set of ordered pairs are the range of the relation, and therefore, the range of the ordered pair is {10, 12, 14}. Notice that the ordered pair (3, 10) and (7, 10) have the same second coordinate of 10, however the 10 is not repeated in the range.

c. The set of ordered pairs from the table is {(2, 8), (3, 12), (5, 16), (9. 19)}.

The first coordinates in a set of ordered pairs are the domain of the relation and the second coordinates are the range of the relation. So, the domain is {2, 3, 5, 9} and the range is {8, 12, 16, 19}.

d. The set of ordered pairs from the table is {(5, 1), (6, 4), (8, 10), (9, 14), (2, -1)}.

The first coordinates in a set of ordered pairs are the domain of the relation, and the second coordinates are the range of the relation. So, the domain is {(2, 5, 6, 8, 9)} and the range is {(-1, 1, 4, 10, 14)}. Notice that both the domain and the range are in order of magnitude from the least number to the greatest number.

Evaluating Functions

A function notation can be used to describe a function. In the function notation, f represents the function, the input value is x and the output value is f(x).

The f(x) is read "f of x." For example, the function $y = 3x + 4$, is written in the function notation form as $f(x) = 3x + 4$.

Example 8

Find $f(-1)$, $f(0)$, $f(3)$, and $f(5)$ of the function $y = 3x + 4$.

Solution

$y = 3x + 4$

$f(x) = 3x + 4$ Function notation or function equation.

$f(-1) = 3(-1) + 4 = -3 + 4 = 1$ Substitute $x = -1$ into the function equation.

$f(0) = 3(0) + 4 = 0 + 4 = 4$ Substitute $x = 0$ into the function equation.

$f(3) = 3(3) + 4 = 9 + 4 = 13$ Substitute $x = 3$ into the function equation.

$f(5) = 3(5) + 4 = 15 + 4 = 19$ Substitute $x = 5$ into the function equation.

Example 9

The relation in the table is a function. Find $f(0)$, $f(2)$, and $f(-1)$.

x	y
-2	-4
-1	-2
0	1
1	3
2	5
3	7

Solution

Use the table to find y for each x value as requested in the question as shown:

f(x) = y	Function notation.
f(0) = 1	Given in the table
f(2) = 5	Given in the table
f(-1) = -2	Given in the table.

Example 10

The graph shows a function. Find f(-1), f(0), and f(3).

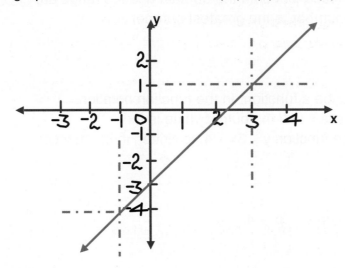

Solution

Use the graph to find y for each value as requested in the question as follows:

f(x) = y	Function notation.
f(-1) = -4	From the graph when x = -1, y = -4.
f(0) = -3	From the graph when x = 0, y = -3.
f(3) = 1	From the graph when x = 3, y = 1.

Exercises

1. Explain "function."

2. What is a domain and a range with respect to a function?

3. Determine if each relationship represents a function. Hint: See Example 1.

    a. y = 3x   **b**. y = 2x + 1   **c**. y = 2x - 1

4. Observe the diagram and determine if the relationship represents a function.
   Hint: See Example 3.

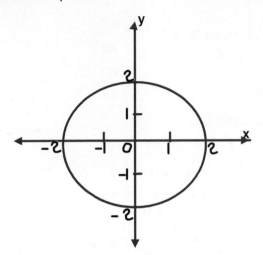

5. Determine whether each set of ordered pairs is a function. Hint: See Example 4.
   a. {(3, 6), (4, 7), (5, 11), (5, 13)}.   **b.** {(2, 3), (3, 6), (5, 11)}.
   c. {(4, 10), (6, 13), (7, 15), (8, 17)}.   **d.** {(5, 7), (6, 9), (8, 9)}.
6. Explain why the relation in Table 1 is not a function but the relation in Table 2 is a
   function. Why is the relation in Table 3 a function but the relation in Table 4 is not a
   function? Hint: See Example 5a.

Table 1

x	y
-1	2
0	4
1	6
1	7

Table 2

x	y
2	3
3	5
4	7
8	2

Table 3

x	y
0	5
1	7
2	9
3	11

Table 4

x	y
3	11
4	13
5	16
3	10

7. Explain why {(5, 7), (6, 9), (8, 11), (5, 8)} is not a function but
   {(4, 8), (5, 11), (7, 15), (9, 18)} is a function. Hint: See Example 5b.
8. Describe the domain and the range of the set of each ordered pair.
   Hint: See Example 6.
   a. {(2, 11), (5, 16), (7, 20)}   **b.** {(4, 3), (6, 7), (8, 12)}
   c. {(6, 2), (8, 0), (10, 3)}   **d.** {(10, 0), (11, 4), (12, 7)}
9. Find the domain and range of the set of each ordered pair. Hint: See Example 7.
   a. (0, 3), (2, 6), (4, 2), (2, 7)}   **b.** {(6, 2), (8, 4), (6, 4)}
10. Find f(-1), f(0), f(2), and f(4) of each function. Hint; See Example 8.
    a. y = 2x + 1   **b.** y = 3x + 1   **c.** y = 2x - 2
11. The relation in each table is a function. Find f(0), f(2), and f(4) of each table.
    Hint: See Example 9.

x	y
-1	4
0	5
2	7
3	12
4	16

a.

x	y
0	1
1	3
2	6
3	7
4	12

b.

x	y
0	12
2	17
3	23
4	29
5	37

c.

12. The graph shows a function. Find f(1), f(0), and f(3).
Hint: See Example 10 and also when $x = 0$, $y = 0$.

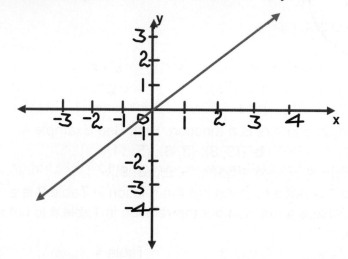

Challenge Questions

13. Give the domain and the range of each function.

x	y
0	12
1	17
6	29
9	44
11	58

a.

x	y
5	2
7	5
9	11
6	2
7	6

b.

c. {(2, 8), (3, 12), (5, 17), (7, 21)}   **d.** {(1, 8), (6, 0), (7, 3), (10, 15)}

14. Explain why the relation in Table 1 is a function but the relation in Table 2 is not a function.

(Tables 1 and 2 are shown on the next page.)

x	y
3	7
4	9
5	10
8	14

Table 1

x	y
2	7
3	18
5	11
3	9

Table 2

LINEAR FUNCTIONS

Any equation of the form $f(x) = 3x + 1$ is a linear function because when the graph of $f(x) = 3x + 1$ is plotted, all the points lie on a straight line. So, the graph of a linear function is a straight line. Note that a linear function does not have any variable that has exponents.

How to Graph a Linear Function or a Linear Equation and How to Tell That an Equation is a Linear Function.

Example 1
a. Graph $y = 3x + 2$
b. Explain why $y = 3x + 2$ is a linear function by using the graph in the solution of Example **1a**.
Solution
a. Step 1: Assign a value to x and then find the corresponding value of y and make a table of the values as shown:

x	y = 3x +2	(x, y)
-1	y = 3(-1) + 2 = -3 + 2 = -1	(-1, -1)
0	y = 3(0) + 2 = 0 + 2 = 2	(0, 2)
1	y = 3(1) + 2 = 3 + 2 = 5	(1, 5)
2	y = 3(2) + 2 = 6 + 2 = 8	(2, 8)

Step 2: From the table in Step 1, the ordered pairs (x, y) are (-1, -1), (0, 2), (1, 5), and (2, 8). Graph the ordered pairs and then draw a line through the points. Label the horizontal axis x and label the vertical axis y.
Hint: Review the chapter on Coordinate Geometry and slope of a line.

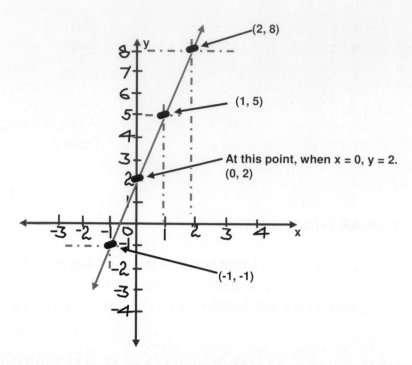

b. $y = 3x + 2$ is a function because the graph of $y = 3x + 2$ in solution **a** is a straight line. So, $y = 3x + 2$ can be written in the function notation as $f(x) = 3x + 2$.

How to Write the Equation for a Linear Function From a Graph

Example 2

Write the rule or the equation for the linear function of the graph.

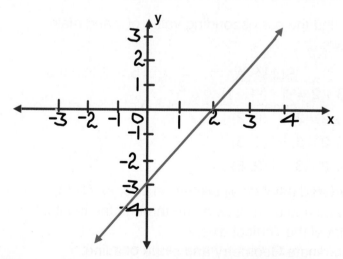

Solution

Setup: The graph is a straight line, and therefore, we can write the general equation of a straight line as $y = mx + b$ where m = slope of the line, b = intercept on the y-axis, x = x coordinate and y = y coordinate. Similarly, we can write $y = mx + b$ in the function form as:

722

$$f(x) = mx + b \text{ ────────────────[A]}$$

(See also the chapter on "Slope of a Line" and also "Coordinate Geometry" in the MathMasters Series.)

Step 1: Find b by identifying the y-intercept from the graph.

The intercept on the y-axis is -3, so, b = -3.

Step 2: Find m by locating a point on the line such as (2, 0) and then substituting (2, 0) and b = -3 into the equation [A] as shown:

$$f(x) = mx + b$$

$$0 = m(2) + (-3)$$ $f(x) = y = 0, x = 2, b = -3.$

$$0 = 2m - 3 \text{ _____[B]}$$

m(2) is the same as 2m and + (- = -, therefore, + (-3 = -3

$$0 + 3 = 2m - 3 + 3$$ Add 3 to both sides of the equation [B] in order to isolate 2m from -3.

$$3 = 2m \text{ _____} [C]$$

$$-3 + 3 = 0$$

$$\frac{3}{2} = \frac{2m}{2}$$ Divide both sides of equation [C] by 2 in order to obtain the value of m.

$$\frac{3}{2} = \frac{\overset{1}{2m}}{\underset{1}{2}}$$

$$\frac{3}{2} = m, \text{ or } m = \frac{3}{2}.$$

The rule or the equation of $f(x) = \frac{3}{2}x + (-3)$. Substitute $m = \frac{3}{2}$ and b = -3 into the general linear equation of $f(x) = mx + b$.

$$= \frac{3}{2}x - 3$$ + (- = -, therefore, + (-3 = -3.

How to Write the Equation for a Linear Function From a Table

Example 3

Write the rule or the equation of the linear function using the ordered pairs in the table.

x	y
-2	-3
-1	-1
0	1
1	3
2	5

Solution

Setup: The general equation for a linear function is $f(x) = mx + b$ where m = slope, b = y-intercept of the line, x = x-coordinate, and y = y-coordinate.

Step 1: Find b from the table. From the coordinate geometry, the y-intercept occurs when $x = 0$, so, from the table, the y-intercept occurs when $x = 0$.

From the table, when $x = 0$, $y = 1$, so, the y-intercept is 1.

From the general equation of a linear function, which is $f(x) = mx + b$, the y-intercept is b, so, $b = 1$. Therefore, $b = f(0) = 1$ as shown:

$$f(x) = mx + b$$
$$f(0) = m(0) + 1, \text{ therefore, } f(0) = 1.$$

Step 2: Find m by substituting another ordered pair in the table such as (1, 3) into the equation $f(x) = mx + b$ with $b = 1$ as shown:

$$f(x) = mx + b$$

$3 = m(1) + 1$ $f(x) = y = 3$, $x = 1$, and $b = 1$.

$3 = m + 1$ ——————————[A]

$3 - 1 = m + 1 - 1$ Subtract 1 from both sides of the equation [A] in order to obtain the value of m.

$2 = m$ $1 - 1 = 0$

The rule or the equation for $f(x) = 2x + 1$ Substitute $m = 2$ and $b = 1$ into the general linear equation of $f(x) = mx + b$.

Exercises

1. Explain what is meant by a linear function. Hint: See the preceding pages.

2. Graph each equation. From your graph, explain why the equation is a linear function. Hint: See Example 1.

    a. $y = 2x + 1$ **b**. $y = 3x - 1$ **c**. $y = 2x + 2$

    d. $y = 3x + 3$ **e**. $y = 2x + 3$ **f**. $y = 2x - 2$

3. Write the rule or the equation for each linear function or graph. Hint: See Example 2.

a.
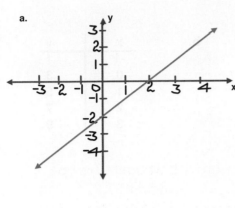

b.
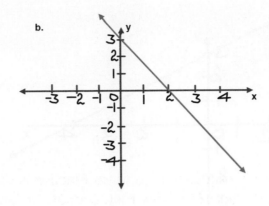

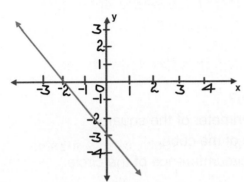

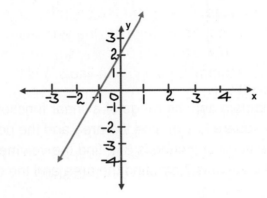

4. Write the rule or the equation for each linear function. Hint: See Example 3

a.

x	y
1	0
2	1
3	3

b.

x	y
0	4
1	2
2	0
3	-2

c.

x	y
-4	0
-2	1
0	2
2	3

Challenge Questions

5. Write the rule or the equation for each linear graph or data.

(The graph and the data are located on the next page.)

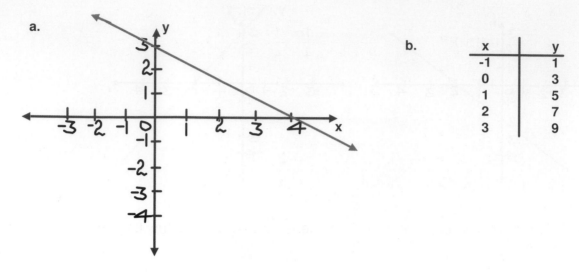

a.

b.

x	y
-1	1
0	3
1	5
2	7
3	9

Cumulative Review

1. What is the domain and the range of a linear function?

2. The side of a square is 2 m, find the area and the perimeter of the square.

3. Given that the edge of a cube is 3 ft, find the volume of the cube.

4. The radius of a circle is 7 cm, find the area and the circumference of the circle.

EXPONENTIAL FUNCTIONS

Exponential functions have the form

$$f(x) = p \cdot a^x, \text{ where } a > 0 \text{ and } a \neq 1.$$

When $x = 0$, $f(x) = p \cdot a^0$

$$= p \cdot 1 \qquad\qquad a^0 = 1$$

$$= p.$$

So, the y-intercept is $f(0) = p$ because at the y-intercept, $x = 0$. Since the expression **a^x is defined for all values x**, the domain of $f(x) = p \cdot a^x$ is all real numbers.

How to Graph Exponential Functions

Example 1

Graph $f(x) = 2^x$

Solution

To graph any exponential function, create a table for the exponential function, and then use the table to graph the function as shown:

Step 1: Create a table for the exponential function by assigning a value to x and then find the corresponding value for y as shown:

726

x	y = f(x) = 2^x	y	(x, y)
-2	$y = f(-2) = 2^{-2} = \dfrac{1}{2^2} = \dfrac{1}{2 \cdot 2} = \dfrac{1}{4}$	$\dfrac{1}{4}$	$(-2, \dfrac{1}{4})$
-1	$y = f(-1) = 2^{-1} = \dfrac{1}{2^1} = \dfrac{1}{2}$	$\dfrac{1}{2}$	$(-1, \dfrac{1}{2})$
0	$y = f(0) = 2^0 = 1$	1	(0, 1)
1	$y = f(1) = 2^1 = 2$	2	(1, 2)
2	$y = f(2) = 2^2 = 2 \cdot 2 = 4$	4	(2, 4)

Step 2: Use the ordered pairs of (x, y) from the table to graph the function as shown:

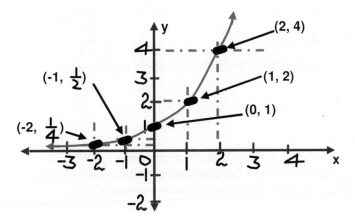

Example 2

Graph $f(x) = 3 \cdot (\dfrac{1}{3})^x$

Solution

To graph any exponential function, create a table for the exponential function and then use the table to graph the function as shown:

Step 1: Create a table for the exponential function by assigning a value to x and then find the corresponding value for y as shown:

x	$y = f(x) = 3 \cdot (\frac{1}{3})^x$	y	(x, y)
-2	$y = f(-2) = 3 \cdot (\frac{1}{3})^{-2} = 3 \cdot \dfrac{1}{(\frac{1}{3})^2} = 3 \cdot (\dfrac{1}{(\frac{1}{9})}) = 3 \cdot (1 \times \dfrac{9}{1}) = 3 \times 9 = 27$	27	(-2, 27)
-1	$y = f(-1) = 3 \cdot (\frac{1}{3})^{-1} = 3 \cdot \dfrac{1}{(\frac{1}{3})^1} = 3 \cdot (\dfrac{1}{\frac{1}{3}}) = 3 \cdot 1 \cdot \dfrac{3}{1} = 3 \times 3 = 9$	9	(-1, 9)
0	$y = f(0) = 3 \cdot (\frac{1}{3})^0 = 3 \cdot 1 = 3$	3	(0, 3)
1	$y = f(1) = 3 \cdot (\frac{1}{3})^1 = 3 \cdot \frac{1}{3} = 1$	1	(1, 1)
2	$y = f(2) = 3 \cdot (\frac{1}{3})^2 = 3 \cdot \dfrac{1^2}{3^2} = 3 \cdot \dfrac{1}{9} = \dfrac{1}{3}$	$\frac{1}{3}$	$(2, \frac{1}{3})$

Step 2: Use the ordered pairs of (x, y) of the table to graph the function as shown:

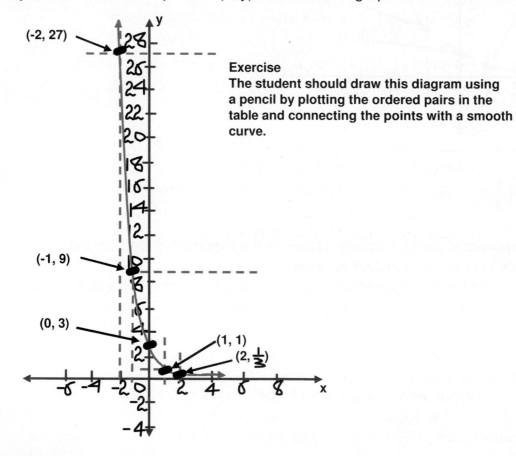

Exercise
The student should draw this diagram using a pencil by plotting the ordered pairs in the table and connecting the points with a smooth curve.

Special Observation
1. Observe that in Example 1, when a > 1, the output f(x) gets larger as the input

728

x gets larger (see both the table and the graph), and this kind of function is called **exponential growth function**.

Recall that the exponential function is in the form $f(x) = p \cdot a^x$ where $a > 0$ and $a \neq 1$, and in the observation of Example 1, $a = 2$.

2. Observe that in Example 2 when $a < 1$, the output $f(x)$ gets smaller as x gets larger (see both the table and the graph), and this kind of function is called an **exponential decay** function. Recall that the exponential function is in the form

$f(x) = p \cdot a^x$ where $a > 0$ and $a \neq 1$, and in the observation of Example 2, $a = \dfrac{1}{3}$.

How to Find f(x) of Exponential Functions

Example 3
Find: **a.** f(-4), **b.** f(0), and **c.** f(3) of the exponential function $f(x) = 2^x$.
Solution

a. $f(x) = 2^x$ —————————————————————[A]

$f(-4) = 2^{-4}$ 　　　　Substitute x = -4 into the equation [A].

$= \dfrac{1}{2^4}$ 　　　　Definition of negative exponents: For all nonzero real

numbers x and all integers n, $x^{-n} = \dfrac{1}{x^n}$. Review exponents.

$= \dfrac{1}{2 \cdot 2 \cdot 2 \cdot 2} = \dfrac{1}{16}$.

b. $f(x) = 2^x$ —————————————————————$\big[B\big]$

$f(0) = 2^0$ 　　　　Substitute x – 0 into the equation $\big[B\big]$.

$= 1$ 　　　　Any nonzero number raised to the power zero = 1.

c. $f(x) = 2^x$ —————————————————————$\big[C\big]$

$f(3) = 2^3$ 　　　　Substitute x = 3 into the equation [C].

$= 2 \cdot 2 \cdot 2$

$= 8$

Exercises
1. Explain an exponential function. Hint: See the preceding pages.
2. How is an exponential graph created? Hint: See Example 1.
3. Graph the following exponential functions. Hint: See Example 1.
　a. $f(x) = 3^x$ 　　　　**b.** $f(x) = 4^x$
4. Graph the following exponential functions. Hint: See Example 2.
　a. $f(x) = 2 \cdot (\dfrac{1}{2})^x$ 　　**b.** $3 \cdot 2^x$ 　　**c.** $4 \cdot (\dfrac{1}{2})^x$ 　　**d.** $f(x) = (\dfrac{2}{3})^x$

5. Find f(-3), f(0), and f(4) for each exponential function.

a. $f(x) = 3^x$ **b .** $f(x) = 10^x$ **c.** $f(x) = 2 \cdot (\frac{1}{2})^x$

6. Explain what is meant by exponential growth function.
   Hint: See the information under "Special Observations."
7. Explain what is meant by exponential decay.
   Hint: See the information under "Special Observations."

Challenge Questions

8. Find f(-2), f(-1), f(0), and f(1) for each exponential function.

   a. $f(x) = 4 \cdot 2^x$ **b.** $f(x) = 2 \cdot 2^x$ **c.** $3 \cdot (\frac{1}{2})^x$

9. Graph the following exponential functions.

   a. $f(x) = 2 \cdot 3^x$ **b.** $f(x) = 4 \cdot (\frac{1}{2})^x$

QUADRATIC FUNCTION

The quadratic function is a function of the form $y = ax^2 + bx + c$ where a, b and c are real numbers and $a \neq 0$. c is the y-intercept. All the graphs of a quadratic function have the same basic shape called a parabola. The simplest quadratic function is $y = x^2$. This can be observed from the equation $ax^2 + bx + c$, when a = 1, b = 0 and c = 0, then $y = x^2$.

How to Make a Graph of the Quadratic Function of the Form $f(x) = ax^2 + bx + c$.

Example 1
Draw a graph of each of the quadratic functions.
a. $y = x^2$, from the graph, what is the minimum value of the function?
b. $y = -x^2$, from the graph what is the maximum value of the function?
c. Compare the minimum and the maximum values in **a** and **b**.
Solution
a. To draw any quadratic function, create a table for the quadratic function, and then use the table to make the graph by assigning numbers to x and then finding the corresponding values for y as shown:
Step 1: Create a table by assigning numbers to x and then finding the corresponding values for y as shown:

x	y = f(x) = x²	y	(x, y)
-2	y = f(-2) = (-2)² = -2 • (-2) = 4	1	(-2, 4)
-1	y = f(-1) = (-1)² = -1 • (-1) = 1	4	(-1, 1)
0	y = f(0) = 0² = 0	0	(0, 0)
1	y = f(1) = 1² = 1 • 1 = 1	1	(1, 1)
2	y = f(2) = 2² = 2 • 2 = 4	4	(2, 4)

Step 2: Use the ordered pairs of (x, y) in the table in Step 1 to graph the function as shown:

Plot the ordered points and then connect them with a smooth curve as shown:

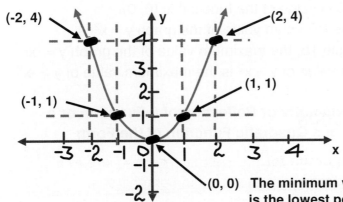

Exercise
The student should draw this graph by plotting the ordered pairs on a graph paper and connect them with a pencil.

The minimum value of the function is the lowest point on the graph, and this lowest point is the vertex. The minimum value or point is (0, 0).

b. Step 1: Create a table by assigning numbers to x and then finding the corresponding values for y as shown:

x	y = f(x) = -x²	y	(x, y)
-2	y = f(-2) = -(-2)² = -(-2) • (-2) = -4	-4	(-2, -4)
-1	y = f(-1) = -(-1)² = -(-1) • (-1) = -1	-1	(-1, -1)
0	y = f(0) = -0² = 0	0	(0, 0)
1	y = f(1) = -(1)² = -(1) • (1) = -1	-1	(1, -1)
2	y = f(2) = -(2)² = -(2) • (2) = -4	-4	(2, -4)

Step 2: Use the ordered pairs of (x, y) in the table in Step 1 to graph the function as shown:

Plot the ordered points and then connect them with a smooth curve.

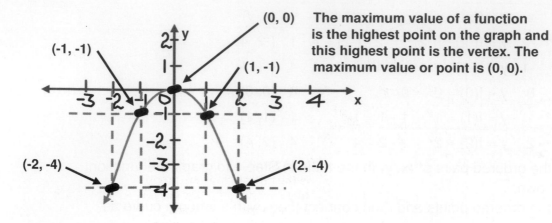

(0, 0) The maximum value of a function is the highest point on the graph and this highest point is the vertex. The maximum value or point is (0, 0).

The maximum value of the function is the highest point on the graph, and the highest point is the vertex. The maximum value of the function is (0, 0).

c. From the solution of Example **1a**, the minimum value of the graph $y = x^2$ is (0, 0) and from the solution of Example **1b**, the maximum value of the graph $y = -x^2$ is (0, 0), and therefore, the minimum value of $y = x^2$ is the maximum value of $y = -x^2$.

How to Solve Problems Involving Symmetry or Reflection of a Function or a Parabola and How to Make a Graph of a Quadratic Function of the Form $f(x) = ax^2 + bx + c$.

Example 2

a. In Example 1, the graphs of $y = x^2$ and $y = -x^2$ are parabolas. Is it correct to say that the function $y = -x^2$ is a reflection of the function $y = x^2$ if both $y = x^2$ and $y = -x^2$ are put on the same graph paper with a common vertex of (0, 0)?

b. Considering the graph of $y = x^2$ or $y = -x^2$ in Example 1, is it correct to state that the vertical line drawn through the vertex (0, 0) is the line of symmetry or the axis of symmetry?

Solution

a. Yes, $y = -x^2$ is the reflection of $y = x^2$ with the x-axis as the line of symmetry or axis of symmetry as shown in the diagram.

(The diagram is on the next page.)

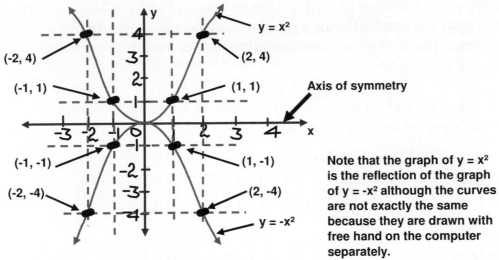

(-2, 4)   y = x²
(2, 4)
(-1, 1)   (1, 1)   **Axis of symmetry**

(-1, -1)   (1, -1)   Note that the graph of y = x²
is the reflection of the graph
(-2, -4)   (2, -4)   of y = -x² although the curves
are not exactly the same
y = -x²   because they are drawn with
free hand on the computer
separately.

Some calculators can be used to draw graphs.

Note: **A flip or a reflection** is the movement of an object by flipping it over a line. The mirror line is known as **a line of reflection**. (See the chapter on Transformations.)

b. Yes, the vertical line drawn through the vertex (0, 0) is the line of symmetry or the axis of symmetry because the vertical line divides the parabola into exactly two equal halves such that one half of the parabola is a reflection of the other half of the parabola as shown:

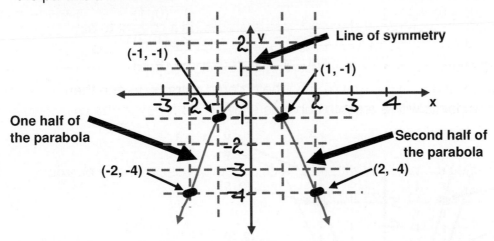

(-1, -1)   **Line of symmetry**
(1, -1)

**One half of
the parabola**   **Second half of
the parabola**

(-2, -4)   (2, -4)

Note: A geometric figure that can be divided into two identical parts is **symmetric**. A line of **symmetry** divides a geometric figure into **exactly two matching halves**.

How to Solve Problems Involving Vertical Translation of Functions or Parabola and How to Draw Graphs of the Quadratic Function of the Form $f(x) = ax^2 + bx + c$. **How to Use Graphs to Solve Functional Problems**

Example 3
a. Graph $y = x^2 - 1$ and $y = x^2 + 1$ on the same coordinate plane.

733

b. Copy the graph of $y = x^2 - 1$ and $y = x^2 + 1$ from the solution of Example **3a**, and then sketch or copy the graph of $y = x^2$ from the solution of Example **1a** on the same coordinate plane. Discuss the **translation** type of the three functions $y = x^2$, $y = x^2 - 1$, and $y = x^2 + 1$.

Solution

a. Step 1: Create a table for $y = x^2 - 1$ by assigning numbers to x and then finding the corresponding values for y as shown:

x	$y = f(x) = x^2 - 1$	y	(x, y)
-2	$y = f(-2) = (-2)^2 - 1 = (-2) \cdot (-2) - 1 = 4 - 1 = 3$	3	(-2, 3)
-1	$y = f(-1) = (-1)^2 - 1 = (-1) \cdot (-1) - 1 = 1 - 1 = 0$	0	(-1, 0)
0	$y = f(0) = 0^2 - 1 = -1$	-1	(0, -1)
1	$y = f(1) = 1^2 - 1 = 1 - 1 = 0$	0	(1, 0)
2	$y = f(2) = 2^2 - 1 = 2 \cdot 2 - 1 = 4 - 1 = 3$	3	(2, 3)

Create a table for $y = x^2 + 1$ by assigning numbers to x and then finding the corresponding values for y as shown:

x	$y = f(x) = x^2 + 1$	y	(x, y)
-2	$y = f(-2) = (-2)^2 + 1 = (-2) \cdot (-2) + 1 = 4 + 1 = 5$	5	(-2, 5)
-1	$y = f(-1) = (-1)^2 + 1 = (-1) \cdot (-1) + 1 = 1 + 1 = 2$	2	(-1, 2)
0	$y = f(0) = 0^2 + 1 = 1$	1	(0, 1)
1	$y = f(1) = 1^2 + 1 = 1 \cdot 1 + 1 = 1 + 1 = 2$	2	(1, 2)
2	$y = f(2) = 2^2 + 1 = 2 \cdot 2 + 1 = 4 + 1 = 5$	5	(2, 5)

Step 2: Graph $y = x^2 - 1$ and $y = x^2 + 1$ by plotting the ordered pairs (x, y) and then connecting the points with a smooth curve as shown:

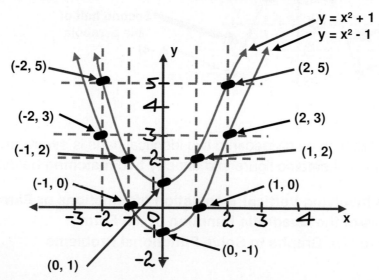

734

b. The 3 graphs $y = x^2 - 1$, $y = x^2 + 1$ and $y = x^2$ are shown below.

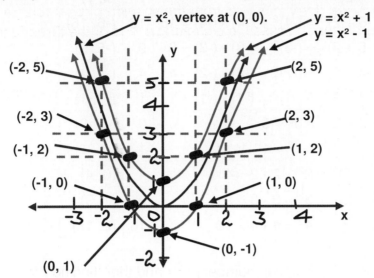

The graphs show that the functions $y = x^2 + 1$ and $y = x^2 - 1$ are vertical translations of the function $y = x^2$ because all the graphs have the same shape, but they are one unit vertically apart on the y-axis. (Hint: **A slide or a translation** is the movement of an object along a straight line. Read more about translation under the chapter on Transformations in the Math Teaching Series.)

How to Solve Problems Involving Horizontal Translation of Functions or Parabolas, and How to Draw Graphs of the Quadratic Function of the Form $f(x) = ax^2 + bx + c$. How to Use Graphs to Solve Functional Problems.

Example 4
a. Draw a graph of the function $y = (x + 2)^2$ and $y = (x - 2)^2$ on the same coordinate plane. Locate where the graphs of $y = (x + 2)^2$ and $y = (x - 2)^2$ intersect and what is the importance of this intersection?
b. Copy the graph of the function $y = (x + 2)^2$ and $y = (x - 2)^2$ from the solution of Example **4a** and then copy the graph of $y = x^2$ from Example **1a** on to the same coordinate plane. Discuss the translation type of the three functions $y = x^2$, $y = (x + 2)^2$, and $y = (x - 2)^2$.
c. Locate where the graphs $y = x^2$ and $y = (x + 2)^2$ intersect. Locate where $y = x^2$ and $y = (x - 2)^2$ intersect.
d. What is the solution of $y = x^2$ and $y = (x + 2)^2$, and $y = x^2$ and $y = (x - 2)^2$?
Solution
a. Step 1: Create a table for $y = (x + 2)^2$ by assigning numbers to x and then finding the corresponding values for y as shown:

x	$y = f(x) = (x + 2)^2$	y	(x, y)
-6	$y = f(-6) = (-6 + 2)^2 = (-4)^2 = (-4) \cdot (-4) = 16$	16	(-6, 16)
-5	$y = f(-5) = (-5 + 2)^2 = (-3)^2 = (-3) \cdot (-3) = 9$	9	(-5, 9)
-4	$y = f(-4) = (-4 + 2)^2 = (-2)^2 = (-2) \cdot (-2) = 4$	4	(-4, 4)
-3	$y = f(-3) = (-3 + 2)^2 = (-1)^2 = (-1) \cdot (-1) = 1$	1	(-3, 1)
-2	$y = f(-2) = (-2 + 2)^2 = 0^2 = 0$	0	(-2, 0)
-1	$y = f(-1) = (-1 + 2)^2 = 1^2 = 1 \cdot 1 = 1$	1	(-1, 1)
0	$y = f(0) = (0 + 2)^2 = 2^2 = 2 \cdot 2 = 4$	4	(0, 4)
1	$y = f(1) = (1 + 2)^2 = 3^2 = 3 \cdot 3 = 9$	9	(1, 9)
2	$y = f(2) = (2 + 2)^2 = 4^2 = 4 \cdot 4 = 16$	16	(2, 16)

Create a table for $y = (x - 2)^2$ by assigning numbers to x and then finding the corresponding values for y as shown:

x	$y = f(x) = (x - 2)^2$	y	(x, y)
-2	$y = f(-2) = (-2 - 2)^2 = (-4)^2 = (-4) \cdot (-4) = 16$	16	(-2, 16)
-1	$y = f(-1) = (-1 - 2)^2 = (-3)^2 = (-3) \cdot (-3) = 9$	9	(-1, 9)
0	$y = f(0) = (0 - 2)^2 = (-2)^2 = (-2) \cdot (-2) = 4$	4	(0, 4)
1	$y = f(1) = (1 - 2)^2 = (-1)^2 = (-1) \cdot (-1) = 1$	1	(1, 1)
2	$y = f(2) = (2 - 2)^2 = 0^2 = 0$	0	(2, 0)
3	$y = f(3) = (3 - 2)^2 = 1^2 = 1 \cdot 1 = 1$	1	(3, 1)
4	$y = f(4) = (4 - 2)^2 = 2^2 = 2 \cdot 2 = 4$	4	(4, 4)
5	$y = f(5) = (5 - 2)^2 = 3^2 = 3 \cdot 3 = 9$	9	(5, 9)
6	$y = f(6) = (6 - 2)^2 = 4^2 = 4 \cdot 4 = 16$	16	(6, 16)

Step 2: Graph $y = x^2 - 1$ and $y = x^2 + 1$ by plotting the ordered pairs (x, y) and then connecting the points with smooth curves as shown:

736

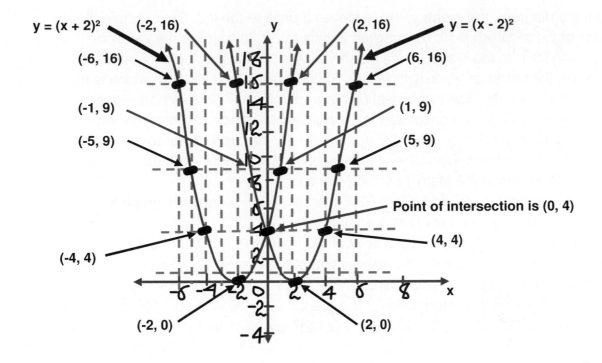

The point of the intersection of $y = (x + 2)^2$ and $y = (x - 2)^2$ on the graph is $(0, 4)$. The point of the intersection of the graph $y = (x + 2)^2$ and the graph $y = (x - 2)^2$ which is $(0, 4)$ is important because the point of the intersection is common to both the graph $y = (x + 2)^2$ and the graph $y = (x - 2)^2$, and therefore, **this common point is the solution to the function** $y = f(x) = (x + 2)^2$ and $y = f(x) = (x - 2)^2$.

b. The graphs of $y = x^2$ (from the solution of Example **1a**), $y = (x + 2)^2$ and $y = (x - 2)^2$ (from the solution of Example **4a**) are shown below.

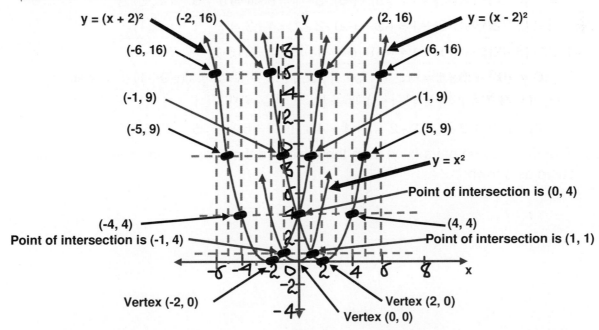

From the diagram, the graph $y = x^2$ is moved 2 units to the left. For example, the vertex of $y = x^2$ which is (0, 0) is moved 2 units to (-2, 0) which is the vertex of $y = (x + 2)^2$. From the diagram, the graph $y = x^2$ is moved 2 units to the right. For example, the vertex of $y = x^2$ which is (0, 0) is moved 2 units to (2, 0) which is the vertex of $y = (x - 2)^2$. The movement of the graph of $y = x^2$, 2 units horizontally to the left and also 2 units horizontally to the right is called **horizontal translation**. Therefore, the functions $y = (x + 2)^2$ and $y = (x - 2)^2$ are **horizontal translations** of $y = x^2$. (Hint: More explanation of translation is given under the topic **Transformations** in the Math Teaching Series.)

c. From the graphs, $y = x^2$ and $y = (x + 2)^2$ intersect at (0, 4), and the graph $y = x^2$ and $y = (x - 2)^2$ intersect at (1, 1).

d. The solution of any function is the point of the intersection of the graphs of the functions. From Example **4c**, the intersection of the graphs $y = x^2$ and $y = (x + 2)^2$ is (0, 4) and therefore the solutions to $y = x^2$ and $y = (x + 2)^2$ are $x = 0$ and $y = 4$. From Example **4c**, the intersection of the graphs $y = x^2$ and $y = (x - 2)^2$ is (1, 1) and therefore, the solutions to $y = x^2$ and $y = (x - 2)^2$ are $x = 1$ and $y = 1$.

Example 5

a. Graph $f(x) = x^2 + x - 1$

b. At what point does the parabola cross the x and y axis?

Solution

a. **Step 1**: Create a table for the quadratic function $f(x) = x^2 + x - 1$ by assigning values to x and then finding the corresponding values of f(x) or y as shown:

x	$f(x) = y = x^2 + x - 1$	y	(x, y)
-3	$f(-3) = (-3)^2 + (-3) - 1 = (-3) \cdot (-3) -3 - 1 = 9 - 4 = 5$	5	(-3, 5)
-2	$f(-2) = (-2)^2 + (-2) - 1 = (-2) \cdot (-2) -2 - 1 = 4 - 3 = 1$	1	(-2, 1)
-1	$f(-1) = (-1)^2 + (-1) - 1 = (-1) \cdot (-1) -1 - 1 = 1 - 2 = -1$	-1	(-1, -1)
0	$f(0) = (0)^2 + 0 - 1 = -1$	-1	(0, -1)
1	$f(1) = (1)^2 + 1 - 1 = 1 \cdot 1 + 1 -1 = 1 + 1 -1 = 1$	1	(1, 1)
2	$f(2) = (2)^2 + 2 - 1 = 2 \cdot 2 + 2 - 1 = 4 + 2 - 1 = 5$	5	(2, 5)

Step 2: Plot the ordered pairs (x, y) from the table and then connect them with a smooth curve as shown:

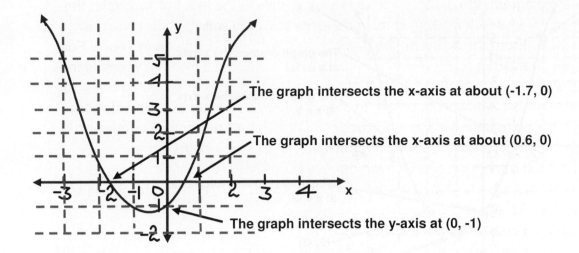

The graph intersects the x-axis at about (-1.7, 0)

The graph intersects the x-axis at about (0.6, 0)

The graph intersects the y-axis at (0, -1)

The intersections on the x-axis may not be correct because the graph is not drawn to scale. The student should try to draw the same graph on actual graph paper and the student may get better values for the points of the intersections because the graph paper is drawn to scale.

b. From the graph of the Solution **5a**, the parabola crosses the x-axis at about x = (0.3, 0) and x = (0.6, 0) and the parabola crosses the y-axis at (0, -1).

Example 6

a. Graph f(x) = (x - 3)(x + 1).

b. Find where the parabola f(x) = (x - 3)(x + 1) crosses the x-axis and the y-axis on the graph.

Solution

a. **Step 1**: Create a table for the parabola or the quadratic function f(x) = (x - 3)(x + 1) by assigning numbers to x and then finding their corresponding y or f(x) values as shown:

x	f(x) = (x - 3)(x + 1)	y	(x, y)
-3	f(-3) = (-3 - 3)(-3 + 1) = (-6)(-2) = 12	12	(-3, 12)
-2	f(-2) = (-2 - 3)(-2 + 1) = (-5)(-1) = 5	5	(-2, 5)
-1	f(-1) = (-1 - 3)(-1 + 1) = (-4)(0) = 0	0	(-1, 0)
0	f(0) = (0 - 3)(0 + 1) = (-3)(1) = -3	-3	(0, -3)
1	f(1) = (1 - 3)(1 + 1) = (-2)(2) = -4	-4	(1, -4)
2	f(2) = (2 - 3)(2 + 1) = (-1)(3) = -3	-3	(2, -3)
3	f(3) = (3 - 3)(3 + 1) = (0)(4) = 0	0	(3, 0)
4	f(4) = (4 - 3)(4 + 1) = (1)(5) = 5	5	(4, 5)

Step 2: Plot the ordered pairs (x, y) from the table and then connect them with a smooth curve as shown:

739

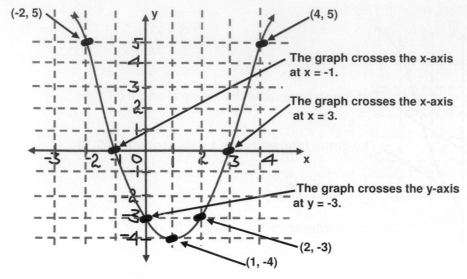

The graph crosses the x-axis at x = -1.

The graph crosses the x-axis at x = 3.

The graph crosses the y-axis at y = -3.

b. From the graph of the solution of Example **6a**, the parabola crosses the x-axis at x = -1 and x = 3.

Exercises

1. State the form or the formula for the quadratic equation. Hint: See the preceding notes.

2. Draw a graph of each quadratic function. Hint: See Example **1**.

   a. $y = 2x^2$ **b**. $y = -2x^2$

   c. From your graphs, what is the minimum value of graph **a**, and what is the maximum value of graph **b**? Select x values from -3 to 3. Hint: See Example 1.

3a. Could you say that the parabola $y = 2x^2$ is a reflection of the parabola $y = -2x^2$ if both parabolas are drawn on the same coordinate plane? Hint: See Example **2a**.

3b. What are the lines of symmetry for the parabolas $y = 2x^2$ and $y = -2x^2$? Hint: See Example **2b**.

4. Create a table for each parabola or quadratic function and use it to make a graph. Hint: See Example **3a**.

   a. $y = x^2 + 2$ **b**. $y = x^2 - 2$ **c**. $y = x^2 - 3$
   d. $y = x^2 + 3$ **e**. $y = x^2 - 4$ **f**. $y = x^2 + 4$

   g. By observing the graphs of your solutions of Exercises **4a**, **4b**, **4c**, and **4d**, discuss the translation type in each case. Hint: See Example **3b**.

5. Create a table for each parabola or quadratic function and use it to make a graph. Hint: See Example **4a**.

   a. $y = (x - 1)^2$ **b**. $y = (x + 1)^2$ **c**. $y = (x + 3)^2$ **d**. $y = (x - 3)^2$

   e. By observing the graphs of your solutions of Exercises **5a**, **5b**, **5c**, and **5d**, discuss the type of translation in each case. Hint: See Example **4b**.

   f. Is it correct to say that the coordinates of the intersecting point of any two graphs is the solution of the equations of the graphs? Hint: See Example **4c**.

6. Graph the following functions. Hint: See Example **5a**.

    a. $f(x) = x^2 - x + 2$ **b.** $f(x) = x^2 + x - 2$ **c.** $f(x) = x^2 + 2x - 1$

    d. $f(x) = 2x^2 - x + 4$ **e.** $f(x) = 2x^2 - x$ **f.** $f(x) = 2x^2 - 2x + 2$

    f. Indicate the points where each graph in your solution to Exercise **6** crosses the x-axis and the y-axis. Hint: See Example **5b**.

7. Graph each function. Hint: see Example **6a**.

    a. $f(x) = (x - 2)(x + 1)$ **b.** $f(x) = (x - 1)(x + 2)$

    c. $f(x) = (x - 3)(x - 1)$ **d.** $f(x) = (x - 2)(x + 2)$

    e. Find where each function crosses the x-axis and the y-axis from your solution to Exercise 7. Hint: See Example **6b**.

Challenge Questions

8. Graph each function of the parabola.

    a. $f(x) = 3x^2$ **b.** $f(x) = (x + 3)(x + 1)$ **c.** $f(x) = 2x^2 - 2x$

    d. $f(x) = -3x^2$ **e.** $f(x) = 2x^2 + 2x - 2$ **f.** $f(x) = (x - 3)^2$

    g. $f(x) = (x + 2)(x - 2)$

REAL WORLD APPLICATIONS OF THE QUADRATIC FUNCTIONS - WORD PROBLEMS

Example 1

Given that $f(x) = -3x^2 + 100x + 250$ represents the profit in dollars for production of x items by a company, how much profit will the company make by producing 15 items?

Solution

f(x) represents the profit of the company when x items are manufactured.

Therefore, f(15) represents the profit in dollars when 15 items are produced.

Find f(15) by substituting x = 15 in the equation $f(x) = 3x^2 + 100x + 250$ as shown:

$f(15) = -3(15)^2 + 100(15) + 250$

       $= -3 \cdot 15 \cdot 15 + 100 \cdot 15 + 250$

       $= -675 + 1{,}500 + 250$ $-3 \cdot 15 \cdot 15 = -675$, $100 \cdot 15 = 1{,}500$

       $= -675 + 1{,}750$ $1{,}500 + 250 = 1{,}750$

       $= 1{,}750 - 675$ Switch the numbers.

       $= 1{,}075$

Therefore, the profit for producing 15 items is $1,075.00.

Example 2

In general, the maximum or the minimum point of a graph is the turning point of a graph. The graph shows the path of a projectile. (Hint: If you throw a baseball in the air, the path of the baseball will be similar to the path of the projectile.)

a. What is the axis of symmetry of the graph of the projectile? Give reasons to support your answer.

b. How long does it take the projectile to return to the ground?

c. Find the maximum height reached by the projectile.

d. Find the time that the projectile takes to reach the maximum height.

e. What is the height of the projectile at 4 seconds and at 12 seconds?

f. How long does it take the projectile to reach a height of 250 feet?

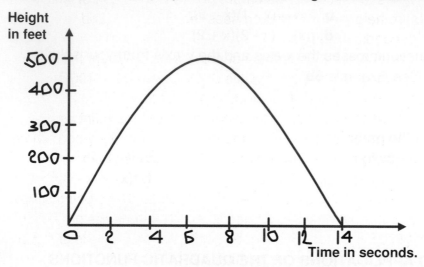

Solution

The graph of the path of the projectile is shown below showing key points of the solutions to the questions. Hint: On the graph, **height in feet** is along the y-axis, and **time in seconds** is along the x-axis.

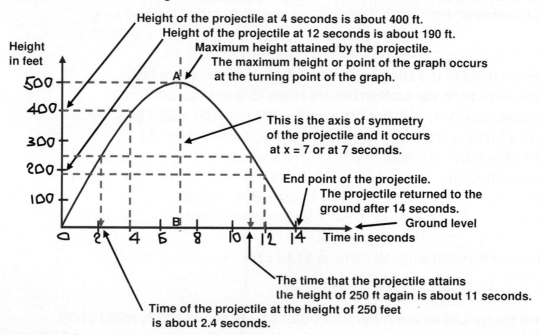

Height of the projectile at 4 seconds is about 400 ft.
Height of the projectile at 12 seconds is about 190 ft.
Maximum height attained by the projectile.
The maximum height or point of the graph occurs at the turning point of the graph.

This is the axis of symmetry of the projectile and it occurs at x = 7 or at 7 seconds.

End point of the projectile.
The projectile returned to the ground after 14 seconds.
Ground level

The time that the projectile attains the height of 250 ft again is about 11 seconds.

Time of the projectile at the height of 250 feet is about 2.4 seconds.

a. The axis of symmetry of the graph of the projectile is x = 7 because x = 7 divides the graph of the projectile into two equal halves such that one half of the graph is a reflection of the other half of the graph.

742

b. The projectile returned to the ground when x = 14, and therefore, the projectile returned to the ground 14 seconds after taking off.

c. The maximum height reached by the projectile occurs at the turning point of the graph which is y = 500 feet. The maximum height on the graph is represented by $\overline{AB}$.

d. The time the projectile takes to reach the maximum height is the point at which the line from the maximum height of 500 feet crosses the time-axis, and from the graph, this occurs at 7 seconds.

e. The height of the projectile at 4 seconds is the y-coordinate at the point the line x = 4 crosses the graph of the path of the projectile and the y-value is 400 feet. Therefore, the height of the projectile at 4 seconds is 400 feet.
The height of the projectile at 12 seconds is the y-coordinate at the point where the line x = 12 crosses the graph of the path of the projectile and this y-coordinate is about 190 feet. So, the height of the projectile at 12 seconds is about 190 feet.

f. The height of 250 feet is the same as y = 250 feet. The x values at the point where y = 250 crosses the graph of the path of the projectile are the times the projectile takes to reach 250 feet which is about 2.4 seconds (while the projectile is going up) and about 11 seconds (while the projectile is coming down).

Exercises

1. Given that $f(x) = -2x^2 + 50x + 150$ represents the profit in dollars for the production of x items by a company, how much will the company make by producing 8 items? Hint: See Example **1**.

2. Given that $f(x) = -3x^2 + 150x + 2750$ represents the cost of making x items in dollars in a certain factory, find the cost of making 10 items at the factory. Hint: See Example **1**.

3. The graph shows the path of a projectile. Hint: See Example 2.
   a. How long does it take the projectile to return to the ground?
   b. Find the time that the projectile takes to reach the maximum height.
   c. What is the axis of symmetry of the graph of the projectile? Give reasons to support your answer.
   d. What is the maximum height reached by the projectile?
   e. How long does it take the projectile to reach a height of 300 feet when going upwards and when going downwards?
   f. What is the height of the projectile at 5 seconds and at 8 seconds?
Hint: See Example **2**.

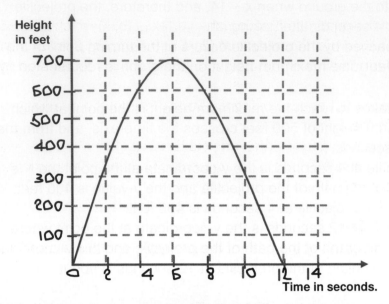

Height in feet

700
600
500
400
300
200
100

0   2   4   6   8   10   12   14
Time in seconds.

4. Is it a true statement that the maximum or the minimum point of a graph is at the turning point of the graph? Hint: See the preceding pages.

Challenge Questions

5. Given that the cost of producing a complex machine is represented in dollars by $f(x) = -2x^2 + 290x + 1200$ where x is the number of the machines produced. Find the production cost if 20 machines are made.

Vertex Form of the Quadratic Function

The vertex form of the quadratic function is:
$y = a(x - h)^2 + k$, where:

　　　　1. (h, k) is the vertex.
　　　　2. the line $x = h$ is the axis of symmetry.
　　　　3. If **a** is positive, the vertex is the minimum or the lowest point on the parabola.
　　　　4. If **a** is negative, the vertex is the maximum or the highest point on the parabola.

Example 1
Find the vertex and the axis of symmetry of each function.
　a. $y = 2(x - 2)^2 - 5$ 　　　　　　　　　　**b.** $y = -(x + 2)^2 + 3$
Solution
a. Compare the vertex form of the quadratic function which is **$y = a(x - h)^2 + k$** to the function $y = 2(x - 2)^2 - 5$ as shown:

$$y = a(x - h)^2 + k$$
$$\downarrow \quad \downarrow\downarrow \quad \downarrow \qquad \downarrow$$
$$y = 2(x - 2)^2 - 5$$

744

From the vertex form of the quadratic function, the vertex is (h, k) which is (2, -5).
Note carefully that considering the vertex of (2, -5), the sign of 2 must always be its opposite in the function and the sign of 5 must always be its sign in the function.

The axis of symmetry is x = 2, because using the vertex form of the quadratic function, the line x = h is the axis of symmetry.

Since the **a** value is 2 which is positive, the vertex is the lowest point on the parabola because using the vertex form of the quadratic function, if **a** is positive, then the vertex is the lowest point on the parabola.

Checking the Answers by Graphing

Graph $y = 2(x - 2)^2 - 5$ by assigning values to x and then finding the corresponding y values as shown:

x	$f(x) = 2(x - 2)^2 - 5$	y	(x, y)
0	$f(0) = 2(0 - 2)^2 - 5 = 2(-2)^2 - 5 = 2(4) - 5 = 8 - 5 = 3$	3	(0, 3)
1	$f(1) = 2(1 - 2)^2 - 5 = 2(-1)^2 - 5 = 2(1) - 5 = 2 - 5 = -3$	-3	(1, -3)
2	$f(2) = 2(2 - 2)^2 - 5 = 2(0)^2 - 5 = 0 - 5 = -5$	-5	(2, -5)
3	$f(3) = 2(3 - 2)^2 - 5 = 2(1)^2 - 5 = 2 - 5 = -3$	-3	(3, -3)
4	$f(4) = 2(4 - 2)^2 - 5 = 2(2)^2 - 5 = 2(4) - 5 = 3$	3	(4, 3)

Plot the ordered pair (x, y) from the table and then connect them with a smooth curve as shown:

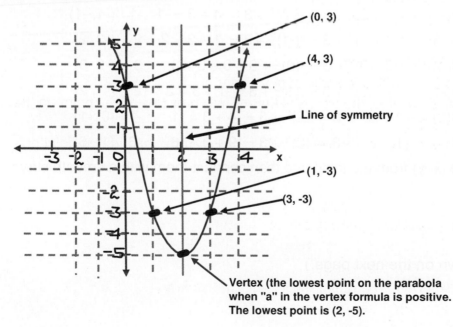

(0, 3)

(4, 3)

Line of symmetry

(1, -3)

(3, -3)

Vertex (the lowest point on the parabola when "a" in the vertex formula is positive. The lowest point is (2, -5).

From the graph:

the vertex is (2, -5),

the line of symmetry is x = 2, and

745

the vertex is the lowest or the minimum point on the parabola.
The graphing confirms the answers when using the vertex formula.

b. Compare the vertex form of the quadratic function which is $y = a(x - h)^2 + k$, to the function $y = -(x + 2)^2 + 3$ as shown:

$$y = a(x - h)^2 + k$$
$$\downarrow \quad \downarrow\downarrow \quad \downarrow \qquad \downarrow$$
$$y = -(x + 2)^2 + 3$$

From the vertex form of the quadratic function, the vertex is (h, k) which is (-2, 3).
Note carefully that when considering the vertex of (-2, 3), the sign of 2 must always be its opposite in the function and the sign of 3 must always be its sign in the function.

The axis of symmetry is x = -2 because using the vertex form of the quadratic function, the line x = h is the axis of symmetry.

Since the **a** value of $-(x + 2)^2$ is -1, [note that the coefficient of $-(x + 2)^2$ is -1 and the coefficient of $(x + 2)^2$ is 1], the sign of **a** is negative, the vertex is the highest point on the parabola, because using the vertex form of the quadratic function, if **a** is negative, the vertex is the highest point on the parabola.

Checking the Answers by Graphing

Graph $y = -(x + 2)^2 + 3$ by assigning values to x and then finding the corresponding y values as shown:

x	$y = f(x) = -(x + 2)^2 + 3$	y	(x, y)
-5	$y = f(-5) = -(-5 + 2)^2 + 3 = -(-3)^2 + 3 = -9 + 3 = -6$	-6	(-5, -6)
-4	$y = f(-4) = -(-4 + 2)^2 + 3 = -(-2)^2 + 3 = -4 + 3 = -1$	-1	(-4, -1)
-3	$y = f(-3) = -(-3 + 2)^2 + 3 = -(-1)^2 + 3 = -1 + 3 = 2$	2	(-3, 2)
-2	$y = f(-2) = -(-2 + 2)^2 + 3 = -(0)^2 + 3 = 0 + 3 = 3$	3	(-2, 3)
-1	$y = f(-1) = -(-1 + 2)^2 + 3 = -(1)^2 + 3 = -1 + 3 = 2$	2	(-1, 2)
0	$y = f(0) = -(0 + 2)^2 + 3 = -(2)^2 + 3 = -4 + 3 = -1$	-1	(0, -1)
1	$y = f(1) = -(1 + 2)^2 + 3 = -(3)^2 + 3 = -9 + 3 = -6$	-6	(1, -6)

Plot the ordered pairs (x, y) from the table and then connect them with a smooth curve as shown:

(The graph is shown on the next page.)

746

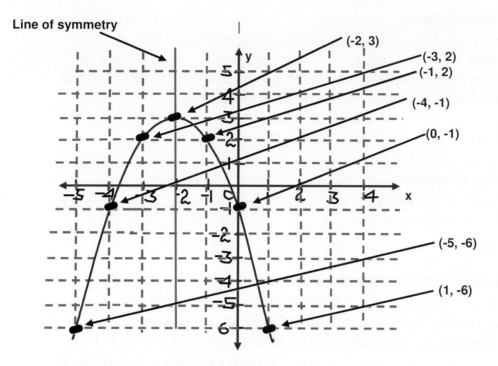

Line of symmetry

(-2, 3)
(-3, 2)
(-1, 2)
(-4, -1)
(0, -1)
(-5, -6)
(1, -6)

From the graph:

the vertex is (-2, 3),
the line of symmetry is x = -2, and
the vertex is the highest point of the parabola.

The graphing confirms the answers when using the vertex formula.

Exercises

1. State the vertex form of the quadratic function and using the vertex form of the quadratic function, state the vertex, the line of symmetry, when the vertex is the lowest point or minimum value of the parabola, and when the vertex is the highest point or the maximum value of the parabola. Hint: See the preceding pages.

2. Use the vertex form of a quadratic function to identify the vertex and the line of symmetry for the graph of each function. Check each answer by graphing. Hint: See Example **1**.

   a. $y = 2(x - 2)^2 + 3$ **b.** $y = (x - 1)^2 - 3$ **c.** $y = 2(x + 3)^2 + 3$
   d. $y = (x + 3)^2 + 1$ **e.** $y = (x - 3)^2 - 4$ **f.** $y = 3(x + 1)^2 - 2$

3. Use the vertex form of a quadratic function to identify the vertex and the line of symmetry for the graph of each function. Check each answer by graphing. Hint: See Example **2**.

   a. $y = -2(x + 2)^2 + 3$ **b.** $y = -(x + 3)^2 + 1$ **c.** $y = -3(x - 1)^2 - 2$
   d. $y = -(x - 3)^2 + 1$ **e.** $y = -2(x + 2)^2 - 3$ **f.** $y = -(x - 2)^2 - 1$

4. Explain how to find the vertex of $y = 2(x - 6)^2 - 4$. Hint: See the vertex form of the quadratic function.

5. Explain how to find the line of symmetry of $y = 2(x - 6)^2 - 5$. Hint: See the vertex

form of the quadratic function.

Challenge Questions

6. Use the vertex form of the quadratic function to identify the vertex and the line of symmetry for each function. Check each answer by graphing.

   a. $y = -2(x + 1)^2 + 1$ **b.** $y = (x - 1)^2 + 2$

   c. $y = -(x - 3)^2 - 1$ **d.** $y = 3(x + 1)^2 - 3$

Answers to Selected Questions

2a. Vertex is (2, 3), line of symmetry: $x = 2$

3a. Vertex is (-2, 3), line of symmetry: $x = -2$

How to Use Zeros to Find the Vertex of a Parabola

The 4 main steps needed to use zeros to find the vertex of a parabola are:

Step 1: Find the zero of the function by setting the function or y equals to 0.

Step 2: Factor the function and set each factored form equals to 0 and solve for x.

Step 3: Find the midpoint of the x-coordinates of the zeros because the parabola is symmetrical and the vertex is halfway between the zeros.

Step 4: Substitute the value for the midpoint of the x-coordinate found in Step 3 for x in the function to find the y-coordinate of the vertex.

Example 1

a. Use the zeros to find the vertex of the graph of $y = x^2 + 7x + 10$.

b. Write the vertex form of the equation.

c. Using the information obtained from solution **a** and **b**, sketch the parabola.

Solution

a. Step 1: Find the zeros of the function by setting the function or y equals to zero as shown:

$$x^2 + 7x + 10 = 0 \qquad \text{Hint: On the x-axis, } y = 0.$$

   Step 2: Factor the function and set each factored form equals to 0 and solve for x as shown:

$$x^2 + 7x + 10 = 0 \text{ ———————————[A]}$$
$$(x + 5)(x + 2) = 0 \text{ ———————————[B]}$$

Hint: The student should understand the chapter on the Factorization of Quadratic Functions before reading this section. How equation [A] becomes equation [B] is explained with the help of **three necessary conditions** and **two diagrams** as shown: The **3 necessary conditions for factoring** $x^2 + 7x + 10$, which are numbered in the diagram k, are that the factors must be such that:

   1. **The product of the first terms in each parenthesis, for example, x · x must be equal to the first term of the function which is x^2.**

   2. **The product of the last terms of each parenthesis, which is 5 · 2, must be**

equal to the last term of the function, **which is 10.**

3. **The product of the outside terms, which is x · 2, added to the product of the inside terms, which is 5 · x, must be equal to the middle term of the function which is 7x.**

Hint: The symbol ( ) is called a parenthesis, and it is also called a grouping symbol.
Diagram k.

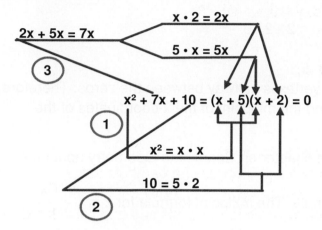

1 gives the first term.

2 gives the last term.

3 gives the middle term.

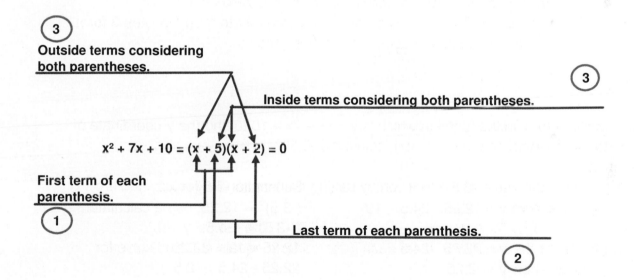

To solve for x in equation [B]:
The equation should be stated that $(x + 5)(x + 2) = 0$, and this means that
either $(x + 5) = 0$ or $(x + 2) = 0$.
If $(x + 5) = 0$,

then $(x + 5) - 5 = -5$	Subtract 5 from both sides of the equation in order to eliminate the 5 at the left side of the equation.
$x + 5 - 5 = -5$	$5 - 5 = 0$

749

$$x + 0 = -5$$
$$x = -5$$

Or, if $(x + 2) = 0$,

then $(x + 2) - 2 = -2$ Subtract 2 from both sides of the equation in order to eliminate the 2 at the left side of the equation.

$$x + 2 - 2 = -2$$
$$x + 0 = -2 \qquad 2 - 2 = 0$$
$$x = -2$$

So, the zeros of the function are -2 and -5.

Since the parabola is symmetrical, the vertex is halfway between the zeros. Therefore, to find the x-coordinate of the vertex, find the midpoint of the x-coordinates of the zeros as shown:

$$x = \frac{-2 + (-5)}{2}$$ Hint: See the chapter on Coordinate Geometry about the

midpoint formula. The midpoint formula for x is $\frac{x_1 + x_2}{2}$.

$$x = \frac{-2 - 5}{2} \qquad \qquad + (- = -$$

$$x = \frac{-7}{2} \qquad \qquad -2 - 5 = -7$$

$$x = -3.5$$

Substitute -3.5 for x in the function which is $y = x^2 + 7x + 10$ to find the y-coordinate of the vertex as shown:

$$y = x^2 + 7x + 10$$
$$y = (-3.5)^2 + 7(-3.5) + 10 \qquad \text{Substitute -3.5 for x.}$$
$$y = 12.25 - 24.5 + 10 \qquad \qquad (-3.5)^2 = 12.25, \text{ use a calculator.}$$
$$\qquad \qquad \qquad \qquad \qquad \qquad 7(-3.5) = -24.5.$$
$$y = 22.25 - 24.5 \qquad \qquad \qquad 12.25 + 10 = 22.25$$
$$y = -2.25 \qquad \qquad \qquad \qquad 22.25 - 24.5 = -2.5$$

So, the vertex is (-3.5, -2.25).

b. From the solution of Example 1a, the vertex form of the equation can be found by substituting the vertex (-3.5, -2.25) into the vertex form of the quadratic function which is **y = a(x - h)² + k** as shown:

$$y = [x - (-3.5)]^2 - 2.25 \qquad \text{(\textbf{h}, \textbf{k}) represent the vertex.}$$
$$y = (x + 3.5)^2 - 2.25 \qquad \qquad - (-3.5) = +3.5$$

c. From the solution of Example 1a, the zeros are -2 and -5 and the zeros are the x values when y = 0.

From the solution of Example 1a, the vertex is (-3.5, -2.25), which is the minimum point of the parabola as shown, so the value of **a** in the quadratic function

$y = a(x - h)^2 + k$ is positive, and in this case, the value of **a** is 1. On the graph, the zeros are -2 and -5.

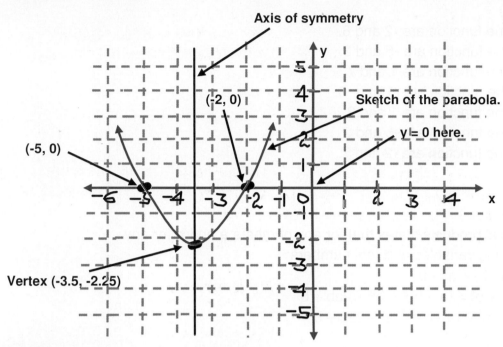

Note: It is possible to sketch the parabola if at least the zeros and the vertex are known and also noting that the parabola is symmetric, the axis of symmetry passes through a point midway between the zeros. Since the parabola is symmetric, one half of the parabola is a mirror image of the other half.

Exercises

It is highly recommended that the students should review the chapter on the **Factoring of Quadratic Function** before attempting these exercises if needed.

1. Use the zeros to find the vertex of each graph. Write the vertex form of the equation. Using your solutions, sketch the parabola. Hint: See Example **1**.

a. $y = x^2 - 6x + 5$ **b.** $y = x^2 - 4x - 12$ **c.** $y = x^2 + 2x - 15$

d. $y = x^2 - 8x + 7$ **e.** $y = x^2 - 3x - 10$ **f.** $y = x^2 + 4x - 5$

2. Use factoring to find the zeros of each function. Hint: See Example 1.

a. $y = x^2 + 4x + 3$ **b.** $y = x^2 - 3x + 2$ **c.** $y = x^2 + 3x - 10$

d. $y = x^2 - 5x - 14$ **e.** $y = x^2 + 2x - 3$ **f.** $y = x^2 - 2x - 3$

g. $y = x^2 - 6x + 5$ **h.** $y = x^2 + 3x + 2$ **i.** $y = x^2 + 5x - 14$

j. $y = x^2 - 3x - 10$ **k.** $y = x^2 - 7x - 18$ **l.** $y = x^2 - 10x + 21$

m. $y = x^2 - 2x - 35$ **n.** $y = x^2 + 6x - 16$ **o.** $y = x^2 + 4x - 5$

p. $y = x^2 - 5x + 6$

Challenge Questions

3. Write the vertex form of the equation $y = x^2 - 4x - 12$ and sketch the parabola.

4. Find the zeros of the function $y = x^2 + 6x - 7$.

Answers to Selected Questions (**partial answers**)

1a. Vertex is (3, 4)

1b. The zeros of the function are -2 and 6.

1c. The zeros of the function are -5 and 3.

1d. The zeros of the function are 1 and 7.

2a. The zeros of the function are -1 and -3.

2b. The zeros of the function are 1 and 2.

2c. The zeros of the function are -5 and 2.

2d. The zeros of the function are -2 and 7.

Special Products

The rules for special products states that for any numbers **a** and **b** for any expressions involving variables and real numbers:

1. $(a + b)(a - b) = a^2 - b^2$
2. $(a + b)(a + b) = (a + b)^2 = a^2 + 2ab + b^2$
3. $(a - b)(a - b) = (a - b)^2 = a^2 - 2ab + b^2$

Example 1

Show that $(a + b)(a - b) = a^2 - b^2$.

Solution

Multiply each term in the first parenthesis by each term in the second parenthesis as shown:

$(a + b)(a - b) = a \cdot a - a \cdot b + b \cdot a - b \cdot b$

$\qquad\qquad\quad = a^2 - ab + ba - b^2 \qquad\qquad\quad a \cdot a = a^2$ and $b \cdot b = b^2$

$\qquad\qquad\quad = a^2 - b^2 \qquad\qquad\qquad\qquad\quad$ ab is the same as ba, and therefore,

$\qquad\qquad\qquad\qquad\qquad\qquad\qquad\qquad\qquad\quad$ $-ab + ba = 0$.

Hint: The symbol ( ) is called a parenthesis, and it is also called a grouping symbol.

Example 2

Show that $(a + b)(a + b) = a^2 + 2ab + b^2$.

Solution

Multiply each term in the first parenthesis by each term in the second parenthesis as shown:

$(a + b)(a + b) = a \cdot a + a \cdot b + b \cdot a + b \cdot b$

$\qquad\qquad\quad = a^2 + ab + ba + b^2 \qquad\qquad\quad a \cdot a = a^2$ and $b \cdot b = b^2$

$\qquad\qquad\quad = a^2 + 2ab + b^2 \qquad\qquad\qquad\quad$ ab is the same as ba, therefore,

$\qquad\qquad\qquad\qquad\qquad\qquad\qquad\qquad\qquad\quad$ $ab + ba = 2ab$.

Example 3

Show that $(a - b)(a - b) = a^2 - 2ab + b^2$.

Solution

Multiply each term in the first parenthesis by each term in the second parenthesis as shown:

$(a - b)(a - b) = a \cdot a - a \cdot b - b \cdot a - b(-b)$

$a \cdot a = a \cdot a, \ a \cdot (-b) = -a \cdot b,$
$-b \cdot a = -b \cdot a$ and $-b \cdot (-b) = -b(-b)$

$= a^2 - 2ab + b^2$

$a \cdot a = a^2, \ -a \cdot b = -ab, \ -b \cdot a = -ba,$
$-ab$ is the same as $-ba$, and therefore,
$-ab - ba = -2ab$ and $-b(-b) = +b^2 = b^2.$

Example 4

Find the product of $(x - 4)(x + 4)$ using the rule for special products.

Solution

$(x - 4)(x + 4)$ can also be written as $(x + 4)(x - 4)$. Now $(x + 4)(x - 4)$ is in the form $(a + b)(a - b)$, where $a = x$ and $b = 4$.

Using the rule, $(a + b)(a - b) = a^2 - b^2$

Similarly, $(x + 4)(x - 4) = x^2 - 4^2$
$= x^2 - 16$

Example 5.

Use the rule for special products to find the product of $(3x + 5)(3x + 5)$.

Solution

$(3x + 5)(3x + 5)$ is in the form $(a + b)(a + b)$ where $a = 3x$ and $b = 5$.

Using the rule, $(a + b)(a + b) = (a + b)^2 = a^2 + 2ab + b^2$.

Similarly, $(3x + 5)(3x + 5) = (3x + 5)^2 = (3x)^2 + 2(3x)(5) + 5^2$
$= 3^2x^2 + 30x + 25 \qquad\qquad 2(3x)(5) = 30x.$
$= 9x^2 + 30x + 25$

Example 6

Use the rule for special products to find the product of $(4x - 3)(4x - 3)$

Solution

$(4x - 3)(4x - 3) = (4x - 3)^2 \qquad\qquad$ In general, $a \cdot a = a^2$

$(4x - 3)^2$ is in the form of $(a - b)^2$ where $a = 4x$ and $b = 3$.

Using the rule, $(a - b)^2 = a^2 - 2ab + b^2$

Similarly, $(4x - 3)^2 = (4x)^2 - 2(4x)(3) + 3^2$
$= 4^2x^2 - 24x + 9 \qquad\qquad 2(4x)(3) = 24x$
$= 16x^2 - 24x + 9$

Exercises

1. Show that $(m + n)(m - n) = m^2 - n^2$. Hint: See Example **1**.
2. Show that $(m + p)(m + p) = m^2 + 2mp + p^2$. Hint: See Example **2**.
3. Show that $(w - r)(w - r) = w^2 - 2wr + r^2$. Hint: See Example **3**.
4. Find each product by using the rules for special products. Hint: See Example **4**.

753

a. (x - 3)(x + 3) **b.** (x + 2)(x - 2) **c.** (2x - 4)(2x + 4)
d. (3x + 2)(3x - 2) **e.** (5x - 2)(5x + 2) **f.** (4x + 1)(4x - 1)

5. Find each product by using the rules for special products. Hint: See Example 5.
   a. (2x + 2)(2x + 2) **b.** (3x + 1)(3x + 1) **c.** (x + 4)(x + 4)
   d. (3x + 3)(3x + 3) **e.** $(2x + 5)^2$ **f.** $(4x + 3)^2$

6. Find each product by using the rules for special products. Hint: See Example 6.
   a. (3x - 2)(3x - 2) **b.** $(2x - 5)^2$ **c.** (4x - 3)(4x - 3)
   d. $(3x - 2)^2$ **e.** (2x - 3)(2x - 3) **f.** (x - 3)(x - 3)

Challenge Questions
7. Find each product by using the rules for special products.
   a. (x - 3)(x - 3) **b.** (3x + 2)(3x + 2) **c.** (4x - 5)(4x + 5)
   d. (2x + 5)(2x - 5) **e.** $(4x + 3)^2$ **f.** $(2x - 3)^2$

Answers to Selected Questions
4a. $x^2 - 9$ **5a**. $4x^2 + 8x + 4$ **6a**. $9x^2 - 12x + 4$

REAL WORLD APPLICATIONS OF THE QUADRATIC FUNCTIONS - WORD PROBLEMS

Example 1
The length of a rectangular farm is 2x + 3 and the width of the farm is 2x - 3.
If the area of the farm is 27 square miles, what is:
a. The value of x?
b. The length of the farm?
c. The width of the farm?

Solution
a. Length of the farm = 2x + 3
   Width of the farm = 2x - 3
   Area of the farm = 27 square miles.
   The formula of the area of a rectangular farm is "Length × Width"
   Therefore, the area of the farm is:
   Area of the farm = Length × Width _____[A]
   Substitute area of the farm = 27 square miles, length of the farm = 2X + 3, and the width of the farm = 2x - 3, into the equation [A] as shown:
   27 = (2x + 3)(2x - 3)
   27 = (2x)(2x) - (2x)(3) + (3)(2x) - (3)(3)   Review special products.
   $27 = 4x^2 - 6x + 6x - 9$
   $27 = 4x^2 - 9$ -6x + 6x = 0
   $27 + 9 = 4x^2 - 9 + 9$ Add 9 to both sides of the equation in order to isolate $4x^2$.

$36 = 4x^2$

$$\frac{36}{4} = \frac{4x^2}{4}$$ Divide both sides of the equation by 4 in order to isolate x^2.

$$\frac{\overset{9}{\cancel{36}}}{4} = \frac{\overset{x^2}{\cancel{4x^2}}}{4}$$
$$\overset{1}{} \qquad \overset{1}{}$$

$9 = x^2$
$3^2 = x^2$ $\qquad\qquad\qquad 9 = 3^2$
$\sqrt{3^2} = \sqrt{x^2}$ $\qquad$ Find the square root of both sides of the equation
to obtain the value for x.

$\pm 3 = x$

b. The length of the farm $= 2x + 3$ _____[B]

Substitute $x = 3$ into the equation [B] in order to obtain the value of the length of the farm as follows:

Length of the farm $= 2x + 3$ $\qquad\qquad$ Given in the question.
$\qquad\qquad\quad = 2(3) + 3$ $\qquad\qquad$ When $x = 3$.
$\qquad\qquad\quad = 6 + 3$
$\qquad\qquad\quad = 9$ miles

Substitute $x = -3$ into the equation [B] in order to obtain the value of the length of the farm as follows:

Length of the farm $= 2x + 3$ $\qquad\qquad$ Given in the question
$\qquad\qquad\quad = 2(-3) + 3$ $\qquad\qquad$ When $x = -3$.
$\qquad\qquad\quad = -6 + 3 = -3$ miles

But the length of the farm cannot be a negative number, and therefore, $x = -3$ is impossible. Therefore, the length of the farm is 9 miles.

c. The width of the farm $= 2x - 3$ _____[C]

Substitute $x = 3$ into the equation [C] in order to obtain the value of the width of the farm as shown:

Width of the farm $= 2x - 3$ $\qquad\qquad$ Given in the question.
$\qquad\qquad\quad = 2(3) - 3$ $\qquad\qquad$ When $x = 3$
$\qquad\qquad\quad = 6 - 3$
$\qquad\qquad\quad = 3$ miles.

Example 2

The side of a square swimming pool is x - 3 kilometers. Given that the area of the square swimming pool is 4 square kilometers,

a. find the value of x,

b. how long is a side of the square swimming pool?

Solution

a. Length of a side of the square swimming pool

$= x - 3$　　　　　　　　　　　　　　　　　　　Given in the question.

Area of the square swimming pool $= 4$ km^2　　　　　Given in the question.

The formula for the area of a square is Side $\times$ Side.

Therefore, the area of the square swimming pool is:

Area of the square swimming pool $=$ (length of a side)(length of a side)

$$= (x - 3)(x - 3)$$
$$= x^2 - 3x - 3x - 3(-3)$$
$$= x^2 - 6x + 9 \qquad\qquad -3(-3) = 9$$

But the question states that the area of the square swimming pool is 4 km^2, therefore:

$x^2 - 6x + 9 = 4$ ————————————————————————————————[A]

Subtract 4 from both sides of the equation [A] so that the right side of the equation will become zero as follows:

$x^2 - 6x + 9 - 4 = 4 - 4$

　$x^2 - 6x + 5 = 0$ ————————————————————————————[B]

Factorize the left side of the equation [B] as follows:

　$x^2 - 6x + 5 = (x - 1)(x - 5) = 0$　　　Hint: Review the chapter on the Factoring Quadratic Functions. Also, see Example 3 for the explanation.

$(x - 1)(x - 5) = 0$ means that either $(x - 1) = 0$ or $(x - 5) = 0$.

　　　　　　　　　　　　　　　　In general, if **ab** $= 0$, such that both **a** and **b** are not equal to zero, then either **a** $= 0$ or **b** $= 0$ in order for **ab** to be equal to zero.

If $(x - 1) = 0$, then $x - 1 = 0$

　　　　　$x - 1 + 1 = 1$　　　　Add 1 to both sides of the equation in order to isolate x.

　　　　　　　$x = 1$　　　　$-1 + 1 = 0$

　　　　　　　$x = 1$ km

If $(x - 5) = 0$, then $x - 5 = 0$

　　　　　$x - 5 + 5 = 5$　　　　Add 5 to both sides of the equation in order to isolate x.

　　　　　　　$x = 5$　　　　$-5 + 5 = 0.$

　　　　　　　$x = 5$ km

b. Length of the side of the square swimming pool $= x - 3$ ———————[C]

　　　　　　　　　　　　　　　　Given in the question.

Substitute $x = 1$ into the equation [C] to obtain the length of the side of the square swimming pool when $x = 1$ km as shown:

Length of the square swimming pool $= x - 3$

　　　　　　　　　　　$= 1 - 3$　　　　　　When $x = 1$.

　　　　　　　　　　　$= -2$ km

Since the length of the side of a swimming pool cannot be a negative number, $x = 1$ km is impossible.

Substitute $x = 5$ into the equation [C] to obtain the length of the side of the square swimming pool when $x = 5$ km as shown:

Length of the side of the square swimming pool $= x - 3$
$$= 5 - 3 \qquad \text{When } x = 5.$$
$$= 2 \text{ km}.$$

Therefore, the length of the square swimming pool is 2 km.

Example 3
Explain how $x^2 - 6x + 5 = 0$ is factored in Example 2a.

Solution
(Hint: First review the solution of Example 1a under **How to Use Zeros to Find the Vertex of a Parabola**, to fully understand how factoring is done).

Lets us explain how $x^2 - 6x + 5 = (x - 1)(x - 5)$ as shown:

The first term in each parenthesis is x.

The last term in the equation $x^2 - 6x + 5 = 0$ is +5, which is the product of -5 and -1, and +5 and +1. The only addition pair which gives -6 as the coefficient for the middle term is -5 and -1 because $-5 + (-1) = -6$. Therefore, $x^2 - 6x + 5 = (x - 1)(x - 5)$.

Exercises
1. The length of a rectangular field is $(2x + 2)$ and the width is $(2x - 2)$. If the area of the field is 40 km^2,
   a. find the value of x,
   b. find the length of the field,
   c. find the width of the field.
   Hint: See Example 1.
2. The length of the sides of a square room is $x - 2$. If the area of the room is 16 m^2,
   a. find the value of x.
   b. find the length of the side of the square room.
   Hint: See Example 2, and also note that $x^2 - 4x - 12 = (x + 2)(x - 6)$.
3. Find the factors of each equation and also find the value of x. Hint: See Example 3.
   a. $x^2 + 4x + 3 = 0$ b. $x^2 + 5x + 6 = 0$ c. $x^2 - 3x + 2 = 0$
   d. $x^2 - 3x - 10 = 0$ e. $x^2 + 11x - 12 = 0$ f. $x^2 + 5x - 6 = 0$

Challenge Questions
4. Show that each of the following expressions have no factors.
   Hint: Note that the expressions have no factors if they cannot be factored.
   So, use the factoring method to factor the expressions and if you cannot factor the expressions, then it means that the expressions have no factors.
   a. $x^2 - 7x - 7$ b. $x^2 + 8x + 9$ c. $x^2 - 3x + 16$

SIMPLE INTEREST

New Terms: **simple interest, principal, rate of interest**.

Simple interest is the money paid for borrowing money and also for saving money. The **interest depends on the principal**, **the rate**, **and the time** for which the money is borrowed and they are related by a formula.
The formula for finding the simple interest is:

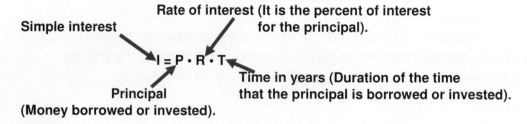

The **sum** of the **principal** and the **interest** is called the **amount**.

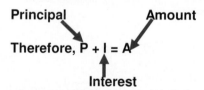

How to Find the Interest and the Amount
Use the simple interest formula to find the interest and then use the amount formula to find the amount.

Example 1
Mary borrowed $2500 from a bank for 3 years to pay her school fees at an annual simple interest rate of 4%.
a. How much interest will she pay if she pays off the loan at the end of the third year?
b. How much is the amount that she will pay.
Solution
a. I = P · R · T   Use the simple interest formula.

Substitute P = $2500, R = 4% = $\frac{4}{100}$ = 0.04 and T = 3 years into the simple interest formula as shown:

I = P · R · T

I = 2500 · 0.04 · 3

= 300   (Depress 2500 × .04 × 3 on the calculator to obtain 300.)

Mary will pay $300 in interest.

b. The amount that Mary will repay on the loan can be found by adding the principal to the interest as shown:

P + I = A   (Formula for the amount is: Principal + interest = Amount).

2500 + 300 = A   Substitute P = $2500 and I = $300 into the formula for finding the amount. (The interest of $300 is already found from the solution of Example **1a**.)

    2800 = A   2500 + 300 = 2800

Mary will repay an amount of $2800.

How to Find the Investment Time or the Duration of Time for Borrowing Money.
In order to find the investment time or the duration of the time for borrowing money, write the formula for finding the simple interest, substitute all the information given into the simple interest formula, and then solve the equation for the investment time or the duration of time for borrowing the money.

Example 2

Eric invested $1500 in a business at a yearly rate of 4%. He earned $200 in interest. How long did he invest the money?

Solution

I = P · R · T   Use the simple interest formula.

We want to find the time which is T. Substitute I − 200, P − 1500, and

$R = 4\% = \dfrac{4}{100} = 0.04$ into the simple interest formula as shown:

I = P · R · T

200 = 1500 · 0.04 · T

200 = 60 · T_____[A]

         (1500 · 0.04 = 60)

Divide both sides of the equation [A] by 60 in order to obtain the value of T as shown:

$$\dfrac{200}{60} = \dfrac{60 \cdot T}{60}$$

$$\dfrac{200}{60} = \dfrac{\overset{1}{\cancel{60}} \cdot T}{\underset{1}{\cancel{60}}} \qquad \text{Divide by 60}$$

3.33333...= T   Depress 200 ÷ 60 = on the calculator to obtain 3.333333...
The money was invested for 3.$\overline{3}$ years.

How to Find the Rate of Interest.

In order to find the rate of interest, write the formula for finding the simple interest, substitute all the information given into the simple interest formula, and then solve the equation for the rate of interest.

Example 3

A farmer borrowed $2000 from a bank for 5 years. If the farmer paid $310 in interest, what is the interest rate?

Solution

$I = P \cdot R \cdot T$ Use the formula for simple interest.

We want to find the rate which is R.

Substitute I = $310, P = $2000, and T = 5 years into the simple interest formula as shown:

$I = P \cdot R \cdot T$

$310 = 2000 \cdot R \cdot 5$

$310 = 10000 \cdot R$ _____ [A]

$$2000 \cdot 5 = 10000$$

Divide both sides of the equation [A] by 10000 in order to obtain the value of R as shown:

$$\frac{310}{10000} = \frac{10000 \cdot R}{10000}$$

$$\frac{310}{10000} = \frac{\overset{1}{\cancel{10000}} \cdot R}{\underset{1}{\cancel{10000}}}$$ Divide by 10000

$0.031 = R$ Use a calculator to find $\dfrac{310}{10000}$ by depressing 310 ÷ 10000 = to obtain

0.031.

So, the farmer borrowed the money at an annual interest rate of

0.031 or 0.031 × 100

    = 3.1%   Review the chapter on Percent if necessary.

Note that the interest rate is expressed in percent (%) by multiplying by 100.

Two-Step Method for Finding the Rate of Interest

Note that at times you will be required to find the rate but the interest is not given directly. In this case, use the formula for finding the amount to find the interest first as shown:

P + I = A _____[B]

Subtract P from both sides of equation [B] in order to isolate I as shown:

P - P + I = A - P

P - P + I = A - P   P - P = 0

I = A - P

The two-step method for finding the interest rate involves finding the interest first and then finding the interest rate as shown in Example 4.

Example 4

Elizabeth borrowed $3500 from the bank for 4 years at a simple interest rate to invest in a business. If she repaid $4000 at the end of the fourth year, at what interest rate did she borrow the money? Round the interest rate to two decimal places.

Solution

I = P · R · T   Simple interest formula which involves the rate, R.

The question gives P = $3500, T = 4 years, and A = $4000. Note that the interest is not given and we do not know the interest rate, and therefore, we cannot find the interest rate directly with the information given in the question. So, we have to find the interest first using the amount formula as shown:

P + I = A   This is the amount formula

Substitute P = $3500, and A = $4000 into the amount formula in order to find I as shown:

P + I = A   This is the amount formula.

3500 + I = 4000 _____[A]

Subtract 3500 from both sides of the equation [A] in order to isolate I and to obtain the value of I as shown:

3500 - 3500 + I = 4000 - 3500

I = 500   3500 - 3500 = 0

4000 - 3500 = 500

She paid $500 in interest.

Now use the interest of $500 in the simple interest formula to find the interest rate as shown:

I = P · R · T   Simple interest formula.

Substitute I = $500, P = $3500, and T = 4 years into the simple interest formula as shown:

I = P · R · T

500 = 3500 · R · 4

500 = 14000 · R   3500 · 4 = 14000

$500 = 14000 \cdot R$ _____[B]

Divide both sides of the equation $[B]$ by 14,000 in order to isolate R and also to obtain the value of R as shown:

$$\frac{500}{14000} = \frac{14000 \cdot R}{14000}$$

$$\frac{500}{14000} = \frac{\overset{1}{\cancel{14000}} \cdot R}{\underset{1}{\cancel{14000}}} \qquad \text{Divide by 14000.}$$

$0.03571... = R$ Use the calculator to find $\dfrac{500}{14000}$ by

depressing $500 \div 14000 =$ on the calculator to obtain 0.03571....

Elizabeth borrowed the money at an annual rate of $0.03571 \times 100 = 3.571...\%$

      $R = 3.57\%$ to two decimal places.

Note that the interest rate is expressed in percent (%) by multiplying by 100.

How to Find the Amount

The formula for finding the amount is:

$P + I = A$ P = Principal, I = Interest, and A = Amount.

So, in order to find the amount, **the principal and the interest must be known**.

Example 5

A school deposited $2000 into a college scholarship fund. How much will the school have in the scholarship fund after four years at a yearly simple interest rate of 5%.

Solution

The money that the school will have at the end of 4 years is the principal plus the interest on the principal, which is the amount The principal = $2000, but the interest is not given. Let us find the interest first as shown:

$I = P \cdot R \cdot T$ Use the simple interest formula.

$I = 2,000 \cdot 0.05 \cdot 4$ Substitute P = $2000, R = 5% = $\dfrac{5}{100}$ = 0.05, and T = 4 years

into the simple interest formula.

$I = 400$ $2000 \cdot 0.05 \cdot 4 = 400$

Now you can use I = 400 in the amount formula which is: $P + I = A$ as follows:

      $P + I = A$ Use the amount formula

$2000 + 400 = A$ Substitute P = $2000 and I = $400 into the amount formula.

     $2400 = A$ $2000 + 400 = 2400$.

The school will have $2400 in the scholarship fund after 4 years.

Example 6

A boy scout club deposited $3200 in a bank. At the end of the third year after the deposit, the club made $341 in interest. Find the amount of money the club had at the bank after the third year.

Solution

$P + I = A$ This is the amount formula.

$3200 + 341 = A$ Substitute P = $3200 and I = $341 into the amount formula.

$3541 = A$ $3200 + 341 = 3541$

So, the club had $3541 in the bank at the end of the third year.

How to Find the Interest, the Principal or the Rate When the Time is Not Given in Years.

Note carefully that the time involving the simple interest, the principal and the rate must always be in years, otherwise the time must be converted to years because the simple interest formula expresses time in years.

Example 7

John borrowed $500 from his mother at 8% simple interest per year.

a. If the $500 was borrowed for 4 months, find the interest and the amount John paid his mother to the nearest cent.

b. If the $500 was borrowed for 19 months, find the interest and the amount John paid his mother to the nearest cent.

Solution

a. The $500 was borrowed for 4 months, and therefore, the time is 4 months. Note that the time involving the simple interest must always be in years, and therefore, we must convert the 4 months into years as shown:

12 months = 1 year   Standard (There are 12 months in 1 year).

4 months = $\dfrac{4}{12}$ years   Note: $\dfrac{\text{Number of months}}{12 \text{ months}}$ = Number of years

Now, let us find the simple interest by using the simple interest formula as shown:

$I = P \cdot R \cdot T$ Simple interest formula.

$I = 500 \cdot 0.08 \cdot \dfrac{4}{12}$ Substitute P = 500, R = 8% = $\dfrac{8}{100}$ = 0.08, and

$T = 4$ months = $\dfrac{4}{12}$ years into the simple interest formula.

$I = 13.3333...$ Depress 4 ÷ 12 × .08 × 500 = on your calculator to obtain 13.3333...

The interest John paid to his mother was $13.33 to the nearest cent.

Let us find the amount that John paid to his mother.

The interest John paid to his mother was $13.33. The money that John borrowed from his mother which is the principal was $500.

Therefore, using the amount formula, the amount John paid to his mother is:

$P + I = A$ Amount formula.

$500 + 13.33 = 513.33.$ Substitute P = \$500 and I = \$13.33 into the amount formula.

So, John paid an amount of \$513.33 to his mother.

b. The \$500 was borrowed for 19 months, and therefore, the time is 19 months. Note that the time involving the simple interest must always be in years, and therefore, we must convert the 19 months into years as shown:

12 months = 1 year.   Standard (There are 12 months in 1 year).

19 months = 1 year 7 months. $19 \div 12 = 1$ remainder 7 which is 1 year and 7 months.

$$= 1\frac{7}{12} \text{ years.}$$

$$\text{Note: } \frac{\text{Number of months}}{\text{12 months}} = \text{Number of years.}$$

Now, let us find the simple interest by using the simple interest formula as shown:

$I = P \cdot R \cdot T$ Simple interest formula.

$I = 500 \cdot 0.08 \cdot 1\frac{7}{12}$ Substitute $P = 500$, $R = 8\% = \frac{8}{100} = 0.08$, and

                              $T = 1\frac{7}{12}$ years into the simple interest formula.

$I = 500 \cdot 0.08 \cdot \frac{19}{12}$ $1\frac{7}{12} = \frac{12 \cdot 1 + 7}{12} = \frac{19}{12}$ (Review improper fractions)

$I = 63.3333...$ Use calculator to find the value of I by depressing

                           $19 \div 12 \times .08 \times 500 =$ on the calculator to obtain 63.3333...

The interest John paid his mother is \$63.33 to the nearest cent.

Let us find the amount that John paid to his mother.

The interest John paid his mother was \$63.33. The money John borrowed from his mother, which is the principal, was \$500. Using the amount formula, the amount John paid his mother was:

$P + I = A$ Amount formula

$500 + 63.33 = 563.33$ Substitute P = \$500 and I = \$63.33 into the amount formula.

So, John paid an amount of \$563.33 to his mother.

Exercises

1. What is the formula for finding the simple interest?

2. What is the formula for finding the amount to be paid involving the simple interest?

3. When finding the simple interest, the principal or the rate, the time must always be expressed in years. True or False? Hint: See Example 7.

4. George borrowed \$2100 from a bank for 4 years to complete a project at an annual simple interest rate of 5%.

   a. How much interest will he pay if he pays off the loan at the end of the 4th year?

   b. How much is the amount he will pay? Hint: See Example 1.

5. Mrs. Brown borrowed $6200 to be repaid after 2 years at an annual simple interest rate of 7%.

   a. How much interest will be due after 3 years?

   b. How much will Mrs. Brown have to repay?

    Hint: See Example 1.

6. Peki Secondary School invested $6800 in a project at a yearly rate of 6%. The school earned $750 in interest. How long did the school invest the money? Hint: See Example 2.

7. Mrs. Johnson invested $5300 in a business with a yearly interest rate of 4.3%. Her total interest on the investment was $950. What was the length of the investment? Hint: See Example 2. (Note: $4.3\% = \dfrac{4.3}{100} = 0.043$)

8. A factory borrowed $8400 from a bank for 6 years. If the factory paid $1200 in interest, what is the interest rate? Hint: See Example 3.

9. A bank loaned a school $12500 at an annual simple interest rate. After 5 years, the school repaid the bank $14000. What was the loan interest rate? Hint: See Example 4

10. Mrs. Ofori borrowed $8300 for 4 years to do some repair on her house. She repaid $10400 at the end of the loan period. At what simple interest rate did she borrow the money? Hint See Example 4.

11. Mr. Jackson borrowed $4750 from a bank to remodel his house 5 years ago at an annual simple interest rate of 6%. How much did Mr. Jackson repay the bank? Hint: See Example 5.

12. Mrs. Amani deposited $6900 into her account at the bank. If the account earned an annual simple interest rate of 4.7%, how much will be in the account after 8 years? Hint: See Example 5. (Note: $4.7\% = \dfrac{4.7}{100} = 0.047$).

13. Ghana High School deposited $9500 in a college scholarship fund for the best students of the school. If the fund earns an annual simple interest rate of 6.2%, how much will be in the fund after 10 years? Hint: See Example 5.

   (**Note**: $6.2\% = \dfrac{6.2}{100} = 0.062$).

14. Girl Scout Club deposited $2400 in a saving account. Five years after the deposit, the club made an interest of $920. Find the amount of money the club had at the bank after the 5th year. Hint: See Example 6.

15. Mr. Jones borrowed $2800 from a bank at 5% simple interest per year.

   a. If the $2800 was borrowed for 9 months, find the interest and the amount that he will pay back to the bank to the nearest cent. Hint: See Example 7.

   b. If the $2800 was rather borrowed for 17 months, find the interest and the amount that he will pay back to the bank. Hint: See Example 7.

16. Find the interest and the amount to the nearest cent of each statement. Hint: See Example 7.

    a. $ 900 at 7% interest rate per year for 5 months.

    b. $ 650 at 5% interest rate per year for 11 months.

    c. $ 1550 at 3% interest rate per year for 13 months.

Challenge Questions

17. A bank loaned a zoo $8550 at an annual simple interest rate. After 6 years, the zoo repaid the bank $12,000. Find the interest rate of the loan.

18. Find the interest and the amount to the nearest cent of each statement.

    a. $625 at 4% simple interest rate per year for 3 years.

    b. $12550 at 6% simple interest rate per year for 8 months.

    c. $800 at 8% simple interest rate per year for 5 years.

    d. $950 at 4.3% simple interest rate per year for 14 months.

    e. $780 at 5.7% simple interest rate per year for 7 months.

    f. $570 at 4.6% simple interest rate per year for 16 months.

19. Mrs. Brown invested $6,500 in a bond with a yearly simple interest rate of 4%. If her interest on the investment was $1250, what was the length of the investment?

20. A certain amount of money was borrowed from the bank at 5% annual interest rate. If after 4 years, the interest on the borrowed money was $1500, find how much was borrowed. Hint: The money borrowed is the principal and since $I = P \cdot R \cdot T$, then P which is the principal can be found as follows:

$I = P \cdot R \cdot T$ Simple interest formula.

$$\frac{I}{R \cdot T} = \frac{P \cdot R \cdot T}{R \cdot T}$$ Divide both sides of the simple interest formula by $R \cdot T$ to isolate P and also obtaining the value of P.

$$\frac{I}{R \cdot T} = \frac{P \cdot \overset{1}{\cancel{R}} \cdot \overset{1}{\cancel{T}}}{\underset{1}{\cancel{R}} \cdot \underset{1}{\cancel{T}}}$$

$$\frac{I}{R \cdot T} = P \underline{\hspace{6cm}}\text{[A]}$$

Substitute the values for I, R, and T into equation [A] in order to obtain the value of P.

21. George borrowed $800 for 3 years. He paid $150 in interest. What was the interest rate per year?

22. Nick borrowed $950 for 5 years He paid $185 in interest. What was the interest rate per year?

23. What principal at 5% interest rate per year for 3 years that will create an interest of $650? Hint: See question 20.

Answers to selected questions

4a. $420   **4b**. $2520

COMPOUND INTEREST

What is compound interest? Compound interest is the interest paid on money, such as savings, and the interest is calculated periodically such as annually (once a year), semiannually (twice a year), quarterly (four times a year or even daily), and the calculation of the current interest is based on the sum of the principal and the interest already earned in the previous period.

How to Calculate Compound Interest and Amount Using a Spreadsheet.
Compound interest: The method of calculating the compound interest is to find the interest of the initial principal. This interest becomes the first compound interest for the first period. The interest of the first period is then added to the initial principal to become the principal for the second period. The interest for the second period is found based on the principal of the second period. The interest for the second period becomes the compound interest for the second period. The interest for the second period is added to the principal of the second period to become the principal for the third period. The compound interest of the third period is based on the sum of the principal of the second period and the interest of the second period. See the solution of Example 7.
Amount: Recall from the chapter on Simple Interest, that P + I = A, similarly, during the first period, the amount is the sum of the initial principal and the interest on the initial principal. The amount at the end of the second period is the sum of the principal of the second period and the interest on the principal of the second period. The amount at the end of the third period is the sum of the principal at the third period and the interest on the principal of the third period. See the solution of Example 1.

Example 1
Samuel deposited $100 in a savings account paying 6%, compounded annually. Find how much money he would have after 3 years by using the spreadsheet method.
Solution
Spreadsheet is just a paper which has lines that forms columns and rows as shown in Table 1. The amount that Samuel made after 3 years can be found by finding the compound interest for each year or period and then adding it to the current principal to obtain the amount for that period as already explained under the section "How to Calculate Compound Interest and Amount Using the Spreadsheet," and as shown in Table 1.

Table 1.

Period/year	Principal ($)	Compound Interest ($)	Amount ($)
1	100	$100 \times 0.06 = 6$	$100 + 6 = 106$
2	$100 + 6 = 106$	$106 \times 0.06 = 6.36$	$106 + 6.36 = 112.36$
3	$106 + 6.36 = 112.36$	$112.36 \times 0.06 = 6.74$	$112.36 + 6.74 = 119.10$

Note in Table 1 that $6\% = \dfrac{6}{100} = 0.06$ Review the topic on Percent.

From Table 1, Samuel made an amount of $119.10 after 3 years.

How to Use the Formula and Calculator to Find the Amount Involving Compound Interest.

The formula for finding the amount involving compound interest is:

$A = P(1 + \dfrac{R}{k})^{n \cdot k}$ where A = amount.

P = Principal or original deposit.
R = rate of annual interest.
n = number of years.
k = number of compounding periods per year.

Example 2

Joshua invested $4000 at 3% annual interest that is compounded semiannually.
Use the amount formula involving compound interest to find the amount after 5 years.

Solution

The formula for finding the amount involving compound interest is:

$A = P(1 + \dfrac{R}{k})^{n \cdot k}$ This is the amount equation.

$A = 4000 (1 + \dfrac{3\%}{2})^{5 \cdot 2}$ Substitute P = 4000, R = 3%, k = 2, and n = 5 into the

amount equation.
Note that k = 2 because the annual interest is compounded semiannually which is twice per year.

$A = 4000 (1 + \dfrac{0.03}{2})^{5 \cdot 2}$ $3\% = \dfrac{3}{100} = 0.03$

$A = 4000 (1 + \dfrac{0.03}{2})^{10}$ Evaluate the exponents, $5 \cdot 2 = 10$

$A = 4000 (1 + 0.015)^{10}$ Evaluate within the parenthesis. Depress $.03 \div 2 =$ on a calculator to obtain 0.015.

$A = 4000 (1.015)^{10}$ Evaluate within the parenthesis. $(1 + 0.015 = 1.015)$

$A = 4000 (1.160540825)$ Evaluate the power. $(1.015)^{10}$ is evaluated by depressing 1.015 y^x 10 = on a calculator to obtain 1.160540825.

(Make sure that your calculator has the y^x button or symbol. Note that calculators vary, so be careful of the type you use.)

A = 4642.1633   Evaluate the product. Depress 4000 × 1.160540825 = on a calculator to obtain 4642.1633.

There would be an amount of $4642.16 rounded to the nearest cent after 5 years.

Example 3

Use the formula for finding the amount involving compound interest to calculate the amount in a savings account after 4 years when $2000 is deposited at 6% per year compounded annually.

Solution

The formula for finding the amount involving compound interest is:

$$A = P(1 + \frac{R}{k})^{n \cdot k}$$ where A = amount.

P = Principal or original deposit.
R = rate of annual interest.
n = number of years.
k = number of compounding periods per year.

$A = 2000(1 + \frac{6\%}{1})^{4 \cdot 1}$ Substitute P = $2000, R = 6%, k = 1, and n = 4 years into the amount equation. Note that k = 1 because the annual interest is compounded annually which is once per year.

$A = 2000(1 + \frac{0.06}{1})^{4 \cdot 1}$ $6\% = \frac{6}{100} = 0.06$. (Review the topic on percent and decimals).

$A = 2000(1 + 0.06)^4$ Evaluate exponents. (4 × 1 = 4) and 0.06 ÷ 1 = 0.06.

$A = 2000(1.06)^4$ Evaluate parentheses. (1 + 0.06 = 1.06).

$A = 2000(1.26247696)$ Evaluate the power. Evaluate $(1.06)^4$ by depressing 1.06 y^x 4 = on a calculator to obtain 1.26247696. (Make sure that your calculator has the y^x button or symbol. Make sure you know how to use the power key on your calculator.)

A = 2524.95392   Evaluate the product. Depress 2000 × 1.26247696 = on a calculator to obtain 2524.95392.

There would be an amount of $2524.95 to the nearest cent at the end of 4 years.

Exercises

1. Use the spreadsheet to find the value of each amount after 3 years, compounded annually. Hint: See Example 1.
    a. $6000 at 4% annual interest.   b. $1000 at 5% annual interest.
    c. $4000 at 8% annual interest.   d. $8000 at 7% annual interest.
2. Use the amount formula involving compound interest to find the value of each amount

or of each investment after 4 years compounded semiannually. Hint: See Example 2.

a. $900 at 7% annual interest
b. $500 at 8% annual interest.

c. $1000 at 6% annual interest.
d. $2000 at 6% annual interest.

3. Use the amount formula involving compound interest to find the value of each amount or each investment after 6 years, compounded annually.
Hint: See Example 3.

a. $700 at 7% annual interest.
b. $3000 at 5% annual interest.

c. $5000 at 7% annual interest.
d. $2500 at 4% annual interest.

Challenge Questions

4. Use a spreadsheet to find the value of each amount after 4 years compounded annually.

a. $1000 at 3% annual interest
b. $2000 at 6% annual interest.

5. Use the amount formula involving compound interest to find the value of each investment.

a. $5500 at 5% annual interest compounded annually for 6 years.

b. $9000 at 4% annual interest compounded semiannually for 7 years.
Hint: compounded semiannually means there were 2 compounding periods per year and therefore $k = 2$ in the amount formula.

c. $5000 at 6.5% annual interest compounded quarterly for 5 years.
Hint: Compounded quarterly means that there were 4 compounded periods per year and therefore $k = 4$ in the amount formula.

d. Determine the value of $10000 investment for 15 years at 7% annual rate of interest that is compounded (1) annually, (2) semiannually, and (3) quarterly.
Hint: Compounding annually means that $k = 1$; compounding semiannually means $k = 2$ and compounding quarterly means $k = 4$ in the amount formula.

e. Find the value of a $8900 savings account paying 5% interest compounded monthly over a 5-year period. Assume no additional deposits or withdrawals are made during that time. Hint: Compounded monthly means compounded 12 times per year because there are 12 months in a year, and therefore, $k = 12$ in the amount formula.

Answers to Selected Questions

2a. $1185.13   3a. $1050.51

QUADRATIC EQUATIONS

Quadratic Equations

If the product of two numbers is 0, then at least one of the numbers must be 0.

If $a \times b = 0$, then either $a = 0$ or $b = 0$.

Example 1

Solve the equation for x.

$(x + 3)(x + 9) = 0$.

Solution

If $(x + 3)(x + 9) = 0$,

then either $x + 3 = 0$ or $x + 9 = 0$.

Find x when $x + 3 = 0$ by subtracting 3 from both sides of he equation $x + 3 = 0$ as shown:

$x + 3 = 0$

$x + 3 - 3 = 0 - 3$ Subtract 3 from both sides of the equation.

$x = -3$ $3 - 3 = 0$

Find x when $x + 9 = 0$ by subtracting 9 from both sides of the equation $x + 9 = 0$ as shown:

$x + 9 = 0$

$x + 9 - 9 = 0 - 9$ Subtract 9 from both sides of the equation

$x = -9$ $9 - 9 = 0$

Therefore, $x = -3$ or $x = -9$.

Example 2

Solve the equation for x

$(2x + 4)(3x + 12) = 0$

Solution

If $(2x + 4)(3x + 12) = 0$,

then either $2x + 4 = 0$ or $3x + 12 = 0$

Find 2x when $2x + 4 = 0$ by subtracting 4 from both sides of the equation $2x + 4 = 0$ as shown:

$2x + 4 - 4 = 0 - 4$

$2x = -4$ $4 - 4 = 0$.

Divide both sides of the equation $2x = -4$ by 2 in order to obtain the value of x as shown:

$2x = -4$

$$\frac{2x}{2} = \frac{-4}{2}$$ Divide both sides of the equation by 2.

$$\begin{array}{cc} \overset{x}{\cancel{\dfrac{2x}{2}}} & = \overset{-2}{\dfrac{\cancel{-4}}{2}} \\ 1 & 1 \end{array}$$ Do the division.

$$x = -2$$

Find 3x when 3x + 12 = 0 by subtracting 12 from both sides of the equation 3x + 12 = 0 as shown:

   3x + 12 - 12 = 0 -12

           3x = -12   12 - 12 = 0

Divide both sides of the equation 3x = -12 by 3 in order to obtain the value of x as shown:

   3x = -12

$$\dfrac{3x}{3} = \dfrac{-12}{3}$$ Divide both sides of the equation by 3.

$$\begin{array}{cc} \overset{x}{\cancel{\dfrac{3x}{3}}} & = \overset{-4}{\dfrac{\cancel{-12}}{3}} \\ 1 & 1 \end{array}$$ Do the division.

$$x = -4$$

Therefore x = -2 or x = -4.

Example 3

Solve for x.

   (x - 2)(7x + 21) = 0

If (x - 2)(7x + 21) = 0,

then either x - 2 = 0 or 7x + 21 = 0.

Find x when x - 2 = 0 by adding 2 to both sides of the equation x - 2 = 0 as shown:

   x - 2 + 2 = 0 + 2

           x = 2   -2 + 2 = 0

Find 7x when 7x + 21 = 0 by subtracting 21 from both sides of the equation 7x + 21 as shown:

   7x + 21 = 0

   7x + 21 - 21 = 0 -21   Subtract 21 from both sides of the equation.

           7x = -21   21 - 21 = 0

Divide both sides of the equation 7x = -21 by 7 in order to obtain the value of x as shown:

   7x = -21

$$\frac{7x}{7} = \frac{-21}{7}$$ Divide both sides of the equation by 7.

$$\frac{\overset{x}{\cancel{7x}}}{\underset{1}{\cancel{7}}} = \frac{\overset{-3}{\cancel{-21}}}{\underset{1}{\cancel{7}}}$$

$$x = -3$$

Therefore, $x = 2$ or $x = -3$.

Example 4
Solve for x

$(5y + 25)(3y - 18) = 0$

Solution
If $(5y + 25)(3y - 18) = 0$,

then either $5y + 25 = 0$ or $3y - 18 = 0$.

Find 5y when $5y + 25 = 0$ by subtracting 25 from both sides of the equation $5y + 25$ as shown:

$5y + 25 - 25 = 0 - 25$ Subtract 25 from both sides of the equation

$5y = -25$ $25 - 25 = 0$

Divide both sides of the equation $5y = -25$ by 5 in order to obtain the value of y as shown:

$$\frac{5y}{5} = \frac{-25}{5}$$

$$\frac{\overset{y}{\cancel{5y}}}{\underset{1}{\cancel{5}}} = \frac{\overset{-5}{\cancel{-25}}}{\underset{1}{\cancel{5}}}$$ Do the division.

$$y = -5$$

Find 3y when $3y - 18 = 0$ by adding 18 to both sides of the equation $3y - 18$ as shown:

$3y - 18 = 0$

$3y - 18 + 18 = 0 + 18$

$3y = 18$ $-18 + 18 = 0$

Divide both sides of the equation $3y = 18$ by 3 in order to obtain the value of y as shown:

$$\frac{3y}{3} = \frac{18}{3}$$

$$\frac{\overset{y}{\cancel{3y}}}{\underset{1}{\cancel{3}}} = \frac{\overset{6}{\cancel{18}}}{\underset{1}{\cancel{3}}}$$

Do the division.

$$y = 6$$

Therefore y = -5 or y = 6.

Example 5

Solve the equation (4p - 20)(3p - 36) = 0

Solution

If (4p - 20)(3p - 36) = 0,

then either 4p - 20 = 0 or 3p - 36 = 0

Find 4p when, 4p - 20 = 0 by adding 20 to both sides of the equation 4p - 20 = 0 as shown:

$$4p - 20 = 0$$
$$4p - 20 + 20 = 0 + 20$$
$$4p = 20$$

Divide both sides of the equation 4p = 20 by 4 in order to obtain the value of p as shown:

$$\frac{4p}{4} = \frac{20}{4}$$

$$\frac{\overset{p}{\cancel{4p}}}{\underset{1}{\cancel{4}}} = \frac{\overset{5}{\cancel{20}}}{\underset{1}{\cancel{4}}}$$

Do the division.

$$p = 5$$

Find 3p when 3p - 36 = 0 by adding 36 to both sides of the equation
3p - 36 = 0 as shown:

$$3p - 36 = 0$$
$$3p - 36 + 36 = 0 + 36$$
$$3p = 36 \qquad\qquad -36 + 36 = 0$$

Divide both sides of the equation 3p = 36 by 3 in order to obtain the value of p as shown:

$$\frac{p}{3p} = \frac{12}{36}$$
$$\frac{3}{3} \qquad \frac{3}{3}$$
$$1 \qquad 1$$

$$p = 12$$

Therefore, p = 5 or p = 12.

Example 6

Solve each of the equations.

   a. w(w + 5) = 0   **b**. k(3k - 15) = 0

Solution

a. If w(w + 5) = 0,

then either w = 0 or w + 5 = 0.

Find w in the equation w + 5 = 0 by subtracting 5 from both sides of the equation
w + 5 = 0 as shown:

$$w + 5 = 0$$
$$w + 5 - 5 = 0 - 5$$
$$w = -5 \qquad\qquad\qquad\qquad 5 - 5 = 0$$

b. If k(3k - 15) = 0,

then either k = 0 or 3k - 15 = 0.

Find 3k in the equation 3k - 15 = 0 by adding 15 to both sides of the equation
3k - 15 = 0 as shown:

$$3k - 15 = 0$$
$$3k - 15 + 15 = 0 + 15$$
$$3k = 15 \qquad\qquad\qquad\qquad -15 + 15 = 0$$

Divide both sides of the equation 3k = 15 by 3 in order to obtain the value of k as
shown:

$$\frac{3k}{3} = \frac{15}{3}$$

$$\begin{array}{cc} k & 5 \\ \frac{3k}{3} & \frac{15}{3} \\ 1 & 1 \end{array}$$

$$k = 5$$

Example 7

Solve each equation.

   a. (m + 6)² = 0   **b**. (2t - 4)² = 0

Solution

$(m + 6)^2 = 0$

$(m + 6)(m + 6) = 0$ $(m + 6)^2 = (m + 6)(m + 6).$

If $(m + 6)(m + 6) = 0$,

then $m + 6 = 0$ twice.

Find m from the equation $m + 6 = 0$ by subtracting 6 from both sides of the equation $m + 6 = 0$ as shown:

$m + 6 = 0$ twice

$m + 6 - 6 = 0 - 6$ twice

$\quad\quad m = -6$ twice $6 - 6 = 0$

b. $(2t - 4)^2 = 0$

$(2t - 4)(2t - 4) = 0$ $(2t - 4)^2 = (2t - 4)(2t - 4)$

If $(2t - 4)(2t - 4) = 0$,

then either $2t - 4 = 0$ or $2t - 4 = 0$

Therefore $2t - 4 = 0$ twice.

Find 2t from the equation $2t - 4 = 0$ by adding 4 to both sides of equation $2t - 4 = 0$ as shown:

$2t - 4 = 0$ twice

$2t - 4 + 4 = 0 + 4$

$\quad\quad 2t = 4$

Divide both sides of the equation $2t = 4$ by 2 in order to obtain the value of t as shown:

$$\frac{2t}{2} = \frac{4}{2}$$

$$\frac{\overset{t}{\cancel{2t}}}{\cancel{2}} = \frac{\overset{2}{\cancel{4}}}{\cancel{2}}$$ Do the division.
$$\quad 1 \quad\quad 1$$

$$t = 2 \quad\quad \text{twice}$$

Exercises

1. Solve each equation. Hint: See Example 1.

   a. $(x + 6)(x + 4) = 0$ **b.** $(x + 2)(x + 7) = 0$ **c.** $(x + 8)(x + 3) = 0$

   d. $(x +)(x + 10) = 0$ **e.** $(x + 11)(x + 5) = 0$ **f.** $(x + 4)(x + 6) = 0$

2. Solve each equation. Hint: See Example 2.

   a. $(2x + 6)(3x + 15) = 0$ **b.** $(2x + 10)(3x + 15) = 0$ **c.** $(3x + 9)(2x + 4) = 0$

   d. $(4x + 16)(2x + 8) = 0$ **e.** $(3x + 6)(2x + 10) = 0$ **f.** $(6x + 12)(2x + 3) = 0$

3. Solve each equation. Hint: See Example 3.

   a. $(x - 5)(3x + 9) = 0$ **b.** $(x - 6)(4x + 12) = 0$ **c.** $(x - 3)(2x + 1) = 0$

d. $(x - 12)(3x + 15) = 0$ **e.** $(x - 4)(4x + 8) = 0$ **f.** $(x - 1)(6x + 12) = 0$

4. Solve each equation. Hint: See Example 4.

   a. $(3x + 6)(4x - 16) = 0$ **b.** $(2x + 8)(3x - 16) = 0$ **c.** $(2x + 10)(3x - 3) = 0$
   d. $(4x + 4)(5x - 15) = 0$ **e.** $(4y + 12)(2y - 9) = 0$ **f.** $(5k + 10)(4k - 16) = 0$

5. Solve each equation. Hint: See Example 5.

   a. $(2w - 10)(3w - 9) = 0$ **b.** $(x - 6)(2x - 11) = 0$ **c.** $(4x - 16)(2x - 6) = 0$
   d. $(2p - 12)(p - 4) = 0$ **e.** $(3k - 5)(4k - 12) = 0$ **f.** $(5v - 15)(v - 7) = 0$

6. Solve each equation. Hint: See Example 6.

   a. $x(x + 4) = 0$ **b.** $w(w + 10) = 0$ **c.** $w(w - 10) = 0$
   d. $a(2a - 4)$ **e.** $m(3m + 15) = 0$ **f.** $x(2x - 9) = 0$

7. Solve each equation. Hint: See Example 7.

   a. $(x + 7)^2 = 0$ **b.** $(m - 3)^2 = 0$ **c.** $(k - 4)^2 = 0$
   e. $(4x - 8)^2 = 0$ **f.** $(3m + 15)^2 = 0$

Challenge Questions

8. Solve for the unknown variable in each equation.

   a. $x(2x - 6) = 0$ **b.** $(2x - 3)(x + 4) = 0$ **c.** $w(2w + 4) = 0$
   d. $(m + 13)^2 = 0$ **e.** $(2x - 4)(3x - 9) = 0$ **f.** $(4a + 4)(3a + 1) = 0$
   g. $(2k - 8)^2 = 0$ **h.** $(3m + 4)(6m - 18) = 0$ **i.** $(5x + 15)(x - 4) = 0$
   k. $a(2a - 6) = 0$

Answers to Selected Questions

1a. x = -6 or x = -4   **2a.** x = -3 or x = -5   **3a.** x = 5 or x = -3
4a. x = -3 or x = 4   **5a.** w = 5 or w = 3   **6a.** x = 0 or x = -4
7a. x = -7 twice

HOW TO SOLVE QUADRATIC EQUATIONS OF THE FORM $x^2 + bx + c = 0$

Quadratic equations are equations of the second degree, and that is, equations in which 2 is the highest power of the variable. An example of a quadratic equation is:

$$x^2 + bx + c = 0$$

Quadratic equations can be solved easily when the quadratic equation can be factored. Recall that many quadratic functions or expressions have already been factored under the chapter "Factoring of Quadratic Functions/Expressions."

The same factoring methods are used to factor the quadratic equations in this chapter.

Special Note: Review and understand the chapter on "Factoring of Quadratic Functions/Expressions" before proceeding with this chapter because the method of finding the factors of the quadratic equations will not be discussed or repeated in this chapter.

Example 1

Solve the equation $x^2 + 7x + 10 = 0$

Solution

From Example 1 under the chapter on the "Factoring of Quadratic Functions/Expressions," $x^2 + 7x + 10$ has already been factored as $(x + 5)(x + 2)$.

Therefore, $x^2 + 7x + 10 = (x + 5)(x + 2) = 0$

If $(x + 5)(x + 2) = 0$, then either $x + 5 = 0$ or $x + 2 = 0$.

Find x in the equation $x + 5 = 0$ by subtracting 5 from both sides of the equation $x + 5 = 0$ as shown:

$x + 5 = 0$

$x + 5 - 5 = 0 - 5$ Subtract 5 from both sides of the equation.

       $x = -5$ $5 - 5 = 0$

Find x in the equation $x + 2 = 0$ by subtracting 2 from both sides of the equation $x + 2 = 0$ as shown:

$x + 2 = 0$

$x + 2 - 2 = 0 - 2$ Subtract 5 from both sides of the equation.

        $x = -2$ $2 - 2 = 0$

Therefore, $x = -5$ or $x = -2$.

Example 2

Solve $x^2 - 9x + 8 = 0$

Solution

From Example 2 under the chapter "Factoring of Quadratic Functions/Expressions," $x^2 - 9x + 8$ has been already factored as $(x - 8)(x - 1)$.

Therefore $x^2 - 9x + 8 = (x - 8)(x - 1) = 0$.

If $(x - 8)(x - 1) = 0$, then either $x - 8 = 0$ or $x - 1 = 0..$

Find x in the equation $x - 8 = 0$ by adding 8 to both sides of the equation $x - 8 = 0$ as shown:

$x - 8 = 0$

$x - 8 + 8 = 0 + 8$

       $x = 8$ $-8 + 8 = 0$

Find x in the equation $x - 1 = 0$ by adding 1 to both sides of the equation $x - 1 = 0$ as shown:

$x - 1 = 0$

$x - 1 + 1 = 0 + 1$

x = 1   -1 + 1 = 0

Therefore, x = 8 or x = 1

Example 3

Solve $x^2 - 4x - 12 = 0$

Solution

From Example 3 under the chapter "Factoring of Quadratic Functions/Expression,"

$x^2 - 4x - 12 = 0$ has been already factored as $(x - 6)(x + 2)$.

Therefore, $x^2 - 4x - 12 = (x - 6)(x + 2) = 0$

If $(x - 6)(x + 2) = 0$, then either $x - 6 = 0$ or $(x + 2) = 0$.

Find x in the equation $x - 6 = 0$ by adding 6 to both sides of the equation $x - 6 = 0$ as shown:

$x - 6 = 0$

$x - 6 + 6 = 0 + 6$ $-6 + 6 = 0$

$x = 6$

Find x in the equation $x + 2 = 0$ by subtracting 2 from both sides of the equation $x + 2 = 0$ as shown:

$x + 2 = 0$

$x + 2 - 2 = 0 - 2$ $2 - 2 = 0$

$= -2$

Therefore, $x = 6$ or $x = -2$

HOW TO SOLVE FOR THE ZEROS OF QUADRATIC EQUATIONS

Example 4

Find the zeros of $y = x^2 + 2x - 15$

Solution

The zeros of the equation are the points where the parabola or the equation $y = x^2 + 2x - 15$ intersects the x-axis. But at the x-axis the y value is 0. **Therefore, in order to find the zeros of a quadratic equation, substitute $y = 0$, factor the equation, and then solve for x in the equation** as shown:

$y = x^2 + 2x - 15$

$0 = x^2 + 2x - 15$ At the x-axis, the y-value is 0.

$0 = (x + 5)(x - 3)$ See Example 4 under the chapter

"Factoring of Quadratic Functions/Expression."

$x^2 + 2x - 15$ has already been factored as $(x + 5)(x - 3)$.

If $0 = (x + 5)(x - 3)$, then either $x + 5 = 0$ or $x - 3 = 0$.

Find x in the equation $x + 5 = 0$ by subtracting 5 from both sides of the equation $x + 5 = 0$ as shown:

$x + 5 = 0$

$x + 5 - 5 = 0 - 5$ Subtract 5 from both sides of the equation.

$$x = -5 \qquad\qquad 5 - 5 = 0$$

Find x in the equation x - 3 = 0 by adding 3 to both sides of the equation x - 3 = 0 as shown:

x - 3 = 0	
x - 3 + 3 = 0 + 3	Add 3 to both sides of the equation x - 3 = 0.
x = 3	-3 + 3 = 0

Therefore, either x = -5 or x = 3

The solutions of the equation are -5 and 3.

These two solutions indicate the points where the graph of $y = x^2 + 2x - 15$ intersect the x-axis. Therefore, the zeros of the function are (-5, 0) and (3, 0). Note that these are the points where the parabola intersects the x-axis. Note also that y values of the zeros which are (-5, 0) and (3,0) are 0 because at the x-axis y – 0, (Review the chapter on Coordinate Geometry).

How to Find the x Values of a Quadratic Equation When the y Value is Given

The method for finding the value of x of a quadratic equation when the y value is given is to change the quadratic equation from two variables in x and y to one variable in x by substituting the given y value into the given quadratic equation, then factor the resulting quadratic equation and finally, solve for x as shown in Example 5.

Example 5

If $y = x^2 - 8x + 15$, find the values of x when y = 8.

Solution

The given function is $y = x^2 - 8x + 15$.

Substitute y = 8 into the given function $y = x^2 - 8x + 15$ because it is given in the question that y = 8. This substitution will eliminate the variable y so that we can factor the equation with just one variable which is x as shown:

$y = x^2 - 8x + 15$	Given function
$8 = x^2 - 8x + 15$	Substitute y = 8. It is given in the question that y = 8.
$8 - 8 = x^2 - 8x + 15 - 8$	Subtract 8 from both sides of the equations $8 = x^2 - 8x + 15$ in order to eliminate the 8 at the left side of the equation.
$0 = x^2 - 8x + 7$	8 - 8 = 0 and 15 - 8 = 7.
$0 = (x - 1)(x - 7)$	See the chapter on the "Factoring of Quadratic Equations."

If 0 = (x - 1)(x - 7), then either x - 1 = 0 or x - 7 = 0.

Find x in the equation x - 1 = 0 by adding 1 to both sides of the equation x - 1 = 0 in order to obtain the value of x as shown:

x - 1 = 0	
x - 1 + 1 = 0 + 1	Add 1 to both sides of x - 1 = 0.
x = 1	-1 + 1 = 0

Find x in the equation x - 7 = 0 by adding 7 to both sides of the equation x - 7 = 0 in order to obtain the value of x as shown:

$x - 7 = 0$

$x - 7 + 7 = 0 + 7$ Add 7 to both sides of the equation $x - 7 = 0$.

$x = 7$ $-7 + 7 = 0$

Therefore, the values of x when $y = 8$ are 1 and 7.

Exercises

1. Solve the equation for x. Hint: See Example 1.

a. $(x + 1)(x + 10) = 0$ **b.** $(x + 5)(x + 6) = 0$ **c.** $(x + 2)(x + 11) = 0$

d. $(x + 4)(x + 5) = 0$ **e.** $(x + 8)(x + 2) = 0$ **f.** $(x + 7)(x + 2) = 0$

2. Solve the equation for x. Hint: See Example 2.

a. $(2x + 2)(4x + 16) = 0$ **b.** $(3x + 9)(2x + 6) = 0$ **c.** $(2x + 5)(3x + 12) = 0$

d. $(2x + 7)(2x + 10) = 0$ **e.** $(3x + 15)(2x + 8) = 0$ **f.** $(2x + 12)(3x + 15) = 0$

3. Solve for x. Hint: See Example 3

a. $(x - 3)(3x + 9) = 0$ **b.** $(3x + 9)(2x + 6) = 0$ **c.** $((x - 7)(2x + 8) = 0$

d. $(x - 10)(3x + 12) = 0$ **e.** $(x - 1)(4x + 16) = 0$ **f.** $(x - 3)(3x + 6) = 0$

4. Solve for y. Hint: See Example 4.

a. $(2y +)(3y - 9) = 0$ **b.** $(3y + 3)(4y - 4) = 0$ **c.** $(3y + 12)(2y - 12) = 0$

d. $(2y + 6)(3y - 6) = 0$ **e.** $(4y + 5)(3y - 9) = 0$ **f.** $(7y + 14)(2y - 10) = 0$

5. Solve for p in the equations. Hint: See Example 3.

a. $(2p - 10)(3p - 9) = 0$ **b.** $(3p - 3)(4p - 8) = 0$ **c.** $(2p - 12)(3p - 9) = 0$

d. $(3p - 12)(2p - 14) = 0$ **e.** $(3p - 7)(3p - 12) = 0$ **f.** $(6p - 24)(5p - 10) = 0$

6. If $y = x^2 - 8x + 15$, find the values of x when $y = 3$. Hint: See Example 5.

7. $y = x^2 + 3x - 15$. Find the values of x when $y = -5$. Hint: See Example 5.

8. Solve each equation. Hint: See Example 6.

a. $x(x + 3) = 0$ **b.** $w(w - 10) = 0$ **c.** $a(a - 12) = 0$

d. $k(k + 2) = 0$ **e.** $n(n - 16) = 0$ **f.** $m(m - 6) = 0$

9. Solve each equation. Hint: See Example 7.

a. $(n + 3)^2 = 0$ **b.** $(3t - 8)^2 = 0$ **c.** $(2x - 6)^2 = 0$

d. $(2k + 12)^2 = 0$ **e.** $(m + 3)^2 = 0$ **f.** $(3n + 15)^2 = 0$

Challenge Questions

10. Solve each equation

a. $(x - 5)(3x + 15) = 0$ **b.** $(m - 36)^2 = 0$ **c.** $(3y + 7)^2 = 0$

d. $(2x - 20)^2 = 0$ **e.** $(2x - 18)^2 = 0$ **f.** $w(w + 4) = 0$

g. $(3x - 15)(2x - 8) = 0$ **h.** $(10v - 30)(v - 9) = 0$ **i.** $a(a + 7) = 0$

j. $m(m - 1) = 0$

11. Find the value(s) of x when $y = -1$ given that $y = x^2 - 8x + 15$.

Answers to Selected Question.

1a. $x = -1$ or $x = -10$ **2a.** $x = -1$ or $x = -4$ **3a.** $x = 3$ or $x = -3$

4a. $y = -4$ or $y = 3$ **5a.** $p = 5$ or $p = 3$ **6a.** $x = 6$ or $x = 2$

8a. $x = 0$ or $x = -3$ **9a.** $n = -3$ twice

MORE TRINOMIALS

Review and understand the chapter on "Factoring of Quadratic Functions/Expressions" with reference to the section on " More Trinomials" because the same method is used to factorize quadratic equations. Therefore, the factoring of the quadratic equation will not be fully discussed in this chapter.

Example 1

Solve the equation $2x^2 + 7x - 15 = 0$.

Solution

To solve for x, first find the factors of the quadratic function $2x^2 + 7x - 15$, and then solve for x.

From the solution of Example 1 under the chapter "Factoring of Quadratic Functions/Expressions," section on "More Trinomials," the factors of $2x^2 + 7x - 15$ are $(2x - 3)(x + 5)$, and therefore, $2x^2 + 7x - 15 = (2x - 3)(x + 5)$.

The question states that $2x^2 + 7x - 15 = 0$, and therefore, we can also state that $(2x - 3)(x + 5) = 0$.

If $(2x - 3)(x + 5) = 0$, then either $2x - 3 = 0$ or $x + 5 = 0$.

Find 2x from the equation $2x - 3 = 0$ by adding 3 to both sides of the equation $2x - 3 = 0$ as shown:

$$2x - 3 = 0$$

$$2x - 3 + 3 = 0 + 3 \qquad \text{Add 3 to the equation } 2x - 3 = 0.$$

$$2x = 3$$

$$\frac{2x}{2} = \frac{3}{2} \qquad \text{Divide both sides of the equation } 2x = 3 \text{ in order}$$

to obtain the value of x.

$$\frac{\overset{x}{\cancel{2x}}}{\underset{1}{\cancel{2}}} = \frac{3}{2} \qquad \text{Do the division.}$$

$$x = \frac{3}{2} = 1\frac{1}{2}$$

Find x from the equation x + 5 = 0 by subtracting 5 from both sides of the equation
x + 5 = 0 as shown:

$$x + 5 = 0$$
$$x + 5 - 5 = 0 - 5$$
$$x = -5$$

Therefore, $x = 1\frac{1}{2}$ or x = -5

Example 2

If $2x^2 - 5x + 3 = 0$, solve for x.

Solution

We can solve for x by first factoring $2x^2 - 5x + 3$. From the solution of Example 2 under the chapter "Factoring of Quadratic Functions/Expressions," section on "More Trinomials," the factors of $2x^2 - 5x + 3$ are (2x - 3)(x - 1), and therefore, $2x^2 - 5x + 3 = (2x - 3)(x - 1)$.
The question states that $2x^2 + 7x - 15 = 0$, therefore, we can state also that (2x - 3)(x - 1) = 0.
If (2x - 3)(x - 1) = 0, then either 2x - 3 = 0 or x - 1 = 0.
Find 2x from the equation 2x - 3 = 0 by adding 3 to both sides of the equation
2x - 3 = 0 as shown:

$$2x - 3 = 0$$
$$2x - 3 + 3 = 0 + 3$$
$$2x = 3 \qquad\qquad -3 + 3 = 0$$

$$\frac{2x}{2} = \frac{3}{2}$$ Divide both sides of the equation by 2 in order

to obtain the value of x.

$$\frac{\overset{x}{\cancel{2x}}}{\underset{1}{\cancel{2}}} = \frac{3}{2}$$

$$x = \frac{3}{2} = 1\frac{1}{2}$$

Find x from the equation x - 1 = 0 by adding 1 to both sides of the equation x - 1 = 0
in order to obtain the value of x as shown:

$$x - 1 = 0$$
$$x - 1 + 1 = 0 + 1$$

$$x = 1 \qquad\qquad -1 + 1 = 0$$

Therefore, $x = 1\dfrac{1}{2}$ or $x = 1$

Example 3

Solve the equation $6n^2 - 7n - 3 = 0$.

Solution

We can solve for n in the equation $6n^2 - 7n - 3 = 0$ by first finding the factors of $6n^2 - 7n - 3$. From the solution of example 3 under the chapter "Factoring of Quadratic Functions/Expressions," section on "More Trinomials," the factors of $6n^2 - 7n - 3$ are $(3n + 1)(2n - 3)$, and therefore, $6n^2 - 7n - 3 = (3n + 1)(2n - 3)$. The question states that $6n^2 - 7n - 3 = 0$, therefore, we can also state that $(3n + 1)(2n - 3) = 0$.

If $(3n + 1)(2n - 3) = 0$, then either $(3n + 1) = 0$ or $(2n - 3) = 0$

Find 3n from the equation $3n + 1 = 0$ by subtracting 1 from both sides of the equation $3n + 1 = 0$ as shown:

$$3n + 1 = 0$$
$$3n + 1 - 1 = 0 - 1$$
$$3n = -1 \qquad\qquad +1 - 1 = 0$$

$$\dfrac{3n}{3} = \dfrac{-1}{3} \qquad\qquad$$ Divide both sides of the equation $3n = -1$ by

3 in order to obtain the value of n.

$$\dfrac{3n}{3} = \dfrac{-1}{3} \qquad\qquad$$ Do the division.

$$\dfrac{\overset{n}{\cancel{3n}}}{\underset{1}{\cancel{3}}} = \dfrac{-1}{3}$$

$$n = -\dfrac{1}{3}$$

Find 2n from the equation $2n - 3 = 0$ as shown:

$$2n - 3 = 0$$
$$2n - 3 + 3 = 0 + 3 \qquad$$ Add 3 to both sides of the equation $2n - 3 = 0$.
$$2n = 3$$

$$\frac{2n}{2} = \frac{3}{2}$$

Divide both sides of the equation $2n = 3$ by 2 in order to obtain the value of n.

$$\frac{\overset{n}{\cancel{2n}}}{\underset{1}{\cancel{2}}} = \frac{3}{2}$$

$$n = \frac{3}{2} = 1\frac{1}{2}$$

Therefore, $n = -\frac{1}{3}$ or $n = 1\frac{1}{2}$

Example 4

Solve $7 - 22n + 3n^2 = 0$.

Solution

We can solve for n in the equation $7 - 22n + 3n^2 = 0$ by first finding the factors of $7 - 22n + 3n^2$. From the solution of example 4 under the chapter "Factoring of Quadratic Functions/Expressions," section on "More Trinomials," the factors of $7 - 22n + 3n^2$ are $(7 - n)(1 - 3n)$, and therefore, $7 - 22n + 3n^2 = (7 - n)(1 - 3n)$.
The equation states that $7 - 22n + 3n^2 = 0$, and therefore, we can also write that $(7 - n)(1 - 3n) = 0$.
If $(7 - n)(1 - 3n) = 0$, then either $7 - n = 0$ or $1 - 3n = 0$.
Find -n from the equation $7 - n = 0$ by subtracting 7 from both sides of the equation $7 - n = 0$ as shown:

$$7 - n = 0$$
$$7 - 7 - n = 0 - 7 \qquad \text{Subtract 7 from both sides of the equation.}$$
$$-n = -7 \qquad \qquad 7 - 7 = 7$$

$$\frac{-n}{-1} = \frac{-7}{-1} \qquad \text{Divide both sides of the equation } -n = -7$$

by -1 in order to obtain the value of n.

$$n = 7 \qquad \text{Review division by a negative number.}$$

Find -3n from the equation $1 - 3n = 0$ by subtracting 1 from both sides of the equation $1 - 3n$ as shown:

$$1 - 3n = 0$$
$$-1 - 3n = 0 - 1 \qquad \text{Subtract 1 from both sides of the equation } 1 - 3n = 0.$$

$$-3n = -1$$

$$\frac{-3n}{-3} = \frac{-1}{-3} \qquad \text{Divide both sides of the equation } -3n = -1$$

by -3 in order to obtain the value of n.

$$\frac{\overset{1}{\cancel{-3}n}}{-3} = \frac{-1}{-3}$$

Do the division.

$$n = \frac{1}{3}$$

Review division by a negative number.

Therefore, $n = 7$ or $n = \dfrac{1}{3}$.

Example 5

Solve for x given that $2x^2 + 23x + 45 = 0$

Solution

We can solve for x in the equation $2x^2 + 23x + 45 = 0$ by first finding the factors for $2x^2 + 23x + 45$. From the solution of example 5 under the chapter "Factoring of Quadratic Functions/Expressions", section on "More Trinomials," the factors of $2x^2 + 23x + 45$ are $(2x + 5)$ and $(x + 9)$, and therefore,

$$2x^2 + 23x + 45 = (2x + 5)(x + 9)$$

The equation states that $2x^2 + 23x + 45 = 0$, and therefore, we can also write that $(2x + 5)(x + 9) = 0$.

If $(2x + 5)(x + 9) = 0$, then either $2x + 5 = 0$ or $x + 9 = 0$

Find 2x from the equation $2x + 5 = 0$ by subtracting 5 from both sides of the equation $2x + 5 = 0$ as shown:

$$2x + 5 = 0$$
$$2x + 5 - 5 = 0 - 5$$

Subtract 5 from both sides of the equation $2x + 5 = 0$.

$$2x = -5$$

$5 - 5 = 0$

$$\frac{2x}{2} = \frac{-5}{2}$$

Divide both sides of the equation by 2 in order to obtain the value of x.

$$\frac{\overset{x}{\cancel{2x}}}{2} = \frac{-5}{2}$$

Do the division.

$$x = \frac{-5}{2} = -2\frac{1}{2}$$

Find x in the equation $x + 9 = 0$ by subtracting 9 from both sides of the equation $x + 9 - 9 = 0 - 9$ as shown:

$$x + 9 = 0$$
$$x + 9 - 9 = 0 - 9 \qquad \text{Subtract 9 from both sides of the equation}$$
$$\qquad\qquad\qquad\qquad x + 9 = 0.$$
$$x = -9 \qquad\qquad 9 - 9 = 0.$$

Therefore, $x = -2\dfrac{1}{2}$ or $x = -9$.

Exercises

1. Solve for the unknown in each equation. Hint: See Example 5.

   a. $n^2 + 4n + 3 = 0$ **b**. $x^2 + 13x + 12 = 0$

   c. $x^2 + 7x + 12 = 0$ **d**. $x^2 + 6x + 9 = 0$

2..Solve for x in each equation. Hint: See Example 1.

   a. $x^2 + 3x - 18 = 0$ **b**. $x^2 + 3x - 10 = 0$

   c. $x^2 + 6x - 16 = 0$ **d**. $x^2 + 5x - 6 = 0$

   e. $3x^2 + x - 2 = 0$ **f**. $3x^2 + 7x - 6 = 0$

3. Solve for x in each equation. Hint: See Example 2.

   a. $2x^2 - 5x + 2 = 0$ **b**. $2x^2 - 10x + 12 = 0$

   c. $2x^2 - 3x + 1 = 0$ **d**. $3x^2 - 11x + 6 = 0$

   e. $2x^2 - 10x + 12 = 0$ **f**. $2x^2 - 15x + 27 = 0$

4. Solve for x in each equation. Hint: See Example 3.

   a. $2x^2 - 5x - 3 = 0$ **b**. $3x^2 - 5x - 8 = 0$

   c. $2x^2 - x - 1 = 0$ **d**. $3x^2 - 14x - 24 = 0$

   e. $3x^2 - 13x - 30 = 0$ **f**. $2x^2 - 15x + 27 = 0$

5. Solve each equation for x. Hint: See Example 4.

   a. $5 - 8x - 4x^2 = 0$ **b**. $7 - 20x - 3x^2 = 0$

   c. $1 + 4x + 3x^3 = 0$ **d**. $35 + 30x - 5x^2 = 0$

Challenge Questions

6. Solve for the unknown variable in each equations.

   a. $2x^2 - 15x + 25 = 0$ **b**. $2x^2 - 15x - 27 = 0$

   c. $7x^2 + 10x + 3 = 0$ **d**. $5 - 7x - 6x^2 = 0$

Answers to Selected Questions

   1a. $n = -1$ or $n = -3$ **2a**. $x = -2$ or $x = 9$

   3a. $x = 2$ or $x = \dfrac{1}{2}$ **4a**. $x = 3$ or $x = -\dfrac{1}{2}$

PYTHAGOREAN THEOREM

The legs and the hypotenuse of a right triangle

A right triangle is a triangle which has one right angle. In a right triangle, the longest side is the hypotenuse and the other two sides of the triangle are called the legs as shown:

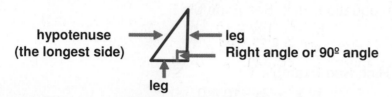

hypotenuse ⟶   ⟵ leg
(the longest side)   **Right angle or 90º angle**

leg

The Pythagorean Theorem states that the sum of the squares of the lengths of the legs of a right triangle is equal to the square of the length of the hypotenuse.

Explanation of the Pythagorean Theorem

1. The Pythagorean Theorem means that in a right triangle,

$$(\text{leg})^2 + (\text{leg})^2 = (\text{hypotenuse})^2$$

or

$$a^2 + b^2 = c^2$$

2. In the Figure 1, the area of the square on leg **a** is 9 square units and the area of the square on leg **b** is 16 square units. The sum of the squares on leg **a** and leg **b** = 9 square units +16 square units.

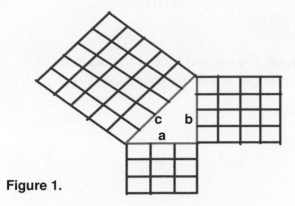

Figure 1.

3. Using Figure 1, the area of the square on the hypotenuse is 25 square units.

4. Since the sum of the areas of the squares on the two legs is 25 square units and the area of the squares on the hypotenuse is also 25 square units, could we conclude that the Pythagorean Theorem is correct?

Special Note: In order to solve problems involving the Pythagorean Theorem, you must know how to find squares and square roots of numbers. Hint: You may review the chapter on Square Roots.

Example 1
a. What is the Pythagorean Theorem used for?
b. Find the value of **c** in the figure.

Solution
a. The Pythagorean Theorem is used to find the length of a side of a right triangle if the lengths of the other two sides are known.
b. Using the Pythagorean Theorem, $a^2 + b^2 = c^2$————————————[A]
   Substitute 3 for **a** and 4 for **b** in the equation [A] as shown:

   $(3 \text{ ft})^2 + (4 \text{ ft})^2 = c^2$
   $9 \text{ ft}^2 + 16 \text{ ft}^2 = c^2$

   $(3 \text{ ft})^2 = 3 \text{ ft} \times 3 \text{ ft} = 9 \text{ ft}^2$
   $(4 \text{ ft})^2 = 4 \text{ ft} \times 4 \text{ ft} = 16 \text{ ft}^2$

   $25 \text{ ft}^2 = c^2$_____[B]

   $9 \text{ ft}^2 + 16 \text{ ft}^2 = 25 \text{ ft}^2$

Find the square root of both sides of the equation [B] in order to obtain the value of **c** as shown:

$$\sqrt{25 \text{ ft}^2} = \sqrt{c^2}$$
$$\sqrt{5^2 \text{ ft}^2} = \sqrt{c^2}$$
$$5 \text{ ft} = c$$

In general, the square root of the square of any number is the number itself. For example, $\sqrt{n^2} = n$.

Example 2

Find b to the nearest tenth.

b   6 cm

3 cm

Solution

Using the Pythagorean Theorem,

$$a^2 + b^2 = c^2 \underline{\hspace{5cm}} \text{[A]}$$

Substitute 3 cm for **a** and 6 cm for **c** into equation [A] as shown:

$$3^2 + b^2 = 6^2 \underline{\hspace{5cm}} \text{[B]}$$

Note that 6 cm is the hypotenuse because it is the longest side of the right triangle. Isolate **b^2** in equation [B] by subtracting 3^2 from both sides of equation [B] as shown:

$$3^2 - 3^2 + b^2 = 6^2 - 3^2$$
$$0 + b^2 = 36 - 9 \qquad\qquad 6^2 = 6 \times 6 = 36 \text{ and } 3^2 = 3 \times 3 = 9$$
$$b^2 = 27 \underline{\hspace{4cm}} \text{[C]}$$

Find the square root of both sides of equation [C] in order to obtain the value of **b** as shown:

$$\sqrt{b^2} = \sqrt{27}$$
$$b = \sqrt{27} \qquad\qquad \sqrt{b^2} = b$$

You may use a calculator to obtain $\sqrt{27}$ by depressing the following keys on the calculator, depending on the type of calculator:

$$27 \sqrt{} = \text{ , or } 2\text{nd} \sqrt{} \; 27 = \text{ , which equals to } 5.196...$$

So, **b** = 5.2 cm to the nearest tenth. On some calculators, 2nd is the same as shift or ctrl.

Exercises

1. State the Pythagorean Theorem.
2. Use the Pythagorean Theorem to find the length n of each right triangle. Round your answer to the nearest tenth. Use a calculator to find the square roots.
   Hint: See Example 1 and Example 2.

a.

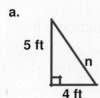

5 ft

n

4 ft

b.

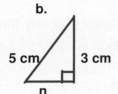

5 cm   3 cm

n

c.

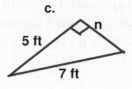

n

5 ft

7 ft

3. Find the length of the diameter of the circle. You may use a calculator to find the square root. Round your answer to the nearest tenth. Hint: The diameter is the hypotenuse and also see Example 1. Note that the triangle ABC is a right triangle, and therefore, we can use the Pythagorean Theorem to find the length of the diameter of the circle.

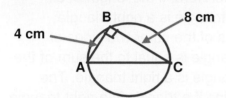

B   8 cm

4 cm

A   C

$\overline{AC}$ is the diameter.

4. Find the length of each rectangle.

a.

A   B

12 cm   4 cm

D   ?   C

b.

A   B

10 cm   3 cm

D   ?   C

Hint: ΔBCD is a right triangle, and therefore, we can use the Pythagorean Theorem to find $\overline{DC}$ which is the length of the rectangle. See Example 2. Round your answer to the nearest tenth.

5. Find the length of the diagonal of each rectangle.

a.

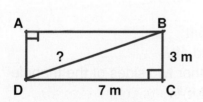

A   B

?   3 m

D   7 m   C

b.

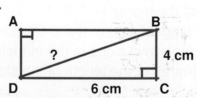

A   B

?   4 cm

D   6 cm   C

Hint: ΔBCD is a right triangle, and therefore, we can use the Pythagorean Theorem to find the length of the diagonal. You may use a calculator to find the square root. Round your answer to the nearest tenth. See Example 2.

Answers to Select Questions

2a. 6.403... ≈ 6.4 ft   **4a**. 11.3137... ≈ 11.3 cm   **5a**. 7.6157...≈ 7.6 m

791

Converse of the Pythagorean Theorem
The converse of the Pythagorean Theorem states that any three positive numbers that make the equation $c^2 = a^2 + b^2$ true are the side lengths of a right triangle.

How to Determine if a Triangle is a Right Triangle When the Length of All the Three Sides are Given

The Pythagorean Theorem states that the sum of the squares of the lengths of the legs of a right triangle is equal to the square of the length of the hypotenuse. The hypotenuse is the longest side of the right triangle, and therefore, if the length of all the three sides are given, we are able to determine if the triangle is a right triangle by squaring the longest side and also squaring the lengths of the other two sides of the triangle and if the square of the longest side of the triangle is equal to the sum of the squares of the lengths of the other two sides, then the triangle is a right triangle. The converse of the Pythagorean Theorem is used to determine if a triangle is a right triangle when the lengths of all the three sides are given. If the side length are all whole numbers, then each set of the three side length is call **Pythagorean Triples**.

Example 3
a. Determine if the triangle with the side lengths of 3 ft, 5 ft, and 4 ft is a right triangle?
b. What is meant by a right angle?
Solution
a. The Pythagorean Theorem states that the sum of the squares of the lengths of the legs of a right triangle is equal to the square of the length of the hypotenuse. The hypotenuse is the longest side of the triangle, and therefore, if the square of the longest side of the triangle is equal to the sum of the squares of the other two sides, then the triangle is a right triangle.
Longest side of the triangle = 5 ft
Square of the longest side of the triangle = $(5 \text{ ft})^2 = 25 \text{ ft}^2$
Length of the other two sides of the triangle are 3ft and 4ft.
Sum of the squares of the length of the sides of the other two sides of the triangle
$$= (3 \text{ ft})^2 + (4 \text{ ft})^2$$
$$= 9 \text{ ft}^2 + 16 \text{ ft}^2$$
$$= 25 \text{ ft}^2$$
Since the square of the longest side of the triangle is equal to the sum of the squares of the other two sides of the triangle which is 25 ft^2, the triangle is a right triangle.
b. Right triangle means that the triangle has a 90 degree angle.

Example 4
Determine if the triangle with the side lengths of 12 cm, 4 cm, and 6 cm is a right angle.
Solution

The Pythagorean Theorem states that the sum of the squares of the lengths of the legs of a right triangle is equal to the square of the length of the hypotenuse. The hypotenuse is the longest side of the triangle, and therefore, if the square of the longest side of the triangle is equal to the sum of the squares of the other two sides, then the triangle is a right triangle.

Longest side of the triangle = 12 cm

Square of the longest side of the triangle = $(12 \text{ cm})^2 = 144 \text{ cm}^2$

Length of the other two sides of the triangle are 4 cm and 6 cm.

Sum of the squares of the length of the sides of the other two sides of the triangle
$$= (4 \text{ cm})^2 + (6 \text{ cm})^2$$
$$= 16 \text{ cm}^2 + 36 \text{ cm}^2$$
$$= 52 \text{ cm}^2$$

Since the square of the longest side of the triangle = 144 cm² and the sum of the squares of the other two sides of the triangle = 52 cm², the square of the longest side of the triangle is not equal to the sum of the square of other two sides of the triangle, so the triangle is not a right triangle.

Exercises

Determine if each triangle with the given length of the sides is a right triangle.
Hint: See Examples 3 and 4. You may use a calculator.

1. 13 ft, 5 ft, 12 ft   **2**. 5 cm, 7 cm, 4 cm   **3**. 15 ft, 8 ft, 17 ft

4. 9 m, 3 m, 5 m   **5**. 16 ft, 34 ft, 30 ft   **6** . 7 m, 9 m, 11 m

7. 6 ft, 10 ft, 8 ft   **8**. 5 m, 4 m, 3 m   **9**. 8 ft, 5 ft, 3 ft

REAL APPLICATIONS - WORD PROBLEMS
Pythagorean Theorem

Example 1

A 10-foot ladder is placed so that the top of it touches a wall. The base of the ladder is 6 feet from the base of the wall. How high is the wall to the top of the ladder?

Solution

Step 1: First draw the diagram.

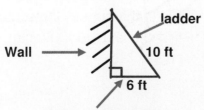

Wall ⟶

ladder

10 ft

6 ft

Distance from the base of
of the ladder to the base of the wall.

793

Step 2: Note that the wall forms a 90 degree angle with the ground level, and therefore, use the Pythagorean Theorem to write an equation involving the length of the ladder, the height of the wall, from the base of the wall to the top of the ladder, and the distance from the base of the ladder to the base of the wall as shown:

Let the height of the wall from the base of the wall to the top of the ladder = H
Length of the ladder = 10 ft
Distance from the base of the ladder to the base of the wall = 6 ft.

Observe the diagram, the longest side of the triangle formed is the length of the ladder, and therefore, the length of the ladder becomes the hypotenuse. Using the Pythagorean Theorem then,

$$(10 \text{ ft})^2 = H^2 + (6 \text{ ft})^2$$
$$100 \text{ ft}^2 = H^2 + 36 \text{ ft}^2 \underline{\hspace{5cm}}[A]$$

$$(10 \text{ ft})^2 = 10 \text{ ft} \times 10 \text{ ft} = 100 \text{ ft}^2,$$
$$(6 \text{ ft})^2 = 6 \text{ ft} \times 6 \text{ ft} = 36 \text{ ft}^2$$

Step 3: Solve for H^2 in equation $[A]$

Subtract 36 ft² from both sides of equation $[A]$ in order to eliminate the 36 ft² from the right side of the equation $[A]$ in order to obtain the value of H^2 as shown:

$$100 \text{ ft}^2 - 36 \text{ ft}^2 = H^2 + 36 \text{ ft}^2 - 36 \text{ ft}^2$$
$$64 \text{ ft}^2 = H^2 + 0$$
$$64 \text{ ft}^2 = H^2 \underline{\hspace{4cm}}[B]$$

Step 4: Solve for H in equation $[B]$.

Find the square root of both sides of equation $[B]$ in order to obtain the value of H as shown:

$$\sqrt{64 \text{ ft}^2} = \sqrt{H^2}$$
$$\sqrt{8^2 \text{ ft}^2} = \sqrt{H^2} \qquad\qquad 8^2 = 64$$

Recall that the square root of any number to the second power is the number itself, therefore 8 ft = H.

Therefore, the height of the wall from the ground level to the top of the ladder is 8 ft.

Example 2

A ladder is placed against a wall. The base of the ladder is 5 m from the base of the wall. If the top of the ladder is 12 m from the base of the wall, how long is the ladder?

Solution

Step 1: First draw the diagram.

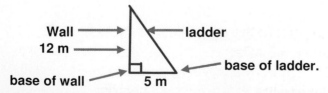

Step 2: Note that the wall forms a 90 degree angle with the ground level, and therefore,

use the Pythagorean Theorem to write an equation involving the length of the ladder, the height of the wall from the top of the ladder to the base of the wall and the distance from the base of the ladder to the base of the wall as shown:

Let the length of the ladder = x

Height of the wall from the top of the ladder to the base of the wall = 12 m.

Distance from the base of the ladder to the base of the wall = 5 m.

Observe the diagram, the longest side of the triangle formed is the length of the ladder. So the length of the ladder becomes the hypotenuse. Using the Pythagorean Theorem then,

$$x^2 = (12 \text{ m})^2 + (5 \text{ m})^2 \qquad\qquad 12^2 = 12 \times 12 = 144$$
$$x^2 = 144 \text{ m}^2 + 25 \text{ m}^2 \qquad\qquad 12^2 = 12 \times 12 = 144 \text{ and } 5^2 = 5 \times 5 = 25$$
$$x^2 = 169 \text{ m}^2 \underline{\hspace{3cm}} [\text{A}]$$

Find the square root of both sides of equation $[\text{A}]$ in order to obtain the value of x as shown:

$$\sqrt{x^2} = \sqrt{169 \text{ m}^2}$$
$$\sqrt{x^2} = \sqrt{13^2 \text{ m}^2} \qquad\qquad\qquad 169 = 13 \times 13 = 13^2$$
$$x = 13 \text{ m} \qquad\qquad \text{Recall that the square root of the square of any number}$$

is the number itself. For an example $\sqrt{n^2} = n$

Note: You may also use a calculator to find $\sqrt{169}$ by depressing $169 \, \sqrt{} \; = \;$ or $2\text{nd} \, \sqrt{} \quad 169 = $ on a calculator to obtain 13.

Example 3

Mary biked 6.2 miles west and then 3.5 miles south. How far is she from her starting point? Round your answer to the nearest tenth.

Solution

Step 1: First draw the diagram.

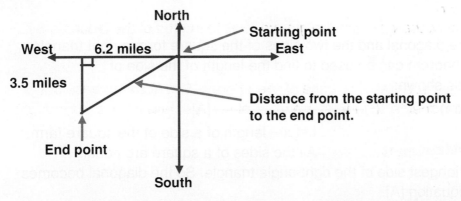

Step 2: Let the distance from the starting point to the end point = d. Note that 6.2 miles west forms a 90 degree angle with the 3.5 miles south. Therefore, the 6.2 miles west and the 3.5 miles south and the distance from the starting point to the end point form a right triangle and we can use the Pythagorean Theorem

to solve the problem as shown:

$$d^2 = (6.2 \text{ miles})^2 + (3.5 \text{ miles})^2$$
$$d^2 = 38.44 \text{ miles}^2 + 12.25 \text{ miles}^2$$

$6.2^2 = 6.2 \times 6.2 = 38.44$

$3.5^2 = 3.5 \times 3.5 = 12.25$

$$d^2 = 50.69 \text{ miles}^2 \underline{\hspace{3cm}} [A]$$

$38.44 + 12.25 = 50.69$

Find the square root of both sides of equation $[A]$ in order to obtain the value of d as shown:

$$\sqrt{d^2} = \sqrt{50.69}$$

$$d = 7.119$$ Use the calculator to obtain the $\sqrt{50.69}$ by depressing

2nd $\sqrt{}$ 50.69 = on the calculator to obtain 7.119.

$d = 7.1$ miles   Rounding to the nearest tenth.

Example 4

A farmer has a farm in the shape of a square with a diagonal of $\sqrt{15 \text{ km}}$.

a. What is the length of the side of the farm?
b. What is the area of the farm?
c. Find the perimeter of the farm.

Solution

a. Step 1: First draw the diagram.

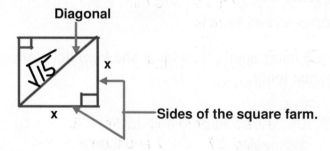

Step 2: Note that the diagonal and the two sides of the square form a right triangle. The Pythagorean Theorem can be used to find the length of the side of the square formed as shown:

$$(\sqrt{15} \text{ km})^2 = x^2 + x^2 \underline{\hspace{3cm}} [A]$$

Let x = length of a side of the square farm.
All the sides of a square are equal.

The diagonal is the longest side of the right angle triangle. So the diagonal becomes the hypotenuse in equation [A].

Step 3: Solve for x^2 in equation $[A]$ as shown:

$$15 \text{ km}^2 = x^2 + x^2$$

The square of the square root of a number is the number. For example, $\sqrt{n^2} = n$.

$$15 \text{ km}^2 = 2x^2 \underline{\hspace{3cm}} [B]$$

Divide both sides of the equation [B] by 2 in order to isolate x^2 and to obtain the value of x^2 as shown:

$$\frac{15 \text{ km}^2}{2} = \frac{2x^2}{2}$$

$$7\frac{1}{2} \text{ km}^2 = x^2 \underline{\hspace{4cm}} \text{[C]}$$

Step 4: Find the square root of the equation [C] in order to obtain the value of x as shown:

$$\sqrt{7\frac{1}{2} \text{ km}^2} = \sqrt{x^2}$$

$$\sqrt{7.5 \text{ km}^2} = \sqrt{x^2} \qquad 7\frac{1}{2} = 7.5$$

$$\sqrt{7.5} \text{ km} = x \qquad$$ Recall that the square root of the square of a number is the number.

2.7386 km = x   Use a calculator to find $\sqrt{7.5}$ by depressing

2nd $\sqrt{}$ 7.5 = on the calculator to obtain 2.7386.

2.7 km ≈ x   To the nearest tenth.

Therefore, the length of the side of the square farm is 2.7 km.

b. From the solution of **a**, the length of the side of the square farm is 2.7 km.
   The formula for finding the area of the square farm is:
   Area = S · S _____[D]
              where S = length of a side of the square farm.
   Substitute S = 2.7 km into the equation [D] as shown:
        Area = 2.7 km × 2.7 km
             = 7.29 km²   Use a calculator to find 2.7 km × 2.7 km by
                                depressing 2.7 × 2.7 and then = on the
                                calculator to obtain 7.29
   Therefore, the area of the square farm is 7.29 km.

c. The perimeter of the square farm is the distance around the farm. The length of
   each side of the square farm is equal.
   The formula of the perimeter of the square farm is:
        Perimeter = S + S + S + S
                  = 4S _____$\left[\text{E}\right]$
                          where S is the length of a side of the square
                          farm.
   Substitute S = 2.7 km into equation $\left[\text{E}\right]$ as shown:
        Perimeter = 4 × 2.7 km
                  = 10.8 km

The perimeter of the square farm = 10.8 km.

Example 5
The length of a side of an equilateral triangular road sign is 3 ft.
a. Find the height of the road sign.
b. Find the area of the road sign.
c. Find the perimeter of the road sign.
Round your answers to the nearest tenth.
Solution
a. Step 1: First draw the diagram.

Height of the triangular sign.
4 ft   4 ft
4 ft

Height of the triangular sign.
B
4 ft   4 ft
A   D   C
2 ft   2 ft

Step 2: The height of the equilateral triangular road sign forms a 90 degree angle with the base of the equilateral triangle and therefore right triangles are formed. $\triangle ABD$ and $\triangle BCD$ are right triangles and therefore we can use the Pythagorean Theorem to find the height of the equilateral triangular road sign as shown:

$$(4 \text{ ft})^2 = (2 \text{ ft})^2 + h^2 \underline{\hspace{4cm}}[A]$$

Let h be the height of the triangle.

Step 3: Find the value of h.
Subtract $(2 \text{ ft})^2$ from both sides of the equation $[A]$ in order to obtain the value of h as shown:

$$(4 \text{ ft}^2) - (2 \text{ ft})^2 = (2 \text{ ft})^2 - (2 \text{ ft})^2 + h^2$$
$$4 \text{ ft} \times 4 \text{ ft} - 2 \text{ ft} \times 2 \text{ ft} = 0 + h^2 \qquad\qquad (2 \text{ ft})^2 - (2 \text{ ft})^2 = 0$$
$$16 \text{ ft}^2 - 4 \text{ ft}^2 = h^2$$
$$12 \text{ ft}^2 = h^2 \underline{\hspace{4cm}}[B]$$

Setup 4: Find the square root of both sides of equation $[B]$ in order to obtain the value of h as shown:

$$\sqrt{12 \text{ ft}^2} = \sqrt{h^2}$$

3.464 ft = h

$\sqrt{h^2}$ = h because the square root of the square of any number is the number.
Use the calculator to find $\sqrt{12}$ by depressing: 2nd then depressing $\sqrt{}$ 12 = on the calculator to obtain 3.464.

3.5 ft ≈ h   To the nearest tenth.

Note that the number 6 in 3.464 is more than 5, and therefore, 3.464 becomes 3.5 to the nearest tenth. Review Rounding of Numbers.

Therefore, the height of the sign is 3.5 ft.

b. The formula for finding the area of a triangle is:

$$\text{Area} = \frac{1}{2} \text{ base} \times \text{height} \underline{\hspace{4cm}} [C].$$

From the solution of Example 5**a**, the height of the road sign = 3.5 ft. The base of the road sign is $\overline{AC}$ which is 4ft. Substitute base = 4 ft and height = 3.5 ft into equation $[C]$ as shown:

$$\text{Area} = \frac{1}{2} \times 4 \text{ ft} \times 3.5 \text{ ft}$$

$$\text{Area} = \frac{\overset{2}{1}}{\underset{1}{2}} \times 4 \text{ ft} \times 3.5 \text{ ft} \qquad \text{Divide by 2.}$$

$$\text{Area} = 2 \text{ ft} \times 3.5 \text{ ft}$$
$$\text{Area} = 7 \text{ ft}^2$$

The area of the road sign is 7 ft².

c. The perimeter of the road sign is the distance around the road sign. Therefore, the perimeter of an equilateral triangular road sign of length of a side of 4 ft
$$= 4\text{ft} + 4\text{ft} + 4 \text{ ft} = 12 \text{ ft.}$$

Example 6
Find the volume of each rectangular prism.
Round your answer to the nearest tenth.

a.

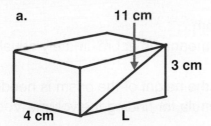

b.

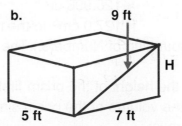

Solution
a. Step 1: Find the length of the prism first because the length is needed in order to find the volume V since the formula for finding the volume of the rectangular prism is:
$$V = \text{Length} \times \text{Width} \times \text{Height.}$$
From the diagram, the length of the diagonal of a face of the rectangular prism = 11 cm.

The diagonal and the two sides of the face of the rectangular prism form a right triangle, and therefore, we can use the Pythagorean Theorem to write an equation to find the length of the prism as shown:
$$(11 \text{ cm})^2 = (3 \text{ cm})^2 + L^2 \underline{\hspace{4cm}} [A]$$

799

Let L represent the length of the prism.
11 cm is the diagonal.

Subtract $(3 \text{ cm})^2$ from both sides of equation $[A]$ in order to isolate L^2 and to obtain the value of L^2 as shown:

$(11 \text{ cm})^2 - (3 \text{ cm})^2 = (3 \text{ cm})^2 - (3 \text{ cm})^2 + L^2$

$11 \text{ cm} \times 11 \text{ cm} - 3 \text{ cm} \times 3 \text{ cm} = 0 + L^2 \qquad\qquad (3 \text{ cm})^2 - (3 \text{ cm})^2 = 0$

$121 \text{ cm}^2 - 9 \text{ cm}^2 = L^2$

$112 \text{cm}^2 = L^2 \underline{\hspace{5cm}} [B]$.

Find the square root of both sides of the equation $[B]$ in order to obtain the value of L as shown:

$$\sqrt{112 \text{ cm}^2} = \sqrt{L^2}$$

$$10.583... \text{ cm} = L$$

The calculator can used to obtain $\sqrt{112}$ by depressing: 2nd and then depressing $\sqrt{}$ 112 = on the calculator to obtain 10.583...

$\sqrt{L^2}$ = L because the square root of a number which is squared is the number.

Step 2: Find he volume of the prism.
The formula for finding the volume of the prism is:

Volume = Length $\times$ Width $\times$ Height $\underline{\hspace{5cm}}[C]$.

From the solution of Example 6**a**, the length ≈ 10.583 cm, from the diagram, the width = 4 cm and the height = 3 cm. Substitute length ≈ 10.583 cm, width = 4 cm and height = 3 cm into equation $[C]$ as shown:

Volume ≈ 10.583 cm $\times$ 4 cm $\times$ 3 cm

$\approx 126.996 \text{ cm}^3$

$\approx 127.0 \text{ cm}^3$ to the nearest tenth.

(Hint: Review Rounding of Numbers.) The symbol $\approx$ means "is approximately equal to."

b. Step 1: Find the height of the prism first because the height of the prism is needed in order to find the volume of the prism since the formula for finding the volume V, of the rectangular prism is:

V = Length $\times$ Width $\times$ Height.

The length of a face of the rectangular prism = 9 ft.
The diagonal and the two sides of the face of the rectangular prism form a right triangle, and therefore, we can use the Pythagorean Theorem to write an equation to find the height of the prism as shown:

$(9 \text{ ft})^2 = (7 \text{ ft})^2 + H^2 \underline{\hspace{5cm}}[D]$

Let H be the height of the rectangular prism.

Subtract $(7 \text{ ft})^2$ from both sides of equation $[D]$ in order to isolate H^2 and also to obtain the value of H^2 as shown:

$(9 \text{ ft})^2 - (7 \text{ ft})^2 = (7 \text{ ft})^2 - (7 \text{ ft})^2 + H^2$

$$9 \text{ ft} \times 9 \text{ ft} - 7 \text{ ft} \times 7 \text{ ft} = 0 + H^2 \qquad (7 \text{ ft})^2 - (7 \text{ ft})^2 = 0.$$
$$81 \text{ ft}^2 - 49 \text{ ft}^2 = H^2 \qquad 9 \text{ ft} \times 9 \text{ ft} = 81 \text{ ft}^2, \; 7 \text{ ft} \times 7 \text{ ft} = 49 \text{ ft}^2.$$
$$32 \text{ ft}^2 = H^2 \underline{\qquad\qquad\qquad\qquad} [E]$$
$$81 \text{ ft}^2 - 49 \text{ ft}^2 = 32 \text{ ft}^2.$$

Find the square root of both sides of equation $[E]$ in order to obtain the value of H as shown:

$$\sqrt{32 \text{ ft}^2} = \sqrt{H^2}$$

$$5.566....\text{ft} \approx H$$

You may use the calculator to find $\sqrt{32}$ by depressing 2nd and then depressing $\sqrt{}$ 32 = on the calculator to obtain 5.656...

$\sqrt{H^2} = H$ because the square root of the square of a number is the number.

Step 2 Find the volume of the prism.
The formula for finding the volume of the rectangular prism is:

$$\text{Volume} = \text{Length} \times \text{Width} \times \text{Height} \underline{\qquad\qquad\qquad} [F]$$

From the solution of Example 6b, the height ≈ 5.656 ft, from the diagram the length = 7 ft and the width = 5 ft. Substitute length = 7 ft, width = 5 ft, and height ≈ 5.656 ft into equation $[F]$ as shown:

$$\text{Volume} = 7 \text{ ft} \times 5 \text{ ft} \times 5.656 \text{ ft}$$
$$= 197.96 \text{ ft}^3$$
$$= 198.0 \text{ ft}^3 \text{ to the nearest tenth. Hint: Review rounding of numbers.}$$

Exercises

1. A 13-foot ladder is placed so that the top of it touches a wall. The base of the ladder is 5 ft from the base of the wall. How high is the wall from the base of the wall to the top of the ladder. Hint: See Example 1.

2. A ladder is placed against a wall. The base of the ladder is 3 m from the base of the wall. If the top of the ladder is 4 m from the base of the wall, how long is the ladder? Hint: See Example 2.

3. John biked 5.8 miles west and then 2.4 miles south. How far is he from his starting point? Round the answer to the nearest tenth. Hint: See Example 3.

4. A boat travelled 4 miles east and then 10 miles north. How far is the boat from its starting point? Hint: See example 3 and also note that the western and the northern directions form a 90 degree angle with each other. Round your answer to the nearest tenth.

5. A square swimming pool has a diagonal of $\sqrt{11}$ km.

   a. What is the length of a side of the swimming pool?
   b. What is the area of the swimming pool?
   c. What is the perimeter of the swimming pool?

Round your answers to the nearest tenth. Hint: See Example 4.

6. A square garden has a diagonal of $\sqrt{10}$ kilometers.

    a. What is the length of a side of the garden?

    b. What is the area of the garden?

    c. What is the perimeter of the garden?

      Round your answers to the nearest tenth. Hint: See Example 4.

7. Find the height, the area, and the perimeter of each equilateral triangle.
Hint: See Example 5. Round your answer to the nearest tenth.

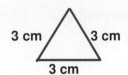 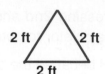 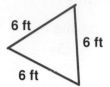

8. Find the volume of each rectangular prism. Round your answer to the nearest tenth.
Hint: See Example 6.

   a. 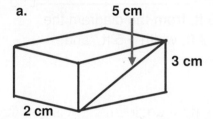   **b.**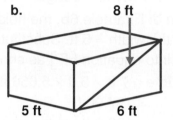

Challenge Questions

9. A square swimming pool has a diagonal of $\sqrt{12}$ **km**.

    a. What is the length of a side of the swimming pool?

    b. What is the area of the swimming pool?

    c. What is the perimeter of the swimming pool?

      Round your answers to the nearest tenth.

10. Nick biked 5 km west and then 4 km south. How far is he from his starting point?
Round your answer to the nearest tenth.

11. A ladder is placed against a wall. The base of the ladder is 5 ft from the base of
the wall. If the top of the ladder is 12 ft from the base of the wall, how long is the
ladder?

12. Find the height, the area, and the perimeter of each equilateral triangle.
Round your answer to the nearest tenth.

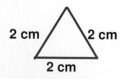 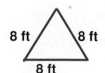 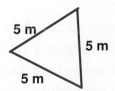

13. Find the volume of each rectangular prism. Round your answer to the nearest tenth.

a.

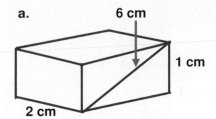

6 cm

1 cm

2 cm

b.

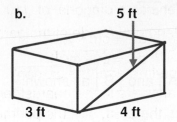

5 ft

3 ft   4 ft

Answers to selected questions

1. 12 ft   **3.** 6.3 miles   **5a.** 2.3 km   **5b.** 5.5 km^2 **5c.** 9.4 km

Proof of the Pythagorean Theorem

We can proof the Pythagorean Theorem by using angle-angle similarity as shown:

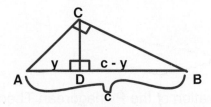

$\triangle$ADC is similar $\triangle$ACB because both triangles have a right angle and $\angle$A is common to both $\triangle$ADC and $\triangle$ACB. ($\angle$ACB = 90^0 and $\angle$ADC = 90^0.)

Therefore, we can write a proportion as shown:

$$\frac{y}{b} = \frac{b}{c}$$

Cross multiply the equation as follows because the cross products of proportions are equal.

$$b^2 = cy \underline{\hspace{8cm}}[A]$$

$\triangle$BDC is similar to $\triangle$ACB because both triangles have a right angle and $\angle$B is common to both $\triangle$BDC and $\triangle$ACB.

($\angle$ACB = 90^0 and $\angle$BDC = 90^0.)

Therefore, we can write a proportion as shown:

$$\frac{c - y}{a} = \frac{a}{c}$$

Cross multiply the equation as follows because the cross products of proportions are equal.

$$\frac{c-y}{a} \times \frac{a}{c}$$

$$a^2 = c(c - y)$$
$$a^2 = c^2 - cy \underline{\hspace{5cm}} [B]$$

Add equations $[A]$ and $[B]$ as shown:

$$b^2 = cy$$
$$+\,a^2 = c^2 - cy$$
$$\overline{a^2 + b^2 = c^2 - cy + cy}$$

$$a^2 + b^2 = c^2 - 0 \qquad\qquad\qquad -cy + cy = 0$$
$$a^2 + b^2 = c^2, \text{ which is the proof of the Pythagorean Theorem.}$$

DISTANCE FORMULA

The distance formula may be considered as the application of the Pythagorean Theorem. Recall from the chapter on the Pythagorean Theorem, the Pythagorean Theorem states that, the sum of the squares of the lengths of the legs of a right triangle is equal to the square of the length of the hypotenuse, which can be stated as shown:

$$(\textbf{leg})^2 + (\textbf{leg})^2 = (\textbf{hypotenuse})^2$$
$$\mathbf{a^2 + b^2 = c^2} \qquad\qquad \textbf{a} = \text{a leg}, \textbf{b} = \text{other leg, and } \textbf{c} = \text{hypotenuse}.$$

Let us use the Pythagorean Theorem to find the length of the hypotenuse $\overline{AB}$ of the right triangle ABC as shown:

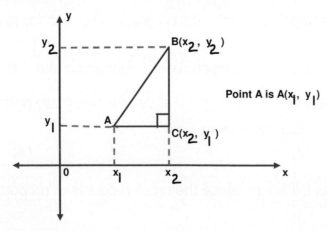

804

$$\overline{AB}^2 = \overline{AC}^2 + \overline{BC}^2 \underline{\hspace{4cm}}[K]$$

Base on the Pythagorean Theorem.

$$\sqrt{\overline{AB}^2} = \sqrt{\overline{AC}^2 + \overline{BC}^2}$$

Take the square root of both sides of the equation [K] in order to obtain the value of $\overline{AB}$.

$$\overline{AB} = \sqrt{\overline{AC}^2 + \overline{BC}^2} \underline{\hspace{2cm}}[L]$$

$\sqrt{\overline{AB}^2} = \overline{AB}$ because the square root of a number that is squared is the number itself.

The distance between two points A and C in the diagram, is the length of $\overline{AC}$, which is the segment with the endpoints of A and C.

$$\overline{AC} = x_2 - x_1$$

If we subtract the distance x_1 from the distance x_2, the result will be the distance AC.

The distance between two points B and C in the diagram, is the length of $\overline{BC}$, which is the segment with the endpoints of B and C.

$$\overline{BC} = y_2 - y_1$$

If we subtract the distance y_1 from the distance y_2, the result will be the distance BC.

Let d represent $\overline{AB}$. Substitute $d = \overline{AB}$, $x_2 - x_1 = \overline{AC}$, and $y_2 - y_1 = \overline{BC}$ into equation [L] as shown:

$$d = \sqrt{(x_2 - x_1)^2 + (y_2 - y_1)^2}$$

This is known as the distance formula.

The distance formula states that the distance between two points $A(x_1, y_1)$ and $B(x_2, y_2)$ is:

$$d = \sqrt{(x_2 - x_1)^2 + (y_2 - y_1)^2}$$

Example 1

Find the distance between each pair of points points. Round your answer to the nearest hundredth.

    a. A(2, 5) and B(6, 9)   **b**. X(8, 6) and Y(2, 4)

Solution

a. Use the distance formula which states that the distance between two points $A(x_1, y_1)$ and $B(x_2, y_2)$ is given by:

$$d = \sqrt{(x_2 - x_1)^2 + (y_2 - y_1)^2} \underline{\hspace{4cm}}[A]$$

Therefore, let the point (2, 5) represent (x_1, y_1) and let the point (5, 9) represent (x_2, y_2). Therefore, we can substitute $2 = x_1$, $5 = y_1$, $5 = x_2$, and $9 = y_2$ into equation [A] as shown:

$$d = \sqrt{(x_2 - x_1)^2 + (y_2 - y_1)^2}$$

$$= \sqrt{(6 - 2)^2 + (9 - 5)^2}$$ ⠀⠀⠀⠀⠀6 - 2 = 4 and 9 - 5 = 4.

$$= \sqrt{4^2 + 4^2}$$ ⠀⠀⠀⠀⠀⠀⠀⠀⠀$4^2 = 4 \times 4 = 16$

$$= \sqrt{16 + 16}$$ ⠀⠀⠀⠀⠀⠀⠀⠀16 + 16 = 32

$$= \sqrt{32}$$ ⠀⠀⠀⠀⠀⠀⠀⠀⠀⠀16 + 16 = 32

$$= 5.656...$$ ⠀⠀⠀⠀⠀⠀⠀⠀Depress: 2nd $\sqrt{}$ 32 = on the calculator to obtain 5.656...

$$= 5.66$$ to the nearest hundredth.

b. Use the distance formula which states that the distance d, between two points $A(x_1, y_1)$ and $B(x_2, y_2)$ is:

$$d = \sqrt{(x_2 - x_1)^2 + (y_2 - y_1)^2}$$ ⠀⠀⠀⠀⠀⠀⠀⠀⠀[B]

Let the point (8, 6) represent (x_1, y_1) and let the point (2, 4) represent (x_2, y_2). Therefore, we can substitute $8 = x_1$, $6 = y_1$, $2 = x_2$, and $4 = y_2$ into equation [B] as shown:

$$d = \sqrt{(x_2 - x_1)^2 + (y_2 - y_1)^2}$$

$$= \sqrt{(2 - 8)^2 + (4 - 6)^2}$$ ⠀⠀⠀2 - 8 = -6 and 4 - 6 = -2

$$= \sqrt{(-6)^2 + (-2)^2}$$

$$= \sqrt{36 + 4}$$ ⠀⠀⠀⠀⠀⠀⠀$(-6)^2 = (-6)(-6) = 36$ and $(-2)^2 = (-2)(-2) = 4$.

$$= \sqrt{40}$$ ⠀⠀⠀⠀⠀⠀⠀⠀⠀36 + 4 = 40.

$$= 6.324...$$ ⠀⠀⠀⠀⠀⠀Depress: 2nd $\sqrt{}$ 40 = on a calculator to obtain 6.324.

$$= 6.32$$ to the nearest hundredth.

Example 2
Find the distance between the points A and B. A(4, -6) and B(5, 3). Round your answer to the nearest hundredth.

Solution
Let (x_1, y_1) represent the coordinate of A which is (4, -6). Let (x_2, y_2) represent the coordinate of B which is (5, 3). The formula for finding the distance d, between two points $A(x_1, y_1)$ and $B(x_2, y_2)$ is:

$$d = \sqrt{(x_2 - x_1)^2 + (y_2 - y_1)^2}$$ ⠀⠀⠀⠀⠀⠀⠀⠀⠀[A]

Therefore, substitute $4 = x_1$, $-6 = y_1$, $5 = x_2$, and $3 = y_2$ into equation [A] as shown:

$$d = \sqrt{(x_2 - x_1)^2 + (y_2 - y_1)^2}$$

$$= \sqrt{(5 - 4)^2 + [3 - (-6)]^2}$$

$$= \sqrt{1^2 + [3 + 6]^2}$$ $- (-6 = + 6$

$$= \sqrt{1 + 9^2}$$ $3 + 6 = 9$

$$= \sqrt{1 + 81}$$ $9^2 = 81$

$$= \sqrt{82}$$ $1 + 81 = 82$

$= 9.055...$ Depress: 2nd $\sqrt{}$ 82 = on a calculator to obtain 9.055.

$= 5.06$ to the nearest hundredth.

Example 3

Find the distance between each pair of points.

a. (4, 3) and (-5, -6)   **b.** (2, 7) and (0, -4).

Round your answer to the nearest hundredth.

Solution

a. Use the distance formula which states that the distance d, between two points $A(x_1, y_1)$ and $B(x_2, y_2)$ is:

$$d = \sqrt{(x_2 - x_1)^2 + (y_2 - y_1)^2}$$ _____[A]

Therefore, let the point (4, 3) represent (x_1, y_1) and let the point (-5, -6) represent (x_2, y_2). Therefore, we can substitute $4 = x_1$, $3 = y_1$, $-5 = x_2$, and $-6 = y_2$ into equation [A] as shown:

$$d = \sqrt{(x_2 - x_1)^2 + (y_2 - y_1)^2}$$

$$= \sqrt{(-5 - 4)^2 + (-6 - 3)^2}$$

$$= \sqrt{(-9)^2 + (-9)^2}$$ $-5 - 4 = -9$ and $-6 - 3 = -9$

$$= \sqrt{81 + 81}$$ $(-9)^2 = (-9)(-9) = 81$

$$= \sqrt{162}$$

$= 12.727...$ Depress: 2nd $\sqrt{}$ 162 = on a calculator to obtain 12.727.

$= 12.73$ to the nearest hundredth.

b. Let the point (2, 7) represent the point (x_1, y_1) and let the point (0, -4) represent (x_2, y_2). Therefore, we can substitute $2 = x_1$, $7 = y_1$, $0 = x_2$, and $-4 = y_2$ into equation [A] which is the distance formula as shown:

$$d = \sqrt{(x_2 - x_1)^2 + (y_2 - y_1)^2}$$

$$= \sqrt{(0 - 2)^2 + (-4 - 7)^2}$$

$$= \sqrt{(-2)^2 + (-11)^2}$$ $0 - 2 = -2$ and $-4 - 7 = -11$

$$= \sqrt{4 + 121}$$ $(-2)^2 = (-2)(-2) = +4 = 4$ and $(-11)^2 = (-11)(-11) = +121$

$$= \sqrt{125}$$

$= 11.180...$ Depress: 2nd $\sqrt{}$ 125 = on a calculator to obtain 11.180...

$= 11.18$ to the nearest hundredth.

Example 4

Find the distance between each pair of points. Round your answer to the nearest hundredth.

    a. (-2, -3) and (-5, -6)   **b**. (-6, -8) and (-1, -4)

Solution

a. Use the distance formula which states that the distance d, between two points $A(x_1, y_1)$ and $B(x_2, y_2)$ is:

$$d = \sqrt{(x_2 - x_1)^2 + (y_2 - y_1)^2} \underline{\hspace{4cm}}[A]$$

Therefore, let the point (-2, -3) represent (x_1, y_1) and let point (-5, -6) represent (x_2, y_2). Therefore we can substitute $-2 = x_1$, $-3 = y_1$, $-5 = x_2$, and $-6 = y_2$ into equation [A] as shown:

$$d = \sqrt{(x_2 - x_1)^2 + (y_2 - y_1)^2}$$

$$= \sqrt{[-5 - (-2)]^2 + [-6 - (-3)]^2}$$

$$= \sqrt{[-5 + 2]^2 + [-6 + 3]^2} \quad\quad - (-2 = +2 \text{ and } - (-3 = +3$$

$$= \sqrt{[-3]^2 + [-3]^2} \quad\quad\quad -5 + 2 = -3 \text{ and } -6 + 3 = -3$$

$$= \sqrt{9 + 9} \quad\quad\quad\quad\quad (-3)^2 = (-3)(-3) = +9 = 9$$

$$= \sqrt{18}$$

$$= 4.242...\quad\quad\quad\quad \text{Depress: 2nd } \sqrt{} \ 18 = \text{ on a calculator to obtain 4.242...}$$

$$= 4.24 \text{ to the nearest hundredth.}$$

b. Use the distance formula which states that the distance d, between two points $A(x_1, y_1)$ and $B(x_2, y_2)$ is:

$$d = \sqrt{(x_2 - x_1)^2 + (y_2 - y_1)^2} \underline{\hspace{4cm}}[A]$$

Therefore, let the point (-6, -8) represent the point (x_1, y_1) and let the point (-1, -4) represent (x_2, y_2). Therefore, we can substitute $-6 = x_1$, $-8 = y_1$, $-1 = x_2$, and $-4 = y_2$ into equation [A] in order to find the distance d, as shown:

$$d = \sqrt{(x_2 - x_1)^2 + (y_2 - y_1)^2}$$

$$= \sqrt{[-1 - (-6)]^2 + [-4 - (-8)]^2}$$

$$= \sqrt{[-1 + 6]^2 + [-4 + 8]^2} \quad\quad - (-6 = +6 = 6 \text{ and } - (-8 = +8$$

$$= \sqrt{[5]^2 + [4]^2} \quad\quad\quad\quad -1 + 6 = 5 \text{ and } -4 + 8 = 4$$

$$= \sqrt{25 + 16} \quad\quad\quad\quad 5^2 = 25 \text{ and } 4^2 = 16$$

$$= \sqrt{41} \quad\quad\quad\quad\quad \text{Use a calculator to find the answer as in Example 4a.}$$

$$= 6.403...$$

= 6.40 to the nearest hundredth.

Exercises

1. State the distance formula.
2. Find the distance between the two pairs of points, A(2, 5) and B(5, 9).
   Hint: See Example 1a.
3. Find the distance between the two pairs of points, P(9, 5) and Q(4, 3).
   Round your answer to the nearest hundredth. Hint: See Example 1b.
4. Find the distance between each pair of points. Round your answers to the nearest
   hundredth. Hint: See Examples 1a and 1b.
   - **a.** (3, 6) and (4, 7)   **b.** (3, 0) and (7, 8)   **c.** (4, 8) and (3, 2)
   - **d.** (0, 4) and (9, 1)   **e.** (5, 2) and (7, 1)   **f.** (0, 0) and (2, 1)
   - **g.** (3, 0) and (2, 5)   **h.** (3, 3) and (4, 0)   **i.** (6, 2) and (0, 0)
   - **j.** (4, 7) and (1, 9)   **k.** (0, 6) and (2, 3)   **l.** (8, 1) and (5, 4)
5. Find the distance between each pair of points. Hint: See Example 2.
   Round your answer to the nearest hundredth.
   - **a.** (3, -4) and (6, 6)   **b.** (5, -8) and (0, 4)   **c.** (2, -3) and (5, 3)
   - **d.** (4, -6) and (8, 7)   **e.** (7, -8) and (2, 4)   **f.** (6, -4) and (2, 3)
6. Find the distance between each pair of points. Round your answers to the nearest
   hundredth. Hint: See Example 3a.
   - **a.** (6, 8) and (-2, -9)   **b.** (5, 7) and (-4, -8)   **c.** (5, 7) and (-3, -2)
   - **d.** (8, 8) and (-3, -5)   **e.** (2, 4) and (-6, -4)   **f.** (0, 0) and (-2, -4)
7. Find the distance between each pair of points. Round your answers to the nearest
   hundredth. Hint: See Example 3b.
   - **a.** (4, 6) and (7, -3)   **b.** (7, 5) and (0, -6)   **c.** (5, 4) and (9, -6)
   - **d.** (2, 7) and (5, -4)   **e.** (7, 2) and (5, -4)   **f.** (4, 6) and (1, -1)
8. Find the distance between each pair of points. Round your answers to the nearest
   hundredth. Hint: See Example 4a.
   - **a.** (-4, -6) and (-7, -8)   **b.** (-1, -3) and (-4, -5)   **c.** (-3, -2) and (-5, -9)
   - **d.** (−4, -2) and (-6, -7)   **e.** (-2, -1) and (-4, -3)   **f.** (-3, -2) and (-4, -3)
9. Find the distance between each pair of points. Round your answers to the nearest
   hundredth. Hint: See Example 4b.
   - **a.** (-7, -4) and (-3, -1)   **b.** (-3, -5) and (-1, -2)   **c.** (-5, -3) and (-4, -2)
   - **d.** (−6, -4) and (-4, -2)   **e.** (-4, -4) and (-2, -2)   **f.** (-5, -6) and (-3, -2)

Answers to selected questions

2. 5 units.   **5a.** 10.44 units.   **6a.** 18.79 units.
7a. 9.49 units.   **8a.** 3.61 units.   **9a.** 5 units.

Challenge questions

10. Find the distance between each pair of points.

a. (-2, 3) and (4, -5)   b. (-2, -4) and (3, -1)   c. (2, 4) and (3, 1)

d. (6, 7) and (4, 5)   e. (3, 4) and (7, 9)   f. (-4, -1) and (-3, -8)

g. (-2, 5) and (4, -7)   h. (-3, -4) and (-2, -1)   i. (1, 6) and (4, 2)

CHAPTER 39

CIRCLES

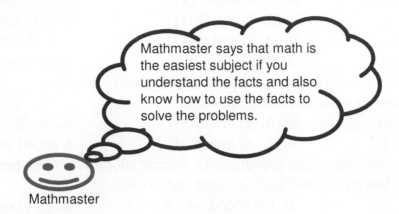

Mathmaster says that math is the easiest subject if you understand the facts and also know how to use the facts to solve the problems.

Mathmaster

A **circle** is a closed plane figure such that all the points on it are the same distance from the center. A **radius** (plural of radius is radii) is the distance from the center of a circle to any point on the circle. Therefore, we can also say that the radius of a circle is the line segment with one endpoint on the circle and the other endpoint at the center of the circle.

Could you give two examples of objects that are in the form of a circle?

An example of an object in the form of a circle is the bicycle wheel. The spokes of the wheel represent the radii of the circle and the spokes join at a fixed point called the center of the wheel or hub, as shown in the picture.

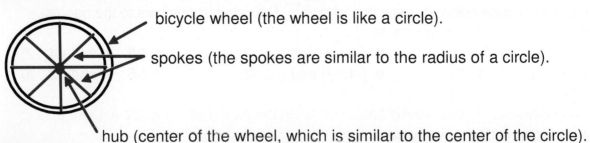

bicycle wheel (the wheel is like a circle).

spokes (the spokes are similar to the radius of a circle).

hub (center of the wheel, which is similar to the center of the circle).

The **chord** of a circle is the line segment that connects two points on a circle.
The **diameter** of a circle is the chord that passes through the center of the circle.
In the diagram,

(1) The fixed point O is the center of the circle.

(2) $\overline{AB}$ is the diameter.

(3) $\overline{AO}$ is a radius.

(4) $\overline{OB}$ is a radius.

(5) $\overline{EO}$ is the radius.

(6) $\overline{CD}$ is the chord.

(7) $\overline{AB}$ and $\overline{CD}$ are chords.

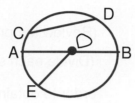

In any specific circle,

1. all radii have the same length
2. any radius is = the diameter ÷ 2
3. the radius is one half of the diameter
4. all the diameters have the same length
5. the longest chord is the diameter
6. diameter = 2 × radius
7. all the radii meet at a fixed point, all the diameters intercept at a fixed point and all the radii and the diameters meet at a fixed point called the center.

Example 1

In the diagram, O is the center of the circle.

(a) $\overline{AB}$ is a diameter?

(b) $\overline{AO}$, $\overline{OG}$, and $\overline{OB}$ are radii?

(c) $\overline{CD}$, $\overline{CE}$, $\overline{DE}$, $\overline{EF}$, and $\overline{DF}$ are chords?

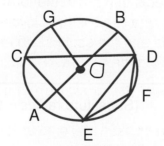

Solution

(a) $\overline{AB}$ is a diameter because $\overline{AB}$ passes through the center of the circle at point O, and $\overline{AB}$ is a chord. (Note that a chord is a line segment that connects two points on a circle and the chord that passes through the center of the circle is the radius.)

(b) $\overline{AO}$, $\overline{OG}$, and $\overline{OB}$ are radii because they are line segments with one endpoint at the center of the circle which is point O and the other endpoints on the circle at points A, G, and B.

811

(c) $\overline{CD}$, $\overline{CE}$, $\overline{DE}$, $\overline{EF}$, and $\overline{DF}$ are chords because they are line segments that connect two points on the circle and they do not pass through the center of the circle.

Example 2
(a) The diameter of a circle is 4 inches. How long is the radius?
(b) The radius of a circle 9 inches. How long is the diameter?

Solution
(a) Diameter = 4 inches

Diameter = 2 × radius   (Review the preceding notes.)

$$\frac{\text{Diameter}}{2} = \frac{2 \times \text{radius}}{2}$$ (Divide each side of the equation in

order to obtain the value of the radius.)

$$\frac{\text{Diameter}}{2} = \frac{2 \times \text{radius}}{2}$$

$$\frac{\text{Diameter}}{2} = \text{radius} \quad\text{———————————————————[A]}$$

$$\frac{4 \text{ inches}}{2} = \text{radius}$$ (Substitute diameter = 4 inches Into

equation [A]).

$$\frac{\overset{2}{4 \text{ inches}}}{\underset{1}{2}} = \text{radius}$$

2 inches = radius

(b) Radius   = 9 inches

Diameter = 2 × radius   ———————————————[B]

Diameter = 2 × 9 inches   (Substitute radius = 9 inches into equation [B].

Diameter = 18 inches.

Exercises
1. In the diagram, the center of the circle is point O.
   (a) List two line segments that passes through the center of the circle .
   (b) List all the diameters, radii, and chords. Hint: See Example 1.

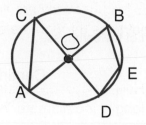

2. In the diagram, classify the line segments as radius, diameter, or chord. Give reasons for your answer. The center of the circle is point O. Hint: See Example 1.

(a) $\overline{DE}$

(b) $\overline{AO}$

© $\overline{AE}$

(d) $\overline{AB}$

(e) $\overline{CO}$

(f) $\overline{BD}$

(g) $\overline{OB}$

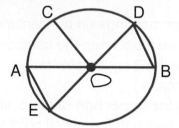

3. (a) The diameter of a circle is 10 inches. How long is the radius? Hint: See Example 2.

(b) The radius of a circle is 7 cm. How long is the diameter? Hint: See Example 2.

How to Draw a Circle

Group Exercise

Objective: To draw a circle which has a radius of 3 centimeters.

Materials that are needed in order to construct a circle are a ruler, a pencil, and a compass.

A compass is a device for drawing circles.

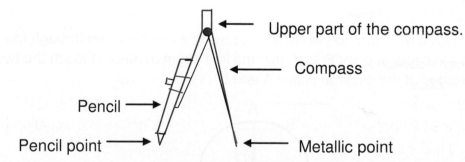

Step 1: Take a pencil and mark a point P which will be the center of the circle.

Point P⟶ •P

Step 2: Take a compass and a ruler. Put the ruler on the table with the centimeter scale showing upwards. Put the metallic point of the compass on the zero mark of the centimeter scale of the ruler and then open the compass such that the pencil point should be on the 3 centimeter mark on the ruler. (Note that how much the compass is opened determines the length of the radius.)

813

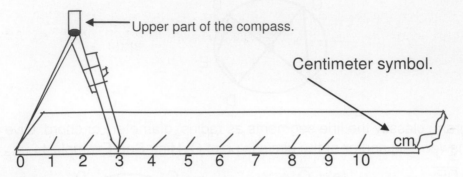

Upper part of the compass.

Centimeter symbol.

cm

0 1 2 3 4 5 6 7 8 9 10

(The smaller markings on the centimeter scale has been omitted.)

Step 3: (Caution: we must keep the compass opening from Step 2 the same in order to maintain the 3 centimeter radius of the circle by holding only the upper part of the compass.)

By holding the upper part of the compass, put the metallic point of the compass on point P and with the pencil point touching the paper swing the pencil point of the compass around (through 360^0) to draw a circle.

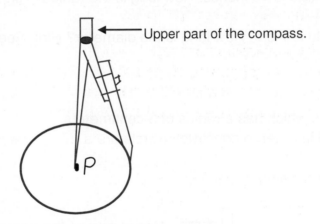

Upper part of the compass.

P

We can draw a diameter to the circle by drawing a line segment through the center of the circle at point P such that the line segment should touch the two opposite sides of the circle at points A and B.

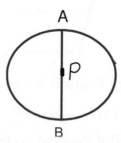

A

P

B

Analysis of the group exercise.

1. Use a ruler to measure the diameter AB. Is the diameter 3 cm? Note that the diameter AB of the circle in this book is not 3 cm because the circle is not drawn to scale and also note that the book just shows you how to draw a circle with any

specific radius.

2. Could you show that the relationship between the radii AP and PB and the diameter AB of a circle by measuring the radii AP and PB and the diameter AB. The relationship is:

Diameter = 2 × radius

Exercise

1. A circle has a radius of 20 cm How long is the diameter? Hint: See Example 2.
2. Draw a circle with each of the radius using a compass. Measure each diameter.
   Hint:
   (a) 2 cm.   (b) 2 in.   (c) 1 in.
   Hint: See the steps under the section "How to Draw a Circle."

Challenge questions

4. Given the following diameter of a circle, find the radius.
   (a) 100 cm   (b) 50 in.   (c) 15 cm   (d) 21 cm
5. Given the following radius of a circle, find the diameter.
   (a) 5 cm   (b) 9 in.   (c) 2 cm   (d) 11 cm

Sum of the Measure of the Angles in a Circle

The sum of the measure of the angles in a circle is 360^0. The sum of the measure of the angles in a circle is similar to the sum of the measure of the angles at a point. The sum of the angles of the circle is: $w^0 + x^0 + y^0 + z^0 = 360^0$.

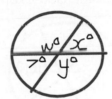

Rule 1: To find the unknown measure of an angle in a circle, find the sum of the measure of the angles that are given in the circle and then subtract that sum from 360^0.

Example 3

Find the value of x^0 in each diagram.

(a)

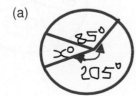

(b)

Solution

(a) The sum of the measure of the angles in a circle = 360^0, and therefore,

815

$$x^0 + 85^0 + 205^0 = 360^0$$
$$x^0 + 290^0 = 360^0$$
$$x^0 + 290^0 - 290^0 = 360^0 - 290^0$$

$(85^0 + 205^0 = 290^0).$

(Subtract 290^0 from each side of the equation in order to eliminate the 290^0 at the left side of the equation and also to obtain the value of x^0.) This is also the application of Rule 1.

$$x^0 + 0 = 70^0$$
$$x^0 = 70^0$$

$(290^0 - 290^0 = 0, 360^0 - 290^0 = 70^0).$

(b) The sum of the measure of the angles in a circle $= 360^0$, and therefore,

$$x^0 + 118^0 + 62^0 + 129^0 = 360^0$$
$$x^0 + 309^0 = 360^0$$
$$x^0 + 309^0 - 309^0 = 360^0 - 309^0$$

$(118^0 + 62^0 + 129^0 = 309^0).$

(Subtract 309^0 from each side of the equation in order to eliminate the 309^0 at the left side of the equation and also to obtain the value of x^0. This is also the application of rule 1).

$$x^0 + 0 = 51^0$$
$$x^0 = 51^0$$

$(309^0 - 309^0 = 0, 360^0 - 309^0 = 51^0).$

Exercise
1. Find the unknown angle measure of each circle.

Let the unknown angle measure be x^0. Hint: See Example 3.

(a)
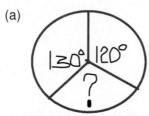

(b)
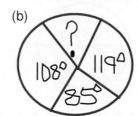

©
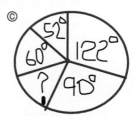

Challenge questions
2. Find the unknown angle measure of each circle.

(a)
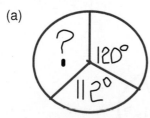

(b)
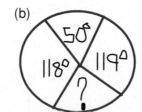

©
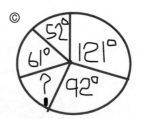

Answers to selected questions
1(a) 110^0 2(b) 73^0

Mixed Review

1. Two lines that intersect to form right angles are called perpendicular lines. True or False.

2. Reduce each fraction to the lowest terms.

   (a) $\dfrac{3}{9}$ (b) $\dfrac{5}{25}$ (c) $\dfrac{6}{36}$

3. What is the difference between an acute angle and an obtuse angle?

4. Solve:

   (a) $-2-6=$ (b) $-9\div3=$ (c) $-12\times2=$

5. Solve:

   (a) $27-2\times4+3=$ (b) $2+18-4\times2=$ (c) $3^2\times2^3=$

6. Explain what is meant by a regular hexagon.

7. What is the sum of the measure of the angles in a triangle?

8. What is the sum of the measure of the angles in a quadrilateral?

9. What is the sum of the measure of the angles formed in a circle?

10. To divide a number by a fraction, we have to multiply the number by the reciprocal of the fraction. True or False?

11. Solve:

   (a) $6\div\dfrac{1}{3}=$ (b) $\dfrac{3}{4}\div\dfrac{1}{8}=$ (c) $3-1\dfrac{1}{5}$ (d) $\dfrac{2}{3}\times\dfrac{3}{2}=$

CHAPTER 40

CIRCUMFERENCE

Mary says that could you use some facts under "place values" to solve some problems in this chapter? What about giving an answer to the nearest tenth?

Mary

The **circumference** is the distance around a circle or a circular object. The ratio of the

817

circumference to the diameter of a circle is called pi which has a symbol π. The value of $\pi = \dfrac{22}{7}$ **which is approximately 3.14.**

Find the distance around an evaporated milk can and the value of π.
Group exercise.
Step 1. The materials needed for the exercise are a can, a string, a ruler, and a pen.
Each group should take a can and wrap a string around the can.
Make a mark on the string at a point where the string first overlaps.

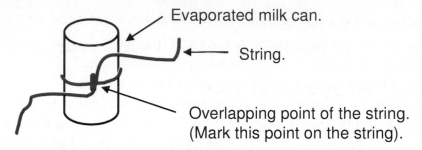

Evaporated milk can.

String.

Overlapping point of the string.
(Mark this point on the string).

Step 2. Put the ruler on the table and stretch the string on the ruler so that one of the marks on the string should be on zero marking and then read the marking on the ruler that corresponds to the second marking on the string. This reading is the length of the string around the evaporated milk can and this is therefore the circumference.

One end of the marking on the string should be on the
zero marking on the ruler.

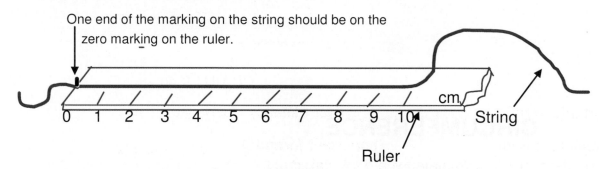

cm

0 1 2 3 4 5 6 7 8 9 10   String

Ruler

Record the circumference and let us represent the circumference by C.
Step 3. Use a pencil to trace the base of the can on a paper, and this trace is the distance around the can. With the zero mark of the ruler on one part of the trace (circle) at point A, move the other end of the ruler on the other side of the trace until you can find the longest distance on the ruler that coincides with the other side of the trace at point B. This distance is the diameter because we can recall that the **longest chord of a circle is the diameter.**
$\overline{AB}$ is the longest chord, which is the diameter. Record the length of the diameter, and let us represent the diameter by d.

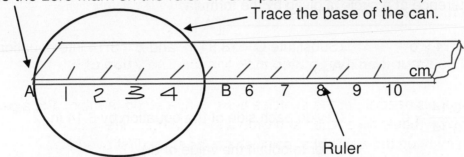

Place the zero mark on the ruler on one part of the trace (circle).

Trace the base of the can.

Ruler

Step 4. Find the ratio of the circumference to the diameter of the circle by dividing the circumference by the diameter which is $= \dfrac{c}{d}$. Record your value for the ratio $\dfrac{c}{d}$. Is your answer approximately 3.14?

Step 5: Find the circumference, the diameter and then the ratio of the circumference to the diameter of four more different size cans using Steps 1 to 4 and record all the data for the group project in the table shown:

Can type	Circumference(c)	Diameter(d)	Ratio = $\dfrac{c}{d}$
1			
2			
3			
4			
5			

Conclusion: The standard ratio $\dfrac{c}{d}$ is approximately $= 3.14 = \pi$.

Therefore, **c $= \pi$d**   (**Important formula**).
(circumference $= \pi \times$ diameter where π is called pi).

Example 1
Find the circumference of a circle that has a diameter of 5 cm.
Solution
The circumference of a circle is given by the formula:

$\quad$ C $= \pi$d, where C is the circumference, $\pi = 3.14$ and d $=$ diameter.
$\quad$ C $= \pi$d ———————————————— [A]
$\quad$ C $= 3.14 \times 5$ cm.   (Substitute $\pi = 3.14$, d $= 5$ cm. into equation [A]).
$\quad$ C $= 15.7$ cm.

Example 2
The circumference of a circle is 18.84 in. (a) Find the diameter. (b) Find the radius.

Solution

(a) The circumference of a circle is given by the formula:

$$C = \pi d \quad\rule{4cm}{0.4pt}\quad [A]$$

$18.84 = 3.14 \times d$ (Substitute C = 18.84 in. and π = 3.14 into equation [A].)

$$\frac{18.84}{3.14} = \frac{3.14}{3.14} \times d$$ (Divide each side of the equation by 3.14 in order to obtain the value of d.)

$$\frac{\overset{6}{\cancel{18.84}}}{\underset{1}{\cancel{3.14}}} = \frac{\overset{1}{\cancel{3.14}}}{\underset{1}{\cancel{3.14}}} \times d$$ (You may use the calculator to divide.)

                                     ($18.84 \div 3.14 = 6$, $3.14 \div 3.14 = 1$.)

$6 = d$

Diameter = 6 in.

(b)   Diameter ÷ 2 = radius. Therefore, the radius = 6 in ÷ 2 = 3 in.

Exercise

1. Find the circumference of a circle that has the following diameter to the nearest tenth. Hint: See Example 1 and review the chapter on "Place Values."
     (a) 3 cm.   (b) 4 ft.   (c) 6 in.   (d) 2.4 cm.

2. The circumference of a circle is 9.42. Find the diameter of the circle.
   Hint: See Example 2.

3. Find the diameter of a circle that has a circumference of 6.28 cm.
   Hint: See Example 2.

Challenge Questions

4. Find the diameter of a circle that has a circumference of 31.4 cm.

5. Find the circumference of a circle that has a radius of 2.3 cm.
   Hint: Change the radius to the diameter first.

6. Find the circumference of each circle.

(a)   (b)   ©

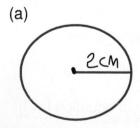 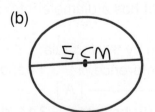 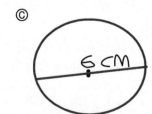

Answer to a selected question

1(a). 9.42 cm.

SYMMETRIC FIGURES

A geometric figure that can be divided into two identical parts is **symmetric**. The line that divides the geometric figure into two identical parts is called the **line of symmetry**. If the geometric figure is folded along the line of symmetry, the two halves will match exactly. **A line of symmetry divides a geometric figure into exactly two matching halves**.
A figure has symmetry if it can be folded into two matching halves exactly.
A geometric figure can have any number of lines of symmetry as shown in the following diagrams.

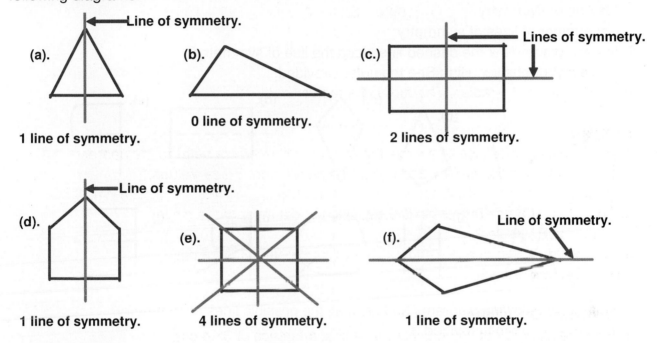

Group Project
Obtain a kite, fold into two matching halves similar to diagram (f).
- Are you able to fold the kite into exactly two matching halves?
- Can you conclude that a kite has symmetry?
- Compare an airplane to the kite. Does the airplane has symmetry? Sketch an airplane and draw the line of symmetry.

Symmetry of Alphabets
The diagrams below show some lines of symmetry of some alphabets as shown:

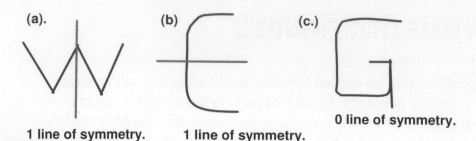

(a). 1 line of symmetry.

(b) 1 line of symmetry.

(c.) 0 line of symmetry.

Exercises

1. Explain what is meant by:
   a. symmetry.
   b. line of symmetry.
   c. number of lines of symmetry.

2. In each diagram, is the dashed line along the line of symmetry?
   Explain your answer. Hint: See the notes provided.

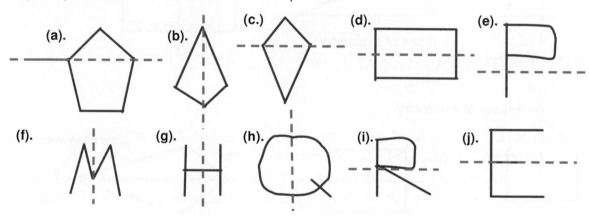

3. Sketch the following diagrams and draw all the possible lines of symmetry.
   Hint: See the notes provided.

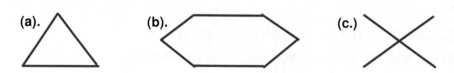

Answer to a Selected Question

2a. The dashed line is not along the line of symmetry because the dashed line does not divide the figure exactly into two matching halves.

Cumulative Review

1. 95% of 20 =

2. 4% of 50 =

3. 6% of 16.2 =

4. .09% of 100 =

5. 900 − 398 =

6. What is an acute angle?

7. The sum of the measure of the angles in a triangle =

8. The sum of the measure of the angles on a line =

9. $4^2 - 2^2 =$ **10.** $24 - 2 \times 4 + 1 =$

11. The sum of the measure of the angles in a rectangle =

12. Find the missing angle.

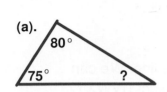 (a).   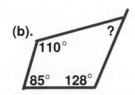 (b).   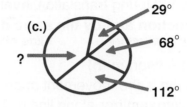 (c.)

13. Sketch and label a figure for each symbol.

    a. $\angle ABC$ **b.** $\overrightarrow{DC}$ **c.** $\overleftrightarrow{XY}$ **d.** $\overline{AR}$

CHAPTER 42

TRANSFORMATION

A movement of objects without changing the size or the shape of the object is called **rigid transformation**. Since during transformation, the size and the shape of the object does not change, **the image is congruent to the preimage or the preimage is congruent to the image.** We can slide (translation), flip (reflection) and turn (rotation) an object as shown:

(a). Translation or slide.   **(b). Reflection or flip.**   **(c.) Rotation or turn.**

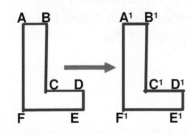   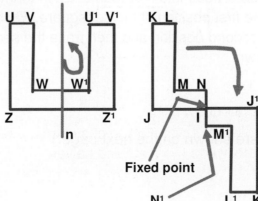

In diagram (c), I is a fixed point and it is also the point of rotation.

Slide (**translation**) - diagram (a) .

A slide or a translation is the movement of an object along a straight line. Figure ABCDEF can slide to a new location at $A^1B^1C^1D^1E^1F^1$. We say that figure $A^1B^1C^1D^1E^1F^1$ is the translation of figure ABCDEF.

The figure ABCDEF is called the preimage and $A^1B^1C^1D^1E^1F^1$ is called the image of ABCDEF. During translation, **every point of the preimage is moved in the same direction and by the same distance**.

Flip (**reflection**) - diagram (b)

A flip or a reflection is the movement of an object by flipping it over a line. We can also think of placing a mirror along line n. The mirror image of the object UVWXYZ is the object $U^1V^1W^1X^1Y^1Z^1$. We say that $U^1V^1W^1X^1Y^1Z^1$ is a reflection of UVWXYZ. The figure UVWXYZ is called the preimage and the figure $U^1V^1W^1X^1Y^1Z^1$ is called the image of the figure UVWXYZ. During reflection, **every point of the preimage is moved across the mirror line so that the perpendicular distance from the preimage to the mirror line is equal to the perpendicular distance from every corresponding points of the image to the mirror line**. The mirror line is also known as line of reflection.

Turn (**rotation**) - diagram (c)

A turn or a rotation is the movement of an object by turning or rotating it around a fixed point. In diagram (c) the object IJKLMN is turned or rotated at the fixed point I, until the object stops at a new position $I^1J^1K^1L^1M^1N^1$. We say that $I^1J^1K^1L^1M^1N^1$ is the rotation of the object IJKLMN. The object IJKLMN is called the preimage and the object $I^1J^1K^1L^1M^1N^1$ is called the image. During rotation, **every point of the preimage is moved by the same angle through a circular direction at a given fixed point known as the center of rotation**.

Group Project 1

The class should be divided into four teams. Each team should put a set-square on a paper and trace the first position of the set-square. Each team should then move the set-square to the second position and then trace the second position of the set-square as shown:

(The diagrams are shown on the next page.)

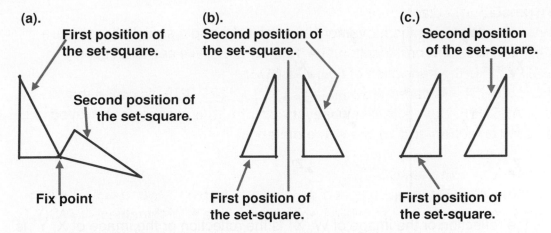

(a).
First position of the set-square.
Second position of the set-square.
Fix point

(b).
Second position of the set-square.
First position of the set-square.

(c.)
Second position of the set-square.
First position of the set-square.

- In each case, write down how the first set-square was moved to the second position of the set-square. Use the terms flip (reflection), slide (translation), and turn (rotation) to explain each movement as applicable.
- Each team should report the result of their project to the whole class.

Group Project 2 - a. How to draw the reflection of points.
                        b. How to find the relationship between the angle formed by the preimage and the mirror line and the angle formed by the image and the mirror line.
                        c. How to find the relationship between the perpendicular distance from the preimage to the mirror line and the perpendicular distance between the image and the mirror line.

Solutions
a. Draw the reflection of the points W, X, Y, and Z across the mirror line n.

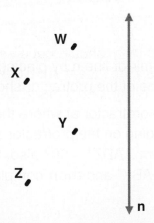

Method: Fold the paper along the mirror line n. Use a sharp object to punch holes through the paper at points W, X, Y, and Z. Unfold the paper and label the new points W^1, X^1, Y^1, and Z^1 as shown on the next page:

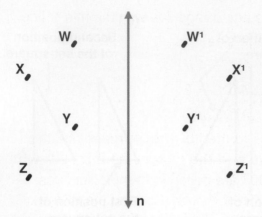

W^1 is the reflection or the image of W, X^1 is the reflection or the image of X, Y^1 is the reflection or the image of Y and Z^1 is the reflection or the image of Z.

b. To find the relationship between the angle formed by the preimage and the mirror line and the angle formed by the image and the mirror line, draw $\overline{WW^1}$, $\overline{XX^1}$, $\overline{YY^1}$, and $\overline{ZZ^1}$ and label the intersection of $\overline{WW^1}$ and the mirror line as A, label the intersection of $\overline{XX^1}$ and the mirror line as B, label the intersection of $\overline{YY^1}$ and the mirror line as C and label the intersection of $\overline{ZZ^1}$ and the mirror line as D as shown:

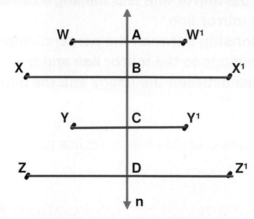

Let us measure the angle formed by $\overline{ZD}$ and the mirror line n by placing the center of the protractor at intersection D and the base line of the protractor should be over $\overline{ZZ^1}$ and then read the number of degrees on the protractor at where the mirror line crosses the protractor degree scale. The reading on the protractor should be 90^0, and this 90^0 shows that $m\angle ZDA = 90^0$ and $m\angle ADZ^1 = 90^0$ also. Similarly, read the $m\angle YCA$, $m\angle ACY^1$, $m\angle XBA$, and $m\angle ABX^1$ and then complete the table on the next page.

Reading of the angles formed by the preimage and image line with the mirror line.	
Preimage side	Image side
$m\angle ZDA = 90^0$	$m\angle ADZ^1 = 90^0$
$m\angle YCA = ?$	$m\angle ACY^1 = ?$
$m\angle XBA = ?$	$m\angle ABX^1 = ?$

We can conclude from the reading of the angles formed by the preimage and the image line with the mirror line that **the preimage and the image line form 90^0 with the mirror line.** Since any two lines that form 90^0 are called perpendicular lines, we can similarly say that the reflection of a point or the preimage and the image of a point are at a perpendicular distance from the mirror line. Further we can state that the **distance from every point of the preimage to the corresponding points of the image form 90^0 with the mirror line.**

c. To find the relationship between the perpendicular distance from the preimage to the mirror line and the perpendicular distance between the image and the mirror line. Take a ruler and measure the following segments from solution b:

$\overline{WA}$ and $\overline{AW^1}$, $\overline{XB}$ and $\overline{BX^1}$, $\overline{YC}$ and $\overline{CY^1}$, $\overline{ZD}$ and $\overline{DZ^1}$, and record each pair of the measurements as shown:

Measurements of the perpendicular distances from the preimage to the mirror line and from the corresponding image to the mirror line.

$$\overline{WA} = ?, \qquad \overline{AW^1} = ?$$
$$\overline{XB} = ?, \qquad \overline{BX^1} = ?$$
$$\overline{YC} = ?, \qquad \overline{CY^1} = ?$$
$$\overline{ZD} = ?, \qquad \overline{DZ^1} = ?$$

We can conclude that since the perpendicular distance from each preimage to the mirror line and the perpendicular distance from each corresponding image to the mirror line is the same, **the perpendicular distance from any preimage to the mirror line is the same as the perpendicular distance from the corresponding images to the mirror line.**

Reflection followed by another reflection across parallel mirror lines.
The transformation type when an object is reflected across two parallel mirror lines is **translation**. This is shown by Example 1.

Example 1
a. Reflect the triangle PQR through two parallel mirror lines.
b. Explain why the transformation across the first mirror line that produces triangle

STU is not a translation.

c. Show that the type of transformation that results from the reflection of the triangle PQR through two parallel mirror lines that produces triangle VWX is a translation by visual inspection.

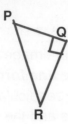

Solution

a. The reflection of the triangle PQR through two parallel mirror lines is shown in the diagram as shown:

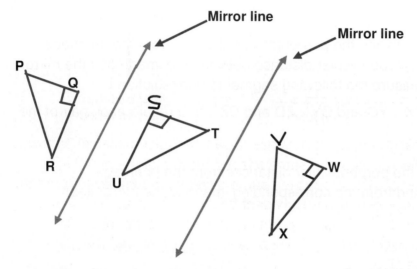

b. The transformation across the first mirror line that produces triangle STU is not a translation because although triangle STU is the image of PQR with the same shape and size, every point of the preimage PQR is not moved the same distance and in the same direction to form the image STU. For example, $\overline{QS}$ is shorter than the $\overline{PT}$ and triangle STU faces the opposite direction to triangle PQR. Translation requires that every point of the preimage which is PQR must be moved the same distance and in the same direction.

c. Show that the type of transformation that results from the reflection of the triangle PQR through two parallel mirror lines that produces triangle VWX is a translation by visual inspection because every point of the preimage which is triangle PQR is moved the same distance and in the same direction to form the new image which is triangle VWX. Translation requires that every point of the preimage which is PQR must be moved the same distance and in the same direction.

Example 2

828

a. Reflect the alphabet F through two parallel mirror lines.

b. Explain why the transformation across the first mirror line is not a translation.

c. Show that the type of transformation that results from the reflection of the alphabet F through two parallel mirror lines is a translation by visual inspection.

Solution

a. The reflection of the alphabet F through two parallel mirror lines is shown as shown:

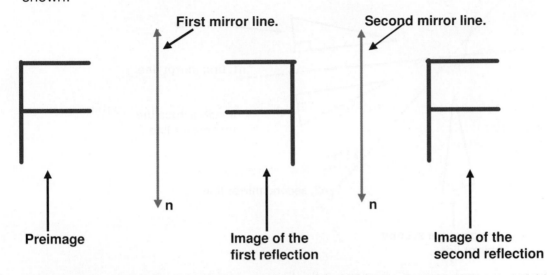

b. The transformation across the first mirror line is not a translation because although the image of the first reflection is of the same shape and size of the preimage, every point of the preimage is not moved the same distance to form every point of the image of the first reflection and this is evident because the image of the first reflection is facing the opposite direction to the preimage of the alphabet F. Translation requires that every point of the preimage must be moved the same distance in the same direction.

c. The type of the transformation that results from the reflection of the alphabet F through two parallel mirror lines is a translation by visual inspection because every point of the preimage is moved the same distance and in the same direction to form the new image after the reflection through two parallel mirror lines. Translation requires that every point of the preimage must be moved the same distance in the same direction.

Reflection Followed by Another Reflection Across Two Intersecting Mirror Lines.

The transformation type when an object is reflected across two intersecting mirror lines is **rotation**. This is shown in Example 3.

Example 3

a. Sketch the reflection of a right-angle triangle across two intersecting mirror lines.

b. Explain why the transformation that occurs when the reflection of a right-angle triangle across two intersecting mirror lines is a **rotation**.

Solution

a. The reflection of a right-angle triangle across two intersecting mirror lines is as shown:

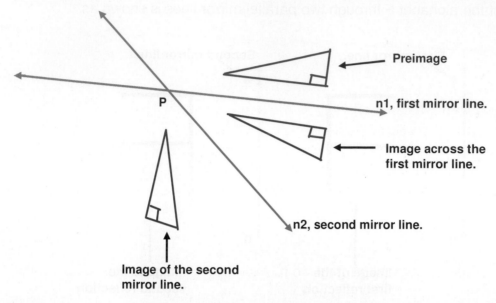

b. The transformation that occurs when the reflection of a right-angle triangle across two intersecting mirror lines is a rotation because every point of the preimage is moved by the same angle through a circular direction at a fixed point P.

Translation Followed by Reflection

Example 4

a. Sketch the translation of figure ABCD to form the image EFGH, followed by a reflection across the line n to form the image IJKL.

b. Give reasons why the figure EFGH is the translation of figure ABCD by visual inspection.

c. Give reasons why the figure IJKL is the reflection of the figure EFGH by visual inspection.

Solution

a. The translation of figure ABCD to form the image EFGH, followed by a reflection across the line n to form the image IJKL is sketched as shown:

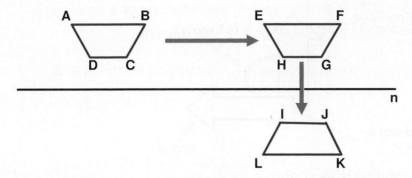

b. The figure EFGH is the translation of figure ABCD because every point of the figure ABCD is moved the same distance in the same direction.

c. The figure IJKL is the reflection of the figure EFGH because every point of the figure EFGH is moved across the mirror line n so that the perpendicular distance from every point of the figure EFGH to the mirror line n is equal to the perpendicular distance from the corresponding points of the image IJKL to the mirror line n.

Example 5

Sketch the image of each figure after the given rotation about the point P.

a. 90º rotation   **b. 180º rotation**   **c. 90º rotation**

      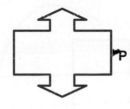

Solution

a. The sketch of the 90⁰ rotation is as shown:

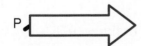

Note that if we join the point of rotation of the preimage and the point of rotation of the image, the angle between the preimage and the image should be be 90⁰ as shown:

(The diagram is shown on the next page.)

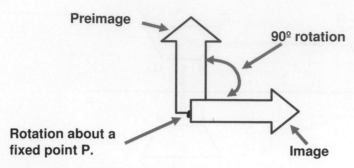

b. The sketch of the 180° rotation is as shown:

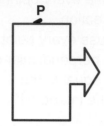

Note that if we join the point of rotation of the preimage and the point of rotation of the image, the angle between the preimage and the image should be 180°, or the image will be under the preimage as shown:

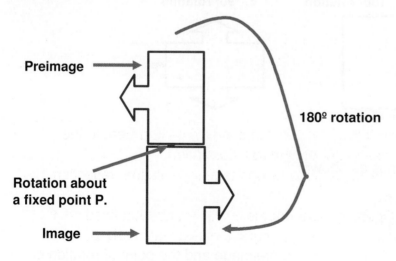

c. The sketch of the 90° rotation is as follows:

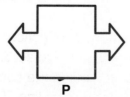

Note that if we join the point of rotation of the preimage and the point of rotation of the image, the angle between the preimage and the image should be 90° as shown:

832

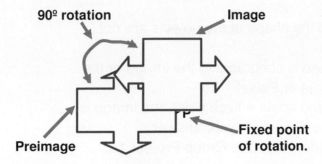

90° rotation   Image

Preimage   Fixed point
of rotation.

Exercise

1. Explain the following terms using a diagram of your own :
   (a) Translation
   (b) Reflection
   (c) Rotation
   Hint : See the preceding notes.
2. Explain how the first figure was moved to the position of the second figure by using the terms rotation, reflection, or translation as applicable.

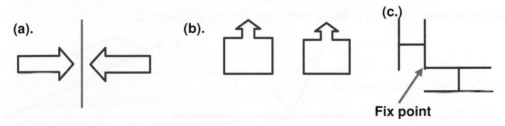

(a).   (b).   (c.)

Fix point

      Hint : See the preceding notes.
3. A polygon is translated, explain if the image of the polygon is congruent to the preimage. Hint: See the information about rigid transformation.
4. How would you classify the following actions using the terms rotation, reflection, or translation as applicable.
   (a) opening a car door. Hint: Opening a car door is a rotation about a fixed point.
   (b) opening the door to your house. Opening a car door is a rotation about a fixed point
   (c) When you see yourself in the mirror
   (d) When a book is moved horizontally in a straight line on a table to a position 6 inches away.
5. The lines from every point of the preimage to the image during reflection is perpendicular to the mirror line. True or False? Hint: See Group Project 2.
6. The perpendicular distance from the preimage to the mirror line is the same as or equal to the perpendicular distance from the image to the mirror line. True or False? Hint: See Group Project 2.
7. The mirror line is also known as the line of reflection. True or False? Hint: See notes on rigid transformations.

8. What is rigid transformation?

9. During rigid transformation, the size and the shape of the objects are not changed? True of False?

10. During rigid transformation, the preimage is congruent to the image or the image is congruent to the preimage. True or False?

11. Judith said that when a polygon is rotated about a fixed point, the image is congruent to the preimage. Is she correct? Explain your answer.

12. Translate each figure along the given line. Hint: See Group Project 1c.

a. 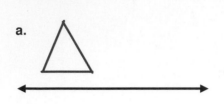   **b.** 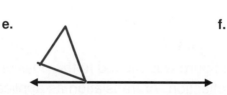   **c.**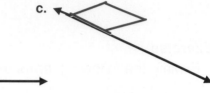

d. 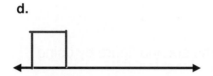   **e.**    **f.**

13. Reflect each figure across the given line. Hint: See Group Project 1b.

a. 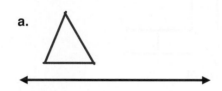   **b.** 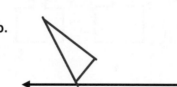   **c.**

d. 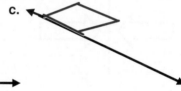   **e.**   **f.**

14. Rotate each figure about the given fixed point P. Hint: See group project 1c.

a.   **b.** 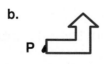   **c.**

15. **a**. Reflect each figure through two parallel mirror lines.
   b. Explain why the transformation across the first mirror line is not a translation.
   c. Show that the type of transformation that results from the reflection of each figure through two parallel mirror lines is a translation by visual inspection.
   Hint: See Example 1.

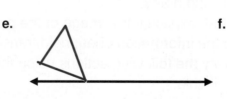
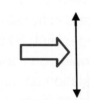

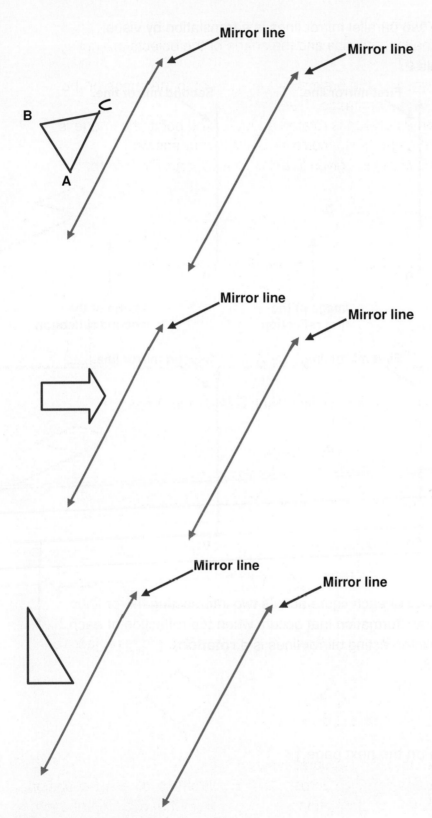

16. **a**. Reflect each alphabet through two parallel mirror lines.
    b. Explain why the transformation across the first mirror line is not a translation.
    c. Show that the type of transformation that results from the reflection of each

alphabet through two parallel mirror lines is a translation by visual inspection.
Hint: See Example 2.

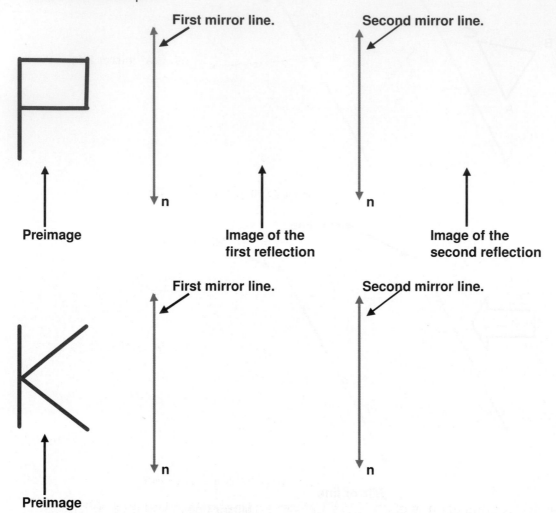

17. a. Sketch the reflection of each figure across two intersecting mirror lines.
   b. Explain why the transformation that occurs when the reflection of each figure across two intersecting mirror lines is a **rotation**.
   Hint: See Example 3.

(The diagrams are on the next page.)

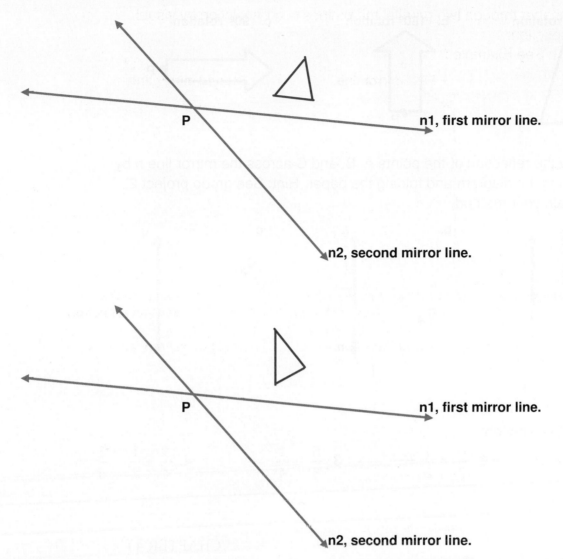

P — n1, first mirror line.

n2, second mirror line.

P — n1, first mirror line.

n2, second mirror line.

18 a. Sketch the translation of each figure to form an image, followed by a reflection across the line n to form a second image.

b. Give reasons why the first image is a the translation of the preimage by visual inspection.

c. Give reasons why the second image is the reflection of the first image by visual inspection.

Hint: See Example 4.

i   ii   iii

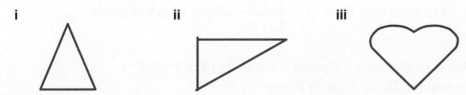

19. Sketch the image of each figure after the given rotation about the point P.

Hint: See Example 5.

a. 90º rotation

P

b. 180º rotation

P

c. 90º rotation

P

20. Draw the reflection of the points A, B, and C across the mirror line n by copying the diagram and folding the paper. Hint: See group project 2. Explain your method.

a.

A

n

b.

B

n

c.

C

n

Cumulative Review

1. $\dfrac{3}{4} \div \dfrac{7}{4} =$

2. $\dfrac{6}{7} \times \dfrac{1}{2} =$

3. $\dfrac{5}{6} - \dfrac{1}{4} =$

4. $\dfrac{1}{4} + \dfrac{1}{2} + \dfrac{3}{4} =$

CHAPTER 43

TOTAL SURFACE AREA AND VOLUME

Cumulative Review

1. The equation of a straight line is $y = mx + b$ where m is the slope, and b is the y-intercept. True or false?

2. If (x_1, y_1) and (x_2, y_2) are on a line, then $m = \dfrac{y_2 - y_1}{x_2 - x_1}$ where m is the slope.

   True or false?

3. Distance = Rate × Time or distance = Speed × Time. True or False?

4. Interest = Principle × Rate × Time. True or False?

5a. 100% of 100 = 100. True or false? 5b. $\dfrac{36}{5} \div \dfrac{4}{5} = ?$

6. Area of a triangle is: $A = \frac{1}{2}$(base) × height. True or false?

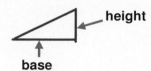
height
base

7. Area of a rectangle is: A = Length × Width. True or False?

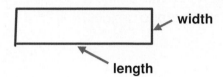
width
length

8. Area of a trapezoid is: $A = \frac{1}{2}$(sum of the parallel sides) × height. True or False?

or

$A = \frac{1}{2}$(sum of the bases) × height. True or False?

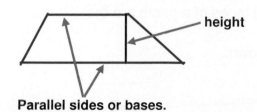
height
Parallel sides or bases.

9. Area of parallelogram is: A = Base × Perpendicular height. True or False?

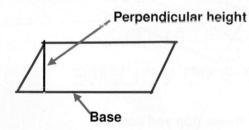
Perpendicular height
Base

10. Area of a circle is: $A = \pi r^2$, where $\pi = \frac{22}{7} \approx 3.14$ and r is the radius. True or False?

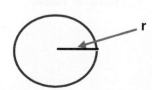
r

11. Circumference of a circle = $2\pi r = \pi d$, where d is the diameter and r is the radius. True or false? Note that 2r = d.

12. In a right triangle: $c^2 = a^2 + b^2$, and this is known as the Pythagorean Theorem. True or False?

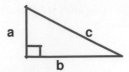

13. Area of a square is: $A = S \times S$ where S is the measure of a side. True or False?

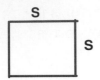

Surface Area of Prisms and Cylinders

What is a surface area of a prism or a cylinder? A **surface area of a prism or cylinder** is the sum of the areas of all surfaces of the prism or cylinder.

What are the **lateral faces of a prism**? The lateral faces of a prism are the parallelograms that connect the bases.

Examples of the shapes of some prisms are as shown:

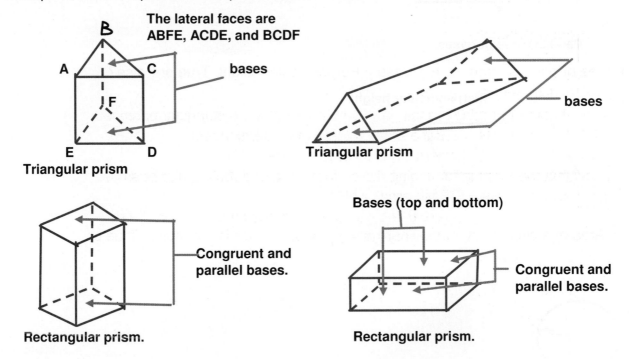

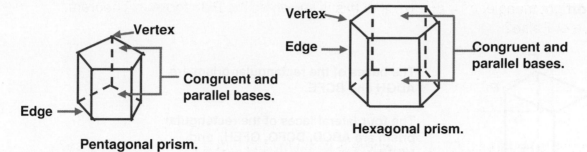

Pentagonal prism.

Hexagonal prism.

What is the **lateral face of a cylinder**? The **lateral surface** of a cylinder is the curved surface of a cylinder. A **cylinder** has two congruent circular bases with curves surface as shown:

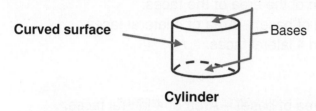

Cylinder

A **prism** has two bases that are congruent polygons and all the other faces of the polygon are parallelograms. The shape of the base of the prism is used to name the prism, for example, a triangular prism has triangular bases and a rectangular prism has rectangular bases.

Rectangular prisms

Example 1

Using the diagram,

a. show that the formula for finding the surface area of a rectangular prism is:

SA = 2(Base area) + (Area of 4 lateral faces)

where SA is the surface area.

b. show that the formula for finding the surface area of a rectangular prism is:

SA = 2(Base area) + hP

where P is the perimeter of the base and h is the height of the rectangular prism.

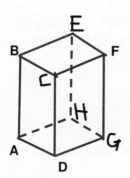

Solution

a.

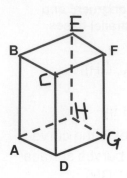

The bases of the rectangular prism are **ADGH** and **BCFE**.

The four lateral faces of the rectangular prism are **ABCD, DCFG, GFEH, and HEBA.**

The surface area of the rectangular prism = sum of the area of the faces.
                           = 2(Area of base) + Area of 4 lateral faces.
Note that the rectangular prism has 2 bases and 4 lateral faces.

b. From Solution **a**:
  The surface area of the rectangular prism = 2(Area of base) + Area of 4 lateral faces.
  Let us represent the above equation as equation $\begin{bmatrix} A \end{bmatrix}$.
  Let us show that the "Area of 4 lateral faces" (see equation A) = hP
                           where P is the perimeter of the
                           base and h is the height of the
                           rectangular prism.

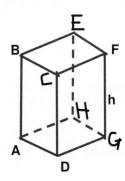

The bases of the rectangular prism are **ADGH** and **BCFE**.

The four lateral faces of the rectangular prism are **ABCD, DCFG, GFEH, and HEBA.**

h is the height of the rectangular prism.

The area of the 4 lateral faces = Area ABCD + Area DCFG + Area GFEH + Area HEBA
                   $= h \times \overline{AD} + h \times \overline{DG} + h \times \overline{GH} + h \times \overline{HA}.$_____[B]
                           (Area of any rectangle = Length × Width,
                           and for example in rectangle ABCD, the
                           length is h and the width is $\overline{AD}$).
                   $= h(\overline{AD} + \overline{DG} + \overline{GH} + \overline{HA}).$
                           (Factor h out in equation $\begin{bmatrix} B \end{bmatrix}$).
                   = h(Distance around rectangle ADGH).
                           $(\overline{AD} + \overline{DG} + \overline{GH} + \overline{HA}$ = Distance around
                           rectangle ADGH).
                   = h(perimeter of rectangle ADGH). _____$\begin{bmatrix} C \end{bmatrix}$

(Perimeter is the distance around any object).

Substitute equation $[C]$ into equation $[A]$ which is:

"The surface area of the rectangular prism = 2(Area of base) + Area of 4 lateral faces" to obtain:

The surface area of the rectangular prism = 2(Area of base) + h(perimeter of rectangle ADGH).

Let the above equation be equation $[D]$.

Notice that the "Area of 4 lateral faces" in equation $[A]$ is replaced by "h(perimeter of rectangle ADGH)" in equation $[D]$.

The surface area of the rectangular prism = 2(Area of base) + h(perimeter of rectangle ADGH)

can then be written as:

The surface area of the rectangular prism = 2(Area of base) + hP,

where P is the perimeter of rectangle ADGH.

We can derive two formulas from Example 1 as shown:
1. **The surface area of the rectangular prism = sum of the area of the faces.**
2. **The surface area of the rectangular prism = 2(Area of base) + hP,**

where P is the perimeter of rectangle ADGH.

Example 2

a. Draw the nets of the figure.

b. Find the surface area of the figure.

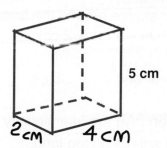

5 cm

2 cm   4 cm

Solution

a. We can draw the nets of the figure as shown:

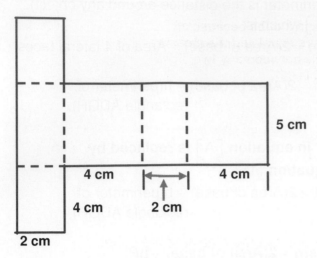

Make sure that every surface area of the figure is shown in the nets diagram.

b. From Example 1a, the formula for finding the surface area of a rectangular prism is:

The surface area of the rectangular prism = **2(Area of base) + hP**,

where P is the perimeter of rectangle.

Therefore,

SA = 2(Area of base) + hP, where SA is surface area.

= 2(Length × Width) + hP, the formula of Area of base is Length × Width.

= 2(4 × 2) + 5(2 + 4 +2 + 4), _____[A]

From the diagram, the length of the base = 4 cm,

the width of the base = 2 cm,

the height, h = 5 cm,

the perimeter P = distance around the base

= 2 cm + 4 cm + 2 cm + 4 cm

From equation [A],

SA = 2 × 8 + 5(12)   From equation [A], 4 × 2 = 8, and 2 + 4 +2 + 4 = 12

= 16 + 60

= 76 cm^2 Note that the units in equation [A] are intentionally omitted so that the equation will not be too long. However, the final answer has units of cm^2. Recall that the units of any area are "square units" such as cm^2.

Cube

If all the six faces of a rectangular prism are squares or all the sides are equal, then the rectangular prism is a cube. Therefore, all the sides of a cube are equal.

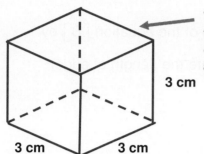

This figure is a cube because all the sides are equal and the measure of the angle between any two sides at a vertex is 90º.

3 cm

3 cm   3 cm

Example 3

The length of a side of a cube is 3 cm. Find the surface area of the cube.

Solution

The formula for finding the surface area of a cube is:

SA = 6 × (Area of a face of the cube).   A cube has 6 faces.

SA = 6 × (Length × Width).   (Length × Width) = Area of a face of a cube.

SA = 6 × (Length of edge)^2.   Since the length and the width of a cube are equal, let us represent the length and width by "length of edge". Therefore, we can represent (Length × Width) as:
(Length of edge) × (Length of edge) = (Length of edge)^2

It is given in the question that the length of a side of the cube is 3 cm, therefore, substitute length of edge in the equation SA = 6 × (Length of edge)^2 as shown:

SA = 6 × (Length of edge)^2

     = 6 × (3 cm)^2

     = 6 × (3 cm) × (3 cm)   (3 cm)^2 = (3 cm) × (3 cm)

     = 6 × 9 cm^2

     = 54 cm^2

Note that the "length of side" of a cube is the same as the "length of edge" of a cube.

Example 4

The surface area of a cube is 24 cm^2. What is the length of the sides or edges of the cube?

Solution

The formula for finding the surface area of a cube is:

SA = 6 x (Length of edge)^2 _____[A]

                    where SA = Surface area.

From the question, the surface area of a cube is 2 cm^2, and therefore, substitute SA = 24 cm^2 into equation [A] as shown:

$24 \text{ cm}^2 = 6 \times (\text{length of edge})^2$ _____ [B]

$\dfrac{24 \text{ cm}^2}{6} = \dfrac{6 \times (\text{length of edge})^2}{6}$

Divide both sides of the equation [B] by 6 in order to isolate the $(\text{length of edge})^2$

$\dfrac{\overset{4 \text{ cm}^2}{\cancel{24 \text{ cm}^2}}}{\underset{1}{\cancel{6}}} = \dfrac{\cancel{6} \times (\text{length of edge})^2}{\underset{1}{\cancel{6}}}$

$4 \text{ cm}^2 = (\text{length of edge})^2$ _____ [C]

$\sqrt{4 \text{ cm}^2} = \sqrt{(\text{length of edge})^2}$

Find the square root of both sides of equation [C] in order to obtain the value of the length of the edge or side.

$\sqrt{2^2 \text{ cm}^2} = \sqrt{(\text{length of edge})^2}$

2 cm = length of edge

$4 = 2^2$

Hint: Review the section on square root. The square root of the square of a number is the number.

REAL WORLD APPLICATIONS - WORD PROBLEM
Cube

Example 5
The surface area of a rectangular tank is 202 m². If the length of the tank is 5 m and the width is 4 m, find the height of the tank.
Solution

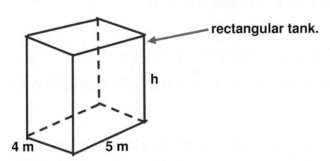

rectangular tank.

The formula for finding the surface area of a rectangular prism or tank is:

SA = 2(Base area) + Ph _____ [A]

where SA = surface area

Base area = (length × width) of the base of the tank.

P = base perimeter (length + width + length + width) of the tank.

h = height of tank.

Substitute Base area = (length × width), P = (length + width + length + width) into

846

equation [A] as shown:

SA = 2((length × width) + (length + width + length + width) × h._____[B].

From the question, substitute SA = 202 m², length = 5 m, and width = 4 m into equation [B] as shown:

202 m² = 2(5 m × 4 m) + (5 m + 4 m + 5 m + 4 m)h

202 m² = 2(20) m² + (18 m)h _____[C]

(5 m × 4 m) = 20 m², and (5 m + 4 m + 5 m + 4 m) = 18 m.

202 m² = 40 m² + (18 m)h. _____[D]

2(20) m² = 40 m².

202 m² - 40 m² = 40 m² - 40 m² + (18 m)h.

Subtract 40 m² from both sides of the equation [D] so as to eliminate 40 m² at the right side of the equation [D].

162 m² = (18 m)h _____[C]

202 m² - 40 m² = 162 m² and
40 m² - 40 m² = 0.

$$\frac{162\ m^2}{18\ m} = \frac{(18\ m)h}{18\ m}$$

Divide both sides of equations [C] by 18 m

to obtain the value of h.

$$\frac{\overset{81\ m}{\cancel{162\ m^2}}}{\underset{9}{\cancel{18\ m}}} = \frac{\overset{h}{(18\ \cancel{m})h}}{\underset{1}{\cancel{18\ m}}}$$

Divide the left side of the equation by 2 m and

divide the right side of the equation by 18 m.

$$\frac{81 m}{9} = h$$

Divide the left side of the equation by 9 to

obtain the value of h.

$$\frac{\overset{9\ m}{\cancel{81\ m}}}{\underset{1}{\cancel{9}}} = h$$

9 m = h

Therefore, the height of the tank is 9 m.

Note: To solve this problem as a homework or a class test, do not give the detail explanations of solving the problem. The MathMasters Series provides detailed explanation about why and how the problem is solved, which leads to the understanding of the problem.

Example 6

Find the missing dimension of the water tank, given that the surface area of the tank is 438 ft^2.

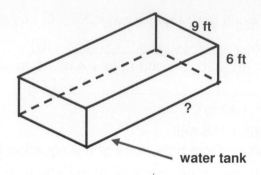

9 ft

6 ft

?

water tank

Solution

From the diagram, we are to find the length of the rectangular tank. Let the length of the rectangular tank be L. The formula for finding the surface area of a rectangular prism or a rectangular tank is:

SA = 2(Base area) + Ph _____[A]

where SA = surface area

Base area = (length x width). This is the formula for finding the area of a rectangle.

P = Base perimeter = (length + width + length + width). Perimeter is the distance around the tank.

h = height of the tank

Substitute Base area = (length x width) and P = (length + width + length + width) into equation [A] as shown:

SA = 2(length x width) + (length + width + length + width)h _____[B].

From the question, SA = 438 ft^2, width = 9 ft, and height = h = 6 ft. Substitute SA = 438 ft^2, width = 9 ft, and height = h = 6 ft into equation [B] as shown:

438 ft^2 = 2(length × 9 ft) + (length + 9 ft + length + 9 ft) × 6 ft _____[C]

Let us represent the length in equation [C] as shown:

438 ft^2 = 2(L × 9 ft) + (L + 9 ft + L + 9 ft) × 6 ft _____[D]

438 ft^2 = 18L ft + (2L + 18 ft) × 6 ft. _____[E]

From equation [D], 2(L × 9 ft) = 18L ft and (L + 9 ft + L + 9 ft) = (2L + 18 ft).

438 ft^2 = 18L ft + 12L ft + 108 ft^2 _____[F]

438 ft^2 = 30L ft + 108 ft^2 _____[G]

From equation [F], 18L ft + 12L ft = 30L ft.

438 ft^2 - 108 ft^2 = 30L ft + 108 ft^2 - 108 ft^2

Subtract 108 ft^2 from both sides of [G] to obtain only 30L ft at the left side of the equation.

$$330 \text{ ft}^2 = 30L \text{ ft} \underline{\hspace{6cm}} [\text{H}]$$

438 ft² - 108 ft² = 330 ft² and 108 ft² - 108 ft² = 0

$$\frac{330 \text{ ft}^2}{30 \text{ ft}} = \frac{30L \text{ ft}}{30 \text{ ft}}$$

Divide both sides of equation $[\text{H}]$ by 30 ft in order

to isolate L which is what we want.

$$\frac{\overset{11 \text{ ft}}{\cancel{330 \text{ ft}}}}{\underset{1}{\cancel{30 \text{ ft}}}} = \frac{\overset{1}{(\cancel{30 \text{ ft}})} L}{\underset{1}{\cancel{30 \text{ ft}}}}$$

11 ft = L

Therefore, the length of the rectangular tank is 11 ft.

Note: If the question in Example 5 is rather to find the width of the rectangular tank, then the same method for the solution of Example 5 can be used to find the width, and the width should be replaced by W where W represents the width of the rectangular tank.

Triangular Prism

Similar to the rectangular prism, the surface area SA of a triangular prism is twice the base area plus the area of the three lateral faces. The area of the three lateral faces is the base perimeter P times the height h.

SA = 2(Base area) + (Area of 3 lateral faces).

   = 2(Base area) + Ph.   P = base perimeter and h = height.

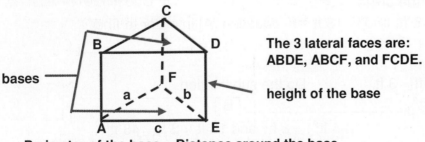

The 3 lateral faces are:
ABDE, ABCF, and FCDE.

height of the base

Perimeter of the base = Distance around the base.
= a + b + c

Example 7 (This example has four sections, **a**, **b**, **c**, and **d** ,which are about the same triangular prism, but it is given to show students how generally one question in mathematics can be twisted or modified to produce other questions.)
a. The base area of a triangular prism is 4 ft², given that the perimeter of the triangular base is 16 ft, and the height of the prism is 3 ft, find the surface area of

849

the prism.

b. Find the base area of a triangular prism given that the perimeter of the triangular base is 16 ft, the height of the prism is 3 ft, and the surface area is 56 ft².

c. Find the perimeter of a triangular prism given that the base area is 4 ft², the surface area is 56 ft², and the height is 3 ft.

d. A triangular prism has a surface area of 56 ft², a base area of 4 ft², and a perimeter of 16 ft, find the height of the perimeter.

Solution

a. The formula for finding the surface area of any prism is:

SA = 2(Base area) + Ph _____[A]

where SA = surface area = ?

Base area = 4 ft²

P = Perimeter of the triangular base = 16 ft

h = height of the prism = 3 ft.

Substitute Base area = 4 ft², P = 16 ft, and h = 3 ft into equation [A] in order to find SA as shown:

SA = 2(Base area) + Ph

SA = 2(4 ft²) + 16 ft × 3 ft.   Do the substitution.

= 8 ft² + 48 ft²   2(4 ft²) = 8 ft² and 16 ft × 3 ft = 48 ft²

= 56 ft²

Therefore, the surface area of the prism is 56 ft².

b. The formula for finding the surface area of any prism is:

SA = 2(Base area) + Ph _____[A]

where SA = surface area = 56 ft².

Base area = ?

P = Perimeter of the triangular base = 16 ft

h = height of the prism = 3 ft.

Substitute SA = 56 ft², P = 16 ft, and h = 3 ft into equation [A] in order to find the base area as shown:

SA = 2(Base area) + Ph

56 ft² = 2(Base area) + 16 ft × 3 ft.   Do the substitution.

56 ft² = 2(Base area) + 48 ft² _____[B]

2(4 ft²) = 8 ft² and 16 ft × 3 ft = 48 ft²

56 ft² - 48 ft² = 2(Base area) + 48 ft² - 48 ft².   Subtract 48 ft² from both sides of the equation [B] in order to to obtain only 2(Base area) at the right side of the equation

8 ft² = 2(Base area) _____[C]

56 ft² - 48 ft² = 8 ft² and 48 ft² - 48 ft² = 0.

Divide both sides of the equation [C] by 2 in order to obtain the value of the base area as shown:

$$\frac{8 \text{ ft}^2}{2} = \frac{2(\text{Base area})}{2}$$

$$\frac{\overset{4 \text{ ft}^2}{\cancel{8 \text{ ft}^2}}}{\underset{1}{\cancel{2}}} = \frac{\overset{1}{\cancel{2}}(\text{Base area})}{\underset{1}{\cancel{2}}}$$

$$4 \text{ ft}^2 = \text{Base area}.$$

c. The formula for finding the surface area of any prism is:

SA = 2(Base area) + Ph _____[A]

          where SA = surface area = 56 ft².

          Base area = 4 ft²

          P = Perimeter of the triangular base = ?

          h = height of the prism = 3 ft.

Substitute SA = 56 ft², Base area = 4 ft², and h = 3 ft into equation [A] in order to find P as shown:

    SA = 2(Base area) + Ph

    56 ft² = 2(4 ft²) + P × 3 ft

    56 ft² = 8 ft² + P × 3 ft   _____[B]

                                   2(4 ft²) = 8 ft²

56 ft² - 8 ft² = 8 ft² - 8 ft² + P × 3 ft   Subtract 8 ft² from both sides of the equation [B] in order to obtain P × 3 ft only at the right side of the equation.

       48 ft² = P × 3 ft   _____[C]

                           56 ft² - 8 ft² = 48 ft² and 8 ft² - 8 ft² = 0.

$$\frac{48 \text{ ft}^2}{3 \text{ ft}} = \frac{P \times 3 \text{ ft}}{3 \text{ ft}}$$ Divide both sides of the equation [C] by

3 ft to obtain the value of P.

$$\frac{\overset{16 \text{ ft}}{\cancel{48 \text{ ft}^2}}}{\underset{1}{\cancel{3 \text{ ft}}}} = \frac{P \times \overset{1}{\cancel{3 \text{ ft}}}}{\underset{1}{\cancel{3 \text{ ft}}}}$$ Do the division.

    16 ft = P

Therefore, the perimeter of the triangular base is 16 ft.

d. The formula for finding the surface area of any prism is:

SA = 2(Base area) + Ph _____[A]

      where SA = surface area = 56 ft^2.

      Base area = 4 ft^2

      P = Perimeter of the triangular base = 16 ft

      h = height of the prism = ?.

Substitute SA = 56 ft^2, Base area = 4 ft^2, and P = 16 ft into equation [A] in order to find h as shown:

    SA = 2(Base area) + Ph

56 ft^2 = 2(4 ft^2) + 16 ft × h. _____[B]

                    Do the substitution.

56 ft^2 = 8 ft^2 + 16 ft × h _____[C]

                  2(4 ft^2) = 8 ft^2

56 ft^2 - 8 ft^2 = 8 ft^2 - 8 ft^2 + 16 ft × h.   Subtract 8 ft^2 from both sides of the equation [C] to obtain only 16 ft × h at the right side of the equation.

        48 ft^2 = 16 ft × h _____[D]

                  56 ft^2 - 8 ft^2 = 48 ft^2 and 8 ft^2 - 8 ft^2 = 0.

$$\frac{48 \text{ ft}^2}{16 \text{ ft}} = \frac{16 \text{ ft} \times h}{16 \text{ ft}}$$

Divide both sides of the equation [D] by

16 ft to obtain the value of h.

$$\frac{\overset{3 \text{ ft}}{\cancel{48 \text{ ft}^2}}}{\underset{1}{\cancel{16 \text{ ft}}}} = \frac{\overset{1}{\cancel{16 \text{ ft}}} \times h}{\underset{1}{\cancel{16 \text{ ft}}}}$$

Do the division.

    3 ft = h

Therefore, the height of the pyramid is 3 ft.

Example 8

Find the surface area of the figure.

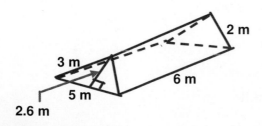

Solution

The figure is a prism. The formula for finding the surface area of a prism is:

SA = 2(Base area) + Ph _____[A]

where:

SA = surface area.

Base area = triangular base area

$= (\frac{1}{2}base \times height\ of\ base)$. This is the formula

for finding the area of a triangle.

P = triangular base perimeter

= (sum of the three sides of the triangular base).

h = height of the prism.

Substitute "Base area" $= \frac{1}{2}base \times height\ of\ base$ into equation [A] as shown:

$SA = 2(\frac{1}{2}base \times height\ of\ base) + Ph$ _____[B]

where base = 5 m, height of base = 2.6 m, P = (3 m + 5 m + 2 m), and h = 6 m. Substitute base = 5 m, height of base = 2.6 m, P = (3 m + 5 m + 2 m), and h = 6 m into equation [B] as shown:

$SA = 2(\frac{1}{2} \times 5\ m \times 2.6\ m) + (3\ m + 5\ m + 2\ m) \times 6\ m.$

$SA = 2(\frac{1}{2} \times 5\ m \times 2.6\ m) + (3\ m + 5\ m + 2\ m) \times 6\ m.$ Divide by 2.

SA = (1 × 5 m × 2.6 m) + (3 m + 5 m + 2 m) × 6 m
SA = (13 m²) + (10 m) × 6 m.   (1 × 5 m × 2.6 m) = 13 m² and
                                       (3 m + 5 m + 2 m) = 10 m.
   = (13 m²) + 60 m²   (10 m) × 6 m = 60 m².
   = 73 m²

Note: The diagram is not drawn to scale, but the solution method is correct.

More on Cylinders
Example 9
Find the surface area of the cylinder.

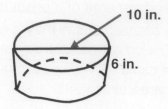

10 in.

6 in.

Solution

The formula for finding the surface area, SA of a cylinder is twice the base area plus the lateral area L, and the lateral area is the base circumference which is $2\pi r$ times the height of the cylinder.

We can therefore write:

SA = 2(Base area) + Lateral area

SA = 2(Base area) + L

SA = 2(Base area) + (Circumference of base)h

SA = $2(\pi r^2) + 2\pi rh$ _____[A]

The formula for the area of a circle is πr^2 and the formula for the circumference of a circle is $2\pi r$.

where SA = Surface area

$\pi \approx 3.14$

r = radius

h = height of the cylinder = 6 in.

Notice that equation [A] which is the formula for finding the surface area has the radius r, but the question is given with the diameter of 10 in. but not the radius. Therefore, we have to change the diameter of 10 in. to radius as shown:

$$radius = \frac{diameter}{2}$$ Recall from grade 5 geometry class.

$$r = \frac{d}{2}$$ where r = radius and d = diameter.

$$r = \frac{10 \text{ in.}}{2}$$ d = 10 in. (from the diagram)

r = 5 in   10 in ÷ 2 = 5 in.

Substitute $\pi \approx 3.14$, r = 5 in, and h = 6 in into the equation [A] which is

SA = $2(\pi r^2) + 2\pi rh$ as shown:

SA $\approx 2[3.14 \times (5 \text{ in})^2] + 2 \times 3.14 \times 5 \text{ in} \times 6 \text{ in}$.   (Note that SA = changes to SA $\approx$ because 3.14 is an approximation.

SA $\approx 2[3.14 \times (5 \text{ in})^2] + 2 \times 3.14 \times 5 \text{ in} \times 6 \text{ in}$.

SA $\approx 2(3.14 \times 5^2 \text{ in}^2) + 188.4 \text{ in}^2$ You may use a calculator. You may depress $2 \times 3.14 \times 5 \times 6 =$ on the calculator to obtain 188.4.

SA $\approx 2(3.14 \times 5 \times 5 \text{ in}^2) + 188.4 \text{ in}^2$ $5^2 = 5 \times 5$

SA ≈ 2 × 3.14 × 5 × 5 in² + 188.4 in²

SA ≈ 157 in² + 188.4 in²   You may use a calculator. You may depress
                                  2 × 3.14 × 5 × 5 = on a calculator to obtain 157.

SA ≈ 345.4 in²   You may use a calculator. You may depress
                                  157 + 188.4 = on a calculator to obtain 345.4.

Therefore, the surface area is approximately 345.4 in².

REAL WORLD APPLICATIONS - WORD PROBLEMS
Cylinders

Example 10

The surface area of a cylindrical water tank is 351.7 m². If the radius of the tank is 4 m, find the height of the tank.

Solution

This is the water tank.

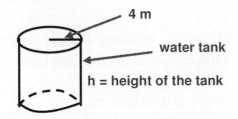

4 m

water tank

h = height of the tank

The formula for finding the surface area, SA of the cylindrical water tank is:

$$SA = 2(\text{Base area}) + (\text{Circumference of base})h$$
$$SA = 2(\pi r^2) + 2\pi rh \underline{\hspace{4cm}}[A]$$

where SA = Surface area – 351.7 m, π ≈ 3.14, and r = 4 m.

Substitute SA = 351.7 m², π ≈ 3.14, and r = 4 m into the equation [A] as shown:

$351.7 \text{ m}^2 \approx 2\left[3.14 \times (4 \text{ m})^2 \right] + 2 \times 3.14 \times 4 \text{ m} \times h$

$351.7 \text{ m}^2 \approx 2 \times 3.14 \times 4 \times 4 \text{ m}^2 + 2 \times 3.14 \times 4 \text{ m} \times h$ $(4 \text{ m})^2 = 4 \times 4 \text{ m}^2.$

$351.7 \text{ m}^2 \approx 2 \times 3.14 \times 4 \times 4 \text{ m}^2 + 2 \times 3.14 \times 4 \text{ m} \times h$

$351.7 \text{ m}^2 \approx 100.48 \text{ m}^2 + 25.12 \text{ m} \times h \underline{\hspace{3cm}}[B]$

You may use a calculator. Depress
2 × 3.14 × 4 × 4 = on your calculator
to obtain 100.48. Depress 2 × 3.14 × 4 =
on your calculator to obtain 25.12.

Subtract 100.48 m² from both sides of the equation [B] so that only 25.12 m × h should remain at the right side of the equation as shown:

$351.7 \text{ m}^2 - 100.48 \text{ m}^2 \approx 100.48 \text{ m}^2 - 100.48 \text{ m}^2 + 25.12 \text{ m} \times h$

$251.22 \text{ m}^2 \approx 25.12 \text{ m} \times h$ _____[B]

$351.7 \text{ m}^2 - 100.48 \text{ m}^2 \approx 251.22 \text{ m}^2$
and $100.48 \text{ m}^2 - 100.48 \text{ m}^2 = 0$.

$$\frac{251.22 \text{ m}^2}{25.12 \text{ m}} \approx \frac{25.12 \text{ m} \times h}{25.12 \text{ m}}$$

Divide both sides of equation [B] by 25.12 m to isolate h or to obtain the value of h.

$$\frac{251.22 \text{ m}^2}{25.12 \text{ m}} \approx \frac{\overset{1}{\cancel{25.12 \text{ m}}} \times h}{\underset{1}{\cancel{25.12 \text{ m}}}}$$

$10.00796 \text{ m} \approx h$

You may use a calculator to divide. Depress $251.22 \div 25.12 =$ on a calculator to obtain 10.00796.

$h \approx 10$ m to the nearest whole number.

Therefore, the height of the cylinder is 10 m.

Example 11

If the surface area of a cylindrical milk tank is 351.68 ft^2, the height of the tank is 10 ft, and the area of the base is 50.24 ft^2, find the circumference of the tank.

Solution

The formula for finding the surface area of a cylindrical milk tank is:

SA = 2(Base area) + (Circumference of base)h

$\text{SA} = 2(\pi r^2) + 2\pi rh$ _____[A]

where SA = surface area = 351.68 ft^2
πr^2 = base area = 50.24 ft^2
$2\pi r$ = circumference of the tank.
h = 10 ft.

Substitute SA = 351.68 ft^2, πr^2 = 50.24 ft^2, and h = 10 ft into equation [A] as shown:

$351.68 \text{ ft}^2 = 2(50.24 \text{ ft}^2) + 2\pi r \times 10 \text{ ft}$

$351.68 \text{ ft}^2 = 2 \times 50.24 \text{ ft}^2 + 2\pi r \times 10 \text{ ft}$

$351.68 \text{ ft}^2 = 2 \times 50.24 \text{ ft}^2 + 2\pi r \times 10 \text{ ft}$

$351.68 \text{ ft}^2 = 100.48 \text{ ft}^2 + 2\pi r \times 10 \text{ ft}$ _____[B]

Subtract 100.48 ft^2 from both sides of the equation [B] in order to eliminate 100.48 ft^2 from the right side of the equation so that we can find $2\pi r$ later as shown:

$351.68 \text{ ft}^2 - 100.48 \text{ ft}^2 = 100.48 \text{ ft}^2 - 100.48 \text{ ft}^2 + 2\pi r \times 10 \text{ ft.}$

$251.2 \text{ ft}^2 = 2\pi r \times 10 \text{ ft}$ _____[C]

$351.68 \text{ ft}^2 - 100.48 \text{ ft}^2 = 251.2 \text{ ft}^2$ and
$100.48 \text{ ft}^2 - 100.48 \text{ ft}^2 = 0$.

Divide both sides of the equation [C] by 10 in order to obtain $2\pi r$ which is the circumference as shown:

$$\frac{251.2 \text{ ft}^2}{10 \text{ ft}} = \frac{2\pi r \times 10 \text{ ft}}{10 \text{ ft}}$$

25.12 ft   1

$$\frac{\overset{}{251.2 \text{ ft}^2}}{\underset{1}{\cancel{10 \text{ ft}}}} = \frac{2\pi r \times \cancel{10 \text{ ft}}}{\underset{1}{\cancel{10 \text{ ft}}}} \qquad\qquad 251.2 \text{ ft}^2 \div 10 \text{ ft} = 25.12 \text{ ft}$$

$25.12 \text{ ft} = 2\pi r$

The circumference of the base is 25.12 ft because $2\pi r$ is the formula of the circumference of the base.

Special notes: You could be requested to find the base area when the circumference and the height are given. Use the formula:
$SA = 2(\pi r^2) + 2\pi rh$
where the base area is πr^2.

Exercises
Let the value of π be 3.14 where needed.
1. What is the formula for finding the surface area of a rectangular prism.
    Hint: See Example 1 or Example 2.
2. Find the surface area of each figure. Hint: See Example 1 or Example 2.

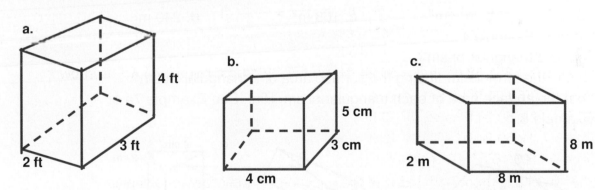

3. Find the missing dimensions. Hint: See Example 5 and Example 6.

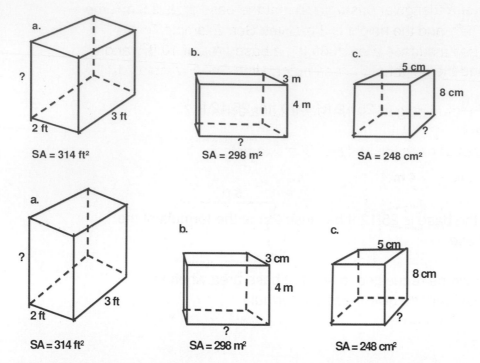

a.
? 3 ft 2 ft 3 ft
SA = 314 ft²

b.
3 m 4 m ?
SA = 298 m²

c.
5 cm 8 cm ?
SA = 248 cm²

a.
? 3 ft 2 ft
SA = 314 ft²

b.
3 cm 4 m ?
SA = 298 m²

c.
5 cm 8 cm ?
SA = 248 cm²

4. What is the formula for finding the surface area of a cube? Hint: See Example 3.

5. What is a cube?

6. What is the surface area of each cube that has the following length of a side.

    a. 5 cm   **b.** 2 ft   **c.** 7 m   **d.** 4 in.

    Hint: See Example 3.

7. Find the length of the sides or edge of each cube that has the following surface areas.

    a. 54 ft²   **b.** 96 cm²   **c.** 168 m²   **d.** 240 m²

    Hint: See Example 4.

8. What is a triangular prism?

9. What is the formula for finding the surface area of a triangular prism?

10. Find the surface area of each triangular prism. Hint: See Example 7a or Example 8.

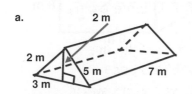

a.
2 m 2 m 5 m 7 m 3 m

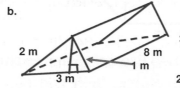

b.
2 m 8 m 1 m 3 m

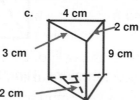

c.
4 cm 2 cm 3 cm 9 cm 2 cm

11. The base area of a triangular prism is 4 m², given that the perimeter of the triangular base is 16 m, and the height of the prism is 3 m, find the surface area of the prism. Hint: See Example 7a.

12. Find the base area of a triangular prism given that the perimeter of the triangular base is 8 ft, the height of the prism is 6 ft, and the surface area is 64 ft². Hint: See Example 7b.

13. Find the perimeter of a triangular prism given that the base area is 8 m², the surface area is 37 m², and the height is 3 m. Hint: See Example 7c.

14. A triangular prism has a surface area of 60 ft², a base area of 10 ft², and a perimeter of 8 ft, find the height of the perimeter. Hint: See Example 7d.

15. What is a cylinder?

16. What is the formula for finding the surface area of a cylinder? Hint: See Example 9.

17. Find the surface area of each figure. Hint: See Example 9.

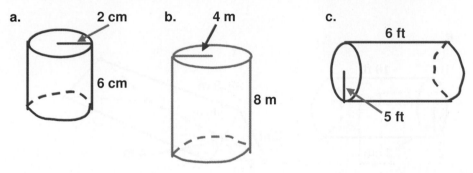

a.   2 cm   b.   4 m   c.   6 ft   5 ft
      6 cm   8 m

18. Find the surface area of each cylinder. Hint: See example 9.

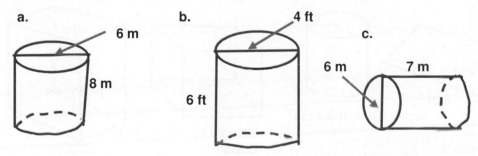

a.   6 m   b.   4 ft   c.   6 m   7 m
      8 m   6 ft

19. The surface area of a cylindrical water tank is 36 m². If the radius of the tank is 5 m, find the height of the tank. Hint: See Example 10.

20. If the surface area of a cylindrical water tank is 336 cm², the height of the tank is 8 cm, and the area of the base of the tank is 48 cm², find the circumference of the tank. Hint: See Example 11.

21. If the surface area of a cylindrical water tank is 345 ft², the height is 6 ft, and the circumference of the base of the tank is 18 ft, find the area of the base of the tank. Hint: Use the formula SA = 2(πr²) + 2πrh, and then solve for πr², which is the formula for the area of the base of the tank. Your solution method should be similar to how the circumference is found in Example 11. See the note at the end of Example 11.

Challenge Questions

22. Find the surface area of each figure.

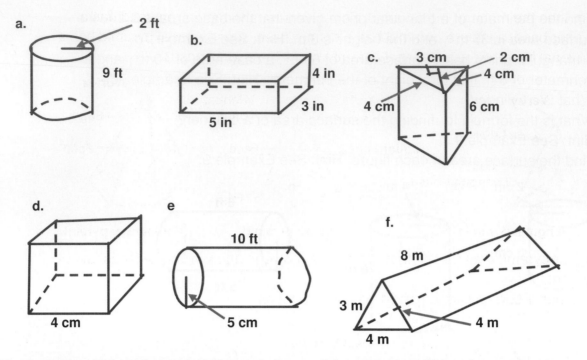

23. Find the missing dimensions in each figure. SA represents the surface area.

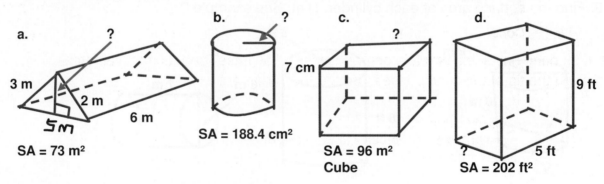

Answers to the Selected Questions

2a. 52 ft²	**3a**. 25.2 ft	**6a**. 150 cm²	**7a**. 3 ft
10a. 76 m²	**17a**. 100.48 cm²	**18a**. 207.24 m²	

SURFACE AREA OF PYRAMIDS AND CONES

A **polyhedron** is a solid figure with flat faces that are polygons. A pyramid is, therefore, a polyhedron with only one base. All the other faces of the **pyramid** are **triangles** that meet at the same **vertex**. The shape of the base of the pyramid determines the name of the pyramid. For examples, a triangular pyramid has a triangular base, a square pyramid has a square base, a pentagonal pyramid has a pentagonal base and a hexagonal pyramid has a hexagonal base.

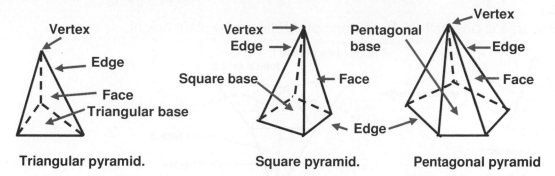

Triangular pyramid.   **Square pyramid.**   **Pentagonal pyramid**

A regular pyramid has a base that is a regular polygon and the lateral faces are all congruent.

A cone has 1 curved surface and 1 flat circular base.

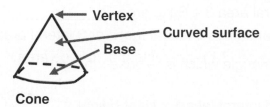

Cone

A right cone has a line which is perpendicular to the base (or the base diameter) through the tip of the cone passes through the center of the base.

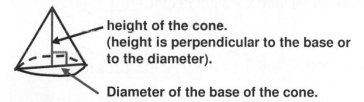

height of the cone.
(height is perpendicular to the base or
to the diameter).

Diameter of the base of the cone.

A slant height of a pyramid and a cone are perpendicular to the edge of their bases and the slant heights are measured along the lateral surfaces of the pyramid or cone.

Slant height

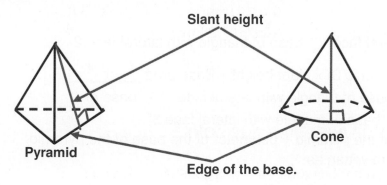

Pyramid   **Cone**

Edge of the base.

Pyramid
Explanation of the Formula

The surface area SA of a regular pyramid is the sum of the lateral area plus the base area.

The lateral area is one-half the base perimeter P times the slant height.

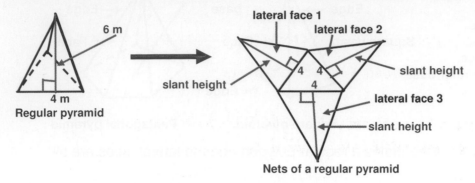

Nets of a regular pyramid

SA = Sum of the lateral areas + Base area.

SA = Lateral area 1 + Lateral area 2 + Lateral area 3 + Base area. _____[A]

A triangular pyramid has 3 lateral faces or 3 lateral areas.

Using the formula for finding the area of a triangle which is $\frac{1}{2}$ base × height:

Lateral area 1 = $\frac{1}{2}$ base of triangle with lateral face 1 × slant height. _____[B].

Lateral area 2 = $\frac{1}{2}$ base of triangle with lateral face 2 × slant height. _____[C].

Lateral area 3 = $\frac{1}{2}$ base of triangle with lateral face 3 × slant height. _____[D].

Notice that $\frac{1}{2}$ and "slant height" are common in equations [B], [C], and [D],

therefore, we can factor out $\frac{1}{2}$ and "slant height", and then rewrite the equation [A] as shown:

SA = $\frac{1}{2}$ (base of triangle with lateral face 1 + base of triangle with lateral face 2

+ base of triangle with lateral face 3) × slant height + Base area _____[E].

Notice from equation [E] that "base of triangle with lateral face 1" + "base of triangle with lateral face 2" + "base of triangle with lateral face 3"

= distance around the base of the pyramid = perimeter of the base of the pyramid.

Therefore, equation [E] can be rewritten as:

SA = $\frac{1}{2}$ (base perimeter) x (slant height) + Base area.

Example 1
Given that the base perimeter of a triangular pyramid is 12 m, with the slant height of 10 m, and the base area is 6.92 m², find the surface area of the pyramid.

Solution

The formula for finding the surface area of a pyramid is:

$$SA = \frac{1}{2}(\text{base perimeter}) \times (\text{slant height}) + \text{Base area} \underline{\hspace{1cm}}[A]$$

where SA = surface area.

Substitute (base perimeter) = 12 m, (slant height) = 10 m, and (base area) = 6.92 m² into equation [A] in order to obtain the value of SA as shown:

$$SA = \frac{1}{2}(12 \text{ m}) \times (10 \text{ m}) + 6.92 \text{ m}^2$$

$$SA = \frac{1}{2} \times 12 \text{ m} \times 1 \text{ m} + 6.92 \text{ m}^2$$

$$SA = \frac{1}{2} \times \overset{6 \text{ m}}{\underset{1}{12}} \text{ m} \times 10 \text{ m} + 6.92 \text{ m}^2 \qquad \text{Divide by 2.}$$

$$SA = 6 \text{ m} \times 10 \text{ m} + 6.92 \text{ m}^2$$
$$SA = 60 \text{ m}^2 + 6.92 \text{ m}^2$$
$$SA = 66.92 \text{ m}^2 \qquad\qquad 60 \text{ m}^2 + 6.92 \text{ m}^2 = 66.92 \text{ m}^2.$$

Therefore, the surface area of the pyramid is 66.92 m².

Example 2
The surface area of a triangular pyramid is 30 cm². If the slant height of the pyramid is 6 cm, and the base perimeter is 8 cm, find the area of the base of the pyramid.

Solution

The formula for finding the surface area of a triangular pyramid is:

$$SA = \frac{1}{2}(\text{base perimeter}) \times (\text{slant height}) + \text{Base area} \underline{\hspace{1cm}}[A].$$

From the question, substitute SA = 30 cm², slant height = 6 cm, and the base perimeter = 8 cm into equation [A] as shown:

$$30 \text{ cm}^2 = \frac{1}{2}(8 \text{ cm}) \times (6 \text{ cm}) + \text{Base area} \underline{\hspace{1cm}}[B]$$

$$30 \text{ cm}^2 = \frac{1}{2}(8 \text{ cm}) \times (6 \text{ cm}) + \text{Base area}$$

$30 \text{ cm}^2 = \dfrac{1}{2}(48 \text{ cm}^2) + \text{Base area}$ $\qquad$ $(8 \text{ cm}) \times (6 \text{ cm}) = 48 \text{ cm}^2$

$\qquad\qquad 24 \text{ cm}^2$

$30 \text{ m}^2 = \dfrac{1}{2}(\overset{\;\;\;\;\;1}{\cancel{48}} \text{ cm}^2) + \text{Base area}$ $\qquad$ Divide by 2.

$30 \text{ m}^2 = 24 \text{ cm}^2 + \text{Base area}$ _____ [C]

$30 \text{ m}^2 - 24 \text{ cm}^2 = 24 \text{ cm}^2 - 24 \text{ cm}^2 + \text{Base area}$ $\quad$ Subtract 24 cm² from both sides of equation [C] to eliminate the 24 cm² from the right side of equation [C].

$\qquad\qquad 6 \text{ m}^2 = \text{Base area}$ $\qquad\qquad$ $30 \text{ m}^2 - 24 \text{ cm}^2 = 6 \text{ cm}^2$.
$24 \text{ cm}^2 - 24 \text{ cm}^2 = 0$

Therefore, the area of the base is 6 m².

Example 3

The surface area of a triangular pyramid is 13.732 m². If the base area of the triangular pyramid is 1.732 m², and the perimeter of the base is 6 m, find the slant height of the pyramid.

Solution

The formula for finding the surface area of the pyramid is:

$\text{SA} = \dfrac{1}{2}(\text{base perimeter}) \times (\text{slant height}) + \text{base area}$ _____ [A].

From the question, substitute SA = 13.732 m², base perimeter = 6 m, and base area = 1.732 m² into equation [A] as shown:

$13.732 \text{ m}^2 = \dfrac{1}{2}(6 \text{ m}) \times (\text{slant height}) + 1.732 \text{ m}^2$ _____ [B]

Subtract 1.732 m² from both sides of the equation [B] in order to eliminate 1.732 m² from the right side of the equation [B] as shown:

$13.732 \text{ m}^2 - 1.732 \text{ m}^2 = \dfrac{1}{2}(6 \text{ m}) \times (\text{slant height}) + 1.732 \text{ m}^2 - 1.732 \text{ m}^2$

$\qquad\qquad 12 \text{ m}^2 = \dfrac{1}{2}(6 \text{ m}) \times \text{slant height})$ $\qquad$ $1.732 \text{ m}^2 - 1.732 \text{ m}^2 = 0$

$\qquad\qquad 12 \text{ m}^2 = \dfrac{1}{2} \times 6 \text{ m} \times (\text{slant height})$

$\qquad\qquad 12 \text{ m}^2 = 3 \text{ m} \times (\text{slant height})$ _____ [C] $\qquad$ $6 \text{ m} \div 2 = 3 \text{ m}$.

Divide both sides of equation [C] by 3 m in order to obtain the value of the slant heights shown:

$$\frac{12 \text{ m}^2}{3 \text{ m}} = \frac{3 \text{ m}}{3 \text{ m}} \times (\text{slant height})$$

$$\begin{array}{cc} 4 \text{ m} & 1 \\ \frac{12 \text{ m}^2}{3 \text{ m}} = \frac{3 \text{ m}}{3 \text{ m}} \times (\text{slant height}) \hspace{2cm} & \text{Do the division.} \\ 1 \hspace{1cm} 1 \end{array}$$

Notice that m ÷ m = 1 and m² ÷ m = m.

$$4 \text{ m} = \text{slant height}$$

Therefore, the slant height of the pyramid is 4 m.

Example 4

The slant height of a square pyramid is 12 ft and the length of a side of the square base is 10 ft. Find the surface area of the square pyramid.

Solution

The net of the square pyramid is shown.

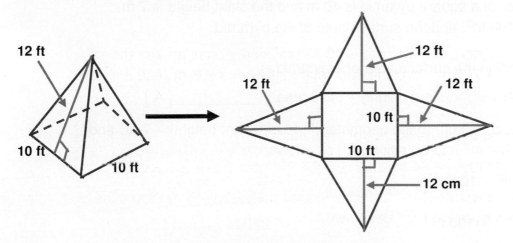

The formula for finding the surface area of a pyramid is:

$$SA = \frac{1}{2}(\text{base perimeter}) \times (\text{slant height}) + \text{base area} \underline{\hspace{4cm}} [A]$$

Where base perimeter = distance around the base.
= 10 ft + 10 ft + 10 ft + 10 ft.
Slant height = 12 ft
Base area = Side × Side.

From the question and the diagram, substitute the base perimeter
= 10 ft + 10 ft + 10 ft + 10 ft, the slant
height = 12 ft, and the base area = 10 ft × 10 ft into the equation [A] to obtain the
value of SA as shown:

$$SA = \frac{1}{2}(10 \text{ ft} + 10 \text{ ft} + 10 \text{ ft} + 10 \text{ ft}) \times 12 \text{ ft} + (10 \text{ ft} \times 10 \text{ ft}).$$

$$SA = \frac{1}{2}(40 \text{ ft}) \times 12 \text{ ft} + 100 \text{ ft}^2 \qquad\qquad 10 \text{ ft} + 10 \text{ ft} + 10 \text{ ft} + 10 \text{ ft} = 40 \text{ ft and}$$

$$(10 \text{ ft} \times 10 \text{ ft}) = 100 \text{ ft}^2.$$

$$SA = \frac{1}{2}\overset{20 \text{ ft}}{\underset{1}{(40 \text{ ft})}} \times 12 \text{ ft} + 100 \text{ ft}^2 \qquad\qquad \text{Divide by 2}$$

$$SA = 20 \text{ ft} \times 12 \text{ ft} \times 100 \text{ ft}^2$$
$$= 240 \text{ ft}^2 + 100 \text{ ft}^2$$
$$= 340 \text{ ft}^2$$

Example 5

The base perimeter of a square pyramid is 40 m and the slant height is 7 m.
The base area is 100 m², find the surface area of the pyramid.

Solution

The formula for finding the surface area of a pyramid is:

$$SA = \frac{1}{2}(\text{base perimeter}) \times (\text{slant height}) + \text{base area} \underline{\hspace{2cm}} [A]$$

From the question, substitute (base perimeter) = 40 m, (slant height) = 7 m, and
the (base area) = 100 m² into equation [A] as shown:

$$SA = \frac{1}{2}(40 \text{ m})(7 \text{ m}) + 100 \text{ m}^2$$

$$SA = \frac{1}{2}(40 \text{ m}) \times 7 \text{ m} + 100 \text{ m}^2$$

$$SA = \frac{1}{2}\overset{20 \text{ m}}{\underset{1}{(40 \text{ m})}} \times 7 \text{ m} + 100 \text{ m}^2 \qquad\qquad \text{Divide by 2.}$$

$$SA = 20 \text{ m} \times 7 \text{ m} + 100 \text{ m}^2$$
$$SA = 140 \text{ m}^2 + 100 \text{ m}^2$$
$$SA = 240 \text{ m}^2$$

Therefore, the surface area is 240 m².

Example 6

Given that the surface area of a square pyramid is 144 m², and the length of a side

866

of the base is 6 in. Find the slant height of the pyramid.

Solution

The pyramid is shown.

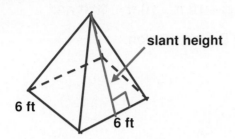

The formula for finding the surface area of a pyramid is:

$SA = \dfrac{1}{2}$(base perimeter) × (slant height) + (base area) _____[A].

From the question, substitute surface area = 144 in^2 , (base perimeter)
= (6 in. + 6 in.+ 6 in. + 6 in.), and (base area) = 6 in. × 6 in. into equation [A] as
shown:

$144 \text{ in}^2 = \dfrac{1}{2}$(6 in. + 6 in. + 6 in. + 6 in.) × (slant height) + (6 in. × 6 in.)

(**Note**: Perimeter of a square base is the distance around the base and the
base area is (side × side).

$144 \text{ in}^2 = \dfrac{1}{2}$(24 in.) × (slant height) + 36 in.^{2} _____[B]

$$(6 \text{ in.} + 6 \text{ in.} + 6 \text{ in.} + 6 \text{ in.}) = 24 \text{ in. and}$$
$$6 \text{ in.} \times 6 \text{ in.} = 36 \text{ in.}^2$$

Subtract 36 in^2 from both sides of equation [B] to eliminate 36 in^2 from the
right side of the equation [B] as shown:

$144 \text{ in}^2 \text{ - } 36 \text{ in}^2 = \dfrac{1}{2}$(24 in) × (slant height) + 36 in^2 - 36 in^2_____[B]

$108 \text{ in}^2 = \dfrac{1}{2}$(24 in) × (slant height)   144 in^2 - 36 in^2 = 108 in^2.

                                          36 in^2 - 36 in^2 = 0.

                 12 in

$108 \text{ in}^2 = \dfrac{1}{2}$(24 in) × (slant height)   Divide the right side of the equation by 2.

                 1

108 in^2 = (12 in) × (slant height) _____[C]

Divide both sides of the equation [C] by 12 in. to obtain the value of the
slant height as shown:

$$\frac{108 \text{ in}^2}{12 \text{ in}} = \frac{(12 \text{ in}) \times (\text{slant height})}{12 \text{ in}}$$

$$\begin{array}{cc} 9 \text{ in} & 1 \\ \dfrac{\cancel{108 \text{ in}^2}}{\cancel{12 \text{ in}}} = \dfrac{(12 \text{ in}) \times (\text{slant height})}{\cancel{12 \text{ in}}} \\ 1 & 1 \end{array}$$

Do the division.

9 in = slant height
Therefore, the slant height = 9 in

Example 7

Given that the surface area of a square pyramid is 336 m², the perimeter of the base is 48 m, and the slant height is 8 m, find:

a. Area of the base

b. Length of a side of the base.

Solution

a. The formula for finding the surface area of a pyramid is:

$$SA = \frac{1}{2}(\text{base perimeter}) \times (\text{slant height}) + \text{base area} \underline{\hspace{2cm}}[A].$$

From the question, substitute SA = 336 m², (base perimeter) = 48 m, and (slant height) = 8 m into equation $[A]$ as shown:

$$336 \text{ m}^2 = \frac{1}{2}(48 \text{ m}) \times (8 \text{ m}) + \text{base area}.$$

$$336 \text{ m}^2 = \frac{1}{2}(\overset{24 \text{ m}}{\cancel{48 \text{ m}}}) \times (8 \text{ m}) + \text{base area}.$$

Do the division.

336 m² = (24 m) × (8 m) + base area

336 m² = 192 m² + base area $\underline{\hspace{2cm}}[B]$

Subtract 192 m² from both sides of the equation $[B]$ to obtain the value of the base area as shown:

336 m² - 192 m² = 192 m² - 192 m² + base area

144 m² = base area $\underline{\hspace{2cm}}[C]$

336 m² - 192 m² = 144 m²

192 m² - 192 m² = 0

Therefore, the base area = 144 m²

b. The formula for finding the area of a square base is = side × side = (side)².
Substitute base area = (side)² into equation $[C]$ as shown:

$144 \text{ m}^2 = (\text{side})^2$

$12^2 \text{ m}^2 = (\text{side})^2$ _____[D]

$144 \text{ m}^2 = 12 \text{ m} \times 12 \text{ m} = (12 \text{ m})^2$

$\sqrt{12^2 \text{ m}^2} = \sqrt{(\text{side})^2}$ Find the square root of both sides of the equation [D] to obtain the value of the measure of the side.

$12 \text{ m} = \text{side}$ Review the Math Teaching Series on Square Root.

Therefore, the length of the side of the base = 12 m.

Exercises

1. What is the formula for finding the surface area of a regular pyramid?
2. Explain how you would find the base area of a regular pyramid.
3. Describe how you would find the surface area of a regular pyramid.
4. Describe how you would find the slant height of a regular pyramid.
5. The base perimeter of a triangular pyramid is 9 m, the area of the base of the pyramid is 3.9 m^2, and the slant height of the pyramid is 8 m, find the surface area of the pyramid. Hint: See Example 1.
6. Find the base area of the triangular pyramid given that the surface area of the pyramid is 39.9 ft^2, the slant height is 8 ft, and the base perimeter is 9 ft. Hint: See Example 2.
7. Given that the surface area of a triangular pyramid is 40 m^2, the base perimeter is 9 m, and the base area is 4 m^2, find the slant height of the pyramid. Hint: See Example 3.
8. Find the surface area of a square pyramid that has a slant height of 12 ft and the length of a side of the square base is 5 ft. Hint: See Example 4.
9. The slant height of a square pyramid is 15 cm. If the base area is 25 cm^2 and the base perimeter is 20 cm, find the surface area of the pyramid. Hint: See Example 5.
10. The surface area of a square pyramid is 160 ft^2, and the measure of a side of the square is 4 ft, find the slant height of the pyramid. Hint: See Example 6.
11. The surface area of a square pyramid is 100 m^2, the perimeter of the base is 24 m and the slant height is 12 m.
    a. What is the area of the base of the square pyramid?
    b. What is the measure of the side of the square base pyramid?
       Hint: See Example 7.

Answers to Selected Questions

5. 39.9 m^2 8. 145 ft^2 9. 175 cm^2

Surface Area of a Cone

Explanation of the Formula for Finding the Area of a Cone
The surface area SA of a right cone is the lateral area plus the base area. The formula for finding the lateral area is one-half the base circumference times the slant height.
Therefore:

SA = $\dfrac{1}{2}$**(circumference of base)** × **(slant height)** + **base area**.

where circumference of base = $2\pi r$, slant height = L, and the base area = πr^2

Therefore,

SA = $\dfrac{1}{2}$**(circumference of base)** × **(slant height)** + **base area**.

SA = $\dfrac{1}{2}$**(2πr)** × **(L)** + $\pi\mathbf{r}^2$

Example 1

Find the surface area of the cone.

2 m   5 m

Solution
The net diagram of the cone is shown.

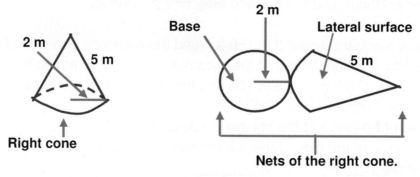

Right cone

Nets of the right cone.

The formula for finding the surface area of a cone is:

SA = $\dfrac{1}{2}$**(circumference of base)** × **(slant height)** + **base area**.

$$SA = \frac{1}{2}(2\pi r) \times (L) + \pi r^2 \underline{\hspace{3cm}} [A]$$

From the diagram substitute r = 2 m, L = 5 m, and π = 3.14 into the equation $[A]$ to find the SA as shown:

$$SA \approx \frac{1}{2}(2 \times 3.14 \times 2\ m) \times (5\ m) + 3.14 \times (2\ m)^2$$

Notice that the symbol $\approx$ is used because $\pi = 3.14$ is an approximation.

$$SA \approx \frac{\overset{1}{\cancel{1}}}{\underset{1}{\cancel{2}}}(2 \times 3.14 \times 2\ m) \times (5\ m) + 3.14 \times (2\ m)^2 \qquad \text{Divide by 2.}$$

$$SA \approx (3.14 \times 2\ m) \times (5\ m) + 3.14 \times (2\ m)^2$$
$$SA \approx 6.28\ m \times (5\ m) + 12.56\ m^2$$

$(2 \times 3.14 \times 2\ m) \approx 6.28$ m.
$3.14 \times (2\ m)^2 \approx 3.14 \times 2\ m \times 2\ m$
$\approx 12.56\ m^2$
Note: $(2\ m)^2 = 2\ m \times 2\ m.$

$$SA \approx 31.4\ m^2 + 12.56\ m^2$$

You may use a calculator.

$$SA \approx 43.96\ m^2$$

Therefore, the surface area of the cone is 43.96 m².

Example 2

Find the surface area of the figure.
Round your answer to the nearest tenth.

4 ft

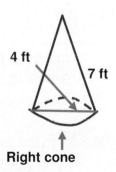

7 ft

Right cone

Solution

The formula for the surface area of a right cone is:

SA = $\frac{1}{2}$(**circumference of base**) × (**slant height**) + **base area**

$$SA = \frac{1}{2}(2\pi r) \times (L) + \pi r^2 \underline{\hspace{3cm}} [A]$$

From the diagram, the diameter of the base = 4 ft. But equation $[A]$ does not have diameter, and therefore, we have to find the radius first as shown:

$$\frac{Diameter}{2} = radius \qquad \text{This is the formula for finding the radius.}$$

871

$\dfrac{4\ \text{ft}}{2} = \text{radius}$ Diameter = 4 ft.

2 ft

$\dfrac{\overset{}{\underset{}{4\ \text{ft}}}}{\underset{1}{2}} = \text{radius}$

2 ft = radius

Now substitute $\pi \approx 3.14$, r= 2 ft, and L = 7 ft into equation $[A]$ to obtain the value of SA as shown:

$$\textbf{SA} = \frac{1}{2}(\textbf{2}\pi\textbf{r}) \times (\textbf{L}) + \pi\textbf{r}^2$$

$$SA \approx \frac{1}{2}(\textbf{2} \times 3.14 \times 2\ \text{ft}) \times (7\ \text{ft}) + 3.14 \times (2\ \text{ft})^2$$

Notice that the symbol $\approx$ is used because $\pi = 3.14$ is an approximation.

$$SA \approx \frac{\overset{1}{1}}{\underset{1}{2}}(2 \times 3.14 \times 2\ \text{ft}) \times (7\ \text{ft}) + 3.14 \times (2\ \text{ft})^2 \qquad \text{Divide by 2.}$$

$SA \approx (\ 3.14 \times 2\ \text{ft}) \times (7\ \text{ft}) + 3.14 \times (2\ \text{ft})^2$
$SA \approx 43.96\ \text{ft}^2 + 12.56\ \text{ft}^2$ _____ $[B]$

$(3.14 \times 2\ \text{ft}) \times (7\ \text{ft}) \approx 43.96\ \text{ft}^2$
$3.14 \times (2\ \text{ft})^2 \approx 3.14 \times 2\ \text{ft} \times 2\ \text{ft} \approx 12.56\ \text{ft}^2$

$SA \approx 43.96\ \text{ft}^2 + 12.56\ \text{ft}^2$
$SA \approx 56.52\ \text{ft}^2$

Therefore, the surface area is 56.5 ft^2 to the nearest tenth.

Example 3

The surface area of a right cone is 44 cm^2. If the radius of the base of the cone is 2 cm find the slant height of the cone.

Solution

The formula for finding the surface area of a right cone is:

$$\textbf{SA} = \frac{1}{2}\textbf{(circumference of base)} \times \textbf{(slant height)} + \textbf{base area}$$

$$\textbf{SA} = \frac{1}{2}(\textbf{2}\pi\textbf{r}) \times (\textbf{L}) + \pi\textbf{r}^2 \ _____[A]$$

From the diagram, substitute the radius of the base = 2 cm, and the surface area = 44 cm^2 into equation $[A]$ to find the slant height as shown:

$$\mathbf{SA} = \frac{1}{2}(2\pi \mathbf{r}) \times (\mathbf{L}) + \pi \mathbf{r}^2$$

$$44 \text{ cm}^2 \approx \frac{1}{2}(2 \times 3.14 \times 2 \text{ cm}) \times (\mathbf{L}) + 3.14 \times (2 \text{ cm})^2$$

Notice that the symbol $\approx$ is used because
$\pi = 3.14$ is an approximation.

$$44 \text{ cm}^2 \approx \frac{\overset{1}{\cancel{1}}}{\underset{1}{\cancel{2}}}(2 \times 3.14 \times 2 \text{ cm}) \times (\mathbf{L}) + 3.14 \times (2 \text{ cm})^2 \qquad \text{Divide by 2.}$$

$$44 \text{ cm}^2 \approx (3.14 \times 2 \text{ cm}) \times (\mathbf{L}) + 3.14 \times (2 \text{ cm})^2$$
$$44 \text{ cm}^2 \approx (6.28 \text{ cm}) \times (\mathbf{L}) + 12.56 \text{ cm}^2. \underline{\hspace{4cm}}[\text{B}]$$

$3.14 \times 2 \text{ cm} = 6.28 \text{ cm}$
$3.14 \times (2 \text{ cm})^2 = 3.14 \times 2 \text{ cm} \times 2 \text{ cm}$
$= 12.56 \text{ cm}^2$

Subtract 12.56 cm^2 from both sides of the equation $[\text{B}]$ to eliminate the 12.56 cm^2 from the right side of the equation $[\text{B}]$ as shown:

$$44 \text{ cm}^2 - 12.56 \text{ cm}^2 \approx 6.28 \text{ cm} \times \text{L} + 12.56 \text{ cm}^2 - 12.56 \text{ cm}^2.$$
$$31.44 \text{ cm}^2 \approx 6.28 \text{ cm} \times \text{L} \underline{\hspace{4cm}}[\text{C}]$$

$44 \text{ cm}^2 - 12.56 \text{ cm}^2 = 31.44 \text{ cm}^2$
$12.56 \text{ cm}^2 - 12.56 \text{ cm}^2 = 0$

$$\frac{31.44 \text{ cm}^2}{6.28 \text{ cm}} \approx \frac{6.28 \text{ cm} \times \text{L}}{6.28 \text{ cm}}$$

Divide both sides of the equation $[\text{C}]$

$$5.006 \text{ cm} \approx \text{L}$$

by 6.28 cm in order to obtain the value of L.
You may use a calculator to divide by
depressing $31.44 \div 6.28 =$ on the
calculator to obtain 5.006.

$$5 \text{ cm} \approx \text{L}.$$

Therefore, the slant height of the cone is approximately 5 cm.

Exercises.

1. Explain how you would find the surface area of a cone?

2. Find the surface area of each of the following cones. Hint: See Example 1.

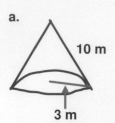 a. 10 m — 3 m

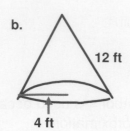 b. 12 ft — 4 ft

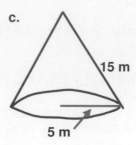 c. 15 m — 5 m

3. Find the surface area of each of the following cones. Hint: See Example 2.

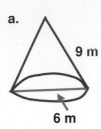 a. 9 m — 6 m

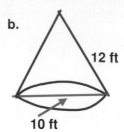 b. 12 ft — 10 ft

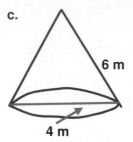 c. 6 m — 4 m

4. The surface area of a right cone is 32 cm². If the radius of the base of the cone is 3 cm, find the slant height of the cone. Hint: See Example 3.

5. Find the slant height of each cone. Hint: See Example 3.

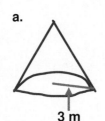 a. 3 m — Surface area = 38 m²

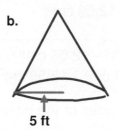 b. 5 ft — Surface area = 36 ft²

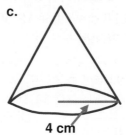 c. 4 cm — Surface area = 48 cm²

Answers to Selected Questions

2a. 122.46 m² **3a**. 113.04 m² **5a**. 1.03 m

SURFACE AREA OF A SPHERE

How to find the surface area of a sphere or the radius of a sphere.
To find the surface area of a sphere or the radius of a sphere use the formula for finding the surface area of a sphere.
The formula for finding the surface area of a sphere is:

$SA = 4\pi r^2$

where SA = surface area, $\pi \approx 3.14$, and r = radius.

The diagram of a sphere is as shown:

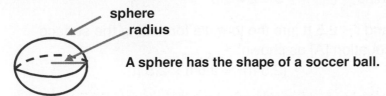

sphere
radius

A sphere has the shape of a soccer ball.

The radius of a sphere is the segment joining the center of the sphere to the circumference or to the surface of the sphere.

The area of a sphere is measured in square units.

Example 1

Find the surface area of the sphere.

3 cm

Solution

The formula for finding the surface area of a sphere is:

$SA = 4\pi r^2$ _____[A]

From the diagram, substitute r = 3 cm into the formula for finding the surface area of a sphere which is equation [A] as shown:

$SA \approx 4 \times 3.14 \times (3\text{ cm})^2$

$SA \approx 4 \times 3.14 \times 3\text{ cm} \times 3\text{ cm}$ Note: $(3\text{ cm})^2 = 3\text{ cm} \times 3\text{ cm}$

$SA \approx 113.04\text{ cm}^2$ You may use a calculator by depressing

                                 $4 \times 3.14 \times 3 \times 3 =$ to obtain 113.04.

Therefore, the surface area of the sphere is 113.04 cm².

Example 2

The diameter of a sphere is 5 ft. Find the surface area of the sphere.

Solution

The sphere is drawn.

The formula for finding the surface area of a sphere is:

         $SA = 4\pi r^2$ _____[A]

The formula for finding the surface area of a sphere has a radius which is r, but the question rather gives the diameter. Therefore, find the radius first as shown:

         $\dfrac{\text{Diameter}}{2} = \text{radius}$ This is the radius formula. Review the

                             Math Teaching Series on Circles.

$$\frac{5 \text{ ft}}{2} = \text{radius} \qquad\qquad \text{Diameter} = 5 \text{ ft.}$$

$$2\frac{1}{2} \text{ ft} = 2.5 \text{ ft} = \text{radius} \qquad\qquad 5 \div 2 = 2.5$$

Now, substitute $\pi = 3.14$, and r = 2.5 ft into the formula for finding the surface area of a sphere which is equation [A] as shown:

SA = 4 × 3.14 × (2.5 ft)² $\qquad\qquad$ (2.5 ft)² = 2.5 ft × 2.5 ft

SA = 4 × 3.14 × 2.5 ft × 2.5 ft

SA = 78.5 ft²

Therefore, the surface area of the sphere is 78.5 ft².

Example 3

If the surface area of a sphere is 113.04 m², find the radius of the sphere.

Solution

The formula for finding the surface area of a sphere is:

$$SA = 4\pi r^2 \underline{\hspace{7cm}}[A]$$

Substitute SA = 113.04 m², and $\pi \approx 3.14$ into the formula for finding the surface area of the sphere which is equation [A] as shown:

113.04 m² = 4 × 3.14 × r²

$$113.04 \text{ m}^2 = 12.56 \times r^2 \underline{\hspace{5cm}}[B]$$

$$4 \times 3.14 = 12.56$$

$$\frac{113.04 \text{ m}^2}{12.56} = \frac{12.56 \times r^2}{12.56} \qquad \text{Divide both sides of the equation } [B] \text{ by 12.56 to}$$

obtain the value of r².

$$9 \text{ m}^2 = r^2 \underline{\hspace{5cm}}[C]$$

113.04 ÷ 12.56 = 9. Divide 113.04 by 12.56 by depressing 113.04 ÷ 12.56 = on the calculator to obtain 9. Notice that 12.56 ÷ 12.56 = 1.

$$\sqrt{9 \text{ m}^2} = \sqrt{r^2} \qquad$$ Find the square root of both sides of the equation [C] to obtain the value of r.

$$\sqrt{3^2 \text{ m}^2} = \sqrt{r^2} \qquad 9 = 3^2$$

$$3 \text{ m} = r$$

The square root of any number that is squared is the number itself. Review the section on Square Root.

Therefore, the radius of the sphere is 3 m.

Exercises

1. Find the surface area of each sphere to the nearest tenth. Hint: See Example 1.
   (Hint: For example, 54.116 to the nearest tenth is 54.1, 6.16 to the nearest tenth is 6.2, and 7.0004 to the nearest tenth is 7.0).

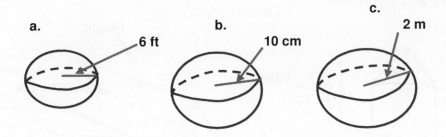

a.   b.   c.   2 m
.6 ft   10 cm

2. Find the surface area of each sphere to the nearest tenth. Hint: See Example 2. (Hint: For example, 3.811 to the nearest tenth is 3.8, and 10.07 to the nearest tenth is 10.1 and 4.3811 to the nearest tenth is 4.4).
   a. diameter = 8 m   b. diameter = 10 ft   c. diameter = 3 cm

3. Find the radius of each sphere which has the following surface areas. Hint: See Example 3. Round your answer to the nearest tenth. (Hint: For example, 1.261 to the nearest tenth is 1.3, 11.09 to the nearest tenth is 1.1 and 2.56 to the nearest tenth is 2.6).
   a. 50 ft^2 **b.** 36 m^2 **c.** 27.9 ft^2 **d.** 47 cm^2

Challenge Questions

4. Find the missing measurements of each sphere to the nearest tenth.
   a. diameter = 18 m   **b.** radius = ?
      radius = ?   diameter = ?
      surface area = ?   surface area = 68 in^2

   c. radius = 12 cm   **d.** radius = ?
      diameter = ?   diameter = ?
      surface area = ?   surface area = 94 cm^2

Answers to Selected Questions

1a. 408.0744 m^2 to the nearest tenth is 408.1 m^2.
2a. 200.96 cm^2 to the nearest tenth is 201.0 cm^2.
3a. 1.9952 ft to the nearest tenth is 2.0 ft.

VOLUME OF PRISMS AND CYLINDERS

The volume of an object is the space occupied by the object, and the volume is measured in cubic units such as cm^3, ft^3, in^3, and m^3.

Diagrams of Prisms and Cylinders

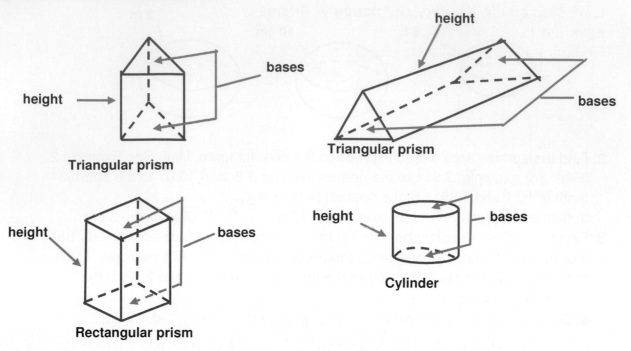

Triangular prism

Triangular prism

Rectangular prism

Cylinder

The volume V of any prism is the area of the base B times the height H. Therefore,

    V = Bh

V = area of base × height

Special cases:

The volume of a rectangular prism, V is:

    V = Length × Width × Height

    V = L × W × H.

        where L × W =area of base.

The volume V, of a cubic prism is:

        V = (length of edge)³

        = Length of edge × Length of edge × Length of edge.

        = S × S × S

        where S × S = area of base.

    S = length of a side of the cube.

Note: A cubic prism is a rectangular prism with all the sides equal.

Volume, V, of a cylinder is the area of the base B times the height h.

        V = area of base × height.

        = Bh

        where area B = area of the base of the cylinder.

            h = height of the cylinder.

How to find the volume or a dimension of a prism.

First start with the formula for finding the volume of a prism.

878

Examples on the Volumes of Triangular Prisms.
Example 1
Find the volume of each triangular prism.

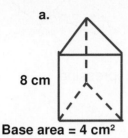

a.

8 cm

Base area = 4 cm²

b.

10 ft

Base area = 15 ft²

Solution
a. The formula for finding the volume of a prism is:

$$V = \textbf{area of base} \times \textbf{height} \underline{\hspace{4cm}}[A].$$

From the diagram, base area = 4 cm², and the height = 8 cm. Substitute base area = 4 cm² and the height = 8 cm into equation [A] as shown:

$$V = 4 \text{ cm}^2 \times 8 \text{ cm}$$
$$V = 32 \text{ cm}^3.$$

Therefore, the volume of the triangular prism is 32 cm³.

b. The formula for finding the volume of a prism is:

$$V = \textbf{base area} \times \textbf{height} \underline{\hspace{4cm}}[B]$$

From the diagram, base area = 15 ft², and the height = 10 ft. Substitute the base area = 15 ft² and the height = 10 ft into equation [B] as shown:

$$V = 15 \text{ ft}^2 \times 10 \text{ ft}$$
$$V = 150 \text{ ft}^3$$

Therefore, the volume of the prism is 150 ft³.

Example 2
The volume of a triangular prism is 18 m³. If the height of the prism is 7 m, find the base area of the prism. Round your answer to the nearest tenth.

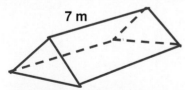

7 m

Volume of the triangular prism is 18 m³

Solution
The formula for finding the volume of a prism is:

$$V = \text{area of base} \times \text{height} \underline{\hspace{4cm}}[A].$$

From the question, the height of the prism = 7 m, and the volume = 18 m³.

Substitute V = 18 m^3 and height = 7 m into equation [A] as shown:

18 m^3 = base area × 7 m _____[B]

Divide both sides of the equation [B] by 7 to obtain the value of the base area as shown:

$$\frac{18 \text{ m}^3}{7 \text{ m}} = \frac{\text{base area} \times 7 \text{ m}}{7 \text{ m}}$$

2.57142 m^2 = base area

> You may use a calculator by depressing 18 ÷ 7 = to obtain 2.57142.
> 7 m ÷ 7 m = 1.

2.6 m^2 = base area   Rounded to the nearest tenth.

Therefore, the base area = 2.6 m^2 to the nearest tenth.

Example 3

The base area of a triangular prism is 13.16 in^2. If the volume of the triangular prism is 34.16 in^3, find the height of the prism to the nearest tenth.

Solution

The formula for finding the volume of a triangular prism is:

V = area of base × height _____[A].

From the question, the base area = 13.16 in^2, and the volume = 34.16^{3}in.

Substitute V = 34.16 in^3 and the base area = 13.16 in^2 into equation [A] as shown:

34.16 in^3 = 13.16 in^2 × height _____[B]

Divide both sides of the equation [B] by 13.16 in^2 to obtain the value of the height as shown:

$$\frac{34.16 \text{ in}^3}{13.16 \text{ in}^2} = \frac{13.16 \text{ in}^2 \times \text{ height}}{13.16 \text{ in}^2}$$

2.595 in = height

> You may use a calculator by depressing 34.16 ÷ 13.16 = to obtain 2.595.

2.6 in = height   (Rounded to the nearest tenth).

Therefore, the height of the triangular prism is 2.6 in.

Examples on the Volume of Cubes

Example 4

One of the measures of the sides or edges of a cube is 3 m.
Find the volume of the cube.

Solution

The formula for finding the volume of a cube is:

V = (length of edge)^3 or V = S × S × S. _____[A]

where V = volume.

S = measure of a side of the cube.

Note: All the sides of a cube are equal.

From the question, the measure of a side or an edge of the cube is 3m. Substitute the "measure of the edge" into the equation for finding the volume of a cube which is equation $[A]$:

$V = $ (length of edge)^3 which is the same as S × S × S.

$V = (3\text{ m})^3$

$V = 3\text{ m} \times 3\text{ m} \times 3\text{ m}$ $(3\text{ m})^3 = 3\text{ m} \times 3\text{ m} \times 3\text{ m}$

$V = 27\text{ m}^3$ $3 \times 3 \times 3 = 27$

Example 5

The volume of a cubic water tank is 12 ft^3. Find the measure of a side or an edge of the tank to the nearest tenth.

Solution

The formula for finding the volume of a cube is:

$V = $ (**length of the edge**)^3 _____[A]

From the question, the volume of the tank is 12 ft^3. Substitute $V = 12$ ft^3 into equation [A] as shown:

12 ft^3 = (length of the edge)^3 _____[B]

Find the cube root of both sides of equation [B] to obtain the value of the "measure of edge" as shown:

$\sqrt[3]{12\text{ ft}^3} = \sqrt[3]{(\text{length of the edge})^3}$

2.289 ft = length of edge

Note: To obtain $\sqrt[3]{12}$, depress 12 2nd $\sqrt[x]{y}$ 3 = on the calculator to obtain 2.289.

$\sqrt[3]{\text{ft}^3}$ = ft. Hint: Review the section on cube root in your MathMasters Series.

Therefore, the "measure of the edge" is 2.3 ft to the nearest tenth.

Example 6

The volume of a cubic water tank is 27 m^3. Find the measure of a side or an edge of the tank.

Solution

The formula for finding the volume of a cube is:

$V = $ (**length of the edge**)^3 _____[A]

From the question, the volume = 27 m^3. Substitute $V = 27$ m^3 into equation [A] as shown:

27m^3 = (length of the edge)^3 _____[B]

Find the cube root of both sides of equation [B] to obtain the value of the "measure of the edge" as shown:

$\sqrt[3]{27\text{ m}^3} = \sqrt[3]{(\text{length of the edge})^3}$ Note: We find the cube root because the "length of the edge" is to the power of 3.

$\sqrt[3]{3\text{ m} \times 3\text{ m} \times 3\text{ m}} = \sqrt[3]{(\text{length of the edge})^3}$

Note: $27 \text{ m}^3 = 3 \text{ m} \times 3 \text{ m} \times 3 \text{ m} = (3 \text{ m})^3$

$$\sqrt[3]{(3 \text{ m})^3} = \sqrt[3]{(\text{length of the edge})^3}$$

$3 \text{ m} = \text{length of the edge.}$ Note: In general, $\sqrt[3]{x^3} = x$, review the section on Cube Root in the Math Teaching Series.

Therefore, the length of the edge is 3 m.

Examples on the Volume of Rectangular Prisms
Example 7
Find the volume of each rectangular block.

a.

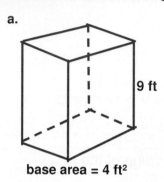

base area = 4 ft²

b.

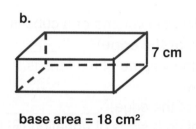

7 cm

base area = 18 cm²

Solution
a. The formula for finding the volume, V, of any prism is:

   V = base area × height _____[A].

From the diagram, the base area = 4 ft², and the height = 9 ft. Substitute base area = 4 ft² and height = 9 ft into equation [A] to obtain the value of the volume as shown:

   $V = 4 \text{ ft}^2 \times 9 \text{ ft}$

   $V = 36 \text{ ft}^3$

Therefore, the volume of the block is 36 ft³.

b. The formula for finding the volume, V, of any prism is:

   V = base area × height _____[B].

From the diagram, the base area = 18 cm², and the height = 7 cm. Substitute the base area = 18 cm² and the height = 7 cm into equation [B] to obtain the value of the volume of the prism shown:

   $V = 18 \text{ cm}^2 \times 7 \text{ cm}$

   $= 126 \text{ cm}^3$

Example 8
a. If a rectangular water tank has a volume of 4 m³ and a base area of 2 cm², find the height of the tank.

b. If a rectangular water tank has a volume of 16.34 ft³ and a height of 5.16 ft, find the base area of the tank to the nearest tenth.

Solution

a. The formula for finding the volume of any prism is:

$$V = \textbf{base area} \times \textbf{height} \hspace{4cm} [A].$$

From the question, the volume = 4 m³, and the base area = 2 m². Substitute
V = 4 m³ and base area = 2 m² into equation [A] as shown:

$$4 \text{ m}^3 = 2 \text{ m}^2 \times \text{height} \hspace{4cm} [B]$$

Divide both sides of equation [B] by 2 m² to obtain the value of the height
of the water tank as shown:

$$\frac{4 \text{ m}^3}{2 \text{ m}^2} = \frac{2 \text{ m}^2}{2 \text{ m}^2} \times \text{height}$$

$$\begin{array}{cc} 2\text{ m} & 1 \\ \dfrac{4 \text{ m}^3}{2 \text{ m}^2} & = \dfrac{2 \text{ m}^2}{2 \text{ m}^2} \times \text{height} \\ 1 & 1 \end{array} \qquad \text{Do the division.}$$

$$m^3 \div m^2 = m \text{ and } m^2 \div m^2 = 1$$

$$2 \text{ m} = \text{height}$$

Therefore, the height of the tank = 2 m.

b. The formula for finding the volume, V, of any prism is:

$$V = \textbf{base area} \times \textbf{height} \hspace{4cm} [C].$$

From the question, the volume = 16.34 ft³, and the height = 5.16 ft.
Substitute V = 16.34 ft³ and the height = 5.16 ft into equation [C] as shown:

$$16.34 \text{ ft}^3 = \text{base area} \times 5.16 \text{ ft} \hspace{3cm} [D]$$

Divide both sides of equation [D] by 5.16 ft to obtain the value of the base
area as shown:

$$\frac{16.34 \text{ ft}^3}{5.16 \text{ ft}} = \frac{\text{base area} \times 5.16 \text{ ft}}{5.16 \text{ ft}}$$

$$\frac{16.34 \text{ ft}^3}{5.16 \text{ ft}} = \frac{\text{base area} \times \overset{1}{\cancel{5.16 \text{ ft}}}}{\underset{1}{\cancel{5.16 \text{ ft}}}} \qquad \text{Do the division.}$$

$$3.166 \text{ ft}^2 = \text{base area} \qquad\qquad \text{Depress } 16.34 \div 5.16 = \text{ on}$$
$$\text{a calculator to obtain } 3.166.$$

Therefore, the base area of the water tank is 3.2 ft² to the nearest tenth.

Hint: Review the section on "Place Values" in other "Math Teaching Series" (Grade 6)
to understand "to the nearest tenth."

Example 9
Find the volume of each rectangular block.

a.
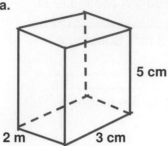

b.
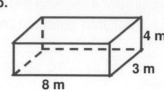

Solution

a. The formula for finding the volume of the rectangular prism or block is:

$$V = \textbf{length} \times \textbf{width} \times \textbf{height} \underline{\hspace{5cm}}[A]$$

From the diagram, length = 3 cm, width = 2 cm, and the height = 5 cm. Substitute length = 3 cm, width = 2 cm, and height = 5 cm into equation $[A]$ to obtain the volume as shown:

$$V = 3 \text{ cm} \times 2 \text{ cm} \times 5 \text{ cm}$$
$$= 30 \text{ cm}^3$$

Therefore, the volume of the block = 30 cm³.
Notice that the question does not involve the base area, and therefore, the formula involving the base area is not used.

b. The formula for finding the volume of the block is:

$$V = \textbf{length} \times \textbf{width} \times \textbf{height} \underline{\hspace{5cm}}[A].$$

From the diagram, length = 8 m, width = 3 m, and height = 4 m. Substitute length = 8 m, width = 3 m, and height = 4 m into equation $[B]$ to obtain the value of the volume of the block as shown:

$$V = 8 \text{ m} \times 3 \text{ m} \times 4 \text{ m}$$
$$V = 96 \text{ m}^3$$

Therefore, the volume of the block is 96 m³.
Notice that the question does not involve the base area, and therefore, the formula involving the base area is not used.

Example 10
a. The volume of a rectangular box is 36 in³. If the height of the box is 4 in and the width is 2 in, find the length of the box.
b. The volume of a swimming pool is 144 m³. If the length of the pool is 15 m and the width is 4.8 m, how deep is the pool?
c. A rectangular aquarium has a volume of 168 ft. If the length of the aquarium is 12 ft and the height is 2 ft, find the width of the aquarium.
Solution

a. The formula for finding the volume of a rectangular box is.

    V = length × width × height _____[A].

From the question, the volume = 36 in³, the height = 4 in, and the width is 2 in.

Substitute V = 36 in³, height = 4 in, and width = 2 in into equation [A] as shown:

  36 in.³ = length × 2 in. × 4 in.

  36 in.³ = length × 8 in.² _____[B]

$$\frac{36 \text{ in}^3}{8 \text{ in.}^2} = \frac{\text{Length} \times 8 \text{ in.}^2}{8 \text{ in.}^2}$$

    Divide both sides of the equation [B] by

    8 in² to obtain the value of the length.

$$\frac{36 \text{ in}^3}{8 \text{ in}^2} = \frac{\text{Length} \times \overset{1}{\cancel{8 \text{ in}^2}}}{\underset{1}{\cancel{8 \text{ in}^2}}}$$

    Do the division.

4.5 in = length   You may use a calculator to find 36 ÷ 8 by depressing

                          36 ÷ 8 = on the calculator to obtain 4.5.

Therefore, the length of the box is 4.5 in.

$$\text{Note: } \frac{\text{in.}^3}{\text{in.}^2} = \frac{\text{in.} \times \text{in.} \times \text{in.}}{\text{in.} \times \text{in.}} = \frac{\overset{1}{\cancel{\text{in.}}} \times \overset{1}{\cancel{\text{in.}}} \times \text{in.}}{\underset{1}{\cancel{\text{in.}}} \times \underset{1}{\cancel{\text{in.}}}} = \text{in.}$$

b. The formula for finding the volume V of a rectangular swimming pool is:

    V = length × width × height _____[C]

Note that the depth of the pool is the same as the height of the pool. From the question, the volume = 144 m³, the length of the pool = 15 m, and the width = 4.8 m. Substitute V = 144 m³, length = 15 m, and the width = 4.8 m into equation [C] as shown:

  144 m³ = 15 m × 4.8 m × height

  144 m³ = 72 m² × height _____[D]

              15 m × 4.8 m = 72 m²

$$\frac{144 \text{ m}^3}{72 \text{ m}^3} = \frac{72 \text{ m}^2 \times \text{height}}{72 \text{ m}^2}$$

    Divide both sides of the equation by 72 m²

    to obtain the value of the height.

$$\frac{\overset{2 \text{ m}}{\cancel{144 \text{ m}^3}}}{\underset{1}{\cancel{72 \text{ m}^2}}} = \frac{\overset{1}{\cancel{72 \text{ m}^2}} \times \text{height}}{\underset{1}{\cancel{72 \text{ m}^2}}}$$

Do the division. Note: $\dfrac{\text{m}^3}{\text{m}^2} = \dfrac{\cancel{\text{m}} \times \cancel{\text{m}} \times \text{m}}{\cancel{\text{m}} \times \cancel{\text{m}}} = \text{m}$

144 ÷ 72 = 2 and 72 ÷ 72 = 1.

2 m = height

Therefore, the height or the depth of the pool is 2 m.

c. The formula for finding the volume V of a rectangular aquarium is:

$$V = \textbf{length} \times \textbf{width} \times \textbf{height} \underline{\hspace{4cm}} [C]$$

From the question, the volume of the aquarium = 168 ft², the length of the aquarium = 12 ft, and the height = 2 ft. Substitute V = 168 ft³, length = 12 ft, and height = 2 ft into equation [C] as shown:

168 ft³ = 12 ft × width × 2 ft.

168 ft³ = 24 ft² × width $\underline{\hspace{5cm}}$ [D]

$$12 \text{ ft} \times 2 \text{ ft} = 24 \text{ ft}^2$$

Divide both sides of the equation [D] by 24 ft² to obtain the width of the aquarium as shown:

$$\frac{168 \text{ ft}^3}{24 \text{ ft}^2} = \frac{24 \text{ ft}^2 \times \text{ width}}{24 \text{ ft}^2}$$

$$\frac{\overset{7 \text{ ft}}{\cancel{168 \text{ ft}^3}}}{\underset{1}{\cancel{24 \text{ ft}^2}}} = \frac{\overset{1}{\cancel{24 \text{ ft}^2}} \times \text{ width}}{\underset{1}{\cancel{24 \text{ ft}^2}}} \qquad \text{Do the division. Note: } \frac{\text{ft}^3}{\text{ft}^2} = \frac{\text{ft} \times \text{ft} \times \text{ft}}{\text{ft} \times \text{ft}} = \text{ft}$$

$$168 \div 24 = 7 \text{ and } 24 \div 24 = 1.$$

7 ft = width

Therefore, the width of the aquarium is 7 ft.

$$\text{Note also that: } \frac{\text{ft}^2}{\text{ft}^2} = \frac{\text{ft} \times \text{ft}}{\text{ft} \times \text{ft}} = \frac{\overset{1}{\cancel{\text{ft}}} \times \overset{1}{\cancel{\text{ft}}}}{\underset{1}{\cancel{\text{ft}}} \times \underset{1}{\cancel{\text{ft}}}} = 1$$

Examples on the Volume of Cylinders

The formula for finding the volume V of a cylinder is the area of the base times the height. Therefore,

$$V = \textbf{base area} \times \textbf{height}$$
$$= \pi \textbf{r}^2 \times \textbf{height}$$

where the formula for the base area of a cylinder is πr^2, $\pi \approx 3.14$, and r = radius.

Example 11

The area of the base of a cylinder is 7 m² and if the height of the cylinder is 10 m,

find the volume of the cylinder.
Solution
The formula for finding the volume V of a cylinder is:

V = area of base × height _____[A].

From the question, the area of the base = 7 m², and the height = 10 m. Substitute the area of base = 7 m² and height = 10 m into equation [A] to obtain the volume of the cylinder as shown:

$V = 7 \text{ m}^2 \times 10 \text{ m}$
$V = 70 \text{ m}^3$

Therefore, the volume of the cylinder is 70 m³.

Example 12

If the volume of a cylindrical water tank is 12 ft³ and the area of the base of the tank is 4 ft², how tall is the tank?

Solution
The formula for finding the volume V of a cylindrical tank is:

V = area of base × height _____[A].

From the question, the volume = 12 ft³, and the area of the base = 4ft². Substitute V = 12 ft³ and the area of the base = 4ft² into equation [A] as shown:

$12 \text{ ft}^3 = 4 \text{ ft}^2 \times \text{height}$ _____[B]

Divide both sides of equation [B] by 4 ft² to obtain the value of the height of the cylinder as shown:

$$\frac{12 \text{ ft}^3}{4 \text{ ft}^2} = \frac{4 \text{ ft}^2 \times \text{height}}{4 \text{ ft}^2}$$

$$\frac{\overset{3 \text{ ft}}{\cancel{12 \text{ ft}^3}}}{\underset{1}{\cancel{4 \text{ ft}^2}}} = \frac{\overset{1}{\cancel{4 \text{ ft}^2}} \times \text{height}}{\underset{1}{\cancel{4 \text{ ft}^2}}}$$

Note: $\dfrac{\text{ft}^3}{\text{ft}^2} = \dfrac{\text{ft x ft x ft}}{\text{ft x ft}} = \text{ft}$

$3 \text{ ft} = \text{height}$

Therefore, the height of the tank is 3 ft.

Example 13

Find the area of the base of the cylinder given that the volume of the cylinder is 36 m³.

4 m

Solution

The formula for finding the volume of a cylinder is:

$\qquad$ V = **area of base** × **height** _____[A]

From the question, the volume of the cylinder is 36 m³ and from the diagram, the height of the cylinder is 4 m. Substitute V = 36 m³ and height = 4 m into equation [A] as shown:

36 m³ = area of base × 4 m _____[B]

Divide both sides of equation [B] by 4 m to obtain the value of the area of the base as shown:

$$\frac{36 \text{ m}^3}{4 \text{ m}} = \frac{\text{area of base} \times 4 \text{ m}}{4 \text{ m}}$$

$$\frac{\overset{9 \text{ m}^2}{\cancel{36 \text{ m}^3}}}{\underset{1}{\cancel{4 \text{ m}}}} = \frac{\text{area of base} \times \overset{1}{\cancel{4 \text{ m}}}}{\underset{1}{\cancel{4 \text{ m}}}} \qquad \text{Note: } \frac{\text{m}^3}{\text{m}} = \frac{\overset{1}{\cancel{\text{m}}} \times \text{m} \times \text{m}}{\underset{1}{\cancel{\text{m}}}} = \text{m}^2$$

9 m² = area of base.

Therefore, the area of the base = 9 m².

Example 14

A cylindrical water tank has a height of 5 ft. If the volume of the tank is 86 ft³ find the radius of the base of the tank. Give your answer to the nearest tenth.

Solution

The formula for finding the volume V of a cylindrical tank is:

$\qquad$ V = **area of base x height**

$\qquad$ V = πr^2 × height _____[A]

$\qquad$ where the formula for the area of the base is πr^2 and r is the radius.

Substitute V = 86 ft³, $\pi \approx 3.14$, and the height = 5 ft into equation [A] to find the value of r as shown:

86 ft³ = 3.14 × r² × 5 ft.

86 ft³ = 15.7 ft × r² _____[B]

$\qquad\qquad\qquad\qquad$ 3.14 × 5 ft = 15.7 ft

Divide both sides of equation [B] by 15.7 ft to obtain the value of r² as shown:

$$\frac{86 \text{ ft}^3}{15.7 \text{ ft}} = \frac{15.7 \text{ ft} \times r^2}{15.7 \text{ ft}}$$

$$\frac{86 \text{ ft}^3}{15.7 \text{ ft}} = \frac{15.7 \text{ ft} \times r^2}{15.7 \text{ ft}}$$

$5.477 \text{ ft}^2 = r^2$ _____[C]

Depress 86 ÷ 15.7 = on a calculator to obtain 5.477.

15.7 ft ÷ 15.7 ft = 1.

Find the radius of both sides of equation [C] to obtain the value r as shown:

$$\sqrt{5.477 \text{ ft}^2} = \sqrt{r^2}$$

2.340 ft = r   Depress 2nd √ 5.477 = on a calculator to obtain 2.340.

$\sqrt{r^2}$ = r because the square root of any number to

the power 2 is equal to the number.

Therefore, the radius of the cylindrical water tank is 2.3 ft to the nearest tenth.

Exercises

1. What is the volume of an object?
2. What is the formula for finding the volume of any prism?
3. What is the formula for finding the volume of a cube?
4. Find the volume of each triangular prism. Hint: See Example 1.

a.   b.

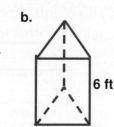   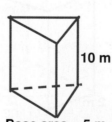

7 cm   6 ft   10 m

Base area = 3 cm²   **Base area = 4 ft²**

c.

Base area = 5 m

5. The height of a triangular prism is 6 cm. If the volume is 20 cm³, find the area of the base to the nearest tenth. Hint: See Example 2.
6. The volume of a triangular prism is 28 cm³. If the base area of the prism is 8.7 cm² find the height of the prism. Hint; See Example 3.
7. Find the volume of each cube if the length of each side or the length of the edge of each cube is given as:

a. 5 cm   **b.** 2 ft   **c.** 3.2 m   **d.** 6.3 m

Hint: See Example 4.

8. Find the length of a side or edge of each cubic tank with the associated volumes. Give your answer to the nearest tenth.

a. 8 m^3 **b.** 128 cm^3 **c.** 11 ft^3 **d.** 16 in^3

Hint: See Example 5 and Example 6.

9. Find the volume of each rectangular block.
    Hint: See Example 7.

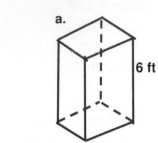

a.

6 ft

base area = 12 ft²

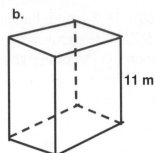

b.

11 m

base area = 15 m²

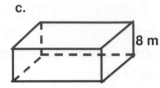

c.

8 m

base area = 16 m²

10. Find each missing number or dimension of each rectangular water tank.
    Hint: You may use the method of Example 8 to find each missing dimension.

Tank type	Volume	area of base	height
Rectangular water tank A	12 m^3	?	3 m
Rectangular water tank B	?	4 ft^2	10 ft
Rectangular water tank C	48 m^3	12 m^2	?
Rectangular water Tank D	60 cm^3	?	15 cm

11. Find the volume of each rectangular block. Hint: See Example 9.

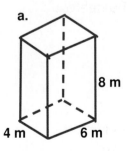

a.

8 m

4 m   6 m

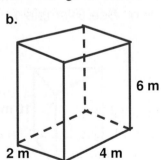

b.

6 m

2 m   4 m

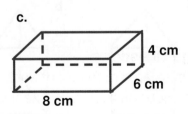

c.

4 cm

6 cm

8 cm

12a. The volume of a rectangular container is 48 m^3. If the height of the container is 2 m and the width is 3 m, find the length of the container. Hint: See Example 10a.

12b. The volume of a swimming pool is 108 m^3. If the length of the pool is 8 m and the width is 6 m, how deep is the swimming pool? Hint: See Example 10b.

12c. If the length of a rectangular aquarium is 8 ft and the height is 3 ft, find the width of the aquarium given that the volume is 120 ft. Hint: See Example 10c.

13. Find the dimension of each rectangular block or tank. Hint: Use the solution methods for Example 9 and Example 10 to find the missing dimensions.

Type of object	Volume	Length	Width	height
Rectangular Tank	50 m^3	10 m	2 m	?
Rectangular block	?	6 in	3 in	2 in
Rectangular aquarium	16 ft^3	4 ft	?	4 m
Rectangular swimming pool	96 m^3	?	3 m	4 m
Rectangular book	24 in^3	6 in	2 in	?

14. The area of the base of a cylinder is 4 m^2 and if the height of the cylinder is 11 m, find the volume of the cylinder. Hint: See Example 11.

15. The height of a cylinder is 8 ft and if the area of the base is 5 ft^2, find the volume of the cylinder. Hint: See Example 11.

16. The area of the base of a cylindrical tank is 5 m^2 and if the volume of the tank is 10 m^3, how tall is the tank? Hint: See Example 12.

17. Find the height of a cylindrical water tank that has a base area of 3 ft^2 and volume of 15 ft^3. Hint: See Example 12.

18. Find the area of the base of the cylinder given that the volume is 24 ft^3. Hint: See Example 13.

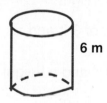

6 m

19. Find the radius of the base of a cylindrical gas tank that has a volume of 36 m^3 and a height of 6 m. Hint: See Example 14. Round your answer to the nearest tenth.

Challenge Questions.

20. Find missing dimension of each rectangular oil tank.
Round your answer to the nearest tenths. Hint: Use the formula for finding the volume of a rectangle prism for each type of tank. Substitute the given dimensions into the formula of each tank type and solve for the unknown dimensions.

Tank type	Volume	Length	Width	Height
Tank A	?	4 ft	3 ft	2.01 ft
Tank B	28 m^3	5 m	2 m	?
Tank C	18 ft^3	4 ft	?	2 ft
Tank D	32 m^3	?	3 m	1.78 m

21. The volume of a cubic tank is 3 m^2. How long is each side of the tank?
22. The side of a cubic tank is 4 ft. What is the volume of the tank.
23. Find the missing dimension of each rectangular Tank. Round your answer to the nearest tenth.

Type of Tank	Volume	Area of base	Height
Tank A	?	8 m^2	10.25 m
Tank B	28 ft^3	9 ft^2	?
Tank C	17 m^3	?	3 m
Tank D	?	11.21 m^2	2 m

24. The area of the base of a triangular prism is 8 ft^2. If the height of the prism is 7 ft, find the volume of the prism.
25. The volume of a triangular prism is 18 m^3. If the area of the base is 9 m^2, find the height of the prism?
26. Find the area of the base of a triangular prism that has a height of 3 ft and a volume of 36 ft^3.
27. Find the volume of a cylindrical tank that has a base area of 6 ft^2 and a height of 5 ft.
28. Find the height of a cylinder that has a volume of 30 m^3 and a base area of 6 m^2.
29. The volume of a cylindrical tank is 19 m^3. If the height is 3 m, find the area of the base to the nearest tenth.
30. The radius of a cylindrical tank is 3 ft and the height is 5.21 ft. Find the volume of the tank to the nearest tenth.

Answer to Selected Questions
4a. 21 cm^3 **7a.** 125 cm^3 **8a.** 2 m   **9a.** 72 ft^3
10. Partial answer: Area of base of tank A = 4 m^2.   **11a.** 192 m^3

VOLUME OF PYRAMIDS AND CONES

Quick cumulative review

1. Explain how you would find the range of a data.

2. Explain what is meant by supplementary angles.

3. Explain what is meant by complementary angles.

4. Explain how you would find the average age of 5 girls.

5. Solve each expression:

  a. $2 + 4 \times 3$ **b.** $4 \times 3 + 2$ **c.** $8 \div 2 \cdot 3$ **d.** $2^2 + 6 \cdot 3 - 5 \cdot 2 =$

  e. $4 - 1.\ 921$ **f.** $20 - (4)(3)(3)$ **g.** $|{-2} - 3|$ **h.** $|2 - (-3)|$

6. Solve each equation.

  a. $3x = 15$ **b.** $\dfrac{3x}{4} = \dfrac{3}{8}$ **c.** $\dfrac{-2}{5} = \dfrac{x}{10}$ **d.** $\dfrac{k}{-2} = 12$

Volume of Pyramids and Cones.

A diagram of a rectangular pyramid, a cone, and a triangular pyramid are shown below.

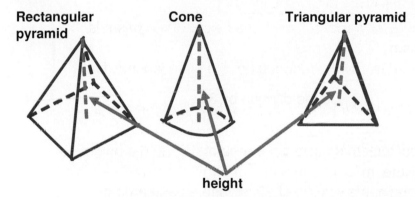

The heights of the pyramids and the cone are perpendicular lines from the highest point on the pyramid and the cone to the base of the pyramid and the base of the cone.

Pyramids

The formula for finding the volume V of a pyramid is:

$$V = \frac{1}{3}(\text{area of base}) \times \text{height}.$$

Cones

The formula for finding the volume V of a cone is:

$$V = \frac{1}{3}(\text{area of base}) \times \text{height}$$

$$= \frac{1}{3}(\pi r^2) \times \text{height}.$$

      where πr^2 is the formula for finding the area of the circular base of the cone.

How to Solve Problems Involving the Volume of Pyramids

To solve problems involving the volume of a pyramid, write the formula for the volume of the pyramid, substitute all the dimensions given about the volume into the formula, and then solve the equation of the formula to find the unknown dimension.

Example 1

Find the volume of a pyramid that has a base area of 3 m² and a height of 7 m.

Solution

The formula for the volume V of a pyramid is:

$$V = \frac{1}{3} \textbf{(area of base)} \times \textbf{height} \underline{\hspace{5cm}} [A]$$

Substitute "area of base" = 3 m² and height = 7 m into equation [A] to obtain the volume of the pyramid as shown:

$$V = \frac{1}{3}(3 \text{ m}^2) \times 7 \text{ m}$$

$$V = \frac{1}{\cancel{3}}(\cancel{3} \text{ m}^2) \times 7 \text{ m} \qquad\qquad \text{Do the division by 3.}$$

$$V = 7 \text{ m}^3 \qquad\qquad \text{Note: } m^2 \times m = m \times m \times m = m^3$$

Example 2

If the volume of a pyramid is 18 ft³ and the height is 4 ft, find the base area of the pyramid.

Solution

The formula for the volume of a pyramid is:

$$V = \frac{1}{3} \textbf{(area of base)} \times \textbf{height} \underline{\hspace{5cm}} [A]$$

Substitute V = 18 ft³ and the height = 4 ft into equation [A] as shown:

$$18 \text{ ft}^3 = \frac{1}{3}(\text{area of base}) \times 4 \text{ ft.}$$

$$18 \text{ ft}^3 = \frac{4}{3} \text{ ft} \times (\text{area of base}) \underline{\hspace{4cm}} \left[B \right]$$

$$\frac{1}{3} \times 4 = \frac{4}{3}$$

894

Multiply both sides of the equation $[B]$ by the reciprocal of $\frac{4}{3}$ ft which is $\frac{3}{4}$ ft in order to eliminate the $\frac{4}{3}$ ft and then to isolate the "area of base" as shown:

$$18 \text{ ft}^3 \times \frac{3}{4}\text{ ft} = \frac{4}{3}\text{ ft} \times \frac{3}{4}\text{ ft} \times (\text{area of base}).$$

$$\overset{9}{\underset{2}{\cancel{18}}} \text{ ft}^3 \times \frac{3}{\underset{}{4}}\text{ ft} = \frac{\overset{1}{\cancel{4}}}{\underset{1}{3}}\text{ ft} \times \frac{\overset{1}{3}}{\underset{1}{\cancel{4}}}\text{ ft} \times (\text{area of base}). \qquad \text{Do the division.}$$

$$9 \text{ ft}^2 \times \frac{3}{2} = \text{area of base}$$

$$\frac{27 \text{ ft}^2}{2} = \text{area of base}$$

Therefore, the area of the base is $13\frac{1}{2}$ ft^2.

Example 3

Find the height of a pyramid that has an area of base of 5.38 m^2 and a volume of 29 m^3. Round your answer to he nearest tenth.

Solution

The formula for finding the volume of a pyramid is:

$$V = \frac{1}{3}(\text{area of base}) \times \text{height} \underline{\hspace{5cm}}[A]$$

Substitute $V = 29$ m^3 and the area of base $= 5.38$ m^2 into equation $[A]$ as shown:

$$29 \text{ m}^3 = \frac{1}{3}(5.38 \text{ m}^2) \times \text{height}$$

$$29 \text{ m}^3 = \frac{5.38 \text{ m}^2}{3} \times \text{height} \underline{\hspace{5cm}}[B]$$

Multiply both sides of the equation by 3 so that the denominator of 3 can be eliminated as shown:

$$29 \text{ m}^3 \times 3 = \frac{5.38 \text{ m}^2}{3} \times 3 \times \text{height}$$

$$29 \text{ m}^3 \times 3 = \frac{5.38 \text{ m}^2}{\underset{1}{\cancel{3}}} \times \overset{1}{\cancel{3}} \times \text{height} \qquad \text{Do the division by 3.}$$

$$87 \text{ m}^3 = 5.38 \text{ m}^2 \times \text{height} \underline{\hspace{5cm}} [C]$$

$$\frac{87 \text{ m}^3}{5.38 \text{ m}^2} = \frac{5.38 \text{ m}^2}{5.38 \text{ m}^2} \times \text{height}$$

Divide both sides of the equation by

5.38 m² to obtain the height.

16.1711 m = height

Therefore, the height of pyramid is 16.2 m to the nearest tenth.

Example 4

The length of the base of a rectangular pyramid is 4 m and the width is 3 m. If the height of the pyramid is 6 m find the volume of the pyramid.

Solution

The formula for finding the volume of a rectangular pyramid is:

$$V = \frac{1}{3}(\text{area of base}) \times \text{height}$$

$$= \frac{1}{3}(\textbf{length} \times \textbf{width}) \times \textbf{height} \underline{\hspace{4cm}} [A]$$

where (length × width) = area of base.

Substitute length = 4 m, width = 3 m, and height = 6 m into equation $[A]$ in order to find the volume as shown:

$$V = \frac{1}{3}(4 \text{ m} \times 3 \text{ m}) \times 6 \text{ m}$$

$$V = \frac{1}{\overset{3}{\underset{1}{3}}}(4 \text{ m} \times \overset{1 \text{ m}}{3 \text{ m}}) \times 6 \text{ m}$$

Do the division by 3.

$$V = 4 \text{ m} \times 1 \text{ m} \times 6 \text{ m}$$
$$V = 24 \text{ m}^3$$

Therefore, the volume of the rectangular pyramid is 24 m³.

Example 5

The volume of the rectangular pyramid is 24 m³. Find the length of he base of the pyramid.

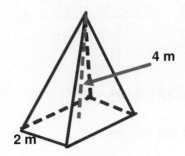

4 m

2 m

Solution

The formula for finding the volume of a rectangular pyramid is:

$$V = \frac{1}{3}(\text{area of base}) \times \text{height}$$

$$= \frac{1}{3}(\textbf{length} \times \textbf{width}) \times \textbf{height} \underline{\hspace{5cm}}[A]$$

Where (length x width) = area of base.

From the diagram, the width of the base of the rectangular pyramid is 2 m, and the height is 4 m. Substitute $V = 24\ m^3$, width of base = 2 m, and height = 4 m into equation $[A]$ in order to find the length of the base as shown:

$$24\ m^3 = \frac{1}{3}(\text{length} \times 2\ m) \times 4\ m$$

$$24\ m^3 = \frac{1}{3} \times \text{length} \times 2\ m \times 4\ m$$

$$24\ m^3 = \frac{1}{3} \times \text{length} \times 8\ m^2 \qquad\qquad 2\ m \times 4\ m = 8\ m^2$$

$$24\ m^3 = \frac{8\ m^2}{3} \times \text{length} \underline{\hspace{5cm}}[B]$$

Multiply both sides of equation $[B]$ by the reciprocal of $\dfrac{8\ m^2}{3}$ which is

$\dfrac{3}{8\ m^2}$ in order to eliminate $\dfrac{8\ m^2}{3}$ in equation $[B]$ and then to obtain the value

of the length as shown:

$$24\ m^3 \times \frac{3}{8\ m^2} = \frac{8\ m^2}{3} \times \frac{3}{8\ m^2} \times \text{length}$$

$3m \quad\quad\quad 1 \quad\quad\quad 1 \quad\quad\quad\quad\quad\quad\quad 1 \quad\quad 1$

$24 \ m^3 \times \dfrac{3}{8 \ m^2} = \dfrac{8 \ m^2}{3} \times \dfrac{3}{8 \ m^2} \times \text{length}$ Note: $\dfrac{m^3}{m^2} = \dfrac{m \times m \times m}{m \times m} = m$

$\quad\quad\quad\quad 1 \quad\quad\quad 1 \quad\quad\quad 1 \quad\quad\quad\quad\quad\quad\quad 1 \quad\quad 1$

$$24 \ m^3 \div 8 \ m^2 = 3 \ m, \ 8 \ m^2 \div 8 \ m^2 = 1,$$
$$3 \div 3 = 1.$$

$3 \ m \times 3 = \text{length}$

$9 \ m = \text{length}$

Therefore, the length of the rectangular base is 9 m.

Example 6

a. Find the width of the base of a rectangular pyramid that has a volume of 36 m³, the length of the base is 6 m, and the height of the pyramid is 3 m.

b. Comparing the width and the length of the base, what name can you give to the pyramid.

Solution

a. The formula for finding the volume of a rectangular pyramid is:

$$\mathbf{V} = \frac{1}{3}(\text{area of base}) \times \text{height}.$$

$$= \frac{1}{3}(\textbf{length} \times \textbf{width}) \times \textbf{height} \rule{5cm}{0.4pt}[\text{A}]$$

where (length × width) = area of base.

Substitute V = 36 m³, length of base = 6 m, and height = 3 m into equation [A] in order to obtain the width of the pyramid as shown:

$$36 \ m^3 = \frac{1}{3}(6 \ m \times \text{width}) \times 3 \ m$$

$$36 \ m^3 = \frac{1}{3} \times 6 \ m \times \text{width} \times 3 \ m$$

$$\overset{\displaystyle 1 \ m}{36 \ m^3 = \frac{1}{\underset{1}{3}} \times 6 \ m \times \text{width} \times \cancel{3} \ m} \qquad\qquad \text{Do the division by 3.}$$

$$36 \ m^3 = 1 \times 6 \ m \times \text{width} \times 1 \ m$$

$$36 \ m^3 = 6 \ m^2 \times \text{width} \rule{5cm}{0.4pt}[\text{B}]$$

$$1 \times 6 \ m \times \text{width} \times 1 \ m = 6 \ m^2.$$

Divide both sides of equation [B] by 6 m² in order to obtain the value of the width as shown:

898

$$\frac{36 \text{ m}^3}{6 \text{ m}^2} = \frac{6 \text{ m}^2}{6 \text{ m}^2} \times \text{width}$$

$$\frac{\overset{6 \text{ m}}{\cancel{36 \text{ m}^3}}}{\underset{1}{\cancel{6 \text{ m}^2}}} = \frac{\overset{1}{\cancel{6 \text{ m}^2}}}{\underset{1}{\cancel{6 \text{ m}^2}}} \times \text{width}$$

$$6 \text{ m} = \text{width}$$

b. Since the width of the base of the pyramid is 6 m and the length of the base of the pyramid is also 6 m, the sides of the base of the pyramid are equal. Therefore, the pyramid can be called a square pyramid.

Example 7

A side of a square pyramid is 4 ft and if the height of the pyramid is 6 ft, find the volume of the pyramid.

Solution

The formula for finding the volume of a square pyramid is:

$$V = \frac{1}{3}(\text{area of base}) \times \text{height}$$

$$= \frac{1}{3}(\textbf{side} \times \textbf{side}) \times \textbf{height} \underline{\hspace{6cm}}[A]$$

where (side × side) of a square pyramid = area of base.

Substitute side = 4 ft and height = 6 ft into equation $[A]$ in order to obtain the volume of the square pyramid as shown:

$$V = \frac{1}{3}(4 \text{ ft} \times 4 \text{ ft}) \times 6 \text{ ft}$$

$$V = \frac{1}{3} \times 4 \text{ ft} \times 4 \text{ ft} \times 6 \text{ ft}$$

$$V = \frac{1}{\cancel{3}} \times 4 \text{ ft} \times 4 \text{ ft} \times \overset{2 \text{ ft}}{\cancel{6 \text{ ft}}} \qquad\qquad \text{Divide by 3.}$$

$$V = 1 \times 4 \text{ ft} \times 4 \text{ ft} \times 2 \text{ ft}$$
$$V = 32 \text{ ft}^3$$

Example 8

Find the length of a side of a square base pyramid that has a volume of 32 ft³ and a height of 6 ft.

Solution

The formula for finding the volume of a square pyramid is:

$$V = \frac{1}{3}(\textbf{area of base}) \times \textbf{height}.$$

$$V = \frac{1}{3}(\textbf{side} \times \textbf{side}) \times \textbf{height} \underline{\hspace{6cm}}[A]$$

where (side × side) = area of base.

Substitute V = 32 ft³ and height = 6 ft into equation $[A]$ in order to find the side as shown:

$$32 \text{ ft}^3 = \frac{1}{3}(\text{side} \times \text{side}) \times 6 \text{ ft}.$$

$$32 \text{ ft}^3 = \frac{1}{\cancel{3}}(\text{side} \times \text{side}) \times \overset{2\text{ ft}}{\cancel{6 \text{ ft}}}. \qquad \text{Divide by 3}$$

$$32 \text{ ft}^3 = (\text{side} \times \text{side}) \times 2 \text{ ft} \underline{\hspace{5cm}}[B]$$

$$\frac{32 \text{ ft}^3}{2 \text{ ft}} = (\text{side} \times \text{side}) \times \frac{2 \text{ ft}}{2 \text{ ft}} \qquad \text{Divide both sides of the equation } [B] \text{ by}$$

2 ft in order to isolate (side × side).

$$\frac{\overset{16\text{ ft}^2}{\cancel{32 \text{ ft}^3}}}{\underset{1}{\cancel{2 \text{ ft}}}} = (\text{side} \times \text{side}) \times \frac{\overset{1}{\cancel{2 \text{ ft}}}}{\underset{1}{\cancel{2 \text{ ft}}}} \qquad \text{Note: } \frac{\text{ft}^3}{\text{ft}} = \frac{\text{ft} \times \text{ft} \times \text{ft}}{\cancel{\text{ft}}} = \text{ft}^2$$

$$32 \text{ ft}^3 \div 2 \text{ ft} = 16 \text{ ft}^2 \text{ and } 2 \text{ ft} \div 2 \text{ ft} = 1.$$

$$16 \text{ ft}^2 = \text{side} \times \text{side}$$
$$16 \text{ ft}^2 = (\text{side})^2 \qquad\qquad \text{side} \times \text{side} = (\text{side})^2$$
$$4^2 \text{ ft}^2 = (\text{side})^2 \underline{\hspace{4cm}}[A]$$

$$4^2 = 4 \times 4 = 16$$

$$\sqrt{4^2 \text{ ft}^2} = \sqrt{(\text{side})^2} \qquad \text{Find the square root of both sides of}$$

equation $[A]$ to obtain the measure of the side.

$$4 \text{ ft} = \text{side} \qquad\qquad \text{Recall that the square root of the square of a}$$

number is the number itself.

Therefore, the length of the side of the square base of the pyramid is 4 ft.

Special Note: If the length of the side were to be $\sqrt{3 \text{ ft}^2}$ such that we cannot easily find the square root of 3 ft², then you may use a calculator as shown: Depress: 2nd $\sqrt{}$ 3 = on your calculator to obtain 1.732 as the length of a side of the square.

Exercises

1. Sketch a triangular pyramid.

2. Explain what is meant by the height of a pyramid.

3. Explain the formula for finding the volume of a pyramid.

4. Explain how you would find the area of the base of a rectangular pyramid.

5. The height of a rectangular pyramid is perpendicular to the base of the pyramid. True or False?

6. Find the volume of a pyramid that has an area of base of 6 cm² and a height of 4 cm. Hint: See Example 1.

7. Find the missing measure of the dimension of each pyramid. Hint: See Example 1.

a. area of base = 9 ft ²
height = 2 ft
volume = ?

b. area of base = 12 m²
height = 4 m
volume = ?

c. area of base = 12 ft²
height = 3 ft
volume = ?

d. area of base = 5 m
height = 3 m
volume = ?

8. If the volume of a pyramid is 12 ft³ and the height of the pyramid is 2 ft, find the area of the base of the pyramid. Hint: See Example 2.

9. Find the missing measure of the dimension of each pyramid. Hint: See Example 2.

a. area of base = ?
volume = 3 m³
height = 5 m

b. area of base = ?
volume = 6 m³
height = 4 m

c. area of base = ?
volume = 7 m³
height = 6 m

d. area of base = ?
volume = 4 ft³
height = 9 ft

10. Find the height of a pyramid that has an area of base of 4.78 m² and a volume of 18.2 m³. Round your answer to the nearest tenth. Hint: See Example 3.

11. Find the missing measure of the dimension of each pyramid. Round your answer to the nearest tenth. Hint: See Example 3.

a. area of base = 9 ft²
height = ?
volume = 17.8 ft

b area of base = 12 m²
height = ?
volume = 27.5 m³

c. area of base = 3.6 ft²

d. area of base = 4.2 m²

height = ?
volume = 15.2 ft³

height = ?
volume = 14.4 m³

12. The length of the base of a rectangular pyramid is 6 ft and the width is 2 ft. If the height of the pyramid is 5 ft, find the volume of the pyramid. Hint: See example 4.

13. Find the missing measure of the dimension of the rectangular pyramid. Hint: See Example 4.

    a. length of base = 5 m
       width of base = 3 m
    height of pyramid = 6 m
    volume of pyramid = ?

    b. length of base = 4 ft
       width of base = 2 ft
    height of pyramid = 3 ft
    volume of pyramid = ?

    c. length of base = 7 ft
       width of base = 2 ft
    height of pyramid = 3 ft
    volume of pyramid = ?

    d. length of base = 6 m
       width of base = 2 m
    height of pyramid = 2 m
    volume of pyramid = ?

14. The volume of a rectangular pyramid is 12 m³. If the width of the base of the pyramid is 2 m and the height of the pyramid is 3 m, find the length of the base of the pyramid. Hint: See Example 5.

15. Find the missing measure of the dimension of the rectangular pyramid. Hint: See Example 5. Round your answer to the nearest tenth.

    a. width of the base = ?
       Length of the base = 5 m
    height of the pyramid = 9 m
    volume of the pyramid = 20 m³

    b. width of the base = ?
       length of the base = 4 ft
    height of the pyramid = 3 ft
    volume of the pyramid = 15 ft³

    c. width of the base = ?
       length of the base = 7 m
    height of the pyramid = 6 m
    volume of the pyramid = 21 m³

    d. width of the pyramid = ?
       length of the base = 8 ft
    height of the pyramid = 9 ft
    volume of the pyramid = 48 ft³

16. The side of a square base of a square pyramid is 5 m and if the height of the pyramid is 9 m, find the volume of the pyramid. Hint: See Example 7.

17. Find the missing measure of the dimension of each square pyramid. Hint: See Example 7.

    a. side of the square base = 4 ft
       height of the pyramid = 6 ft
       volume of the pyramid = ?

    b. side of the square base = 3 m
       height of the pyramid = 7 m
       volume of the pyramid = ?

    c. side of the square base = 5 ft
       height of the pyramid = 9 ft
       volume of the pyramid = ?

    d. side of the square base = 2 m
       height of the pyramid = 6 m
       volume of the pyramid = ?

18. Find the length of a side of a square base of a square pyramid that has a volume of 16 ft³ and a height of 3 ft. Hint: See Example 8.

19. Find the length of a side of a square base of a square pyramid that has a volume of 25 m³ and a height of 3 m. Hint: See Example 8.

Answers to Selected Questions

6. 8 cm³	**7a.** 6 ft³	**8.** 18 ft²	**9a.** 1.8 m²	**10.** 11.4 m
11. 5.9 ft	**13a.** 30 cm³	**15a.** 1.3 m	**17a.** 32 ft³	

Cones

How to Solve Problems Involving the Volume of a Cone.

To solve problems involving the volume of a cone, write the formula for finding the volume of a cone, substitute all the dimensions about the volume given into the formula and then solve the equation of the formula to find the unknown dimension.

The formula for finding the volume of a cone is:

$$V = \frac{1}{3}(\text{area of base}) \times \text{height.}$$

$$V = \frac{1}{3}(\pi r^2) \times \text{height.}$$

where πr^2 is the formula for finding the area of the base

Example 9

Find the volume of a cone that has a base area of 3 ft² and a height of 4 ft.

Solution

The formula for finding the volume of a cone is:

$$V = \frac{1}{3}(\text{area of base}) \times \text{height.} \underline{\hspace{6cm}} [A]$$

It is given in the question that the (area of base) = 3 ft² and the height of the cone = 4 ft.

Substitute the (area of base) = 3 ft² and the height = 4 ft into equation $[A]$ to find the volume of the cone as shown:

$$V = \frac{1}{3}(3 \text{ ft}^2) \times 4 \text{ ft}$$

$$= \frac{1}{3} \times 3 \text{ ft}^2 \times 4 \text{ ft}$$

$$= \frac{1}{3} \times \overset{1 \text{ ft}^2}{\cancel{3 \text{ ft}^2}} \times 4 \text{ ft.} \qquad \text{Do the division by 3.}$$

903

$$= 4 \text{ ft}^3$$

Therefore, the volume of the cone is 4 ft^3.

Example 10

The radius of a cone is 3 m and the height is 4 m. Find the volume of the cone. Round your answer to the nearest tenth.

Solution

The formula for the volume of a cone is:

$$V = \frac{1}{3}(\text{area of base}) \times \text{height}$$

$$V = \frac{1}{3}(\pi r^2) \times \text{height} \underline{\hspace{5cm}}[A]$$

where $\pi \approx 3.14$ and r = radius of the base.

It is given in the question that r = 3 m and the height = 4 m.

Substitute $\pi \approx 3.14$, r = 3 m, and height = 4 m into equation $[A]$ to find the volume of the cone as shown:

$$V = \frac{1}{3}\left[3.14 \times (3 \text{ m})^2\right] \times 4 \text{ m}.$$

$$V = \frac{1}{3}\left[3.14 \times 3 \text{ m} \times 3 \text{ m}\right] \times 4 \text{ m}. \qquad\qquad (3 \text{ m})^2 = 3 \text{ m} \times 3 \text{ m}$$

$$V = \frac{1}{3}\left[3.14 \times \overset{1 \text{ m}}{3 \text{ m}} \times 3 \text{ m}\right] \times 4 \text{ m} \qquad\qquad \text{Divide by 3.}$$
$$\underset{1}{}$$

$$V = 3.14 \times 1 \text{ m} \times 3 \text{ m} \times 4 \text{ m}$$
$$= 37.68 \text{ m}^3 \qquad\qquad\qquad \text{You may use your calculator.}$$

(Depress $3.14 \times 1 \times 3 \times 4 =$ on your calculator to obtain 37.68. Note that m × m × m = m^3.)

V = 37.7 m^3 rounded to the nearest tenths. Therefore, the volume of the cone is 37.7 m^3.

Example 11

Find the volume of the cone.

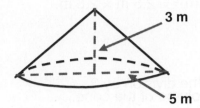

3 m

5 m

Solution

The formula for finding the volume of a cone is:

$$V = \frac{1}{3}(\text{area of base}) \times \text{height}$$

$$= \frac{1}{3}(\pi r^2) \times \text{height} \underline{\hspace{5cm}} [A]$$

where $\pi \approx 3.14$ and r = radius of base.

πr^2 is the formula for finding the (area of base).

From the diagram, the height of the cone is 3 m, and the diameter of the cone is 5 m. The formula for finding the volume of a cone involves the radius but not the diameter. Therefore, let us find the radius first before substituting the value of the radius into the formula of the cone as shown:

$$\text{Diameter} = 2 \times \text{radius} \underline{\hspace{5cm}} [B]$$

$$\frac{\text{Diameter}}{2} = \frac{2 \times \text{radius}}{2} \qquad \text{Divide both sides of the equation } [B] \text{ by 2}$$

to obtain the radius.

$$\frac{\text{Diameter}}{2} = \frac{\overset{1}{2} \times \text{radius}}{\underset{1}{2}}$$

$$\frac{\text{Diameter}}{2} = \text{radius}$$

$$\frac{5 \text{ m}}{2} = \text{radius} \qquad\qquad \text{Diameter} = 5 \text{ m.}$$

$$2\frac{1}{2} \text{ m} = 2.5 \text{ m} = \text{radius.} \qquad\qquad 5 \div 2 = 2\frac{1}{2}$$

Substitute $\pi \approx 3.14$, radius = 2.5 m, and height = 3 m into equation $[A]$ as shown:

$$V = \frac{1}{3}\left[3.14 \times (2.5 \text{ m})^2 \times 3 \text{ m}\right].$$

$$V = \frac{1}{3}(3.14 \times 2.5 \text{ m} \times 2.5 \text{ m} \times 3 \text{ m}) \qquad\qquad (2.5 \text{ m})^2 = 2.5 \text{ m} \times 2.5 \text{ m}.$$

$$V = \frac{1}{\underset{1}{3}}(3.14 \times 2.5 \text{ m} \times 2.5 \text{ m} \times \overset{1 \text{ m}}{3 \text{ m}}) \qquad\qquad \text{Do the division by 3.}$$

$$V = 3.14 \times 2.5 \text{ m} \times 2.5 \text{ m} \times 1 \text{ m}$$
$$= 19.625 \text{ m}^3 \qquad \text{You may use a calculator by depressing}$$

$3.14 \times 2.5 \times 2.5 =$ on your calculator to obtain 19.625. Note: m $\times$ m $\times$ m $=$ m^3

$$V = 19.6 \text{ m}^3 \text{ rounded to the nearest tenth.}$$

Therefore, the volume of the cone is 19.6 m^3.

Example 12

Find the area of the base of a cone that has a volume of 19 ft^3 and a height of 4 ft.

Solution

The formula for finding the volume of a cone is:

$$\mathbf{V = \frac{1}{3}(area\ of\ base) \times height} \underline{\hspace{5cm}} \text{[A]}$$

It is given in the question that $V = 19$ ft^3 and the height $= 4$ ft.

Substitute $V = 19$ ft^3 and height $= 4$ ft into equation [A] as shown:

$$19 \text{ ft}^3 = \frac{1}{3}(\text{area of base}) \times 4 \text{ ft} \underline{\hspace{5cm}}\text{[B]}$$

Multiply both sides of the equation [B] by 3 to eliminate the 3 at the right side of the equation as a denominator as shown:

$$19 \text{ ft}^3 \times 3 = \frac{1}{3}(\text{area of base}) \times 4 \text{ ft} \times 3.$$

$$9 \text{ ft}^3 \times 3 = \frac{1}{\underset{1}{3}}(\text{area of base}) \times 4 \text{ ft} \times \overset{1}{3}. \qquad\qquad \text{Do the division by 3.}$$

$$57 \text{ ft}^3 = (\text{area of base}) \times 4 \text{ ft.} \underline{\hspace{5cm}}\text{[C]}$$

Divide both sides of the equation [C] by 4 ft to obtain the area of the base as shown:

$$\frac{57 \text{ ft}^3}{4 \text{ ft}} = \frac{(\text{area of base}) \times 4 \text{ ft}}{4 \text{ ft}}$$

$$\frac{57 \text{ fi}^3}{4 \text{ ft}} = \frac{(\text{area of base}) \times \overset{1}{\cancel{4 \text{ ft}}}}{\underset{1}{\cancel{4 \text{ ft}}}}$$
Do the division.

14.25 ft² = area of base
14.3ft² = area of base to the nearest tenth.

Review the Math Teaching Series for grade 6 on Place Values and Rounding of Number.

Example 13
A cone has a base area of 6 m² and a volume of 25 m³, find the height of the cone.
Solution
The formula for finding the volume of a cone is:

$$V = \frac{1}{3}(\text{area of base}) \times \text{height} \underline{\hspace{4cm}}[A]$$

Substitute V = 25 m³ and the area of the base = 6 m² into equation [A] as shown:

$$25 \text{ m}^3 = \frac{1}{3}(6 \text{ m}^2) \times \text{height.}$$

$$25 \text{ m}^3 = \frac{1}{\cancel{3}}(\overset{2 \text{ m}^2}{\cancel{6 \text{ m}^2}}) \times \text{height.} \qquad \text{Do the division by 3.}$$

$$25 \text{ m}^3 = 2 \text{ m}^2 \times \text{height} \underline{\hspace{4cm}}[B]$$

Divide both sides of equation [B] by 2 in order to obtain the value of the height as shown:

$$\frac{25 \text{ m}^3}{2 \text{ m}^2} = \frac{2 \text{ m}^2 \times \text{height}}{2 \text{ m}^2}$$

$$\frac{25 \text{ m}^3}{2 \text{ m}^2} = \frac{\overset{1}{\cancel{2 \text{ m}^2}} \times \text{height}}{\underset{1}{\cancel{2 \text{ m}^2}}}$$

$$12\frac{1}{2} \text{ m} = \text{height.} \qquad 25 \div 2 = 12\frac{1}{2} \text{ and } \frac{\text{m}^3}{\text{m}^2} = \frac{\overset{1}{\cancel{\text{m}}} \times \overset{1}{\cancel{\text{m}}} \times \text{m}}{\underset{1}{\cancel{\text{m}}} \times \underset{1}{\cancel{\text{m}}}} = \text{m.}$$

12.5 m = height

Example 14

Find the radius of a cone that has a volume of 9 ft³ and a height of 4 ft. Round your answer to the nearest tenth.

Solution

The formula for finding the volume of a cone is:

$$V = \frac{1}{3}(\textbf{area of base}) \times \textbf{height}$$

$$V = \frac{1}{3}(\pi r^2) \times \textbf{height} \underline{\hspace{7cm}} [A]$$

where πr^2 is the formula for finding the area of the base and $\pi = 3.14$.

Substitute V = 9 ft³, $\pi \approx 3.14$, and height = 4 ft into equation [A]:

$$9 \text{ ft}^3 = \frac{1}{3}(3.14 \times r^2) \times 4 \text{ ft} \underline{\hspace{5cm}} [B]$$

Multiply both sides of the equation [B] by 3 to eliminate the denominator 3 from the right side of the equation as shown:

$$9 \text{ ft}^3 \times 3 = \frac{1}{3} \times 3 \times (3.14 \times r^2) \times 4 \text{ ft}$$

$$9 \text{ ft}^3 \times 3 = \frac{1}{\underset{1}{\cancel{3}}} \times \overset{1}{\cancel{3}} \times (3.14 \times r^2) \times 4 \text{ ft}$$

$$9 \text{ ft}^3 \times 3 = 1 \times 1 \times 3.14 \times r^2 \times 4 \text{ ft}$$

$$9 \text{ ft}^3 \times 3 = 3.14 \times r^2 \times 4 \text{ ft}$$

Divide both sides of the equation by 3.14×4 ft to obtain the value of r^2 as shown:

$$\frac{9 \text{ ft}^3 \times 3}{3.14 \times 4 \text{ ft}} = \frac{3.14 \times r^2 \ 4 \text{ ft}}{3.14 \times 4 \text{ ft}}$$

$$\frac{9 \text{ ft}^3 \times 3}{3.14 \times 4 \text{ ft}} = \frac{\overset{1}{\cancel{3.14}} \times r^2 \ \overset{1}{\cancel{4 \text{ ft}}}}{\underset{1}{\cancel{3.14}} \times \underset{1}{\cancel{4 \text{ ft}}}}$$

$$\frac{9 \text{ ft}^3 \times 3}{3.14 \times 4 \text{ ft}} = r^2$$

$$\frac{27 \text{ ft}^3}{12.56 \text{ ft}} = r^2 \qquad\qquad 9 \text{ ft}^3 \times 3 = 27 \text{ ft}^3,\ 3.14 \times 4 \text{ ft} = 12.56 \text{ ft}$$

$$2.14968 \text{ ft}^2 = r^2 \underline{\hspace{8cm}} [C]$$

Depress $27 \div 12.56 =$ on a calculator to obtain 2.14968.

Find the square root of both sides of the equation $[C]$ in order to find the value of r as shown:

$$\sqrt{2.14968 \text{ ft}} = \sqrt{r^2}$$

1.466 ft = r.   Depress: 2nd $\sqrt{}$ 2.14968 = on a calculator to obtain 1.466 17.

Therefore, the radius of the cone is 1.5 ft to the nearest tenth.

Exercises

1. Sketch: **a.** a cone   **b.** a triangular pyramid.
2. Describe the height of a cone.
3. Explain how you would find the volume of a cone.
4. What is the formula for finding the volume of a cone?
5. By comparing the formula of a pyramid to the formula of a cone, would you say that both formulas are similar? True or False?
6. Find the volume of a cone that has an area of base of 6 cm^2 and a height of 4 cm. Hint: See Example 9.
7. Find the missing measure of dimensions of each cone.
   Hint: See Example 9.

   a. area of base = 9 ft^2 **b** area of base = 6 m^2
   　　　height = 3 ft   　　　height = 4 m
   　　　volume = ?   　　　volume = ?

   c. area of base = 12 ft^2 **d.** area of base = 4 m
   　　　height = 3 ft   　　　height = 3 m
   　　　volume = ?   　　　volume = ?

8. If the volume of a cone is 12 ft^3 and the height is 2 ft, find the area of the base of the cone. Hint: See Example 12.
9. Find the missing measure of dimension of each cone. Hint: See Example 12.

   a. area of base = ?   **b.** area of base = ?
   　　　volume = 6 m^3 　　　volume = 3 m^3
   　　　height = 5 m   　　　height = 4 m

c. area of base = ?
    volume = $7 m^3$
    height = 9 m

d. area of base = ?
    volume = $4 ft^3$
    height = 6 ft

10. Find the height of a cone that has an area of base of $4.78 m^2$ and a volume of $18.2 m^3$. Round your answer to the nearest tenth. Hint: See Example 3.

11. Find the missing measure of each cone. Round your answer to the nearest tenth. Hint: See Example 13.

    a. area of base = $6 ft^2$
        height = ?
        volume = $17.8 ft^3$

    b area of base = $12 m^2$
        height = ?
        volume = $27.5 m^3$

    c. area of base = $3.6 ft^2$
        height = ?
        volume = $15.2 ft^3$

    d. area of base = $4.2 m^2$
        height = ?
        volume = $14.4 m^3$

12. Find the volume of a cone that has a radius of 6 m and a height of 7 m. Hint: Round your answer to the nearest tenth. Hint: See Example 10.

13. Find the missing measure of the dimension of each cone. Round your answer to the nearest tenth. Hint: See Example 10.

    a. radius of the base = 2 m
        height = 6 m
        volume = ?

    b. radius of the base = 4 ft
        height = 3 ft
        volume = ?

    c. radius of the base = 2 ft
        height = 7 ft
        volume = ?

    d. radius of the base = 5 m
        height = 2 m
        volume = ?

14. Find the missing measure of the dimension of each cone. Round your answer to the nearest tenth. Hint: See Example 11.

    a. diameter of the base = 4 m
        height = 5 m
        volume = ?

    b. diameter of the base = 5 ft
        height = 7 ft
        volume = ?

    c. diameter of the base = 10 m
        height = 6 m
        volume = ?

    d. diameter of the base = 9 ft.
        height = 10 ft
        volume = ?

Challenge Questions

15. Find the volume of a cone that has an area of base of $6 ft^2$ and a height of 5 ft.

16. Find the missing measure of the dimension of each cone.

    a. area of base = $9 m^2$
        height = 5 m
        volume = ?

    b. area of base = $7 ft^2$
        height = 5 ft
        volume = ?

Answers to Selected Questions
7a. 9 ft³   **9a**. 3.6 m²   **11a**. 8.9 ft
13a. 25.1 m³   **14a**. 20.9 m³

SPHERE
Recall from the section on the surface area that a sphere has the shape of a soccer ball. The formula for finding the volume of a sphere is:

$$V = \frac{4}{3}\pi r^3$$

where V = volume, $\pi \approx 3.14$, and r = radius.

Example 1
Find the volume of a sphere that has a radius of 2 cm. Round your answer to the nearest tenth.
Solution.
The formula for finding the volume of a sphere is:

$$V = \frac{4}{3}\pi r^3 \underline{\hspace{6cm}}[A]$$

From the question, the radius of the sphere is 2 cm, and therefore, substitute r = 2 cm and $\pi \approx 3.14$ into equation $[A]$ as shown:

$$V = \frac{4}{3}\pi r^3$$

$$V \approx \frac{4}{3} \times 3.14 \times (2 \text{ cm})^3 \qquad\qquad \pi \approx 3.14 \text{ and r} = 2 \text{ cm}.$$

$$V \approx \frac{4}{3} \times 3.14 \times 2^3 \text{ cm}^3 \qquad\qquad (2 \text{ cm})^3 = 2^3 \text{ cm}^3$$

$$V \approx \frac{4}{3} \times 3.14 \times 8 \text{ cm}^3 \qquad\qquad 2^3 = 2 \times 2 \times 2 = 8$$

$$V \approx \frac{100.48 \text{ cm}^3}{3}$$

$$V \approx 33.493... \text{ cm}^3$$

$$V \approx 33.5 \text{ cm}^3 \text{ to the nearest tenth.}$$

Example 2
The volume of a sphere is 50.78 m³. Find the radius of the sphere. Round your

answer to the nearest tenth.

Solution

The formula for finding the volume of a sphere is:

$$V = \frac{4}{3}\pi r^3 \hspace{6cm} [A]$$

From the question, the volume of the sphere is 50.78 m³. Therefore, substitute $V = 50.78$ m³ and $\pi \approx 3.14$ into equation $[A]$ as shown:

$$V = \frac{4}{3}\pi r^3$$

$$50.78 \text{ m}^3 \approx \frac{4}{3} \times 3.14 \times r^3 \hspace{2cm} V = 50.78 \text{ m}^3 \text{ and } \pi \approx 3.14.$$

$$50.78 \text{ m}^3 \approx \frac{12.56}{3} \times r^3 \hspace{5cm} [B]$$

$$4 \times 3.14 \approx 12.56$$

Multiply both sides of the equation $[B]$ by 3 to eliminate the denominator of 3 as shown:

$$50.78 \text{ m}^3 \times 3 \approx \frac{12.56}{3} \times r^3 \times 3$$

$$50.78 \text{ m}^3 \times 3 \approx \frac{12.56}{\cancel{3}_1} \times r^3 \times \cancel{3}^1 \hspace{3cm} \text{Do the division.}$$

$$50.78 \text{ m}^3 \times 3 \approx 12.56 \times r^3 \hspace{5cm} [C]$$

Divide both sides of the equation $[C]$ by 12.56 to obtain the value of r^3 as shown:

$$\frac{50.78 \text{ m}^3 \times 3}{12.56} \approx \frac{12.56 \times r^3}{12.56}$$

$$\frac{50.78 \text{ m}^3 \times 3}{12.56} \approx \frac{\cancel{12.56}^1 \times r^3}{\cancel{12.56}_1} \hspace{2cm} \text{Do the division.}$$

$$\hspace{8cm} 12.56 \div 12.56 = 1$$

$$\frac{50.78 \text{ m}^3 \times 3}{12.56} \approx r^3$$

$$\frac{152.34 \text{ m}^3}{12.56} \approx r^3 \hspace{2cm} 50.78 \text{ m}^3 \times 3 = 152.34 \text{ m}^3.$$

$$12.12898 \text{ m}^3 \approx r^3 \underline{\hspace{5cm}} [D]$$

$$152.34 \text{ m}^3 \div 12.56 = 12.12898 \text{ m}^3.$$
Use a calculator to divide.

Find the cube root of both sides of the equation $[D]$ to obtain the value of r as shown:

$$\sqrt[3]{12.12898 \text{ m}^3} \approx \sqrt[3]{r^3}$$

$2.29760 \text{ m} \approx r$ Use a calculator to find the cube root of 12.12898 by depressing 2nd $\sqrt[3]{}$ 12.12898 = on a calculator to obtain 2.29760.

$\sqrt[3]{r^3} = r$ because the cube root of a number to the power 3 is the number itself.

$\sqrt[3]{m^3} = m$ because the cube root of a number to the power 3 is the number itself.

$r \approx 2.3 \text{ m}$ rounded to the nearest tenth.

Exercises
1. Find the volume of each sphere that has a radius of:
   a. 1 m   **b.** 3 ft   **c.** 4 cm   **d.** 2.5 m
   Round your answer to the nearest tenths. Hint: See Example 1.
2. Find the missing dimension of each sphere.
   a. $V = 54 \text{ cm}^3$ **b.** $V = 48 \text{ m}^3$ **c.** $V = 60 \text{ m}^3$ **d.** $V = 42 \text{ ft}$
   $r = ?$ $r = ?$ $r = ?$ $r = ?$
   Round your answer to the nearest tenths. Hint: See Example 2.

Challenge questions.
3. Find the missing dimension of each sphere.
   a. $V = 44 \text{ cm}^3$ **b.** $V = ?$ **c.** $V = 70 \text{ m}^3$ **d.** $V = ?$
   $r = ?$ $r = 2.6 \text{ m}$ $r = ?$ $r = 4 \text{ ft}$
   Round your answer to the nearest tenth.

Answers to Selected Questions.
1a. 4.2 m^2 **2a.** 2.4 cm

INDEX OF GRADE 8

D

ones 32
opposite integers 389-391
order integers 392
order of operations 17, 18
ordered pair 580, 582, 714, 715
origin 580-593
outcome 462, 469, 470, 471, 499-506
output value 713, 716

P

parabola 732, 733, 735, 740, 746, 748
parallel and perpendicular lines 629, 630, 665
parallel lines 602, 606
parentheses 21-30
pattern 2
pentagonal pyramid 861
percent 56-124
percent of decrease 122, 123, 125, 126
percent of increase 119-122, 125, 126
percent rate 107
percentage 107
perfect square 295, 300-307, 310, 311
perimeter 803
PERMDAS 290
perpendicular distance 827
perpendicular lines 604, 605, 606, 704
pints 452-454
place value 31
placement 681
points 239-248, 251-255
point-slope form 625-628
positive correlation 631, 632
positive integer 398, 399, 400, 401,415,
positive numbers 4
positive slope 596, 607, 610
positive strong correlation 633
positive symbol 199
positive weak correlation 633
power 128, 134, 142, 165, 167
preimage 823, 824, 825, 829, 831, 832, 833, 836, 837
prime factorization 129
prime number 315
principal 758, 768

X

x-axis 580-604
x-coordinate 580-604
x-intercept 614, 615, 621, 622

Y

yard 432-434
y-axis 357, 580-604
y-coordinate 580-604
y-intercept 614, 615, 621, 622, 624

Z

zero pair 397, 398, 399, 401
zero power 135-137
zero slope 596, 607, 610

When the logic of the mathematics is understood, students may use calculators and other computer softwares as applications of technology. The two pictures below show the two out of the three main components of the TI-nspire calculator. Some of the applications of the TI-nspire are shown. Refer to the manual of your calculator or computer program for detail applications.

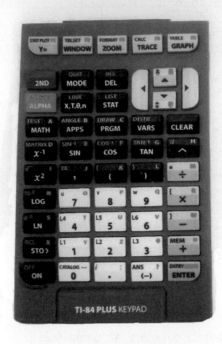

	Menu Option List	Overview of Tool Actions	Press:
▶	1: Actions	Provides tools to access the pointer, hide or show various graph features, add text, delete all objects in the work area, open the calculator, and access attributes for an object or function.	(menu) (1)
	2: View	Provides tools to manipulate the work area features and display.	(menu) (2)
	3: Graph Type	Enables you to select the type of graph to plot: function, parametric, or scatter plot.	(menu) (3)
	A: Transformation	Provides tools for symmetry, reflection, translation, rotation, and dilation.	(menu) (A)

Graphing inequalities

Function mode enables you to define a function that uses a symbol other than the equal sign. To change = to a different sign and graph the inequality:

1. Position the cursor to the right of the equal sign.

    Press (clear) to delete the equal sign.

2. Type the desired sign or use the Symbol Palette to enter the appropriate inequality. The possible inequalities are: $>$, $<$, $\leq$, and $\geq$.

3. Type the rest of the inequality expression.

    Press (enter) to graph it.

TI-*nspire* Learning Handheld
Quick Reference

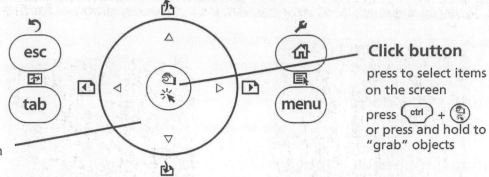

NavPad

press in any direction
to move the cursor

Click button

press to select items
on the screen

press (ctrl) + (🖱)
or press and hold to
"grab" objects

Shortcuts

(ctrl) + (esc) undo; (CAPS⇧) + (esc) redo

(ctrl) + (🏠) provides tools to manage and edit your document

(ctrl) + (menu) provides options available to current application

(esc) closes menus and dialog boxes

(tab) moves to the next field in a dialog or between fields in an expression template

(🏠) allows you to add applications, manage documents, or view system information

(menu) opens the application menu for working with the current application

(ctrl) alternates between primary and secondary functions on keyboard

(🄿) applies language-specific accents or punctuation to international characters

---

Moving around in documents

(ctrl) + ▶ displays next page

(ctrl) + ◀ displays previous page

(ctrl) + (tab) moves to next application in a split layout

(tab) moves between fields within the application

Navigation

(ctrl) + ▲ from page, displays Page Sorter
from Page Sorter, displays My Documents

(ctrl) + ▼ from My Documents, displays Page Sorter
from Page Sorter, displays page

(ctrl) + (7) Home

(ctrl) + (1) End

(ctrl) + (9) Page Up

(ctrl) + (3) Page Down

Managing Files and Folders

(🏠) (7) opens My Documents

(ctrl) (N) opens a new document

(ctrl) (I) inserts a new page

Changing Mode Settings

(🏠)(8)(1) Current document settings

(🏠)(8)(2) System settings

Entering Math Expressions

(📖) opens catalog

(ctrl) + (📖) opens symbol palette

(ctrl) + (📐) opens math templates

Opening a document

1. Press ⌂ 7 to open My Documents.

2. Press ▲ or ▼ to highlight the folder than contains the document.

3. Press ▶ to expand the folder.

4. Press ▲ or ▼ to highlight the document you want to open.

5. Press ⏎ or the click button to open the document.

Creating a new document

Press ⌂ 6 or ctrl N to open a new document.

Creating a split-page layout

1. Press ctrl ⌂ 5 2 to view the standard layouts.
2. Press the number of the layout to apply it to the page.

-OR-

1. Press ctrl ⌂ 5 1 to apply a custom split to a layout.
2. Use arrow keys to move the splitter bar.

3. Press ⏎ to select a layout.

Adding a problem to a document

Press ctrl ⌂ 4 1.
A new problem with one page is added.

Adding a page to a problem

Press ctrl ⌂ 4 2 or ctrl I to add a blank page.

A new page is added to the current problem.

-OR-

Press ⌂ and then select an application. A new page with that application is added.

Saving a document

To save your document, press ctrl ⌂ 1 3 or press ctrl S.

Using the Page Sorter

1 From the document view, press ctrl ▲.

2. Press ▲, ▼, ▶ or ◀ to highlight the page or problem you want to move.

3. Press and hold the click button until it the "grab" hand displays on the screen.
4. Drag the page to the desired location and drop it in place.

Using the catalog

1. From the document view, press 📖 to open the catalog.

2. Press tab to highlight the tabs, then press ▲, ▼, ▶ or ◀ to move to the tab that contains the function, symbol or expression you want to insert into your problem.

3. Press tab until the item you want to insert is highlighted.

4. Press ⏎ to insert the item.